# Spread Spectrum Techniques

OTHER IEEE PRESS BOOKS

Electronic Switching: Central Office Systems of the World, *Edited by A. E. Joel, Jr.*
Electromagnetic Horn Antennas, *Edited by A. W. Love*
Waveform Quantization and Coding, *Edited by N. S. Jayant*
Communcation Satellite Systems: An Overview of the Technology, *Edited by the Satellite Systems Panel*
Literature Survey of Communication Satellite Systems and Technology, *Edited by J. H. W. Unger*
Solar Cells, *Edited by C. E. Backus*
Computer Networking, *Edited by R. P. Blanc and I. W. Cotton*
Communications Channels: Characterization and Behavior, *Edited by B. Goldberg*
Large-Scale Networks: Theory and Design, *Edited by F. T. Boesch*
Optical Fiber Technology, *Edited by D. Gloge*
Selected Papers in Digital Signal Processing, II, *Edited by the Digital Signal Processing Committee*
A Guide for Better Technical Presentations, *Edited by R. M. Woelfle*
Career Management: A Guide to Combating Obsolescence, *Edited by H. G. Kaufman*
Energy and Man: Technical and Social Aspects of Energy, *Edited by M. G. Morgan*
Magnetic Bubble Technology: Integrated-Circuit Magnetics for Digital Storage and Processing, *Edited by H. Chang*
Frequency Synthesis: Techniques and Applications, *Edited by J. Gorski-Popiel*
Literature in Digital Processing: Author and Permuted Title Index (Revised and Expanded Edition), *Edited by H. D. Helms, J. F. Kaiser, and L. R. Rabiner*
Data Communications via Fading Channels, *Edited by K. Brayer*
Nonlinear Networks: Theory and Analysis, *Edited by A. N. Willson, Jr.*
Computer Communications, *Edited by P. E. Green, Jr. and R. W. Lucky*
Stability of Large Electric Power Systems, *Edited by R. T. Byerly and E. W. Kimbark*
Automatic Test Equipment: Hardware, Software, and Management, *Edited by F. Liguori*
Key Papers in the Development of Coding Theory, *Edited by E. R. Berlekamp*
Technology and Social Institutions, *Edited by K. Chen*
Key Papers in the Development of Information Theory, *Edited by D. Slepian*
Computer-Aided Filter Design, *Edited by G. Szentirmai*
Laser Devices and Applications, *Edited by I. P. Kaminow and A. E. Siegman*
Integrated Optics, *Edited by D. Marcuse*
Laser Theory, *Edited by F. S. Barnes*
Digital Signal Processing, *Edited by L. R. Rabiner and C. M. Rader*
Minicomputers: Hardware, Software, and Applications, *Edited by J. D. Schoeffler and R. H. Temple*
Semiconductor Memories, *Edited by D. A. Hodges*
Power Semiconductor Applications, Volume II: Equipment and Systems, *Edited by J. D. Harnden, Jr. and F. B. Golden*
Power Semiconductor Applications, Volume I: General Considerations, *Edited by J. D. Harnden and F. B. Golden*
A Practical Guide to Minicomputer Applications, *Edited by F. F. Coury*
Active Inductorless Filters, *Edited by S. K. Mitra*
Clearing the Air: The Impact of the Clean Air Act on Technology, *Edited by J. C. Redmond, J. C. Cook, and A. A. J. Hoffman*

# Spread Spectrum Techniques

Edited by
**Robert C. Dixon**
Consultant

A volume in the IEEE PRESS Selected Reprint Series,
prepared under the sponsorship of the
IEEE Communications Society.

IEEE PRESS

The Institute of Electrical and Electronics Engineers, Inc. New York

International Standard Book Numbers: Clothbound: 0-87942-077-4
Paperbound: 0-87942-078-2

Library of Congress Catalog Card Number 76-18432

PRINTED IN THE UNITED STATES OF AMERICA

# Contents

# Preface

This volume consists primarily of selected papers on spread spectrum communications and/or navigation techniques, and closely related subjects, that have appeared since 1949. Spread spectrum systems and techniques have grown along with information and coding theory, applying many of the premises and conclusions almost as soon as they were formulated. Indeed, in some cases, spread spectrum systems have been the necessity that mothered the invention of new theorems, especially in the coding area. The first spread spectrum systems developments began in the late 1940's, and references to some of them appeared in popular literature [1], [2] in the early 1960's.

The papers included in this volume have been selected because (in this editor's opinion) they best represent the thinking that has shaped developments in a particular area, or else because they represent some technique that is important but not discussed elsewhere. A number of papers exist that are just as important and that are written just as well as those included here; so selection has been quite difficult.

I have attempted to minimize overlapping coverage in order to present the maximum amount of material. In a few cases, however, the import of the material or the impact of a result on the field is such that the paper cannot reasonably be omitted. A few of the areas into which the book has been divided have been much more heavily documented than others, and in those areas it has been necessary to choose between a number of outstanding papers. Where this is so, a listing of alternative papers is given. It is also worthy of note that there have been a few publications that have concentrated on spread spectrum techniques [3]–[6]. Rather than try to reprint all of the many excellent papers that appeared in these few sources, I have chosen to include only one paper here, and that one only because I can find no other that provides an equivalent up-to-date survey in its subject area. Instead, it is recommended that anyone who is interested in spread spectrum techniques see those sources referenced *in toto*, in their original publications. This is reasonable, since the prime reason for the existence of this volume is to gather together those papers of importance to the spread spectrum field that have been scattered throughout several publications and over a 26-year period.

This book is divided into two general sections. The first is an introduction to the spread spectrum field, its whys and wherefores, and a summary and a projection of where we might go from here. The second section, Parts I through XI, contains the papers that have been selected for reprinting here. The papers in the second section are divided into 11 categories, arranged chronologically within each category, with introductory remarks to give the reader some perspective on the impact of the papers included there. A bibliography of papers on spread spectrum techniques and closely related subjects is included at the end of the book for the reader's use in researching the field. This bibliography and the information it represents should fill some of the gaps that must inevitably exist in any finite set of references and give the reader an entry into the remainder of the body of information that has accumulated in and around spread spectrum systems.

I am indebted to a number of people for material contained in that part of the introduction entitled Historical Notes (and Some Contemporary Systems). J. Allen of the Naval Research Laboratory, J. Flatz of the Air Force Avionics Laboratory, H. Mayer of the Aerospace Corporation, and W. Richards and R. Mifflin of the Air Force Rome Air Development Center were instrumental in supplying information of historical interest as well as information on contemporary developments. The photographs used in Figs. 8 through 11 and 15 are courtesy of the Advanced Products Division, Magnavox Company., Figs. 12 through 14 and Figs. 17 through 21 were furnished by the Air Force Rome Air Development Center. Figure 16 was furnished by the Ground Systems Group, Hughes Aircraft Company.

Those centers who have, through the years, been most active in sponsoring and carrying out spread spectrum work have been the Air Force's Avionics Laboratory and Rome Air Develeopment Center, the Navy's Naval Research Laboratory, and the Army's

Satellite Communications Agency. The entire spread spectrum field owes a debt to these farsighted groups. In addition, there have been many others who have made important contributions, both as sponsors and developers. To those who are not specifically named here, let me also give a vote of thanks, for they have also contributed to making spread spectrum systems what they are—the single best hope for providing reliable interference-free communications and navigation in a world that requires ever increasing communications to survive.

Responsibility for selection of the papers reprinted here is mine. If better or more applicable information exists, then it has been omitted only because I am ignorant of that existence, or else because the information is not available for publication here. At least this is a place to start, and that place has been and will continue to be needed, for I am sure that I can safely assert that spread spectrum techniques are here to stay.

R. C. Dixon
*Editor*

## REFERENCES


[1] K. Gilmore, "The secret keepers," *Popular Electron.*, Aug. 1962.
[2] A. Pfansteil, "Intelligent noise," *Analog Sci. Fiction*, 1961.
[3] IEEE Transactions on Microwave Theory and Techniques (Special Issue) April, 1973.
[4] *Proc. 1973 Symp. Spread Spectrum Commun.*, Naval Electronics Lab., Mar. 1973.
[5] C. R. Cahn, "Spread spectrum applications and state of the art equipments," AGARD-NATO Lecture Ser. 58, May 1973.
[6] R. C. Dixon, *Spread Spectrum Systems.* New York: Wiley, 1975

# Spread Spectrum Techniques

# Introduction

## SPREAD SPECTRUM TECHNIQUES

Spread spectrum techniques and spread spectrum systems have come about because of a desire on the part of communications systems designers and users to protect their signals from detection, demodulation, and/or interference. One way of doing this is to transmit as little signal as possible (or at least as little as possible that the unauthorized receiver will recognize as a signal). A second way is to disguise the signal so that it looks as little like something desirable as possible. One might even encode the information so that if an unauthorized receiver does pick it up, it will mean nothing to him. Further, one might vary the frequency used as well as using prearranged transmission times to keep his signals from unauthorized parties. Current spread spectrum systems employ all of these techniques to keep their information contained and to satisfy the goal of protecting the signals they send from interference at the same time. These systems, though made up of subsystems that are in many ways identical to other contemporary communications systems, employ them in slightly different ways and extend their requirements beyond those that exist in the more conventional applications. The point is that there is very little in spread spectrum systems that is new from a microscopic viewpoint, but when viewed from the system design level they depart materially from conventional systems.

A spread spectrum system is one that employs a great deal more modulated RF bandwidth in transmitting its information than would normally be required. To be classified as a spread spectrum system, the modulated signal bandwidth should be at least 10 to 100 times the information rate, and the information itself should not be a factor in setting the modulated signal bandwidth. Under these rules, it is seen that techniques such as wide-band (high deviation) FM and high rate digital modulation are not spread spectrum systems even though they may employ more RF bandwidth than another system that does meet the spread spectrum criteria. Put another way, the spread spectrum systems designer must go out of his way to use a great deal more RF bandwidth than he would need to use if all he desired to do was to send a signal.

Spread spectrum signals are divided into four basic types:

1) direct sequence modulated;
2) frequency hopping;
3) pulse-FM or chirp;
4) time hopping.

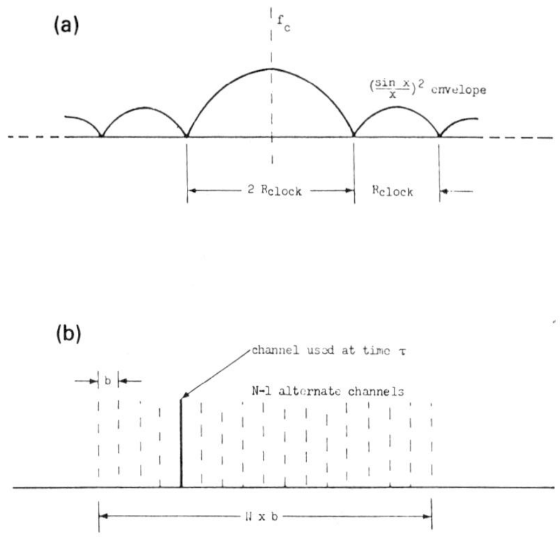


Fig. 1. Power versus frequency spectra for the most common forms of spread spectrum signals. (a) Direct sequence. (b) Frequency hopping.

These basic spread spectrum systems are differentiated by their modulation formats. Other formats that are really combinations of these are also often used.

*Direct Sequence:* Direct sequence signals are generated by modulating a carrier with a code sequence; therein is the origin of the "direct sequence" title. In a direct sequence system (also called pseudonoise or direct spread) the incoming information signal is digitized if it is not in a digital format, and modulo 2 added to a higher speed code sequence.[1] The combined information and code then are used to suppressed-carrier modulate an RF carrier. Since the high speed code sequence dominates the modulating function, it determines the RF signal bandwidth [see Fig. 1(a)] and gives rise to the spread spectrum signal. In comparison, digital communications systems have been built that employ the same kind of modulation with high speed bit streams, but in those instances the bit streams are the information being sent, rather than a high speed information-masking signal.

[1]The code sequences considered here are binary bit streams, may be of lengths from a few thousand to trillions of bits, and may be linear or nonlinear in their construction.

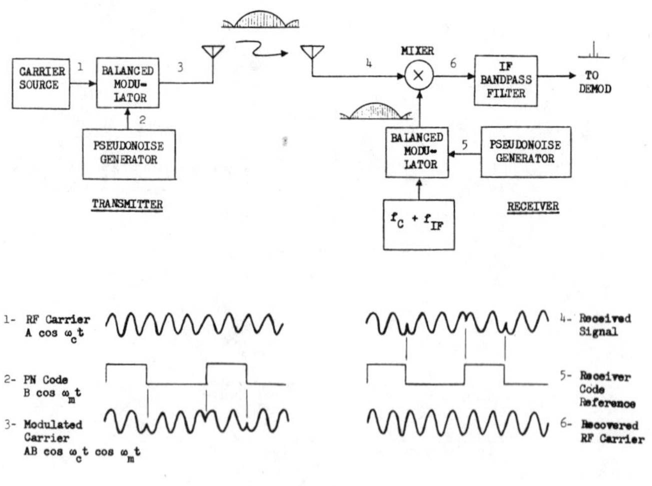


Fig. 2. Direct sequence system block diagram.

Fig. 2 is a block diagram of a simplified direct sequence system. The RF carrier is modulated with the digitized information ⊕ code stream by phase-shift keying (PSK) the carrier. Biphase or quadriphase PSK is employed in one of its forms almost universally. The result of this modulation process is the signal spectrum shown in Fig. 3, where the main lobe bandwidth of the signal is equal to twice the clock rate of the code $R_c$, and each sidelobe is $R_c$ wide. The signal envelope is sin $x/x$. Fig. 4(a) and (b) shows the result of employing a special form of quadriphase PSK, discussed in Kwan's paper (see Part IX, RF Effects), which is especially well adapted to confining the direct sequence signal to a reasonable bandwidth. After all, even though one may be interested in spreading a signal to take advantage of the benefits that accrue, he may not be prepared to transmit sidelobes that stretch out over the entire electromagnetic spectrum. The double-binary modulation technique permits filtering and subsequent limiting of the signal without sidelobe regeneration such as occurs when a simple biphase or quadriphase PSK signal is filtered and limited.

The direct sequence receiver operates by multiplying the received wide-band signal with a locally generated replica, which has the effect of remapping or collapsing the wide-band signal into a bandwidth which is commensurate with the information alone. The signal that passes through the narrow-band IF and is presented to the demodulator is a carrier that is PSK modulated with the information only, just as if the direct sequence modulation had never existed on the carrier. Direct sequence systems (and indeed all spread spectrum systems) are thus said to be "transparent" to their information channels.

The prime problem in direct sequence systems, as in all spread spectrum systems, is to synchronize the code sequences used in their transmitters and receivers and to keep them synchronized. Synchronization is discussed in detail in Part X and in the references listed in the bibliography at the end of this volume. Here we will only state with all due emphasis that spread spectrum systems will not work properly without code synchronization (with the possible exception of the chirp systems) and that the synch acquisition and maintenance problem is the toughest that the designer faces.

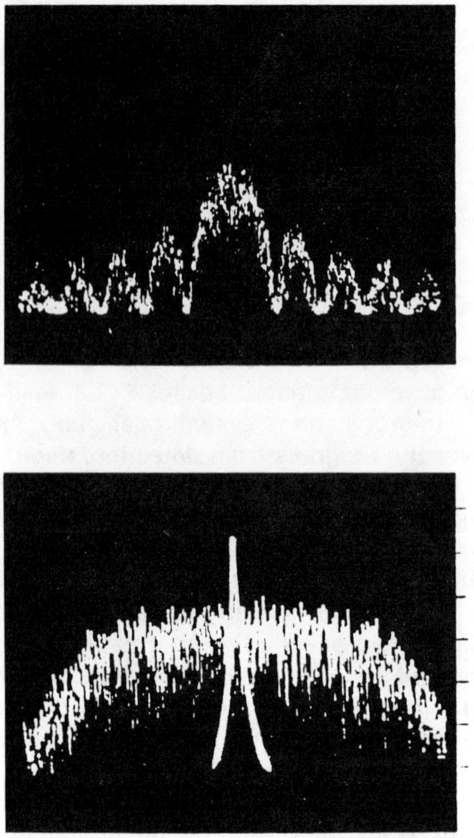

(a)

(b)

Fig. 3. Typical direct sequence spectra. (a) Direct sequence signal spectrum, biphase modulation, showing first four sidelobes. (b) Main lobe of direct sequence signal compared to equal power continuous wave signal. Code rate: 1 Mbit/s. Vertical calibration: 10 dB/div.

A direct sequence system spreads any uncorrelated signal that appears at its input over at least its local reference bandwidth, forcing the interference to occupy a wide bandwidth and reducing its average power per hertz. Direct sequence systems are therefore said to be "averaging" systems from the standpoint of their interference handling process. This reduced average power level then is all that is seen by the direct sequence system's demodulator.

*Frequency Hopping:* Frequency hopping is an extension of the idea that a good way to prevent an unintended receiver from receiving a message, or to prevent an unwanted signal from interfering with reception of a desired signal, is to move around in the frequency domain in such a way that the undesirable receivers cannot find the operating frequency. Where the early radio operator used a time schedule, frequency hopping systems employ a code sequence to determine what frequency is to be employed at any particular time. These code sequences are the same type as those used by the direct sequence systems, with the exception

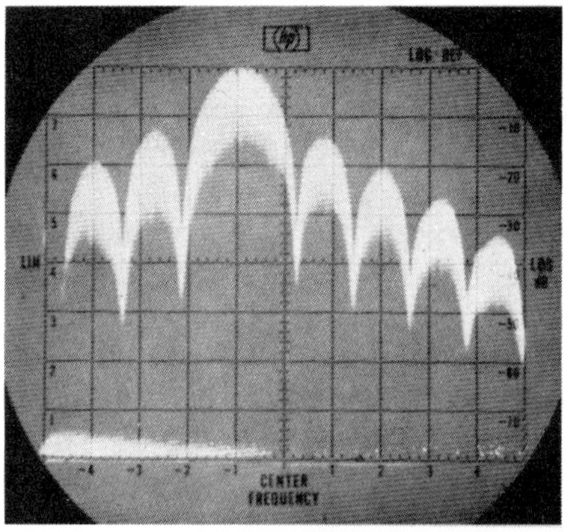


(a)

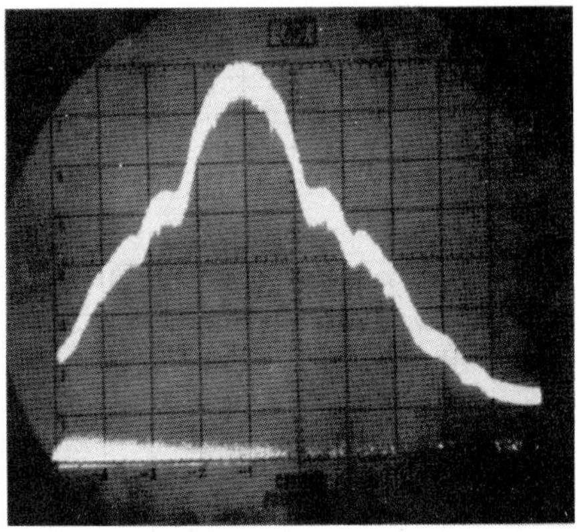

(b)

Fig. 4. Comparison of QPSK signal spectra with double-binary signal. (a) Filtered and limited PQSK signal. Note that the sidelobe level is the same as if filtering had not occurred. (This reaction is typical of both biphase and quadriphase direct sequence signals.) Filter bandwith: 2 $R_{clock}$ (b) Identical filtering and limiting of double-binary or staggered quadriphase signal. First sidelobe level is now down 25 dB, or 12 dB below level of the signal in (a).

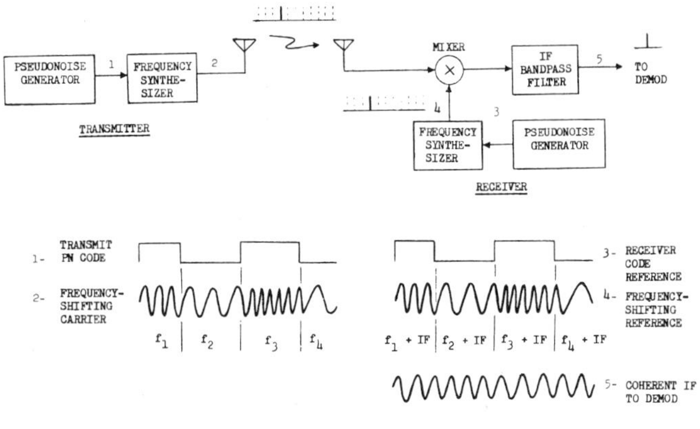


Fig. 5. Frequency hopping system block diagram.

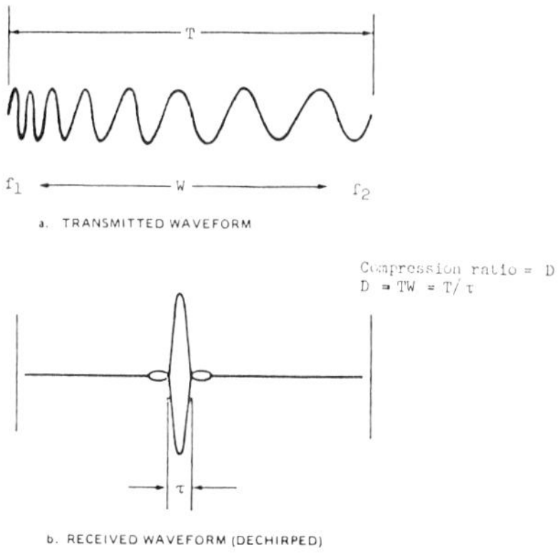


Fig. 6. Typical chirp signals.

that the code clock rate is usually slower. (Where direct sequence code rates are usually in the 1-Mbit/s to 100-Mbit/s range, frequency hopping codes do not normally exceed a few hundred Kilobits per second.) See Fig. 1(b).

Figure 5 is a simplified diagram of a frequency hopping system. Note the similarity (on a block diagram basis) between the previous direct sequence diagram and this diagram for a frequency hopper. When compared at this level, it appears that the only difference between the two types of systems is in that the frequency hopper includes an extra subsystem—its frequency synthesizer. This particular consideration has blocked the use of frequency hopping systems in the past, but improved small frequency synthesizers have recently opened the way for widespread use of frequency hoppers in those applications where they can operate best.

*Pulse-FM:* Pulse-FM or chirp systems are familiar to many from their use in radar. The signals used are simple and do not (at least in their fundamental form) employ coding as the other forms of spread spectrum modulation do to spread their transmitted signal bandwidth. The signals used are just swept-frequency pulses, just as one might see in a single sweep from a laboratory sweep generator. The secret is in the receiver, which employs a dispersive filter to match the swept signal and to compress it into a much narrower time slot such that it behaves in the same way a high power (but narrower) pulse does. See Fig. 6. Fig. 12 shows a chirp system.

*Time Hopping:* Time hopping systems control their transmission time and period with a code sequence in the same way that frequency hoppers control their frequency. In fact, time hopping is most often used in conjunction with frequency hopping, and the two together form the basis for one form of time-division multiple-access (TDMA) system. Time hopping alone can be viewed as pulse modulation under code sequence control, and a diagram for a time hopper can be generated by adding carrier on–off control to the direct sequence diagram. Such control could be on a code chip basis or on the basis of some code-derived signal.

*Hybrids:* Hybrid spread spectrum systems made up by combining two or more of the four basic modulation techniques are also possible and sometimes offer the only viable approach to implementing very wide-band and/or very high process gain systems. The hybrid techniques, in fact, are now being employed in most of the newest systems at this time. This trend is expected to continue, and future spread spectrum systems will probably seldom employ a single form of modulation. The reason for this is that no code generator is expected to run at a rate that provides the entire spectrum spreading, and likewise no frequency synthesizer is expected to produce a number of frequencies that would cover the entire spread signal bandwidth of a system. Therefore both code and frequency synthesis requirements may be relaxed without degrading the system's overall performance. For example, suppose that a particular requirement called for a system with a spread spectrum bandwidth of 500 MHz. This bandwidth would require a code generator with at least 250-Mbit/s clocking, or else a frequency synthesizer that could fill the band with frequencies spaced at approximately the data rate. (If the data rate were 10 kbit/s, then $5 \times 10^8/1 \times 10^4 = 50\,000$ frequencies would be required, and the hopping rate would be at least 10 khop/s.) An alternate hybrid approach could provide similar performance with a 10-Mbit/s code sequence generator and a frequency synthesizer that generates only 50 frequencies. The frequency synthesizer output would be direct sequence modulated with the 10-Mbit/s code, and this would produce a hybrid frequency hop/direct sequence signal that meets the 500-MHz bandwidth requirement. Implementation of the code generator and the frequency synthesizer for the hybrid system would be significantly simpler than either the code generator or the synthesizer for the straightforward direct sequence of frequency hopping system approach.

### *Spread Spectrum Processing Advantages*

It would be foolhardy to employ spread spectrum modulation, using all of the bandwidth required and constructing complex modulators and demodulators if significant advantages did not come about. Indeed, the process of spreading a signal's bandwidth and then collapsing it through coherent correlation with a stored reference signal contained in the receiver offers a unique combination of advantages:

1) selective addressing;
2) code-division multiple access;
3) low density output signals;
4) inherent message privacy/security;
5) high resolution ranging;
6) interference rejection.

There are, of course, disadvantages. Chief among these are:

1) more difficult frequency allocation;
2) greater system complexity.

*Selective addressing* is possible through use of the modulating code sequences to recognize a particular signal. Assignment of a particular code to a given receiver would allow it to be contacted only by a transmitter which is using that code to modulate its signal. With different codes assigned to all of the receivers in a network, a transmitter can select any one receiver for communication by simply transmitting that receiver's code; then only that receiver will receive the message.

*Code-division multiplexing* is similar, in that a number of transmitters and receivers can operate on the same frequency at the same time by employing different codes. Either continuous transmission or time-division transmission is facilitated, since the synchronization inherent to transmission and reception of spread spectrum signals provides an excellent time base for on and off timing.

*Low-density* transmitted signals are used to advantage in preventing interference to other systems as well as in providing a low probability of intercept. The low density of spread spectrum signals is an inherent property which exists because of the bandwidth expansion. In a direct sequence system, for instance, where the spectrum-spreding code is at a 20-Mbit/s rate, the transmitted output is at least 24 MHz wide (at the 3-dB points) and the power of the transmitter is spread over this bandwidth. In that 24-MHz band, a 10-W transmitter would average a power density of approximately 4.16 $\mu$W/Hz. To a narrow-band receiver with a 50-kHz bandwidth, this 10-W signal would have less effect than a 200-mW transmitter of anything less than 50-kHz bandwidth. In addition, a spread spectrum output signal appears to be incoherent and is therefore often less objectionable (from a subjective point of view) than a narrow-band signal.

*Message privacy* is inherent in spread-spectrum signals because of their coded transmission format. Of course, the degree of privacy, or security, is a function of the codes used. Spread spectrum systems have been constructed to employ every kind of code from the relatively simple linear maximals[2] to the truly secure nonlinear encryption types. Proper design of the system can provide for substitution as required, when higher or lower level message security is desired.

Spread spectrum signals of the direct sequence type excel in their capability to provide *high resolution range measurements.* Again, this property is due to the high speed codes used for modulation. Since synchronizing a spread spectrum receiver depends on the receiver matching its code reference to the signal it receives to within 1 bit (typically, a spread spectrum receiver's code will be matched to the incoming signal's code to within one-tenth to one-hundredth of a bit), the inherent resolution capability of the signal is better than the range which corresponds to a bit period. Given that same system with a 20-Mbit/s code, the range between transmitter and receiver can easily be measured to within 50 ns, or 50 ft, and little difficulty is found in narrowing the resolution to 5 ft or less. An added ad-

[2]Linear maximal codes, or $m$-sequences, are the longest sequences that can be generated by a given length shift register ($2^n - 1$ bits for an $n$-stage register).

TABLE I
SPREAD SPECTRUM SYSTEM PROCESS GAIN

| Technique | Approximate $G_p$ |
|---|---|
| Direct sequence (DS) | RF bandwidth/information rate |
| Frequency hopping (FH) | number of channels |
| Chirp | $TW = T/\tau$ |
| Time hopping (TH) | $(\text{duty factor})^{-1}$ |
| Hybrids | |
| DS/FH | $G_{pDS} + G_{pFH}$ |
| DS/TH | $G_{pDS}$/duty factor |
| FH/TH | $G_{pFH}$/duty factor |

vantage of spread spectrum systems in the range area is that their range resolution is minimally affected by range. That is, a spread spectrum ranging system that provides 50-ft basic resolution capability at 10 mi will also provide that same resolution capability at 100 mi or 500 mi. Direct sequence ranging techniques have been more than proved on deep space probes, where they provide accurate tracking for space probes millions of miles[3] away. In addition, spread spectrum ranging has been employed in high-performance aircraft where accurate tracking has been demonstrated at 300-mi ranges with 2-W transmitter power.

Spread spectrum systems provide an *interference rejection capability* that cannot be matched in any other way. Both deliberate and unintentional interference are rejected by a spread spectrum receiver, up to a maximum which is known as the "jamming margin" for that receiver. This jamming margin is also a function of the code sequence rate (in a direct sequence system) or the number of frequency channels available (in a frequency hopper). A chirp system's jamming margin is set by the frequency band it covers during its pulse time, or may be better expressed by its compression ratio. Chirp systems have received a great deal more attention in radar systems, to provide better transmitter power efficiency and range resolution, than in communications systems for interference rejection.

### *Process Gain and Jamming Margin*

*Process Gain:* Interference rejection, selective addressing, and code-division multiplexing occur as a result of the spectrum spreading and consequent despreading necessary to the operation of a spread spectrum receiver. In a particular system, the ratio of the spread or transmitted bandwidth to the rate of the information sent is called the "process gain" of that system. For a system in which the transmitted signal bandwidth is 20 MHz and the baseband is 10 kbit/s, process gain would be approximately $10 \log 2 \times 10^7/1 \times 10^4 = 33$ dB. This system would offer a 33 dB improvement in the signal-to-noise ratio between its receiver's RF input and its baseband output, less whatever might be lost in imperfect implementation. Table I compares the process gain $G_p$ that can be expected from various types of spread spectrum systems.

*Jamming Margin:* Jamming Margin is determined by a system's process gain (jamming margin cannot exceed process gain), acceptable output signal-to-noise ratio, and implementation losses. This margin, sometimes called the antijamming (AJ) margin, is the amount of interference that a receiver can withstand while operating and producing an acceptable output signal-to-noise ratio. For the preceding system, which has a 33-dB process gain, if the minimum acceptable output signal-to-noise ratio is 10 dB and implementation losses are 2 dB, then the jamming margin is 33 – 12 = 21 dB.

Figs. 2 and 5 show simplified direct sequence and frequency hopping systems, respectively. Both operate in much the same way. In either the direct sequence or the frequency hopping transmitter, the spread spectrum transmitted signal is generated as a function of the code sequence. (As it happens, the direct sequence transmitter is directly modulated by the code, while the frequency hopper goes through a code-to-frequency translation.) In either case, the signal transmitted is a wide-band signal, with information imbedded it it, and that is the signal matched to the receiver's local reference.

Expressed as a formula,

$$M_j = G_p - (L_{sys} + S/N_{out})$$

where $M_j$ is the jamming margin; $G_p$ is the process gain, equal to the RF bandwidth/information rate; $L_{sys}$ is the system implementation losses; and $S/N_{out}$ is the acceptable receiver output $S/N$.

A 21-dB jamming margin would permit a receiver to operate in an environment in which its desired signal is 121 times smaller than the interference at its input. Expressed another way, an interfering transmitter can have 121 times more power output than the desired signal's transmitter (if their distances are equal) before it affects the receiver's operation.

Typical spread spectrum transmitters are much simpler than their receiving counterparts. (Here we neglect any consideration of frequency translations and power amplifiers.) Information input to a spread spectrum transmitter is usually digitized, if not already in digital form, and imbedded within the code used for spectrum spreading. In the chirp systems, where there is no code, the chirp itself may be used, by sending a downchirp (decreasing frequency) to represent a "one," and an upchirp to represent a "zero." Once the information to be sent is imbedded in the code (by simple modulo-2 addition of the digitized information with a code), the code is used to balanced-modulate a carrier or to control the frequency output of a frequency synthesizer.

In general, one might say that direct sequence transmitters exist only to generate the kind of signals that are needed by the receiver to allow it to discriminate against undesired inputs, and the transmitter must generate that signal and send it with minimum distor-

[3]The code sequences used in ranging systems are chosen to be long enough that no ambiguity exists at the maximum range for which they are to be employed.

tion. The signal then is at the mercy of the transmission medium and all of the would-be interferors within the receiver's field of view.

At the receiver, the local reference (which is a replica of the transmitted signal, except that it does not contain the transmitter's imbedded information) is multiplied with the incoming signal, performing the operation $\int f(t)g(t-\tau)\,dt$. When the local code and received codes are matched, then $f(t) = g(t)$, and $\tau = 0$, which "despreads" the received signal, leaving only information-modulated carrier, which is then demodulated to yield the desired information by the conventional methods. In the same process in which the desired signal is despread, or "correlated" by multiplication with the receiver's wide-band local reference, any non-synchronous incoming signal is spread or decorrelated by being multiplied with that same wide-band local reference. Therefore, by passing the despread desired signal (now in a bandwidth commensurate with the information that was sent) through a bandpass filter that is just wide enough to pass the information-bearing carrier, the receiver rejects the undesired signal. This process allows rejection of most of the power contained in an undesired signal, since the undesired signal is forced to occupy a bandwidth that is equal to the covariance of the undesired signal and the local reference. (That is, any undesired signal has a bandwidth at least as wide as the receiver's local reference, once it is convolved with that local reference.) Therefore, the process gain that was previously discussed comes about through the remapping of a desired signal to fit within a narrow-band filter that is able to reject almost all of the undesired signal input, which has been spread and (pseudo) randomized by convolution with the local reference.

The process is the same, whether in a direct sequence or frequency hopping system, with a bandwidth trade being made to the advantage of the receiver through the convolution or correlation process. No bandwidth trade is made in chirp receivers, but an analogous process is carried out wherein the chirp filter compresses a desired input signal while not changing the signals that are not matched to the filter. In each case, process gain is realized in the receiver through processing that takes advantage of the spread spectrum waveform sent by the desired transmitter.

## HISTORICAL NOTES (AND SOME CONTEMPORARY SYSTEMS)

It is difficult to say when the concept of spread spectrum first came to light, or what its precepts were. We do know, however, that Shannon[4] had the idea of empolying coded wide-band signals for communicating in the presence of noise when he wrote the paper having to do with that subject in the 1940's. Costas affirms that he knew of such techniques in his 1959 paper.[4] Cryptic references to early systems with names like Phantom and Cherokee appeared in the literature in the early 1960's, but that same literature gave only very sketchy information on the inner workings of these systems and in fact did not say what form of modulation was employed. It is known, however, that Army, Navy, and Air Force programs existed for investigating the properties and capabilities if the then-new spread spectrum techniques. Some of these early programs are listed in Table II. Other programs are shown in Fig. 7, and some of the systems themselves are described in the paragraphs that follow.

TABLE II

| Program | Developer | Sponsor |
|---|---|---|
| NOMACS | M.I.T. Lincoln Lab. | Army |
| Cherokee | Martin | |
| Phantom | General Electric | Air Force |
| Blades | | Navy |
| Hush Up | Sylvania | Air Force |

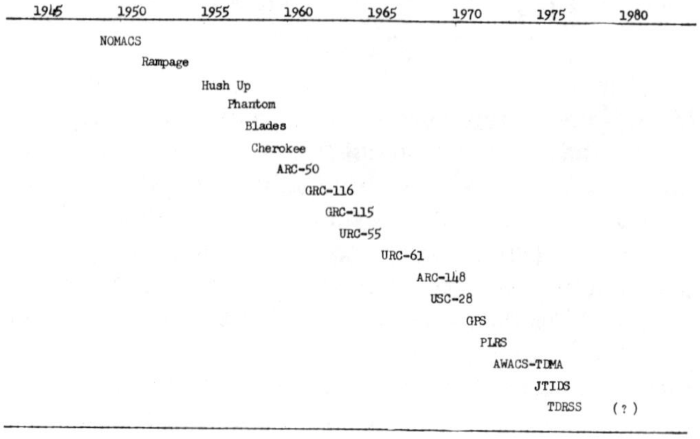


Fig. 7. Some spread spectrum systems developed since 1945. (Dates are approximate.)

Fig. 7 shows the lines of development of spread spectrum systems, at least within the United States. Other systems also exist, and it is not intended that this chart show anything other than a time line to give the reader an idea of the contemporary state of the spread spectrum field over the years. It is sure that spread spectrum systems also exist, or at least the requisite knowledge to construct them exists, in the iron curtain countries, although no specific information is available to this author to support such an opinion. Observance of Soviet literature in the communications and information theoretic areas leads to the conclusion that not only is the knowledge there, but also a basic understanding of the need for and capabilities of spread spectrum techniques.

Although Fig. 7 appears to show that developments and progress in the spread spectrum area followed an orderly progression, with new systems being built on the foundation of the old, such was not necessarily the case. System developers often had little or no knowledge of others working in the same area or of other

[4]See Part I, Anti-interference.

work that had preceded their own. Most often, in fact (as has happened many times before in the scientific world), the researchers and designers had to rediscover the principles on which spread spectrum systems work and reinvent the techniques for implementing them.

It is of some interest to note that the process gain[5] possessed by some of the very earliest systems would be considered to be quite respectable today. Although there has been improvement in performance, the prime advances have come about primarily as a result of the availability of solid state components. The first spread spectrum systems were implemented with vacuum tubes and were literally rooms full of equipment. Then, as switching transistors became available that could be used for code sequence generation in the megabit range, and could be used for the RF sections of spread spectrum systems, the systems became more practical and certainly more attractive from the user's viewpoint. In the late 1950's Western Electric's 2N560 transistor (selected) was used to implement a 5-Mbit code sequence generator using the transistors to drive two 2.5-Mbit/s delay line shift registers. (The delay line outputs were multiplexed together to give a 5-Mbit code.) Then, in the early 1960's, the Fairchild 2N706 and the higher beta Texas Instruments 2N744 made it possible to construct completely transistorized code generators that could run at bit rates well in excess of the 5 Mbit needed at that time. Until the advent of high speed, high gain transistors, spread spectrum systems were not really practical.

Integrated circuits have also made a significant impact on spread spectrum systems, just as they have on all other kinds of electronic equipment. Where a code generator in the 1960's often employed 500 or more transistors and thousands of other components, the same generator can be readily constructed today with less than a hundred components. Further, the integrated circuits field is sufficiently advanced that the entire code sequence generator could be implemented on a single integrated circuit, and it is certain that this will happen once circuit manufacturers see that such a circuit is salable. As a case in point, the phase-lock-loop integrated circuits that are now available from several manufacturers were just as useful in 1965 as they are now, but no manufacturer was interested in them as a market at that time. (This author talked to several uninterested prospective developers for phase-lock circuits then.)

Many of the early spread spectrum systems were intended to provide low detectability or minimum interference to other systems which were to share the bands they operated in. Prospective users soon discovered the other capabilities that were available

[5]Process gain is that property of a spread spectrum system that gives it its prime capabilities. It may be determined, in general, as the ratio of the RF bandwidth employed compared to the information rate.

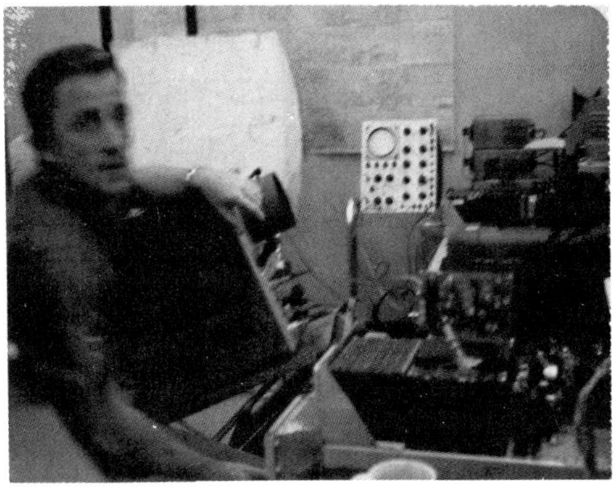

Fig. 8. ARC-50 engineering model in initial testing.

to do other jobs, however, and the emphasis has now been diverted to interference rejection and very high resolution ranging. These are the primary uses of spread spectrum systems today.

### *Some Spread Spectrum System and Subsystem Developments*

*NOMACS:* One of the very first (if not the first) spread spectrum systems was built by the M.I.T. Lincoln Lab., Lexington, Mass., and the Army Electronics Command, Fort Monmouth, N.J., and was called NOMACS (Noise Modulation and Correlation System). The system was built and tested in the late 1940's. It was direct sequence modulated, had a 10-kHz spread bandwidth at HF, employed a Rake tap combining receiver, and had a 25-dB process gain. The system's chief drawback was that it was constructed with vacuum tubes and therefore consisted of a roomful of equipment. Nevertheless, some systems were built, but they were never used operationally because of problems in operator training and maintenance. The system was demonstrated extensively in tests between the Lincoln Lab. and the Army Electronic Command as well as from the West Coast to the Army Electronics Command. The initial system employed a transmitted reference, but this was later changed in favor of a stored reference.

*Phantom I and II:* Phantom was one of the early spread spectrum systems, developed by the General Electric Company under contract to the Rome Air Development Center. Frequency hopping was employed as the basic spectrum-spreading medium. (See [1].)

*ARC-50:* The ARC-50 modem [2] was the first successful airborne spectrum modem. It was started by Sylvania under the Hush Up program and after several versions was finally implemented as a completely solid state modem with a 90 percent solid state companion transceiver, built by Magnavox. This system spawned a series of derivatives that have application in many areas. Fig. 8 shows one of the engineering development models under test in 1960. The author is standing in the left of the photo.

*URC-55:* The URC-55 modem [2] grew directly from the ARC-50-developed technology, but extended its

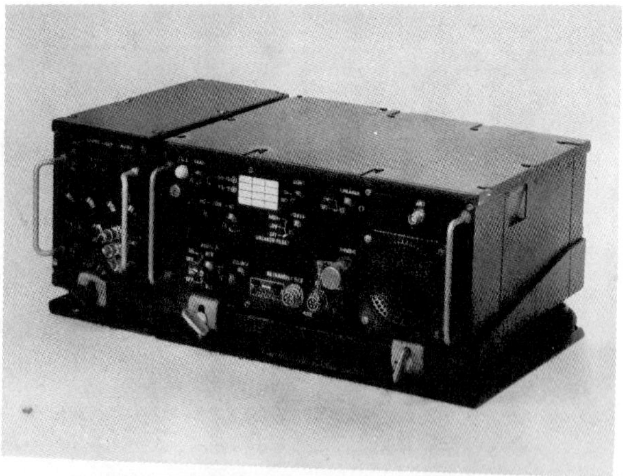

Fig. 9. Left: MX-170 spread spectrum modem for VHF. Right: VHF transceiver, VRC-12. (Courtesy Magnavox Co.)

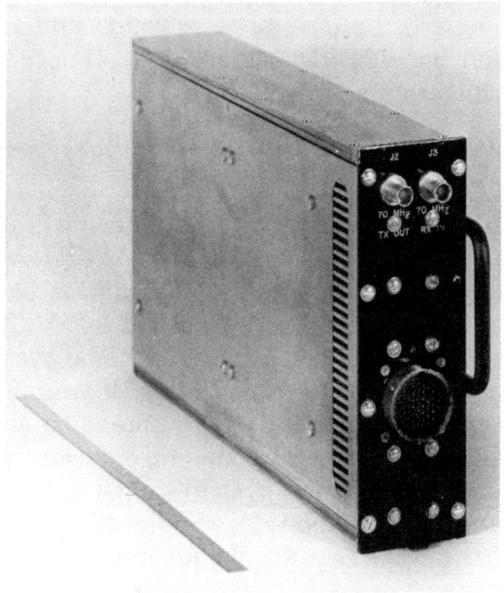

Fig. 10. Spread spectrum modem for use with 70-MHz IF. (Courtesy Magnavox Co.)

capability for use with a number of baseband signals through a wide-band and repeating satellite. The URC-55 is a direct sequence system and is packaged in two relay racks. The URC-55 was the first spread spectrum production system for satellite communications.

*URC-61:* The URC-61 modem [2] is compatible with the URC-55, but does not handle as many baseband signals. A frequency hopping synchronization mode was provided for the URC-61, however, that was not provided in the URC-55. The URC-61 was packaged in a single rack.

*MX-170 Modem:* Fig. 9 shows a spread spectrum modem that was developed for use in the VHF band (30 to 76 MHz) in conjunction with VRC-12 radio sets. The modem used direct sequence modulation for voice signal protection and also could provide range information to a similar terminal. The MX-170 [see (7)] was the first spread spectrum modem to employ Gold codes. The first developmental models were demonstrated in 1964.

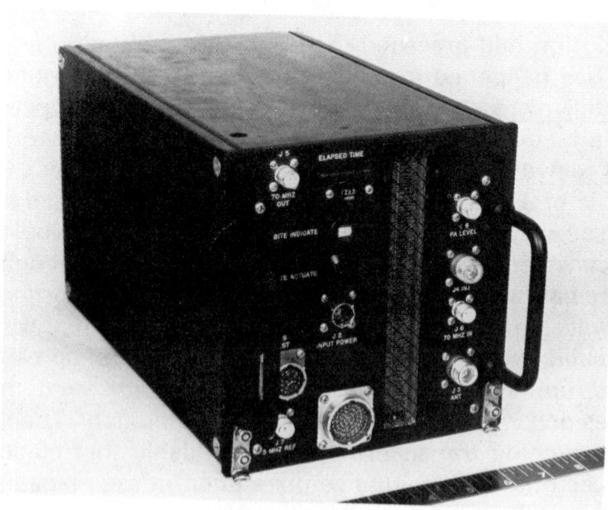

Fig. 11. UHF transceiver with wide-band 70-MHz IF. (Courtesy Magnavox Co.)

*UHF Modem:* The modem shown in Fig. 10 was developed for use in the military UHF (225- to 400-MHz) band and was designed to be able to do everything the earlier ARC-50 could do, and more. The modem is packaged in about one-fourth the volume of an ARC-50 modem, however, which was made possible by developments in the integrated circuits area, primarily. This modem operates at a 70-MHz IF.

*UHF Transceiver:* The UHF transceiver shown in Fig. 11 was specifically configured to handle wide-band signals at a 70-MHz IF, such as those produced by the modem shown in Fig. 10. In addition, this transceiver can perform all of the functions of a conventional UHF modem, including AM and frequency-shift keying (FSK) signal transmission and reception. One feature of the modem is its completely solid state circuitry, including its RF power amplifier.

*USC-28:* The newest version of a spread spectrum modem for Army use through Defense Satellite Communication System (DSCS) satellites is the USC-28 [2], which features full TDMA operation. This modem will replace the URC-55 and URC-61 modems and has greatly extended capabilities. The USC-28 has been under development since 1968 and was due for engineering development model delivery during 1975. Many advanced design features are included in the USC-28, including computer control and modem testing. It occupies three racks.

*Wide-band Command and Control Modem (WCCM):* Remotely piloted vehicles (RPV's) [4] have received prime attention within recent years because of the possibility that they will eventually be able to relieve human pilots of some of the riskier missions. Critical to the success of such vehicles, however, is the capability of a remote controller to send signals to them and to receive position or other information back from them. Spread spectrum techniques offer the ability to reject the jamming signals that could be expected

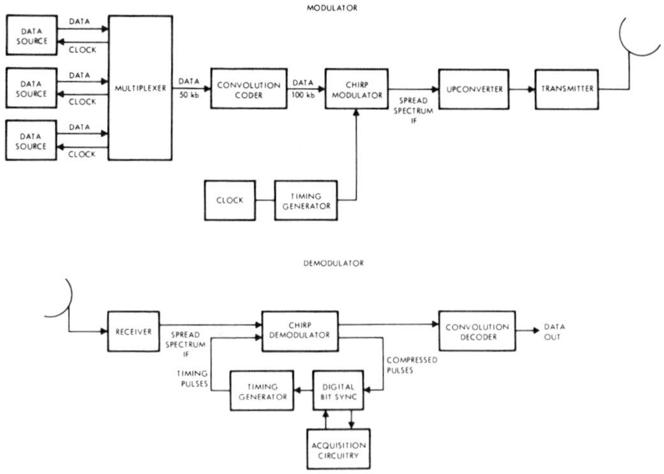


Fig. 12. Block diagram of chirp modem. (Courtesy Rome Air Development Center.)

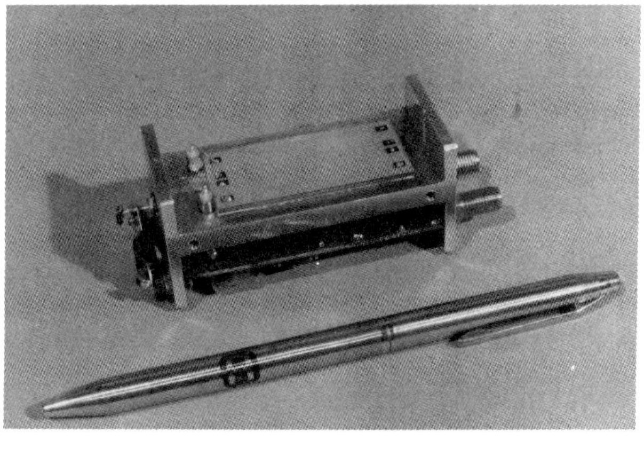

Fig. 13. Chirp filter for WCCM modem. (Courtesy Rome Air Development Center.)

in such operations and to protect the information sent from unauthorized reception. Two developmental approaches to a spread spectrum system for such use are briefly described in the following paragraphs.

*Chirp approach:* A block diagram of a chirp-type modem for RPV command and control is shown in Fig. 12. This modem is designed to operate with up to 25 vehicles at once, using time-division multiplexing. RF bandwidth of the spread spectrum signal is 38.4 MHz. The chirp filter, a reflective array compressor, surface wave device, is shown in Fig. 13.

*Direct sequence approach:* A WCCM was also developed that employed direct sequence modulation as its spectrum-spreading format. This system also controlled up to 25 vehicles at once. Its modulating code sequence operated at a 60-Mbit/s rate and continuous phase shift modulation (CPSM) was used to modulate the modem's carrier. Time-division multiplex was empolyed on the control link, while the return link from the vehicle used code-division multiplex. The developmental modem itself is shown in Fig. 14.

*Global Positioning System (GPS), or NAVSTAR:* (GPS) [8] is a system in which up to 24 satellites will be employed to provide signals that can be processed

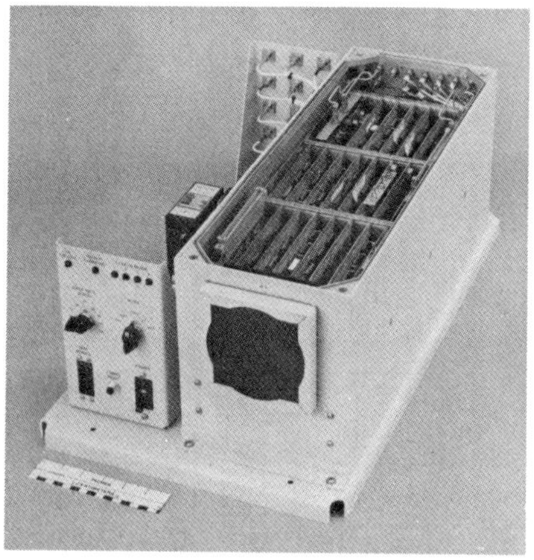

Fig. 14. RPV modem, pallet mounded and weighing approximately 35 lb. (Courtesy Rome Air Development Center.)

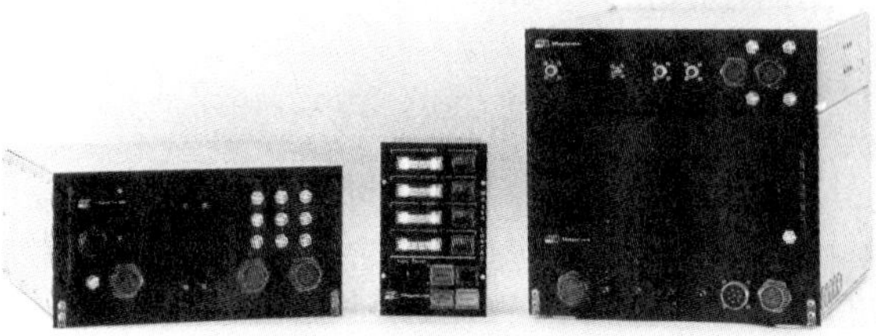

Fig. 15. Four-channel navigation receiver. (Courtesy Magnavox Co.)

by system users to derive precise time, position, and velocity information. GPS provides: 1) accurate three-dimensional positioning and velocity; 2) worldwide common grids; 3) passive and all weather operations; 4) real time and continuous information; 5) support of an unlimited number of users; 6) denial to unauthorized users; 7) resistance to jamming.

These services will be provided through use of a direct sequence signal that is transmitted from each satellite. A receiver uses the direct sequence signals coming from the satellites to measure the range to the satellites and then to combine the range measurements to determine its own position. This is done by multilateration. A number of GPS receiver configurations have been postulated, covering applications for fixed or shipboard to hand-held users; at this writing several development programs for various receiver configurations are under way. Fig. 15 shows a typical four-receiver navigation signal reception subsystem built to present standards. It is expected that by the time that GPS is fully operational, a full-capability GPS navigation receiver will be available in a 3/4 ATR short package. GPS is expected to be partly operational, with two-dimensional navigation capacity (9 satellites) in early 1981. Full operation, with 24 satellites, is scheduled for 1984.

*Position Location Reporting System (PLRS)*: PLRS [9] is primarily a position location system, although it does permit transfer of digital messages. Position location in PLRS is performed by combining time of arrival

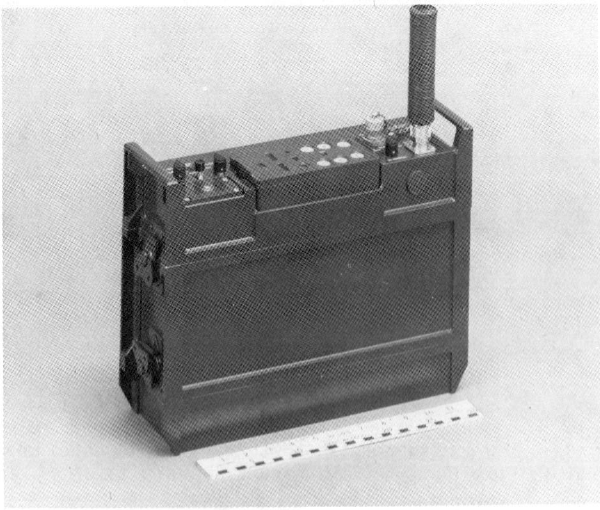

Fig. 16. PLRS user unit. (Courtesy Hughes Aircraft Co.)

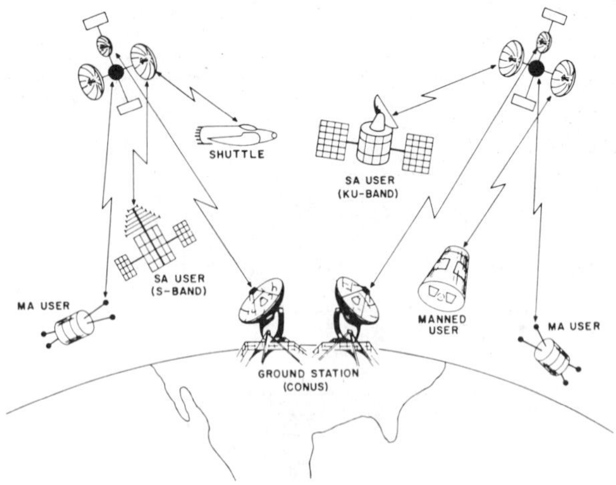


Fig. 17. TDRSS system concept.

(TOA) measurements from a number of units within a network to determine their positions with respect to a master unit. Positions of all the units in a network can be derived by processing TOA information generated as the various units receive transmissions from each other. PLRS employs time-division multiplexing to allow a large number of users to occupy a single network.

Two separate PLRS programs were let, and the resulting systems were under test by the Marine Corps. at the time of this writing. Fig. 16 shows the Hughes development model user unit (the man-packed portion of the system). PLRS, when fully operational will permit a field commander to know precisely where each element of his force is at any time and also to keep those elements, whether a single infantryman or a vehicle, in touch with the master unit.

*Seek Bus/Joint Tactical Information Distrubution System (JTIDS)*: Seek bus, or JTIDS [10], is a high capacity TDMA information distribution system for tactical communications, intended to be operational in the late 1970's. The system has the following characteristics: 1) TDMA; 2) 1280 time slots in 10 s; 3) operation in the 962–1215-MHz band; 4) omnidirectional antennas only; 5) 56.2-kHz information bandwidth; 6) jamming resistance; 7) cryptographic security; 8) line of signt or relay operation; 9) no dedicated fixed terminals; 10) high survivability; and 11) high availability.

The system will share an operating frequency band with two other systems: tactical air navigation (TACAN) and identification friend or foe (IFF). The waveform used has been selected to produce minimum interference to these other systems, and it is expected that they will be able to continue to operate as they do at the present time, without modification to their waveforms or equipment. This is made possible by employing both frequency hopping and direct sequence modulations in the seek bus/JTIDS signal structure. Thus, those frequencies that could cause a problem for the less capable IFF and TACAN systems can be avoided, while the direct sequence modulation gives minimum signal density for interference at those frequencies that are not specifically being avoided. The process gain available is a product of both the direct sequence and frequency hopping modulations.

The first application of the seek bus/JTIDS system is in the AWACS program, but it is expected that system will be expanded to include all military tactical users in the future.

*Tracking and Data Relay Satellite System (TDRSS)*: The TDRSS program [11] is a NASA program that is intended to provide support to a large number of earth-orbiting vehicles by giving them a path for communicating with a ground station in the continental United States, even when they are far out of the field of view of that ground station. The TDRS satellites act as relays for the ground station and various users, such as the space shuttle vehicle. Spread spectrum modulation is employed to provide both time-division and code-division multiple access advantages. The primary modulation method used is direct sequence, but frequency hopping is also employed to enable rapid code synchronization. The system is expected to be operational in the 1980's. Fig. 17 shows the concept of TDRSS.

*Some Recent Subsystem Developments:* Contemporary matched filter circuitry employing surface acoustic waves is illustrated by the two examples that follow. The first of these is a 31-bit fully programmable unit developed by Motorola under contract to Rome Air Development Center. Fig. 18 shows why such circuits are so attractive from a size, weight, and production standpoint: there are 36 potential matched filters on the one wafer shown here. A packaged circuit (minus cover) is shown in Fig. 19. This surface wave matched filter package includes a read-only memory (ROM) controlled 31-bit silicon MOSFET biphase tap structure and a zinc oxide film layer transducer structure. The

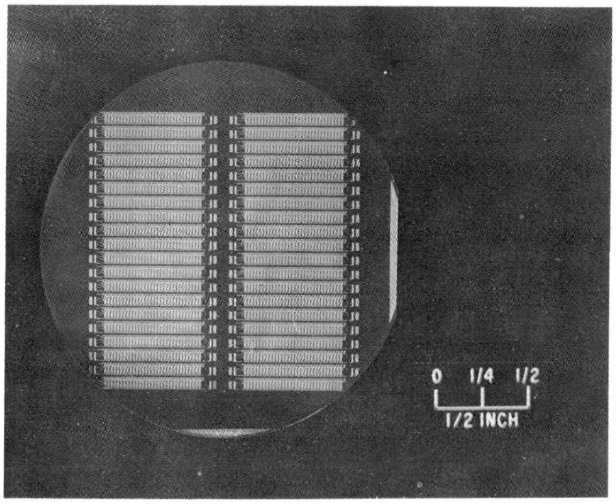


Fig. 18. Wafer showing matched filters. (Courtesy Rome Air Development Center.)

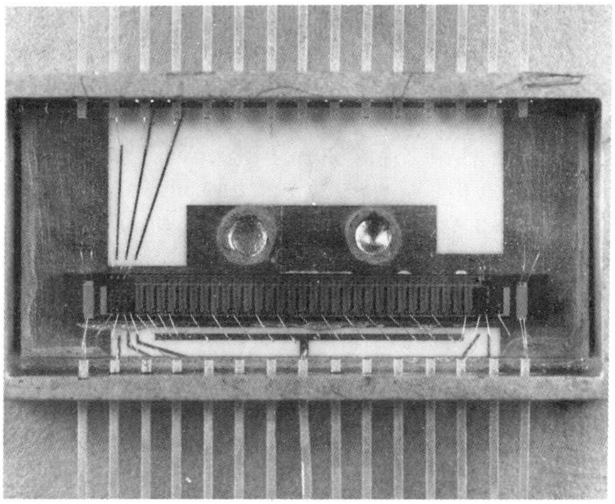

Fig. 19. Packaged matched filter. (Courtesy Rome Air Development Center.)

entrie matched filter was integrated on a single silicon chip measuring 770 by 75 mil.

Conversion efficiency of the 10 finger pair zinc oxide film layer transducers is good enough to produce only 15-dB loss, and coupling efficiency is approximately 40 dB per tap. Overall losses total 78 dB from pulsed input to coded output. Operating as a code sequence generator, the output code to noise ratio is 17 dB. In the reverse direction (code modulated input and pulse output) loss is 44 dB. The peak to sidelobe ratio is 12 dB for autocorrelation and 8 dB for cross correlation.

This development demonstrates that zinc oxide–silicon MOSFET acoustic surface wave devices can be developed in monolithic form to produce high performance matched filters.

A second matched filter, implemented with quartz as a medium and with hybrid integrated circuits for its interfaces and drivers was also developed. This time the matched filter had 127 delay elements, fully programmable, at a 10-Mbit/s chip rate. Some of its operating parameters are

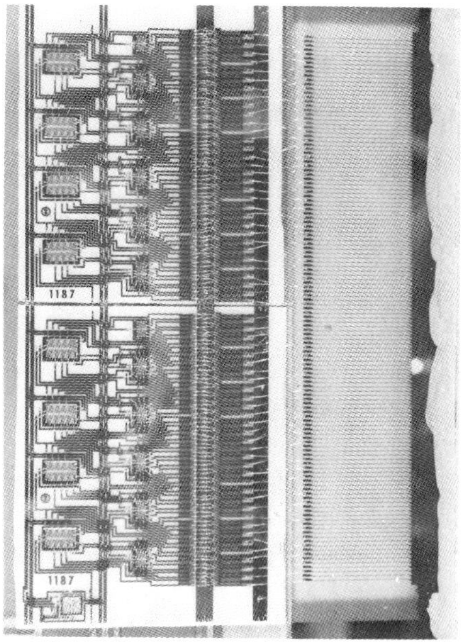


Fig. 20. 127-bit matched filter. (Courtesy Rome Air Development Center.)

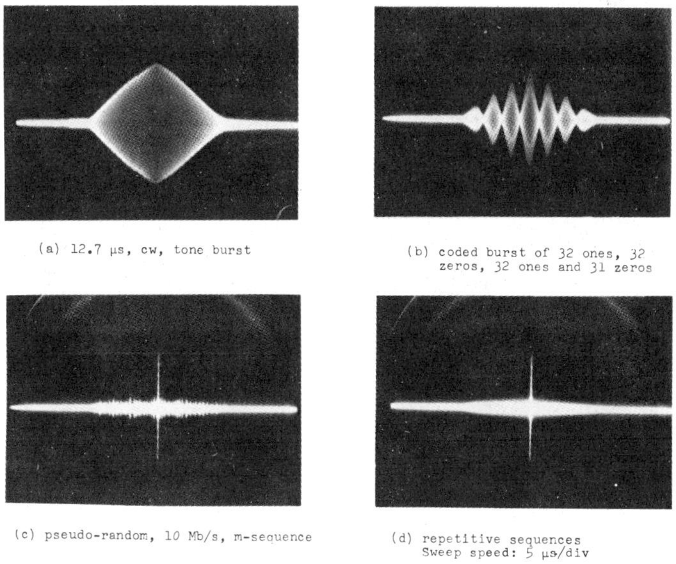


Fig. 21. 127-bit matched filter waveforms. (Courtesy Rome Air Development Center.)

| | |
|---|---|
| insertion loss | 58.7 dB |
| process gain | 20.0 dB |
| time sidelobes | -18.2 dB |
| center frequency shift | 7.32 kHz/30°C (differential) |
| compressed pulse amplitude shift | 0.6 dB/30°C (differential) |
| code change time | 25.4 µs |
| length | 127 elements |
| element length | 100 ns |
| operating frequency | 60 MHz. |

A photograph of this matched filter is shown in Fig. 20. Its overall size is 3 by 4 by 1.25 in. Quartz was selected for the delay medium because of its low temperature and coupling coefficients. Performance of this matched filter is shown in Fig. 21.

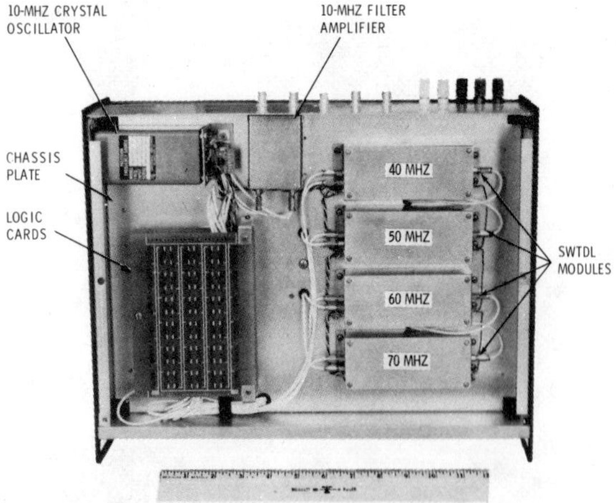


Fig. 22. FH/PN modem. (Courtesy Rome Air Development Center.)

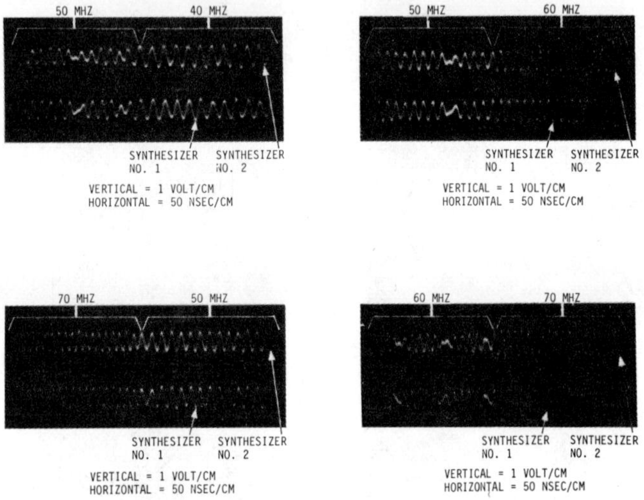


Fig. 23. FH/PN waveforms. (Courtesy Rome Air Development Center.)

A coherent synthesizer that should be of interest is shown in Fig. 22. This synthesizer employs acoustic surface wave delay lines to generate signals at 40, 50, 60, and 70 MHz. Each surface wave device has an impulse that is a carrier biphase modulated with a 127-bit maximal PN code, at a 10-Mbit/s rate. The overall output bandwidth of the four-frequency synthesizer is 40 MHz. At room ambient temperature, the synthesizer maintains its coherence within 18° rms. For 30° temperature differential, coherence degrades by approximately 4.5°. Fig. 23 shows waveforms at the synthesizer output.

## REMAINING PROBLEMS

A number of problems remain to be solved in the spread spectrum systems world. In fact, this list of problems looks a great deal like a list that could have been generated more than 20 years ago. One can hardly assume, therefore, that spread spectrum systems have come to their maturity, even though they have found a number of uses in those 20-plus years. The following are some of the problems that remain:

*Frequency Assignment:* Spread spectrum modulation offers minimum interference to other types of receivers, but this does not solve the problem for such receivers when they must operate near a high power spread spectrum transmitter. Future use of spread spectrum signals will depend on assignment of other types of systems in the same band, since there is no reason to expect that exclusive use of any part of the spectrum will be assigned for exclusive use. The burden of noninterference will have to be borne by the spread spectrum user.

*Standardized Signal Formats:* No standards exist with respect to the various signal formats. Every system in existence employs a modulation scheme that is different from all others, and therefore none can transmit to a receiver that was not specifically designed to receive the signal from that particular transmitter. That is, equipment of one particular type will talk from unit to unit, but other equipment from the same manufacturer but different vintage will not do so. The prime reason for this is the rapid advances in components and techniques that have occurred, with the resultant lack of uniformity as equipment capability has been improved. The time has come, however, to bring some uniformity to the spread spectrum world in such areas as code rates and IF, at least. This would not preclude advances or even specialized applications, but would begin to allow common use of the available frequency spectrum and pave the way for more general use of spread spectrum systems.

*Common Terminology:* Allied to the problem of standards is the fact that no common terminology is in existence for spread spectrum systems and subsystems. This problem should be addressed along with format standardization.

*Operator Training and maintenance:* Operators and maintenance personnel for spread spectrum systems are in short supply. This is because of the relative complexity of spread spectrum systems and the fact that the synchronization requirement brings an operational constraint that is unfamiliar. This problem will be solved of its own accord as more systems are deployed and as they move into commercial applications.

*Size, Weight, and Cost:* The size, weight, and cost of spread spectrum systems are being minimized as rapidly as the integrated circuit art improves. The first spread spectrum systems were made up of rooms full of vacuum tubes. The next generation gave better performance with a cubic foot of transistors and a few tubes in their RF sections. Today's systems are about one-half a cubic foot, and they employ both integrated circuits and discrete transistors—with no vacuum tubes as long as operation is below a few gigahertz. Tomorrow's systems will probably consist of a score of large scale integrated circuits with perhaps a few hybrid circuits for the higher frequency functions.

In addition to these problems, further advances are needed to improve processing gain and ranging resolution, preferably without increasing the RF bandwidth

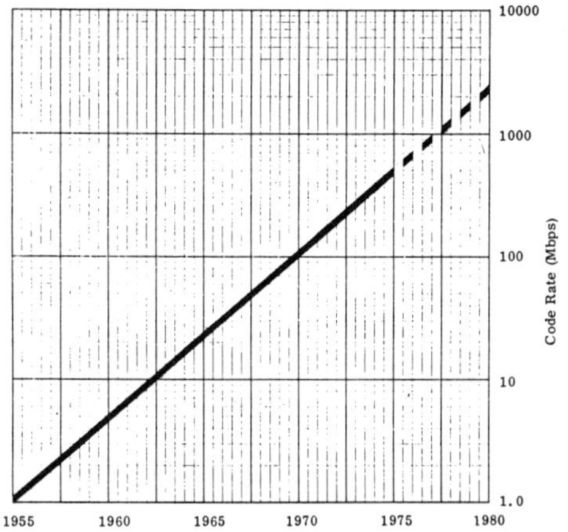


Fig. 24. Projection of code rate capability for direct sequence systems through 1980.

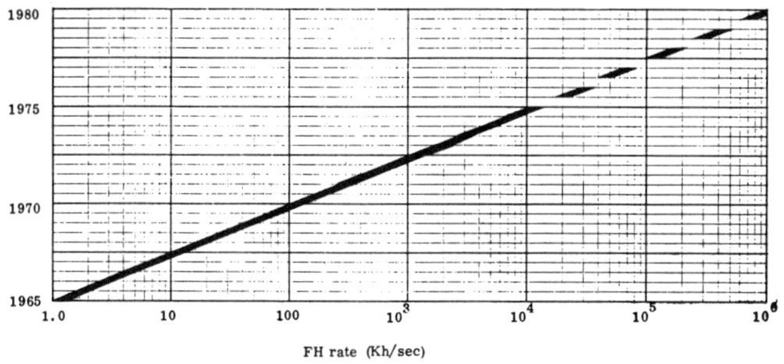


Fig. 25. Projection of hopping rate for frequency hopping synthesizers with 100 to 10 000 available frequencies through 1980.

required. The engineer just now entering the field need not think that all the problems have been solved and that he cannot find a fresh area to which to contribute. Indeed, just the opposite is true: a whole new communications area lies waiting to be explored and to be brought within the useful repertoire of all communicators. Some specific areas that presently appear to be most challenging and that offer high rewards are

1) development of practical long matched filter detectors capable of more than 40-dB jamming margins;
2) employment of small computers (minicomputers and microcomputers) for system control, code generation and decoding, and signal demodulation;
3) analog/digital signal conversion for voice and video basebands, with data compression to provide maximum process gains;
4) surface acoustic wave and charge coupled devices to minimize the size, weight, and cost of spread spectrum processors;
5) development of new coding structures that enable many link users at once, but that ease synchronization and signal encryption where it is required;
6) development of new spread spectrum-compatible RF subsystems that enhance their operation, rather than degrade it.

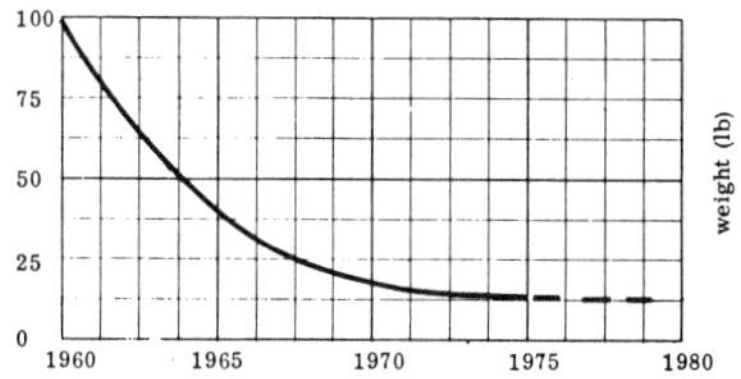


Fig. 26. Projection of weight for spread spectrum systems through 1980.

A place already exists for any of these, and this will continue to be true for as long as the need to reject interference, range with high resolution, or any of the other things at which spread spectrum systems excel continue to exist.

## PROJECTION OF FUTURE CAPABILITY

Spread spectrum communication and navigation systems, though existing in practical form for some 15 years (since the advent of sufficiently economical high speed junction transistors), have not yet realized their potential in either use or capability. This is true in part because of system cost and complexity, and in part because of a lack of widespread knowledge of system capabilities. The general tendency, in fact, has been to doubt the existence of practical spread spectrum systems or equipment.

The first practical spread spectrum systems (including transmitter) capable of airborne operation employed approximately 600 discrete transistors and several electron tubes, weighed over 100 lbs, and had a volume of 1.2 $f^3$. Today's equivalent system contains half the semiconductors, no electron tubes, weighs one-fourth as much and takes up one-third the volume of the earlier system, even though its capability is greatly expanded. It is expected that systems developed in the next 5 to 10 years can take full advantage of various large scale integrated circuit techniques available even now to produce systems weighing 15 lb or less, occupying 500 $in^3$, and employing less than 100 separate semiconductor packages.

Today, spread spectrum technology is in a state of development such that not only is equipment available to operate in an airborne environment and to perform the job of protecting vulnerable signals, but the state of spread spectrum development is reasonably predictable through 1980. Figs. 24, 25, and 26 show the capabilities of direct sequence and frequency hopping systems in recent years, with projections of future capability.

For most applications, the present spread spectrum systems are adaptable, though not optimum. Functionally, these systems include far more capability and flexibility than is necessary in most applications. (Present configurations allow, for instance, selection of any one of millions of codes from a pilot's control panel.)

Fig. 24 shows code rate capability for direct sequence systems. The code rate determines spread spectrum bandwidth in a direct sequence system and this in turn determines the system's advantage against jamming, its range resolution, etc. Spread spectrum bandwidth is approximately twice the code rate, so that in 1976 one might expect to be able to generate direct sequence RF bandwidths 900 MHz wide and by 1980, up to 5 GHz wide. It must be noted, however, that reliable and economical code generation for RPV environments could dictate the use of much slower codes.

Frequency hopping synthesizer capability is plotted in Fig. 25. Based on improvements of the past 5 years, frequency synthesizers could reach 10 million hops per second in 1976. Again, however, practicality will restrict the usable rate. The projection of Fig. 2 shows hopping rate reading 1 gigahop per second by 1980. It is felt, however, that this is an overly optimistic estimate, and that hopping rates will not be greater than 10 million hops per second even in 1980 unless some completely new method of frequency synthesis is developed in the interim period.

Fig. 26 shows the reduction in weight achieved in spread spectrum systems since 1960. Equipment used in 1980 is not expected to be significantly lighter than that available now, since the bulk of weight is in RF translation and power amplification, and this is not expected to change significantly because of power dissipation requirements.

Equipment in existence today is capable of many communication systems requirements for antijamming and multiple access. Only wide baseband bandwidths (such as video) would require more than modifications to present equipment to satisfy either control or data link requirements. Equipment used in 1980 will be restricted by the same reliability and power dissipation problems expected in the 1976 designs. Therefore, it is reasonable to expect that a 1980 spread spectrum system receiver–transmitter will weigh approximately 10 to 20 lb, employ code rates in the 200-Mbit/s (or less) range (with auxiliary frequency hopping), and have approximately 100 W output power in the 200- to 400-MHz band.

## REFERENCES


[1] K. Gilmore, "The secret keepers," *Popular Electron.*, Aug. 1962.

[2] G. D. LaRue, "The evolution of spread spectrum equipment for the defense satellite system communications," *Signal*, Aug. 1975.

[3] J. N. Birch, "Spread spectrum technology applications," *Signal*, Aug. 1975.

[4] H. M. Federhan, "RPV command and control," *Signal*, Aug. 1975.

[5] K. Kronlund, "A fighter pilot's view of JTIDS," *Signal*, Aug. 1975.

[6] R. C. Dixon, "Why spread spectrum," *IEEE Commun. Soc. Dig.*, July 1975.

[7] ——, "MX-170 voice process modem," Magnavox Res. Lab., Torrance, Calif.

[8] ——, "NAVSTAR—Global positioning system," Air Force Space and Missiles Systems Org., Los Angeles, Calif.

[9] ——, "PLRS—Position location reporting system," Marine Corps Development and Education Command, Quantico, Va.

[10] C. E. Ellingson, "SEEK BUS—Description and status," Mitre Corp., Sept. 1974.

[11] ——, "Tracking and data relay satellite system (TDRSS) user's guide," NASA Goddard Space Flight Center, May 1975.

# Part I
# Anti-Interference

This part contains five papers that deal specifically with what is probably the most sought after property of spread spectrum systems, the capability to reject interference. The first paper, by C. E. Shannon, was published in 1949 in the *Proceedings of the IRE* and presented in 1947 to the New York Section of the IRE. This was before publication of his more famous paper, "A Mathematical Theory of Communication," in 1948 in the *Bell System Technical Journal*, a paper that is claimed by information theorists, coding theorists, and spread spectrum communicators as a basis for their branch of science. Shannon's paper was chosen here because is presents the concept that the error rate in a channel can be set arbitrarily low by properly coding the information being sent (and that is what a spread spectrum system endeavors to do), while spreading the bandwidth of the signal being sent. The second paper, by J. P. Costas, introduces the notion that "if intentional jamming is a consideration, one must of necessity choose a broad-band technique."

The remaining papers in this part are oriented to more direct concerns. Sussman and Ferrari discuss the effects of employing a notch filter or filters to remove narrow-band interference from a composite spread spectrum/interference signal. The discussion centers on the effects on the receiver of losing narrow portions of the desired signal due to the notch filter of filters. Digital matched filters are addressed by C. R. Cahn, with the filters having interference and dither applied to them, and a minimax design optimization technique is given. In the remaining paper, Freeman analyzes the effect of dither and interference on correlators.

Interference rejection in spread spectrum systems is important not only to the military communicator who has important traffic to send, but is also of interest to those who must contend with ever more crowded radio bands. It has been suggested that more efficient use of the available spectrum might be made by assigning both narrow-band and wide-band users the same frequencies for concurrent use. Under the right conditions, such concurrent use would be quite practical. The burden of achieving practicality would necessarily fall on the spread spectrum users, however, because of the fact that most of the frequency spectrum is already filled with narrow-band users who got there first, and the cost of modifying the present narrow-band sets to accommodate spread spectrum users would be astronomical. The approach then would be to let the present users go on about their business, but overlay spread spectrum users on the present networks. The spread spectrum systems would then not only be required to furnish minimum interference to the conventional systems, but also operate well in the presence of many interfering signals.

At present, it is unthinkable to suggest that a spread spectrum radio network might occupy the television band, but it is feasible, and in the future may prove to be the only alternative to doing without sorely needed communication channels. The same is true of the rest of the usable frequency spectrum. Future radio systems will depend on their capability to reject unwanted signals, and spread spectrum techniques are alone in their ability to resist interference without regard as to its type or direction of origin.

## OTHER PAPERS OF INTEREST


1) J. M. Aein and R. D. Turner, "Effect of co-channel interference on CPSK carriers," *IEEE Trans. Commun. Technol.*, June 1966.
2) C. R. Cahn, "Data coding to reduce vulnerability to pulse Jamming," Magnavox Res. Labs., Rep. STN-13, Nov. 1964.
3) ——, "Comparison of frequency hopping and PN for AJ data transmission," Magnavox Res. Labs., Rep. STN-15, Dec. 1964.
4) H. J. Friedman, "Jamming susceptibility," *IEEE Trans. Aerosp. Electron. Syst.*, July 1968.
5) S. L. Levine, "Anti-jam communications systems," ASTIA Doc., AD445897, Apr. 1964.
6) W. C. Morchin, "Radar range in a jamming environment," *Microwave J.*, June 1968.
7) J. L. Sevy, "The effect of limiting a biphase or quadriphase signal plus interference," this reprint volume.
8) R. Thorensen, "On the theory of jam-resistant communication systems," Magnavox Res. Labs., Rep. R-502, Apr. 1962.
9) A. J. Viterbi, "Maximum problems in coding for jammed channels," Magnavox Res. Labs., Rep. STN-27, June 1966.
10) ——, "Bandspreading combats multipath and RFI in tactical satellite net," *Commun. Designer's Dig.*, Dec. 1969.

# Communication in the Presence of Noise*

CLAUDE E. SHANNON†, MEMBER, IRE

*Summary*—**A method is developed for representing any communication system geometrically. Messages and the corresponding signals are points in two "function spaces," and the modulation process is a mapping of one space into the other. Using this representation, a number of results in communication theory are deduced concerning expansion and compression of bandwidth and the threshold effect. Formulas are found for the maximum rate of transmission of binary digits over a system when the signal is perturbed by various types of noise. Some of the properties of "ideal" systems which transmit at this maximum rate are discussed. The equivalent number of binary digits per second for certain information sources is calculated.**

* Decimal classification: 621.38. Original manuscript received by the Institute, July 23, 1940. Presented, 1948 IRE National Convention, New York, N. Y., March 24, 1948; and IRE New York Section, New York, N. Y., November 12, 1947.

† Bell Telephone Laboratories, Murray Hill, N. J.

## I. Introduction

A GENERAL COMMUNICATIONS system is shown schematically in Fig. 1. It consists essentially of five elements.

1. *An information source.* The source selects one message from a set of possible messages to be transmitted to the receiving terminal. The message may be of various types; for example, a sequence of letters or numbers, as in telegraphy or teletype, or a continuous function of time $f(t)$, as in radio or telephony.

2. *The transmitter.* This operates on the message in some way and produces a signal suitable for transmission to the receiving point over the channel. In teleph-

Reprinted from *Proc. IRE*, vol. 37, pp. 10–21, Jan. 1949.

ony, this operation consists of merely changing sound pressure into a proportional electrical current. In teleg-

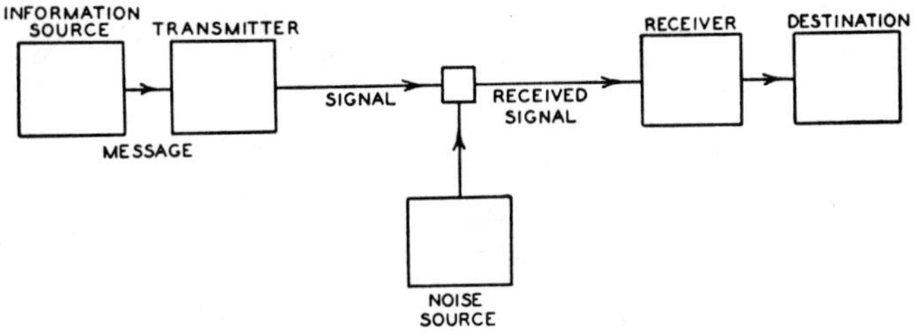


Fig. 1—General communications system.

raphy, we have an encoding operation which produces a sequence of dots, dashes, and spaces corresponding to the letters of the message. To take a more complex example, in the case of multiplex PCM telephony the different speech functions must be sampled, compressed, quantized and encoded, and finally interleaved properly to construct the signal.

3. *The channel.* This is merely the medium used to transmit the signal from the transmitting to the receiving point. It may be a pair of wires, a coaxial cable, a band of radio frequencies, etc. During transmission, or at the receiving terminal, the signal may be perturbed by noise or distortion. Noise and distortion may be differentiated on the basis that distortion is a fixed operation applied to the signal, while noise involves statistical and unpredictable perturbations. Distortion can, in principle, be corrected by applying the inverse operation, while a perturbation due to noise cannot always be removed, since the signal does not always undergo the same change during transmission.

4. *The receiver.* This operates on the received signal and attempts to reproduce, from it, the original message. Ordinarily it will perform approximately the mathematical inverse of the operations of the transmitter, although they may differ somewhat with best design in order to combat noise.

5. *The destination.* This is the person or thing for whom the message is intended.

Following Nyquist[1] and Hartley,[2] it is convenient to use a logarithmic measure of information. If a device has $n$ possible positions it can, by definition, store $\log_b n$ units of information. The choice of the base $b$ amounts to a choice of unit, since $\log_b n = \log_b c \log_c n$. We will use the base 2 and call the resulting units binary digits or bits. A group of $m$ relays or flip-flop circuits has $2^m$ possible sets of positions, and can therefore store $\log_2 2^m = m$ bits.

If it is possible to distinguish reliably $M$ different signal functions of duration $T$ on a channel, we can say that the channel can transmit $\log_2 M$ bits in time $T$. The *rate* of transmission is then $\log_2 M/T$. More precisely, the *channel capacity* may be defined as

$$C = \lim_{T\to\infty} \frac{\log_2 M}{T}. \tag{1}$$

A precise meaning will be given later to the requirement of reliable resolution of the $M$ signals.

## II. The Sampling Theorem

Let us suppose that the channel has a certain bandwidth $W$ in cps starting at zero frequency, and that we are allowed to use this channel for a certain period of time $T$. Without any further restrictions this would mean that we can use as signal functions any functions of time whose spectra lie entirely within the band $W$, and whose time functions lie within the interval $T$. Although it is not possible to fulfill both of these conditions exactly, it is possible to keep the spectrum within the band $W$, and to have the time function very small outside the interval $T$. Can we describe in a more useful way the functions which satisfy these conditions? One answer is the following:

Theorem 1: *If a function $f(t)$ contains no frequencies higher than $W$ cps, it is completely determined by giving its ordinates at a series of points spaced $1/2W$ seconds apart.*

This is a fact which is common knowledge in the communication art. The intuitive justification is that, if $f(t)$ contains no frequencies higher than $W$, it cannot change to a substantially new value in a time less than one-half cycle of the highest frequency, that is, $1/2W$. A mathematical proof showing that this is not only approximately, but exactly, true can be given as follows. Let $F(\omega)$ be the spectrum of $f(t)$. Then

$$f(t) = \frac{1}{2\pi}\int_{-\infty}^{\infty} F(\omega)e^{i\omega t}d\omega \tag{2}$$

$$= \frac{1}{2\pi}\int_{-2\pi W}^{+2\pi W} F(\omega)e^{i\omega t}d\omega, \tag{3}$$

since $F(\omega)$ is assumed zero outside the band $W$. If we let

$$t = \frac{n}{2W} \tag{4}$$

where $n$ is any positive or negative integer, we obtain

$$f\left(\frac{n}{2W}\right) = \frac{1}{2\pi}\int_{-2\pi W}^{+2\pi W} F(\omega)e^{i\omega \frac{n}{2W}}\,d\omega. \tag{5}$$

On the left are the values of $f(t)$ at the sampling points. The integral on the right will be recognized as essentially the $n$th coefficient in a Fourier-series expansion of the function $F(\omega)$, taking the interval $-W$ to $+W$ as a fundamental period. This means that the values of the samples $f(n/2W)$ determine the Fourier coefficients in the series expansion of $F(\omega)$. Thus they determine $F(\omega)$, since $F(\omega)$ is zero for frequencies greater than $W$, and for

[1] H. Nyquist, "Certain factors affecting telegraph speed," *Bell Syst. Tech. Jour.*, vol. 3, p. 324; April, 1924.
[2] R. V. L. Hartley, "The transmission of information," *Bell Sys. Tech. Jour.*, vol. 3, p. 535–564; July, 1928.

lower frequencies $F(\omega)$ is determined if its Fourier coefficients are determined. But $F(\omega)$ determines the original function $f(t)$ completely, since a function is determined if its spectrum is known. Therefore the original samples determine the function $f(t)$ completely. There is one and only one function whose spectrum is limited to a band $W$, and which passes through given values at sampling points separated $1/2W$ seconds apart. The function can be simply reconstructed from the samples by using a pulse of the type

$$\frac{\sin 2\pi Wt}{2\pi Wt}. \tag{6}$$

This function is unity at $t=0$ and zero at $t=n/2W$, i.e., at all other sample points. Furthermore, its spectrum is constant in the band $W$ and zero outside. At each sample point a pulse of this type is placed whose amplitude is adjusted to equal that of the sample. The sum of these pulses is the required function, since it satisfies the conditions on the spectrum and passes through the sampled values.

Mathematically, this process can be described as follows. Let $x_n$ be the $n$th sample. Then the function $f(t)$ is represented by

$$f(t) = \sum_{n=-\infty}^{\infty} x_n \frac{\sin \pi(2Wt - n)}{\pi(2Wt - n)}. \tag{7}$$

A similar result is true if the band $W$ does not start at zero frequency but at some higher value, and can be proved by a linear translation (corresponding physically to single-sideband modulation) of the zero-frequency case. In this case the elementary pulse is obtained from $\sin x/x$ by single-side-band modulation.

If the function is limited to the time interval $T$ and the samples are spaced $1/2W$ seconds apart, there will be a total of $2TW$ samples in the interval. All samples outside will be substantially zero. To be more precise, we can define a function to be limited to the time interval $T$ if, and only if, all the samples outside this interval are exactly zero. Then we can say that any function limited to the bandwidth $W$ and the time interval $T$ can be specified by giving $2TW$ numbers.

Theorem 1 has been given previously in other forms by mathematicians[3] but in spite of its evident importance seems not to have appeared explicitly in the literature of communication theory. Nyquist,[4,5] however, and more recently Gabor,[6] have pointed out that approximately $2TW$ numbers are sufficient, basing their arguments on a Fourier series expansion of the function over the time interval $T$. This gives $TW$ sine and $(TW+1)$ cosine terms up to frequency $W$. The slight discrepancy is due to the fact that the functions obtained in this way will not be strictly limited to the band $W$ but, because of the sudden starting and stopping of the sine and cosine components, contain some frequency content outside the band. Nyquist pointed out the fundamental importance of the time interval $1/2W$ seconds in connection with telegraphy, and we will call this the Nyquist interval corresponding to the band $W$.

The $2TW$ numbers used to specify the function need not be the equally spaced samples used above. For example, the samples can be unevenly spaced, although, if there is considerable bunching, the samples must be known very accurately to give a good reconstruction of the function. The reconstruction process is also more involved with unequal spacing. One can further show that the value of the function and its derivative at every other sample point are sufficient. The value and first and second derivatives at every third sample point give a still different set of parameters which uniquely determine the function. Generally speaking, any set of $2TW$ independent numbers associated with the function can be used to describe it.

## III. Geometrical Representation of the Signals

A set of three numbers $x_1$, $x_2$, $x_3$, regardless of their source, can always be thought of as co-ordinates of a point in three-dimensional space. Similarly, the $2TW$ evenly spaced samples of a signal can be thought of as co-ordinates of a point in a space of $2TW$ dimensions. Each particular selection of these numbers corresponds to a particular point in this space. Thus there is exactly one point corresponding to each signal in the band $W$ and with duration $T$.

The number of dimensions $2TW$ will be, in general, very high. A 5-Mc television signal lasting for an hour would be represented by a point in a space with $2\times 5 \times 10^6 \times 60^2 = 3.6\times 10^{10}$ dimensions. Needless to say, such a space cannot be visualized. It is possible, however, to study analytically the properties of $n$-dimensional space. To a considerable extent, these properties are a simple generalization of the properties of two- and three-dimensional space, and can often be arrived at by inductive reasoning from these cases. The advantage of this geometrical representation of the signals is that we can use the vocabulary and the results of geometry in the communication problem. Essentially, we have replaced a complex entity (say, a television signal) in a simple environment (the signal requires only a plane for its representation as $f(t)$) by a simple entity (a point) in a complex environment ($2TW$ dimensional space).

If we imagine the $2TW$ co-ordinate axes to be at right angles to each other, then distances in the space have a simple interpretation. The distance from the origin to a

[3] J. M. Whittaker, "Interpolatory Function Theory," Cambridge Tracts in Mathematics and Mathematical Physics, No. 33, Cambridge University Press, Chapt. IV; 1935.

[4] H. Nyquist, "Certain topics in telegraph transmission theory," *A.I.E.E. Transactions*, p. 617; April, 1928.

[5] W. R. Bennett, "Time division multiplex systems," *Bell Sys. Tech. Jour.*, vol. 20, p. 199; April, 1941, where a result similar to Theorem 1 is established, but on a steady-state basis.

[6] D. Gabor, "Theory of communication," *Jour. I.E.E.* (London), vol. 93; part 3, no. 26, p. 429; 1946.

point is analogous to the two- and three-dimensional cases

$$d = \sqrt{\sum_{n=1}^{2TW} x_n^2} \tag{8}$$

where $x_n$ is the $n$th sample. Now, since

$$f(t) = \sum_{n=1}^{2TW} x_n \frac{\sin \pi(2Wt - n)}{\pi(2Wt - n)}, \tag{9}$$

we have

$$\int_{-\infty}^{\infty} f(t)^2 dt = \frac{1}{2W} \sum x_n^2, \tag{10}$$

using the fact that

$$\int_{-\infty}^{\infty} \frac{\sin \pi(2Wt - m)}{\pi(2Wt - m)} \frac{\sin \pi(2Wt - n)}{\pi(Wt - n)} dt = \begin{cases} 0 & m \neq n \\ \frac{1}{2W} & m = n. \end{cases} \tag{11}$$

Hence, the square of the distance to a point is $2W$ times the energy (more precisely, the energy into a unit resistance) of the corresponding signal

$$\begin{aligned} d^2 &= 2WE \\ &= 2WTP \end{aligned} \tag{12}$$

where $P$ is the average power over the time $T$. Similarly, the distance between two points is $\sqrt{2WT}$ times the rms discrepancy between the two corresponding signals.

If we consider only signals whose average power is less than $P$, these will correspond to points within a sphere of radius

$$r = \sqrt{2WTP}. \tag{13}$$

If noise is added to the signal in transmission, it means that the point corresponding to the signal has been moved a certain distance in the space proportional to the rms value of the noise. Thus noise produces a small region of uncertainty about each point in the space. A fixed distortion in the channel corresponds to a warping of the space, so that each point is moved, but in a definite fixed way.

In ordinary three-dimensional space it is possible to set up many different co-ordinate systems. This is also possible in the signal space of $2TW$ dimensions that we are considering. A different co-ordinate system corresponds to a different way of describing the same signal function. The various ways of specifying a function given above are special cases of this. One other way of particular importance in communication is in terms of frequency components. The function $f(t)$ can be expanded as a sum of sines and cosines of frequencies $1/T$ apart, and the coefficients used as a different set of co-ordinates. It can be shown that these co-ordinates are all perpendicular to each other and are obtained by what is essentially a rotation of the original co-ordinate system.

Passing a signal through an ideal filter corresponds to projecting the corresponding point onto a certain region in the space. In fact, in the frequency-co-ordinate system those components lying in the pass band of the filter are retained and those outside are eliminated, so that the projection is on one of the co-ordinate lines, planes, or hyperplanes. Any filter performs a linear operation on the vectors of the space, producing a new vector linearly related to the old one.

## IV. Geometrical Representation of Messages

We have associated a space of $2TW$ dimensions with the set of possible signals. In a similar way one can associate a space with the set of possible messages. Suppose we are considering a speech system and that the messages consist of all possible sounds which contain no frequencies over a certain limit $W_1$ and last for a time $T_1$.

Just as for the case of the signals, these messages can be represented in a one-to-one way in a space of $2T_1W_1$ dimensions. There are several points to be noted, however. In the first place, various different points may represent the same message, insofar as the final destination is concerned. For example, in the case of speech, the ear is insensitive to a certain amount of phase distortion. Messages differing only in the phases of their components (to a limited extent) sound the same. This may have the effect of reducing the number of essential dimensions in the message space. All the points which are equivalent for the destination can be grouped together and treated as one point. It may then require fewer numbers to specify one of these "equivalence classes" than to specify an arbitrary point. For example, in Fig. 2 we have a two-dimensional space, the set of points in a square. If all points on a circle are regarded as equivalent, it reduces to a one-dimensional space—a point can now be

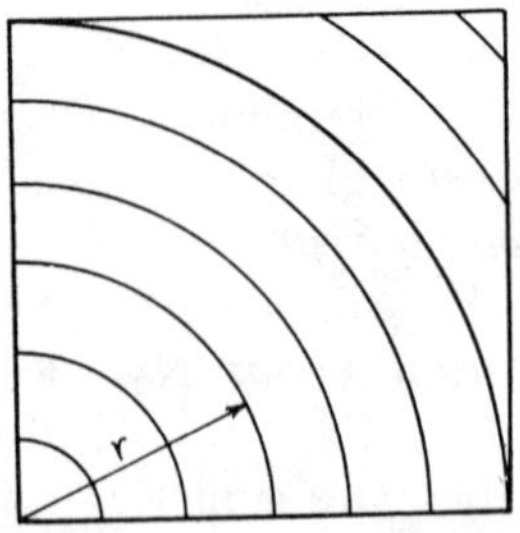


Fig. 2—Reduction of dimensionality through equivalence classes.

specified by one number, the radius of the circle. In the case of sounds, if the ear were completely insensitive to phase, then the number of dimensions would be reduced by one-half due to this cause alone. The sine and cosine components $a_n$ and $b_n$ for a given frequency would not need to be specified independently, but only $\sqrt{a_n^2+b_n^2}$; that is, the total amplitude for this frequency. The reduction in frequency discrimination of the ear as frequency increases indicates that a further reduction in dimensionality occurs. The vocoder makes use to a considerable extent of these equivalences among speech sounds, in the first place by eliminating, to a large degree, phase information, and in the second place by lumping groups of frequencies together, particularly at the higher frequencies.

In other types of communication there may not be any equivalence classes of this type. The final destination is sensitive to any change in the message within the full message space of $2T_1W_1$ dimensions. This appears to be the case in television transmission.

A second point to be noted is that the information source may put certain restrictions on the actual messages. The space of $2T_1W_1$ dimensions contains a point for *every* function of time $f(t)$ limited to the band $W_1$ and of duration $T_1$. The class of messages we wish to transmit may be only a small subset of these functions. For example, speech sounds must be produced by the human vocal system. If we are willing to forego the transmission of any other sounds, the effective dimensionality may be considerably decreased. A similar effect can occur through probability considerations. Certain messages may be possible, but so improbable relative to the others that we can, in a certain sense, neglect them. In a television image, for example, successive frames are likely to be very nearly identical. There is a fair probability of a particular picture element having the same light intensity in successive frames. If this is analyzed mathematically, it results in an effective reduction of dimensionality of the message space when $T_1$ is large.

We will not go further into these two effects at present, but let us suppose that, when they are taken into account, the resulting message space has a dimensionality $D$, which will, of course, be less than or equal to $2T_1W_1$. In many cases, even though the effects are present, their utilization involves too much complication in the way of equipment. The system is then designed on the basis that all functions are different and that there are no limitations on the information source. In this case, the message space is considered to have the full $2T_1W_1$ dimensions.

## V. Geometrical Representation of the Transmitter and Receiver

We now consider the function of the transmitter from this geometrical standpoint. The input to the transmitter is a message; that is, one point in the message space. Its output is a signal—one point in the signal space. Whatever form of encoding or modulation is performed, the transmitter must establish some correspondence between the points in the two spaces. Every point in the message space must correspond to a point in the signal space, and no two messages can correspond to the same signal. If they did, there would be no way to determine at the receiver which of the two messages was intended. The geometrical name for such a correspondence is a mapping. The transmitter maps the message space into the signal space.

In a similar way, the receiver maps the signal space back into the message space. Here, however, it is possible to have more than one point mapped into the same point. This means that several different signals are demodulated or decoded into the same message. In AM, for example, the phase of the carrier is lost in demodulation. Different signals which differ only in the phase of the carrier are demodulated into the same message. In FM the shape of the signal wave above the limiting value of the limiter does not affect the recovered message. In PCM considerable distortion of the received pulses is possible, with no effect on the output of the receiver.

We have so far established a correspondence between a communication system and certain geometrical ideas. The correspondence is summarized in Table I.

TABLE I

| *Communication System* | *Geometrical Entity* |
|---|---|
| The set of possible signals | A space of $2TW$ dimensions |
| A particular signal | A point in the space |
| Distortion in the channel | A warping of the space |
| Noise in the channel | A region of uncertainty about each point |
| The average power of the signal | $(2TW)^{-1}$ times the square of the distance from the origin to the point |
| The set of signals of power $P$ | The set of points in a sphere of radius $\sqrt{2TW\,P}$ |
| The set of possible messages | A space of $2T_1W_1$ dimensions |
| The set of actual messages distinguishable by the destination | A space of $D$ dimensions obtained by regarding all equivalent messages as one point, and deleting messages which the source could not produce |
| A message | A point in this space |
| The transmitter | A mapping of the message space into the signal space |
| The receiver | A mapping of the signal space into the message space |

## VI. Mapping Considerations

It is possible to draw certain conclusions of a general nature regarding modulation methods from the geometrical picture alone. Mathematically, the simplest types of mappings are those in which the two spaces have the same number of dimensions. Single-sideband amplitude modulation is an example of this type and an especially simple one, since the co-ordinates in the signal space are proportional to the corresponding co-ordinates in the message space. In double-sideband transmission the signal space has twice the number of co-ordinates, but they occur in pairs with equal values. If there were only one dimension in the message space and two in the signal space, it would correspond to mapping a line onto a square so that the point $x$ on the line is represented by $(x, x)$ in the square. Thus no significant use is made of the extra dimensions. All the messages go into a subspace having only $2T_1W_1$ dimensions.

In frequency modulation the mapping is more involved. The signal space has a much larger dimensionality than the message space. The type of mapping can be suggested by Fig. 3, where a line is mapped into a three-dimensional space. The line starts at unit distance from

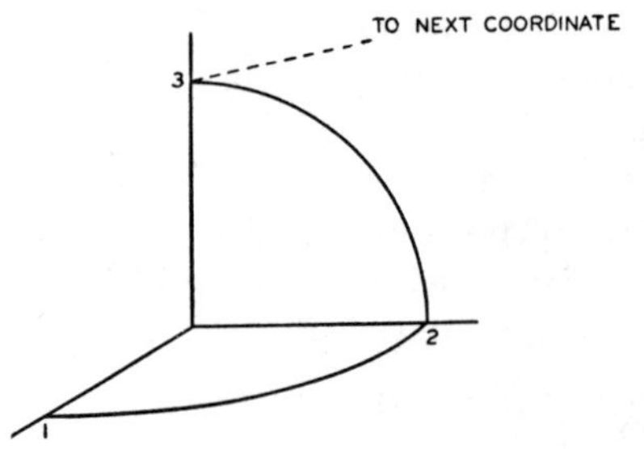


Fig. 3—Mapping similar to frequency modulation.

the origin on the first co-ordinate axis, stays at this distance from the origin on a circle to the next co-ordinate axis, and then goes to the third. It can be seen that the line is lengthened in this mapping in proportion to the total number of co-ordinates. It is not, however, nearly as long as it could be if it wound back and forth through the space, filling up the internal volume of the sphere it traverses.

This expansion of the line is related to the improved signal-to-noise ratio obtainable with increased bandwidth. Since the noise produces a small region of uncertainty about each point, the effect of this on the recov-

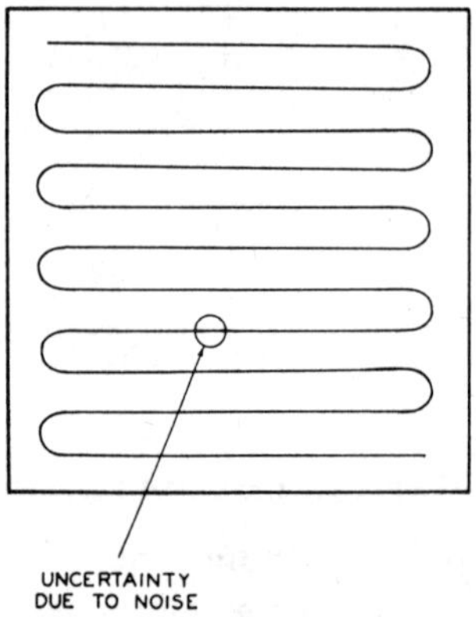


Fig. 4—Efficient mapping of a line into a square.

ered message will be less if the map is in a large scale. To obtain as large a scale as possible requires that the line wander back and forth through the higher-dimensional region as indicated in Fig. 4, where we have mapped a line into a square. It will be noticed that when this is done the effect of noise is small relative to the length of the line, provided the noise is less than a certain critical value. At this value it becomes uncertain at the receiver as to which portion of the line contains the message. This holds generally, and it shows that *any system which attempts to use the capacities of a wider band to the full extent possible will suffer from a threshold effect when there is noise.* If the noise is small, very little distortion will occur, but at some critical noise amplitude the message will become very badly distorted. This effect is well known in PCM.

Suppose, on the other hand, we wish to reduce dimensionality, i.e., to compress bandwidth or time or both. That is, we wish to send messages of band $W_1$ and duration $T_1$ over a channel with $TW < T_1W_1$. It has already been indicated that the effective dimensionality $D$ of the message space may be less than $2T_1W_1$ due to the properties of the source and of the destination. Hence we certainly need no more than $D$ dimension in the signal space for a good mapping. To make this saving it is necessary, of course, to isolate the effective co-ordinates in the message space, and to send these only. The reduced bandwidth transmission of speech by the vocoder is a case of this kind.

The question arises, however, as to whether further reduction is possible. In our geometrical analogy, is it possible to map a space of high dimensionality onto one of lower dimensionality? The answer is that it is possible, with certain reservations. For example, the points of a square can be described by their two co-ordinates which could be written in decimal notation

$$x = .a_1a_2a_3 \cdots$$
$$y = .b_1b_2b_3 \cdots . \tag{14}$$

From these two numbers we can construct one number by taking digits alternately from $x$ and $y$:

$$z = .a_1b_1a_2b_2a_3b_3 \cdots . \tag{15}$$

A knowledge of $x$ and $y$ determines $z$, and $z$ determines both $x$ and $y$. Thus there is a one-to-one correspondence between the points of a square and the points of a line.

This type of mapping, due to the mathematician Cantor, can easily be extended as far as we wish in the direction of reducing dimensionality. A space of $n$ dimensions can be mapped in a one-to-one way into a space of one dimension. Physically, this means that the frequency-time product can be reduced as far as we wish when there is no noise, with exact recovery of the original messages.

In a less exact sense, a mapping of the type shown in Fig. 4 maps a square into a line, provided we are not too particular about recovering exactly the starting point, but are satisfied with a near-by one. The sensitivity we noticed before when increasing dimensionality now takes a different form. In such a mapping, to reduce $TW$, there will be a certain threshold effect when we perturb the message. As we change the message a small amount, the corresponding signal will change a small amount, until some critical value is reached. At this point the signal will undergo a considerable change. In topology it is shown[7] that it is not possible to map a region of higher dimension into a region of lower dimension *continuously*. It is the necessary discontinuity which produces the threshold effects we have been describing for communication systems.

[7] W. Hurewitz and H. Wallman, "Dimension Theory," Princeton University Press, Princeton, N. J.; 1941.

This discussion is relevant to the well-known "Hartley Law," which states that "... an upper limit to the amount of information which may be transmitted is set by the sum for the various available lines of the product of the line-frequency range of each by the time during which it is available for use."[2] There is a sense in which this statement is true, and another sense in which it is false. It is not possible to map the message space into the signal space in a one-to-one, continuous manner (this is known mathematically as a *topological* mapping) unless the two spaces have the same dimensionality; i.e., unless $D=2TW$. Hence, if we limit the transmitter and receiver to continuous one-to-one operations, there is a lower bound to the product $TW$ in the channel. This lower bound is determined, not by the product $W_1T_1$ of message bandwidth and time, but by the number of *essential* dimension $D$, as indicated in Section IV. There is, however, no good reason for limiting the transmitter and receiver to topological mappings. In fact, PCM and similar modulation systems are highly discontinuous and come very close to the type of mapping given by (14) and (15). It is desirable, then, to find limits for what can be done with no restrictions on the type of transmitter and receiver operations. These limits, which will be derived in the following sections, depend on the amount and nature of the noise in the channel, and on the transmitter power, as well as on the bandwidth-time product.

It is evident that any system, either to compress $TW$, or to expand it and make full use of the additional volume, must be highly nonlinear in character and fairly complex because of the peculiar nature of the mappings involved.

## VII. The Capacity of a Channel in the Presence of White Thermal Noise

It is not difficult to set up certain quantitative relations that must hold when we change the product $TW$. Let us assume, for the present, that the noise in the system is a white thermal-noise band limited to the band $W$, and that it is added to the transmitted signal to produce the received signal. A white thermal noise has the property that each sample is perturbed independently of all the others, and the distribution of each amplitude is Gaussian with standard deviation $\sigma=\sqrt{N}$ where $N$ is the average noise power. How many different signals can be distinguished at the receiving point in spite of the perturbations due to noise? A crude estimate can be obtained as follows. If the signal has a power $P$, then the perturbed signal will have a power $P+N$. The number of amplitudes that can be reasonably well distinguished is

$$K\sqrt{\frac{P+N}{N}} \tag{16}$$

where $K$ is a small constant in the neighborhood of unity depending on how the phrase "reasonably well" is interpreted. If we require very good separation, $K$ will be small, while toleration of occasional errors allows $K$ to be larger. Since in time $T$ there are $2TW$ independent amplitudes, the total number of reasonably distinct signals is

$$M=\left[K\sqrt{\frac{P+N}{N}}\right]^{2TW}. \tag{17}$$

The number of bits that can be sent in this time is $\log_2 M$, and the rate of transmission is

$$\frac{\log_2 M}{T}=W\log_2 K^2\frac{P+N}{N}\ \text{(bits per second)}. \tag{18}$$

The difficulty with this argument, apart from its general approximate character, lies in the tacit assumption that for two signals to be distinguishable they must differ at some sampling point by more than the expected noise. The argument presupposes that PCM, or something very similar to PCM, is the best method of encoding binary digits into signals. Actually, two signals can be reliably distinguished if they differ by only a small amount, provided this difference is sustained over a long period of time. Each sample of the received signal then gives a small amount of statistical information concerning the transmitted signal; in combination, these statistical indications result in near certainty. This possibility allows an improvement of about 8 db in power over (18) with a reasonable definition of reliable resolution of signals, as will appear later. We will now make use of the geometrical representation to determine the exact capacity of a noisy channel.

Theorem 2: *Let $P$ be the average transmitter power, and suppose the noise is white thermal noise of power $N$ in the band $W$. By sufficiently complicated encoding systems it is possible to transmit binary digits at a rate*

$$C=W\log_2\frac{P+N}{N} \tag{19}$$

*with as small a frequency of errors as desired. It is not possible by any encoding method to send at a higher rate and have an arbitrarily low frequency of errors.*

This shows that the rate $W\log(P+N)/N$ measures in a sharply defined way the capacity of the channel for transmitting information. It is a rather surprising result, since one would expect that reducing the frequency of errors would require reducing the rate of transmission, and that the rate must approach zero as the error frequency does. Actually, we can send at the rate $C$ but reduce errors by using more involved encoding and longer delays at the transmitter and receiver. The transmitter will take long sequences of binary digits and represent this entire sequence by a particular signal function of long duration. The delay is required because the transmitter must wait for the full sequence before the signal is determined. Similarly, the receiver must wait for the full signal function before decoding into binary digits.

We now prove Theorem 2. In the geometrical representation each signal point is surrounded by a small region of uncertainty due to noise. With white thermal noise, the perturbations of the different samples (or co-ordinates) are all Gaussian and independent. Thus the probability of a perturbation having co-ordinates $x_1, x_2, \cdots, x_n$ (these are the differences between the original and received signal co-ordinates) is the product of the individual probabilities for the different co-ordinates:

$$\prod_{n=1}^{2TW} \frac{1}{\sqrt{2\pi 2TWN}} \exp - \frac{x_n^2}{2TWN}$$
$$= \frac{1}{(2\pi 2TWN)^{TW}} \exp \frac{-1}{2TW} \sum_1^{2TW} x_n^2.$$

Since this depends only on

$$\sum_1^{2TW} x_n^2,$$

the probability of a given perturbation depends only on the *distance* from the original signal and not on the direction. In other words, the region of uncertainty is spherical in nature. Although the limits of this region are not sharply defined for a small number of dimensions ($2TW$), the limits become more and more definite as the dimensionality increases. This is because the square of the distance a signal is perturbed is equal to $2TW$ times the average noise power during the time $T$. As $T$ increases, this average noise power must approach $N$. Thus, for large $T$, the perturbation will almost certainly be to some point near the surface of a sphere of radius $\sqrt{2TWN}$ centered at the original signal point. More precisely, by taking $T$ sufficiently large we can insure (with probability as near to 1 as we wish) that the perturbation will lie within a sphere of radius $\sqrt{2TW(N+\epsilon)}$ where $\epsilon$ is arbitrarily small. The noise regions can therefore be thought of roughly as sharply defined billiard balls, when $2TW$ is very large. The received signals have an average power $P+N$, and in the same sense must almost all lie on the surface of a sphere of radius $\sqrt{2TW(P+N)}$. How many different transmitted signals can be found which will be distinguishable? Certainly not more than the volume of the sphere of radius $\sqrt{2TW(P+N)}$ divided by the volume of a sphere of radius $\sqrt{2TWN}$, since overlap of the noise spheres results in confusion as to the message at the receiving point. The volume of an $n$-dimensional sphere[8] of radius $r$ is

$$V = \frac{\pi^{n/2}}{\Gamma\left(\frac{n}{2}+1\right)} r^n \cdot \qquad (20)$$

Hence, an upper limit for the number $M$ of distinguishable signals is

$$M \leqq \left(\sqrt{\frac{P+N}{N}}\right)^{2TW}. \qquad (21)$$

Consequently, the channel capacity is bounded by:

$$C = \frac{\log_2 M}{T} \leqq W \log_2 \frac{P+N}{N} \cdot \qquad (22)$$

[8] D. M. Y. Sommerville, "An Introduction to the Geometry of $N$ Dimensions," E. P. Dutton, Inc., New York, N. Y., 1929; p. 135.

This proves the last statement in the theorem.

To prove the first part of the theorem, we must show that there exists a system of encoding which transmits $W \log_2 (P+N)/N$ binary digits per second with a frequency of errors less than $\epsilon$ when $\epsilon$ is arbitrarily small. The system to be considered operates as follows. A long sequence of, say, $m$ binary digits is taken in at the transmitter. There are $2^m$ such sequences, and each corresponds to a particular signal function of duration $T$. Thus there are $M=2^m$ different signal functions. When the sequence of $m$ is completed, the transmitter starts sending the corresponding signal. At the receiver a perturbed signal is received. The receiver compares this signal with each of the $M$ possible transmitted signals and selects the one which is nearest the perturbed signal (in the sense of rms error) as the one actually sent. The receiver then constructs, as its output, the corresponding sequence of binary digits. There will be, therefore, an over-all delay of $2T$ seconds.

To insure a frequency of errors less than $\epsilon$, the $M$ signal functions must be reasonably well separated from each other. In fact, we must choose them in such a way that, when a perturbed signal is received, the nearest signal point (in the geometrical representation) is, with probability greater than $1-\epsilon$, the actual original signal.

It turns out, rather surprisingly, that it is possible to choose our $M$ signal functions at random from the points inside the sphere of radius $\sqrt{2TWP}$, and achieve the most that is possible. Physically, this corresponds very nearly to using $M$ different samples of band-limited white noise with power $P$ as signal functions.

A particular selection of $M$ points in the sphere corresponds to a particular encoding system. The general scheme of the proof is to consider all such selections, and to show that the frequency of errors averaged over all the particular selections is less than $\epsilon$. This will show that there are particular selections in the set with frequency of errors less than $\epsilon$. Of course, there will be other particular selections with a high frequency of errors.

The geometry is shown in Fig. 5. This is a plane cross section through the high-dimensional sphere defined by a typical transmitted signal $B$, received signal $A$, and the origin 0. The transmitted signal will lie very

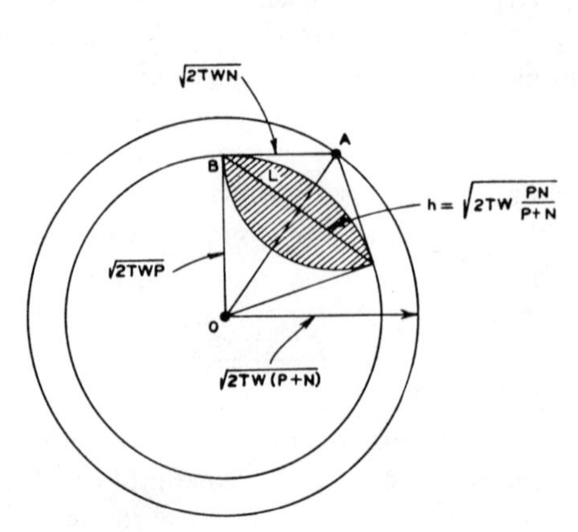


Fig. 5—The geometry involved in Theorem 2.

close to the surface of the sphere of radius $\sqrt{2TWP}$, since in a high-dimensional sphere nearly all the volume is very close to the surface. The received signal similarly will lie on the surface of the sphere of radius $\sqrt{2TW(P+N)}$. The high-dimensional lens-shaped region $L$ is the region of possible signals that might have caused $A$, since the distance between the transmitted and received signal is almost certainly very close to $\sqrt{2TWN}$. $L$ is of smaller volume than a sphere of radius $h$. We can determine $h$ by equating the area of the triangle $OAB$, calculated two different ways:

$$\tfrac{1}{2}h\sqrt{2TW(P+N)} = \tfrac{1}{2}\sqrt{2TWP}\sqrt{2TWN}$$
$$h = \sqrt{2TW\frac{PN}{P+N}}.$$

The probability of any particular signal point (other than the actual cause of $A$) lying in $L$ is, therefore, less than the ratio of the volumes of spheres of radii $\sqrt{2TW\,PN/P+N}$ and $\sqrt{2TWP}$, since in our ensemble of coding systems we chose the signal points at random from the points in the sphere of radius $\sqrt{2TWP}$. This ratio is

$$\left(\frac{\sqrt{2TW\frac{PN}{P+N}}}{\sqrt{2TWP}}\right)^{2TW} = \left(\frac{N}{P+N}\right)^{TW}. \tag{23}$$

We have $M$ signal points. Hence the probability $p$ that all except the actual cause of $A$ are *outside* $L$ is greater than

$$\left[1-\left(\frac{N}{P+N}\right)^{TW}\right]^{M-1}. \tag{24}$$

When these points are outside $L$, the signal is interpreted correctly. Therefore, if we make $P$ greater than $1-\epsilon$, the frequency of errors will be less than $\epsilon$. This will be true if

$$\left[1-\left(\frac{N}{P+N}\right)^{TW}\right]^{(M-1)} > 1-\epsilon. \tag{25}$$

Now $(1-x)^n$ is always greater than $1-nx$ when $n$ is positive. Consequently, (25) will be true if

$$1-(M-1)\left(\frac{N}{P+N}\right)^{TW} > 1-\epsilon \tag{26}$$

or if

$$(M-1) < \epsilon\left(\frac{P+N}{N}\right)^{TW} \tag{27}$$

or

$$\frac{\log(M-1)}{T} < W\log\frac{P+N}{N} + \frac{\log\epsilon}{T}. \tag{28}$$

For any fixed $\epsilon$, we can satisfy this by taking $T$ sufficiently large, and also have $\log(M-1)/T$ or $\log M/T$ as close as desired to $W \log P+N/N$. This shows that, with a random selection of points for signals, we can obtain an arbitrarily small frequency of errors and transmit at a rate arbitrarily close to the rate $C$. We can also send *at* the rate $C$ with arbitrarily small $\epsilon$, since the extra binary digits need not be sent at all, but can be filled in at random at the receiver. This only adds another arbitrarily small quantity to $\epsilon$. This completes the proof.

## VIII. Discussion

We will call a system that transmits without errors at the rate $C$ an ideal system. Such a system cannot be achieved with any finite encoding process but can be approximated as closely as desired. As we approximate more closely to the ideal, the following effects occur: (1) The rate of transmission of binary digits approaches $C=W\log_2(1+P/N)$. (2) The frequency of errors approaches zero. (3) The transmitted signal approaches a white noise in statistical properties. This is true, roughly speaking, because the various signal functions used must be distributed at random in the sphere of radius $\sqrt{2TWP}$. (4) The threshold effect becomes very sharp. If the noise is increased over the value for which the system was designed, the frequency of errors increases very rapidly. (5) The required delays at transmitter and receiver increase indefinitely. Of course, in a wide-band system a millisecond may be substantially an infinite delay.

In Fig. 6 the function $C/W=\log(1+P/N)$ is plotted with $P/N$ in db horizontal and $C/W$ the number of bits per cycle of band vertical. The circles represent PCM systems of the binary, ternary, etc., types, using positive and negative pulses and adjusted to give one error in about $10^5$ binary digits. The dots are for a PPM system with two, three, etc., discrete positions for the pulse.[9]

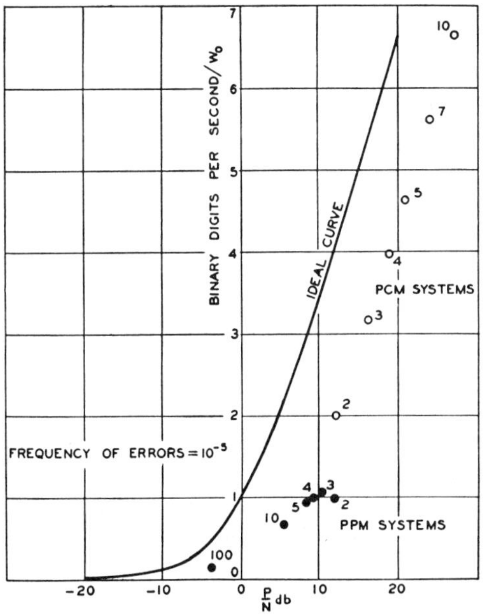


Fig. 6—Comparison of PCM and PPM with ideal performance.

[9] The PCM points are calculated from formulas given in "The philosophy of PCM," by B. M. Oliver, J. R. Pierce, and C. E. Shannon, Proc. I.R.E., vol. 36, pp. 1324–1332; November, 1948. The PPM points are from unpublished calculations of B. McMillan, who points out that, for very small $P/N$, the points approach to within 3 db of the ideal curve.

The difference between the series of points and the ideal curve corresponds to the gain that could be obtained by more involved coding systems. It amounts to about 8 db in power over most of the practical range. The series of points and circles is about the best that can be done without delay. Whether it is worth while to use more complex types of modulation to obtain some of this possible saving is, of course, a question of relative costs and valuations.

The quantity $TW \log(1+P/N)$ is, for large $T$, the number of bits that can be transmitted in time $T$. It can be regarded as an exchange relation between the different parameters. The individual quantities $T$, $W$, $P$, and $N$ can be altered at will without changing the amount of information we can transmit, provided $TW \log(1+P/N)$ is held constant. If $TW$ is reduced, $P/N$ must be increased, etc.

Ordinarily, as we increase $W$, the noise power $N$ in the band will increase proportionally; $N=N_0W$ where $N_0$ is the noise power per cycle. In this case, we have

$$C = W \log\left(1 + \frac{P}{N_0W}\right). \tag{29}$$

If we let $W_0=P/N_0$, i.e., $W_0$ is the band for which the noise power is equal to the signal power, this can be written

$$\frac{C}{W_0} = \frac{W}{W_0}\log\left(1 + \frac{W_0}{W}\right). \tag{30}$$

In Fig. 7, $C/W_0$ is plotted as a function of $W/W_0$. As we increase the band, the capacity increases rapidly until the total noise power accepted is about equal to the

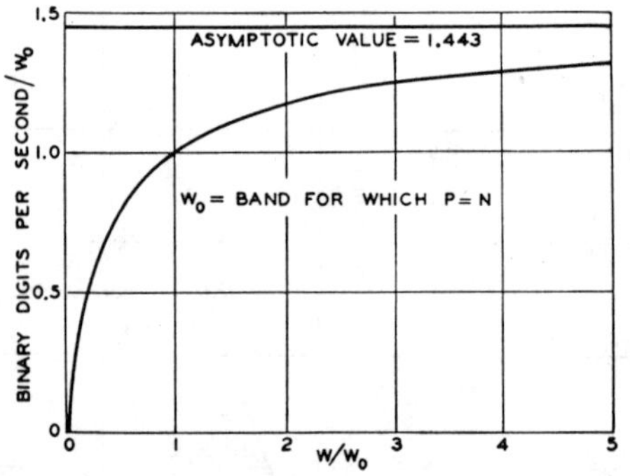


Fig. 7—Channel capacity as a function of bandwidth.

signal power; after this, the increase is slow, and it approaches an asymptotic value $\log_2 e$ times the capacity for $W=W_0$.

## IX. Arbitrary Gaussian Noise

If a white thermal noise is passed through a filter whose transfer function is $Y(f)$, the resulting noise has a power spectrum $N(f)=K|Y(f)|^2$ and is known as Gaussian noise. We can calculate the capacity of a channel perturbed by any Gaussian noise from the white-noise result. Suppose our total transmitter power is $P$ and it is distributed among the various frequencies according to $P(f)$. Then

$$\int_0^W P(f)df = P. \tag{31}$$

We can divide the band into a large number of small bands, with $N(f)$ approximately constant in each. The total capacity for a given distribution $P(f)$ will then be given by

$$C_1 = \int_0^W \log\left(1 + \frac{P(f)}{N(f)}\right)df, \tag{32}$$

since, for each elementary band, the white-noise result applies. The maximum rate of transmission will be found by maximizing $C_1$ subject to condition (31). This requires that we maximize

$$\int_0^W \left[\log\left(1 + \frac{P(f)}{N(f)}\right) + \lambda P(f)\right]df. \tag{33}$$

The condition for this is, by the calculus of variations, or merely from the convex nature of the curve $\log(1+x)$,

$$\frac{1}{N(f)+P(f)} + \lambda = 0, \tag{34}$$

or $N(f)+P(f)$ must be constant. The constant is adjusted to make the total signal power equal to $P$. For frequencies where the noise power is low, the signal power should be high, and vice versa, as we would expect.

The situation is shown graphically in Fig. 8. The curve is the assumed noise spectrum, and the three lines correspond to different choices of $P$. If $P$ is small, we cannot make $P(f)+N(f)$ constant, since this would require negative power at some frequencies. It is easily shown, however, that in this case the best $P(f)$ is obtained by making $P(f)+N(f)$ constant whenever possible, and making $P(f)$ zero at other frequencies. With low values of $P$, some of the frequencies will not be used at all.

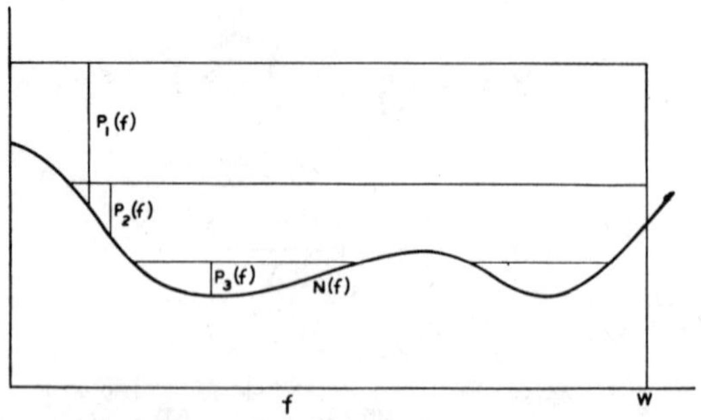


Fig. 8—Best distribution of transmitter power.

If we now vary the noise spectrum $N(f)$, keeping the total noise power constant and always adjusting the signal spectrum $P(f)$ to give the maximum transmission, we can determine the worst spectrum for the noise. This turns out to be the white-noise case. Although this only shows it to be worst among the Gaussian noises, it will be shown later to be the worst among all possible noises with the given power $N$ in the band.

## X. The Channel Capacity with an Arbitrary Type of Noise

Of course, there are many kinds of noise which are not Gaussian; for example, impulse noise, or white noise that has passed through a nonlinear device. If the signal is perturbed by one of these types of noise, there will still be a definite channel capacity $C$, the maximum rate of transmission of binary digits. We will merely outline the general theory here.[10]

Let $x_1, x_2, \cdots, x_n$ be the amplitudes of the noise at successive sample points, and let

$$p(x_1, x_2, \cdots, x_n)dx_1 \cdots dx_n \tag{35}$$

be the probability that these amplitudes lie between $x_1$ and $x_1+dx_1$, $x_2$ and $x_2+dx_2$, etc. Then the function $p$ describes the statistical structure of the noise, insofar as $n$ successive samples are concerned. The *entropy*, $H$, of the noise is defined as follows. Let

$$H_n = -\frac{1}{n}\int \cdots \int p(x_1, \cdots, x_n) \cdot \log_e p(x_1, \cdots, x_n)dx_1, \cdots, dx_n. \tag{36}$$

Then

$$H = \lim_{n\to\infty} H_n. \tag{37}$$

This limit exists in all cases of practical interest, and can be determined in many of them. $H$ is a measure of the randomness of the noise. In the case of white Gaussian noise of power $N$, the entropy is

$$H = \log_e \sqrt{2\pi e N}. \tag{38}$$

It is convenient to measure the randomness of an arbitrary type of noise not directly by its entropy, but by comparison with white Gaussian noise. We can calculate the power in a white noise having the same entropy as the given noise. This power, namely,

$$\overline{N} = \frac{1}{2\pi e}\exp 2H \tag{39}$$

where $H$ is the entropy of the given noise, will be called the ***entropy power*** of the noise.

A noise of entropy power $\overline{N}$ acts very much like a white noise of power $\overline{N}$, insofar as perturbing the message is concerned. It can be shown that the region of uncertainty about each signal point will have the same volume as the region associated with the white noise. Of course, it will no longer be a spherical region. In proving Theorem 1 this volume of uncertainty was the chief property of the noise used. Essentially the same argument may be applied for any kind of noise with minor modifications. The result is summarized in the following:

Theorem 3: *Let a noise limited to the band $W$ have power $N$ and entropy power $N_1$. The capacity $C$ is then bounded by*

$$W\log_2\frac{P+N_1}{N_1} \leqq C \leqq W\log_2\frac{P+N}{N_1} \tag{40}$$

*where $P$ is the average signal power and $W$ the bandwidth.*

If the noise is a white Gaussian noise, $N_1=N$, and the two limits are equal. The result then reduces to the theorem in Section VII.

For any noise, $N_1<N$. This is why white Gaussian noise is the worst among all possible noises. If the noise is Gaussian with spectrum $N(f)$, then

$$N_1 = W\exp\frac{1}{W}\int_0^W \log N(f)df. \tag{41}$$

The upper limit in Theorem 3 is then reached when we are above the highest noise power in Fig. 8. This is easily verified by substitution.

In the cases of most interest, $P/N$ is fairly large. The two limits are then nearly the same, and we can use $W\log(P+N)/N_1$ as the capacity. The upper limit is the best choice, since it can be shown that as $P/N$ increases, $C$ approaches the upper limit.

## XI. Discrete Sources of Information

Up to now we have been chiefly concerned with the channel. The capacity $C$ measures the maximum rate at which a random series of binary digits can be transmitted when they are encoded in the best possible way. In general, the information to be transmitted will not be in this form. It may, for example, be a sequence of letters as in telegraphy, a speech wave, or a television signal. Can we find an equivalent number of bits per second for information sources of this type? Consider first the discrete case; i.e., the message consists of a sequence of discrete symbols. In general, there may be correlation of various sorts between the different symbols. If the message is English text, the letter $E$ is the most frequent, $T$ is often followed by $H$, etc. These correlations allow a certain compression of the text by proper encoding. We may define the entropy of a discrete source in a way analogous to that for a noise; namely, let

$$H_n = -\frac{1}{n}\sum_{i,j,\cdots,s} p(i,j,\cdots,s)\log_2 p(i,j,\cdots,s) \tag{42}$$

where $p(i, j, \cdots, s)$ is the probability of the sequence of symbols $i, j, \cdots, s$, and the sum is over all sequences of $n$ symbols. Then the entropy is

$$H = \lim_{n\to\infty} H_n. \tag{43}$$

[10] C. E. Shannon, "A mathematical theory of communication," *Bell Sys. Tech. Jour.*, vol. 27, pp. 379–424 and 623–657; July and October, 1948.

It turns out that $H$ is the number of bits produced by the source for each symbol of message. In fact, the following result is proved in the Appendix.

THEOREM 4. *It is possible to encode all sequences of n message symbols into sequences of binary digits in such a way that the average number of binary digits per message symbol is approximately H, the approximation approaching equality as n increases.*

It follows that, if we have a channel of capacity $C$ and a discrete source of entropy $H$, it is possible to encode the messages via binary digits into signals and transmit at the rate $C/H$ of the original message symbols per second.

For example, if the source produces a sequence of letters $A$, $B$, or $C$ with probabilities $p_A=0.6$, $p_B=0.3$, $p_C=0.1$, and successive letters are chosen independently, then $H_n=H_1=-[0.6 \log_2 0.6+0.3 \log_2 0.3 +0.1 \log_2 0.1]=1.294$ and the information produced is equivalent to 1.294 bits for each letter of the message. A channel with a capacity of 100 bits per second could transmit with best encoding $100/1.294=77.3$ message letters per second.

## XII. Continuous Sources

If the source is producing a continuous function of time, then without further data we must ascribe it an infinite rate of generating information. In fact, merely to specify exactly one quantity which has a continuous range of possibilities requires an infinite number of binary digits. We cannot send continuous information *exactly* over a channel of finite capacity.

Fortunately, we do not need to send continuous messages exactly. A certain amount of discrepancy between the original and the recovered messages can always be tolerated. If a certain tolerance is allowed, then a definite finite rate in binary digits per second can be assigned to a continuous source. It must be remembered that this rate depends on the nature and magnitude of the allowed error between original and final messages. The rate may be described as the rate of generating information *relative to the criterion of fidelity*.

Suppose the criterion of fidelity is the rms discrepancy between the original and recovered signals, and that we can tolerate a value $\sqrt{N_1}$. Then each point in the message space is surrounded by a small sphere of radius $\sqrt{2T_1W_1N_1}$. If the system is such that the recovered message lies within this sphere, the transmission will be satisfactory. Hence, the number of different messages which must be capable of distinct transmission is of the order of the volume $V_1$ of the region of possible messages divided by the volume of the small spheres. Carrying out this argument in detail along lines similar to those used in Sections VII and IX leads to the following result:

THEOREM 5: *If the message source has power $Q$, entropy power $\overline{Q}$, and bandwidth $W_1$, the rate $R$ of generating information in bits per second is bounded by*

$$W_1 \log_2 \frac{\overline{Q}}{N_1} \leqq R \leqq W_1 \log_2 \frac{Q}{N_1} \tag{44}$$

*where $N_1$ is the maximum tolerable mean square error in reproduction. If we have a channel with capacity $C$ and a source whose rate of generating information $R$ is less than or equal to $C$, it is possible to encode the source in such a way as to transmit over this channel with the fidelity measured by $N_1$. If $R>C$, this is impossible.*

In the case where the message source is producing white thermal noise, $\overline{Q}=Q$. Hence the two bounds are equal and $R=W_1 \log Q/N_1$. We can, therefore, transmit white noise of power $Q$ and band $W_1$ over a channel of band $W$ perturbed by a white noise of power $N$ and recover the original message with mean square error $N_1$ if, and only if,

$$W_1 \log \frac{Q}{N_1} \leqq W \log \frac{P+N}{N}. \tag{45}$$

## Appendix

Consider the possible sequences of $n$ symbols. Let them be arranged in order of decreasing probability, $p_1 \geqq p_2 \geqq p_3 \cdots \geqq p_s$. Let $P_i=\sum_1^{i-1} p_j$. The $i$th message is encoded by expanding $P_j$ as a binary fraction and using only the first $t_i$ places where $t_i$ is determined from

$$\log_2 \frac{1}{p_i} \leqq t_i < 1 + \log_2 \frac{1}{p_i}. \tag{46}$$

Probable sequences have short codes and improbable ones long codes. We have

$$\frac{1}{2^{t_i}} \leqq p_i \leqq \frac{1}{2^{t_i-1}}. \tag{47}$$

The codes for different sequences will all be different. $P_{i+1}$, for example, differs by $p_i$ from $P_i$, and therefore its binary expansion will differ in one or more of the first $t_i$ places, and similarly for all others. The average length of the encoded message will be $\sum p_i t_i$. Using (46),

$$-\sum p_i \log p_i \leqq \sum p_i t_i < \sum p_i (1 - \log p_i) \tag{48}$$

or

$$nH_n \leqq \sum p_i t_i < 1 + nH_n. \tag{49}$$

The average number of binary digits used per message symbol is $1/n \sum p_i t_i$ and

$$H_n \leqq \frac{1}{n} \sum p_i t_i < \frac{1}{n} + H_n. \tag{50}$$

As $n \to \infty$, $H_n \to H$ and $1/n \to 0$, so the average number of bits per message symbol approaches $H$.

# Poisson, Shannon, and the Radio Amateur*

J. P. COSTAS†, SENIOR MEMBER, IRE

*Summary*—**Congested band operation as found in the amateur service presents an interesting problem in analysis which can only be solved by statistical methods. Consideration is given to the relative merits of two currently popular modulation techniques, SSB and DSB. It is found that in spite of the bandwidth economy of SSB this system can claim no over-all advantage with respect to DSB for this service. It is further shown that there are definite advantages to the use of very broadband techniques in the amateur service.**

**The results obtained from the analysis of the radio amateur service are significant, for they challenge the intuitively obvious and universally accepted thesis that congestion in the radio frequency spectrum can only be relieved by the use of progressively smaller transmission bandwidths obtained by appropriate coding and modulation techniques. In order to study the general problem of spectrum utilization, some basic results of information theory are required Some of the significant work of Shannon is reviewed with special emphasis on his channel capacity formula. It is shown that this famous formula, in spite of its deep philosophical significance, cannot be used meaningfully in the analysis and design of practical, present day communications systems. A more suitable channel capacity formula is derived for the practical case.**

**The analytical results thus obtained are used to show that broadband techniques have definite merit for both civil and military applications. Furthermore, such techniques will result in far more efficient spectrum utilization in many applications than any practical narrow-band, frequency-channelized approach. Thus broad-band techniques can, in many cases, increase the number of available "channels." With regard to military communications it is shown that the ability of a communication system to resist jamming varies in direct proportion to the transmission bandwidth for a given data rate. Thus narrow-band techniques lead progressively to more expensive communications systems and less expensive jammers. It is concluded that in the military field broad-band techniques are not only desirable but also often mandatory.**

## I. Introduction

Most common usage of the radio frequency spectrum involves operation at specified frequencies as assigned by the appropriate regulatory agencies in the various countries. In contrast, the radio amateur service is assigned various bands of frequencies and properly licensed stations are permitted to operate at any frequency within these bands. This freedom of choice of frequency is necessitated by the obviously impossible administrative problem of assigning specific frequencies to specific stations and, furthermore, the available bandwidths fall short by several orders of magnitude of providing exclusive channels to each authorized station. Thus, as one might suspect, the situation in the amateur bands is a chaotic one in terms of mutual interference. There is very little tendency to "channelize" for several reasons. The crowded conditions normally leave no empty spaces in frequency so that a station starting operation has no choice but to transmit "in between" two strong stations or on top of a weaker station. Furthermore, at the higher HF frequencies, the ionospheric "skip" makes it impossible to choose a good operating frequency by listening, since the signal situation will be radically different between two points spaced many miles apart. Thus, the very nature of the amateur service would lead one to expect that any meaningful analysis of this problem must be based on a statistical approach.

A mathematical study of amateur radio communications can be of use in other important areas. Consider, for example, military communications where allocation of frequencies cannot possibly prevent interference due to the use of the same frequencies by the opposing forces. It is not hard to imagine that under such conditions each operator will shift frequency and take other appropriate action in order to get his message through. Thus, in a combat area we might well expect to find the very same chaos in the communications services that we observe in the amateur bands today. Certainly in such situations interference cannot be eliminated by allocation; interference will exist and we must simply learn to live with it. We are not speaking here of intentional jamming but rather of the casual interference which is inevitable when two opposing military forces (which today depend heavily on radio) attempt to operate independently and use the same electromagnetic spectrum. The problem of intentional jamming will be treated in detail in Section VI.

In the analysis of the radio amateur problem which follows, three modes of operation are compared. It is first assumed that all stations employ suppressed-carrier single-sideband (SSB). Then exclusive use of suppressed-carrier AM (DSB) is assumed. Finally, a frequency diversity system is examined in which each station transmits a large number of identical signals at randomly selected frequencies in the band. Intuitively we might suspect that SSB would be superior to DSB because of the two-to-one difference in signal bandwidths. The frequency diversity system is intuitively ridiculous because it apparently "wastes" bandwidth rather indiscriminantly. As we shall see, intuition is a poor guide in these matters. The feeling that we should always try to "conserve bandwidth" is no doubt caused by an environment in which it has been standard practice to share the RF spectrum on a frequency basis. Our emotions do not alter the fact that bandwidth is but one dimension of a multidimensional situation.

* Original manuscript received by the IRE, April 21, 1959; revised manuscript received, June 13, 1959.
† General Electric Co., Syracuse, N. Y.

Reprinted from *Proc. IRE*, vol. 47, pp. 2058–2068, Dec. 1959.

## II. Congested Band Analysis

### SSB Case

We shall first consider the case of exclusive use of SSB. The spectral situation is shown in Fig. 1 as it might

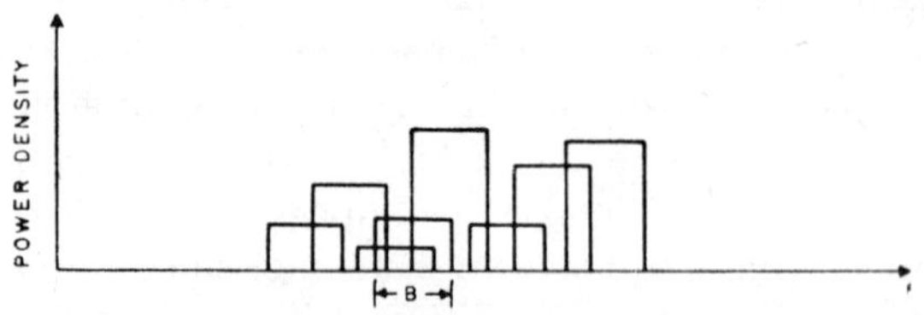


Fig. 1—Power density spectra—SSB case.

appear to a particular receiver. Each signal occupies a bandwidth $B$ (equal to the baseband bandwidth for SSB), has a location in frequency independent of all other signal locations, and has an amplitude of power density independent of all other signal amplitudes. The signal amplitudes will have a probability distribution which will be specified at a later time. While the frequency locations of the various signals are distributed at random, it can be said that, on the average, there are a given number of signals per given unit of bandwidth. Thus, we may specify the density of loading of the band by a quantity $k$ which represents the average number of signals per unit bandwidth. It happens that we shall need to know the probability of having a given number of signals $\nu$ falling in a bandwidth $B$. This, of course, is given for the conditions specified by the celebrated distribution of Poisson as

$$P(\nu, B) = \frac{(kB)^\nu}{\nu!} e^{-kB}, \tag{1}$$

where $P(\nu, B)$ is the probability of having $\nu$ signals in the bandwidth $B$ if there are $k$ signals per unit bandwidth on the average.

The choice of the distribution function for the signal power densities is somewhat arbitrary and, as far as the final results are concerned, apparently not particularly critical. It is physically reasonable and mathematically convenient to choose the chi-squared distribution[1]

$$p_\nu(x) = \frac{x^{\nu/2-1}e^{-x/2}}{2^{\nu/2}\Gamma(\nu/2)} \qquad (x \geq 0), \tag{2}$$

where $p_\nu(x)$ is the probability density function of the spectral amplitude which results from the summation of $\nu$ independent signals. For $\nu = 1$ the distribution has a mean of unity. This specifies that the average signal strength at the receiver is unity which results in no loss of generality for this application.

For convenience only, we shall assume that we are receiving a signal of average strength and want to find the probability that the Signal-to-Noise Ratio at the receiver output will equal or exceed a specified value. For SSB operation, the SNR at RF is the same as the SNR at the receiver output. We shall estimate the effective noise level at the receiver input by noting the interference level at the center of the pass band. We shall now determine the probability that the interference level will be less than or equal to $J$, which means that the SNR at the receiver output will be equal to or greater than $1/J$, since the desired signal is assumed to be of average strength of unity. Let $P_{SSB}(SNR \geq 1/J)$ be this probability. Then

$$P_{SSB}(SNR \geq 1/J) = P(0, B) + P(1, B)\int_0^J p_1(x)dx + P(2, B)\int_0^J p_2(x)dx + P(3, B)\int_0^J p_3(x)dx + \cdots, \tag{3}$$

which states that the event will occur if there are no signals in $B$, if there is one signal in $B$ with amplitude less than $J$, if there are two signals in $B$ the sum of whose amplitudes is less than $J$, etc. It should be clear that if an interfering signal is to contribute to the measurement of interference, its lowest frequency must fall somewhere within a frequency band extending from the center of the pass band to $B$ cycles below. It is to this event that the terms $P(\nu, B)$ in (3) refer. Substituting (1) and (2) into (3) one obtains

$$P_{SSB}(SNR \geq 1/J) = e^{-kB}\left[1 + \sum_{\nu=1}^{\infty} \frac{(kB)^\nu}{\nu!} \int_0^J \frac{x^{\nu/2-1}e^{-x/2}}{2^{\nu/2}\Gamma(\nu/2)} dx\right]. \tag{4}$$

Evaluation of (4) for a fixed $J$ and variable $k$ will give the probability of exceeding a certain receiver output SNR as a function of band loading. For example, for $J = 1$ the expression gives the probability of exceeding a 0-db SNR when receiving a signal of average strength, or of exceeding a +3-db SNR when receiving a signal of twice (power) average strength, etc. Fortunately, the integral function in (4) is tabulated[2] and the series converges rather rapidly, so that the numerical work involved in evaluating (4) is not too difficult.

### DSB Case

As might be suspected, the analysis of the case involving exclusive use of DSB is quite similar to the SSB analysis. There are two important differences to be noted. First, since all transmitted signals have twice the baseband bandwidth it is to be expected for a given band loading there will be more interfering signals involved than in the case of SSB. In the DSB analysis then, we will be concerned with the probability of having $\nu$ interfering signals in a bandwidth $2B$, using the same estimate of effective receiver input noise level as before.

[1] H. Cramer, "Mathematical Methods of Statistics," Princeton University Press, Princeton, N. J., ch. 18; 1946.

[2] C. D. Hodgman, "Mathematical Tables," Chemical Rubber Publishing Co., Cleveland, Ohio, p. 257; 1946.

Thus the Poisson distribution $P(\nu, 2B)$ must be used in the equation equivalent to (3) for the DSB analysis. This represents a loss caused by increased transmission bandwidth; there is a compensating gain as will be seen. The second difference between the SSB and DSB analysis involves the relationship between the predetector and postdetector SNR's. In SSB these two ratios are the same. In DSB the postdetector SNR is 3 db better than the predetector value. This difference arises because of the coherent addition of upper and lower sideband components of the signal and incoherent addition of the corresponding interference components in the synchronous detector. Thus, for identical output SNR's the interference power density will be two times as great relative to desired signal density in DSB as compared to SSB. Consequently, in the equation equivalent to (3) the upper limit on all integrals must be changed from $J$ to $2J$ in order that $J$ have the same meaning in both cases.

When the two changes discussed above are made, the probability of exceeding an output SNR of $1/J$ for a desired signal of mean strength (unity) becomes

$$P_{\mathrm{DSB}}(\mathrm{SNR} \geq 1/J) = e^{-2kB}\left[1 + \sum_{\nu=1}^{\infty} \frac{(2kB)^{\nu}}{\nu!} \int_0^{2J} \frac{x^{\nu/2-1}e^{-x/2}}{2^{\nu/2}\Gamma(\nu/2)}\, dx\right]. \quad (5)$$

A comparison of (4) and (5) shows that the increased bandwidth of DSB has in some ways been detrimental ($2kB$ in place of $kB$ in the Poisson distribution), and in other ways beneficial ($2J$ in place of $J$ in the integral expression). As later calculations show, the increased bandwidth of DSB does not affect the relative congested band performance as compared to SSB in any significant manner. We might begin to suspect that the efficient use of broader bandwidths in a congested operating band is not necessarily a bad idea. The broader bandwidth signals will increase the tendency of frequency overlap and tend, in a sense, to cause more interference. This is obvious. *What is not so obvious is the fact that the increased bandwidth gives to the receiving system an increased ability to discriminate between the desired signal and the interference.* In order to investigate further the effects of increasing transmission bandwidth, a rather simple form of broad-band technique will now be analyzed.

*Frequency Diversity Case*

For this example we shall use the SSB mode of transmission (although the DSB mode would yield identical results), in a somewhat unusual manner. Each station will transmit not one but $M$ (where $M$ is a large number) identical signals at randomly chosen frequencies in the congested band. The receiver must know these frequency locations so that all $M$ signals may be received, detected, and added coherently to produce the receiver output signal. With each station transmitting $M$ identical signals, the interference spectrum amplitude will, with nearly unit probability, be very nearly equal to a constant value at all frequencies for sufficiently large $M$. This value may be determined quite easily by inspection.

Consider first the normal SSB situation without diversity. The received signals are distributed in amplitude of power density about a mean of unity. Thus, the average received power is $B$ watts per station. Since there are $k$ stations per cycle on the average, the mean interference power density will be $kB$ watts per cycle. Going from one transmission to $M$ transmissions per station (assuming the power of each station is now split evenly between the $M$ signals) does not alter the value of the average interference power density. In the diversity case this *average* value will be very nearly the *actual* value of interference density level which will exist at all frequencies and at all times. The diversity receiver output SNR may now be easily calculated.

Each of the $M$ signals will have a power $B/M$ (for the average signal strength case) and the noise power accepted in receiving each of the $M$ signals will be $kB^2$. The RF SNR at each of the $M$ frequencies will be $1/MkB$ and coherent addition of $M$ such signals will yield an output SNR of $1/kB$. So then

$$(\mathrm{SNR})_{\mathrm{Div}} = \frac{1}{kB} \quad (6)$$

on a power basis for a desired signal of mean strength. Note that in (6) we are able to specify the precise SNR, while in the SSB and DSB cases of (4) and (5) we can only predict the probability or the percentage time the SNR will exceed a given value.

## III. Results and Discussion—Congested Band

The results represented by (4)–(6) may be interpreted in many different ways. For the purposes of this discussion let us assume that voice communications is involved and that message reception will be considered successful if the receiver output SNR equals or exceeds unity or 0 db. Keep in mind that this is not a commerical service but rather a service where the operator is willing to exert some effort in order to understand what is being said. Thus, the 0-db choice is probably reasonable with regard to sentence intelligibility where the interference is of an incoherent nature. The three equations will then be used to calculate the circuit reliability for signals at 0, +3, +6, and +9 db relative to mean signal strength as a function of $kB$, the band loading expressed in average number of stations per audio bandwidth. The resulting graphs are shown in Figs. 2 through 5. Turning first to Fig. 2, which assumes a received signal of mean strength, we note that the circuit reliability drops rather rapidly with band loading for both SSB and DSB. SSB shows some advantage, but of a small amount, at loadings which result in a reasonable reliability percentage. An estimate of the increased number of users for the same performance which results from SSB use may be obtained by drawing a line horizonally from any given

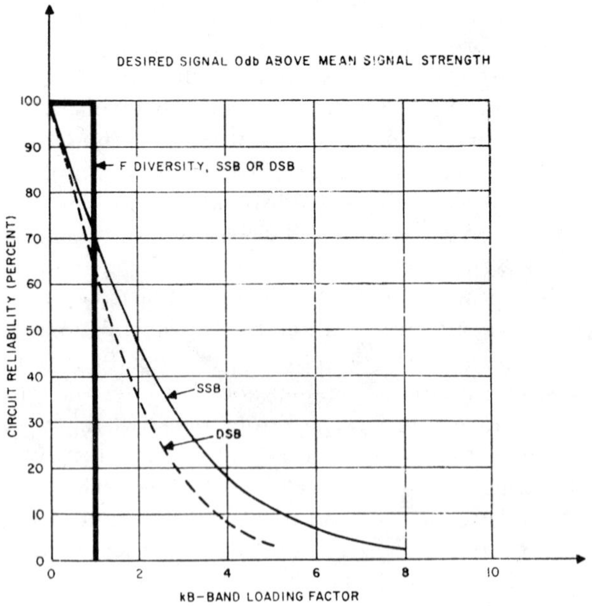


Fig. 2—Per cent circuit reliability vs band loading.

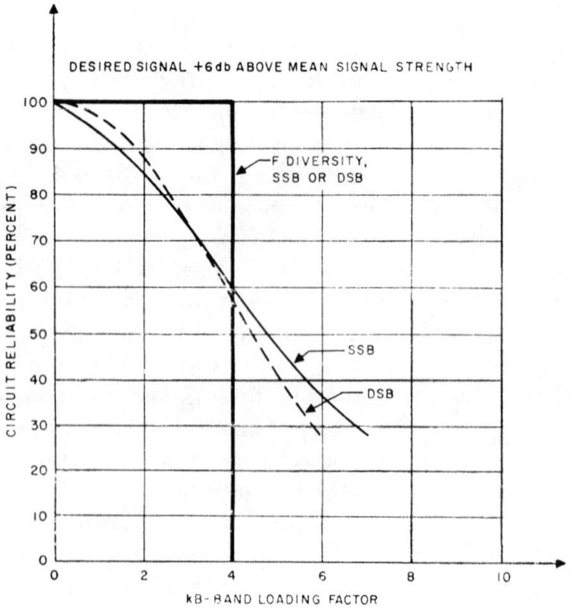


Fig. 4—Per cent circuit reliability vs band loading.

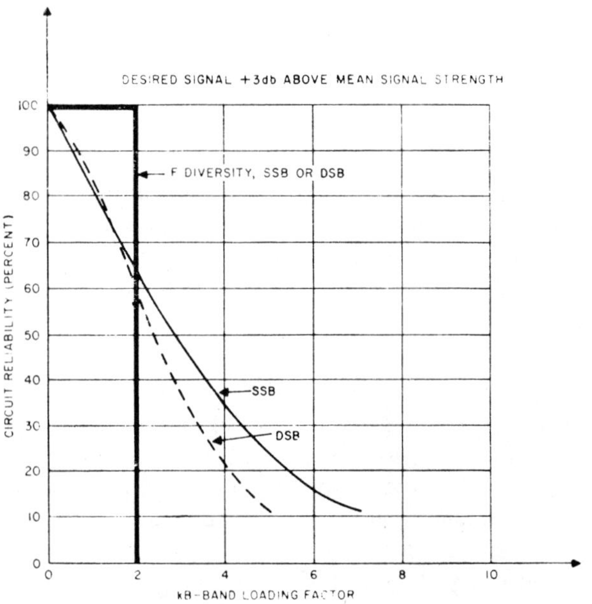


Fig. 3—Per cent circuit reliability vs band loading.

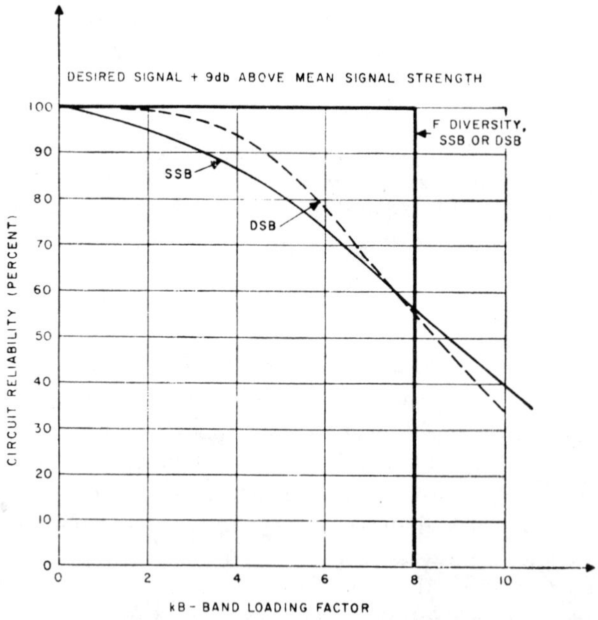


Fig. 5—Per cent circuit reliability vs band loading.

ordinate value and noting the $kB$ values at which this line interesects the SSB and DSB curves. The two-to-one increase in loading which we might at first expect from SSB certainly does not materialize, except at values of circuit reliability which are so low as to be meaningless. Thus, the randomness of band occupancy has a significant effect on performance, and any intuitive conclusions based on orderly channel assignments are subject to considerable error. Note in particular that the circuit reliability for SSB at $kB=1$ is 70 per cent. At this loading there are enough channels to satisfy all needs, and 100 per cent reliability could be had if some organization could be obtained. About the only conclusions to be drawn from Fig. 2 are that SSB and DSB give nearly the same performance and that it is usually hopeless to try to communicate with a station whose signal strength is only average at times when the band is crowded. This last conclusion will come as no surprise to the experienced operator.

As the strength of the desired signal increases above the mean value the situation improves rather rapidly, as shown by Figs. 3–5. The SSB and DSB curves now "cross over" and both curves tend to stay at higher reliability values as $kB$ is increased, which is to be expected. Note in Fig. 5 that DSB shows a slight advantage over SSB for the lower loading values and the cross-over occurs when the reliability factor is 63 per cent. In total these results show the futility of claiming any advantage for either SSB or DSB in this service. If one is insistent upon claiming an advantage, the specific conditions under which the comparisons are made must be given.

In our attempt to determine the sensitivity of the calculated results with respect to the choice of the amplitude distribution function, an exponential distribution was tried in place of the chi-squared. The exponential distribution gave more weight to signals above the mean than did the chi-squared. However, the final results were very nearly the same. A further calculation involving a delta-function distribution (all interfering signals of the same strength) showed no significant differences. Thus, one is led to believe that the results obtained are not particularly sensitive to the choice of any reasonable distribution function for the signal strengths.

The performance of the frequency diversity system shows up in a rather unusual manner in the graphs. This is due in part to the way in which we chose to interpret the results, and in part to the fact that in this case the interference is not random but constant. In the narrow-band cases the interference level changes considerably in short periods of time because of the random appearances and disappearances of signals close to the operating frequency. In the broad-band case, the interference observed is the net result of *nearly all* the stations on the band so that the actions of *any one* station have a negligible effect on the interference level at the output of an appropriate broad-band receiving system. Thus, for a given loading, the interference level stays fixed and only the signal strengths of the various stations to which the receiver is "tuned" will be found to vary. Some signals will be sufficiently above the noise to be understood all of the time, while others will be below the noise and will not be heard at all. We have made a rather interesting trade in going from narrow- to broad-band operation. In narrow-band operation, we can copy a strong signal most of the time and a weak signal just part of the time. In broad-band operation, we can copy a strong signal all of the time but a weak signal cannot be copied at all. The reason for the shape of the frequency diversity curves should now be clear, and the nature of the "trade-off" may be evaluated by an examination of Figs. 2–5.

Amateur band operation with broad-band systems will prove to be somewhat different in certain respects. There will be fewer stations with which contact may be established (since the weaker signals which were formerly heard intermittently will now not be heard at all), but once contact is established the conversation can be expected to continue without interruption for a considerable period of time. Since the amateur is not normally concerned with communicating with a specific person, the exchange of some freedom of choice of possible contacts for reliability of communications will probably be welcomed.

In the case of military communications, the problem is more difficult, since specific messages must be transmitted to specific stations. If the signal strengths are weak, the narrow-band approach certainly offers no solution since, as we have seen, the circuit reliability will be poor. The message will have to be repeated over and over again before it is received with any reasonable degree of completeness and accuracy. Thus, under such adverse conditions *we have been forced to lower the data rate* because the necessity for repetition has increased the time required for the transmission of a given message. Broad-band operation under the same adverse conditions will suffer the same fate, but to a lesser degree. The data rate will have to be lowered (this can be done without decreasing the bandwidth) but since the interference level will be fixed at some average value we can lower the rate by just the amount necessary to keep the error rate below the acceptable maximum. With narrow-band operation, practical considerations will no doubt force us to reduce the data rate to a value determined by the *maximum* interference level. Thus, for congested-band operation, broad-band systems appear to offer a more orderly approach to the problem and a potentially higher average traffic volume than narrow-band systems.

Nothing that has been said so far should be construed as meaning that broad-band systems will always give us the traffic volume we would like to have, or feel we must have to support operations. As the congestion becomes worse it will be impossible to avoid reducing the data rate per circuit. The important point here is that the broad-band philosophy *accepts interference as a fact of life* and an attempt is made to do the best that is possible under the circumstances. The narrow-band philosophy essentially denies the existence of interference since there is an implied assumption that the narrow-band signals can be placed in non-overlapping frequency bands and thereby prevent interference. It is perhaps redundant to state that the realities of most practical military situations almost completely destroy the validity of such reasoning.

At this point we shall leave the problem of the radio amateur and turn our attention to other communications areas. We have seen that the operating environment of the amateur is not unique to his service but that in other services, especially the military, conditions in actual practice will quite often degenerate to the congested situation of the amateur service. Under such conditions we have shown the necessity for a statistical approach to the problem. It has been further demonstrated that the efficient use of additional transmission bandwidth does not constitute a "waste" in the basic sense of the word. The policy of "conserving bandwidth" is not based on sound physical principles but is based rather on a very common but still myopic view of communications. Such a policy will, in many situations, conserve only the opportunity to communicate as efficiently as might otherwise be possible. Even worse, this point of view quite often leads to the design of systems which have little or no true military capability because of extreme sensitivity to intentional interference. These and other matters will be discussed in Sections VI and VII in more detail. First, it is necessary to derive some rather simple results from information theory.

## IV. Information Theory

Consider the problem of data transmission by electrical means. We transmit pulses over a noisy circuit and the pulses, together with the noise, are received and interpreted. Errors in interpretation of the message occur because of this noise. If the error rate is too high and the transmitter power is fixed, we have traditionally lowered the data rate in order to reduce the errors. This has always worked and the reason given was very simple. A lower data rate means that the pulse lengths can be increased, which in turn allows narrower bandwidths to be used, thereby reducing the amount of noise accepted by the receiver. Thus, it became axiomatic that lower error rates could be obtained only by corresponding decreases in bandwidth and data rate. To almost everyone in the communications art the validity of this axiom was unquestioned since there was a great deal of experience in support and none in contradiction. It remained for Shannon to show that systems could be constructed, in theory at least, which would behave quite differently from what our previous experience would lead us to expect. First of all, he showed that the data rate could be held at a constant value (provided this value were below a certain maximum) and at the same time the error rate could be reduced to arbitrarily small values. As for the general belief that one should always use the minimum possible bandwidth in order to reduce the noise accepted by the receiver, Shannon showed that in the ideal case, with a white-noise background, the system bandwidth should be increased to the point where the accepted noise power is at least equal to the signal power.[3] This new theory presented a radically different picture of the limiting behavior of communications systems.

A very superficial study of Shannon-type systems will now be made in the belief that many readers, who are not specialists in information theory, might find a practical discussion of this topic interesting and perhaps useful. Fig. 6 shows a form of communications system suggested by Shannon's work. The channel has a bandwidth $W$ and average (white) noise power $N$. The transmitter is limited to an average power $P$. Consider a white-noise generator having a bandwidth $W$. We record $M$ different samples of the generator output, each sample having a duration of $T$ seconds. These waveforms are now designated $f_1(t)$, $f_2(t)$, $f_3(t)$, $\cdots$, $f_k(t)$, $\cdots$, $f_M(t)$ and are made available as transmitted symbols, as indicated in the figure. Copies of each of the $M$ waveforms are made and placed at the receiver in the corresponding operator units $O_1$, $O_2$, $\cdots$, $O_k$, $\cdots$, $O_M$. In operation, one of the $M$ waveforms (say the $k$th one) is selected for transmission. Waveform $f_k(t)$ plus channel noise is received by each of the operator units. The operator units subtract the waveform stored within each unit from the received signal, square this difference, integrate the square for $T$ seconds (which is the duration of the symbols), and indicate this mean-square value as shown. If $T$ is sufficiently large, each meter (except for the $k$th one) will with almost unit probability read very nearly a value corresponding to $2P+N$, which is the average power of the difference voltage in each case. The $k$th meter will give a reading corresponding to very nearly $N$ (again with almost unit probability), since the $f_k(t)$ portion of the received signal is completely removed in the subtraction process and only the channel noise remains. Thus, by noting which meter has the lowest reading we can identify which of the $M$ symbols was transmitted. Of course, because of the channel noise we will make an occasional error and identify the wrong symbol.

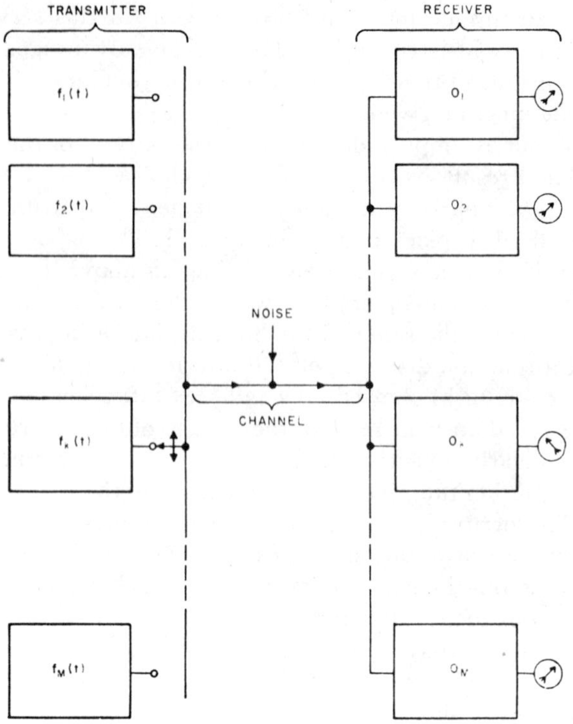


Fig. 6—An ideal communications system.

Before investigating the problem of errors we should examine the relationships between data rate $R$, symbol duration $T$, and number of symbols $M$. Assume that in each $T$ seconds of time the system receives $S$ binary digits (0, 1) to transmit. $R$ will then be $S/T$ bits per second. Since our symbol length is $T$, we must be prepared to indicate a choice of one out of $2^S$ possibilities with each symbol transmitted, since this is the number of different sequences of $S$ binary digits. Then clearly

[3] C. E. Shannon, "Communication in the presence of noise," Proc. IRE, vol. 37, pp. 10–21; January, 1949.

$M = 2^S$ and

$$R = \frac{S}{T} = \frac{\log_2 M}{T} \text{ bits per second.} \tag{7}$$

Note that if the symbol length $T$ is increased, the number of symbols $M$ used must increase *exponentially* with $T$ in order to keep a constant data rate. Thus, if $T$ is *doubled*, $M$ will have to be *squared* for the same data rate. In general terms

$$M = A^T \tag{8}$$

and

$$R = \log_2 A. \tag{9}$$

Returning again to Fig. 6, assume the $k$th symbol has been transmitted. Thus, we look to see if the $k$th meter gives the lowest reading. If this is so, there is no error. If any one of the other meters gives a lower reading, an error in selection will occur. The probability that any meter will read less than the $k$th one can be made progressively smaller by increasing $T$, which increases the integration time in the operator units. However, this is only part of the story. As $T$ is increased to lower the probability of any one meter indicating lower than the $k$th, the number of such comparisons needed rises according to (8) in order that the data rate remain fixed. Thus, we have two conflicting trends as $T$ is increased. The probability of error per comparison drops, but the number of comparisons necessary to arrive at a selection rises with increasing $T$. Shannon shows that we can always reduce the over-all probability of error in selection to as small a value as we may choose by letting $T$ become large, *provided* that $M$ does not increase with $T$ faster than

$$M = \left(1 + \frac{P}{N}\right)^{TW}. \tag{10}$$

This maximum permissible rate of increase of $M$ with $T$ determines the maximum data rate which can be supported with an arbitrarily small error rate. This maximum rate is known as the channel capacity $C$ and is obtained by substituting (10) into (7) to obtain

$$C = W \log_2 (1 + P/N). \tag{11}$$

Of course, we do not have to send data at the rate given by (11). We may send slower, and enjoy arbitrarily low, error rates. We may even send faster than $C$, but then we must accept a certain irreducible error rate.

As remarkable as (11) may be, the engineer concerned with practical system design needs more information than has been given thus far. We now know that multi-symbol systems of the type shown in Fig. 6 are capable, practical considerations aside, of making the most efficient possible use of the communications channel. There are two engineering constraints which must be considered carefully. First, there is an inherent delay of $2T$ seconds involved in data transmission because a $T$-second length sample of input binary data must be available before choice of transmitted symbol may be made, and another $T$ seconds is required for processing at the receiver before identification may be made. What will be the order of magnitude of this transmission delay? Secondly, how many different symbols $M$ will be required in a given situation? This last consideration is of special importance because it determines, rather directly, system complexity. We might suspect that any attempt to operate at or very near the rate $C$ would require intolerably large $T$ and $M$ since this rate represents a limiting condition. Similarly, large $T$ and $M$ would be expected to result at operating rates lower than $C$ if the error rate is specified at a very small value. What we really need to know is the behavior of $T$ and $M$ for a practical error rate, say $10^{-5}$, as the data rate is varied from zero to 100 per cent of capacity. Rice, in an excellent paper,[4] gives us a good indication of the orders of magnitude involved. Rice assumed an SNR of 10 and an error rate of $10^{-5}$. He then determined the number of bits per symbol $S$ which would be necessary for various values of the ratio of actual data rate to channel capacity. The results are shown plotted in Fig. 7. Notice

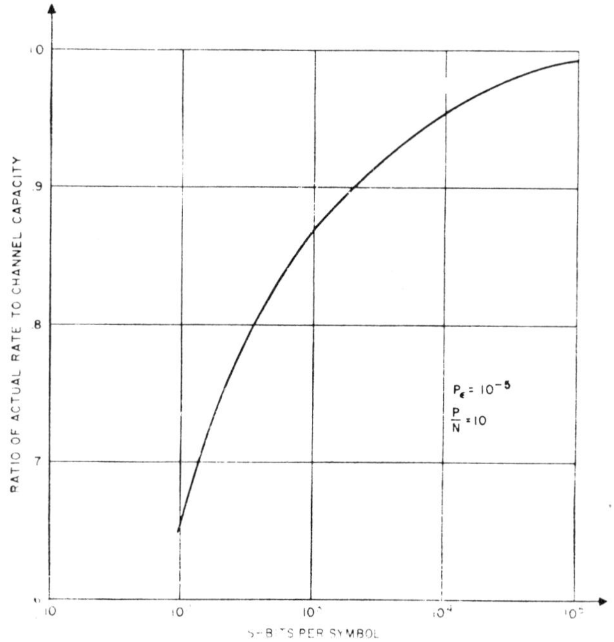


Fig. 7—Curve from Rice showing approach to capacity.

that the numbers $S$ of bits per symbol are quite large, and keep in mind that the number of symbols $M$ is $2^S$. We need no numerical examples to conclude that the number of symbols needed will be fantastically large and that it is completely impractical to attempt to build systems which operate at rates close to the Shannon capacity under the conditions assumed above. (An

[4] S. O. Rice, "Communication in the presence of noise," *Bell Sys. Tech. J.*, vol. 29, pp. 60–93; January, 1950.

interesting piece of work by Stutt[5] shows that the situation is not quite so unreasonable if the SNR is low and the symbol waveforms are chosen systematically rather than at random.)

In brief retrospect, we (as communications engineers) have been shown by Shannon that there is an upper limit to what we can do no matter how hard we may try or how ingenious we may be. That it may be extremely difficult to achieve or even approach this upper limit in practice can hardly be blamed on Shannon. He has located the top of our mountain; the problem of reaching the peak is ours, not his.

## V. A Practical System of High Efficiency

It is quite clear that any analysis of a communications problem which uses the capacity formula without careful qualification may give results of doubtful practical value. If a system of high efficiency and of reasonable complexity could be found, perhaps problem analysis could be carried out with results which would be significant in practice. Consider once more the system of Fig. 6, but now let there be only two symbols used, $f_1(t)$ and $f_2(t)$. Shannon's idea of using noise-like symbols is quite intriguing. This will be retained except that $f_2(t)$ will be the negative of $f_1(t)$ instead of being chosen at random as before. Thus, $f_1(t)$ is now transmitted for mark (or binary 1) and $-f_1(t)$ for space (or binary 0). For obvious reasons we shall refer to this two-symbol system as the binary system.

In the analysis of this binary system it is convenient to recall one form of the sampling theorem which states that a time function of $T$-seconds duration and of $W$-cycles bandwidth is completely specified by $2TW$ equally-spaced sample values of the funtion. Thus, we will represent the function $f_1(t)$ by the sequence of numbers $\{x_1, x_2, \cdots, x_{2TW}\}$, which are the values of the function at the sampling times. The function $f_1(t)$ will be noise-like except that we shall adjust the function so that we obtain the exact relationship

$$\frac{1}{2TW}\sum_{1}^{2TW} x_j^2 = P, \tag{12}$$

where $P$ is the average transmitter power. In a like manner the channel noise, which has an average power $N$, will be represented by the sequence of numbers $\{n_1, n_2, \cdots, n_{2TW}\}$, where the $n_j$ are independent normal variables with zero mean and variance $N$. If one performs the operations described for Fig. 6 one obtains the following for the probability of error $P_\epsilon$:

$$P_\epsilon = \text{Prob.}\left[\frac{1}{2TW}\sum_{1}^{2TW} x_j n_j < -P\right]. \tag{13}$$

The summation term may be shown to be Gaussian with zero mean and variance $PN/2TW$. If operating conditions yield a low error probability, then

$$P_\epsilon = \frac{e^{-\gamma}}{2\sqrt{\pi}(\gamma)^{1/2}}, \tag{14}$$

where

$$\gamma = \frac{P}{N}TW. \tag{15}$$

A plot of $\log_{10} P_\epsilon$ as a function of $\gamma$ is shown in Fig. 8.

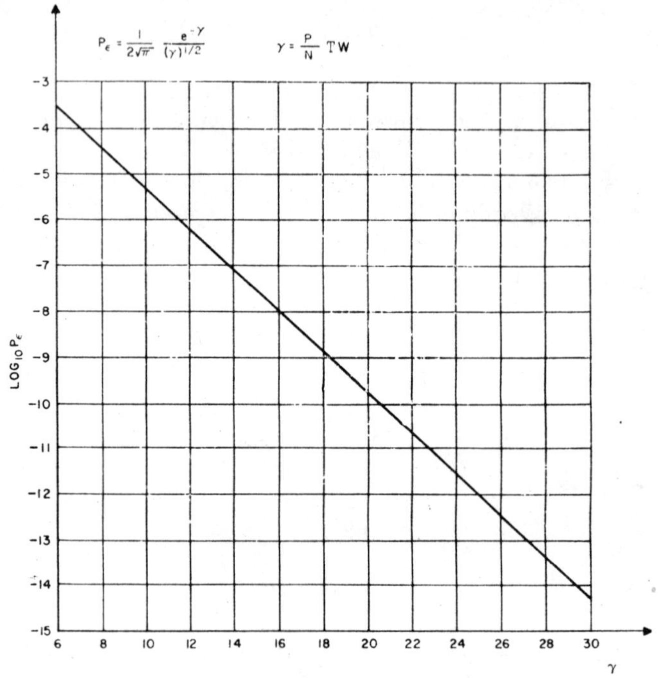


Fig. 8—Plot of $\log_{10} P_\epsilon$ vs $\gamma$ for the binary system.

Note that once the system error probability is fixed, the relationship between SNR, bandwidth, and data rate ($1/T$ bits per second) is immediately determined.

We might inquire now as to how good our binary system is. It is certainly as good as any two-symbol system can be. Better results can be obtained only by increasing the number of symbols. The gain in doing this, however, does not generally appear to be worth the effort. For example, Stutt[5] shows that for a $P/N$ of 1/10 and error probabilities in the neighborhood of $10^{-4}$ to $10^{-6}$, the most efficient symbol choice requires the use of about 100 symbols in order to increase the data rate over binary by a factor of five. Note, however, that at a fixed error rate the data rate of the binary system may be made 5 times as large by inceasing transmitter power by 7 db. Thus, we must evaluate the relative costs of a 7-db transmitter power increase vs the increase in symbols from two (actually one in terms of equipment complexity) to 100. We must conclude, therefore, that our binary system performance represents about the best that can be done in practice. Better results may be obtained by using more symbols but the rate of improve-

[5] C. A. Stutt, "Regular Polyhedron Codes," Research Laboratory, General Electric Co., Schenectady, N. Y., Tech. Rept. No. 59-RL-2202; February, 1959.

ment will generally prove to be low.[6]

This places us in a good position to derive expressions for the channel capacity in the practical case from (14) and (15). Before doing so we should understand that for high SNR's these equations may yield rates in bits per second far in excess of the bandwidth in cycles per second. There is a mathematical limitation which prevents this. This limitation will not be discussed except to mention the fact that in theory the binary system is limited to a maximum rate $2W$ regardless of SNR.[7] In practice it is usually quite difficult to achieve even $W$ as a rate; we shall choose this as our limiting value.

Since the rate $R$ is $1/T$, the channel capacity $C_p$ in the practical case may be obtained from (15) as

$$C_p = \frac{W}{\gamma}\frac{P}{N}, \tag{16}$$

$$C_p \leq W, \tag{16a}$$

where $\gamma$ is fixed by the desired error probability according to (14). For an error probability of $10^{-5}$, $\gamma$ is approximately 9.2.

Admittedly, the result (16) is not as elegant as (11). Keep in mind, however, that the concise nature of the capacity formula (11) is made possible by a limiting process in mathematics which cannot be duplicated in practice. A valid objection could also be raised to the application of the term "capacity" to the rate indicated by (15) and expressed in (16). From purely theoretical considerations, such an objection is certainly justified. From a practical point of view, (16) does, in a sense, qualify as a capacity since the performance indicated may only be approached by the most efficient use of modulation and processing techniques. It is quite doubtful that there exist at present any operating systems which perform as well as (16) indicates is obtainable. The main point to remember is that for many years to come (16) will represent a sensible, realizable (but not easily realizable) design goal for the communications engineer; the capacity formula (11) can never serve this purpose. As processing and storage techniques improve, it is to be expected that at some future time multisymbol systems may be built whose performance will exceed that indicated by (16). This does not in any way lessen the utility of (16) as a frame of reference.

## VI. Jamming

From the work of the previous section, we now derive some rather simple results which are well-known to information theory specialists the world over, but whose significance is apparently not appreciated by many engineers, at least in this country.

Consider first the performance of the binary system in a white-noise background having a density of $n_0$ watts per cycle. The effective noise power $N$ will then be

$$N = n_0 W, \tag{17}$$

and (15) will read in this case

$$\gamma = \frac{PT}{n_0} = \frac{E}{n_0}, \tag{18}$$

where $E$ is the energy per transmitted symbol. We now have derived the well-known result that for binary systems of this type operating against flat channel noise, the error probability is independent of bandwidth and is a function only of energy per symbol and noise power density. Thus, for fixed average signal power and fixed data rate, the error probability does not change as the system bandwidth is increased. It is clear that as the bandwidth increases, the noise power accepted by the receiver increases, and for large bandwidths the received noise power becomes quite large compared to received signal power. Thus, systems of this type can operate with SNR's far below unity, or put another way, these systems can be made to operate satisfactorily in the presence of very large amounts of noise power. One might begin to suspect that a broad-band system would be fairly immune to intentional jamming, since in normal operation it is contending (satisfactorily) with such large amounts of natural noise that the additional noise contributed by the jammer would be insignificant by comparison. That this is precisely the case will be made more definite in what follows.

Consider a binary communications system designed to operate in a white-noise background of power density $n_0$ watts per cycle. Let practical considerations demand that the error probability be kept at or below a critical value $P_{e0}$ corresponding to a $\gamma$ value of $\gamma_0$. Then the channel capacity will be from (16):

$$C_p = \frac{W}{\gamma_0}\frac{P}{n_0 W} \tag{19}$$

as far as natural noise is concerned. For the sake of argument, we shall choose to operate at a data rate $R$ corresponding to one-half capacity. Then,

$$R = \frac{1}{T} = \frac{C_p}{2} = \frac{P}{2\gamma_0 n_0}. \tag{20}$$

Consider now the appearance of a jamming signal of average power $J$ in the channel and let us investigate the effect of $J$ on $\gamma$, since this factor must be kept above the assumed critical value of $\gamma_0$. The noise term $N$ in (15) will now be

$$N = n_0 W + J, \tag{21}$$

and when (20) and (21) are substituted into (15) we obtain

$$\gamma = \gamma_0 \frac{2n_0}{n_0 + J/W}. \tag{22}$$

[6] This, like all generalizations, will have exceptions. One can conceive of situations in which the multisymbol system would have sensible application. In such cases the work of Stutt, *ibid.*, should prove quite useful.

[7] See discussion of sampling theorem which precedes (12).

This last equation tells a very interesting story. First of all, note the appearance of the $J/W$ term in the denominator. This indicates that the effectiveness of a given average jamming power varies *inversely* as system bandwidth. The broader the bandwidth the less effective will be the resultant jamming. In particular, in order to disrupt the circuit ($\gamma = \gamma_0$) one needs an amount of average jamming power $J_0$ equal to

$$J_0 = n_0 W \tag{23}$$

under the conditions specified. Thus, the relationships between bandwidth and jamming power become quite clear and may be summarized as follows: *If the most efficient system design is assumed for a fixed data rate in each case, the necessary power required to jam the ciruit varies in direct proportion to system bandwidth. The broader the bandwidth the more difficult it will be to jam the circuit. Conversely, the narrower the bandwidth the easier it becomes to jam the circuit.*

It should be quite clear that if intentional jamming is a consideration, one must of necessity choose a broad-band technique. The narrow-band approach can only lead to eventual disaster.

## VII. The Question of Channels

The well-known, but not necessarily sufficiently appreciated, relationship between jamming immunity and system bandwidth discussed above leads to a natural concern over loss of channels if broad-band techniques are employed, as obviously they must be in many applications. It is the purpose of this section to discuss the general problem of "channels" somewhat more thoroughly than before, through use of the practical channel capacity formula (16).

Consider the following problem. Communications service must be provided which requires that a total of $K$ stations be permited to transmit messages at *any* time. Let $\alpha$ be the average fraction of time each station is active. The average signal strength (power) at a particular receiver will be denoted by $\overline{P}$ and it is assumed that $\Omega$ cycles of total bandwidth are allocated to this service. Background or natural noise will be ignored. Thus:

$\Omega$ = Total bandwidth allocated to service.
$K$ = Number of stations, each of which must be permitted to transmit at any time.
$\alpha$ = Average fraction of time each station is actually transmitting.
$\overline{P}$ = Mean signal power at a receiving site (one station).
$C_{pN}$, $C_{pB}$ = Practical channel capacity per circuit in narrow- and broad-band operation, respectively.

We now wish to inquire as to the relative merits of narrow- and broad-band techniques for this service.

First let us assume an environment in which *all* stations are under the complete control of a central authority. Under this special condition, frequency division will result in circuit bandwidths of $\Omega/K$ and, since there will be no interference and background noise is ignored, the capacity per circuit will be, using (16a),

$$C_{pN} = \frac{\Omega}{K}\,. \tag{24}$$

By comparison, the broad-band approach would yield a circuit bandwidth of $\Omega$ and a noise power $N$ of $\alpha K\overline{P}$, which, if an average strength signal were being received, would result in a capacity per circuit of

$$C_{pB} = \frac{\Omega}{\gamma\alpha K}, \tag{25}$$

using (16). Comparing (25) and (24) we see that if such a well-disciplined environment can be found, the narrow-band system would be superior *provided* that the duty cycle factor $\alpha$ is kept high. For example, if $\alpha = 1$ (each station transmitting continuously) the narrow-band system appears to offer about a ten-to-one data rate advantage (for $\gamma = 10$). If, due to operational considerations, the average duty cycle is low (say, 10 per cent or even 1 per cent or less as may quite often be the case), then the broad-band system, even under such ideal conditions, becomes superior.

The reasons for this are quite clear. If the duty cycle is low, the narrow-band system wastes spectrum since most of the allocated channels in $\Omega$ will be idle at any time. This cannot be avoided since each of the $K$ stations must have access to communications at any time. The broad-band system takes immediate advantage of a low-duty cycle since this keeps the "noise" level at low values and increases the per-circuit capacity. The narrow-band approach guarantees complete elimination of interference between stations (orthogonality, as the specialist would say), while in the broad-band case each station appears as noise to the others. Thus, at high duty cycles the narrow-band system is superior because it avoids this "noise" problem completely. We must conclude then that the narrow-band system has sensible application under very special conditions (such as in radio broadcasting), but that even where complete control of all transmitters is possible, the broad-band system can easily prove to be the more efficient user of spectrum.

We shall now consider the same communications service problem as before, except that we shall abandon any hope of a disciplined use of the bandwidth $\Omega$. In most military applications, a congested band assumption is much more realistic for several reasons. Certainly two opposing military forces will have planned their spectrum usage independently. Under such conditions interference will be the expected rather than the unusual event. If narrow-band systems have been chosen, it is quite likely that each operator will shift frequency when severe interference is encountered in an attempt to maintain service. This is only the natural and sensible thing to do. Furthermore, under conditions where signals propagate over distances of many thousands of miles, interference will no doubt be quite common even between stations that are a part of the same military force. It seems unrealistic to expect that interference can be prevented by administrative means when the total number of users is large and when the geographic distances between groups of users is great. It must be presumed then that, in spite of careful allocation attempts, the narrow-band approach will not prevent interference and that congested operating conditions will certainly prevail.

Consider the problem that an operator faces when trying to clear messages in a congested band using narrow-band systems. As we have shown, the SNR in such a case is a statistical quantity varying from very good at one time to hopelessly poor minutes or even seconds later. If the data rate is set too high (based on those times when the SNR is good), much of the traffic will be lost and repetition will be necessary. In order to know what messages or parts of messages were lost, a return link is required, but this will also suffer from interference. Such operation is quite inefficient and it would soon be discovered that the data rate would have to be determined by the *least favorable* SNR anticipated during the operating period. Thus, the per-circuit channel capacity in this case may be approximated roughly by

$$C_{pN} = \left(\frac{P}{N}\right)_{\min} \frac{\Omega}{\gamma K}, \tag{26}$$

using (16).

The assumption of congestion does not alter the performance of the broad-band system so that (25) still holds. A rough estimate of the relative performance of these two approaches to the problem of congested band operation may now be obtained by taking the ratio of (25) to (26):

$$\frac{C_{pB}}{C_{pN}} = \frac{1}{\alpha(P/N)_{\min}}. \tag{27}$$

As rough as this approximation may be it still seems rather certain that in a congested band the broad-band system will normally far outperform the narrow-band system.

Eq. (25) may then be taken as the average capacity per circuit of a congested band. In slightly modified form we have:

$$C_{pB} = \frac{1}{\gamma k} \text{ bits per second,} \tag{28}$$

where $k$ is the average number of actual users per cycle of bandwidth and $\gamma$ is determined by the required error probability according to (14).

It might be mentioned at this point that with broad-band operation the DSB and SSB methods of modulation give identical results for the same transmission bandwidth. As a practical matter, the DSB system offers a two-to-one increase in transmission bandwidth in the modulation process over and above the bandwidth increase obtained by coding processes at baseband. This may sound strange to engineers accustomed to design work aimed at conserving bandwidth. It is still true that there are practical difficulties involved in designing equipment which uses more bandwidth *efficiently* and that the bandwidth doubling which may be obtained in the modulation process with DSB will prove quite helpful in general.

## VIII. Conclusions

Since the invention, many years ago, of the frequency-selective filter, it has been common practice to share the inherent capacity of the RF spectrum among users on the basis of frequency allocations. As the number of users increased, methods were found for reducing transmission bandwidths so that new services could be accommodated in the existing spectrum. Extrapolating the past into the future has led to the natural attempt to continue this evolutionary process of seeking methods for the further narrowing of transmission bandwidths, thus providing service for the increasing user population.

This philosophy of spectrum usage is based on a particular course of development which the radio art happened to take, rather than on any fundamental physical principles. The inherent communication capacity of the spectrum can be shared in ways other than by frequency allocation and for many applications the frequency division approach represents a very poor choice indeed. In the field of military communications in particular, the tendency to follow the trends of the past quite often leads to systems having negligible military capability although good intentions may be to the contrary.

This is not to say that broad-band systems have been completely ignored in the past. It could safely be said, however, that the magnitude of the effort thus far expended on the broad-band approach is far out of proportion to the importance of this technique.

## Acknowledgment

The author wishes to express appreciation to his many colleagues at the General Electric Company who assisted in the work upon which this paper is based. Special thanks are due to J. C. Kovarik who contributed much original material for the congested-band analysis and to S. Applebaum and Dr. H. D. Friedman for their constructive discussions of information theory problems.

# Performance of Digital Matched Filter Correlator With Unknown Interference

C. R. CAHN

***Abstract*—The $S/N$ loss due to amplitude quantization is examined in connection with a digital matched filter correlator for a binary coded signal. A minimax binary quantizing concept is described, which adds an optimized noise dither prior to hard clipping. The design philosophy is minimax; i.e., the loss from an ideal analog correlator is minimized in the presence of the worst interference constrained to a specified average power. The resulting worst performance degradation is 4.8 dB, and occurs for constant amplitude interference. The extension of the minimax approach to a multilevel randomized quantizing concept is sketched. With four-level quantization, an upper bound on the performance degradation is 2.3 dB. The effect of finite time estimation of the interference power is determined, with the conclusion that a short-term power averaging can be used with only a small additional loss. Computer simulation results are in accordance with theoretical predictions.**

Paper approved by the Communication Theory Committee of the IEEE Communication Technology Group for publication without oral presentation. Manuscript received April 26, 1971; revised July 6. 1971.

The author is with the Magnavox Research Laboratories, Torrance, Calif. 90503.

## Introduction

In a variety of different applications, one example being measurement of propagation time to extract range [1], the transmitted signal is phase shift modulated by a binary code, and correlation detection with a stored replica is performed in a receiver. Adjusting the epoch of the replica so as to give maximum correlation in the receiver output then is a plausible criterion for estimating the unknown time of arrival of the signal received in the presence of unknown interference. One possible receiver implementation is based on use of a matched filter [2] whose impulse response forms the stored replica over a specified number of code digits. In effect, the matched filter acts as a correlator and serves to detect the instant in time when the received signal appears to be best aligned with the finite-duration stored replica. Analog implementations based on tapped delay lines have been the typical design concept of a matched

Reprinted from *IEEE Trans. Commun. Technol.*, vol. COM-19, pt. II, pp. 1163–1172, Dec. 1971.

filter for a binary coded waveform; however, digital implementations appear to have significant packaging and cost advantages for the future when advantage is taken of the burgeoning technology of large scale integration. The losses associated with the requisite quantization in a digital system are of concern in the following.

The basic digital matched-filter configuration is shown in Fig. 1 for a biphase modulated signal where, as is typically the case, the carrier phase of the desired received signal is unknown. As indicated, the received signal plus interference is product detected to quadrature low-pass components, which are individual inputs to baseband matched filters. These would be tapped delay lines in an analog system. In a digitized system as discussed here, shift registers replace the tapped delay lines, and it is necessary to time sample the signal and then amplitude quantize each sample appropriately. For the present discussion, however, only the effects of amplitude quantization will be of concern, and it is presumed that adequate time sampling can be made inherent in the system design.[1]

Directing attention to either of the product detector outputs in Fig. 1, the analog correlation process ideally would be

$$v = \sum_{i=1}^{K} s_i(s_i + n_i) \tag{1}$$

where $s_i = 1$ or $-1$ in accordance with the binary coded signal and $K$ samples of signal plus interference are integrated. Equation (1) is written for the instant when the desired signal is aligned with the replica. The interference samples $n_i$ are assumed independent of the signal samples; hence, for a random selection of code digits, one may define an output signal-to-noise ratio as

$$\left(\frac{S}{N}\right)_{\text{analog}} = \frac{\{E(v)\}^2}{E(v^2) - \{E(v)\}^2} = \frac{K}{\sigma^2}. \tag{2}$$

In (2) the averaging is taken over the ensemble of binary codes, and $\sigma^2$ is defined as the average interference power per sample

$$\sigma^2 = \frac{1}{K} \sum_{i=1}^{K} n_i^2. \tag{3}$$

Typically, interest is connected with the case $\sigma^2 \gg 1$ and large $K$, and to the extent that the central limit theorem can be invoked, the performance of the matched filter correlation process will be independent of the individual $n_i$ values except through the parameters $\sigma$ and $K$.

When the amplitude quantization is introduced, there is a degradation in output $S/N$ depending on the statistics of the interference. For example, with binary quantization by infinite clipping, which retains only polarity of $s + n$, the loss is well known to be $2/\pi$ when the interference samples are Gaussian distributed with zero mean and variance $\sigma^2 \gg 1$. However, if all $|n_i| > 1$, as would be the case for square wave interference as an example, the polarity of $s + n$ is dominated by the interference, and the binary code structure of the signal is destroyed by the infinite clipping process. This condition of signal suppression implies a very large performance degradation, compared with an analog implementation.

Since binary quantization leads to the simplest digital matched filter implementation, a concept avoiding the inherent suppression effect is sought. Such a concept is that of dither, i.e., noise introduced to randomize the quantization process [3]–[5]. The problem addressed in this paper is to select the dither so as to minimize the worst degradation from (2), for the presumed number of quantization levels. A related game theory problem of this type has previously been treated for binary quantization [6]. The design philosophy may be described as minimax and is appropriate for such situations where the interference statistics are not *a priori* known.

## Binary Quantization

The binary quantization process attempts to derive the polarity of $s$ from the received sample $s + n$. If the polarity decisions are independent and the probability of error in determining polarity is $P$, the output signal-to-noise ratio of the binary correlation process may be defined [7] as

$$\left(\frac{S}{N}\right)_{\text{binary}} = K\,\frac{(1 - 2P)^2}{4P(1 - P)}, \tag{4}$$

which is optimized by a quantization process yielding the minimum $P$. For $P \to 0.5$, as will be the case for $\sigma^2 \gg 1$,

$$\left(\frac{S}{N}\right)_{\text{binary}} = K(1 - 2P)^2 \tag{5}$$

and one needs only the average probability of error to characterize performance. Then, comparison of (2) and (5) determines the degradation due to binary quantization. (Again, the central limit theorem is invoked for large $K$.)

In order to obtain the worst degradation, the minimax design concept utilizes a quantizing process that can be defined to guarantee an upper bound on $P$ for any interference with a specified bound on average power, i.e.,

$$\frac{1}{K} \sum_{i=1}^{K} n_i^2 \le \sigma^2. \tag{6}$$

Then, it is anticipated that the suppression effect noted above for infinite clipping can be avoided, at the expense of additional degradation for Gaussian interference. This quantizing process is now described.

## Minimax Dither Concept for Binary Quantization

To establish a minimax dither concept, consider one sample of the received signal plus interference. Let the interference have an unknown probability density with second moment not exceeding $\sigma^2$. Following Root [6], a dither voltage $\beta$ is introduced on the sample amplitude

[1] For example, two or more samples can be taken over the duration of each code digit and segregated into parallel shift registers.

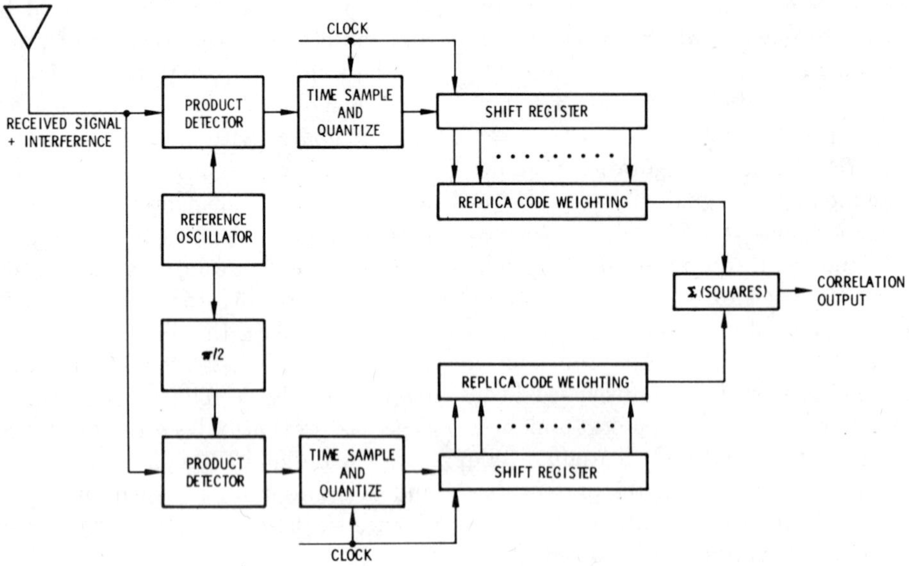


Fig. 1. Concept of digital matched filter.

prior to polarity quantizing. The dither is chosen for each sample independently in accordance with a probability density $g(\beta)$. It is required to find $g(\beta)$ to minimize the probability of quantizing to the incorrect polarity when the probability density $p(n)$ of interference is selected within the second moment constraint so as to maximize probability of quantizing to the incorrect polarity. For a particular $\beta$, the probability of error averaged over the two signal polarities can be written as

$$\begin{aligned} P_\beta &= \tfrac{1}{2} \Pr(n - \beta > 1) + \tfrac{1}{2} \Pr(n - \beta < -1) \\ &= \tfrac{1}{2} - \tfrac{1}{2} \Pr(-1 < n - \beta < 1) \end{aligned} \tag{7}$$

since the signal and interference are statistically independent. The ensemble average probability of error is then obtained by averaging over $\beta$ to give

$$P = \frac{1}{2} - \frac{1}{2} \int_{-\infty}^{\infty} g(\beta)\, d\beta \int_{-1+\beta}^{1+\beta} p(n)\, dn. \tag{8}$$

If the noise probability density $p(n)$ is known, the probability of error is minimized by setting $\beta$ so that

$$\int_{-1+\beta}^{1+\beta} p(n)\, dn = \text{maximum} \tag{9}$$

and

$$\min P = \frac{1}{2} - \frac{1}{2}\left[\int_{-1+\beta}^{1+\beta} p(n)\, dn\right]_{\text{max over } \beta}. \tag{10}$$

It is seen that any probability density of interference that has its maximum ordinate at zero will tend to call for a threshold setting at $\beta = 0$. As a simple generalization, Gaussian noise with a nonzero mean calls for $\beta$ to be set at the mean in order to maximize the correlation.

If the probability distribution of interference is unknown, the minimax (game theory) concept causes the threshold shift to be selected in accordance with a probability density $g(\beta)$ that is defined to minimize the probability of error for the worst noise distribution. Equation (10) gives a lower bound for the worst probability of error, since the threshold shift density $g(\beta)$ was selected to combat a specific noise density $p(n)$. If a uniform distribution satisfying the average power constraint,

$$p(n) = \frac{1}{2\sqrt{3}\sigma}, \qquad -\sqrt{3}\sigma < n < \sqrt{3}\sigma \tag{11}$$

is substituted in (10), one obtains (assuming $\sigma > 1/\sqrt{3}$)

$$\text{max-min } P \geq \frac{1}{2} - \frac{1}{2\sqrt{3}\sigma}. \tag{12}$$

A corresponding upper bound is to be found next.

Now, assume a threshold shift density $g(\beta)$ and compute the noise density $p(n)$ that yields the maximum probability of error. It is desired to find $g(\beta)$, which yields the least upper bound. As a suitable approximation for the following, assume $\sigma \gg 1$ so that $g(\beta)$ is essentially constant over a region of width 2. Then, after reversing the order of integration, (8) may be approximated as

$$\begin{aligned} P &= \frac{1}{2} - \frac{1}{2} \int_{-\infty}^{\infty} p(n)\, dn \int_{-1+n}^{1+n} g(\beta)\, d\beta \\ &\cong \frac{1}{2} - \int_{-\infty}^{\infty} p(x) g(x)\, dx. \end{aligned} \tag{13}$$

A solution is sought corresponding to selection of nonnegative density functions $p(x)$ and $g(x)$ which, respectively, maximize and minimize (13), subject to the constraints

$$\int_{-\infty}^{\infty} g(x)\, dx = 1 \tag{14}$$

$$\int_{-\infty}^{\infty} p(x)\, dx = 1 \tag{15}$$

$$\int_{-\infty}^{\infty} x^2 p(x)\, dx \leq \sigma^2. \tag{16}$$

If the Euler equation for a constrained extremal is applied, one obtains

$$p(x) - \lambda_1 = 0$$
$$g(x) - \lambda_2 - \lambda_3 x^2 = 0. \tag{17}$$

The form of (17) suggests the solution

$$g(\beta) = \frac{\sqrt{3}}{4\sigma}\left(1 - \frac{\beta^2}{3\sigma^2}\right), \qquad -\sqrt{3}\,\sigma < \beta < \sqrt{3}\sigma, \tag{18}$$

which turns out to be the desired probability density of threshold shift, as will now be demonstrated by considering an arbitrary $p(n)$ satisfying the constraints (15) and (16). Substituting $g(x)$ from (18), (13) becomes

$$P = \frac{1}{2} - \frac{\sqrt{3}}{4\sigma}\int_{-\sqrt{3}\sigma}^{\sqrt{3}\sigma}\left(1 - \frac{x^2}{3\sigma^2}\right)p(x)\,dx$$
$$\leq \frac{1}{2} - \frac{\sqrt{3}}{4\sigma}\int_{-\infty}^{\infty}\left(1 - \frac{x^2}{3\sigma^2}\right)p(x)\,dx \leq \frac{1}{2} - \frac{\sqrt{3}}{4\sigma}\left(1 - \frac{1}{3}\right). \tag{19}$$

Hence,

$$\text{min-max } P \leq \frac{1}{2} - \frac{1}{2\sqrt{3}\sigma} \tag{20}$$

irrespective of $p(n)$. In view of (12) and (20), the minimax solution—within the approximation in (13)—has been found for probability of error. Using this solution, (5) is evaluated to give

$$\left(\frac{S}{N}\right)_{\text{binary worst case}} = K(1 - 2P)^2 = \frac{K}{3\sigma^2} = \frac{1}{3}\left(\frac{S}{N}\right)_{\text{analog}}. \tag{21}$$

Thus, the minimax loss of signal-to-noise ratio is 4.8 dB, regardless of the actual distribution of the interference, and the suppression effect of infinite clipping has been avoided.

## Estimation of Interference Power

The minimax strategy for obtaining the guaranteed loss of (21) may be described as randomized binary quantizing, which shifts the threshold for each sample within the range $-\sqrt{3}\,\sigma < \beta < \sqrt{3}\,\sigma$ in accordance with the probability density in (18). Note that the range is determined by the average interference power $\sigma^2$ to be tolerated in the receiver; hence, the minimax dither function and the resulting minimax performance are dependent on knowledge of $\sigma^2$. In general, this quantity must be derived from the received signal by an estimation process, which may, for convenience, be called automatic gain control (AGC). Conceptually, a short-term power measurement is a basis for deriving AGC that can follow changes in the interference level.

In practice, the power estimation must be accomplished prior to the occurrence of the sample to be quantized (unless a short-term analog memory is incorporated). Thus, to follow changes in the interference level, the time constant of the power measurement should be kept short. This leads to a performance degradation due to the statistical fluctuations of a short-term measurement.

To illustrate the loss and indicate the required averaging interval, consider coherent square-wave interference at a given power level $\sigma^2 > 1$. Assume the value of $\sigma^2$ is estimated simply as the mean square over $k$ received samples, each of which can have either of the equally likely amplitudes $\sigma \pm 1$. Thus, the estimate is obtained

$$\sigma_k^2 = \frac{\sigma^2}{\sigma^2 + 1}\frac{1}{k}\sum_{i=1}^{k}(s_i + n_i)^2, \tag{22}$$

which has a binomial distribution of values for the postulated interference.

The actual probability of error over the $k$ samples may now be computed, on the basis that an independent random dither is added to each sample, using the distribution of (18) with $\sigma$ equal to the estimate $\sigma_k$. By integration, the probability of error for each sample of amplitude $\sigma - 1$ is

$$P_- = 0.5 + \frac{\sqrt{3}}{4}\left\{\frac{\sigma - 1}{\sigma_k} - \frac{1}{9}\left(\frac{\sigma - 1}{\sigma_k}\right)^3\right\} \tag{23}$$

and for each sample of amplitude $\sigma + 1$ is

$$P_+ = 0.5 - \frac{\sqrt{3}}{4}\left\{\frac{\sigma + 1}{\sigma_k} - \frac{1}{9}\left(\frac{\sigma + 1}{\sigma_k}\right)^3\right\}, \qquad \sigma + 1 > \sqrt{3}\sigma_k$$
$$= 0, \qquad \sigma + 1 < \sqrt{3}\sigma_k. \tag{24}$$

These may be averaged over the binomial distribution of $\sigma_k^2$ to give $P$. Typical results are displayed in Fig. 2 in terms of $S/N$ degradation from (21); in other words, $3\sigma^2(1 - 2P)^2$ is plotted expressed in decibels.

Let us now generalize the analysis using the same approximation as introduced in (13) for the case $\sigma \gg 1$. Letting $n_i$ be a set of interference samples, the estimate of $\sigma^2$ over $k$ samples may be written

$$k\sigma_{k+}^2 = (1 + n_j)^2 + \sum_{i \neq j}^{k}(s_i + n_i)^2$$
$$k\sigma_{k-}^2 = (-1 + n_j)^2 + \sum_{i \neq j}^{k}(s_i + n_i)^2 \tag{25}$$

where the notation is intended to indicate the dependence of $\sigma_k$ on the polarity of the $j$th sample of the desired signal. One may simply write $\sigma_k$ except where the small difference between $\sigma_{k+}$ and $\sigma_{k-}$ becomes significant.

Assuming an arbitrary dither distribution $g(\beta)$, the probability of error averaged over the two polarities for the $j$th sample is

$$P_j = \frac{1}{2}\int_{-\infty}^{-(1+n_j)/\sigma_{k+}} g(\beta)\,d\beta + \frac{1}{2}\int_{(1-n_j)/\sigma_{k-}}^{\infty} g(\beta)\,d\beta$$
$$= \frac{1}{2} - \frac{1}{2}\int_{(n_j-1)/\sigma_{k-}}^{(n_j+1)/\sigma_{k+}} g(\beta)\,d\beta$$
$$\cong \frac{1}{2} - \frac{1}{2}\left(\frac{n_j + 1}{\sigma_{k+}} - \frac{n_j - 1}{\sigma_{k-}}\right)g\left(\frac{n_j}{\sigma_k}\right). \tag{26}$$

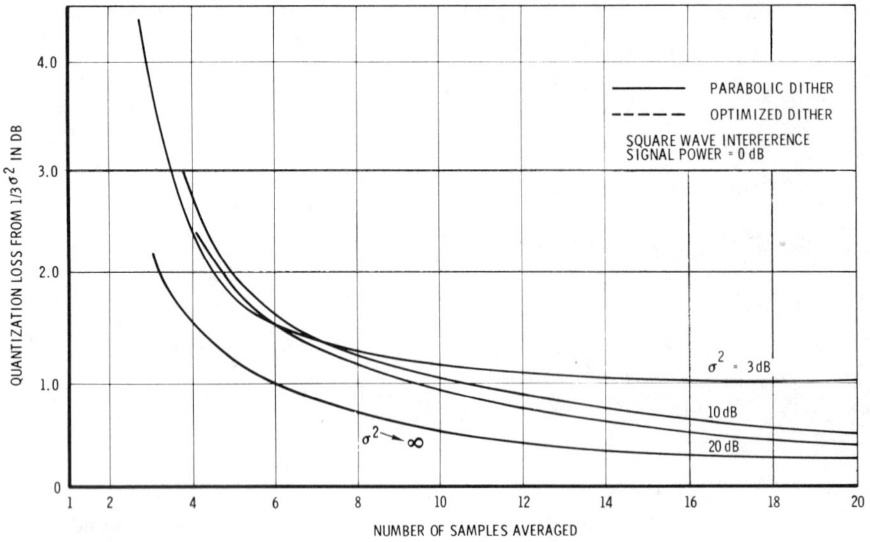


Fig. 2. Performance with short-duration interference averaging.

Now, observe from (25) that

$$\sigma_{k+}^2 - \sigma_{k-}^2 = (\sigma_{k+} + \sigma_{k-})(\sigma_{k+} - \sigma_{k-}) = \frac{4}{k}\, n_j. \qquad (27)$$

Using (27), (26) may be further approximated as

$$P_j \cong \frac{1}{2} - \frac{1}{\sigma_k}\, g\left(\frac{n_j}{\sigma_k}\right)\left(1 - \frac{n_j^2}{k\sigma_k^2}\right) \qquad (28)$$

and averaged over the $k$ samples to give

$$P \cong \frac{1}{2} - \frac{1}{k\sigma_k} \sum_{j=1}^{k} g\left(\frac{n_j}{\sigma_k}\right)\left(1 - \frac{n_j^2}{k\sigma_k^2}\right). \qquad (29)$$

It is now desired to find the least upper bound of this approximate expression for $P$ subject to the constraint of a maximum average interference power over the $k$ samples. Then,

$$k\sigma_k^2 = \sum_{i=1}^{k} n_i^2 \le k\sigma_k\Big]_{\max}^2. \qquad (30)$$

In similarity with the derivation leading to (18), define the probability density of dither

$$g_k(u) = f(\gamma_k)\,\frac{1 - (u/\gamma_k)^2}{1 - u^2/k}, \qquad |u| < \gamma_k \qquad (31)$$

where $f(\gamma_k)$ is the value that normalizes $g_k(u)$. Substituting (31) into (29) and using (30), the upper bound is obtained

$$P \le \frac{1}{2} - \frac{f(\gamma_k)}{\sigma_k]_{\max}}\,(1 - \gamma_k^{-2}) \qquad (32)$$

and the least upperbound as a function of $\gamma_k$ may be computed. From this, the resulting $S/N$ degradation is plotted in Fig. 2 and shows the same behavior with $k$ as was computed in a straightforward manner for square-wave interference, above.

It may be noted from Fig. 2 that estimation of the interference power over roughly 10 samples suffices to reduce the degradation to a small loss from the result for a long time constant averaging. Hence, the baseband portion of the minimax design concept for the digital matched filter with binary quantizing can be detailed as shown in Fig. 3. As previously suggested, the analog delay corresponds to the short-term averaging interval.

## Worst Allocation of Interference Power

It has been shown in the above that the output $S/N$ for integration over $k$ binary quantized samples becomes

$$\left(\frac{S}{N}\right)_{\text{binary}} \cong \frac{k}{3\sigma_k^2} \qquad (33)$$

for $k$ reasonably large, where $\sigma_k^2$ is the average interference power over the $k$ samples, according to (30). Now consider integration over $K/k$ disjoint sets of samples, where $K/k$ is taken as an integer for simplicity. The resulting output $S/N$ may be expressed as

$$\left(\frac{S}{N}\right)_{\text{binary}} = \frac{k^2}{3K}\left(\sum_{i=1}^{K/k} \frac{1}{\sigma_k^{(i)}}\right)^2 \qquad (34)$$

where $\sigma_k^{(i)}$ is the average interference power over the $i$th set of $k$ samples. If the total interference is specified, as in (6), one has

$$\sum_{i=1}^{K/k} [\sigma_k^{(i)}]^2 \le K\sigma^2/k \qquad (35)$$

as a constraint.

The worst allocation of interference power to the different sets of $k$ samples is now to be found, which minimizes (34) subject to the constraint of (35). Applying the Schwarz inequality, as previously done for a similar problem with a bandpass limiter [8], shows that the worst-case occurs for $\sigma_k^{(i)} = \sigma$, for all $i$. Thus, square-wave interference, in fact, represents an example of worst interference for binary quantizing when the optimized

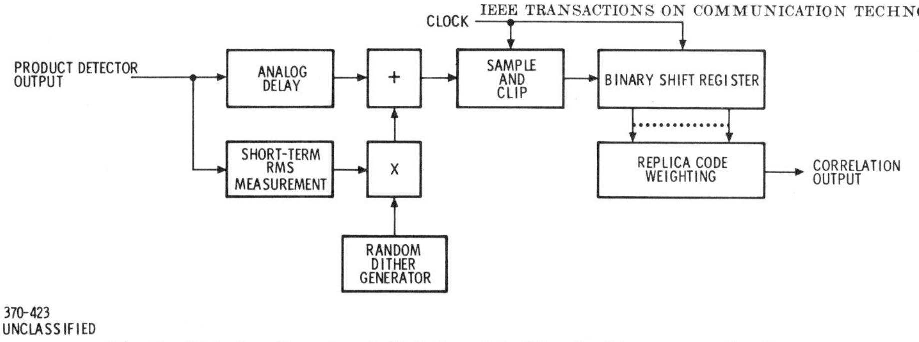


Fig. 3. Details of baseband digital match filter for binary quantization.

dither is introduced and (21) is the resulting performance.

## Multilevel Quantization

An approach toward extending the minimax theory to multilevel quantization will now be sketched. For this, dither is to be interpreted as a randomization process that assigns each sample of received signal plus interference to one of $Q = 2^B$ quantization levels, as suggested in Fig. 4.

The general formulation of the randomized quantizing process is to define transition probabilities $p(q/r)$, conditional on the received amplitude $r$. Then, by definition

$$\sum_{q=1}^{Q} p(q/r) = 1 \tag{36}$$

for all $r$. If the signal assumes the value $s$, the overall channel transition probabilities including the quantizing are

$$\begin{aligned} p_0(q/s) &= \int p(q/r)p(r-s)\,dr \\ &\cong \int p(q/r)p(r)\,dr - s\int p(q/r)p'(r)\,dr \\ &= p_q - s\int p(q/r)p'(r)\,dr \end{aligned} \tag{37}$$

where $p(n)$ is the interference distribution and the expansion is predicated on the signal amplitude being typically small compared with the interference (very noisy channel [9]). Letting $s = \pm 1$ for transmitting binary digits

$$\begin{aligned} p_0(q/\pm 1) &\cong p_q \pm \left\{-\int p(q/r)p'(r)\,dr\right\} \\ &= p_q \pm \epsilon_q \end{aligned} \tag{38}$$

where $\epsilon_q$ is to be small compared with $p_q$.

Suppose that the $q$th level is assigned the metric weighing $\gamma_q$, so that the correlation process for multilevel quantizing is

$$v = \sum_{i=1}^{K} s_i \gamma_{q_i} \tag{39}$$

where $q_i$ is the level assigned to the $i$th sample. Then, averaging over the two equally likely digit polarities and using (38)

$$\begin{aligned} E(v) &= K \sum_q \epsilon_q \gamma_q \\ E(v^2) &\cong K \sum_q p_q \gamma_q^2 \end{aligned} \tag{40}$$

when the desired signal is aligned with the replica. The mean is zero otherwise. By the definition (2), we can write

$$\left(\frac{S}{N}\right)_{\text{quantized}} = K \frac{\left[\sum_q \epsilon_q \gamma_q\right]^2}{\sum_q p_q \gamma_q^2} \leq K \sum_q \epsilon_q^2/p_q \tag{41}$$

where the upper bound is achieved by setting (with an arbitrary constant of proportionality).

$$\gamma_q = \epsilon_q/p_q \tag{42}$$

Let $\epsilon_q^*$ and $p_q^*$ minimize this maximum $S/N$ over the convex set of allowed interference distributions. Then, by arguments paralleling those applied by Stiglitz [10] for a similar problem in bounding probability of error for random code words and unknown interference, one can show that

$$\left(\frac{S}{N}\right)_{\text{quantized}} \geq K \sum_q \epsilon_q^{*2}/p_q^* \tag{43}$$

if the metric weightings

$$\gamma_q^* = \epsilon_q^*/p_q^* \tag{44}$$

are employed. Equation (43) includes binary quantizing as a special case and shows how the improvement in minimax performance with multilevel quantizing can be computed, at least in principle.

## Lower Bound on Performance With Four Quantization Levels

With four-level quantizing and an arbitrary noise interference distribution constrained by its average power, a lower bound on guaranteed performance with a binary coded signal is derived by presuming any distribution of dither on the quantizing thresholds and then finding the worst interference distribution that minimizes (43). The metric weightings are computed for this worst interference distribution. Because the binary digits are equi-

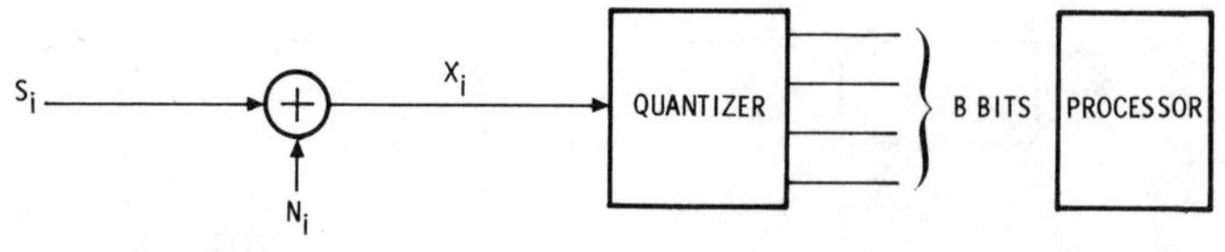


Fig. 4. Channel and quantized receiver.

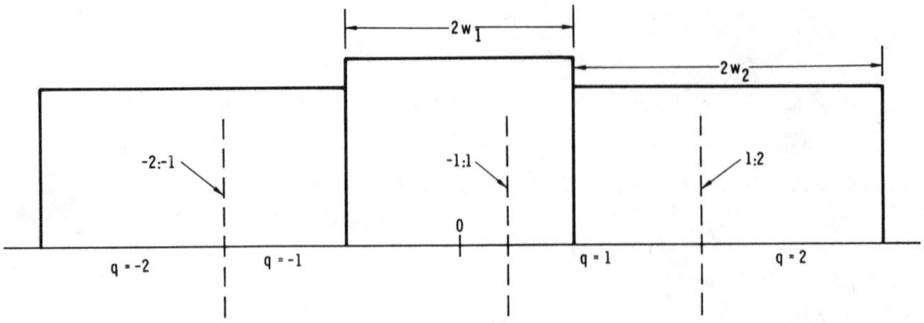


Fig. 5. Probability densities of quantizing dithers.

probable, only symmetrical interference distributions need be considered.

With four symmetrical quantizing levels, let the transition probabilities in the absence of signal be $p_1 = p_{-1}$, $p_2 = -p_2$. The binary signal of unit amplitude causes increments $\pm\epsilon_1$, $\pm\epsilon_2$. Thus, by (43), the output $S/N$ associated with quantizing may be written

$$(S/N)_{4\text{-level}} = 2K\left(\frac{\epsilon_1^{\,2}}{p_1} + \frac{\epsilon_2^{\,2}}{p_2}\right), \tag{45}$$

which can be computed for a given situation.

The quantizing concept presumed to find a lower bound is shown in Fig. 5, which gives the probability densities of the quantizing thresholds separating the four output regions. A uniform distribution for each is presumed. Thus, the probability densities of the locations of the quantizing thresholds are

$$p(1\!:\!2) = p(-2\!:\!-1) = \frac{1}{2w_2}$$

$$p(-1\!:\!1) = \frac{1}{2w_1} \tag{46}$$

where $w_1$ and $w_2$ are to be determined. If the received signal plus interference occurs in one of the regions, the corresponding metric weighting is applied. It is seen that the quantities $\epsilon_1$ and $\epsilon_2$ are determined by the probability that the signal will displace the interference from one quantizing region to another.

Observe the following. If the interference value $n$ lies anywhere within $-w_1 < n < w_1$, the increment $\epsilon_1$ due to the signal of unit amplitude is given by

$$\epsilon_1 = \frac{1}{2w_1}, \tag{47}$$

which expresses the probability of crossing from region $-1$ to 1. The strategy for the worst interference in this region should be to utilize $n = 0$, which takes no power. The probability $P_0$ is yet to be found. If the interference lies anywhere within $w_1 < n < w_1 + 2w_2$, the increments $\epsilon_1$ and $\epsilon_2$ are given by

$$\epsilon_1 = -\frac{1}{2w_2}$$

$$\epsilon_2 = \frac{1}{2w_2}, \tag{48}$$

which are found from the probability of crossing from region 1 to 2. In this range, the strategy for the worst interference should be to utilize the single value $n = A$, since the average value of $n$ within the range sets the $p_1$, $p_2$ result, and the power is minimized for a constant value. The value $A$ and its probability $P_A$ are still to be determined. Finally, if the interference exceeds $w_1 + 2w_2$, the signal has no effect and the minimum interference power causing this situation occurs for $n = w_1 + 2w_2$. Note that $w_1 + 2w_2 > \sigma$ is therefore a requirement to avoid complete suppression.

The general form of the worst interference distribution has thus been found since it minimizes the required power to produce any given set of transition probabilities. The distribution is discrete, and

$$n = 0, \quad \text{with probability } P_0$$

$$n = A, -A, \quad \text{each with probability } P_A$$

$$n = w_1 + 2w_2, -w_1 - 2w_2,$$

$$\text{each with probability } 0.5 - 0.5P_0 - P_A. \tag{49}$$

If $A$ and $P_0$ are taken as parameters to be optimized to find the worst interference, $P_A$ is computed by solving

$$2A^2P_A + 2(w_1 + 2w_2)^2(0.5 - 0.5P_0 - P_A) = \sigma^2 \tag{50}$$

where the constraints $P_A \geq 0$ and $0.5 - 0.5\,P_0 - P_A \geq 0$ specify the permissible values of $P_0$ and $A$. Then, the transition probabilities $p_1$ and $p_2$ and the increments $\epsilon_1$

and $\epsilon_2$ may be computed. The resulting $S/N$ is thus obtained from (45) as a function of $w_1$, $w_2$, $A$, and $P_0$.

The interference parameters $A$ and $P_0$ are to be varied so as to minimize $S/N$ while the quantizing parameters $w_1$ and $w_2$ are adjusted to maximize $S/N$. A computer search, yields the approximate saddle point

$$\begin{aligned}(S/N)_{4\text{-level}} &= 0.59K/\sigma^2\\ w_1 &= 0.61\sigma\\ w_2 &= 0.92\sigma\\ A &= 0.98\sigma\\ P_0 &= 0.38\end{aligned}\tag{51}$$

Thus, the loss in $S/N$ from the unquantized case is guaranteed not to exceed 2.3 dB for this method of four-level quantizing.

The proper metric weightings of the two quantizing levels (1 and 2) may be computed after solving for $\epsilon_1$, $\epsilon_2$, $p_1$, $p_2$ from the numerical results of (51) to give

$$\begin{aligned}\epsilon_1/p_1 &= 0.406\\ \epsilon_2/p_2 &= 1.565\end{aligned}\tag{52}$$

Only the ratio 3.85 of the two weightings is significant.

## Computer Simulation

To demonstrate the validity of the minimax design concept, a computer simulation of the sampled system was implemented. Using a random number generator, the simulation generates a sequence of $K$ random binary signal digits and adds interference to each digit. Thus, $K$ samples of signal plus interference are thereby obtained. The AGC was implemented simply as a single-pole smoothing process, according to

$$\sigma_{\text{new}}^2 = e^{-\alpha}\sigma_{\text{old}}^2 + (1 - e^{-\alpha})(s + n)^2 \tag{53}$$

where $\alpha^{-1}$ is the number of samples in the time constant of AGC averaging. In the simulation, this time constant was set typically at 10 samples and $\sigma^2$ was initialized as its true average value.

Binary quantizing is performed by generating a dither value for each sample using the AGC's estimate of interference power at that sample and clipping the resultant of signal plus interference plus dither to $\pm 1$. The dither distribution of (18) was approximated very closely for convenience of computation by

$$g(\beta) = \left(\frac{\pi}{4\sqrt{3}\sigma}\right) \cos(\pi\beta/2\sqrt{3}\sigma). \tag{54}$$

An analog delay of half the AGC time constant was presumed. In other words, the value of $\sigma^2$ computed in (53) was used when quantizing a digit received 5 samples earlier, for an averaging time constant of 10 samples. The quantized samples were then correlated with the known signal digits over the $K$ samples. The results of the simulation may be expressed as an output signal-to-noise ratio defined by

$$S/N = 20\log_{10}\left\{\frac{\text{correlation amplitude}}{\text{rms with uncorrelated signal}}\right\} \tag{55}$$

where the rms fluctuation in the absence of correlation is that of the binomial distribution produced by the sum of $K$ binary digits equally likely to be positive or negative.

With four-level quantizing, the same simulation model described above applies except that quantizing was performed by generating two uniformly distributed dithers, $\beta_1$ and $\beta_2$, where from (51)

$$\begin{aligned}-0.61\sigma &< \beta_1 < 0.61\sigma\\ 0.61\sigma &< \beta_2 < 2.45\sigma.\end{aligned}\tag{56}$$

Then, a received sample $r$ is quantized so that

$$\begin{aligned}\text{amplitude} &= 1.0;\ |r| \le \beta_2\\ &= 3.85;\ |r| > \beta_2\\ \text{polarity} &= \text{sign}\,(r - \beta_1).\end{aligned}\tag{57}$$

These quantized samples are correlated with the known signal digits over the $K$ samples. The output signal-to-noise ratio is still defined by (55); however, the rms fluctuation in the absence of correlation was measured simultaneously with the correlation amplitude.

In the simulation, several forms of interference were generated for a filter with $K = 2000$, a theoretical processing gain of 33 dB according to (2). The interference forms were constant, random binary, sinusoidally varying, ON–OFF pulsed, and Gaussian.

The results of the simulation are plotted in Figs. 6 and 7. For reference, the theoretical relation between $(S/N)_0$ and $(S/N)_i$ for analog integration is plotted for $K = 2000$. Also plotted in Fig. 6 is the theoretical relation for a digital matched filter with binary quantizing using the minimax dither of (18); this is simply displaced from the linear integration curve by 4.8 dB according to (21). In Fig. 7, the theoretical relation with four-level quantizing is displaced by 2.3 dB.

The performance results for both constant interference and random binary-modulated interference are identical within the scatter of a Monte Carlo simulation. The performance appears to be below the theoretical curve for quantizing by a fraction of 1 dB, and this is attributed to the short time constant of AGC averaging, as indicated in Fig. 2.

Two extremes may be examined for time-varying interference, depending on whether the amplitude variation is fast or slow compared with the AGC time constant. If the variation is fast, the AGC will remain essentially constant and the basic arguments leading to the mini-

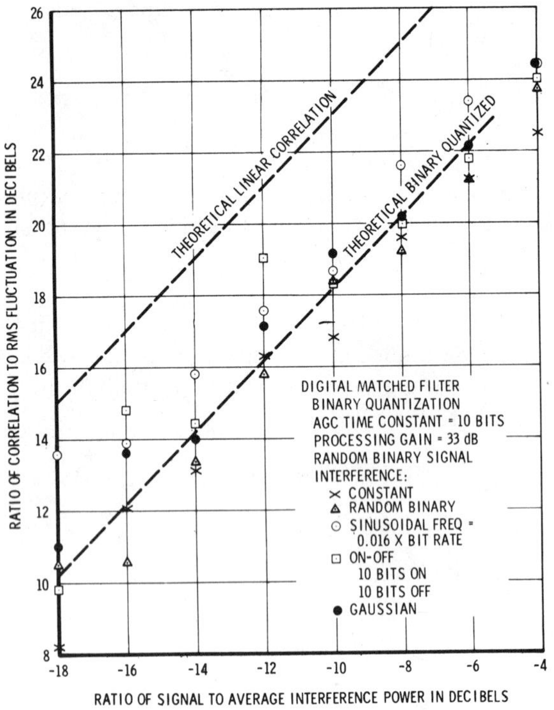


Fig. 6. Performance of digital matched filter with binary quantizing.

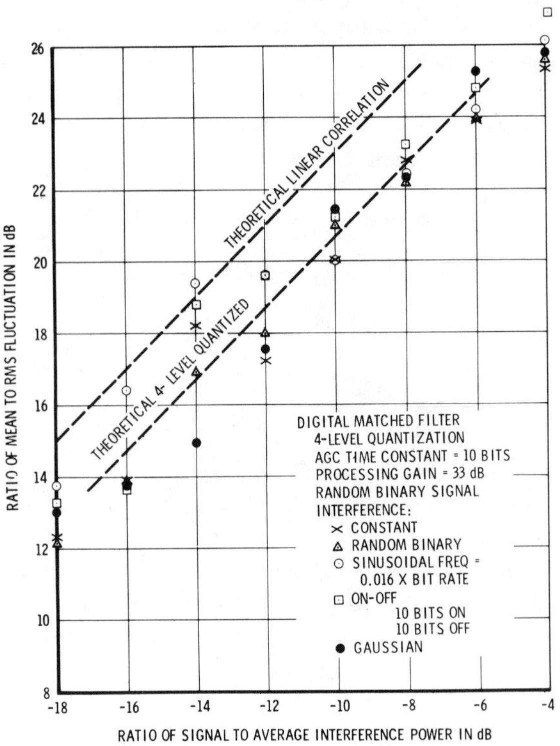


Fig. 7. Performance of digital matched filter with four-level quantizing.

max solution are applicable. On the other hand, if the amplitude variation is slow, the AGC will tend to follow, and the interference is then less effective.

Sinusoidally varying interference was tested at two frequencies, 0.16 × bit rate and 0.016 × bit rate. Those are, respectively, fast and slow compared with the AGC averaging time constant. The former yielded results essentially the same as constant interference. The latter is plotted in Figs. 6 and 7 and displays a decrease in effectiveness.

Next, ON–OFF pulsed interference was introduced. In an attempt to find a potential effect related to the AGC averaging time constant, the ON and OFF intervals were both set equal to the time constant, 10 samples. The results plotted show a slight decrease in effectiveness compared with constant interference and no effect associated with AGC averaging is apparent. Similar conclusions are observed for Gaussian interference with binary quantizing. With four-level quantizing, Gaussian interference is as effective as constant interference.

In addition to the computation of correlation with the replica signal, the simulation also monitored correlation for a one-sample time shift of the replica, for which the correlation should average to zero. No correlation value was observed, which would be highly improbable based on the rms fluctuation in the absence of signal correlation.

## Conclusions

It has been shown that a digital matched filter correlator can be designed for a binary coded signal on the basis of binary quantization. Suppression of the desired signal, normally a potential problem when the interference is unknown, can be avoided provided that a random dither is added to each sample of signal plus interference prior to the clipping process. The dither requires an estimation of interference power, such as by a short-term power averaging. For binary quantization, the worst-case loss in output $S/N$ is 4.8 dB compared with an analog correlator, irrespective of the distribution of interference power.

It may be observed that a digital matched filter can be designed with the alternate approach of multilevel amplitude quantization. This approach [11] can reduce the loss (at most by 4.8 dB) but at the expense of increased filter complexity (proportional to the number of bits to represent the quantizing levels). Dither is useful here also for the same purpose; namely, avoid signal suppression due to the quantization. In the general quantizing problem, dither is to be interpreted as a randomization process leading to a definable set of transition probabilities for the quantizer. In this way, the minimax concept employed here for binary quantization can, in principle, be extended to multilevel quantization. With four-level quantization, the loss is at most 2.3 dB, a bound obtained by postulating a particular dither scheme. Thus, binary quantization and four-level quantization are almost equivalent when measured in terms of digital matched filter complexity to achieve a specified output $S/N$.

Computer simulations show that the performance of a digital matched filter conforms closely to theoretical expectations. The concept of employing a square law AGC with a short time constant of averaging is demonstrated to give $S/N$ enhancement almost independent of the form of interference, taking average power as the measure of the interference level. As expected, slow variations in amplitude tend to decrease the effectiveness of the interference.

## References


[1] S. W. Golomb *et al., Digital Communications with Space Applications.* Englewood Cliffs, N. J.: Prentice-Hall, pp. 65–105, 1964.

[2] R. M. Lerner, "A matched filter detection system for complicated Doppler shifted signals," *IRE Trans. Inform. Theory,* vol. IT-6, pp. 373–385, June 1960.

[3] G. A. Korn, *Random-Process Simulation and Measurement.* New York: McGraw-Hill, pp. 136–139, 1966.

[4] H. Berndt, "Correlation function estimation by a polarity method using stochastic reference signals," *IEEE Trans. Inform. Theory,* vol. IT-14, pp. 796–801, Nov. 1968.

[5] K.-Y. Chang and A. D. Moore, "Modified digital correlator and its estimation errors," *IEEE Trans. Inform. Theory,* vol. IT-16, pp. 699–706, Nov. 1970.

[6] W. L. Root, "Communications through unspecified additive noise," *Inform. Control,* vol. 4, pp. 15–29, Mar. 1961.

[7] J. V. Harrington, "An analysis of the detection of repeated signals in noise by binary integration," *IRE Trans. Inform. Theory,* vol. IT-1, pp. 1–9, Mar. 1955.

[8] C. R. Cahn, "A note on signal-to-noise ratio in band-pass limiters," *IRE Trans. Inform. Theory,* vol. IT-7, pp. 39–43, Jan. 1961.

[9] R. G. Gallager, *Information Theory and Reliable Communication.* New York: Wiley, pp. 147–149, 1968.

[10] I. G. Stiglitz, "Coding for a class of unknown channels," *IEEE Trans. Inform. Theory,* vol. IT-12, pp. 189–195, Apr. 1966.

[11] C. R. Cahn, "Worst interference for coherent binary channel," *IEEE Trans. Inform. Theory,* vol. IT-17, pp. 209–210, Mar. 1971.

# The Effects of Notch Filters on the Correlation Properties of a PN Signal


**Abstract**

**With wideband pseudo-noise (PN) communications systems, it is sometimes desirable to supplement the inherent interference rejection capabilities by adding notch filters to attenuate relatively narrowband interference. This correspondence presents an investigation of the effects of notch filters on the performance of PN correlation receivers. A theoretical analysis of the correlation drop due to filter distortion has been conducted and confirmed by experimentation. Additional measurements and analysis have established the trade-off between correlation drop and interference suppression as a function of interference bandwidth. A typical result is that by incurring a penalty of a 1-dB drop in correlation peak, interfering signals having bandwidths of 2 to 3 percent of the PN chip rate can be attenuated by 25 dB.**


## I. Introduction

Wideband pseudo-noise (PN) signals have been utilized as information carriers or range measurement waveforms in numerous applications. The motivation for such signals includes interference rejection, multipath discrimination, multiple access, or, simply, range resolution with minimum peak power. Although PN systems employing correlation detectors for reception have inherent capability to reject co-channel interference, it is sometimes desirable to supplement the inherent immunity by adding notch filters to attenuate relatively narrowband interference.

The bandwidth of the notch filters which are used is determined, on one hand, by the bandwidth of the interfering signal and the total suppression of that signal which is required. Given an interference signal bandwidth and the amount of suppression desired, the bandwidth of the notch filter is essentially established. On the other hand, the band-rejection filter will distort the desired signal which passes through it. In the case of a desired PN signal, the effect of passing the signal through a notch filter is to reduce the correlation peak and increase correlation sidelobe responses in the receiver. Thus, a trade-off is required between the requirements for high attenuation of wide bandwidth interference signals and low degradation of the receiver correlation function. This correspondence presents the analytical and experimental criteria for making the trade-off between correlation drop and interference suppression.


Manuscript received May 31, 1973; revised Ausust 29, 1973.

This work was performed while the authors were with Teledyne ADCOM, Cambridge, Mass., and was partially supported by NASA-Goddard SFC under contract NAS 5-20226.



Reprinted from *IEEE Trans. Aerosp. Electron. Syst.*, vol. AES-10, pp. 385–390, May 1974.

TABLE I

Initial Values of High-Pass Tchebycheff Impulse-Response Curves (From [1])

| n | $h_g(0)$ | | |
|---|---|---|---|
| | $\rho$ = 0.5 | $\rho$ = 1 | $\rho$ = 2 |
| 1 | -0.349 | -0.508 | -0.765 |
| 2 | -0.888 | -0.887 | -0.776 |
| 3 | -2.145 | -2.521 | -3.127 |
| 4 | -2.554 | -2.401 | -1.995 |
| 5 | -4.206 | -4.726 | -5.621 |
| 6 | -4.307 | -3.972 | -3.247 |
| 7 | -6.306 | -6.958 | -8.131 |
| 8 | -6.079 | -5.554 | -4.505 |
| 9 | -8.416 | -9.197 | -10.645 |
| 10 | -7.856 | -7.139 | -5.765 |

## II. Effect of Notch Filter Bandwidth on Receiver Correlation Peak

The insertion of a signal-distorting filter in the path of one input to a correlator will cause a degradation in the output SNR relative to optimum. The filter will have an effect on both the signal and the noise. However, for applications considered here, the notch filters are relatively narrowband, compared to the PN signal bandwidth, and the change in noise power is not significant. The main consequence of the filter is to cause a degradation in the correlation peak. This degradation can be calculated as follows. Let $s(t)$ be the undistorted signal that forms one input to the correlator. The same signal has passed through a filter with impulse response $h(t)$. The filter output is

$$y(t) = \int_0^\infty h(\tau)s(t-\tau)\,d\tau. \tag{1}$$

The correlator performs the integral

$$w(T) = \int_0^T y(t)s(t-\sigma)\,dt \tag{2}$$

where we have allowed for a time shift $\sigma$ in the local reference to account for a possible delay through the filter. Inserting for $y(t)$ gives

$$w(T) = \int_0^T dt \int_0^\infty d\tau\, h(\tau)s(t-\tau)s(t-\sigma). \tag{3}$$

The $t$ integral can be recognized as the correlation function of the signal over an interval $T$:

$$R_T(\sigma-\tau) = \int_0^T s(t-\tau)s(t-\sigma)\,dt, \tag{4}$$

whence

$$w(T) = \int_0^\infty h(\tau)R_T(\sigma-\tau)\,d\tau. \tag{5}$$

The correlation function for a square-wave PSK pseudo-noise signal is given by

$$R_T(\sigma) = R_c(\sigma)\cos\omega_c\sigma. \tag{6}$$

Here $\omega_c$ is the carrier frequency and $R_c(\sigma)$ is the code autocorrelation given by the familiar triangle function

$$R_c(\sigma) = R_c(0)[1-(|\sigma|/\Delta)] \tag{7}$$

where $\Delta$ is the chip duration.

The filter impulse response is represented by

$$h(\tau) = 2h_e(\tau)\cos\omega_f\tau. \tag{8}$$

Here $\omega_f$ is the notch filter center frequency and $h_e(\tau)$ is the impulse response envelope.

Inserting the preceding into (5) yields

$$\begin{aligned} w(T) &= \int_0^\infty 2h_e(\tau)\cos\omega_f\tau R_c(\sigma-\tau)\cos\omega_c(\sigma-\tau)\,d\tau \\ &= \int_0^\infty h_e(\tau)\cos[(\omega_f-\omega_c)\tau+\omega_c\sigma]R_c(\sigma-\tau)\,d\tau \\ &\quad + \text{vanishing integral of sum frequency term.} \end{aligned} \tag{9}$$

We now invoke the properties of the filter impulse response. The envelope $h_e(\tau)$ is derived from the equivalent high-pass filter, which, when translated to $\omega_f$, produces a notch.

Impulse responses of conventional high-pass filters have been investigated in the literature [1]. Unfortunately, only the Tchebycheff variety has been computed to the extent necessary for the present evaluation [2]. The impulse response consists of an impulse at the origin and a slowly varying decaying term. Table I gives the initial value of the slowly varying term for the Tchebycheff filter. Treating these two components separately, the integral $w(T)$ can be evaluated approximately as follows. Let

$$h_e(\tau) = \delta(\tau) + g(\tau) \tag{10}$$

and assume that the correlation $R_c(\sigma)$ can be regarded as an impulse compared to $g(\tau)$, while being, of course, slowly varying in relation to the impulse $\delta(\tau)$. Under these conditions,

$$\begin{aligned} w(T) &\approx \int_0^\infty [\delta(\tau)+g(\tau)]\cos[(\omega_f-\omega_c)\tau+\omega_c\sigma] \\ &\quad \cdot R_c(\sigma-\tau)\,d\tau \\ &\approx R_c(\sigma)\cos\omega_c\sigma + g(\sigma)\int_0^\infty R_c(\sigma-\tau)\cos[(\sigma-\tau) \\ &\quad \cdot(\omega_c-\omega_f)+\omega_f\sigma]\,d\tau. \end{aligned} \tag{11}$$

With phase-coherent demodulation and synchronized code correlation, one may set $\sigma = 0$, whereupon

$$w(T) \approx R_c(0) + g(0)\int_0^\infty R_c(\tau) \cos(\omega_c - \omega_f)\tau \, d\tau. \quad (12)$$

For the triangular correlation function,

$$w(T) \approx R_c(0) + g(0)R_c(0)(\Delta/2) \cdot \{[\sin(1/2)\Delta(\omega_c - \omega_f)]/[(1/2)\Delta(\omega_c - \omega_f)]\}. \quad (13)$$

There now remain only the normalization factors. Since the calculated impulse responses $h_n(t)$ are normalized for unit bandwidth, a frequency scaling factor to a bandwidth $B$ must be applied. The transfer function of the high-pass filter $H_e(s)$ is found from the normalized one, $H_n(\lambda)$, by

$$H_e(s) = H_n[s/(2\pi B)]. \quad (14)$$

The impulse response is

$$\begin{aligned} h_e(t) &= [1/(2\pi)]\int_{-\infty}^{\infty} e^{st} H_e(s)\, ds \\ &= 2\pi B[1/(2\pi)]\int_{-\infty}^{\infty} \exp\{[s/(2\pi B)](2\pi Bt)\} \\ &\quad \cdot H_n[s/(2\pi B)]\,[ds/(2\pi B)] \\ &= 2\pi B h_n(2\pi Bt). \end{aligned} \quad (15)$$

The scale factor applies only to the continuous part of the impulse response, because the impulse at the origin arises from a portion of the transfer function that is independent of the variable $s$.

With these factors,

$$w(T) = R_c(0)[1 + (\pi/2)g_n(0) \cdot (2B\Delta)\{[\sin(1/2)\Delta(\omega_c - \omega_f)]/[(1/2)\Delta(\omega_c - \omega_f)]\}^2]. \quad (16)$$

From Table I, $g_n(0) \approx -2.5$ for third- and fourth-order Tchebycheff filters of moderate ripple factors. Employing this as a representative value, we get

$$w(T) = R_c(0)[1 - 4(2B\Delta) \cdot \{[\sin(1/2)\Delta(\omega_c - \omega_f)]/[(1/2)\Delta(\omega_c - \omega_f)]\}^2]. \quad (17)$$

The parameter $(2B\Delta)$ is the notch bandwidth between the ripple points (1 dB in this case) normalized by the chip rate.

Two situations of interest are: 1) filter centered on the carrier, $\omega_c = \omega_f$, and 2) filter displaced by 50 percent of the chip rate, $(\omega_c - \omega_f) = \pi/\Delta$. Since $w(T)$ is a voltage, the degradation in decibels for the two cases is

$$20 \log [w(T)/R_c(0)] = 20 \log [1 - 4(2B\Delta)] \quad \text{(centered filter)} \quad (18)$$

$$\begin{aligned} 20 \log [w(T)/R_c(0)] &= 20 \log [1 - 4(2/\pi)^2(2B\Delta)] \quad \text{(50\% offset).} \quad (19) \\ &= 20 \log [1 - 1.6(2B\Delta)] \end{aligned}$$

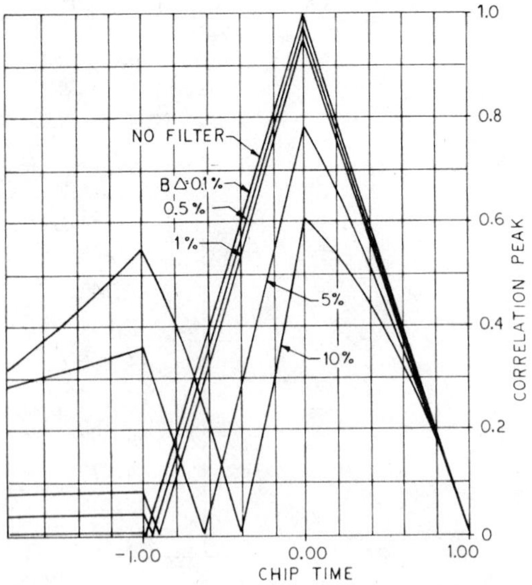


Fig. 1. Effect of the notch bandwidth on correlation for the third-order Butterworth filter.

Equations (18) and (19) permit plotting the drop in correlation peak which is incurred by passing the PN desired signal through a notch filter as a function of the product of the notch bandwidth and the chip rate. This prediction is compared with experiments in Section III.

Independent predictions have been made on the effect of the notch filter bandwidth on correlation in a PN receiver. Koerner [3] has plotted correlation for a third-order Butterworth band-reject filter as a function of 10-dB notch bandwidth normalized to the chip rate. This curve is reproduced in Fig. 1.

## III. Measurement of the Effects of the Notch Filter Bandwidth on the PN Receiver Correlation Peak

A number of experiments have been conducted in order to verify the predictions of the effect of notch filters on the correlation characteristics of a PN signal. Two filters were used in the experimental evaluation. These included an approximate fourth-order Butterworth characteristic and a two-pole Butterworth notch filter. As indicated above, the theoretical predictions obtained from Section II are applicable only to Tchebycheff filters. Also, the predictions from Koerner [3] are only for a third-order Butterworth notch filter. Thus, the experimental results will only provide a partial verification of the theoretical prediction. These results do, however, indicate how the various categories of notch filters can be expected to affect a PN signal.

A set of measurements was taken using a crystal notch filter approximating a four-pole Butterworth response. The first test was conducted with the PN signal carrier equal to the center frequency of the notch filter. The results of this

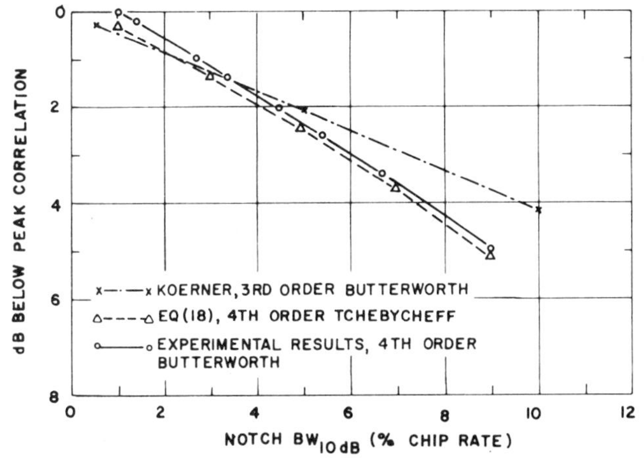


Fig. 2. Effect of notch filter on correlation peak ($f_0 = f_c$).

Fig. 3. Effect of notch filter on correlation peak ($f_0 = f_c + (1/2)\Delta$; $\Delta$ = chip interval).

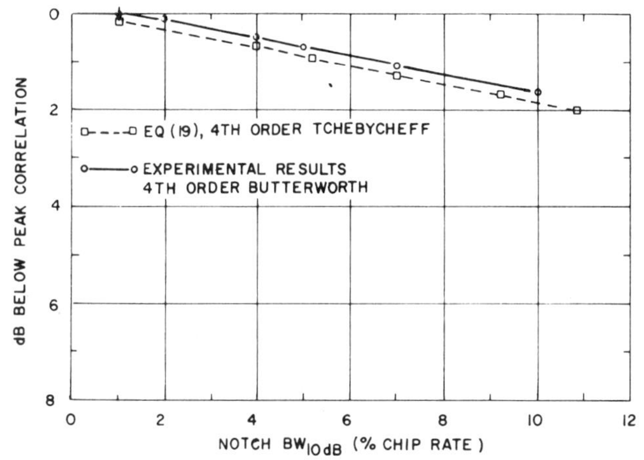


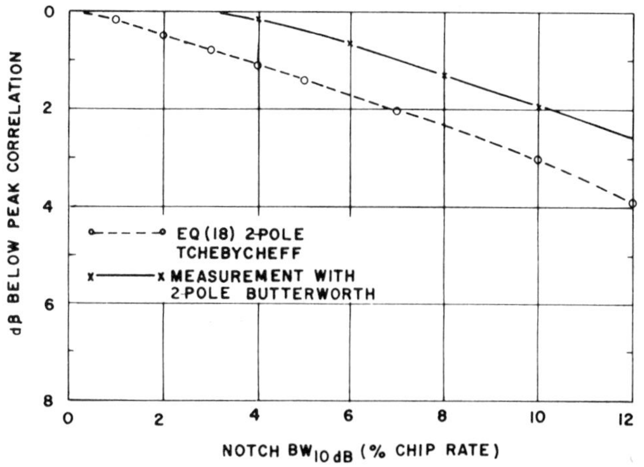


Fig. 4. Effect of two-pole notch filter on correlation peak ($f_0 = f_c$).

Fig. 5. Effect of two-pole notch filter on correlation peak ($f_0 = f_c + (1/2\Delta)$; $\Delta$ = chip interval).

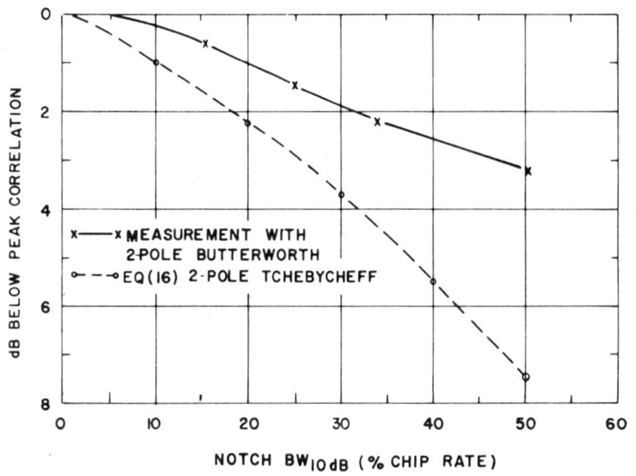


test are shown in Fig. 2, which plots the drop in correlation peak against the 10-dB notch bandwidth as a percentage of chip rate. Fig. 2 also shows the theoretical predictions from [3] on a third-order Butterworth notch filter, and the prediction from (18) based on a fourth-order Tchebycheff notch filter. In general, the experimental results support the theoretical predictions. As might be expected, the correlation drop with a fourth-order Butterworth is greater than the prediction for a third-order Butterworth filter. The measurements nearly coincide with the prediction for a fourth-order Tchebycheff filter.

The above data was repeated with the carrier of the PN signal offset from the center of the notch filter by one-half of the chip rate. The results of the experiment and the predictions from (19) are shown in Fig. 3. Note that the notch filter has substantially less distorting effect on the PN signal when it is offset from the center of the PN signal. In particular, where a 1-dB correlation drop was caused by a 3 percent notch bandwidth, when the notch was centered on the PN carrier, a 1-dB correlation drop is caused by a 7 percent notch bandwidth for a notch offset by one-half of the chip rate. This indicates that much wider notch filters can be tolerated at the edge of the signal spectrum than in the center. Again, the experimental results on the Butterworth filter show a smaller drop in correlation than predicted for the Tchebycheff filter.

A second set of experiments was conducted using a two-pole Butterworth notch filter. The results of the test are shown in Fig. 4, along with a prediction for a two-pole Tchebycheff filter. Comparison of the results obtained with the two-pole and four-pole filters indicates that substantially lower distortion is introduced by a two-pole notch filter of the same bandwidth.

The effect of offsetting the two-pole notch filter by one-half the chip rate from the PN signal carrier is shown in Fig. 5. Once again, it can be seen that the offset notch introduces much less distortion than the notch centered on the PN signal carrier.

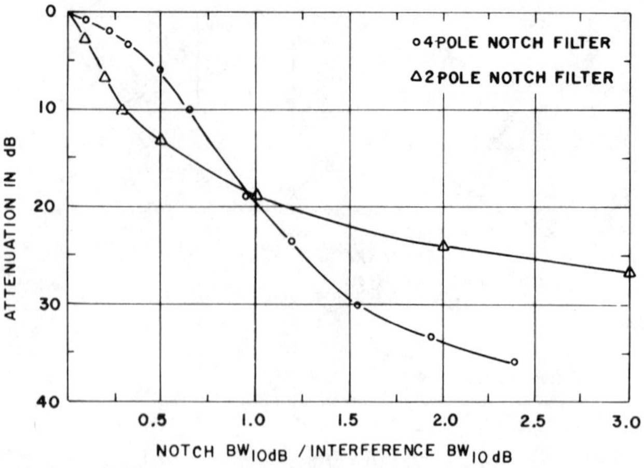

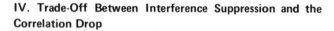

Fig. 6. Attenuation of interference signal through notch filter; four-pole interference baseband.

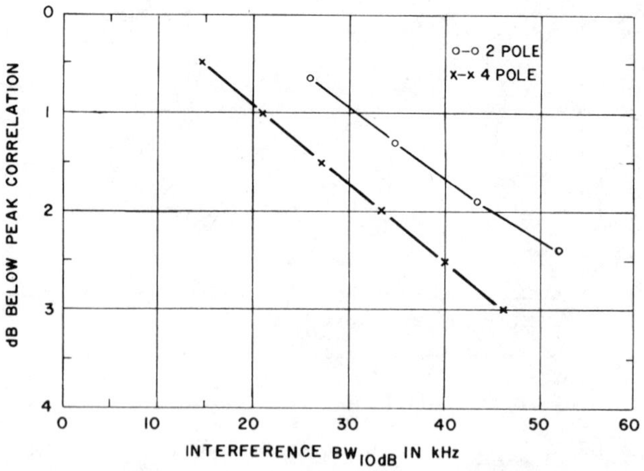


Fig. 7. Correlation drop versus bandwidth of interfering signal for 25-dB suppression ($f_0 = f_c$).

Fig. 8. Correlation drop versus bandwidth of interfering signal for 25-dB suppression ($f_0 = f_c + (1/2\Delta)$).

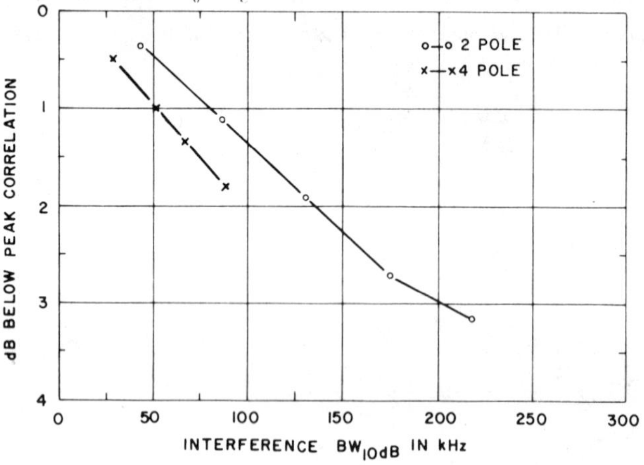


## IV. Trade-Off Between Interference Suppression and the Correlation Drop

In order to suppress interfering signals, the notch filter bandwidth must be somewhat wider than the interference bandwidth. However, as the interference bandwidth, and, hence, the required notch filter bandwidth increases, the receiver correlation peak will decrease. Thus, there is a trade-off between an acceptable degradation of the receiver correlation peak and the bandwidth of the interference signal which can be suppressed.

The attenuation capabilities of the notch filters investigated here have been measured in order to permit a prediction of the suppression of interference signals as a function of bandwidth. An interference signal was simulated by generating a double-sideband suppressed-carrier signal using a baseband noise signal, and the attenuation of this signal was then measured. The bandwidth of the noise was controlled by the variable low-pass filter having a fourth-order roll off, which gives the RF signal into the notch filter a fourth-order bandpass characteristic.

The attenuation properties of the second- and fourth-order notch filters are shown in Fig. 6. The graph indicates that the fourth-order notch filter can provide 25 dB of attenuation to an interference signal whose 10-dB bandwidth is $1/1.25 = 0.8$ of the notch 10-dB bandwidth. For the second-order notch filter, an interference suppression of 25 dB is obtained when the 10-dB interference signal bandwidth is 0.45 of the notch 10-dB bandwidth. It is clear from Fig. 6 that for large attenuations ($>$ 20 dB), the higher order notch filters can provide greater interference suppression for the same relative bandwidth. However, as indicated in Section III, the higher order notch also imposes a greater penalty in degradation of the correlation peak.

By combining the data for drop in the correlation peak from Figs. 2 and 4 with that for interference suppression from Fig. 6, a curve can be generated showing the trade-off between the drop in the correlation peak and the permissible interference signal bandwidth for a given amount of suppression of the interference signal. Fig. 7 is a plot of this trade-off for the case of a notch filter centered at the carrier frequency of the PN signal. The data is plotted for an interference signal suppression of 25 dB, assuming a 1-MHz chip rate for the desired signal. The upper curve of Fig. 7 indicates that if the drop in correlation peak is restricted to 1 dB or less, then a single interfering signal with a bandwidth up to 21 kHz can be attenuated by 25 dB. This attenuation is accomplished with a four-pole notch having a 10-dB bandwidth of 26 kHz.

The trade-off for a two-pole notch filter is also shown in Fig. 7. It can be seen that for interference signal suppression of 25 dB and a correlation drop of 1 dB or less, interference signal bandwidths up to 31 kHz can be suppressed.

Curves showing the same data for a notch filter offset from the PN signal carrier by one-half the chip rate are shown in Fig. 8. Comparison of Figs. 8 and 3 indicates that much wider notch bandwidths and, hence, interfering signal bandwidths can be tolerated for offset notch filters.

## V. Conclusions

This correspondence has presented an investigation of the effects of notch filters on the performance of PN correlation receivers. A theoretical analysis of the correlation drop due to filter distortion has been conducted and confirmed by experimentation. Additional measurements and analysis have established the trade-off between correlation drop and interference suppression as a function of interference bandwidth. The results indicate that for a penalty of a 1-dB drop in correlation peak, interfering signals having bandwidths of 2 to 3 percent of the PN chip rate can be attenuated by 25 dB.

### References


[1] K.W. Henderson and W.H. Kautz, "Transient response of conventional filters," *IRE Trans. Circuit Theory*, vol. CT-5, December 1958.

[2] G.A. Beck, "Comments on transient responses of conventional filters," *IRE Trans. Circuit Theory*, vol. CT-8, p. 166, June 1961.

[3] M.A. Koerner, "Effect of premodulation filtering on the correlation and error signals in a pseudo-noise receiver," Jet Propulsion Lab., Pasadena, Calif., Program Summary 36-64, vol. 3, September 1970.



STEVEN M. SUSSMAN
M.I.T. Lincoln Lab.
Lexington, Mass.

EUGENE J. FERRARI
D.O.T.–T.S.C.
Cambridge, Mass.

# The Action of Dither in a Polarity Coincidence Correlator

J. J. FREEMAN, SENIOR MEMBER, IEEE

*Abstract*—An analysis has been made of how dither added to the input of a polarity coincidence correlator eliminates capture of a weak signal by an unwanted signal. For certain interfering environments the output signal-to-noise ratio of various correlators with three specific input dithers is analyzed. The correlators considered were a polarity coincidence correlator with: 1) no dither, 2) dither of random amplitude uniformly distributed between the chosen plus-and-minus peak values, 3) sinusoidal dither, and 4) Gaussian dither. Each correlator was analyzed for the cases of Gaussian-noise, rectangular-wave, and sinusoidal interference and compared with the classical correlator.

The choice of dither amplitude based upon the measured value of the noise power was studied. A uniformly distributed dither is shown to be slightly superior to sinusoidal dither, and both superior to Gaussian noise.

Paper approved by the Associate Editor for Communication Theory of the IEEE Communications Society for publication without oral presentation. Manuscript received April 11, 1973; revised February 22, 1974.

The author is with the Naval Research Laboratory, Washington, D. C. 20375.

## I. INTRODUCTION

One way of decreasing the susceptibility of electromagnetic radiation to interference as well as decreasing its interfering effect is to distribute the radiated energy widely in time and frequency in a complicated fashion. One possible receiver implementation for this type of transmission is based on the use of a matched filter. Cost, reliability, and flexibility considerations suggest the use of a similar but simpler device employing shift registers. This study analyzes the performance of such a device, known as a polarity coincidence correlator (PCC), for various types of input signals.

This concise paper aims at a detailed examination of how dither, the addition of a large, suitably fluctuating component to the input of a digital correlator or matched filter, can eliminate the phenomenon of "capture" of a weak signal by an unwanted stronger one.

Although there exist various papers [1]–[3] on the use of dither with digital correlators, it appears that the only article immediately dealing with the use of dither in matched filters in a communication context is the one by Cahn [4]. Cahn applies game theoretic concepts to determine the optimum distribution of dither against unknown jamming. This concise paper analyzes the behavior of a

Reprinted from *IEEE Trans. Commun.*, vol. COM-22, pp. 857–862, June 1974.

TABLE I

| Interference Type | $(S/N)_0$ for a Signal Having $N$ Pulses With Amplitude $\pm S$ | | | | |
|---|---|---|---|---|---|
| | Classical Correlation Detector | Polarity Coincidence Detector | | | |
| | | Without Dither | With Uniform Dither $-d_0 \leqslant d(t) \leqslant d_0$ | With $CW$ Dither ($A$) | With Gaussian Dither |
| Gaussian Noise | $NS^2/\sigma_n^2$ | $\frac{2}{\pi} NS^2/\sigma_n^2$ | $N\left[\frac{S}{d_0} \operatorname{erf}\left(\frac{d_0}{\sqrt{2}\sigma_n}\right)\right]^2$ | $\frac{2NS^2}{\pi\sigma_n^2} e^{-A^2/2\sigma_n^2} I_0^2\left(\frac{A^2}{4\sigma_n^2}\right)$ | $\frac{2NS^2}{\pi(\sigma_n^2 + \sigma_d^2)}$ |
| Rectangular Wave ($C$) | $NS^2/C^2$ | $0,\ C > S$<br>$\infty,\ C < S$ | $NS^2/d_0^2,\ C < d_0$<br>$0,\ C > d_0$ | $\frac{4}{\pi^2} NS^2/(A^2 - C^2),$ $C < A-S$<br>$0,\ C > A+S$ | $\frac{2NS^2}{\pi\sigma_d^2} e^{-C^2/\sigma_d^2}$ |
| $CW$ ($J$)<br>$J \sin \omega t$ | $2NS^2/J^2$ | $4NS^2/\pi^2J^2$ | $NS^2/d_0^2,\ J < d_0$<br>$N\left[\frac{2}{\pi}\frac{S}{d_0} \sin^{-1} \frac{d_0}{J}\right]^2,$ $J > d_0$ | $\frac{16NS^2}{\pi^4A^2} K^2\left(\frac{J}{A}\right),\ J+S < A$<br>$\frac{16NS^2}{\pi^4J^2} K^2\left(\frac{A}{J}\right),\ A+S < J$ | $\frac{2NS^2}{\pi\sigma_d^2} e^{-J^2/2\sigma_d^2} I_0^2(J^2/4\sigma_d^2)$ |

$(S/N)_o = \bar{z}^2/\sigma_z^2$ for different detectors under different interference conditions, for signal power negligible compared to interference power.

PCC with specific dithers for certain specific interference environments. In particular, the output signal-to-noise ratio $(S/N)_o$ for the PCC with and without dither is derived for three types of interference, namely Gaussian, sinusoidal, and rectangular wave. Three types of dither are considered, namely a random uniformly distributed voltage, a sinusoidal one,[1] and a Gaussian one. The results are summarized in Table I.

We will see that if the baseband signal consists of a sequence of bipolar pulses, and if the baseband jamming has the same waveform but a larger peak amplitude, then the output from a polarity coincidence detector will consist of all interference and no signal. However, if a dither voltage is added whose peak exceeds that of the interference then the complete capture of the receiver by the interference is avoided. On the other hand, if the dither voltage is too large then the $(S/N)_o$ will become degraded. Accordingly, we analyze the situation in which the interference power is continuously measured and the peak dither voltage is continuously adjusted so as to exceed the peak interference by a given factor, say $g$, which at least exceeds unity. Graphs of $(S/N)_o$ resulting from this procedure are given as a function of $g$ for the different types of interference. We will find that uniformly distributed random dither is superior to the sinusoidal type which is superior to the Gaussian dither for the interfering environments considered. For uniform dither at the value of $g$ which maximized the $(S/N)_o$ for the worst case of interference considered, the $(S/N)_o$ was 4.3 dB below the value which would have resulted from the optimum classical correlator.

## II. BACKGROUND

Consider a signal $s(t)$ consisting of a sequence of $N$ bipolar pulses, each of width $\Delta$, and defined by

$$s(t) = S \sum_{j=1}^{N} u_j h(t - j\Delta) \tag{1}$$

where $u_j = \pm 1$, $S$ is the signal amplitude, and $h(t) = 1$ for $-\Delta < t < 0$ and 0 elsewhere.

Let $n(t)$ designate the input noise or interference (sinusoidal, normal, or whatever), and let $s'(t)$ designate a stored replica of $s(t)$ with unit amplitude, so that $s(t) = Ss'(t) = S \operatorname{sgn} s(t)$, where

$$\operatorname{sgn} x \triangleq \begin{cases} 1, & x > 0 \\ 0, & x = 0 \\ -1, & x < 0. \end{cases}$$

Letting $n_j \triangleq n(t_j)$ and $s_j \triangleq s(t_j)$, the output of the classical correlation detector is characterized by

$$z_c = \frac{1}{N} \sum_{j=1}^{N} (Ss_j' + n_j)s_j' \tag{2}$$

at the instant that the $N$th signal and replica samples coincide.

We are interested in evaluating the relative effectiveness of different detectors for a whole class of signals. Accordingly, we consider the $s_j$ as independent random parameters which take on specific values for a given message, but over the entire set of possible messages the $s_j$ will be assumed to take on the values $\pm S$ with equal probability. Thus, $\overline{s_j} = 0$, and $\overline{s_j s_k} = \bar{s}_j \bar{s}_k = 0$, $j \neq k$. Since $\bar{s}_j^2 = S^2$, $\overline{s_j s_k} = \delta_{kj} S^2$, where $\delta_{kj} = 0$, $j \neq k$, $\delta_{kj} = 1$, $j = k$.

Although the classical correlator is optimum (for additive white Gaussian noise), its implementation leads to many practical difficulties. The configuration of Fig. 1, taking the dotted option labeled (a), known as a PCC, is adaptable to implementation by microelectronic techniques with the advantages of increased reliability and decreased weight, size, and cost. This configuration compares the corresponding signs of the sampled input with that of the stored signal replica and yields an output proportional to the number of agreements of sign.

The output $z_P$ of a PCC at the instant the sampled input and the stored replica coincide, is given by

$$z_p = \frac{1}{N} \sum_{j=1}^{N} \operatorname{sgn} s_j \operatorname{sgn} (s_j + n_j). \tag{3}$$

Unfortunately, the PCC suffers from the defect that a rectangular-wave interfering signal can completely capture the receiver. However, this defect can be remedied by introducing a suitable noise or dither, in series with the input, as in Fig. 1(b). If we designate the dither by $d(t)$, then the output for the detector in Fig. 1(b) is given by

$$z_d = \frac{1}{N} \sum_{j=1}^{N} \operatorname{sgn} s_j \operatorname{sgn} (s_j + n_j + d_j) \tag{4}$$

where $d_j = d(t_j)$.

For analytical convenience we will use the $(S/N)_o$ ratio defined by[2]

$$(S/N)_o = \bar{z}^2/\overline{(z - \bar{z})^2} \tag{5}$$

as the criterion of performance, and compute $(S/N)_o$ for the case that a) $d(t) = A \sin \omega_0 t$, b) $d(t)$ is a Gaussian random variable, and c) $d(t)$ is randomly and uniformly distributed over the range $[-d_0, d_0]$. We assume that the values of $d(t_j)$ and $d(t_k)$ are statistically independent for $j \neq k$ for cases b) and c).

For case a), consider for the moment that

$$d(t) = A \sin (\omega t + \varphi)$$

so that (4) reads

$$z_d = \frac{1}{N} \sum_{j=1}^{N} \operatorname{sgn} s_j \operatorname{sgn} (s_j + n_j + A \sin (\omega_0 t_j + \varphi)).$$

[1] For brevity we use CW to designate a sinusoidal wave.

[2] The $N$ (for noise) in $(S/N)_o$ will not be confused with the $N$ designating the number of elements in the shift register [also the number of pulses in $s(t)$].

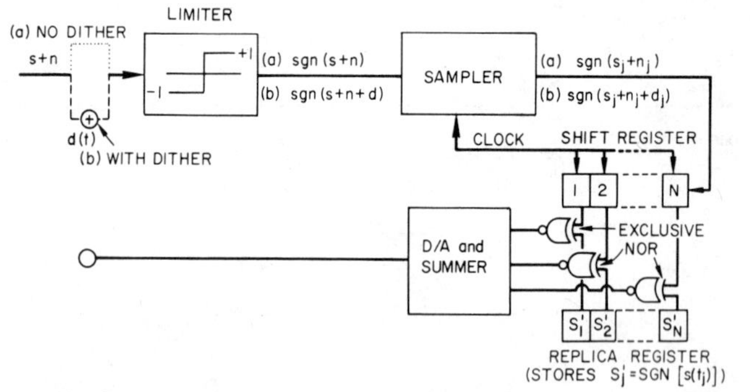


Fig. 1. Polarity coincidence detector (a) without and (b) with dither.

For a given sum, $\varphi$ will be constant. However, for different observations $z_d$, $\varphi$ will be a random variable since there is no relation between the state of the oscillator in the receiver and the time origin which is the instant the signal is received by the message source. Since we are interested in the average of $z_d$ and $z_d^2$ over all possible observations $z_d$, that is, over all possible values of $\varphi$, as well as words (sequences of $s_j$), we consider $\varphi$ to be uniformly distributed. Thus the probability density of $d = A \sin(\omega t_j + \varphi)$ is given by

$$p_d(x) = \frac{1}{\pi(A^2 - x^2)^{1/2}}, \qquad |x| < A$$
$$= 0, \qquad |x| > A.$$

## III. DERIVATION OF THE $(S/N)_o$ RATIO

*Case 1: Classical Correlation Detector*

For this case it is easy to show that, taking into account the assumed distribution of the $s_j$, one has for any type of noise or interference

$$(S/N)_o = \bar{z}_c^2/\overline{(z_c - \bar{z}_c)^2} = NS^2/\bar{n}^2 = N(S/N)_i \tag{6}$$

where $(S/N)_i$ indicates the $S/N$ power ratio at the input.

We derive $(S/N)_o$ for a PCC a) with randomly and uniformly distributed dither, b) with sinusoidal dither, c) with Gaussian dither. Letting

$$n_j + d_j = n_j' \tag{7}$$

and averaging (4) over the independent random variables $s_j$ which take on the values $\pm S$ each with probability 1/2,

$$\bar{z}_d^{s_j} = \frac{1}{2N} \sum_{j=1}^{N} [\text{sgn}(S + n_j') - \text{sgn}(-S + n_j')]. \tag{8}$$

Averaging now over the $n_j'$

$$\bar{z}_d = \tfrac{1}{2}[\text{Prob}(S + n' > 0) - \text{Prob}(S + n' < 0) - \text{Prob}(-S + n' > 0) + \text{Prob}(-S + n' < 0)]. \tag{9}$$

Since the probability density of the $n_j'$ is symmetric about the origin so that Prob $(-S + n' < 0)$ = Prob $(-S - n' < 0)$, equation (9) reduces to

$$\bar{z}_d = 2\,\text{Prob}(0 < n' < S). \tag{10}$$

Consider now the square of (4), namely

$$z_d^2 = \frac{1}{N^2} \sum_{j=1}^{N} \sum_{k=1}^{N} \text{sgn}\, s_j\, \text{sgn}\, s_k\, \text{sgn}(s_j + n_j')\, \text{sgn}(s_k + n_k'). \tag{11}$$

For the case that the signal power is small compared to the interference, the output fluctuations when the signal is present will differ only negligibly from those occuring when the signal is absent. Accordingly, we may replace sgn $(s_j + n_j')$ by sgn $n_j'$ in (11). On averaging (11) over the $s_j$ and $n_j'$, one finds immediately that for small input $S/N$ ratios

$$\overline{z_d^2} \approx 1/N \tag{12}$$

regardless of the probability density function of the noise. Accordingly, for small signal power compared to the interference,

$$(S/N)_o = 4N[\text{Prob}(0 < n + d < S)]^2. \tag{13}$$

If $p_{n'}(z)$ designates the probability density of $n'$,

$$p_{n'}(z) = \int_{-\infty}^{\infty} p_n(x) p_d(z - x)\, dx = \int_{-\infty}^{\infty} p_d(x) p_n(z - x)\, dx \tag{14}$$

since $n(t)$ and $d(t)$ are statistically independent. Also

$$\text{Prob}(0 < n' < S) = \int_0^S \int_{-\infty}^{\infty} p_n(x)\, p_d(z - x)\, dx dz. \tag{15}$$

In the situations of interest the signal power will be much smaller than the interference power, so that

$$\text{Prob}(0 < n' < S) = \int_0^S p_{n'}(z)\, dz \simeq S p_{n'}(0) \tag{16}$$

where $p_{n'}(x)$ is continuous in the neighborhood of the origin. Accordingly,

$$\text{Prob}(0 < n' < S) \simeq S \int_{-\infty}^{\infty} p_n(x) p_d(-x)\, dx. \tag{17}$$

In the Appendix the $(S/N)_o$ for the various types of dither and interference is explicitly computed and the resulting formulas are entered in Table I.

## IV. COMPARISON OF $(S/N)_o$ FOR VARYING DITHER AMPLITUDES

Table I shows that rectangular-wave interference whose peak amplitude exceeds that of the signal will completely suppress or capture the signal of a polarity coincidence detector with no dither. However, the addition of sinusoidal or uniformly distributed dither whose peak exceeds that of the interference eliminates capture. On the other hand, values of peak dither exceeding the necessary threshold will decrease the $(S/N)_o$. In order for the dither to be large enough to avoid capture, and yet not so large that the $(S/N)_o$ is unnecessarily degraded, it is necessary for the receiver to continuously monitor the interference power, and to adjust the peak dither voltage to be a prescribed safety factor, say $g$, of the interference peak, the factor at least exceeding unity. Thus, if $P$ is the measured interference power, we choose $d_0 = gC = gP^{1/2}$ for the case of sinusoidal dither.

For the case of Gaussianly distributed dither, Table I shows that there is no dither threshold below which an interfering rectangular waveform can always capture the receiver. Rather, there is a dither power at which the $(S/N)_o$ is maximized, namely when $\sigma_d^2 = C^2 = P$, the $(S/N)_o$ decreasing continuously on either side of this maximum, where again $P$ is the measured interference power. However, since we are interested in how $(S/N)_o$ varies with the amount of dither we write $\sigma_d = gP^{1/2}$, where now the only stipulation on $g$ is that $g > 0$.

Generally speaking, however, the interference may not have a rectangular waveshape, it might be either Gaussian noise or a sinusoidal waveform, or whatever. Whatever the waveshape may be, to avoid possible capture (in the case of sinusoidal or uniform dither) or considerable degradation (in the case of Gaussian dither) the receiver will assume the worst case, and ascribe the measured interference power $P$ to a rectangular waveform. Thus one chooses $d_0 = gP^{1/2}$, $A = gP^{1/2}$, $\sigma_d = gP^{1/2}$, depending upon whether one uses uniform-, sinusoidal-, or Gaussian-type dither. Also one has $C = P^{1/2}$, $J = 2^{1/2}P^{1/2}$, $\sigma_n^2 = P$, depending upon whether the interference was rectangular, sinusoidal, or Gaussian. Substituting the values of these parameters into the formulas of Table I one obtains Table II, giving $(S/N)_o$ in terms of $P$ and $g$. Figs. 2–4 graph $(S/N)_o/(NS^2/P)$, the $S/N$ ratio divided by that of the classical correlator, as a function of $g$ for the three different types of interference studied, for the case of uniform, sinusoidal, and Gaussian dither, respectively. Since we are interested in insuring that the system performance always meets a minimum specification, we define the optimum value of $g$ as that value which maximizes the minimum possible $(S/N)_o$ among the possible types of interference considered, namely rectangular wave, sinusoidal, and Gaussian.

Fig. 2 shows that with uniform dither the worst case $(S/N)_o$ is maximized by choosing $g = 1.36$, where the minimum $(S/N)_o$ equals $0.37NS^2/P$, which is 4.3 dB below the theoretical optimum.

TABLE II

| Interference Type | $(S/N)_0$ Values (and Comparison With Correlator Values) | | | | | |
|---|---|---|---|---|---|---|
| | Classical Correlation Detector | Polarity Coincidence Detector | | | | |
| | | Without Dither | With Uniform Dither | With *CW* Dither | With Gaussian Dither |
| Gaussian Noise | $NS^2/P$ | $\frac{2}{\pi} NS^2/P$ | $\frac{NS^2}{Pg^2} \operatorname{erf}^2\left(\frac{g}{\sqrt{2}}\right), g > 1$ | $\frac{2NS^2}{\pi P}\left[e^{-g^2/4} I_0(g^2/4)\right]^2, g > 1$ | $\frac{2NS^2}{\pi P (g^2+1)}$ |
| Rectangular Wave | $NS^2/P$ | $0, \quad C > S$<br>$\infty, \quad C < S$ | $NS^2/Pg^2, \quad 1 < g$<br>$0, \quad 1 > g$ | $4NS^2/\pi^2(g^2-1)P, \quad g > 1$<br>$0, \quad g < 1$ | $\frac{2NS^2 e^{-1/g^2}}{\pi g^2 P}$ |
| *CW* | $NS^2/P$ | $2NS^2/P\pi^2$ | $NS^2/Pg^2, g > \sqrt{2}$<br>$\frac{NS^2}{P}\left[\frac{2 \arcsin (g/\sqrt{2})}{\pi g}\right]^2$<br>$0 < g < \sqrt{2}$ | $\frac{16NS^2}{P} K^2(\sqrt{2}/g), g > \sqrt{2}$<br>$\frac{8NS^2 K^2(g/\sqrt{2})}{\pi^4 P}, 1 < g < \sqrt{2}$ | $\frac{2NS^2 e^{-1/g^2} I_0^2(1/2g^2)}{\pi g^2 P}$ |

Values obtained from Table I under the conditions that $d_0 = A = \sigma_d = gP^{1/2}$, and $\sigma_n^2 = C^2 = J^2/2 = P$. Assumes the signal power is negligible compared to the interference power.

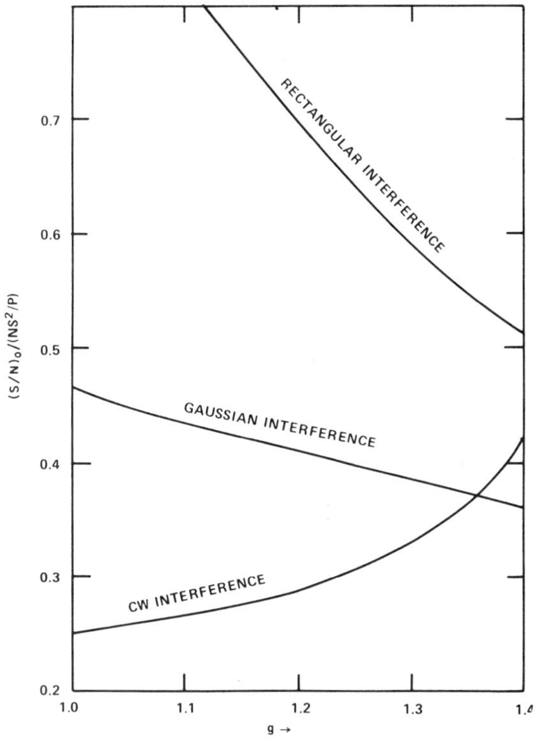


Fig. 2. $(S/N)_o$ of a polarity coincidence detector with uniformly distributed dither divided by $(S/N)_o$ of a classical correlator as a function of $g$, for small signal power.

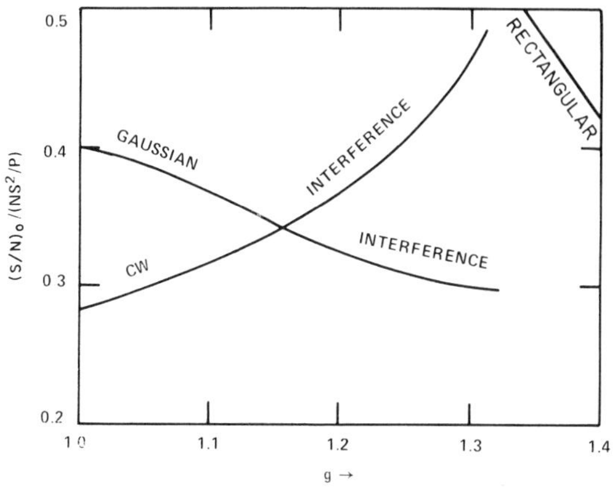


Fig. 3. $(S/N)_o$ of a polarity coincidence detector with sinusoidal dither divided by $(S/N)_o$ of a classical correlator as a function of $g$, for small signal power.

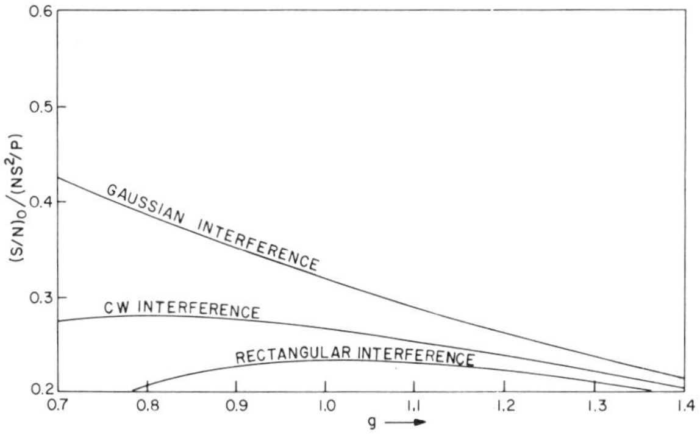


Fig. 4. $(S/N)_o$ of a polarity coincidence detector with Gaussian dither divided by $(S/N)_o$ of a classical correlator as a function of $g$, for small signal power.

Fig. 3 shows that with sinusoidal dither the worst case $(S/N)_o$ is maximized at $g = 1.16$ where $(S/N)_o = 0.34NS^2/P$, 4.7 dB below the theoretical optimum. For Gaussian dither Fig. 4 shows that at $g = 1$ the maximum $(S/N)_o = 0.23NS^2/P$ for the worst case noise, which is 1.7 dB below the optimum value for sinusoidal dither, and 2.1 dB below the optimum value for uniform dither. Accordingly, uniform dither is somewhat superior to sinusoidal dither, and both are fairly superior to Gaussian dither, according to the criterion of maximizing the worst case $(S/N)_o$, when the possible cases are rectangular-wave, sinusoidal, or Gaussian interference.

## APPENDIX

Formulas for $(S/N)_o$ are derived for different types of dither and interference.

*Case A: Uniformly Distributed Dither*

For this case

$$p_d(x) = \frac{1}{2d_0}, \quad |x| < d_0 \qquad 0, \quad |x| > d_0. \tag{A1}$$

Equation (17) then becomes

$$\text{Prob } (0 < n' < S) = \frac{S}{2d_0} \int_{-d_0}^{d_0} p_n(x)\, dx. \tag{A2}$$

For Gaussian noise of zero mean and variance $\sigma_n^2$

$$p_n(x) = [1/(2\pi)^{1/2}\sigma_n] \exp(-x^2/2\sigma_n^2). \tag{A3}$$

Substituting (A3) into (A2),

$$\text{Prob}\ (0 < n' < S) = \frac{S}{2d_0(2\pi)^{1/2}\sigma_n} \int_{-d_0}^{d_0} \exp\ (-x^2/2\sigma_n^2)\ dx$$

$$= \frac{S}{2d_0} \text{erf}\ (d_0/\sigma_n\sqrt{2}). \tag{A4}$$

For rectangular pulse interference

$$p_n(x) = \tfrac{1}{2}\delta(x - C) + \tfrac{1}{2}\delta(x + C) \tag{A5}$$

where $C$ is the pulse height.

Substituting (A5) into (A2),

$$\text{Prob}\ (0 < n' < S) = \begin{cases} S/2d_0, & C < d_0 \\ 0, & C < d_0. \end{cases} \tag{A6}$$

For sinusoidal interference

$$n(t) = J \sin\ (\omega t + \varphi) \tag{A7}$$

and

$$p_n(x) = \begin{cases} 1/\pi(J^2 - x^2)^{1/2}, & |x| < J \\ 0, & |x| > J. \end{cases} \tag{A8}$$

Equation (A2) becomes

$$\text{Prob}\ (0 < n' < S) = \frac{S}{\pi d_0} \sin^{-1}\ (d_0/J), \qquad J > d_0$$

$$= S/2d_0, \qquad J < d_0. \tag{A9}$$

*Case B: Sinusoidal Dither*

Here

$$d(t) = A \sin\ (\omega_0 t + \varphi)$$

and

$$p_d(x) = \begin{cases} \dfrac{1}{\pi(A^2 - x^2)^{1/2}}, & |x| < A \\ 0, & |x| > A. \end{cases} \tag{A10}$$

For Gaussian noise, on substituting (A10) and (A3) into (17),

$$\text{Prob}\ (0 < n' < S) = \frac{S}{(2\pi)^{1/2}\sigma_n \pi} \int_{-\pi/2}^{\pi/2} \exp\ (-A^2 \sin^2 \varphi / 2\sigma_n^2)\ d\varphi. \tag{A11}$$

Substituting $\sin^2 \varphi = (1 - \cos 2\varphi)/2$ into (A11) and simplifying

$$\text{Prob}\ (0 < n' < S) = \frac{S \exp\ (-A^2/4\sigma_n^2)}{(2\pi)^{1/2}\sigma_n} \left[ \int_{-\pi}^{\pi} \frac{\exp\ (-A^2 \cos \beta / 4\sigma_n^2)}{2\pi}\ d\beta \right]$$

$$= \frac{S \exp\ (-A^2/4\sigma_n^2)}{(2\pi)^{1/2}\sigma_n} I_0(A^2/4\sigma_n^2) \tag{A12}$$

since the expression within brackets equals the modified Bessel function [6, p. 193].

For pulse interference, on substituting (A5) into (14),

$$p_{n'}(z) = \tfrac{1}{2}\{p_d(z - C) + p_d(z + C)\}. \tag{A13}$$

Substituting (A13) into (15) and simplifying

$$\text{Prob}\ (0 < n' < S) = \frac{1}{2} \int_{C-S}^{C+S} p_d(u)\ du. \tag{A14}$$

Or, on substituting (A10) into (A14) and integrating,

$$\text{Prob}\ (0 < n' < S) = \begin{cases} 0, & A < C - S \\ \dfrac{1}{2\pi}\left[\dfrac{\pi}{2} - \sin^{-1}\left(\dfrac{C - S}{A}\right)\right], & C - S < A < C + S \\ \dfrac{1}{2\pi}\left[\sin^{-1}\left(\dfrac{C + S}{A}\right) - \sin^{-1}\left(\dfrac{C - S}{A}\right)\right], & A > C + S. \end{cases} \tag{A15}$$

For $S \ll C$, (A15) simplifies to

$$\text{Prob}\ (0 < n' < S) = \begin{cases} 0, & A < C - S \\ S/\pi(A^2 - C^2)^{1/2}, & A > C + S. \end{cases} \tag{A16}$$

For sinusoidal interference, one substitutes (A8) and (A10) into (11), obtaining

$$p_{n'}(z) = \frac{1}{\pi^2} \int_{\text{Max}[-J,z-A]}^{\text{Min}[J,A+z]} \frac{dx}{[(A^2 - (x - z)^2)^{1/2}(J^2 - x^2)]^{1/2}}. \tag{A17}$$

For $A > J + S$ the limits of integration are $\pm J$. For $A < J - S$ the limits of integration are from $z - A$ to $z + A$. Fortunately, we do not require the evaluation of (A17) for $J - S < A < J + S$, which is more complicated than the other two cases. Thus, letting $z = 0$ in (A17) and substituting the result into (16), one obtains

$$\text{Prob}\ (0 < n' < S) = \frac{S}{\pi^2} \int_{-J}^{J} \frac{dx}{(A^2 - x^2)^{1/2}(J^2 - x^2)^{1/2}}$$

$$= \frac{2SK(J/A)}{\pi^2 A}, \qquad J + S < A. \tag{A18a}$$

Similarly, we find that

$$\text{Prob}\ (0 < n' < S) = \frac{S}{\pi^2} \int_{-A}^{A} \frac{dx}{(A^2 - x^2)^{1/2}(J^2 - x^2)^{1/2}}$$

$$= \frac{2SK(A/J)}{\pi^2 J}, \qquad A + S < J. \tag{A18b}$$

Here

$$K(b) = \int_0^{\pi/2} \frac{d\varphi}{(1 - b^2 \sin^2 \varphi)^{1/2}} \tag{A19}$$

is the complete elliptic integral of the first kind.

*C. Gaussian Dither*

Here $d(t)$ is a zero mean Gaussian random variable of variance $\sigma_d^2$, so that if $n(t)$ is Gaussian noise of zero mean and variance $\sigma_n^2$, (17) becomes

$$\text{Prob}\ (0 < n' < S) = \frac{S}{2\pi\sigma_d\sigma_n} \int_{-\infty}^{\infty} \exp\left[-\frac{x^2}{2}\left(\frac{1}{\sigma_d^2} + \frac{1}{\sigma_n^2}\right)\right] dx$$

$$= \frac{S}{(2\pi)^{1/2}(\sigma_n^2 + \sigma_d^2)^{1/2}}. \tag{A20}$$

If $n(t)$ is a random rectangular wave whose probability density is given by (A5), then (17) becomes

$$\text{Prob}\ (0 < n' < S) = \frac{S \exp\ (-C^2/2\sigma_d^2)}{(2\pi)^{1/2}\sigma_d}. \tag{A21}$$

The case when $n(t)$ is sinusoidal has already been treated under the category of sinusoidal dither and Gaussian noise, (A12), so with a slight change in notation, we obtain

$$\text{Prob}\ (0 < n' < S) = \frac{S \exp\ (-J^2/4\sigma_d^2)}{(2\pi)^{1/2}\sigma_d} I_0(J^2/4\sigma_d^2). \tag{A22}$$

The various formulas for Prob $(0 < n' < S)$ have been substituted into (13) and the resulting $(S/N)_o$ formulas for the various cases are collected in Table I. Also included are the formulas for no dither, obtained as a limiting case.

## ACKNOWLEDGMENT

The author wishes to thank Prof. W. C. Linsey and Dr. S. J. Lee for various helpful suggestions to improve the manuscript.

## REFERENCES

[1] G. A. Korn, *Random-Process Simulation and Measurement.* New York: McGraw-Hill, 1966, pp. 136–139.
[2] K.-Y. Chang and A. D. Moore, "Modified digital correlator and its estimation errors," *IEEE Trans. Inform. Theory*, vol. IT-16, pp. 699–706, Nov. 1970.
[3] H. Berndt, "Correlation function estimation by a polarity method using stochastic reference signals," *IEEE Trans. Inform. Theory*, vol. IT-14, pp. 796–801, Nov. 1968.
[4] C. R. Cahn, "Performance of digital matched filter correlator with unknown interference," *IEEE Trans. Commun. Technol. (Part II of Two Parts)*, vol. COM-19, pp. 1163–1172, Dec. 1971.
[5] B. O. Pierce, *Table of Integrals.*, 3rd rev. ed. Boston, Mass.: Ginn, 1969, p. 64.
[6] W. Grosner and N. Hofreiter, *Integraltafel*, part II, 3rd ed. Vienna, Austria: Springer, 1961.

# Part II
# Applications

It would be difficult to show that any one of the papers included in this reprint volume is not eligible for inclusion in this part on applications of spread spectrum techniques. Here, however, the concentration is on specific use of some spread spectrum method that is especially advantageous for solution of a particular problem. The first paper, on code-division multiplexing, published in 1964, discusses the use of spread spectrum signals for multiple access, a subject still of major interest. The second paper is also concerned with signal multiplexing using PN-coded signals.

While the first two papers are concerned with the use of codes for multiplexing, the other papers in this part are more concerned with employing a spread spectrum technique to some task now being carried out by other types of systems. The Rake technique employed by Bitzer *et al.* was suggested by Price and Green (see paper 10 in the following listing. Other Papers of Interest) for use in overcoming multipath transmission problems, and certainly there are few paths that have a higher degree of associated multipath propagation than a troposcatter link.

Spread spectrum signal processing on board an active communications satellite is discussed by Huang and Hooten. Satellite systems, because of their visibility and because of their high value, are at once the most potentially vulnerable and yet most useful tools available for long range communications. Their vulnerability (due to their constant visibility) makes the use of spread spectrum techniques almost indispensable, for not only is a satellite uplink forced to operate in the presence of all the transmitters in the world (literally) but it is a very tempting target for a would be jammer, since it often sits in the same location for long periods of time, and it often carries the most valuable communications traffic. Combine the inherent time-division and code-division multiplexing capabilities of spread spectrum systems with their interference rejection capability and they are quickly seen to be especially valuable for satellite systems use, even at the cost of increased on-board complexity.

Berni and Gregg discuss the use of chirp signals as a method of sending digital data. Such a technique is of great interest, since the advent of inexpensive chirp matched filters that have *TW* products on the order of 30 dB (see Part IV, Chirp Techniques).

Certainly there are many other applications for which spread spectrum signaling can make a significant improvement in communications or navigation system operation. Here I have included papers that describe four applications. Many more possibilities exist. For other ideas, try the following other papers of interest, or take a look at your most difficult current problem. You may well find that your problem is a natural for one of the spread spectrum methods.

## OTHER PAPERS OF INTEREST


1) B. B. Barrow, L. G. Abraham, Jr., S. Stein, and D. Bitzer, "Tropospheric-scatter propagation tests using a Rake receiver," presented at the IEEE Commun. Conv., June 1965.
2) H. Blasbalg, H. Najjar, R. D'Antonio, and R. Haddad, "Air-ground, ground-air communications using pseudo-noise through a satellite," this reprint volume.
3) D. Chesler, "Performance of a multiple access RADA system," *IEEE Trans. Commun. Technol.*, Aug. 1966.
4) C. E. Cook, "Pulse compression—Key to more efficient radar transmission," this reprint volume.
5) R. C. Dixon, "A spread spectrum ranging technique for aerospace vehicles," this reprint volume.
6) P. R. Drouilhet, Jr., and S. L. Bernstein, "TATS—A bandspread modulation–demodulation system for multiple access tactical satellite communication," this reprint volume.
7) R. Y. Huang and P. Hooten, "Communication satellite processing repeaters," this reprint volume.
8) R. M. Hultberg, F. H. Jean, and M. C. Jones, "Time division access for military communications satellites," *IEEE Trans. Aerosp. Electron Syst.*, Dec. 1965.
9) R. Price and P. E. Green, Jr., "A communication technique for multipath channels," *Proc. IRE.*, Mar. 1958.
10) R. B. Ward, "Digital communications on a pseudo-noise tracking link using sequence inversion modulation," this reprint volume.

# Multiplexing Using Quasiorthogonal Binary Functions

W. J. JUDGE
ASSOCIATE MEMBER AIEE

**Summary:** The process of correlation detection is briefly reviewed and the properties of binary codes are stated for the purpose of utilizing these codes as a quasiorthogonal multiplexing function. The maximal linear code is shown to exhibit the best properties, particularly those generated by a Mersenne prime. The relationship between system bandwidth and code length is derived.

RECENTLY, substantial interest has been generated in systems employing quasiorthogonal functions for multiplexing, particularly binary codes (sequences). For example, if two different codes are linearly added and sent over the same channel, a receiver can accept one code and reject the other by the process of correlation detection. This may be shown mathematically: let $S_1(t)$ and $S_2(t)$ = two codes; $S_1(t)+S_2(t)$ = the receiver input; $S_1(t)$ = the stored code at the receiver; $T$ = the data integration time. The correlator output will be

$$Y(t)=\frac{1}{T}\int_0^T [S_1(t)+S_2(t)]S_1(t)dt$$

$$=\frac{1}{T}\int_0^T S_1(t)^2dt+\frac{1}{T}\int_0^T S_1(t)S_2(t)dt \quad (1)$$

= desired signal + interference

The interference level is therefore determined by the cross-correlation of $S_1(t)$ and $S_2(t)$. The usefulness of the system will be determined by the cross-correlation of the codes used which in turn will set the interchannel cross-talk.

In studying correlation, it is probably best to consider autocorrelation first on the premise that a set of codes, belonging to the same ensemble, each having satisfactory autocorrelation will also exhibit satisfactory cross-correlation. The sequences (codes) to be studied can be classified into four categories: maximal linear, nonmaximal linear, maximal nonlinear, and nonmaximal nonlinear. The maximal linear sequences exhibit the best autocorrelation,[1] that is

$$Kf(t)=\sum_{n=1}^{k} S(t)S(t+\tau)=\begin{cases} K \text{ if } \tau=0 \\ -\frac{1}{L} \text{ if } 1<\tau<L \end{cases}$$

where $L$ is the length of the sequences $S(t)$. The function $K\,f(t)$ is two-valued for whole bit increments of $\tau$; see Fig. 1(A). The maximal nonlinear sequence has autocorrelation which is a function of $\tau$ Fig. [1(B)] and is clearly not two-valued.[2] A nonmaximal linear sequence has autocorrelation which may take on all integral values between $1/L$ and $(L-2)/L$. Very little is known about the nonmaximal nonlinear sequence although there is no reason to expect its correlation is any better than the nonmaximal linear.

The superiority of the maximal linear sequence autocorrelation is due to two characteristics of sequences of this type, namely, the randomness and the shift-and-add properties. The maximal sequences (linear and nonlinear) have a balance in ones and zeros with disparity not greater than one. The maximal linear sequence has a normal run-length distribution. This, however, is not quite true of the nonlinear maximal. Balance and run-length distribution determine the randomness properties. Maximal linear sequences exhibit the shift-and-add property, the sequence shifted and added back on itself (mod 2) produces the same sequence. Nonlinear maximal sequences do not exhibit this property and the new nonlinear sequences so generated do not necessarily have balance. Since shift-and-add is essentially autocorrelation, one might say that sequences which do not exhibit the shift-and-add property also exhibit poor autocorrelation.

Next it is necessary to consider the cross-correlation of linear maximal codes belonging to the same ensemble which can also be viewed as the binary sum of the output of two shift register sequence generators of equal length. Each generator may be represented by a characteristic equation:

$$A^n+\ldots+A^k+\ldots+I=0$$

and

$$A^n+\ldots+A^j+\ldots+I=0$$

The binary sum is the operation of multiplication of the two characteristic equations. The resultant equation is of order $2n$ and has as factors the two original equations. This means that the binary sum of the two generators is equivalent to producing a nonmaximal sequence from a generator of length equal to the sum of the two original generator lengths. Since a nonmaximal sequence cannot be expected to produce good randomness properties (balance and run distribution) then neither can the cross-correlation of two maximal sequences. The lack of balance determines the amplitude of the interchannel crosstalk whenever quasiorthogonal binary functions are used for multiplexing. Of equal importance is the spectral distribution of the crosstalk. Ideally, the spectral distribution should duplicate the spectral properties of a maximal sequence. For nonmaximal sequences this desirable distribution is not even approximately realized except for long sequences. Poor run-length distribution produces subcycles and "lumpy" spectral properties. Analytical and empirical results indicate that reasonable spectral properties are not usually realized until the code lengths exceed 1,000 bits. Maximal linear codes, of course, exhibit a normally distributed run-length property producing smooth pseudorandom line spectra having a sin $x/x$ envelope. Consequently, multiplexing utilizing the quasiorthogonal characteristics of binary sequences requires the use of long sequences. This fact is necessarily true for systems using direct sequence transmission, frequency hopping, or combinations thereof such as frequency-time systems.

The cross-correlation integral from equation 1

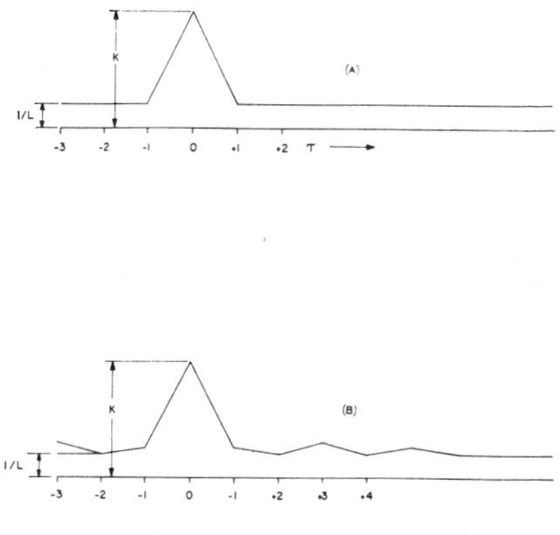


**Fig. 1. Autocorrelation of maximal sequences**

A—Linear
B—Nonlinear

Paper 62-51, recommended by the AIEE Radio Communication Systems Committee and approved by the AIEE Technical Operations Department for presentation at the AIEE Winter General Meeting, New York, N. Y., January 28–February 2, 1962. Manuscript submitted June 19, 1961; made available for printing November 27, 1961.

W. J. JUDGE is with Magnavox Research Laboratories, Torrance, Calif.

Reprinted from *AIEE Trans. Commun. Electron.*, vol. 81, pp. 81–83, May 1962.

**Table I. $C_{max}$ (Long-Term) for Maximal Linear Codes Plus Other Useful Data**

| Generator Length (n) | Number of Possible Maximal Codes | Code Length | Prime Factors | C(max) | C(max), Db |
|---|---|---|---|---|---|
| 3* | 2 | 7 | | 0.714 | − 3 |
| 4 | 2 | 15 | 3, 5 | 0.466 | − 6.6 |
| 5* | 6 | 31 | | 0.291 | −10.8 |
| 6 | 6 | 63 | 3, 3, 7 | | |
| 7* | 18 | 127 | | 0.134 | −17.5 |
| 8 | 16 | 255 | 3, 5, 17 | | |
| 9 | 42 | 511 | 7, 73 | | |
| 10 | 60 | 1,023 | 3, 11, 31 | | |
| 11 | 176 | 2,047 | 23, 89 | 0.047 | −26.6 |
| 12 | 144 | 4,095 | 3, 3, 5, 7, 13 | 0.078 | −22.2 |
| 13* | 630 | 8,191 | | 0.016 | −36 |

* Mersenne primes.

$$\frac{1}{T}\int^{T} S_1(t)S_2(t)dt$$

has been evaluated in the laboratory for $T\to\infty$ (long-term correlation) for maximal shift register generated codes up to 8,191 bits in length. For Mersenne prime coders ($M$ is a Mersenne prime if $2^M-1=$ a prime) the long-term cross-correlation

$$\frac{2\left(\frac{n+1}{2}\right)+1}{2^n-1} \geq C_M \geq \frac{1}{2^n-1} \quad (2)$$

where $n$ is the register length. For non-Mersenne prime coders, the maximum cross-correlation $C_{\max}$ is greater than $C_M$(max) and is a function of the number of prime factors in the code length.

The greater number of prime factors in the code length, the worse the cross-correlation. For example, the length $2^{11}-1=2{,}047$ which has two factors (23, 89) has maximum long-term cross-correlation of $96/2{,}047=0.0468$. The length $2^{12}-1=4{,}095$ has four prime factors (3, 5, 7, 13) and exhibits long-term cross-correlation of $321/4{,}095=0.0783$. Thus, codes produced by an 11-bit generator show 4.5 decibels less long-term cross-correlation than those produced by a 12-bit register even though the latter codes are twice as long as the former. Table I indicates the maximum cross-correlation for codes produced by generator lengths up to 13. The values for generator lengths 6, 8, 9, and 10 were not computed since it is doubtful much interest will be developed in these lengths for multiplexing. Data on the short lengths (3 to 7) were included because of the ease of computation and to demonstrate the futility of considering short sequences for multiplexing.

The usefulness of a code sequence for multiplexing may be assessed by considering the basic communications system model of Fig. 2 first. For simplicity the case for multiplexing two signals of equal power in a common channel was examined and the output of one receiver was evaluated. The data $D_1(t)$ are binary added to the code sequence $S_1(t)$ producing the signal $D_1(t)\ S_1(t)$ for transmission; the signal $D_2(t)\ S_2(t)$ is similarly produced. The two signals are linearly added into a common communications channel. Receiver 1 stores the code sequence $S_1(t)$. Cross-correlation of $S_1(t)$ with the received signal after integration produces the following:

$$Y(t)=\frac{1}{T}\int_0^T D_1(t)S_1^2(t)dt + \frac{1}{T}\int_0^T S_1(t)D_2(t)S_2(t)dt \quad (3)$$

and since $S_1(t)=\pm 1$ (binary)

$$Y(t)=D_1(t)+\frac{1}{T}\int_0^T S_1(t)D_2(t)S_2(t)dt$$

where $1/T=$ the maximum bit rate of $D_1(t)$. Thus

$$Y(t)=\text{desired signal } [D_1(t)] + \text{interference}\left[\frac{1}{T}\int_0^T D_2(t)S_1(t)S_2(t)dt\right] = S+N$$

It can be seen that the noise (interference) term is determined by the cross-correlation of $S_1(t)$ and $S_2(t)$ over the integration period $T$. Neglecting for a moment the data term $D_2(t)$, the noise term $N$ is a function of the length and bit rate of the codes $S_1(t)$ and $S_2(t)$. Assuming $S_1(t)$ and $S_2(t)$ are maximal linear codes of equal length $L$ and bit rate $1/T_o$, the product $S_1(t)\ S_2(t)$ is a nonmaximal linear code $S_3(t)$ of length $L$ and bit rate $1/T_o$. The repetition rate of $S_3(t)$ is $1/LT_o$. The value of $N$ measured over the period $T$, therefore, is proportioned to the average (d-c) value of $S_3(t)$ plus any spectral components occurring at frequency $1/LT_o$, $2/LT_o$, $3/LT_o$, .... $<1/T$. Thus, since $S_3(t)$ is pseudorandom, the rms noise voltage over the period $T$ may generally be written as

$$E_n=(K_1^2+MK_2^2)^{1/2}$$

where $K_1=$ amplitude of the d-c term; $K_2=$ amplitude of the spectral components (assuming all are equal on the average); $M=$ the number of spectral components of frequency less than $1/T$.

Note that

$$\lim_{L\to\infty} E_n = K_2\sqrt{M}$$

which is proportional to $T_o/T$, and

$$\lim_{T_o\to 0} E_n = K_1$$

which is proportional to $L$.

Thus, for infinite length codes, the noise is proportional to the ratio of the integration rate and the code bit rate; and for infinite code bit rate, the noise is proportional to the code length. The latter is the long-term cross-correlation discussed earlier and shows up as an a-c rather than d-c term because of the data term $D_2(t)$. Consequently, since infinite code bit rate and infinite code length constitute design extremes, a practical compromise in the choice of $L$ and $T_o$ might allow $K_1\approx K_2\sqrt{m}$ as a means of minimizing $E_n$. This permits a fairly even noise distribution

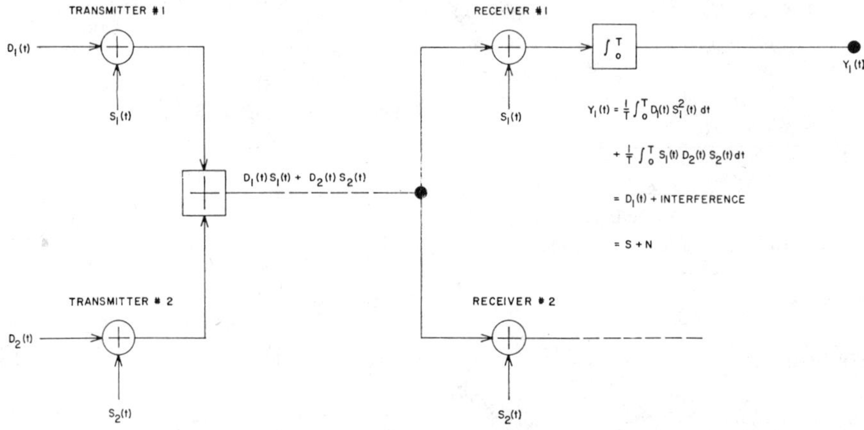


Fig. 2. Multiplexing using quasiorthogonal binary codes

across the band 0 to $1/T$ and is probably best for most applications.

Assuming a flat distribution of the spectral components which occur at frequencies less than $1/T$, the normalized value of $K_2 = (1/L)^{1/2}$. If the repetition frequency of $S_3(t)$ is $1/LT_o$, then $M = LT_o/T$ and therefore $K_2\sqrt{M} = (T_o/T)^{1/2}$ which is independent of the code length as previously stated. For two channels in multiplex

$$\left[\frac{S}{N}\right]_2 = \frac{S}{\left(K_1^2 + \frac{T_o}{T}\right)^{1/2}}$$

and for $b$ channels in multiplex (that is, $b$ channels plus the desired channel)

$$\left[\frac{S}{N}\right]_b = \frac{S}{\left[b\left(K_1^2 + \frac{T_o}{T}\right)\right]^{1/2}} \quad (4)$$

assuming all codes belong to the same ensemble and worst-case values of $K_1$. The $K_1$ values can be computed for Mersenne prime codes; see equation 2. An expression for non-Mersenne prime codes has not been derived by W. Judge although this should not be too difficult to do.

Table II shows the performance which can be expected for systems utilizing maximal linear codes generated by registers of respective lengths 11, 12, and 13. Two specific cases for the noise are given

$$(a) K_1 = \left(\frac{T_o}{T}\right)^{1/2}$$

$$(b) T_o/T = 1/500$$

The number of channels allowable under maximum loading for a given $S/N$ in the baseband output of one channel is shown. The two cases were chosen because they will be representative of systems using quasiorthogonal binary functions (maximal linear codes) for multiplexing. From the table, it can be seen that the Mersenne prime coder (13) is substantially better than lengths 11 and 12 for both cases and that 12 is poor for both cases. This is because 12 has so many factors in its length. It is also obvious that lengths less than 11 will not be useful for multiplexing.

**Table II. Performance for Systems Using Maximal Linear Codes**

| | | | |
|---|---|---|---|
| Register length | 11 | 12 | 13 |
| Code length | 2047 | 4095 | 8191 |
| $K_1$ (from Table I) | 0.047 | 0.078 | 0.016 |
| $T_o/T = K_1^2$ | $2.6 \times 10^{-3}$ | $8.85 \times 10^{-3}$ | $2.56 \times 10^{-4}$ |
| $b$ (for $S/N = 6$ db) | 48 | 14 | 488 |
| $T_o/T$ | $2 \times 10^{-3}$ | $2 \times 10^{-3}$ | $2 \times 10^{-3}$ |
| $b$ ($S/N = 6$ db) | 54 | 23 | 113 |
| $b$ ($S/N$ 10 db) | 24 | 10 | 50 |

## Conclusions

To implement a coded correlation system successfully for the purpose of multiplexing, the code sequences utilized must have length and correlation properties consistent with the required number of channels. For modest channel capability, it has been shown that code lengths of several thousand bits are necessary since the long-term cross-correlation is an inverse function of code length. In addition, the relationship between system bandwidth and code length is derived based on the use of maximal linear codes.

Because this type of multiplexing function is quasiorthogonal, it will probably find greatest application in random access systems in which the number of subscribers greatly exceeds the number of channels available.

## References


1. Introduction to Linear Shift Register Generated Sequences, **T. G. Birdsall, M. P. Ristenblatt.** *Report no. 90*, Electronic Defense Group, University of Michigan, Ann Arbor, Mich., Nov. 1958.

2. An Investigation of Iterative Boolean Sequences, **Scott, Welch.** *Report 8-543*, Jet Propulsion Laboratories, California Institute of Technology, Pasadena, Calif., 1955.

# Multiple Access to a Hard-Limiting Communication-Satellite Repeater

JOSEPH M. AEIN

*Summary*—This paper analyzes the communication capability of a hard-limiting satellite repeater when spread-spectrum signals are used for asynchronous access multiplexing. It derives formal results which indicate the most suitable system bandwidth and the resulting maximum number of simultaneous users as a function of the ratio of the received signal power (over the entire system bandwidth) from the satellite to the available noise power density at the ground station receiver. Equally important, the paper sets forth the assumptions and approximations necessary to achieve the formal results and examines their weaknesses.

THE BASIC FEASIBILITY of communication-satellite systems has now been demonstrated, and it is likely that one will be placed in operation in the next few years. The usefulness of any such system depends heavily upon solving the problem of multiple access, *i.e.*, the problem of making the satellite repeater simultaneously available to more than one pair of geographically separated ground stations whenever the need arises.[1] Decisions affecting multiple access also affect the signaling process and are therefore fundamental to the design of the system.

This paper presents and solves an illustrative multiple-access problem. The treatment is introductory rather than comprehensive. It proceeds from several assumptions regarding the system as a whole to a formal derivation of the most suitable bandwidth for the system and the corresponding maximum number of simultaneous users, as a function of the ratio of two quantities: the signal power received from the satellite over the entire system bandwidth, and the noise power density at the ground-station receivers. It concludes with a critical examination of the assumptions and approximations upon which the formal analysis rests.

The hypothetical communication-satellite system analyzed here has uncontrolled random access,[2] or simultaneous asynchronous multiplexing, through a hard-limiting satellite repeater. The multiplexed carriers are binary-phase-coded, constant-envelope signals; the message information is modulated into the carriers by binary complementation of $n$-length sub-blocks of the bit stream. The message source is speech digitally converted to $q$-bit pulse-code modulation (PCM).

Manuscript received July 28, 1964.

The author is with the Research and Engineering Support Division, Institute for Defense Analyses, Arlington, Va.

[1] In a strict sense, a single duplex communication link routed through a satellite represents multiple access to the satellite, but as used here the term multiple access denotes simultaneous access by more than one duplex link.

[2] As opposed to controlled synchronous access, *e.g.*, time-division multiplexing.

The object of the following analysis is to determine the maximum number of simultaneous signals (denoted by $M$) that the satellite repeater can handle simultaneously. Consequently, the maximum number of simultaneous simplex users is $M$; the maximum number of simultaneous duplex users is $M/2$.

## I. Preliminary Problem

Before considering the complete satellite problem, one is restricted to a much less ambitious problem which has not yet been fully examined: that of detecting a sine wave with binary phase coding buried deeply in Gaussian noise after passage through a hard limiter. Fig. 1 depicts the situation.

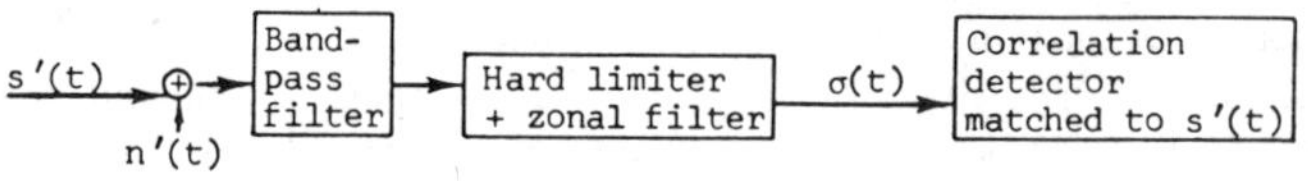


Fig. 1—Hard-limiting correlation detector.

In Fig. 1

$$s'(t) = \sum_{l=0}^{n-1} \alpha \operatorname{rect}_{\Delta T} (t - l\Delta T) \cos (\omega_0 t + \mu_l \pi/2)$$

$$n'(t) = \text{white Gaussian noise}$$

$$\sigma(t) = \text{output of hard limiter}$$

where

$\alpha$ = signal amplitude, the sign of which carries the message information

$\operatorname{rect}_{\Delta T}(x)$ = 1 if $0 \leq x < \Delta T$
= 0 otherwise

$\mu_l$ = $\pm 1, \cdots$ } phase coding sequence
$l$ = $0, 1, \cdots, n-1$ }

$n$ = number of phase-coded samples

$\Delta T$ = length of each phase sample

$T$ = $n\Delta T$ = total signaling time per message bit

$1/T$ = message bit rate

$\omega_0$ = carrier frequency.

This channel structure has received some attention in the past as it is a form of constant false-alarm rate (CFAR) fix for radar and sonar detection. Doyle and Reed [1] recently carried through an elegant analysis of this type of channel in some detail. They analyzed the channel with the correlation detector of Fig. 1 replaced by a narrow-band filter centered on the frequency $\omega_0$ followed by an envelope detector. They considered a sine-

Reprinted from *IEEE Trans. Space Electron. Telem.*, vol. SET-10, pp. 159–167, Dec. 1964.

wave signal and obtained the probability density functions of the detector output for both noise only and signal present cases. For the purpose of this paper, coherent detection will be presumed. Their formulation of the problem will be adopted and the central limit theorem will be applied to avoid the difficult task of evaluating the probability density function of the correlator output.

One now makes the following three assumptions:

*Assumption 1*: The band-pass filter (BPF) is an ideal filter of bandwidth $W = 1/\Delta T$ and gain $1/\sqrt{N_0 W}$ where $N_0$ is the noise power density. (It is further assumed that the BPF passes $s'(t)$ with negligible distortion.)

*Assumption 2*: The zonal filter in the hard limiter passes only those harmonic components centered on the carrier frequency $\omega_0$.

*Assumption 3*: The noise samples are uncorrelated over $\Delta T$ intervals.

It follows that $n = TW$. By Assumption 1, the noise power at the hard limiter is unity. The signal portion of the hard-limiter input, denoted by $s(t)$, is given by

$$s(t) = \frac{s'(t)}{\sqrt{N_0 W}} = \sum_{l=0}^{n-1} a \operatorname{rect}_{\Delta T} (t - l\Delta T) \cdot \cos(\omega_0 t + \mu_l \pi/2) \quad (1)$$

where

$$a = \frac{\alpha}{\sqrt{N_0 W}}$$

Thus

$$\frac{1}{T}\int_0^T s^2(t)\,dt = \frac{1}{T}\sum_{l=0}^{n-1} a^2 \cdot \int_0^{\Delta T} \cos^2(\omega_0 t + \mu_l \pi/2)\,dt$$

$$= \frac{1}{T}\frac{a^2}{2} n\Delta T = \frac{a^2}{2} = \frac{\alpha^2/2}{N_0 W}$$

But $\alpha^2/2$ is the input power in $s'(t)$ and $N_0 W$ is the noise power in the band $W$, so that $a^2/2$ is the input signal-to-noise ratio at the hard limiter.

By Assumption 2, one is only interested in the components of the limiter output at the frequency $\omega_0$. Thus, $\sigma(t)$ is given by

$$\sigma(t) = \operatorname{sgn} a \sum_{l=0}^{n-1} \operatorname{rect}_{\Delta T}(t - l\Delta T) \cdot \cos(\omega_0 t + \mu_l \pi/2) \quad (2$$

where

$$\operatorname{sgn} a = 1 \text{ if } a \geq 0$$
$$= -1 \text{ if } a < 0$$

$$\varphi(t) = \tan^{-1} \frac{y(t)}{a + x(t)}$$

The functions $x(t)$ and $y(t)$ are the quadrature components of the Gaussian noise (centered on $\omega_0$) at the input to the hard limiter. The correlator output $V$ is given by

$$V = \frac{\operatorname{sgn} a}{\sqrt{n}} \sum_{k=0}^{n-1} \int_{k\Delta T}^{(k+1)\Delta T} \frac{2}{\Delta_T} \cos(\omega_0 t + \mu_k \pi/2) \cdot \cos\left[\omega_0 t + \mu_k \pi/2 + \varphi(t)\right] dt$$

$$= \frac{\operatorname{sgn} a}{\sqrt{n}} \sum_{k=0}^{n-1} \frac{1}{\Delta_T} \int_{k\Delta T}^{(k+1)\Delta T} \cos \varphi(t)\,dt \quad (3)$$

where $2/(\sqrt{n}\ \Delta T)$ = the correlator gain normalizing factor.

This motivates our next assumption. Since by Assumption 3 the noise $(x, y)$ is uncorrelated over $\Delta T$ intervals and is hence statistically independent, one expects $\varphi(t)$ to be statistically independent over $\Delta T$ intervals also. In order to avoid the mathematical difficulties inherent in the stochastic integral of (3), one assumes[3] the following:

*Assumption 4*: The correlator output $V$ may be approximated by

$$V \approx \frac{\operatorname{sgn} a}{\sqrt{n}} \sum_{k=0}^{n-1} \cos \varphi_k \frac{1}{\Delta T} \int_{k\Delta T}^{(k+1)\Delta T} dt \quad (4)$$

$$V \approx \operatorname{sgn} a \sum_{k=0}^{n-1} \frac{1}{\sqrt{n}} \cos \varphi_k \quad (5)$$

where $\varphi_k$ are identically distributed statistically independent random variables.

It is well known [2] that if $a = 0$, the $\varphi_k$ are distributed uniformly over the interval $(0, 2\pi)$. Thus,

$$E(V^2 | a = 0) = \frac{1}{n} \sum_{k=0}^{n-1} E \cos^2 \varphi_k = \tfrac{1}{2} \quad (6)$$

where $E$ is the expectation operator. Since the noise has a mean value of zero, and if

$$Pr(a > 0) = Pr(a < 0) = \tfrac{1}{2},$$

one has a symmetric binary channel and the error probability $P_e$ is given by

$$P_e = Pr(V < 0 | a > 0)$$

Thus, if $a > 0$, $V$ is given by

$$V = \sum_{k=0}^{n-1} \frac{1}{\sqrt{n}} \cos \varphi_k$$

and

$$\varphi_k = \tan^{-1} \frac{y}{x + a} \quad (7)$$

where $x$ and $y$ are zero-mean, unit-variance, uncorrelated Gaussian random variables. It can be shown [3] that $p(\varphi_k) = p(\varphi)$ can be approximated (for small values of $a^2$) by

$$p(\varphi) = \frac{1}{2\pi}\left(1 + \sqrt{\frac{\pi}{2}}\, a \cos \varphi\right), \qquad 0 \leq \varphi < 2\pi, \quad (8)$$

[3] A similar technique is used in [2].

to within terms of order $a^2$. Note that $p(\varphi) \geq 0$ implies that

$$\frac{a^2}{2} < \frac{1}{\pi}$$

Note further that

$$E(V) = \frac{1}{\sqrt{n}} \sum_{k=0}^{n-1} \int_0^{2\pi} \left(\cos\varphi + \sqrt{\frac{\pi}{2}}\, a \cos^2 \varphi\right) \frac{d\varphi}{2\pi} = \frac{a}{2}\sqrt{\frac{n\pi}{2}} \tag{9}$$

Dividing the square of (9) by (6) yields

$$\frac{[E(V)]^2}{E(V^2 \mid a = 0)} = na^2 \frac{\pi}{4} \tag{10}$$

Now let

$$d^2 \triangleq \frac{[E(V)]^2}{E(V^2 \mid a = 0)}$$

If no hard limiter is present,

$$d^2 = 2\frac{TS}{N_0}$$

where $S$ = the average power of the signal $s'(t)$. Observe that

$$d^2 = 2\frac{TS}{N_0} = 2TW\left(\frac{S}{N_0 W}\right)$$

But

$$\frac{S}{N_0 W} = \frac{a^2}{2}$$

which is the input signal-to-noise ratio at the hard limiter. Furthermore,

$$TW = n$$

and therefore

$$d^2 = na^2 \tag{11}$$

From a comparison of (10) and (11), it is evident that the hard limiter degrades the output detection threshold by $\pi/4$ or 1.0 db.

In order to obtain the probability density function for $V$ as given by (7), the central limit theorem is invoked in a form [3] which states that if all quantities $\lambda_k$ ($k = 0, 1, 2, \cdots$) are statistically independent and if for some $\delta > 0$ they satisfy the relation

$$\tau = \lim_{n\to\infty} \frac{\sum_{k=0}^{n-1} E\,|\lambda_k - \bar{\lambda}_k|^{2+\delta}}{\left(\sum_{k=0}^{n-1} E\,|\lambda_k - \bar{\lambda}_k|^2\right)^{1+\delta/2}} = 0 \tag{12}$$

where $\bar{\lambda}_k = E\lambda_k$, then the random variable

$$y(n) = \frac{1}{\sqrt{n}} \sum_{k=0}^{n-1} \lambda_k$$

approaches a Gaussian random variable as $n \to \infty$. For this case, $\lambda_k = \cos\varphi_k$ and $\bar{\lambda} = b/2 = a/2\sqrt{\pi/2}$. For $\delta = 2$,

$$E\,|\lambda_k - \bar{\lambda}_k|^4 = \int_0^{2\pi} (\cos\varphi - b/2)^4 (1 + b\cos\varphi) \frac{d\varphi}{2\pi}$$

$$< \int_0^{2\pi} (\cos\varphi - b/2)^4 \frac{d\varphi}{\pi} < 2^5; \text{ for small } a^2/2$$

$$E\,|\lambda_k - \bar{\lambda}_k|^2 = \tfrac{1}{2}(1 - b^2/2)$$

Whence the test $\tau$ becomes

$$\tau = \lim_{n\to\infty} n \frac{2^5}{n^2(1 - b^2/2)} = 0$$

Consequently, one concludes that for sufficiently large $n$ (*i.e.*, for sufficiently large time-bandwidth product), $V$ is Gaussian with mean $\sqrt{n}\, b/2$ and variance $\frac{1}{2}(1 - b^2/2)$. Thus

$$(d')^2 = \frac{(EV)^2}{\sigma_v^2} = \frac{n\frac{\pi}{8}a^2}{\frac{1}{2}\left(1 - \frac{\pi}{4}a^2\right)}$$

$$\approx n\frac{\pi}{4}a^2\left(1 + \frac{\pi}{4}a^2\right) \approx \frac{n\pi}{4}a^2 \tag{13}$$

for small $a^2/2$. Therefore (see (10)),

$$(d')^2 = d^2$$

It is the above argument which leads to the statement that the hard limiter is a quasi-linear device that degrades the signal-to-noise ratio by 1.0 db. Of course it is important to know the relation between the size of $n$ and the non-Gaussianness of $V$, especially when dealing with very low error rates.

## II. Hard-Limiting Satellite Link

In this section the satellite down link is incorporated into the framework of Section I. Fig. 2 is the corresponding block diagram. In Fig. 2, $n_1'(t)$ and $n_2(t)$ are statistically independent zero-mean Gaussian random variables.

If $\rho^2$ is the space loss (power attenuation), normalized to a hard-limiter output power of $\frac{1}{2}$ watt (see (2)), a block diagram equivalent to Fig. 2 is Fig. 3.

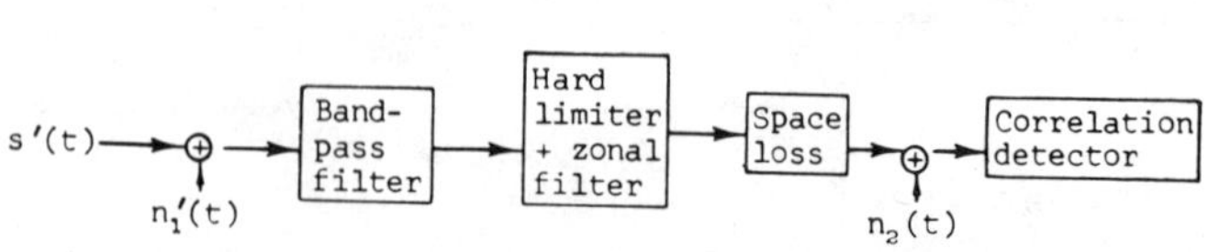


Fig. 2—Hard-limiting communication channel.

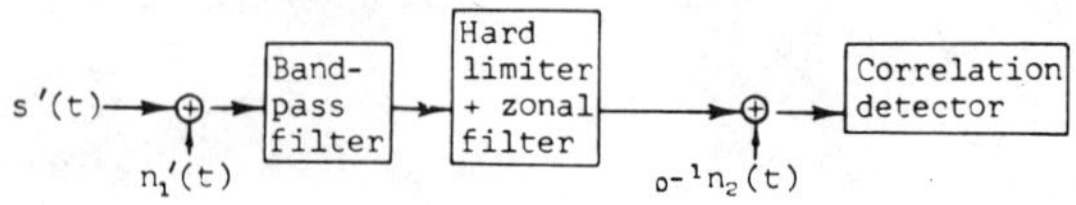


Fig. 3—Equivalent hard-limiting satellite communication channel.

Since the system following the hard limiter is linear, one may use superposition and apply the results of Section I. Namely, the correlator output $V$ can be considered as the sum of two random variables $V_1$ and $V_2$ which, due to the independence of $n_1'(t)$ and $n_2(t)$, are also statistically independent. Furthermore, $V_2$ will be Gaussian with zero mean and a variance which one now calculates.

The function $n_2(t)$ will have an available noise power density of $KT_r$ watts/cps, where $K$ is Boltzmann's constant and $T_r$ is the effective receiver noise temperature. Consequently, the noise power density at the input to the correlator of Fig. 3 is $\rho^{-2}KT_r$. Thus,

$$V_2 = \frac{1}{\sqrt{n}} \sum_{k=0}^{n-1} \frac{2}{\Delta T} \int_{k\Delta T}^{(k+1)\Delta T} \cos\left(\omega_0 t + \mu_k \frac{\pi}{2}\right) \rho^{-1} n_2(t)\, dt$$

and

$$EV_2^2 = \frac{1}{n} \frac{4}{(\Delta T)^2} \sum_{k=0}^{n-1} \int_{k\Delta T}^{(k+1)\Delta T} \frac{\rho^{-2}}{2} KT_r \cos^2\left(\omega_0 t + \mu_k \frac{\pi}{2}\right) dt$$

$$= \frac{\rho^{-2}KT_r}{\Delta T} = \rho^{-2}KT_r W \qquad (14)$$

If $V_1$ is regarded as Gaussian with mean $(a/2)\sqrt{n\pi/2}$ and variance $\frac{1}{2}(1 - \pi a^2/4) \approx \frac{1}{2}$ (see (13), then $V = V_1 + V_2$ is also Gaussian with mean $(a/2)\sqrt{n/\pi 2}$ and variance $\frac{1}{2} + \rho^{-2}KT_r W$, and the average error rate $P_e$ (assuming a binary symmetric channel) is given by

$$P_e = \int_d^\infty \exp\left[-\frac{x^2}{2}\right] \frac{dx}{\sqrt{2\pi}} \qquad (15)$$

where

$$d^2 = \frac{m_r^2}{\sigma_v^2} = \frac{n \frac{\pi}{2} \frac{a^2}{2}}{1 + 2\rho^{-2}KT_r W}$$

The quantity $a^2/2$, as before, is the input signal-to-noise ratio at the limiter (assumed to be small).

## III. Multiple Access Utilizing Spread-Spectrum Signals

Since the necessary mathematical framework is contained in (15), this section is devoted to the application of (15) to the problem of multiple-access to a hard-limiting communications satellite with spread-spectrum signals. Fig. 4 depicts the situation.

It is assumed that there are $m$ unsynchronized spread-spectrum signals of *equal power* at the input to the satellite. A generic signal is singled out and denoted by $s'(t)$. The other $(m - 1)$ signals are added together; their sum is denoted by $n_1'(t)$. It is our aim to endow $n_1'(t)$ with the statistical properties of Gaussian noise, white over the frequencies passed by the BPF and of a power $m - 1$ times that of $s'(t)$. Of course, the correlation detector of Fig. 4 is that receiver which is tuned to $s'(t)$. If $m$ is reasonably large (?), if the binary phase codings appear well distributed, if the constant RF reference phase of each signal is independent of all others, and if the signals are unsynchronized, then it is customary to bless $n_1'(t)$ with Gaussian noise properties and assert that $n_1'(t)$ is statistically independent of $s'(t)$.[4] This is justifiable by the central limit theorem. If these assumptions are accepted and if the thermal noise at the satellite input is neglected, (15) is valid for an input signal-to-noise ratio of $1/m - 1$. It should be borne in mind, however, that as the system bandwidth increases, the satellite thermal noise may no longer be neglected. Appendix I discusses the influence of this noise source on the system, but for the moment one shall continue to neglect it even to the point of letting the system bandwidth go to infinity, because by doing so one obtains meaningful results which may then be reinterpreted in the light of Appendix I. The derivation of (15) presupposed a small input signal-to-noise ratio, which corresponds to the necessity of a large $m$.

One's purpose now is to obtain the number of simultaneous users $m$ as a function of the RF bandwidth, given the quality of message transmission $q$ and the receiver signal-to-noise ratio. From [3] and [4] one makes use of some well-known formulas relating PCM to output signal-to-noise ratios. Let $q$ be the number of bits used to encode speech samples at a rate of $f_s$ cps. That is to say, speech is sampled every $1/f_s$ seconds and quantized into $2^q$ levels. There are (nominally) two sources of noise for PCM: quantization noise and channel noise. The quantization noise is independent of the channel and results from the quantization process. It is a function of the choice of quantization levels and the input-signal probability distribution. However, if the quantization levels are chosen to match the input signal statistics

[4] This assumption is discussed further in Section IV.

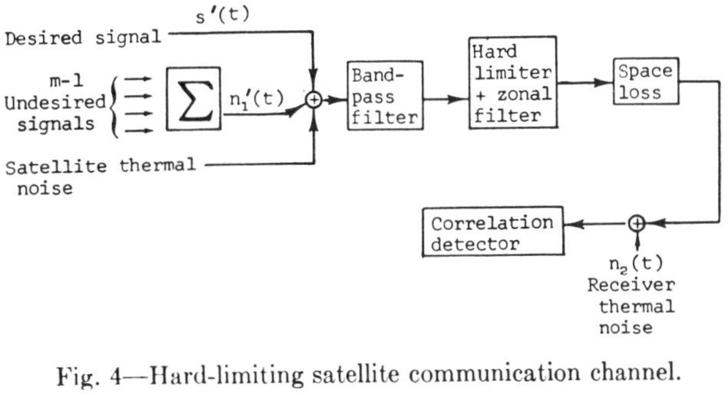


Fig. 4—Hard-limiting satellite communication channel.

(the process known as companding), then the signal-to-noise ratio $S/N$ of the process is given [4] to a close approximation by

$$S/N = 4^q \tag{16}$$

The other source of noise is channel dependent, *i.e.*, it arises from the errors introduced by the channel in decoding the PCM word. If $P_e$ is the channel error probability and if $P_e \leq 10^{-2}$, then the output signal-to-noise ratio due to channel errors is closely approximated [5] by

$$S/N = \frac{1}{4P_e} \tag{17}$$

Equating the right-hand members of (16) and (17) defines a very sharp threshold on $P_e$ so that for small $P_e$, the output signal-to-noise ratio is quickly dominated by the quantizing noise. This follows from the fact that for reasonably small $P_e$ (*i.e.*, $P_e < 10^{-2}$), a 1-db increase in channel noise decreases $P_e$ by an order of magnitude. Thus, $P_e$ at threshold denoted by $P_{e,t}$, is given by

$$P_{e,t} = 4^{-(q+1)} \tag{18}$$

The system parameters are uniquely related by introducing (15) as follows:

$$P_{e,t} = 4^{-(q+1)} = \int_{d_t}^{\infty} \exp\left[-\frac{x^2}{2}\right] \frac{dx}{\sqrt{2\pi}} \tag{19a}$$

$$d_t^2 = \frac{\frac{\pi}{2} TW \frac{1}{(M-1)}}{1 + 2\rho^{-2}KT_rW} \tag{19b}$$

where

$d_t^2$ = detectability at PCM threshold
$M$ = maximum number of simultaneous users, $m$
$T$ = $1/qf_s$ = sampling interval
$W$ = $1/\Delta T$ = RF bandwidth
$\rho^2$ = normalized space loss
$K$ = Boltzmann's constant
$T_r$ = effective system noise temperature.

Eq. (19a) can be solved for $d_t$ as a function of $q$, the PCM bit size. Then from (19b), threshold values of the indicated parameters may be computed.

The quantity $2\rho^{-2}KT_r$ has an interesting interpretation. The numerator is the space loss normalized to a power output of $\frac{1}{2}$ watt. If the satellite *total* output power is $P_r$ watts and the actual space loss is $L^2$, then the *total* received power at any one station $P_r$ is equal to $L^2P_r$. Writing $P_r$ as $\frac{1}{2}\mu$, one sees that $P_r = \frac{1}{2}\mu L^2 = \frac{1}{2}\rho^2$ or $\rho^2 = 2P_r$.

Consequently,

$$\frac{\rho^2}{2KT_r} = \frac{P_r}{KT_r} \tag{20}$$

is the *total* received satellite power-to-thermal-noise density ratio. From (19b) and (20),

$$d_t^2 = \frac{\frac{\pi}{2}\frac{1}{q}(M-1)^{-1}\frac{P_r}{KT_rf_s}\left(\frac{W}{W_0}\right)}{1 + \frac{W}{W_0}} \tag{21}$$

where $W_0 = P_r/KT_r$.

Let $d_t(q)$ be the solution to (19a) for a given value of $q$. Then

$$(M-1) = \frac{\frac{\pi}{2}[qd_t^2(q)]^{-1}\left(\frac{P_r}{N}\right)\frac{W}{W_0}}{1 + \frac{W}{W_0}} \tag{22}$$

where

$$\left(\frac{P_r}{N}\right) = \frac{P_r}{KT_rf_s} = \text{total received satellite power-to-noise ratio referred to the sampling bandwidth.}$$

Eq. (22) yields the *maximum* number of simultaneous spread-spectrum users[5] of a hard-limiting satellite repeater as a function of the RF bandwidth for a given output signal-to-noise quality $4^q$ and total received power-to-noise ratio (*referred to the sampling bandwidth*). If one assumes that the actual number of simultaneous users $m$ exceeds $M$, the system as a whole will break threshold. If $m$ is less than $M$, the output signal-to-noise quality of the users will increase to the value $4^q$. If $m$ equals $M$, the system is at threshold and the resulting output quality is 3 db down from $4^q$ (*i.e.*, $\frac{1}{2}4^q$). Thus, one sees that this system has a user loading characteristic which saturates sharply, an effect which is attributable to the PCM mode of message modulation.

Notice that (22) is of the form

$$(M-1) = \frac{(M_\infty - 1)W/W_0}{1 + W/W_0} \tag{22a}$$

which resembles the transfer function of a simple high-pass $RC$ filter with break frequency $W_0$ and gain $(M_\infty - 1)$. Thus the value that $M$ approaches asymptotically as $W$ approaches infinity, denoted by $M_\infty$, is given by

$$M_\infty - 1 = \frac{\pi}{2}\left(\frac{P_r}{N}\right)[qd_t^2(q)]^{-1} \tag{23}$$

and the critical RF bandwidth $W_0$ is given by

$$W_0 = \frac{P_r}{KT_r} \tag{24}$$

where

$q$ = PCM bit size
$d_t^2(q)$ = the function of $q$ given by the solution to (19a)
$P_r$ = total received satellite power
$K$ = Boltzmann's constant
$T_r$ = effective noise temperature of the ground station
$N$ = $KT_rf_s$ = noise power referred to the sampling bandwidth.

[5] As noted in the introduction, one duplex communication link comprises two simultaneous users.

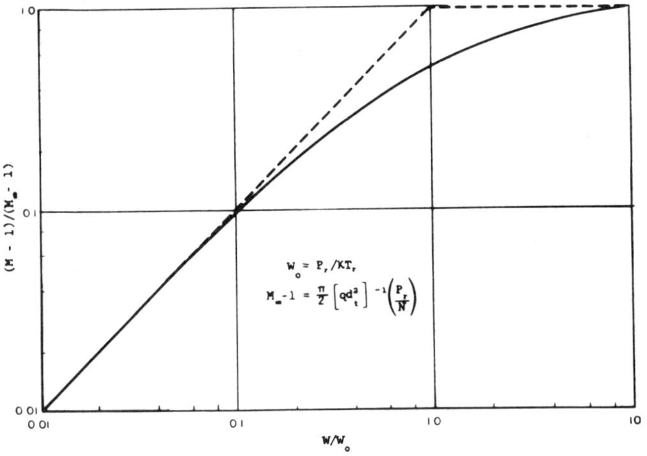


Fig. 5—Normalized plot of $M-1$ vs $W$.

TABLE I

$d_t$ SOLUTIONS OF (19a)

| $q$ | $d_t$ | $[q\ d_t^2]^{-1}$ | $(\pi/2)[q\ d_t^2]^{-1} = (M_\infty - 1)(P_r/N)^{-1}$ |
|---|---|---|---|
| 4 | 3.094 | 0.0262 | 0.041 |
| 5 | 3.489 | 0.0164 | 0.026 |
| 6 | 3.843 | 0.0114 | 0.018 |
| 7 | 4.169 | 0.00823 | 0.013 |

Fig. 5 is a normalized plot of $(M - 1)/M_\infty - 1)$ as a function of $W/W_0$. Table I presents $d_t$ solutions of (19a) together with values of $(\pi/2)[q\ d_t^2]^{-1}$.

One takes as an example the parameters of a medium-altitude communications satellite wherein a $P_r/KT_r$ of 67 db is available (see Appendix II) which implies that the critical RF bandwdith $W_0$ is 5 Mcps. This in turn implies that any RF bandwidth greater than 5 Mcps increases $M$ marginally. Let us arbitrarily choose $W = 10$ Mcps. At least a 3-db margin must be provided for uncontrollable losses (*e.g.*, rain); consequently, if $f_s = 8$ kcps, the available $P_r/N$ is given by

$$P_r/N = (64 - 39)\text{ db} = 25\text{ db}$$

and substitution of values from Table I for 5-bit PCM and from Fig. 5 for $W/W_0 = 4$, yields[6]

$$M - 1 = (0.8)(0.026)(315) = 6.5$$

Therefore,

$$M = 7$$

Thus, there is seen in this example a set of parameters which seriously strains the assumption used to model the access problem; namely, that $P_r/KT_rf_s$ is not sufficiently large to produce $M$-values greater than 10. Under this condition, the above $M$-value of 7 can only be taken as a qualitative indication. This example was chosen because the characteristics of a communications-satellite repeater with an isotropic antenna are of current interest. If gravity stabilization of the satellite proves feasible, then it may well turn out that a 10-db increase in $P_r/KT_r$ is possible, in which case $W_0$ becomes 50 Mcps and $M$ about 70.

[6] Note than when $P_r$ fades 3 db, $W_0$ is halved.

It is worthwhile to compare these results to some ideal systems. The first is one where it is assumed

1) that the ground station-to-repeater input links are free from interference and noise;
2) that the repeater output is multiplexed among $M_\perp$ orthogonal subchannels;
3) that the modulation is $q$-bit, binary PCM with a sampling frequency of $f_s$ cps; and
4) that the ground-station receivers are perturbed by white Gaussian noise of available power density $KT_r$ watts.

With the above assumptions, one may use (19a) and modify (19b). Our measure of performance is the same as that used for the spread-spectrum analysis. Thus $d_t^2$ is the same as before, being uniquely specified once $q$ is selected. It is well known that $d^2$ is given by

$$d^2 = 2E/KT_r$$

where $E$ is the energy available for transmission of one bit of each PCM sample word. Thus

$$E = \frac{2}{qf_s}\left(\frac{P_r}{M_\perp}\right)$$

where $P_r$ = total average received signal power from the repeater. Whence

$$M_\perp = 2\,[qd_t^2]^{-1}\left(\frac{P_r}{N}\right) \tag{25}$$

or

$$\frac{M_\infty - 1}{M_\perp} = \frac{\pi}{4} \tag{26}$$

Consequently, the channel output obtainable with the spread-spectrum technique can be as high as $\pi/4$ times the output of the ideal orthogonally multiplexed channel.

Next one compares the spread-spectrum technique to an ideal linear, average-power-limited Shannon channel. The information rate on the Shannon channel with infinite bandwidth $R_\infty$ is given by

$$R_\infty = \frac{P_r}{KT_r} \tag{27}$$

where

$P_r$ = average received power
$KT_r$ = available noise power density.

Each of the $M_\infty - 1$ communication links of the spread-spectrum system produces $qf_s \log_e 2$ natural bits per second. Thus the spread-spectrum multiplex efficiency $\eta$ can be defined as

$$\eta \triangleq \frac{(M_{\infty} - 1)qf_s \log_e 2}{P_r/KT_r} \tag{28}$$

$$= \frac{\pi}{2} \log_e 2d_t^{-2}$$

$$= 1.1d_t^{-2}$$

where $d_t$ as a function of $q$ is given in Table I.

Note that $\eta$ is a function only of the quality of the communication system. Table II presents $\eta$ as a function of $q$.

TABLE II
UPPER BOUNDS ON MULTIPLEX EFFICIENCY

| Quality of Transmission, $q$ Dimensionless | Multiplex Efficiency, $\eta$ per cent | System Output Quality, $S/N$ db |
|---|---|---|
| 4 | 11 | 24 |
| 5 | 9 | 30 |
| 6 | 7 | 36 |
| 7 | 6 | 42 |

## IV. CRITICAL REVIEW

The following paragraphs summarize the critical deficiencies in the foregoing analysis. These deficiencies are attributable to sins of omission and sins of commission; they will be reviewed in that order.

### *A. Undiscussed Problems*

Two problems have been overlooked: the choice of the actual bit-stream codes and bit-stream synchronization. Directly related to the coding problem is the microscopic interference between bit streams which can cause loss of synchronization between the transmitting and receiving stations of a particular link. This, in effect, places another threshold (loss of synchronization) into the system aside from that induced by signaling errors $P_e$. Given that a system is coded reasonably well, this threshold should be below the signaling threshold and the analysis of Section III then applies. However, the coding must be chosen somewhat intelligently. In this context, it will be important to establish, for a given coding method, the relationships between the bit-stream length, the correlation length $n = TW$, the totality of the addresses (potential ground stations), and the maximum number of simultaneous users, so as not to lose bit-stream synchronization.

Also of importance is the actual acquisition and maintenance of bit-stream synchronization by the receiving stations. Doppler tracking at the ground stations may be an important consideration for medium-altitude (6000 n.mi.) satellite systems.

### *B. Analytical Deficiencies*

Perhaps the greatest weakness of the analysis presented is that for a $q$ as small as 4, the channel $P_{e,t}$ is of the order of $10^{-3}$. Consequently, one must work with the tail of the distribution of the correlator output voltage $V$. Thus, all expedient assumptions regarding the Gaussian nature of a sum of $M-1$ binary-phase-coded sinusoids are critical. Even granting this assumption, it is clear that this sum does not have a white spectrum. Moreover, the assumptions leading to the technique of obtaining the correlator output in Section I (especially Assumption 4) need a closer examination.

Further justification is needed for the use of the Central Limit Theorem in Section III in summing the undesired signals to Gaussian noise which is then also assumed to be *independent* of the desired signal. The difficulty is that some small but nonzero correlation between the phase-coded bit-stream generators does exist. However, an argument [6] for justifying the statistical independence of these bit streams can be based upon the fact that each transmitter adds an arbitrary, completely independent, and random RF reference phase to the transmitted bit stream.

A further serious deficiency is the assumption that all the signals arriving at the satellite input are of equal power. This point must be examined much more closely. If one signal has an average power slightly greater than the sum of the average powers of the other signals, there are indications that the strong signal will capture the limiter. In fact, the analysis of Section I specifically assumes that such is not the case; for if one considered the strong signal as $s(t)$, the signal-to-noise ratio would not be sufficiently small for the analysis to hold and (8) would be quite erroneous. Thus future work must devote considerable attention to the strong-signal case.

It may be objected that the satellite BPF before the hard limiter has a gain normalized to $1/\sqrt{N_0W}$, and that in the multiple-access case $N_0W$ is directly proportional to $m$, the number of users. However, this gain was chosen to set the average power in the output of the BPF equal to the input signal-to-noise ratio. Any fixed value of gain for the BPF will provide analytically identical results (to within the dynamic range of the equipment used).

## V. CONCLUSIONS

The foregoing analysis permits the following conclusions:

1) Spread-spectrum signals with PCM digitized speech message sources produce a system loading characteristic exhibiting sharp saturation with an increase in the number of users. This effect is due to the performance of PCM encoded speech. Graceful degradation (soft saturation) is not an inherent attribute of the spread-spectrum multiplexing modulation, although systems can be designed which do have this property (*e.g.*, spread-spectrum carriers with the message information contained in a narrow-band FM subcarrier). This suggests that the total modulating process be analytically factored into the

component modulations of carrier multiplexing and message encoding so that generalized statements regarding system behavior can be more easily understood.

2) The selection of the system RF bandwidth is of great importance. The foregoing analysis suggests that this bandwidth is intimately related to the received power-to-noise density ratio $P_r/KT_r$ at a typical ground station. That $P_r/KT_r$ is a critical bandwidth is gratifying since it is the Shannon limit for an average, power-limited channel. An increase in this ratio is necessary to obtain desired increases of multiple-access capability. This, in turn, requires an increase in satellite bandwidth. Ever increasing bandwidth will eventually force the designer to be concerned with thermal noise at the satellite input.

## Appendix I

### Effects of Satellite Thermal Noise

This Appendix accounts for the effects of the satellite thermal noise terms of the hard-limiting satellite communication channel shown in Fig. 4. It is assumed that this noise is white, Gaussian, and statistically independent of $n_2(t)$, and that it has an available single-sided power density of $KT_s$ watts/cps. Thus, the input of the satellite contains a signal $s'(t)$ of power $P_TL$ and Gaussian noise of power $(m-1)P_TL + KT_sW$, where it is assumed that all ground stations transmit $P_T$ watts with the same ground-to-satellite power loss factor $L$. Thus $(S/N)_{in}$, the input signal-to-noise ratio at the limiter (see (15)), is given by

$$\left(\frac{S}{N}\right)_{in} = \frac{P_TL}{P_TL(m-1) + KT_sW} = \frac{1}{(m-1) + KT_sW/P_TL} \tag{29}$$

Normalizing $W$ to $W_0$ produces

$$\left(\frac{S}{N}\right)_{in} = \frac{1}{(m-1) + \alpha\dfrac{W}{W_0}} \tag{30}$$

$$W_0 = \frac{P_r}{KT_r}$$

$$\alpha = \frac{KT_s}{P_TL}\cdot\frac{P_r}{KT_r}$$

If the down-link losses are assumed equal to the up-link losses, $P_r$ is equal to $P_sL$, where $P_s$ is the satellite transmitter power in watts, and $\alpha$ is then the power-temperature product ratio

$$\alpha = \frac{P_sT_s}{P_TT_r}$$

Consequently, the expression for $d_i^2$ becomes

$$d_i^2 = \frac{\dfrac{\pi}{2q}\dfrac{P_r}{N}\dfrac{W}{W_0}}{\left[1 + \dfrac{W}{W_0}\right]\left[(M-1) + \alpha\dfrac{W}{W_0}\right]} \tag{31}$$

Eq. (31) is easily put into the following form:

$$\frac{(M-1)}{(M_\infty - 1)} = \frac{\left(\dfrac{W}{W_0}\right)}{\left[1 + \dfrac{W}{W_0}\right]\left[1 + \dfrac{\alpha}{M-1}\dfrac{W}{W_0}\right]} \tag{32}$$

where

$$W_0 = \frac{P_r}{KT_r} = \frac{P_sL}{KT_r}$$

$$M_\infty - 1 = \frac{\pi}{2}[qd_i^2]^{-1}\left(\frac{P_r}{N}\right)$$

Thus, it is seen that (22a) is modified by the term

$$\left[1 + \frac{\alpha}{M-1}\frac{W}{W_0}\right]^{-1}$$

To calculate the effects of this term one considers as an example the following system parameters:

$$P_s = 4 \text{ watts}; \qquad T_s = 2000^0\text{K}$$

$$P_T = 1 \text{ kw}; \qquad T_r = 200^0\text{K}$$

$$\frac{W}{W_0} = 4.$$

Whence

$$\alpha = 4 \times 10^{-2}$$

$$\alpha\frac{W}{W_0} = 0.16$$

and since $(M-1)$ must be no less than six

$$\left[1 + \frac{0.16}{(M-1)}\right]^{-1} \approx 1 - \frac{0.16}{(M-1)}$$

which is a negligible correction even for an $M$ as small as six. Note, however, that if $W/W_0$ is made sufficiently large, this correction is not negligible. In fact, if $W$ becomes too large, the maximum number of simultaneous users decreases. This follows from the fact that the satellite input power contributed by the spread-spectrum signals remains fixed, whereas the satellite noise power increases linearly with $W$.

The foregoing suggests the existence of an optimum system bandwidth $W^*$. Solving (32) for $(M-1)$ yields

$$(M-1) = \left[\frac{M_\infty - 1}{1 + \dfrac{W}{W_0}} - \alpha\right]\frac{W}{W_0} \tag{33}$$

Differentiating (33) with respect to $W/W_0$ and setting the result equal to zero, yields the value of $W^*$ that maximizes $M$. That is to say,

$$\frac{W^*}{W_0} = \sqrt{\frac{(M_\infty - 1)}{\alpha}} - 1 \tag{34}$$

and

$$\frac{M^* - 1}{M_\infty - 1} = \left(1 - \sqrt{\frac{\alpha}{(M_\infty - 1)}}\right)^2$$

where $M^*$ denotes the maximum value of $M$. This implies that for an optimum bandwidth to exist the following condition must be satisfied:

$$\frac{M_\infty - 1}{\alpha} > 1$$

or

$$\frac{P_T L}{KT_s f_s} > \frac{2}{\pi} q d_i^2 \tag{35}$$

The quantity $P_T L/KT_s f_s$ is the received power-to-noise ratio at the input to the satellite from *one* ground station referred to the sampling bandwidth. Condition (35) simply states that the up-link signal-to-noise ratio must exceed the PCM threshold. If condition (35) is not met, the system will break the PCM threshold established by equating channel noise to quantizing noise.

For the example cited above, $\alpha = 4 \times 10^{-2}$ so that

$$\frac{M_\infty - 1}{\alpha} = (25)\,(M_\infty - 1) > 1$$

If $(M_\infty - 1)$ is as small as six, then

$$\frac{W^*}{W_0} = 11$$

and

$$\frac{M^* - 1}{M_\infty - 1} = 0.85$$

In practice a $W^*/W_0$ of more than four would seem implausible. The example considered here seems to emphasize this even more, because for $W/W_0 = 4$ and $(M_\infty - 1) = 6$,

$$\frac{M^* - 1}{M_\infty - 1} = \left(1 - \frac{0.16}{6}\right)(0.82) = 0.8$$

That is to say, with a bandwidth one-third of optimum one has come within 95 per cent of the maximum number of users. If $P_T L/KT_s f_s$ is increased, a $W/W_0$ of four decreases the yield of simultaneous users to a floor of 82 per cent of the optimum number that could be obtained with ever increasing bandwidths.

## Appendix II

### Pertinent Characteristics of a Medium-Altitude Communications Satellite System

This Appendix presents the satellite to ground-station power budget associated with a proposed medium-altitude (6000 n.mi.) communications satellite system. The pertinent features of the system are: 1) a 4-watt satellite output into an isotropic antenna, and 2) a 30-foot dish at the ground station feeding a receiver with a noise temperature of 200°K and an operating frequency of 8 kMcps.

The up-link budget provides satellite input signal-to-natural-noise ratios exceeding 20 db; so that in comparison to the noise of the $(m - 1)$ unwanted signals, the natural noise is neglected (see Appendix I).

| | |
|---|---|
| $P_s$ (=4 watts) | 6 dbw |
| $G_s$ (=0 db) | 0 db |
| losses | −3 db |
| $G_r$ (30-foot dish) | +54 db |
| $16\pi^2$ | −22 db |
| $\lambda^2 = (0.123)^2$ | −18 db |
| tracking losses | −2 db |
| $D^2$ (maximum slant range) | −154 db |
| $P_r$ | −139 dbw |
| $KT_r$ ($T_r$ = 200°K) | −206 dbw |
| $P_r/KT_r$ | 67 db |

### Acknowledgment

The author wishes to thank R. A. Hoover of the Institute for Defense Analyses (IDA) for his careful editing of the manuscript, and W. E. Bradley, J. Kaiser, and J. W. Schwartz of IDA for their stimulating discussions of the subject of this paper.

### References

[1] W. Doyle and J. S. Reed, "Approximate band pass limiter envelope distributions," IEEE Trans. on Information Theory, vol. IT-10, pp. 180–184; July, 1964.
[2] P. Bello and W. Higgins, "Effect of hard limiting on the probabilities of incorrect dismissal and false alarm at the output of an envelope detector," IRE Trans. on Information Theory, vol. IT-7, pp. 60–66; April, 1961.
[3] W. B. Davenport, Jr., and W. L. Root, "An Introduction to the Theory of Random Signals and Noise," McGraw-Hill Book Co., Inc., New York, N. Y.; 1958.
[4] B. Smith, "Instantaneous companding of quantized signals," *Bell System Tech. J.*, vol. 36, pp. 653–708; May, 1957.
[5] H. F. Mayer, "Principles of pulse code modulation," in "Advances in Electronics," Academic Press, Inc., New York, N. Y., vol. 3; 1951. See p. 251.
[6] J. M. Aein, "Multiple Access Capability of a Hard-Limiting Communication Satellite Repeater with Spread-Spectrum Signals," IDA/RESD, Washington, D. C., Research Paper P-121; April, 1964.

# A Rake System for Tropospheric Scatter

D. R. BITZER, D. A. CHESLER, MEMBER, IEEE, R. IVERS, MEMBER, IEEE, AND S. STEIN, SENIOR MEMBER, IEEE

*Abstract*—**Experimental equipment has been developed which adapts the Rake concept to tropospheric scatter. This equipment enables experimental tests of multipath diversity effectiveness for communications. Its delay-resolution capabilities and circuit stability also allow effective use of the equipment for novel propagation research. The underlying concepts and equipment design are described, along with initial propagation test results.**

## I. Introduction

### *Review of the Rake Concept*

In a classic paper, Price and Green [1] introduced the Rake concept and described its implementation in equipment for HF operation. For communicating over a fading multipath radio channel in which the maximum multipath time-delay spread is a value $T_M$, the Rake concept utilizes a special wide-band signal of bandwidth $W$, where $W \gg 1/T_M$. The signal is structured to have a pseudo-random character, with autocorrelation width of the order $1/W$. The receiver comprises a bank of cross-correlators, mutually synchronized with respect to overall nominal propagation delay from transmitter to receiver, but each operates with successive relative delays of $1/W$. Each successive cross-correlator then extracts from the total received signal only that portion corresponding to contributions arriving from a particular $1/W$ — time width segment of the multipath. When the multipath spread is $T_M$, this makes available a total of $M = T_M/(1/W) = T_M W$ versions of the transmitted signal, hopefully fading independently, which can then be combined by standard diversity-combining techniques. This technique thus allows the antifading advantages of $M$-fold diversity, without requiring the replication in RF equipment (antennas, transmitters, receivers) usually associated with diversity.

The equipment described is an adaptation of the Rake concept to experimental equipment which tests possible usefulness of Rake techniques in tropospheric scatter operation. In addition to being designed for a greatly different bandwidth and multipath spread than associated with long-distance HF communications, the system differs in some details from the implementation described by Price and Green. These are all described in Section II. The kind of propagation tests carried out with this equipment are also of interest with respect to improving the understanding of the radiophysics of the troposcatter mechanism.

Manuscript received December 27, 1965. Presented as paper CP 65-456 at the 1965 IEEE Communications Convention, Boulder, Colo.

D. R. Bitzer is with the Department of Defense, Washington, D. C.

D. A. Chesler and S. Stein are with the Applied Research Laboratory, Sylvania Electronic Systems Division, Sylvania Electric Products, Inc., Waltham, Mass.

R. Ivers is with Sylvania Electronic Systems–Central, a division of Sylvania Electric Products, Inc., Buffalo, N. Y.

### *System Parameters*

The equipment developed comprises transmitter and receiver terminals, suitable for mating with any standard tropospheric-scatter radio set. Since the widest RF bandwidth commonly available in such equipment is 10 Mc/s, this was the bandwidth chosen for design. In the tests run the terminals were mated to the radio-frequency portions of an AN/MRC-98, military troposcatter equipment operating at 910 Mc/s with a nominal 10 Mc/s bandwidth.

The basic pseudo-random signal structure is achieved by direct phase-reversal modulation of a carrier by a pseudo-random bipolar 10-megabaud waveform, as achieved via an $M$ sequence (see Section II). Use of a 10-megabaud sequence implies that the entire system runs synchronized to within 0.1 $\mu$s. This synchronization is maintained in the stable clock, from which all heterodyning frequencies and other timing functions are derived; the latter, hence, implicitly operate within this accuracy.

The multiple cross-correlators comprising the basic Rake receiver correspondingly operate with 0.1 $\mu$s relative delays. In order to limit costs of the experimental equipment, the number of cross-correlators used has been limited to 10. This is adequate to capture all multipath delay components when the multipath spread is 1.0 $\mu$s or less. (This corresponds to path lengths up to about 400 km.) For short troposcatter paths of length 200 to 300 km, where the multipath spread is about 0.3–0.4 $\mu$s, only three or four of these cross-correlators are usually active (extracting fading signals). A Rake communications receiver would then provide triple or quadruple diversity for this path. (A wider bandwidth radio equipment, allowing finer resolution of the multipath, would provide higher order diversity.) For longer path lengths, up to tenth-order diversity, is available with the ten taps. However, while this 10-correlator system would still provide tenth-order diversity on paths longer than about 400 km (1 $\mu$s multipath spread), some fraction of the total arriving energy would be lost because of the failure to extract it in any of the cross-correlators.

As part of a diversity combining operation, an appropriate smoothing would be done on all or part of each cross-correlator output, to derive envelope and phase estimates of the *instantaneous* fading state for that segment of the arriving energy. A band-pass filter of bandwidth 200 c/s in the present equipment corresponds to this purpose. It is the set of outputs of these 200 c/s filters which provide the propagation research data. Hence, as constructed, the equipment can validly provide data on channels whose fad-

Reprinted from *IEEE Trans. Commun. Technol.*, vol. COM-14, pp. 499–506, Aug. 1966.

ing power spectra extend to about ± 100 c/s. This appears adequate within the scope of the tests performed, but wider filters could be readily employed in future tests, if it seemed desirable.

*Propagation Experiments*

The multipath resolution capability implied in Rake operation involves a detailed probing, both in envelope *and* phase, of the impulse response of the propagation channel. The utility of this troposcatter Rake system as an instrument for propagation research has been enhanced by deriving all system frequencies and timing propagation experiments from well synchronized, highly stable oscillators and clocks, accurate to several parts in $10^{10}$ per day, and in the short terms, as well.

Some data taken on a 251 km (156 mile) path are described and discussed in Section III. The data described include the following parameters:

1) Observations of selective fading over the total 10-Mc/s bandwidth received signal, with a resolution of 15 kc/s (panoramic receiver)
2) Envelope fluctuations of resolved multipath at rates up to 100 c/s
3) Delay stabilities of the medium over periods of several minutes, with accuracy of about five parts in $10^{10}$
4) Total received signal power over periods of hours with time constant of one second and drift/hour approximately 10 percent.

Data were collected for approximately 100 hours in two one-week periods, three months apart. Initial data reduction has enabled qualitative observations concerning the following:

1) Diurnal phenomena, and "ducting" effects
2) Correlation bandwidth of the medium
3) Effects of aircraft in the common volume
4) Fading rates and depths
5) Usefulness of Rake concept as a diversity combining technique
6) Delay stability of the link
7) Number of resolvable paths, total delay spread, and stability of particular propagation events
8) Comparison of theoretical predictions for path loss, antenna radiation patterns and delay spread with experimental results.

Abraham et al. [2] describes tests in which the resolved multipath return is separated into quadrature components, and the so-called complex auto- and cross-convariances calculated. The corresponding power spectra, for each time-delay segment of the multipath spread, are directly interpretable in terms of radiophysical parameters such as Doppler distribution, whereas all known previous measurements (confined to envelope covariances) allow no such direct interpretation. In addition, the cross-covariances between resolved components can indicate translational motion (drifts, aircraft) in the medium.

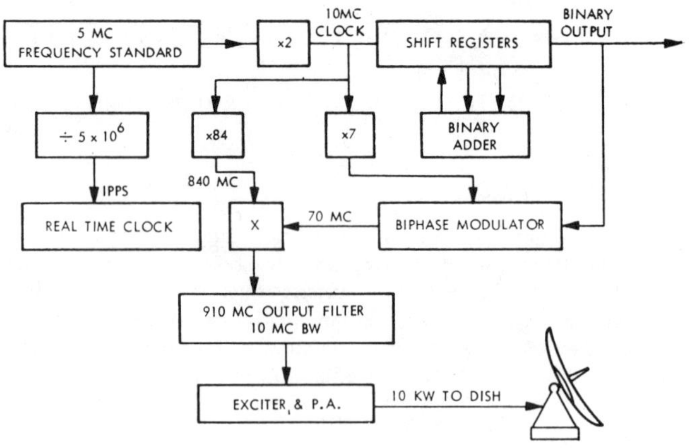


Fig. 1. Transmitter.

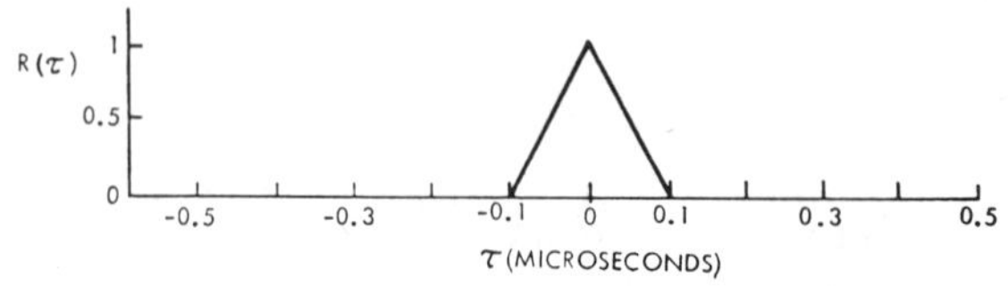


Fig. 2. Autocorrelation function of binary stream.

## II. Description of Troposcatter Rake Equipment

*Transmitter Terminal*

A block diagram of the transmitter terminal is shown in Fig. 1. All frequencies and timing are synthesized from a precision 5-Mc/s crystal oscillator. Its measured stability is typically five parts in $10^{10}$ over periods of five minutes, and one part in $10^{10}$ over periods of 48 hours.

A binary sequence is generated at a rate of ten megabits per second, using standard feedback shift-register techniques, with a sufficient number of stages to eliminate the time ambiguity and remove granularity from the power density spectrum. As is well known, any short (several hundred bit) segment of such a sequence has pseudorandom properties, with successive binary states highly uncorrelated. Simple tests on the binary sequence generator verified that the probability of $+1$ or $-1$ is 0.5, the probability of two successive bits alike is 0.5, the probability of three successively alike is 0.25, etc. The binary sequence is obtained in the form of a bipolar rectangular waveform. The autocorrelation function of any reasonably long $N$-bit segment ($N$ = several hundred bits) of this waveform has the form shown in Fig. 2, with *sidelobe* peaks of the order of $1/\sqrt{N}$.

The bipolar waveform is used to biphase modulate (phase positions 0, $\pi$) a 70 Mc/s subcarrier, which is in turn heterodyned to 910 Mc/s for compatibility with the AN/MRC-98 radio equipment. The 910 Mc/s signal is filtered to a $-3$-dB bandwidth of 10 Mc/s by a high-order Butterworth filter. The envelope of the autocorrelation of the resulting signal is like that of the original sequence. The filtering results in a small widening of the autocorrelation function, and rounding of the triangular center peak, but it can be shown that these effects are negligible for the test results described here.

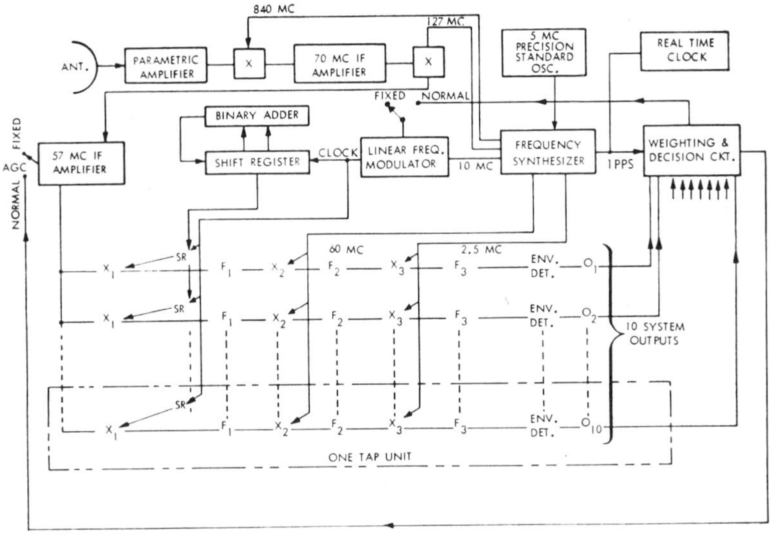


Fig. 3. Receiver.

The 910 Mc/s signal is then applied to the exciter and power amplifier of the AN/MRC-98 transmitting equipment, resulting in a power level of 10 kW fed to the transmitting antenna.

*Rake Receiving Terminal*

The heart of the instrumentation is the receiving terminal equipment, described in the block diagram of Fig. 3. Again a 5-Mc/s precision oscillator, of the same type as used in the transmitting terminal, is used to synthesize all frequencies and timing. The incoming signal is pre-amplified in a low-noise parametric amplifier, heterodyned, and amplified at 70-Mc/s intermediate frequency (10-Mc/s bandwidth). It is then heterodyned again to 57 Mc/s where it is fed through a 10-fold branching circuit into ten *tap units;* the *tap unit* terminology is carried over from the HF Rake (Price and Green [1]).

In the HF Rake equipment, the received *signal* was passed into a tapped delay line, so that the multiple correlation operation is achieved by correlating several relatively-delayed versions of the signal against a single correlation reference. This was termed a *delayed-signal* Rake. In the 10-Mc/s troposcatter Rake, it appeared simpler to implement a *delayed-reference* Rake (also discussed in Price and Green [1]), as shown in Fig. 3. Here, the stored reference is generated as a video bipolar waveform, identical to the one at the transmitter, and synchronized to take into account the propagation delay. The shift register is driven by a linear frequency modulator (LFM) clock, whose function in correcting for synchronization drift is described later. At each of the 10 successive tap units, the sequence is applied through one additional shift-register stage (creating the relative delay of 0.1 μs).

In each tap unit, the first mixer ($X_1$) effectively multiplies the total received signal plus noise against the reference waveform, at the particular time delay. This is accomplished by $(0, \pi)$ phase modulation again. The pseudo-random phase modulation is effectively cancelled for those

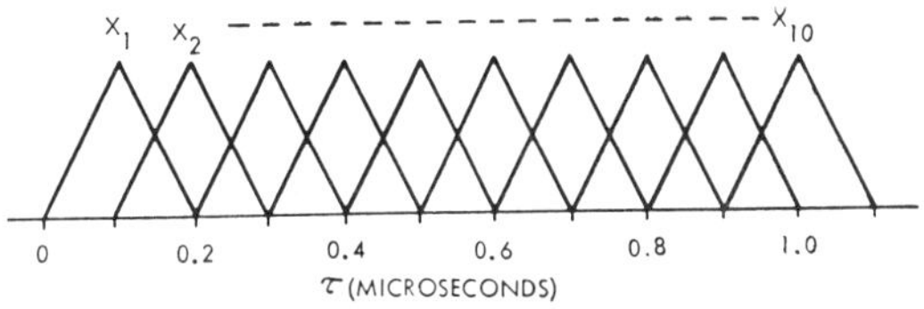


Fig. 4. Receiver correlation function.

signal components arriving via the particular time delay to which the tap circuit is synchronized. In later smoothing (200 c/s bandwidth filters) in this tap unit, these signal components will add coherently. Others, relatively delayed in propagation time from the correlation reference by intervals exceeding 0.1 μs, will appear noise-like in these latter filters and be rejected (to the extent that the autocorrelation "sidelobes" discussed earlier are nearly zero). The subsequent filtering and mixing operations ($F_1$, $X_2$, $F_2$, $X_3$, $F_3$), result in filtering the signal to a bandwidth of 200 c/s at a frequency of 500 kc/s. Double conversion is employed here to reduce image responses and eliminate foldover problems.

For the ten tap units, with the ideal autocorrelation, the successive correlations with signal would overlap as shown in Fig. 4. With the smoothing time of the 200 c/s filter (~10 ms) the number of sequence bits over which the smoothing (cross-correlation) is carried out is thus of the order of $10^5$. Thus, the correlation sidelobes at the filter outputs will be of the order of 50 dB below the main peak (the same statement can alternately be derived by considering the result of 200 c/s bandwidth filtering of a 10 Mc/s bandwidth noise-like signal).

The 500 kc/s filter outputs are envelope-detected for the measurements reported here in Section III, Abraham et al. [2], providing measurements of the relative amplitude of the fading signal arriving via the particular corresponding segment of the multipath structure of the medium. A typical example of the outputs, for a 2-path signal, is shown in Fig. 5.

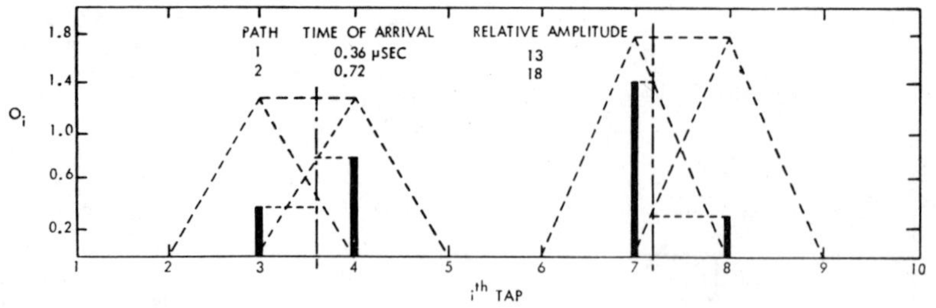


Fig. 5. Typical 2-path signal.

The ten envelope outputs, designated $0_i$, are used to keep the received signal *centered* in the Rake receiver. The following weights are assigned to each output:

$$\begin{aligned} 0_1 &= 1.0 & 0_6 &= 0 \\ 0_2 &= 0.5 & 0_7 &= -0.25 \\ 0_3 &= 0.33 & 0_8 &= -0.33 \\ 0_4 &= 0.25 & 0_9 &= -0.5 \\ 0_5 &= 0 & 0_{10} &= -1.0 \end{aligned}$$

The weighted outputs are summed together, and a decision is made once per second as to whether the output is positive or negative. A 10-ns clock timing correction is sent to the LFM based on this decision. This circuit thus produces corrections for synchronization drift either in the medium or between transmitter and receiver clocks. It is denoted below as the center-of-gravity circuit. It can track delay changes at rates up to about 0.6 μs/min (path length changes up to 200 m/min). For some propagation experiments, the LFM is operated without the correction pulses; drifts observed across the ten tap outputs which exceed the known clock instabilities are then directly attributable to instabilities or drifts in the medium.

An unweighted sum of the envelope outputs was used, through a suitable time constant smoothing, to control the gain of the 57 Mc/s intermediate frequency amplifier when AGC action is desired.

*Link Synchronization*

Synchronization is easily accomplished by aligning the clocks at both ends with WWV signals, and then proceeding through a routine synchronization phase. An agreed initial setting is inserted into the shift register in the sequence generators, the receiver clock start pulse is offset by the estimated path delay plus time uncertainty, and then both transmitter and receiver pattern generators are started on a pre-agreed time-marker (WWV second pulse). It then remains to search for the correlation peak by advancing or retarding the stream generators by using the linear frequency modulator.

In automatic search the linear frequency modulator can advance the timing at a rate of $10^3$ clock pulses per second. Time can be blocked into 1 μs segments for synchronization search, because of the simultaneous use of all ten delay-line taps. Thus, the linear frequency modulator advances 1 μs (10 pulses) during an interval 10 ms long, following which the filter outputs are allowed to build-up over a 15-ms interval. If any outputs exceed a preset threshold, the automatic search is stopped and the center-of-gravity circuit activated. If the threshold is not exceeded, the linear frequency modulator is advanced another 1 μs. Since each step of the search requires 25 ms, the actual search rate in the time uncertainty is 1 μs per 25 ms, or 40 μs/s. Since the time uncertainty between transmitting and receiving sites during these tests was less than 1 ms, the maximum search time is 25 seconds.

Once initial synchronization has been achieved, the inherent short-term clock stability has allowed disabling of the center-of-gravity circuit for long periods (15 minutes or more). This has been particularly important (see also Abraham et al. [2]) in taking data for propagation research purposes where it is desired to observe the existence of any time-delay drifts (physically relatable to drift mechanisms in the medium) without the intrusion of circuit compensations of the type needed for maintaining communications continuity. Any drifts which exceed the residual clock drift thus become measurable with high confidence.

## III. Initial Propagation Tests

*Description of the Link*

Initial tests with detailed data collection were carried out during March and June 1964. A standard Air Force transportable troposcatter communications equipment, the AN/MRC-98, was modified for use in these tests. The MRC-98 equipment normally operates in quadruple diversity, with two spaced transmitting antennas, differing in polarization, at the transmitting end. For the troposcatter Rake tests, only one antenna at each terminal and one transmitter were used, with the Rake system transmitter feeding the MRC-98 exciter and the Rake receiver operating from a single IF output of the MRC-98.

The transmitting site was located at the south terminal approximately 60 km southwest of Richmond, Va. The lower edge of the 8.5-meter (28-foot) antenna was about 3.5 meters above ground. Using a field intensity meter in a helicopter, the −3 dB beamwidth was found to be 3° ±0.5° in both the azimuth and elevation planes. The foreground is flat for 1500 meters (an abandoned airport), with 0° elevation to the visual horizon. The antenna was vertically polarized, and the signal was transmitted at a center frequency of 910 Mc/s.

The receiving site was located at the north terminal, approximately 20 km northeast of Washington, D. C., a great-circle distance of 251 km (156 statute miles) from the transmitter. The lower edge of the 8.5-meter receiving

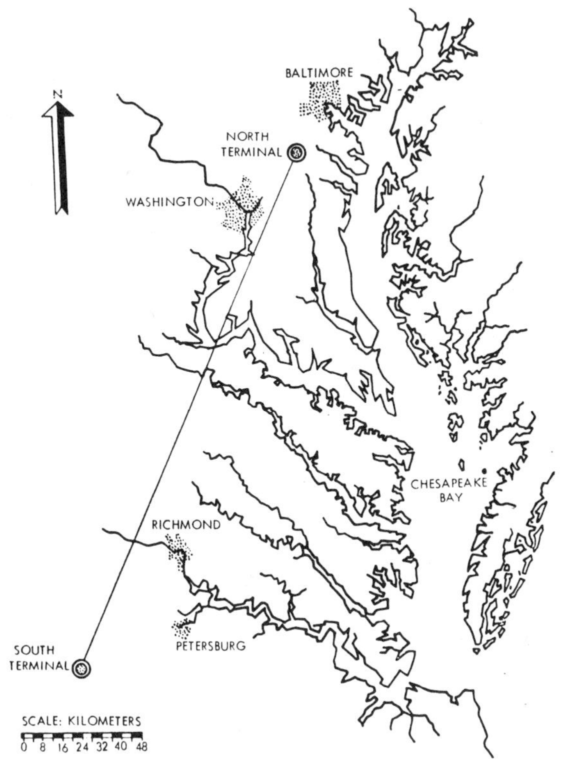


Fig. 6. Location of propagation path.

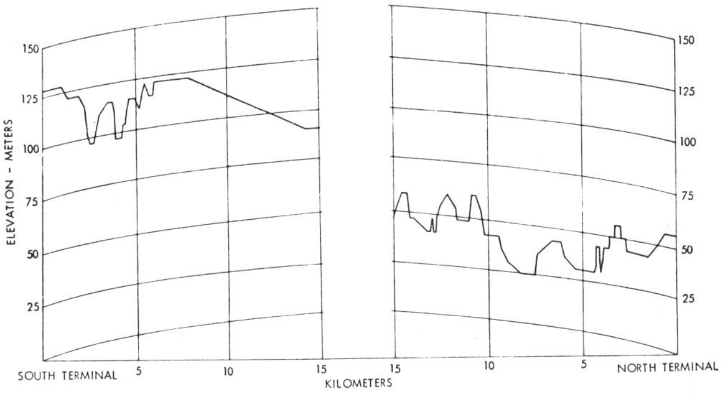


Fig. 7. Path profile near terminals.

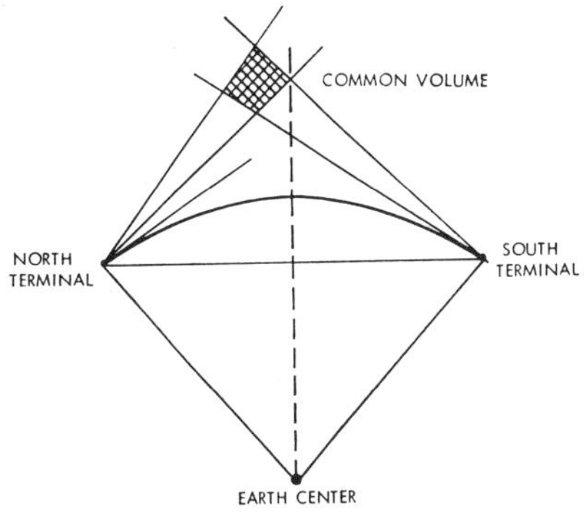


Fig. 8. Common volume geometry.

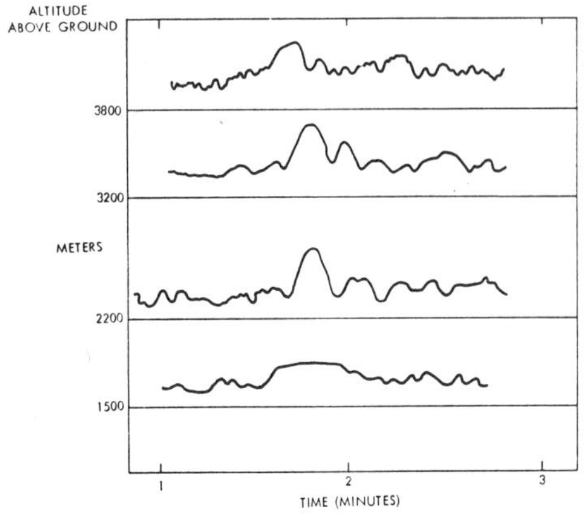


Fig. 9. Typical records for aircraft flying through common volume near midpath.

TABLE I

PATH LOSS ESTIMATES

| | |
|---|---|
| KTB | −134 dB W |
| N.F. | 2 dB |
| Free Space Loss | 140 dB |
| Beyond-Horizon Loss | 67 dB (Median) |
| Terminal Losses | 5 dB |
| Radiated Power | 40 dB W |
| Total Antenna Gains | 68 dB |
| SNR (Median) | 28 dB |

antenna was about 3.5 meters above ground. The RF front end utilized a parametric amplifier with 2-dB noise figure. The foreground at the receiving site was concave, with a maximum depression of about 10 meters at 150 meters from the antenna. The visual horizon was about 600 meters away, at $\alpha$ $+3°$ elevation. The beamwidths at this terminus were also checked and determined to be $3° \pm 0.5°$. The map of Fig. 6 shows the path; the path profile is shown in Fig. 7.

Antennas were aligned coarsely on the basis of surveys and then aligned for maximum received signal by vertical and horizontal beam-swinging measurements. In the vertical plane, the boresight at each terminal was then found to be pointing approximately 1.5° above the visual horizon. A sketch indicating the common volume geometry is shown in Fig. 8. On the basis of 4/3 earth radius, the common volume defined by the −3-dB beamwidths of the antennas ranges from a minimum altitude of about 1400 meters to a maximum of about 8000 meters.

In addition, a cooperating aircraft was flown back and forth in the region of midpath at thousand-foot intervals from 2000 feet (600 meters) to 12 000 feet (3600 meters) while signal strength fluctuations were observed at the receiving terminal. Radio communications between the plane and ground allowed determination of the shape of the common volume, from data such as shown in the sketch of Fig. 9.

Estimates of the annual median path loss for this link are shown in Table I based on standard methods [3]. Tests were primarily carried out in daytime, from early morning through early evening. During most of the test

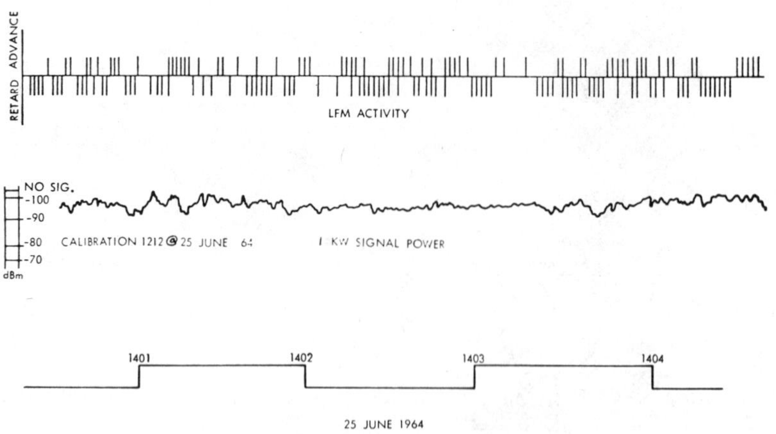


Fig. 10. Typical chart record.

period, the mean SNR appeared to be within 3 dB of the value shown. On almost all days, a consistent *sundown* effect was noted, in which the median signal strength dropped 12 to 16 dB for about three hours beginning shortly before sundown (but during which fading was still typical of troposcatter). On several occasions, signal enhancements of 14 to 32 dB were observed, that lasted for periods of 3 to 24 hours.

*Data Collection Procedures*

Data were collected by hand, multipen chart recorder, multichannel magnetic tape, and still and motion pictures. The chart recorder ran throughout the tests at a rate of 1.0 mm/s. A typical chart record is shown in Fig. 10. One channel recorded received signal strength, taken from the 70-Mc/s IF amplifier using a square-law detector and a low-pass integrator with a time constant of one second. A second channel recorded time of occurrence and direction of the 10-ns corrections to the linear frequency modulator when automatic synchronization correction was in use. A third channel recorded AGC voltage, which was used mainly to indicate whether or not the system was in synchronism. A fourth channel indicated real time.

A spectrum analyzer was used to observe the received signal at the output of the 70-Mc/s IF amplifier of the MRC-98. Motion pictures of the CRT display were made from time to time. The horizontal and vertical deflection voltages were recorded with FM electronics on separate channels of a tape recorder running at 15 in/s. A third channel of this tape recorder was used to record PCM data described in detail below, and a fourth channel recorded timing pulses for the PCM data.

For ten days preceding each field test, the frequency standards were slowly brought into precise frequency alignment with the 20-kc transmission from WWVL by using commercial phase tracking receivers and phase comparators. During the tests, clock checks were made several times each day with WWV using the configuration shown in Fig. 11. By displaying one cycle of the 1-kc modulation during the WWV second-pulses across 10 cm of scope face, time resolutions of better than 20 $\mu$s can be observed. It can be shown that the time uncertainty $T$ due to receiver noise is then

$$T = \frac{10^{-3}}{2\pi\beta} \text{ seconds}$$

where $\beta$ is the ratio of peak signal-to-rms noise voltages. For $\beta = 10$, $T = 16$ $\mu$s, so no difficulty was encountered with clock alignment.

Collection of envelope data from the ten outputs was a more complicated problem. In addition to a visual display for immediate observation, a permanent record was required for later data reduction. A 10-channel recorder was rejected because of cost, required frequency response, dynamic range, and drift problems, in favor of the following system: each tap output envelope was sampled sequentially to form a time-division-multiplexed signal, with each analog sample converted to a 4-bit digital word. The number of bits per word was determined by the SNR available at the coder. The 4-bit PCM, which provides a maximum SNR of about 28.5 dB, was chosen. Each output was sampled 417 times per second, along with a level 0 and a level 15 for frame sync recovery, giving a multiplexed PCM stream at 20 000 baud.

To record this data on magnetic tape, the wave was converted to a 3-level signal, Trinary $A$, using the following rule: if the baseband is 0, $A = 0$; and if baseband is $+1$, $A$ alternates between $+1$ and $-1$ during successive intervals. The state diagram and transition probabilities are shown in Fig. 12. The power density spectrum of this signal is readily shown to be

$$\Phi(f) = \frac{\sin^4(\pi f/f_0)}{2f_0(\pi f/f_0)^2}$$

where in our case, $f_0 = 20$ kc/s. This spectrum is suitable for recording directly on tape recorders with a 20-kc/s frequency response, as it contains no dc and low-level highs. This signal is placed on the third channel of the tape recorder, thus making available a simultaneous display

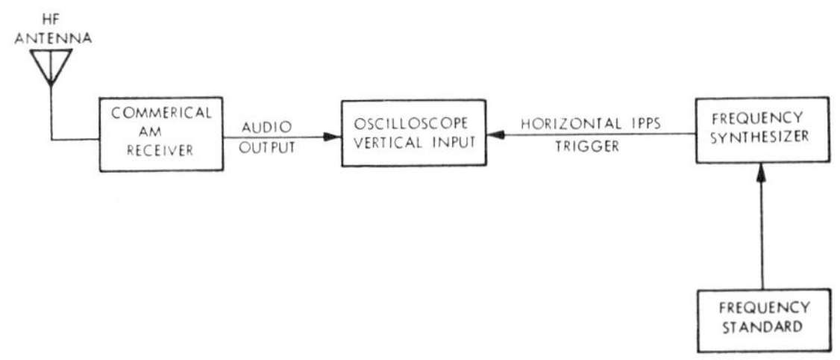


Fig. 11. Clock comparator.

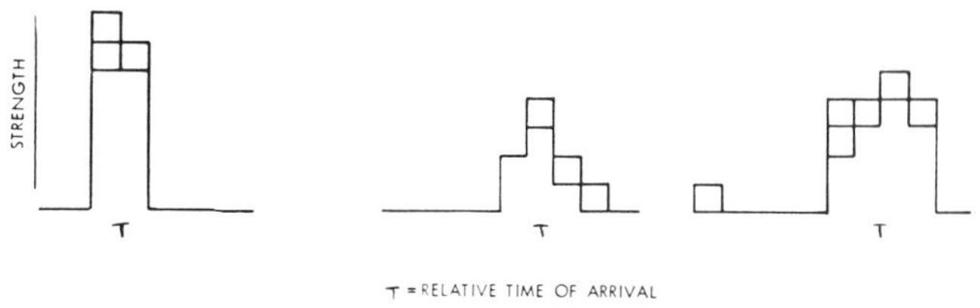


Fig. 13. Typical multipath displays, March 10, 1964.

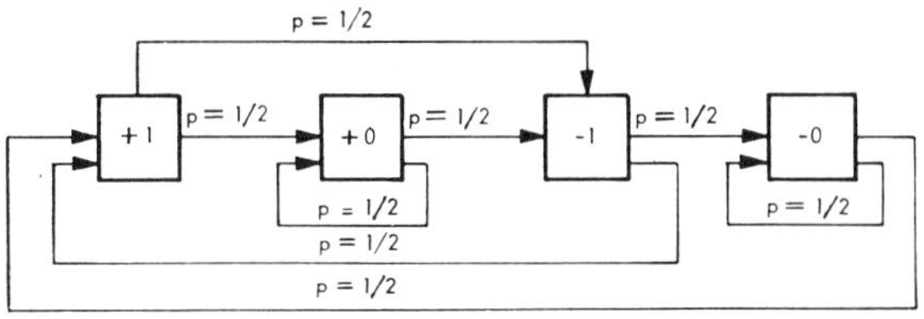


Fig. 12. State diagram for trinary $A$.

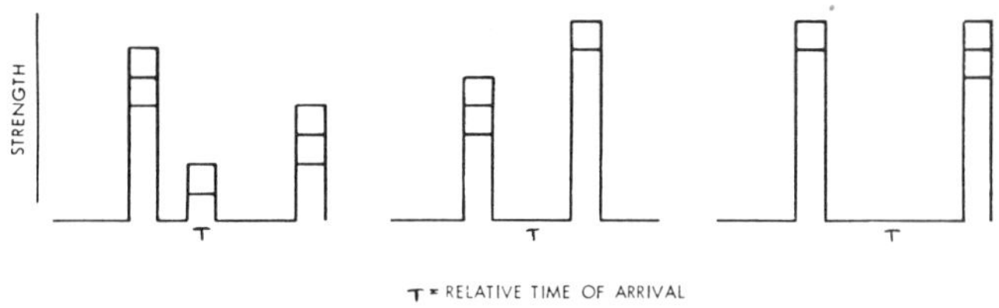


Fig. 14. Typical displays with two resolvable paths, June 25, 1964.

of both the panoramic analyzer and the multipath intensity profile (time delay spread). The 3-level signal is decoded by full-wave rectification. Frame sync is recovered by passing the baseband through an 8-bit register and looking for the 00001111 pattern indicating frame sync. The PCM can be coverted to PAM and displayed on an oscilloscope, which in turn is triggered by the frame-sync pulse. Motion pictures were also made of the CRT display.

### *Initial Results*

*Multipath spread, including aircraft:* Pending more detailed analysis, much useful observation on the multipath structure was done by replaying the tape records of the PCM data into the visual display. Typical occurrences are shown in Fig. 13, with earliest time of arrival at the left. Most often, two to four active taps are observed.[1] The total delay spread observed is in the range 0.2–0.4 $\mu$s, in accordance with the original predictions and, hence, supporting the expected diversity capability.

Occasionally, two distinct paths would appear, as indicated in Fig. 14, with separation sometimes exceeding 0.5 $\mu$s. This could occur, on the basis of random volumetric interaction, because of strong contributions coming momentarily from only the bottom and top of the common volume. Moreover, quite often, the delayed path appeared to be correlated with an indication (changes in fade rate and a momentary signal enhancement) of an aircraft skin echo.

The patterns typified in Figs. 13 and 14 usually exhibited observable changes in a fraction of a second, and complete changes in detail (although not in the overall multipath spread) every few seconds. This is expected from the fade rates at this carrier frequency.

[1] For the geometry involved, each tap corresponds roughly to scatterers confined between confocal ellipsoidal surfaces (the terminal being the foci), with the shell thus defined having a thickness in altitude of about 1000 m at midpath, for 0.1 $\mu$s resolution.

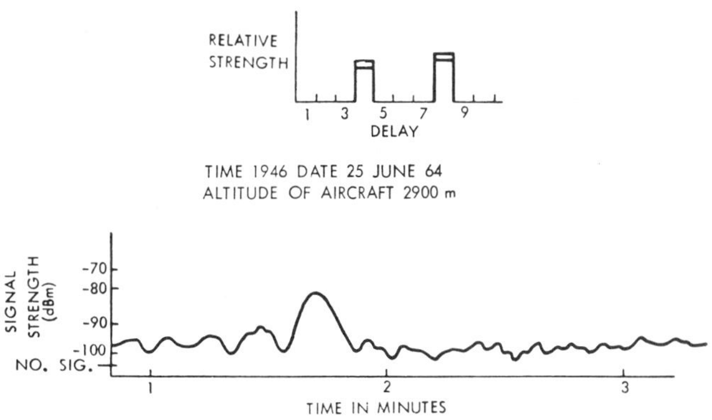


Fig. 15. Effect of aircraft passing through the common volume.

Aircraft passing through the common volume were accompanied by an increase in signal strength, changes in the fading rate, and an observed strong path. A typical example is shown in Fig. 15. The LFM also usually showed unusual activity during such periods, presumably due to the relatively rapid changes observed by the center-of-gravity circuit. In the cooperating aircraft flights, aircraft echoes appeared to occur only for altitudes exceeding 1600 meters (5000 feet) at mid-path (Fig. 9).

*Spectrum analysis:* The relatively flat spectrum of the transmitted 10-Mc/s signal allowed interesting observation of selective fading effects (frequency-domain effects due to the multipath spread), by observing the variations in the *instantaneous* power spectrum of the received signal. Typical observed spectra are shown in Fig. 16. Correlations in the simultaneity of fading at spaced frequencies in the spectra appeared high for spacings up to about 250 kc/s. Fading seems to be largely uncorrelated for spacings exceeding 1 Mc/s.

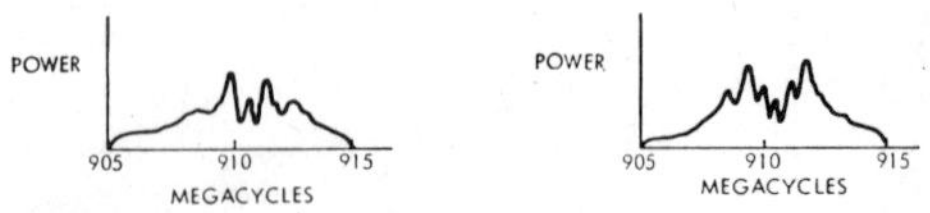


Fig. 16. Typical spectra observed on panoramic analyzer.

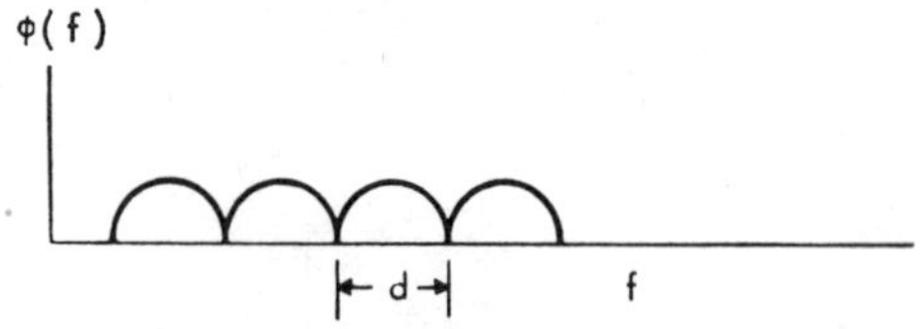


Fig. 17. Spectrum for two equal amplitude paths.

In examining Fig. 16, it is interesting to compare with the easily shown result that the spectrum of a signal consisting of two equal energy signals at a relative delay $\tau$ from each other has the shape shown in Fig. 17. The distance between nulls $d$ is inversely proportional to $\tau$,

$$d(\text{Mc}) = \frac{1}{\tau(\mu\text{s})}.$$

## IV. Further Plans

It is planned to process the PCM data on a CDC 1604 computer, to provide more precise data on the statistics of the fading envelope at the various taps. This will include power spectra, and auto- and cross-correlations. It is also planned to run additional tests on paths in the 400-to 600-km range.

In addition to the test results described here, the equipment has been utilized with auxiliary instrumentation, to provide the first known measurements of the so-called complex correlations of the fading signal. These involve auto- and cross-correlations among quadrature components of the signals observed at each tap of the Rake receiver. The corresponding power spectra can be directly interpreted in terms of Doppler spreads, and the complex cross-correlations may be quite illuminating on drift mechanism. These measurements will be reported separately (Abraham et al. [2]).

## Acknowledgment

The equipment and tests described here involved the efforts and support of a large group. Among these, the authors wish to especially note contributions by the following: B. F. Price and B. B. Barrow, Applied Research Laboratory, Sylvania Electronic Systems, Waltham, Mass.; R. Hileman, J. Lindholm, D. Fast, F. Tomtishen, and R. Hartley, Amherst Laboratories, Sylvania Electronic Systems-Central, Buffalo, N. Y.; Capt. T. O. Duff, M. H. Klein, J. N. Birch, and H. Rosenblum, Department of Defense, Washington, D. C.; and C. Garrison and R. Simmons, Bendix Radio Corp., Towson, Md.

## References

[1] R. Price and P. E. Green, Jr., "A communication technique for multipath channels," *Proc. IRE*, vol. 46, pp. 555–570, March 1958.

[2] L. G. Abraham, B. B. Barrow, D. R. Bitzer, and S. Stein, "Tropospheric-scatter propagation tests using a Rake receiver," *1965 IEEE Communications Conv. Conf. Rec.*, pp. 685–690; also abstracted in "Preliminary report on trophospheric-scatter propagation tests," *Proc. IEEE* (Correspondence), vol. 53, pp. 649–651, June 1965.

[3] *Reference Data for Radio Engineers*, 4th Ed. ITT, pp. 757–761.

# Communication Satellite Processing Repeaters

ROBERT Y. HUANG AND PHILLIP HOOTEN

Abstract—Two kinds of processing repeaters which may find application on communication satellites in the near future are described. The type I repeater allows access only if the transmitted signal contains a predetermined code structure. This serves three purposes: first, unauthorized users are excluded, second, co-channel interfering signals are not retransmitted on the downlink, so as not to waste a portion of the satellite transmitter power, and, third, removal of the interference signal at the satellite avoids having to do this at the ground receiving terminal. Thus such a repeater would find particular application where there are a large number of ground receiving stations. The type 2 repeater routes signals received at its $N$ input terminals to be transmitted at $N$ output terminals, thus acting as a "switchboard in the sky." Two purposes are served: first, the satellite capacity is more fully utilized in the presence of fluctuating traffic demands, and, second, single-frequency transmission and reception are possible for user ground stations, thus simplifying these stations and still allowing communication to any station in the network. It is established when the type 1 repeater is able to increase the satellite communication capability beyond that of a simple repeater and further that fairly simple filtering is sufficient on the satellite. For the type 2 repeater, a proposed frequency control plan minimizes the filtering required on the satellite where frequency division multiplex is used and reduces the amount of switching required on the satellite to $N$ single-pole $N$-throw switches where time division multiplex is used without the requirement of any memory on the satellite. A summary of present-day translating repeaters, as used in the Intelsats III and IV and DSCS II satellites, is included.

Manuscript received October 21, 1970.
R. Y. Huang is with Systems Group of TRW, Inc., Redondo Beach, Calif. 90278.
P. Hooten is with the Naval Research Lab., Washington, D. C.

## I. Introduction and Summary

THIS PAPER describes what we envision to be the next step in communication satellite repeaters beyond those presently in use or being designed to be in use. The present-day repeaters are of various types—channelized or not, saturating or linear, etc.,—but may categorically be described as simply translating in frequency the signals received on the satellite uplink to be retransmitted on the downlink. The primary reasons for this relative repeater simplicity are the constraints on repeater size and weight imposed by launch vehicle capability and the requirement for high reliability as a consequence of the large initial in-orbit cost.

This situation is rapidly changing as the communication satellite technology matures. Available operational boosters such as the Titan III-C can place payloads of two to three thousand pounds in synchronous orbit; by comparison, the present generation of commercial comsats, the Intelsat III satellite weighs 268 lb without the apogee motor. In addition, the advent of microelectronic techniques for circuit fabrication will reduce considerably the size and weight of a circuit to perform a given function. Secondly, the reliability of electronic components in a space environment is now well proven, and, in most cases, the factors that need to be

Reprinted from *Proc. IEEE*, vol. 59, pp. 238–252, Feb. 1971.

controlled to increase their mean time to failure are understood. Thus the technology needed to build large complex communication satellites, to place them in orbit, and to operate them with high reliability is presently available or soon to be available.

One may envision several applications for a satellite repeater which does more than retransmit the uplink signal. We have named such repeaters "processing repeaters" to supply a connotation of complexity beyond that of simple frequency translation. In this paper, we consider specifically two types of processing repeaters: an interference-removal repeater, and a switching and routing repeater. The objective of the first type, as is evident in its name, is to remove the effect of an interferer on the downlink transmission. Two purposes are served: first, the major portion of the satellite radiated power is not wasted in retransmitting the undesired interference signal, and, second, the modulation forms of the desired signals may be rearranged for downlink transmission, thus simplifying the ground receiver. Thus it may be expected that such a repeater would find an application where interference on the uplink is substantially larger than the desired signals and where the increased repeater complexity more than offsets the alternative solution of increasing the repeater transmitted power. Such a repeater would find additional application when there are a large number of ground receiving stations, so that an attractive tradeoff exists in increasing the repeater complexity to simplify the many ground station receivers.

The switching and routing repeater finds two applications: first, in reuse of an assigned frequency band and, second, in simplifying the ground station transmitting and receiving equipment. Frequency reuse is a major item of concern, particularly for commercial applications. It is envisioned that by using multiple antennas on a satellite with narrow enough beamwidths, the amount of relative mutual isolation available between antennas—perhaps with the aid of polarization discrimination—would allow the same frequency band to be used by several of the antennas simultaneously. Some form of processing repeater, which is able to route signals between antennas, would be necessary —or at least desirable—with such a satellite. At present, the Intelsat system uses multidestination carriers; i.e., each ground station transmits at only one frequency but needs to be able to receive at the carrier frequency of the ground station with which it is communicating. This arrangement is cumbersome and does not fully utilize the satellite repeater capacity unless all ground stations are transmitting at their maximum rates. SPADE, an experimental frequency division multiple access (FDMA) demand assignment system built by COMSAT Corporation [1], is an attempt to overcome part of these objections. A switching and routing satellite, which is able to allow each ground station to transmit and receive at fixed frequencies, would allow a more complete solution.

The idea of a communication satellite processing repeater is not a new one. Perry [2] describes various such repeaters, as does Sullivan [3] for military applications. Both Schmidt [4] and DeBrunner and Neu [5] propose schemes for processing repeaters for spectrum conservation, the former for frequency reuse, the latter for minimizing interference with terrestrial radio links. In this paper, we do not attempt a comprehensive categorization of various processing repeaters and applications but concentrate instead on the two types previously described.

Section II discusses those satellite repeater parameters that are of interest from a user's standpoint, i.e., the repeater characteristics that most affect a satellite user. Four ways of accessing a satellite repeater are compared in Section III, while Section IV describes three present-day satellite repeaters and their advantages and disadvantages with respect to the previously mentioned parameters. Sections V and VI describe the two processing repeaters that are the subjects of this paper.

## II. Satellite Repeater Parameters

From the standpoint of a user, the communication satellite may be considered to be a communication node which may be accessed from a large area on the earth's surface. The areas that may access this node are determined by the satellite receive and transmit antenna coverage patterns. Typically, these antennas provide earth coverage, but even the "spot" beams on the Intelsat IV and DSCS II satellites still provide broad coverage—from 2°–4° (approximately 1000 to 2000 miles for a satellite at synchronous altitude).

This broad geographical coverage is both a desirable and an undesirable attribute of communication satellites: desirable in the single-node accessibility over a large area, undesirable in that any emitter in this area and in the same frequency range having adequate effective radiated power (ERP) acts as an interference source on the satellite uplink. This is particularly objectionable for a military communication satellite, since signals originating from a remote location can interrupt communications through such a satellite at critical times. The interference-removal type of processing repeater discussed in Section V is considered to be a partial solution to this problem.

In addition to the geographical ability to access the satellite, the repeater as a communication node possesses three other features that are of direct user interest: ease of access, uplink and downlink bandwidths, and downlink ERP. We discuss each in turn.

The downlink bandwidth and ERP of the satellite jointly determine the maximum data rate transmitting to a specified receiving ground terminal. It is convenient to determine this maximum rate by first assuming only the ERP constraint. The receiving ground terminal can be simply characterized by the parameter $G/T$, where $G$ is the gain of the receiving antenna and $T$ is the effective noise temperature in degrees Kelvin. $G/T$ is usually expressed in decibels, where $T$ in decibels is referred to 1°K. As an example, Fig. 1 plots the maximum permissible data rates against ground terminals of various sizes for some representative satellite repeaters. The ordinate is the noise bandwidth in which a 10-dB signal-to-noise ratio can be obtained, while the abscissa is the parameter $G/T$. Various points along the abscissa are marked with the $G/T$ of some representative

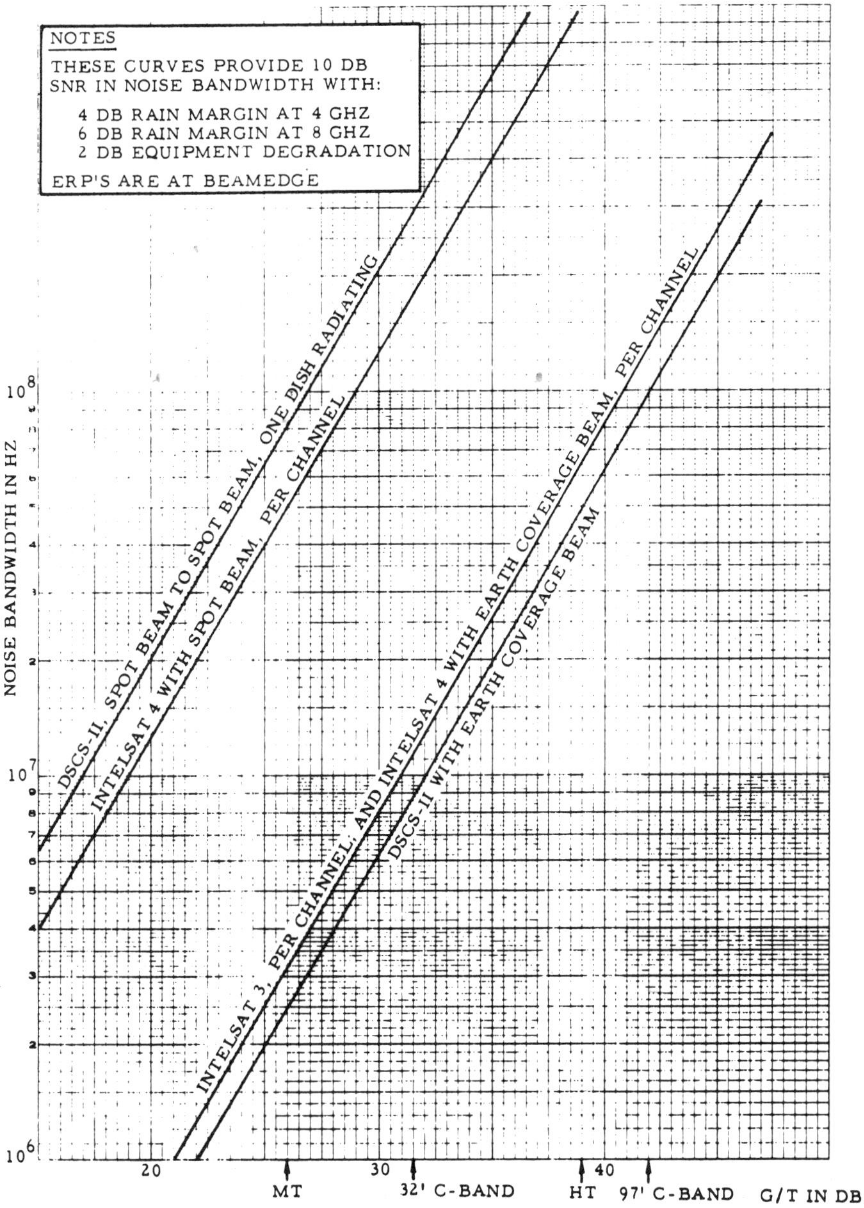


Fig. 1. Present repeater capacities downlink ERP.

ground terminals; the 32′ *C* band and 97′ *C* band refer to receiving antennas of the given sizes to be used with Intelsats III and IV, while MT and HT refer respectively to a Medium Transportable terminal with an 18′ dish and a Heavy Transportable terminal with a 60′ dish to be used with the DSCS II satellite. If several ground terminals of the same type are used to receive from the same satellite repeater, the total data rate to these terminals is upper-bounded by Fig. 1, using the $G/T$ of one terminal. This assumes that the satellite is able to share its ERP among the data to be transmitted to the terminals by making the power proportional to the data rate to each terminal. In fact, this maximum data rate is usually not achievable due to backoff in the output tube to avoid excessive intermodulation where multiple carriers are used and loss due to time guard bands and synchronization where time division multiplex is used. With a mix of ground terminals, the satellite should apportion its power proportional to $R_i/(G/T)_i$, where $R_i$ is the data rate to the $i$th terminal.

It is important to note in Fig. 1 the range of noise bandwidths for which a 10-dB signal-to-noise ratio exists with planned terminals—in the range of 50–1000 MHz for the spot beams in DSCS II and Intelsat IV and 10–150 MHz for Intelsat III. Thus in many cases it is not the satellite ERP that limits the downlink data rate but the repeater bandwidth.

In the case of the satellite uplink, it is almost always true that the uplink bandwidth is the limiting factor on data rate. Here, the normally large ERPs of the ground transmitting terminals often result in over 20 dB of excess power on the satellite uplink. On the other hand, this excess power does not solve the interference problem due to other ground-based emitters. Spread-spectrum operation, as discussed in Section V, is a partial solution to this problem. However, the extent of interference suppression is limited by the bandwidth of the uplink.

Finally, the ease of access is an important characteristic of the satellite repeater as a communication node. In some cases, a major consideration is the complexity of the ground terminal equipment: for example, the requirement to generate, transmit, or receive over a broad range of frequencies, the amount of data storage and synchronization equipment required, the necessity for multiple receivers for simultaneous reception from multiple user transmitters, etc. In other cases, operational considerations are paramount: the degree to which network discipline must be maintained and the degradation of communication capacity with the loss of such discipline, the time required to access the satellite, the degree to which *a priori* information is needed in accessing, etc. These problems are affected not only by the multiple access method but by the satellite repeater design.

## III. Multiple Access Techniques

The techniques for multiple access to a spacecraft have generally been categorized into one of the following types: FDMA, time division multiple access (TDMA), code division multiple access (CDMA), and pulse address multiple access (PAMA). Systems which use PAMA are in reality a hybrid combination of the techniques employed in FDMA and CDMA, so little additional discussion will be provided.

The techniques employed in FDMA are probably the simplest in terms of ground equipment complexity. The modulation can be in the form of frequency modulation (FM) or phase-shift keying (PSK), with multiple access being achieved through frequency band discrimination, either in the ground receiver in the case of a wide-band frequency translating repeater, or in the satellite in the case of the frequency channelized satellite. The advantage of using FDMA in a wide-band frequency translating repeater is that it allows the simplest ground station configuration requiring no timing by the user and further allows easy determination of repeater loading. The disadvantages in a wide-band frequency translating repeater are that intermodulation products generated in the spacecraft rob a percentage of downlink radiated power, that uplink power coordination is required to allow different user information rates, and that the system is vulnerable to discretionary jamming.

TDMA provides the highest degree of satellite efficiency but requires that the earth station complex be synchronized to a high degree of precision and be capable of high peak power transmission. TDMA avoids power robbing of the spacecraft transmitter by intermodulation products, since only one user accesses the spacecraft at any time. Additional advantages are that uplink power coordination is not required and a large variation in ground station ERP can be tolerated. One drawback is that selective jamming of a single user is possible unless time slot scrambling is employed.

CDMA is usually divided into two subclasses: frequency hopping and direct sequence. In the former, a user imposes a preselected frequency hopping sequence on his normal transmission so that mutual interference between two such users occurs only when they are hopped to the same frequency at the same time. In the latter, the transmission is characterized by a phase-modulated carrier with a total bandwidth occupancy much wider than the information bandwidth. The data are added to the multiple access carrier as either frequency or phase modulation. A pseudonoise code is used to spread the spectrum and is typically a maximal length shift register code [6], [7]. The degree of mutual interference between two such users is determined by the (aperiodic) cross correlation between the pseudonoise codes of the two users, hence the utilization of codes with low cross correlation is important in maximizing the total number of simultaneous users. A class of multiple access codes described by Gold [8] is an example of such codes. These Gold codes are not maximal length sequences and have bounded cross correlation properties. In the same manner, frequency hopping codes can be chosen to have minimal mutual interference and have been proposed by Cooper [9] and Solomon [10]. Perhaps the distinctive feature of CDMA is that it allows a potential number of users much larger than the maximum number of simultaneous users, with no necessity for system monitoring and control, by assigning each user a different multiple access code. On the other hand, the number of allowable simultaneous users is usually much less than is possible with techniques such as FDMA and TDMA (approximately 0.1), due to mutual interference.

PAMA is a combination of code addressing, as in CDMA, and FDMA where the code is used to generate a particular frequency pattern for use as a method of multiple access. In general, PAMA exhibits the following characteristics: rapid synchronization, no requirement for network timing, and a relatively large number of accesses. Spira [11] has defined a class of codes particularly applicable to PAMA systems.

A comprehensive study of multiple access techniques has been prepared by Kaiser [12] and Aein [13]. The best technique depends on the application and on particular user parameters.

## IV. Present-Day Repeaters

This Section compares the repeaters in three present-day communication satellites: the Intelsat III, Intelsat IV, and DSCS II satellites. The pertinent repeater characteristics from a user's standpoint are listed in Table I, while simplified block diagrams of these repeaters are shown in Fig. 2.

While Intelsat III is an operational satellite, both Intelsat IV and DSCS II are presently being constructed and are planned to be launched in 1971. It is interesting to compare the differences between Intelsats III and IV, as well as between the latter and DSCS II.

Aside from the obviously larger transmitter power available in Intelsat IV as compared to Intelsat III, two differences are worthy of note: first, the much narrower bandwidth per channel for Intelsat IV (36 MHz as compared to 225 MHz) and, second, the use of spot beam antennas in addition to the global coverage antenna. The twelve 36-MHz channels for Intelsat IV occupy the same total bandwidth as the two 225-MHz channels for Intelsat III. However, because of the spot beam antennas, the former tends to be bandwidth limited, while the latter is ERP limited (Fig. 1). The receive antennas are earth coverage on Intelsat IV since, as mentioned in Section II, uplink power is gen-

TABLE I
PRESENT-DAY REPEATER CHARACTERISTICS

| | Intelsat III | Intelsat IV | | | DSC II | | | |
|---|---|---|---|---|---|---|---|---|
| | | Global | Spot Beam | Spot Beam | Global to Global | Spot Beam to Global | Spot Beam to Spot Beam | Global to Spot Beam |
| Number of channels | 2 | 4 | 4 | 4 | 1 | 1 | 1 | 1 |
| Channel bandwidth (MHz) | 225 | 36 | 36 | 36 | 125 | 50 | 185 | 50 |
| Channel center spacing (MHz) | 265 | 40 | 40 | 40 | | | | |
| Receive bands (MHz) | 5930–6420 | 5932–6418 | | | 7975–8100 | 8125–8175 | 8215–8400 | 7900–7950 |
| Transmit bands (MHz) | 3705–4195 | 3700–4200 | 3707–3993 | 3747–4033 | 7250–7375 | 7400–7450 | 7490–7675 | 7700–7750 |
| Antenna beamwidths (deg) | 17 | 17 | 4.5 | 4.5 | 17 global, 2½ spot beams | | | |
| ERP at beamedge (dBW) | 23.0 | 23.0 | 34.7 | 34.7 | 28.1—global<br>41.2—spot beam, 2 dishes radiating<br>44.6—spot beam, 1 dish radiating | | | |
| Repeater type | frequency-translating<br>nonchannelized<br>global coverage | frequency-translating<br>channelized[a]<br>global coverage receive,<br>selected coverage transmit | | | frequency-translating<br>nonchannelized,<br>cross strapped<br>global and spot beam receive<br>global and spot beam transmit | | | |

[a] Channelized is defined here as having more than one frequency channel per beam.

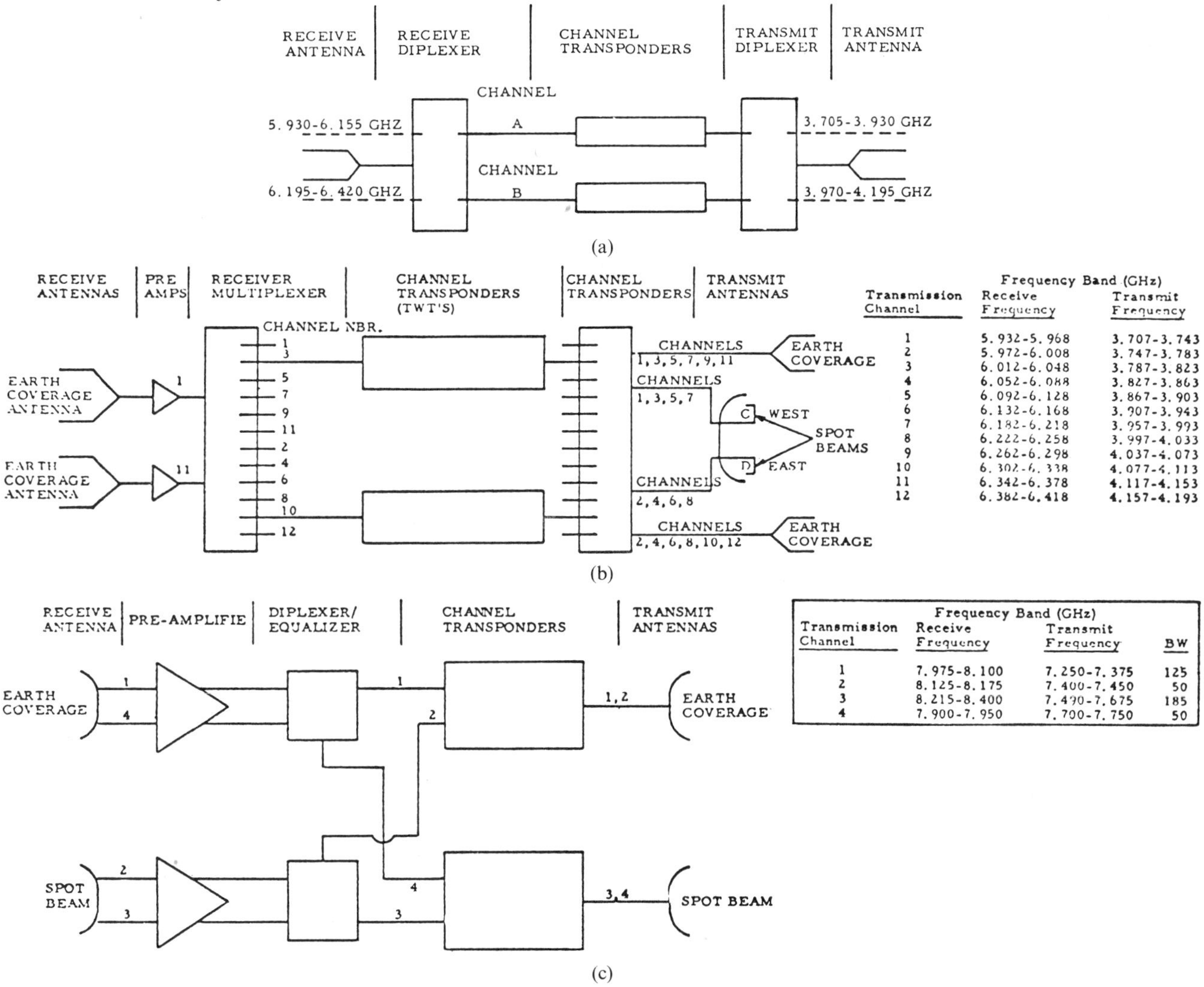


| Transmission Channel | Frequency Band (GHz) Receive Frequency | Transmit Frequency |
|---|---|---|
| 1 | 5.932-5.968 | 3.707-3.743 |
| 2 | 5.972-6.008 | 3.747-3.783 |
| 3 | 6.012-6.048 | 3.787-3.823 |
| 4 | 6.052-6.088 | 3.827-3.863 |
| 5 | 6.092-6.128 | 3.867-3.903 |
| 6 | 6.132-6.168 | 3.907-3.943 |
| 7 | 6.182-6.218 | 3.957-3.993 |
| 8 | 6.222-6.258 | 3.997-4.033 |
| 9 | 6.262-6.298 | 4.037-4.073 |
| 10 | 6.302-6.338 | 4.077-4.113 |
| 11 | 6.342-6.378 | 4.117-4.153 |
| 12 | 6.382-6.418 | 4.157-4.193 |

| Transmission Channel | Frequency Band (GHz) Receive Frequency | Transmit Frequency | BW |
|---|---|---|---|
| 1 | 7.975-8.100 | 7.250-7.375 | 125 |
| 2 | 8.125-8.175 | 7.400-7.450 | 50 |
| 3 | 8.215-8.400 | 7.490-7.675 | 185 |
| 4 | 7.900-7.950 | 7.700-7.750 | 50 |

Fig. 2. (a) Intelsat III. (b) Intelsat IV. (c) DSCS II.

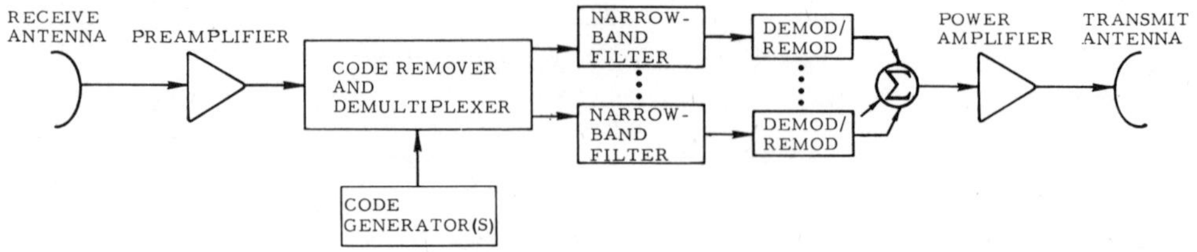


Fig. 3.

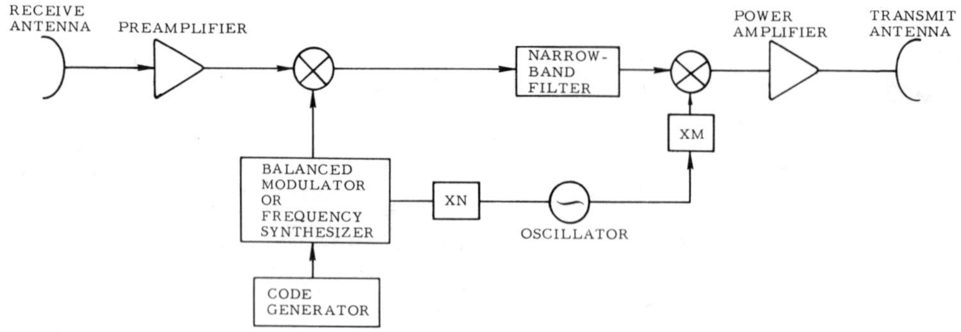


Fig. 4.

erally excessive, but each of the two spot beam antennas for transmit, as well as the earth coverage antenna on transmit, only transmit 4 each of the 12 total channels. Thus Intelsat IV reflects technological advancement in the use of spot beam antennas to achieve higher ERPs. It also reflects a desire to use multiple channelized narrower band repeaters rather than a few much wider band repeaters. Wide-band repeaters require many users to share the same repeater; since the amount of downlink power allocated to a particular signal is proportional to its strength as received at the satellite, and since optimum use of satellite power requires proportioning the downlink ERP to the data rate (Section II), satellite ERP is utilized efficiently only by relatively careful control of the ERP of each transmitting ground terminal.

In addition, to avoid excessive intermodulation between the multiple carriers in a wide-band repeater, it is often necessary to operate the repeater in a quasi-linear mode, by setting the gain so that the output tube is slightly backed off from saturation. Again, this requires the user ground transmitting terminals to hold their ERPs constant and does not use the satellite ERP efficiently. The narrower band channelized repeater results in one or sometimes only a few users per channel. Thus power control and intermodulation problems are reduced. More importantly, the large ERP in the 36-MHz bandwidth can allow the use of TDMA even for the smaller terminals. In such a case, since only one carrier is present in the repeater at any time, no power control and intermodulation problems exist.

By comparison, the primary differences between the Intelsat IV and the DSCS II are that, first, the latter is not channelized and, second, it has a spot beam receive antenna in addition to a global coverage receive antenna. The reason for the spot beam receive antenna for DSCS II is for interference rejection purposes only, since, as previously discussed, there is excess uplink power available.

It is worthwhile noting the wide-band repeaters on DSCS II compared to the narrow-band ones on Intelsat IV. The difference is primarily due to two factors: the degradation in transmission quality due to a temporary loss of net control is a direct financial loss in a commercial application, while in a military application even unfriendly interferers have to be tolerated; second, much more bandwidth is needed for interference suppression reasons than is strictly required from that supportable by a given signal power.

## V. Processing Repeater—Type 1

The type 1 processing repeater allows access only if a predetermined code structure is imbedded in the transmitted signal. Three purposes are served: first, unauthorized transmitters are not able to use the satellite as a communication repeater; second, an interference signal not containing the predetermined code is not retransmitted on the downlink which otherwise wastes some portion of the downlink ERP; and, third, the ground terminal receivers can be simple since all the uplink interference rejection is performed at one place, viz., the satellite, rather than separately at each ground terminal.

A general block diagram of such a processing repeater is shown in Fig. 3. The ground terminal transmitted signals have the form of CDMA signals and may be either direct sequence or frequency hopping. The pseudonoise code used in the direct sequence modulation or the code which dictates the frequency hopping sequence constitute the "key" which allows the ground transmitter to access the satellite repeater. Each ground transmitter is assigned such a key, which may or may not be identical for all transmitters. The box labelled "code remover and demultiplexer" in Fig. 3 provides $n$ separate channels containing the $n$ uplink transmissions. Any authorized users or interference signals not having the proper key are spread in frequency and are attenuated when passed through the subsequent narrow-band filters. These filter outputs may be further demodulated and remodulated in a format suitable for downlink transmission. Alternatively, this operation may be omitted.

### A. Single Access Repeater

Consider first the type 1 processing repeater designed only for a single access. A block diagram is shown in Fig. 4.

When does such a processing repeater increase the satellite capacity beyond that of a simple repeater? Consider the simple translating repeater. Given a signal modulation technique and a ground receiving terminal $G/T$, two constraints on maximum downlink bit rate exist: first, the finite downlink ERP limits this to some value $R_1$ bit/s, say, based perhaps on a maximum acceptable bit error probability; alternatively, the finite repeater bandwidth limits this to another value $R_2$ bits per second, based perhaps on a maximum acceptable amount of distortion. If $R_1 \neq R_2$, the modulation technique may be changed to provide an increased bit rate. Where $R_1 < R_2$, a higher order alphabet or error correction coding may be used to increase the former. Where the reverse is the case, a modulation scheme such as multiphase PSK may be used which requires less bandwidth for a given bit rate, but is perhaps less efficient in power utilization.

For a given modulation scheme, and for a particular satellite–ground terminal combination, suppose that $R_1/R_2 = \alpha$. Suppose also that the desired transmitter has only $1/k$ times the power of an uplink interference signal. For the simple repeater, only $1/(1+k)$ of the downlink ERP is used for the desired signal, and so the maximum downlink data rate due to the downlink ERP constraint is

$$R'_1 = R_1/(1 + k)$$

where $R_1$ is the maximum data rate in the absence of interference. Thus it would appear that whenever $R'_1 < R_2$, a processing repeater is able to increase the satellite downlink capacity. This is not, however, completely true.

This would be the case if the interference signal were narrow-band and *a priori* known. In this case, the ground transmitter merely avoids the frequency of the interference signal, and the processing repeater may simply notch out the narrow-band interference. In a more realistic case, the interference signal frequency is unknown, may not be narrow-band, and there may in fact be more than one interference signal. In this case, the direct sequence or frequency hopping modulation used allows discrimination against arbitrary interference signals, provided that they do not contain the proper key. The penalty in the use of these spread-spectrum modulations is that they require more bandwidth than is strictly needed for information transmission, in fact, typically, $\gamma k$ times larger, where $\gamma$ is approximately equal to 10.[1] Thus the use of a processing repeater for a given repeater bandwidth constraint would result in a maximum data rate of

$$R'_2 = R_2/\gamma k$$

where $R_2$ is the maximum data rate without the use of spread spectrum. Hence

$$\frac{R'_1}{R'_2} = \gamma\alpha \frac{k}{1 + k} \approx \gamma\alpha \qquad (1)$$

for large $k$.

This says that if $\alpha > 1$, $R'_1 > R'_2$. In other words, if the simple repeater is bandwidth limited rather than ERP limited in the absence of interference, the processing repeater cannot increase the satellite capacity in the presence of interference. Alternatively, if $\alpha\gamma < 1$, then $R'_1 < R'_2$, or that if the simple repeater is strongly ERP limited rather than bandwidth limited in the absence of interference, then the use of the processing repeater can increase the satellite capacity in the presence of interference.

From Fig. 1, it is seen that even for the smallest downlink ERP considered (DSCS II with earth coverage beam) and for the smallest ground terminal indicated (MT), the supportable downlink bit rate due to the ERP constraint is approximately 20 Mbit/s, while the repeater bandwidth is between 50 and 125 MHz. Thus the ground receiving terminal would need to have a $G/T$ much less than that for the MT terminal before a processing repeater is beneficial.

Thus it is seen that with satellites of the DSCS II class or larger, the primary utility of this repeater is in connection with small ground receiving terminals. Not only can it increase the satellite capacity for these terminals, but it also simplifies the receiving equipment by performing the spread-spectrum code removal on the spacecraft. This is particularly advantageous where there are a large number of small receiving terminals.

The previous arguments can be extended in regard to the narrow-band filter in Fig. 4. Suppose that the repeater bandwidth is $B$ and that the filter bandwidth is $\beta B$. Suppose further that with such a filter the uplink interference signal is attenuated by $\beta$ (a reasonable approximation). Then the maximum downlink data rate due to the downlink ERP constraint is

$$R''_1 = R_1/(1 + k\beta)$$

where $R_1$ is the maximum data rate in the absence of interference. Decreasing $\beta$ increases $R''_1$, but there is no advantage in increasing it beyond $R'_2$. Hence the $\beta$ which does not degrade satellite capacity is where $R''_1 \geq R'_2$, or

$$\frac{R_2}{\gamma k} \leq \frac{R_1}{1 + k\beta},$$

or

$$\beta \leq \gamma\alpha - \frac{1}{k} \approx \gamma\alpha \qquad (2)$$

for large $k$.

On the other hand, $\beta$ is constrained to be no less than $1/\gamma k$ since that is the filter bandwidth needed to reject the interference to the desired degree at the ground terminal

[1] The spread-spectrum process may be modelled as follows: let $s(t)$ be the signal before spread-spectrum modulation. The transmitted signal has the form $s[t-x(t)]$, where $x(t)$ represents either phase or frequency modulation and spreads $s(t)$, say, by a factor $\gamma k$. The received signal is $y(t)=s[t-x(t)]+I(t)$, where $I(t)$ is an interference signal. The receiver performs the inverse operation, i.e., $y[t+x(t)]=s(t)+I[t+x(t)]$, which spreads $I(t)$ to the same bandwidth as $s[t-x(t)]$. The signal-to-noise ratio in the bandwidth of $s(t)$ is approximately $\gamma$ which has to be about 10 for good detection performance.

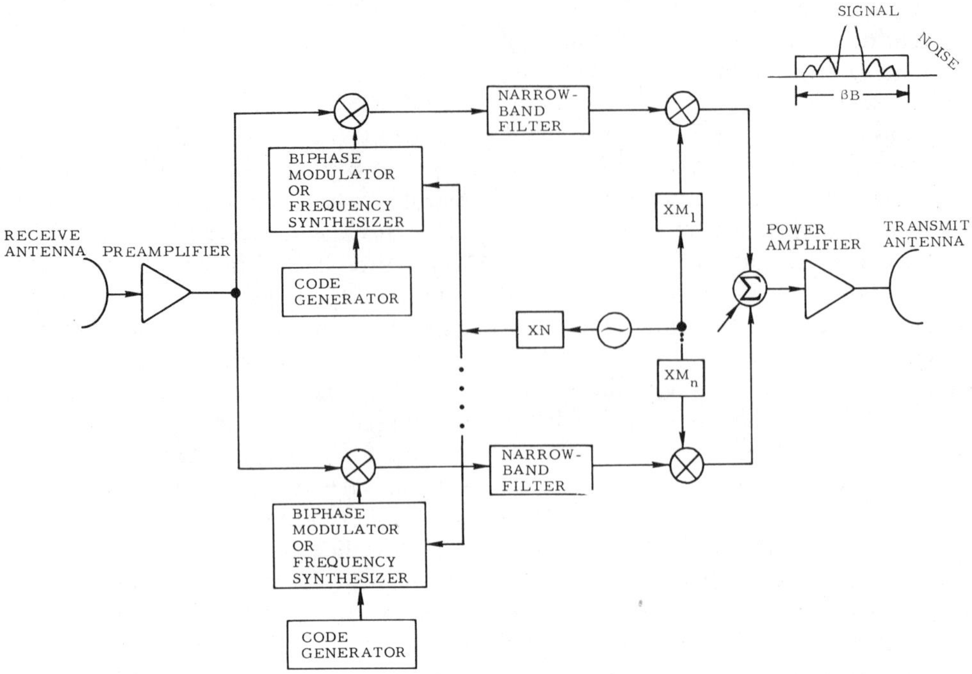


Fig. 5.

receiver. Setting

$$\gamma\alpha \geq \frac{1}{\gamma k}$$

we see that if $\alpha \geq 1/\gamma^2 k$, $\alpha\beta$ can be chosen which will attenuate the uplink interference sufficiently so as not to cause the downlink ERP to be a constraint on data rate, yet sufficiently large that it does not cause a decrease in maximum data rate by the filter being too narrow-band. Thus aside from the case of extremely small ground receiving terminals, the filter used on the satellite for interference rejection purposes can normally be much wider than the information bandwidth, thus it may be sufficiently wide to allow for carrier frequency uncertainties due to Doppler and drift. Therefore, it is likely that simple passive filters, rather than tracking filters, are sufficient.

### *B. Multiple Access Repeater*

Spread-spectrum modulation is used on the uplink to deny access to unauthorized transmitters and for interference rejection. This same modulation may also be used for multiple access. A block diagram of a repeater using CDMA is shown in Fig. 5, where the biphase modulator is used if direct sequence is the spread-spectrum method and the frequency synthesizer is used if frequency hopping is the spread-spectrum method. Suppose that there are $n$ users, each having the same data rate and ground transmitter power. In CDMA, the $(n-1)$ other users appear as interference to each user. The arguments in Section V-A would lead one to the same conclusion as (1); i.e., the condition when a type 1 processing repeater is beneficial is independent of whether it is a single or multiple access repeater. This conclusion can be expected by imagining the rest of the accesses $(n-1)$ as included in the total interference power $k$. The bandwidth $\beta B$ of each narrow-band filter in each channel in Fig. 5 is further constrained than is given by (2). The reason is the possible overlapping of the unfiltered noise of one channel into the desired signal of another channel in the summation node in Fig. 5. For this reason in addition to (2), $\beta$ must also be no larger than $2/n$.

Alternatively, it is possible to combine the spread-spectrum modulation with a more conventional multiple access technique, such as FDMA and TDMA. In the case of the former, each user transmitter is assigned the same pseudonoise code (for direct sequence) or frequency hopping pattern, but each transmitter is offset appropriately in carrier frequency. Thus the output of the first mixer in Fig. 4 exhibits the normal FDMA spectrum. A single narrow-band filter could be used to filter out interference signals, and the entire FDMA spectrum is translated in frequency for downlink transmission. Thus the $n$ channels of Fig. 5 can be replaced by the single channel of Fig. 4. Frequency guard bands are necessary between channels, as usual, to allow for transmitter frequency uncertainties due to Doppler or oscillator drift. One advantage of this scheme is that mutual interference between users is avoided, hence is attractive where $n$ approaches $k$. A problem with the single channel configuration of Fig. 4 is the necessity for control of the user transmitter ERPs, as in a conventional FDMA scheme.

TDMA may also be used, and, as in conventional TDMA, user transmitter ERPs need not be controlled. In this case, each transmitter simply transmits in its assigned time slot using the spread-spectrum code appropriate at that time. Instead of the frequency guard bands necessary in FDMA for frequency uncertainty, time guard bands are needed in TDMA. These depend on the accuracy to which time synchronization can be achieved and it is discussed in Section V-C, as well as in Section VI. The increase in transmitted instantaneous data rate from each ground terminal necessary for TDMA also means a lesser interference rejection capability for a fixed repeater bandwidth $B$ which needs to be offset by an increase in instantaneous transmitter power.

### C. Synchronization

Perhaps the principal problem in using spread-spectrum modulation is that of synchronization. The transmit and receive codes need to be aligned in time; how long it takes to do this is a function of both the available initial and desired final timing uncertainties. The latter depends on the spread-spectrum technique used. In general, frequency hopping does not require as accurate final timing uncertainties as direct sequence and is preferable from this standpoint. The former depends on the clock stabilities used and the time elapsed since synchronization was last established. Standard results are available in this area.

For synchronization, there are important differences in the type 1 processing repeater compared to the standard spread-spectrum communication system. The satellite repeater configuration requires only that the transmitter be synchronized to it; one has the option of varying the satellite clock to synchronize with each ground transmitter or of varying each ground transmitter to synchronize with a (free-running) satellite clock. The first option would require a separate satellite clock and separate synchronization circuitry for each ground transmitter; this is clearly undesirable. The problem in the second option is that of conveying the information that synchronization has been achieved when it has so that the ground transmitter can stop its search. The two parts to this problem are: complication of detection circuitry on the satellite to decide that synchronization has been achieved and the round trip delay of approximately 0.2 s (to a synchronous satellite) which would result in an unacceptably long synchronization time.

Both of these difficulties can be alleviated by allowing the satellite clock to be broadcast, so that each transmitting ground terminal can adjust its clock to be synchronous with that in the satellite. However, for the ground terminal transmission to be in time synchronism with the satellite clock when it arrives at the satellite requires further that the range from the ground transmitting terminal to the satellite be accurately known. Conventional space–ground ranging systems provide accuracies on the order of 50 ft; thus the ground transmission may be received at the satellite in time error by the equivalent of 100 ft, or 0.1 $\mu$s. Thus if it is necessary to synchronize to an accuracy better than this, fine synchronization of some kind is needed on board the satellite with attendant complexity.

## VI. Processing Repeater—Type 2

The type 2 processing repeater may be classified as either fixed or variable routing depending on whether message routing within the repeater may or may not be changed. A simple example of a fixed routing repeater is the DSCS II repeater, as shown in Fig. 2(c).

Consider the repeater as a communication node having $n$ input and $n$ output ports. The signal received at the $i$th input port needs to be routed to one or more output ports for retransmission. Further, which portions of the signal go to which output port may change with time, depending on traffic requirements. A representation of such a repeater is shown in Fig. 6, illustrating a satellite with $k$ antennas, all presumably disjoint in area of coverage with $m_i$ transmitters and receivers attached to the $i$th antenna (this assumes downlink capacity equals the uplink capacity for each antenna). The $m_i$ transmitters are presumed disjoint in frequency band and similarly for the $m_i$ receivers. With

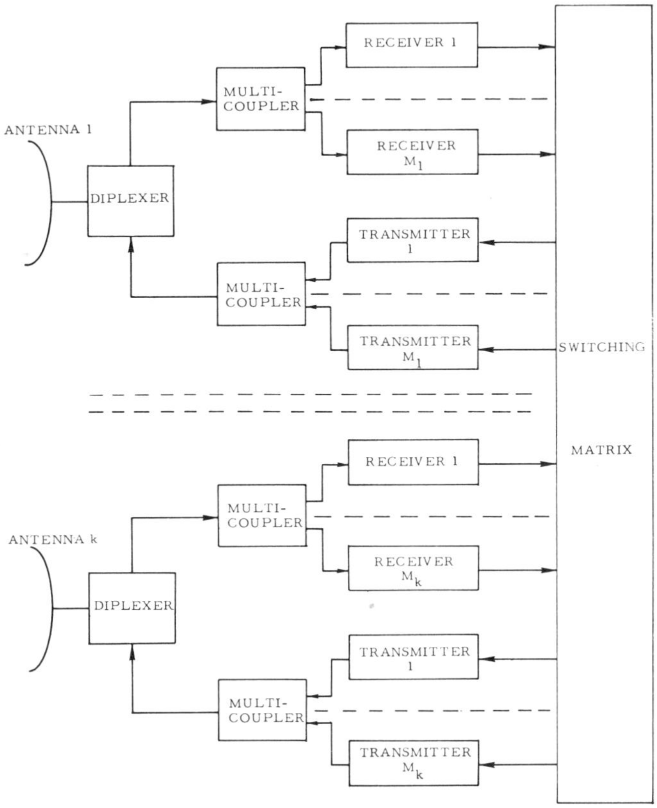

Fig. 6. Switching and routing repeater block diagram.

$$\sum_{i=1}^{k} m_i = n$$

Fig. 6 may be considered as an $n$-port repeater having $k$ antennas. Fig. 6 may be envisioned to be a future enlargement of the Intelsat IV satellite, for example, having $m_i$ channelized repeaters on the $i$th antenna, with $k$ fairly large ($>4$).

### A. Frequency Reuse

The principal reason for the $k$ antennas is "frequency reuse." This is a term implying that several uplinks on the same satellite may share the same frequency band, and it is similar for the downlinks. This may be achieved by providing sufficient mutual isolation between the antennas; its practicality is presently still being investigated. Fuenzalida and Podraczky [14] have studied some of the factors in providing this isolation; here we briefly review some of the considerations.

How closely one can place two antenna beams without unacceptable interference depends on the beam shape and sidelobe levels. A typical beam shape for a parabolic reflector is shown in Fig. 7. A first consideration is whether the

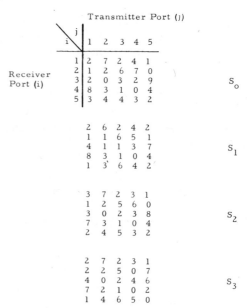

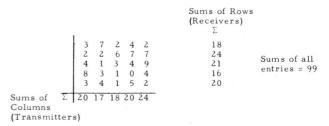

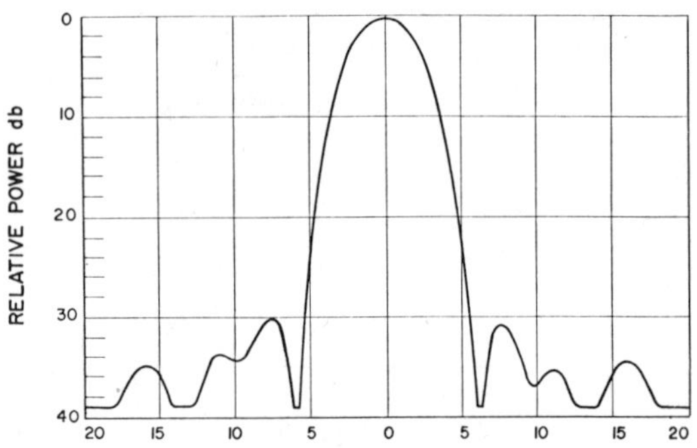


Fig. 7. Paraboloid power pattern $H$ plane.

Transmitter Port (j); Receiver Port (i)

| State | i \ j | 1 | 2 | 3 | 4 | 5 |
|---|---|---|---|---|---|---|
| $S_o$ | 1 | 2 | 7 | 2 | 4 | 1 |
| | 2 | 1 | 2 | 6 | 7 | 0 |
| | 3 | 2 | 0 | 3 | 2 | 9 |
| | 4 | 8 | 3 | 1 | 0 | 4 |
| | 5 | 3 | 4 | 4 | 3 | 2 |
| $S_1$ | | 2 | 6 | 2 | 4 | 2 |
| | | 1 | 1 | 6 | 5 | 1 |
| | | 4 | 1 | 1 | 3 | 7 |
| | | 8 | 3 | 1 | 0 | 4 |
| | | 1 | 3 | 6 | 4 | 2 |
| $S_2$ | | 3 | 7 | 2 | 3 | 1 |
| | | 1 | 2 | 5 | 6 | 0 |
| | | 3 | 0 | 2 | 3 | 8 |
| | | 7 | 3 | 1 | 0 | 4 |
| | | 2 | 4 | 5 | 3 | 2 |
| $S_3$ | | 2 | 7 | 2 | 3 | 1 |
| | | 2 | 2 | 5 | 0 | 7 |
| | | 4 | 0 | 2 | 4 | 6 |
| | | 7 | 2 | 1 | 0 | 2 |
| | | 1 | 4 | 6 | 5 | 0 |

Fig. 8. An assumed traffic pattern with four states.

| | | | | | | Sums of Rows (Receivers) Σ |
|---|---|---|---|---|---|---|
| | 3 | 7 | 2 | 4 | 2 | 18 |
| | 2 | 2 | 6 | 7 | 7 | 24 |
| | 4 | 1 | 3 | 4 | 9 | 21 |
| | 8 | 3 | 1 | 0 | 4 | 16 |
| | 3 | 4 | 1 | 5 | 2 | 20 |
| Sums of Columns (Transmitters) Σ | 20 | 17 | 18 | 20 | 24 | Sums of all entries = 99 |

Fig. 9. Maximum traffic matrix for Fig. 8.

sidelobes are sufficiently suppressed; if not, the beams have to be spaced far enough so that the large sidelobes of one antenna do not appear on the main beams of any of the other antennas. If all sidelobes are acceptably low, the steepness of the main beams determines how closely two such beams can be placed. For example, in Fig. 7 the 3-dB beamwidth is 1.5°. If the antenna gain were to drop abruptly at that point, two such beam centers could be located within 3° of each other. In the actual case, assuming that the 30-dB down first sidelobe is acceptable, two such beams can be placed no closer than 5° apart.

Polarization diversity is seen to be another means of increasing mutual isolation, with two adjacent antenna beams being either cross-circularly or cross-linearly polarized. The latter is easier to feed with lower cross-polarized components; the former does not require polarization tracking, certainly an attractive feature, and should be less susceptible to atmospheric effects. Several factors contribute to the amount of cross polarization for a parabolic antenna: the amount of reflector curvature ($f/D$ ratio), strut and feed scattering, and the kind of feed used. Horn feeds, in particular, can provide excellent polarization purity. The amount of polarization isolation practically achievable is still unknown; Fuenzalida and Podraczky [14] state that 10 dB is achievable with cross-linear polarization. This is perhaps conservative but is also a function of the total bandwidth over which polarization isolation is desired.

*B. Traffic Considerations*

The degree of variation of traffic between the $n$ ports determines the amount of routing flexibility the repeater has to provide. Between the $m_i$ ports connected to the $i$th antenna, one has the option of minimizing the variation in traffic flow by requiring the user ground terminals to access a different port on the same antenna by changing its frequency, at the expense of increasing the terminal complexity On the other hand, no such option exists when traffic requirements between antennas change with time.

Here we consider the case where it is desired to route even between repeaters connected to the same antenna, thus allowing each ground terminal to transmit and receive always on the same frequency, regardless of the destination or source of the messages. The desired traffic at any time between the $n$ ports may be expressed as an $n \times n$ matrix, with the $ij$th entry being the data rate from the $i$th receiver port to the $j$th transmitter port. This matrix changes with time according to traffic demands; an example may be as shown in Fig. 8. Here $n=5$ and it is assumed that each channel has the same capacity, normalized to 16 (MHz). At state $S_0$, for instance, a message with bandwidth of 7 MHz is passed from the second receiver port to the fourth transmitter port. At $S_0$, it is seen that all channels are fully loaded (sums of all rows and all columns equal 16). On the other hand, at $S_1$, this is no longer the case since, for instance, the sum along the second row gives 14 instead of 16.

Suppose that the four states $S_0, \cdots, S_3$ represent the the total traffic variations. First of all we see that the channel capacities [16] are never exceeded, so that the satellite capacity is adequate if sufficient routing flexibility is provided by the repeater. On the other hand, suppose that no routing flexibility is provided. One has the alternative of increasing the capacities of each of the receivers and transmitters to accommodate the maximum demand. Fig. 9 shows this maximum traffic matrix which has as its $ij$th entry the largest of the $ij$th entries in the four states of Fig. 8. On the other hand, Fig. 9 also gives the sums of the rows and columns of this maximum traffic matrix. It is seen that the receiver capacities all have to be increased (with one exception). The total receiver capacity required is increased from 80 MHz ($16 \times 5$) for the repeater with switching, to 99 MHz for the repeater without switching, and similarly for the transmitter capacity.

This example merely illustrates the degree to which

traffic variations determine the desirability of a repeater with variable or fixed routing. It is seen that even the relatively minor traffic variations between the four states in Fig. 8 require a repeater with 25 percent greater capacity if fixed routing is employed.

### C. Repeater Configurations

We first consider a repeater with fixed routing, using the traffic matrix of Fig. 9 as an illustrative example. In order to route signals received at port 1 to be distributed for transmission through ports 1–5, one must have a means of separating the received signals at port 1. If the signals at port 1 consist of a single bit stream on one carrier, one may demodulate the bit stream, identify the destination of the various bits if they are suitably coded, and redistribute them. However, aside from the complexity, it is desirable that the repeater structure be flexible enough to accommodate multiple earth terminal origins for the signals at each port so that these signals will not in general be on a single bit stream on a single carrier. One could of course demodulate each earth terminal transmission separately, but this would be excessively complicated. The other obvious alternatives are frequency and time division multiplex.

In time division multiplex, the time-location of a message is its destination code. Consider first the fixed routing case, using Fig. 9 as an illustration. For receiver port 1, the time slot may be divided into 18 equal parts, each of duration, say, $T_0$. From $t=0$ to $t=3T_0$, receiver port 1 is connected to transmitter port 1; from $t=3T_0$ to $t=10T_0$, receiver port 1 is connected to transmitter port 2, etc. A problem with this straightforward approach is that more than one receiver port carrying more than one message may be simultaneously connected to a transmitter port. A solution is a suitable memory on the satellite repeater to properly format the signals for retransmission. However, this is obviously an unattractive solution.

The question arises as to whether, given any traffic matrix, it is possible to format the ground terminal transmissions so that no two messages destined for the same transmitter port are allowed to occur simultaneously; for then, the satellite repeater could consist of memoryless switches. It can be shown that if the sums of each row and column of the traffic matrix are identical, as in state $S_0$ of Fig. 8, this can always be done. The proof follows: consider a permutation matrix $P$ of order $n$, meaning a matrix possessing exactly one nonzero element of value one in each row and column. If a traffic matrix is a permutation matrix, the required switching can obviously be satisfied with fixed switches, with the $i$th receiver port permanently connected to the $j$th transmitter port if the $ij$th matrix element is one. Second, a traffic matrix (with capacity normalized to one) is a doubly stochastic matrix, where the elements of a doubly stochastic matrix, by definition, satisfy the conditions

$$a_{ij} \geq 0$$
$$\sum_j a_{ij} = 1$$
$$\sum_i a_{ij} = 1$$

2 2 2 2 2 1 1 4 4 4 3 3 4 2 1 2 5 5 - - - - - - -
3 3 3 3 3 4 4 5 5 2 5 5 5 4 4 4 2 1 3 1 4 4 5 5
5 5 5 5 5 5 5 1 1 1 4 4 3 3 2 3 4 4 1 - 5 5 - -
1 1 1 1 1 2 2 2 3 5 1 1 1 5 5 5 - - - - - - - - -
4 4 4 4 4 3 3 3 2 3 2 2 2 1 3 1 1 3 5 5 - - - -
t=0 $\quad$ t=5T$_0$ $\quad$ t=10T$_0$ $\quad$ t=15T$_0$ $\quad$ t=20T$_0$

TIME →

Fig. 10. Time division format for fixed routing.

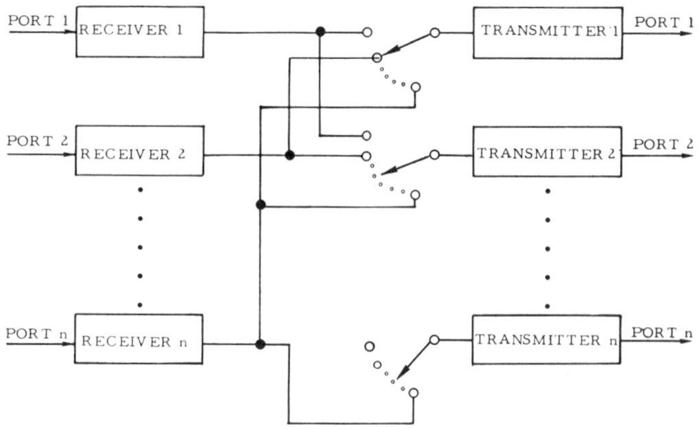


Fig. 11. Repeater configuration for time division multiplex.

Third, it is obvious that any (normalized) finite sum of permutation matrices is a doubly stochastic matrix and, further, that any traffic matrix constituted in this way can be implemented with a switch matrix consisting of the switch positions specified by each permutation matrix sequentially switched. Finally, any doubly stochastic matrix can be written as a (normalized) finite sum of permutation matrices, the last result being due to Birkhoff [15].

The question arises when the rows and columns of the traffic matrix do not have identical sums. In this case, it is necessary for all data rates transmitted and received by the satellite to be identical and in synchronism so that all lower capacity ports (from a traffic requirement standpoint) need to have the capacity of the highest capacity port. For instance, for the matrix of Fig. 9 even though receiver port 1 only requires 18 MHz, it has to operate at the rate of the highest capacity port, receiver port 2, which requires 24 MHz. Thus receiver port 1 would be idle $(24-18)/24=25$ percent of the time.

An example of the receive–transmit format using memoryless switches for the traffic matrix of Fig. 9 is shown in Fig. 10. Here the rows represent the receive ports, and the numbers represent the transmit port to which the receive port is connected at the given time. The abscissa is in units of time, quantized to, say, $T_0$. For example, Fig. 10 shows that receiver port 1 is connected to transmitter port 2 from $t=0$ to $t=5T_0$, to transmitter port 1 from $t=5T_0$ to $t=7T_0$, etc. That no transmitter port is connected to more than one receiver port simultaneously is evidenced by the fact that no two numbers are alike in every column of Fig. 10. The times when the receiver ports are idle are indicated in Fig. 10 by a dash mark.

The repeater configuration for this case is given in Fig. 11 with the $n$ receive and transmit ports connected by $n$ single-

| | | | | | | | | | | | | | | | | |
|---|---|---|---|---|---|---|---|---|---|---|---|---|---|---|---|---|
| 2 | 2 | 2 | 2 | 4 | 4 | 4 | 4 | 2 | 2 | 2 | 1 | 1 | 3 | 5 | 3 | |
| 4 | 4 | 4 | 4 | 3 | 3 | 3 | 3 | 4 | 4 | 4 | 3 | 3 | 2 | 2 | 1 | |
| 5 | 5 | 5 | 5 | 5 | 5 | 5 | 5 | 3 | 3 | 3 | 4 | 4 | 1 | 1 | 5 | $S_o$ |
| 1 | 1 | 1 | 1 | 1 | 1 | 1 | 1 | 5 | 5 | 5 | 2 | 2 | 5 | 1 | 2 | |
| 3 | 3 | 3 | 3 | 2 | 2 | 2 | 2 | 1 | 1 | 1 | 5 | 5 | 4 | 4 | 4 | |

| | | | | | | | | | | | | | | | | |
|---|---|---|---|---|---|---|---|---|---|---|---|---|---|---|---|---|
| 2 | 2 | 2 | 2 | 2 | 4 | 4 | 4 | 3 | 3 | 1 | 1 | 5 | 2 | 1 | 2 | |
| 4 | 4 | 4 | 4 | 4 | 3 | 3 | 3 | 2 | 2 | 3 | 3 | 1 | 4 | - | - | |
| 5 | 5 | 5 | 5 | 5 | 1 | 1 | 1 | 4 | 4 | 5 | 5 | 4 | 3 | 3 | 5 | $S_2$ |
| 1 | 1 | 1 | 1 | 1 | 5 | 5 | 5 | 1 | 1 | 2 | 2 | 3 | 5 | 2 | - | |
| 3 | 3 | 3 | 3 | 3 | 2 | 2 | 2 | 5 | 5 | 4 | 4 | 2 | 1 | 4 | 1 | |

| | | | | | | | | | | | | | | | | |
|---|---|---|---|---|---|---|---|---|---|---|---|---|---|---|---|---|
| 2 | 2 | 2 | 2 | 2 | 4 | 4 | 4 | 1 | 1 | 2 | 5 | 3 | 3 | 4 | 5 | |
| 4 | 4 | 4 | 4 | 4 | 3 | 3 | 3 | 3 | 3 | 3 | 2 | - | - | 5 | 1 | |
| 5 | 5 | 5 | 5 | 5 | 1 | 1 | 1 | 5 | 5 | 1 | 4 | 4 | 4 | 3 | 2 | $S_1$ |
| 1 | 1 | 1 | 1 | 1 | 5 | 5 | 5 | 2 | 2 | 5 | 1 | 1 | 1 | 2 | 3 | |
| 3 | 3 | 3 | 3 | 3 | 2 | 2 | 2 | 4 | 4 | 4 | 3 | 5 | 5 | 1 | 4 | |

| | | | | | | | | | | | | | | | | |
|---|---|---|---|---|---|---|---|---|---|---|---|---|---|---|---|---|
| 2 | 2 | 2 | 2 | 2 | 4 | 4 | 4 | 1 | 1 | 3 | 5 | 2 | 2 | 3 | - | |
| 3 | 3 | 3 | 3 | 3 | 5 | 5 | 5 | 2 | 2 | 5 | 1 | 5 | 5 | 1 | 5 | |
| 5 | 5 | 5 | 5 | 5 | 1 | 1 | 3 | 4 | 4 | 4 | 4 | 1 | 3 | 5 | - | $S_3$ |
| 1 | 1 | 1 | 1 | 1 | 2 | 2 | 1 | 5 | 5 | 1 | 3 | - | - | - | - | |
| 4 | 4 | 4 | 4 | 4 | 3 | 3 | 2 | 3 | 3 | 2 | 2 | 3 | 1 | 2 | 3 | |

Fig. 12. Time division with variable routing for four states.

pole $n$-throw switches. Fig. 11 is shown with the single pole connected to the transmitter port rather than to the receiver port, since one never desires to connect two receivers to the same transmitter, but one may sometimes desire to connect two or more transmitters to the same receiver, as in a broadcast mode.

A penalty for this relative repeater simplicity is a further increase in required satellite capacity. For the example of Fig. 9 each port has to have the capacity of the highest capacity port, viz., 24, resulting in a total required satellite capacity of $(24 \times 5) = 120$ MHz or a further increase of approximately 20 percent.

On the other hand, the repeater configuration of Fig. 11 can be used without modification for variable routing, and there is no reason to suffer the degradation due to fixed routing. For example, the four states in Fig. 8 are implemented as shown in Fig. 12. Since the maximum port capacity required in all four states of Fig. 8 is 16 MHz, this is also the capacity required for each port, and the total satellite capacity requirement is simply $(16 \times 5) = 80$ MHz, the minimum achievable with variable routing. Thus the previously mentioned method of time division multiplex appears as a very attractive possibility for a variable routing satellite repeater.

The second alternative is frequency division multiplex. Consider first the situation with fixed routing. For the assumed traffic of Fig. 8, the maximum traffic matrix of Fig. 9 still applies. The traffic entering the $i$th receiver port has to be separated in frequency by the use of filters and reassembled at each transmitter port. The difficulty is that the signals from the $n$ receivers are in general at the wrong frequencies for reassembly without an intermediate frequency conversion, and the difficulty is exactly analogous to the problem of having more than one receiver connected to the same transmitter at the same time in the time division multi-

| | | | | |
|---|---|---|---|---|
| 2 | 6 | 2 | 3 | 1 |
| 1 | 1 | 5 | 0 | 0 |
| 2 | 0 | 1 | 2 | 6 |
| 7 | 2 | 1 | 0 | 2 |
| 1 | 3 | 4 | 3 | 0 |

Fig. 13. Minimum traffic matrix for Fig. 8.

plex case, and which can be solved in a similar way if desired. In this case, considering the abscissa as a frequency rather than a time axis, Fig. 10 may be viewed as a frequency plan for the five receive ports for the traffic matrix of Fig. 9. For instance, 0 to 5 MHz (reading from left to right) is reserved for those earth terminals wishing to transmit to receive port 1 to be retransmitted through transmit port 2; 5 to 7 MHz is reserved for retransmission through transmit port 1, etc. As Fig. 10 shows, frequency conversion is necessary to reassemble the signals at the transmitter ports, since all frequencies need to be disjoint at the transmitter port. Unlike time division multiplex, where each channel has to have the capacity of the largest channel, this is not the case in frequency division. For instance, receiver port 1 only has to have a bandwidth of 18 MHz, while the maximum bandwidth, for receiver port 2, requires 24 MHz. On the other hand, the frequency plan is not perfectly efficient, as evidenced by receiver port 3 requiring 22 MHz instead of its minimum of 21 as given by Fig. 9. Also, transmitter ports 3 and 4 require 1 and 2 more MHz than necessary, as will be seen by inspecting Fig. 10. On the other hand, what is now needed are sixteen 1-MHz filters for each receive port with only a simple summation at each transmit port.

Consider next the receiver with variable routing. For a given traffic pattern, one may identify a minimum traffic matrix having an $ij$th entry which is the smallest of the $ij$th entries for the traffic matrices constituting the specified traffic pattern. For example, Fig. 13 is the minimum traffic matrix for Fig. 8. The minimum traffic matrix specifies that portion of the traffic pattern that does not vary as the traffic pattern varies and, thus in the present context, represents the maximum amount of fixed routing that may be accepted without requiring an increase in repeater capacities. Thus the receiver may be conceived of as having two parts: a part with fixed routing, as specified by the minimum traffic matrix, and a part with variable routing. A possible configuration, for the case of Fig. 8, is the following: divide the traffic flow into integral factors of the smallest unit of traffic flow, in this case 1 (MHz). Each ground terminal transmits multiple carriers, each carrying 1 MHz of data, the number of carriers depending on the total data rate. For instance, referring to Fig. 8, the ground terminal(s) transmitting to receive port 1 uses 16, 16, 16, and 15 carriers respectively over the four states. A repeater configuration may be as shown in Fig. 14. The top halves of the two parts of Fig. 14 show the fixed routing of Fig. 13. The lower halves are those parts for which variable routing is needed. The division simplifies the required switch matrix and reduces the number of frequency conversions required. However, Fig. 14 does not show, explicitly, frequency synthesizers (or equivalent) to convert to a variety of frequencies, nor does it show the filters required to eliminate spurious products.

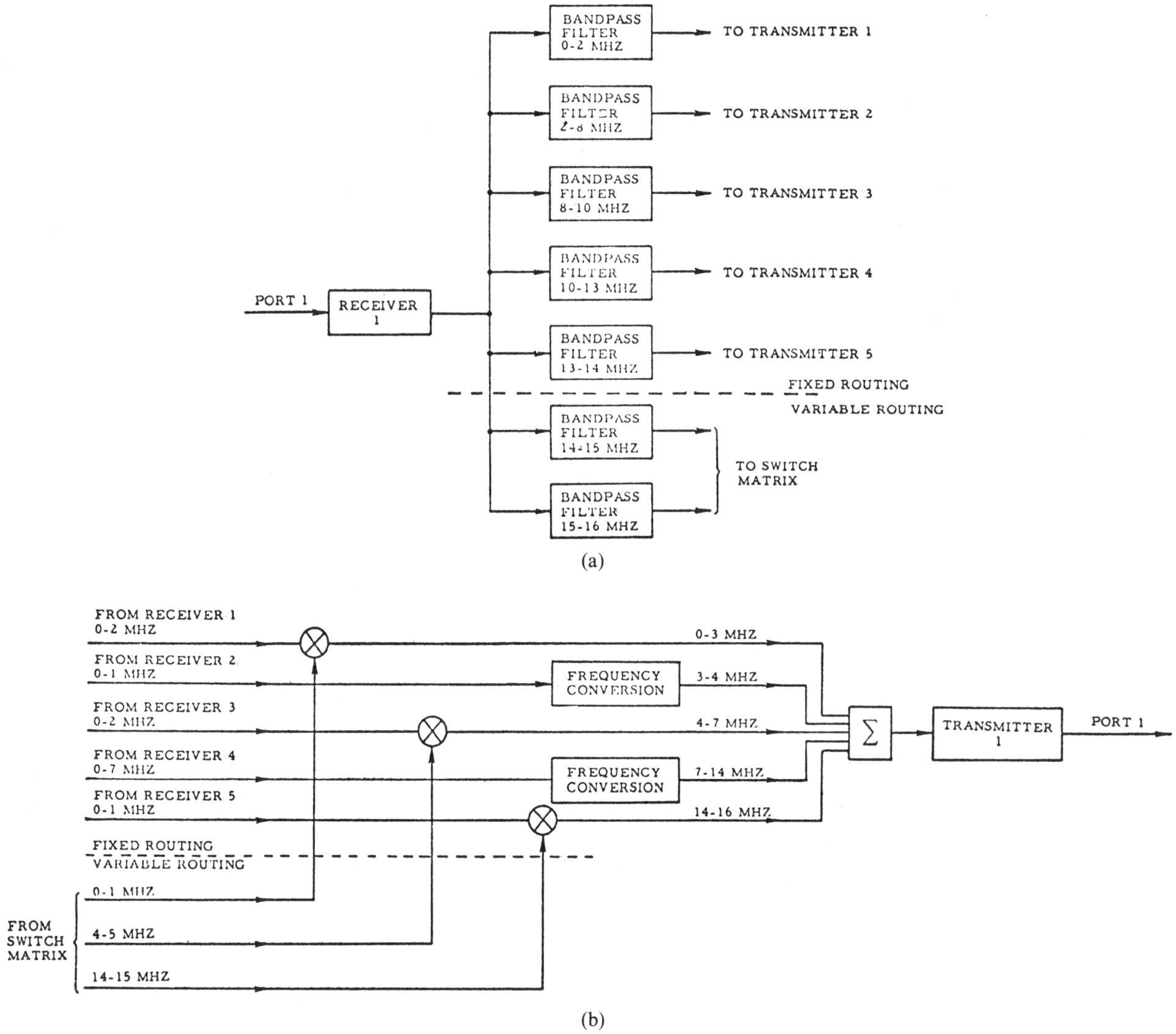


Fig. 14. Repeater configuration with variable routing (state $S_2$ of Fig. 8 shown). (a) Receiver port 1. (b) Transmitter port 1.

These frequency conversion problems can also be eliminated by a frequency management scheme as given by Fig. 12 for the case with variable routing. Here the outputs of each 1-MHz filter are connected to a switch matrix which would connect them to the appropriate transmitter port depending on the state $S_i$. For instance, the output of receiver port 1 in the frequency range 15–16 MHz (right-most position) would be connected to transmitter ports 3, 5, and 2 for states $S_0$, $S_1$, and $S_2$, respectively. For state $S_3$, the receiver port is not used. As in time division multiplex, one has the alternative of connecting a receive port to one of several transmit ports or of connecting a transmit port to one of several receive ports, the latter providing a broadcast capability. In the former case, $p$ single-pole $n$-throw switches are needed at each receive port where $p$ is the ratio of the port capacity to the lowest data rate to be switched (in this case, 16); hence $np$ single-pole $n$-throw switches are required altogether. In the latter case, one single-pole $np$-throw switch is needed at each transmit port, hence $n$ single-pole $np$-throw switches are required altogether. Similarly, $np$ filters are needed altogether, one at each receive port. The number of switches and filters needed for a specified traffic pattern, such as in Fig. 8, may be reduced from the previously stated number by taking advantage of the minimum traffic matrix of Fig. 13, since a possibly substantial portion of the traffic need not be switched.

In comparing frequency and time division multiplex, it appears that both can be implemented with either fixed or variable routing with a reasonably modest amount of equipment complexity. Time division is attractive in that no multiple-carrier intermodulation problems are present, and, in addition, it does not require multiple frequency separation filters at the spacecraft and requires less complex switching. Further, it is compatible with presently planned TDMA modems. The main disadvantages of time division multiplex are two: the requirement for fast switching and the control logic necessary for fast switching. We discuss some detailed problems in Section VI-D.

### *D. Time Division Multiplex*

It is envisioned that, together with the repeater configuration of Fig. 11, the ground terminal transmitters and receivers operate similarly to the presently planned TDMA mode [16]–[18]. Between each burst of data with duration

$T_0$, there is a guard band, together with a data preamble, which allows timing errors and reacquisition. It has been estimated that a guard time of 100 ns is adequate for a synchronous satellite with a simple repeater. Where the repeater is required to switch between bursts as in Fig. 11, additional guard time needs to be allowed for switch timing errors, switching time, etc. The switching time can be a function of the number of positions $n$ of the switch, the loss through the switch, and the isolation desired. $T_0$ is chosen long enough so that a relatively small proportion of it is used for guard time and synchronization and yet short enough so that ground terminal data buffering requirements are minimal. The maximum data buffering required is over a frame time where a frame, in the case of Fig. 8, would be 16 $T_0$. Thus the ratio of the frame time to $T_0$ is the ratio of the maximum port capacity to the lowest data rate to be separated for retransmission. An attractive solution to reducing this ratio is the use of what is equivalent to subcommutation. In this way, the high data rate ground terminals would operate at a higher frame rate, the low data rate terminals at a lower frame rate, allowing one to adjust the data storage/buffering requirements to fit the ground terminal size.

The presently envisioned TDMA mode of operation with a simple satellite repeater uses a ground station as the master clock. This master ground station transmits a periodic burst through the satellite repeater, allowing any other transmitter to receive this burst and to time-phase its transmission through the satellite with respect to the burst. The satellite is indifferent to the user system timing. This is not the case, however, for the repeater configuration of Fig. 11 since the times at which the switches operate must be in synchronism with the user transmissions. This requirement is similar to the type 1 processing repeater discussed in Section V, and it is similarly proposed that the satellite may be kept simple by allowing all ground terminals to synchronize to it. In this case, the satellite contains a master oscillator, which determines the time $T_0$ at which the switches should operate, but receives instructions from a master ground control station as to the connectivity as a function of time. Since it is envisioned that traffic requirements change relatively slowly ($\sim$hours), instructions from a master ground station are loaded into a memory on the satellite which is read out every $T_0$ seconds.

It is necessary for each ground terminal to synchronize its transmission to the satellite clock to an accuracy of approximately 100 ns. This can be simply done by letting the satellite transmit a burst in place of that presently to be transmitted by a master ground station, provided that each ground terminal transmitter can receive its own transmission through the satellite repeater. The latter may not be the case with $k$ antennas with disjoint ground coverage if the repeater is configured only to satisfy traffic requirements (i.e., traffic requirements may not necessitate connecting the transmitter for node 1 to the receiver for node 1 at any time). In this case, some additional capacity would be needed to allow each ground terminal to receive at least part of its own transmission to allow synchronization.

Finally, synchronization to within 100 ns requires digital logic on the satellite to operate in the range 1–10 Mbit/s, certainly acceptably modest.

## VII. Conclusions

In this paper, we have examined in some detail two types of processing repeaters. The type 1 processing repeater is able to discriminate against unauthorized users, to conserve the capacity of the repeater to only those users who possess a predetermined key. At the same time, undesired interference signals are rejected. It appears that such a repeater is most useful in the situation where there are a large number of small receiving terminals to optimize the satellite capacity with respect to these terminals and to simplify the processing otherwise needed at these terminals. The type 2 repeater acts somewhat as a "switchboard in the sky" in being able to route signals transmitted through one antenna at one frequency to another antenna at another frequency where the desired routing may be changed as a function of time. In this way, the satellite capacity is utilized fully in the face of changing traffic demands. Also, transmitting and receiving terminals are simplified.

In both of these processing repeaters, complexity is added for two reasons: to fully utilize the satellite capacity and to simplify the user ground terminals. As communication satellites become larger, so that a small saving in communication capacity may allow the addition of substantially more equipment, and as users of these satellites become more and more numerous, it appears to us that one or both of these processing repeaters will find application in the near future.

## Acknowledgment

The authors wish to thank Dr. D. R. Anderson who pointed out the proof available in [15].

## References

[1] A. M. Werth, "SPADE: A PCM FDMA demand assignment system for satellite communications," in *Proc. Intelsat/IEE Int. Conf. on Digital Satellite Commun.*, 1969, pp. 51–68.

[2] A. D. Perry, Jr. "Electronics-communications," *Space/Aeronaut.*, July 31, 1968, pp. 81–84.

[3] D. P. Sullivan, "Future trends in military communication satellite repeaters," *IEEE Trans. Aerosp. Electron. Syst.*, vol. AES-6, Mar. 1970, pp. 129–136.

[4] W. G. Schmidt, "An on-board switched multiple access system for millimeter wave satellites," in *Proc. Intelsat/IEE Conf.*, pp. 399–407.

[5] W. DeBrunner and W. Neu, "Efficient PCM satellite communication with minimum interference to terrestrial radio links," in *Proc. Intelsat/IEE Conf.*, pp. 253–261.

[6] T. G. Birdsall and M. P. Ristenblatt, "Introduction to linear shift register generated sequences," University of Michigan Res. Inst., Ann Arbor, Mich., Tech. Rep. 90, Oct. 1958.

[7] S. W. Golomb, *Shift Register Sequences.* San Francisco, Calif.: Holden-Day, 1967.

[8] R. Gold, "Study of correlation properties of binary sequences," AF Avionics Lab., Wright-Patterson AF Base, Dayton, Ohio, Tech. Rep. TR-66-234.

[9] G. Cooper, "A method of time-frequency coding for multiple access systems," in *3rd Haw. Conf. Syst. Sci.*, 1970, pp. 598–602.

[10] G. Solomon, "Optimum frequency hopping codes," Inter. Memo.

[11] P. M. Spira, "A class of codes for multiple access satellite communication systems," Rand Corp. Memo. RM-5131-NASA.

[12] J. Kaiser, Ed., "Modulation techniques and their application," in "Multiple Access to a Communication Satellite with a Hard-Limiting Repeater," IDA Rep. R-108, Jan. 1965, vol. 1.

[13] J. M. Aein and J. Schwartz, Ed., "Proceedings of the IDA multiple-

access summer study," in "Multiple Access to a Communication Satellite with a Hard-Limiting Repeater," IDA Rep. R-108, Apr. 1965, vol. 2.
[14] J. C. Fuenzalida and E. Podraczky, "Reuse of the frequency spectrum at the satellite," presented at the 3rd Communication Satellite Syst. Conf., Los Angeles, Calif., Apr. 1970.
[15] R. Bellman, *Introduction to Matrix Analysis*. New York: McGraw-Hill, 1960, p. 267.
[16] T. Sekimoto and J. G. Puente, "A satellite TDMA experiment," *IEEE Trans. Commun. Technol.*, vol. COM-16, August 1968, pp. 581–588.
[17] W. G. Schmidt, O. G. Gabbard, E. R. Cacciamani, W. G. Maillet, and W. W. Wu, "MAT-1, intelsat's experiment 700-channel TDMA/DA system," in *Proc. Intelsat/IEE Int. Conf. Digital Satellite Commun.*, 1969, pp. 428–440.
[18] R. M. Hultberg, F. H. Jean, and M. E. Jones, "Time division access for military communications satellites," *IEEE Trans. Aerosp. Electron. Syst.*, vol. AES-1, Dec. 1965, pp. 272–282.

# On the Utility of Chirp Modulation for Digital Signaling

ALBERT J. BERNI AND WILLIAM D. GREGG

*Abstract*—The issue of signal selection in binary data transmission is presented. The question of the relative utility of linear frequency sweeping (LFS or chirp), compared to PSK and FSK, in terms of error probability and spectrum usage, is discussed. The transmission media considered are the coherent, partially coherent, Rayleigh, and Rician channel models. Theoretically, LFS has unconditionally superior characteristics in the partially coherent and fading cases, for certain ranges of channel conditions. This is due to the more negative values of cross-coherence parameters possible with the LFS signal set over the FSK signal set. For the fading channel, theoretical supremacy of LFS over FSK depends upon the specular-to-Rayleigh signal power ratio and the adjustability of in-phase cross coherence, with a constraint upon quadrature phase cross coherence.

From a practical standpoint, coherent reception of the LFS signal set has severe limitations. These are manifested primarily in two aspects: the need for phase synchronization of a chirp signal set, and the fact that the optimum value of cross coherence is highly sensitive to synchronization channel signal-to-noise ratio (SNR), and/or spectral-to-Rayleigh signal power ratio. The latter would require that modulation characteristics track the channel conditions in order to achieve the supremacy in performance theoretically predicted by optimization of the cross-coherence parameter in LFS.

## INTRODUCTION

This paper deals with the issue of signal selection in binary data transmission and is motivated by a recurrent interest [1]-[3] in the use of linear-frequency-swept signal sets for transmission of digital data. This paper takes up some of the questions raised in the literature. In particular, a comparison of linear frequency sweeping (LFS), PSK, and FSK is made on the basis of error probability, data rate, and spectrum usage. The channel models are coherent, partially coherent, and nonselective fading.

## SIGNAL REPRESENTATION

This paper considers the utility of linear frequency modulation (LFS), sometimes referred to as a chirp signal set, for use in digital data transmission. The problem of optimal signaling has been treated by Kotelnikov [4], Middleton [5], and Van Trees [6]. Work in [4]-[6] has shown that the bit error probability depends upon certain parameters that can be defined on a general signal set. The physical parameter of primary concern in this paper is the cross-coherence factor $\rho$. For equal energy signals, $\rho$ is defined as

$$\rho \triangleq \frac{1}{E}\int_0^T s_1(t)s_2(t)\,dt \tag{1}$$

where $E$ is the bit pulse energy

$$E \triangleq \int_0^T s_i^2(t)\,dt, \qquad i = 1, 2.$$

Paper approved by the Communication Theory Committee of the IEEE Communications Society for publication without oral presentation. Manuscript received March 10, 1972; revised November 29, 1972. This research was supported in part by the Department of Electrical Engineering and the Bureau of Engineering Research, College of Engineering, University of Texas, Austin, under Grant TX 78712.

A. J. Berni is with the Electro Science Laboratory, Department of Electrical Engineering, Ohio State University, Columbus, Ohio 43221.

W. D. Gregg is with the Department of Electrical Engineering, University of Texas at Austin, Austin, Tex. 78712.

Application of Schwarz's inequality to (1) reveals that the cross coherence is bounded as $-1 \leqslant \rho \leqslant +1$.

The three modulation schemes considered are PSK, FSK, and LFS or chirp.

The PSK signal set is

$$\begin{aligned} s_1(t) &= A\cos[\omega_c t] \\ s_2(t) &= A\cos[\omega_c t + \pi], \qquad 0 \leqslant t \leqslant T. \end{aligned} \tag{2}$$

Since $s_1(t) = -s_2(t)$, the signal energy is the same for both signals:

$$E = \int_0^T A^2\cos^2[\omega_c t]\,dt = A^2 T/2$$

and also $\rho = -1$. This assumes that the period of the carrier frequency is small with respect to the bit interval. A bandwidth of $2/T$ Hz centered at the carrier frequency contains 90 percent of the signal energy. This is usually taken as the nominal bandwidth for PSK.

The FSK signal set is given by

$$\begin{aligned} s_1(t) &= A\cos[\omega_1 t] \\ s_2(t) &= A\cos[\omega_2 t], \qquad 0 \leqslant t \leqslant T. \end{aligned} \tag{3}$$

In an FSK system the carrier frequency is shifted in accordance with the information bit being conveyed. If, as just stated, the carrier frequency is large compared to the reciprocal of the baud length, the signal energy is again $A^2T/2$.

The cross-coherence coefficient (1) is more involved for FSK. Neglecting the integral over high frequencies yields

$$\rho = \frac{\sin[\Delta\omega T]}{\Delta\omega T} \tag{4}$$

where

$$\Delta\omega = \omega_2 - \omega_1 .$$

The value of $\rho$ varies as $\sin x/x$, where $x$ is the product of frequency separation and baud length for the signal set. The bounds on $\rho$ for FSK are

$$-0.218 \leqslant \rho \leqslant 1 \text{ FSK}. \tag{5}$$

Note that this definition of FSK requires phase coherency between the two signal states; this requirement is also made for the LFS signal set.

The spectral occupancy of the FSK signal follows from (3):

$$\begin{aligned} S(j\omega) &= S_1(j\omega) + S_2(j\omega) \\ s_i(j\omega) &= \tfrac{1}{2}AT\,\frac{\sin[(\omega_i+\omega)\frac{1}{2}T]}{[(\omega_i+\omega)\frac{1}{2}T]}\exp\{-j[(\omega_i+\omega)\tfrac{1}{2}T]\} \\ &\quad + \tfrac{1}{2}AT\,\frac{\sin[(\omega_i-\omega)\frac{1}{2}T]}{[(\omega_i-\omega)\frac{1}{2}T]}\exp\{+j[(\omega_i-\omega)\tfrac{1}{2}T]\}. \end{aligned} \tag{6}$$

From the amplitude spectra of (6), it is conventionally assumed that band limiting is achieved at the first zero points. The bandwidth of each signal in the FSK set is equal to that of PSK.

$$W = \frac{4\pi}{T}\ \text{rad/s}.$$

Reprinted from *IEEE Trans. Commun.*, vol. COM-21, pp. 748–751, June 1973.

The general LFS signal set is

$$s_1(t) = A \cos [\omega_1 t + \tfrac{1}{2} m t^2]$$
$$s_2(t) = A \cos [\omega_2 t - \tfrac{1}{2} m t^2]. \quad (7)$$

Taking the overall frequency change $mT$ to be much less than the carrier frequencies, the signal energy is also $A^2 T/2$.

The cross-coherence coefficient for LFS cannot be expressed in simple form. Employing (7) in (1) yields a Fresnel integral,

$$\rho = \frac{1}{T} \int_0^T \cos [(\omega_1 - \omega_2) t + m t^2] \, dt \quad (8)$$

where the integral over the high-frequency terms is not significant. The integral can be rewritten into a standard Fresnel form [7]:

$$\rho = \frac{1}{g} \{\cos [\tfrac{1}{2} \pi p^2] [C_f(p) - C_f(p - g)] + \sin [\tfrac{1}{2} \pi p^2] [S_f(p) - S_f(p - g)]\} \quad (9)$$

where

$$p = \frac{\omega_2 - \omega_1}{(2\pi m)^{1/2}}; \; g = \left(\frac{2m}{\pi}\right)^{1/2} T$$

$$C_f(x) = \int_0^x \cos \tfrac{1}{2} \pi t^2 \, dt; \; S_f(x) = \int_0^x \sin \tfrac{1}{2} \pi t^2 \, dt. \quad (10)$$

Numerical evaluation indicates that $\rho$ is bounded by

$$-0.629 \leqslant \rho \leqslant +1 \text{ LFS}. \quad (11)$$

Fig. 1 illustrates the variation of $\rho$ dependent upon $T$, the bit duration, and hence the data rate; the values of $\rho$ will be likewise dependent upon $T$. However, the optimum value of $\rho$ for any data rate can be obtained by the variation of the sweep rate $m$ and the frequency range $\Delta\omega$.

The overall frequency sweep in a baud length of $T$, $mT$ is, to a good approximation, the radian frequency bandwidth $W$.

Manipulation of (10) yields the following interdependence of bandwidth, initial frequency spacing, and data rate:

$$\Delta\omega = p g \pi / T$$
$$mT = \pi g^2 / 2T \quad (12)$$

where $W$ is the radian half-power bandwidth of the signal, and $\Delta\omega$ is the initial frequency spacing $\omega_1 - \omega_2$.

This establishes the relative values of spectrum occupancy, energy, and cross-coherence coefficient for the PSK, FSK, and LFS signal sets. The parameters are employed in terms of the effects upon bit error probability for various channels.

## Coherent Reception

This channel situation is analytically specified with the received waveform given by the original transmitted signal and additive zero-mean Gaussian noise,

$$r(t) = A \cos [\omega_i t + m_i(t)] + n(t), \qquad i = 1, 2.$$

The additive noise is taken to be of flat spectral density over the frequency range of interest.

Since the preceding model is simple, it best serves to introduce the signal selection issue.

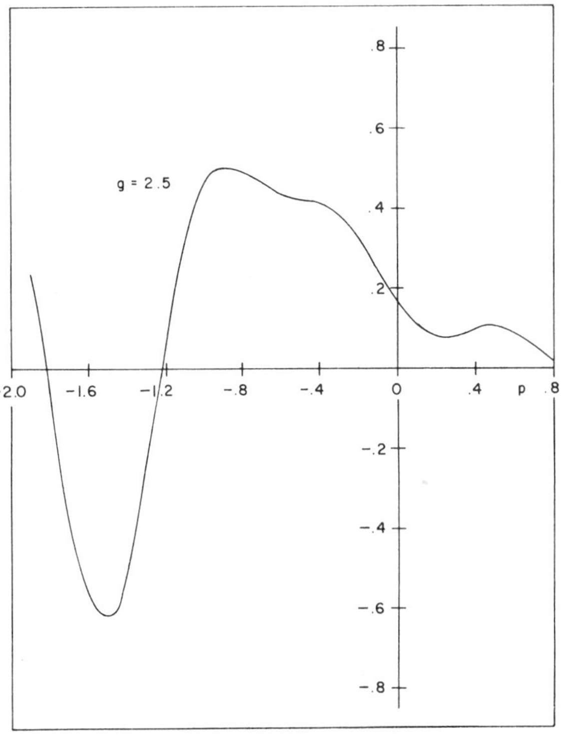


Fig. 1. Real part of cross-coherence coefficient for LFS signals.

The signal set parameters are

$$m_1(t) = 0, m_2(t) = \pi; \omega_1 = \omega_2 \text{ PSK}$$
$$m_1(t) = 0, m_2(t) = 0; \omega_1 \neq \omega_2 \text{ FSK}$$
$$m_1(t) = \tfrac{1}{2} m t^2, m_2(t) = \tfrac{1}{2} m t^2 \text{ LFS}.$$

In general, the $\{m_i(t)\}$ can be any waveforms that are low pass with respect to the carrier frequencies.

For equal *a priori* signal probabilities, flat noise spectral density with two-sided height $N_0/2$, assuming equal energy signals, the error probabilities of the first and second kind [6] are

$$\alpha = \text{erfc}\left(\frac{\delta}{2}\right) = \tfrac{1}{2} - \text{erf}\left(\frac{\delta}{2}\right)$$

$$\beta = \tfrac{1}{2} - \text{erf}\left(\frac{\delta}{2}\right)$$

where

$$\delta^2 \triangleq \frac{4}{N_0} E(1 - \rho).$$

The overall probability of error is then

$$P(e) = P(H_1)\alpha + P(H_2)\beta = \tfrac{1}{2} - \text{erf}\left(\frac{\delta}{2}\right) \quad (13)$$

and decreases with an increase in $\delta$; in the limit $\text{erf}_{\delta \to \infty}(\delta/2) = \frac{1}{2} = P(e)_{\delta \to \infty} = 0$.

The parameter $\delta$ is specified by design considerations. The signal energy $E$ is a quantity fixed by transmitter power and transmission characteristics, $N_0/2$ is the noise power spectral density level set by the receiver noise figure, leaving the cross-coherence parameter $\rho$ to be optimized. It can be seen from (13) that $\delta$ increases monotonically as $\rho$ decreases for fixed energy to noise ratio $E/N_0$. The most negative value of $\rho$ possible is $-1$, indicating that an antipodal signal set is optimum. Referring to (2), it is seen that the PSK signal set is optimal for this channel. Direct numerical evaluation shows that FSK is capable of achieving a cross-coherence coefficient of $-0.218$, while LFS can be as negative as $-0.629$. From Fig. 1 this value of the cross-coherence coefficient is produced for the LFS signal set when $p = 1.53$, $g = 2.50$. For these values, (12) yields

$$W = 9.85\left(\frac{1}{T}\right); \ \Delta\omega = 12\left(\frac{1}{T}\right) \text{ LFS.}$$

Since the signals are sweeping into one another, the overall radian frequency bandwidth of the signal set for this case is determined by the initial frequency separation

$$B = \Delta\omega = 12\left(\frac{1}{T}\right).$$

An FSK signal set with cross-coherence coefficient of $-0.218$ yields from (4)

$$\Delta\omega = \frac{4.4}{T}, \ W = 4\pi\left(\frac{1}{T}\right) = 12.5\left(\frac{1}{T}\right).$$

The overall system bandwidth $B$ is then

$$B = \Delta\omega + W = 17\left(\frac{1}{T}\right).$$

Table I gives a comparison of FSK, PSK, and LFS for equal probability of error in terms of energy and bandwidth requirements. There is a 2.12-dB improvement from FSK to PSK, and a 1.3-dB improvement from FSK to LFS. A comparison of the three modulation techniques shown in Table I indicates that there is no motivation for the use of LFS over PSK. However, LFS is superior to FSK in terms of required signal energy and bandwidth for a given probability of error.

## Partially Coherent Reception

In partially coherent reception, precisely synchronous detection is not achieved. This is analytically represented as the exact knowledge of the RF phase of the received signal component not being available to the receiver. The phase is then treated as a random variable with some appropriate probability distribution. The received waveform is

$$r(t) = A\cos[\omega_i t + m_i(t) + \theta] + n(t), \qquad i = 1, 2.$$

The statements pertaining to $m(t)$, $\omega$, etc., for the various modulation schemes are the same as in the coherent case. The phase variable $\theta$ is taken to have a probability density function $p(\theta)$ modeled [9] by

$$p(\theta) \triangleq \frac{\exp[\Gamma\cos\theta]}{2\pi I_0(\Gamma)}; \ \Gamma = \frac{A\tau}{N_0/2}, \qquad 0 \leqslant \theta \leqslant 2\pi$$
$$= 0, \qquad \text{elsewhere}$$

where $I_0(\Gamma)$ is the zeroth-order Bessel function of the first kind, and $\tau$ is a measure of the phase instability/drift.

As $\Gamma \to \infty$, $p(\theta) \to \delta(\theta)$ and the receiver LO becomes coherent; when $\Gamma = 0$, $p(\theta)$ is uniform, corresponding to the noncoherent situation. In practice, the situation is more nearly one of partial coherence, such as when $\theta$ is acquired through the use of a pilot carrier or phase lock loop, etc.

The probability of error is evaluated assuming that the test

TABLE I

| Modulation | Bandwidth $B$ (rad/s) | Relative Signal Energy $E$ |
|---|---|---|
| PSK | 6.283 $(1/T)$ | $E_0$ |
| FSK | 17 $(1/T)$ | 1.64 $E_0$ |
| LFS | 12 $(1/T)$ | 1.22 $E_0$ |

statistic is conditionally Gaussian given the phase variable $\theta$, by averaging over $\theta$

$$P(e) = \int_{-\pi}^{\pi} p(e)P(e/\theta)\,d\theta. \tag{14}$$

It has been shown by Viterbi [9] that the conditional error probability is

$$P(e/\theta) = Q\left(\frac{k_1}{\sqrt{2}}, \frac{k_2}{\sqrt{2}}\right) - \tfrac{1}{2}\exp\left\{-\frac{k_1^2 + k_2^2}{4}\right\} I_0\left(\frac{k_1 k_2}{2}\right) \tag{15}$$

where

$$Q(x, y) \triangleq \int_y^{\infty} \exp\{-(t^2 + x^2/2\} I_0(xt)\,dt$$

is the Marcum $Q$ function [10].

To obtain the average probability of error $P(e)$, (15) is substituted into (14) and the expression is integrated numerically. The analytical results are plotted versus $\Gamma$ for fixed signal-to-noise ratio (SNR) $d$ and quantized values of coherence coefficients $\rho_1$ and $\rho_2$, where the parameters are

$$d^2 = 2E/N_0$$

$$k_1^2 = (E[y_1])^2 + (E[y_2])^2 \ k_2^2 = (E[y_3])^2 + (E[y_4])^2$$

$$E\begin{bmatrix} y_1 \\ y_2 \\ y_3 \\ y_4 \end{bmatrix} = \frac{1}{\nu d[2(2+\nu)]^{1/2}} \begin{bmatrix} \Gamma(1+\nu-\rho_1) + d^2(1+\nu)\cos\theta \\ \Gamma\rho_2 + d^2\nu(1+\nu)\sin\theta \\ \Gamma(1+\nu-\rho_1) + d^2\nu(\rho_1\cos\theta - \rho_2\sin\theta) \\ -\Gamma\rho_2 + d^2\nu(\rho_1\sin\theta + \rho_2\cos\theta) \end{bmatrix}$$

$$\nu = (1 - \rho_1^2 - \rho_2^2)^{1/2}$$

$$\rho_1 = \frac{A^2}{E}\int \cos[\omega_1 t + m_1(t)]\cos[\omega_2 t + m_2(t)]\,dt$$

$$\rho_2 = \frac{A^2}{E}\int \sin[\omega_1 t + m_1(t)]\cos[\omega_2 t + m_2(t)]\,dt.$$

The results indicate that $P_e$ is an increasing function of the magnitude of the quadrature cross-coherence coefficient $|\rho_2|$ and has a minimum at $\rho_2 = 0$ for any quantization of $\rho_1$. One such case, Fig. 2, is for $\rho_2 = 0$ and values of $\rho_1$ corresponding to FSK, PSK, and LFS. It can be seen that for values of $\Gamma$ between 2 and 8, partially coherent reception, a signal set with an intermediate value of cross coherence excels over PSK. Fig. 3 shows $|\rho_2|$ for LFS and indicates that values of $\rho_1$ near the minimum are obtainable with $|\rho_2| = 0$. The use of FM modulation to achieve the desired cross coherence has an advantage over an AM technique in view of the peak-to-average-power limitations of high power transmission. However, the required phase recovery system for LFS, presumably a phase locked pilot tone, and sensitivity of the optimal modulation

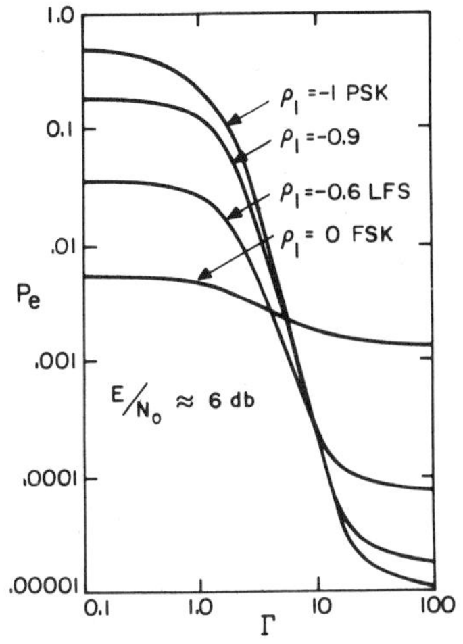


Fig. 2. Bit error probability for partially coherent reception, zero quadrature cross coherence $p_2 = 0$.

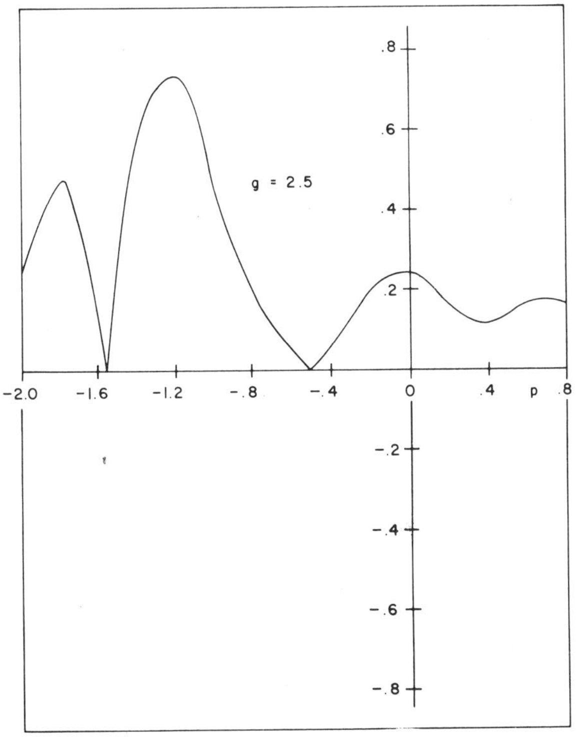


Fig. 3. Magnitude of imaginary part of the cross-coherence coefficient for LFS signals.

parameters to channel conditions (Fig. 2) make LFS unappealing for most applications.

## Fading Channel

For transmission over a Rician channel, the received waveform is modeled by a deterministic component and a scatter component whose envelope is specified by a Rayleigh probability distribution and a uniformly distributed phase. The fading is assumed not frequency selective and slow compared to $T$.

The received waveform is

$$r(t) = vA \cos\left[\omega_i t + m_i(t) + \theta\right] + A \cos\left[\omega_i t + m_i(t)\right] + n(t), \qquad T_1 \leqslant t \leqslant T_2, i = 1, 2.$$

The random variables $v$ and $\theta$ are Rayleigh and uniformly distributed, respectively.

Turin [11] has shown that the generalized orthogonal signal set $\rho_1 = 0$; $\rho_2 = 0$ is desirable for the range of spectral-to-Rayleigh ratios encountered in most applications. Thus the PSK signal set is excluded while the FSK and LFS signal sets are candidates. However, the relatively simpler implementation of FSK rules out the use of LFS for orthogonal signaling in the nonselective slow fading channel.

## Discussion

For ideal (coherent) reception over stable channels, the antipodal signal set PSK excels over FSK and LFS, in terms of both error probability and bandwidth. For partially coherent reception, a signal set intermediate to the antipodal (PSK) and orthogonal (FSK) signal sets would be optimum; the extent of cross coherence desirable would be dependent upon the degree of phase coherency.

For the Rician channel, for large values of spectral-to-Rayleigh, a situation similar to that for partially coherent reception prevails. The fading case parallels partially coherent reception with the added complexity of a fluctuating signal amplitude. Thus, in both instances, the error rate is an increasing function of $|\rho_2|$; the inquadrature cross coherence should be zero and the optimum value of in-phase cross coherence $\rho_1$ is dependent upon the spectral-to-Rayleigh ratio.

Theoretical analyses based upon the relationship of error probability to the signal parameters $\rho_1$, $\rho_2$ overlook certain practical constraints. Since the modulation cannot be removed in a manner such as squaring in PSK, a pilot tone is required in addition to the data transmission. Comparisons between modulation schemes must be made at equal total power levels and data rate; an analysis based upon power division between pilot signal and data is then required as well.

Finally, an obvious limitation is manifested in the implications of Fig. 2; the optimal value of the cross-coherence coefficient is highly sensitive to the SNR in the phase synchronization channel, for a wide range of SNR. Since communication systems almost always have a requirement to operate over a range of SNR's, and since the modulation characteristics would be exceedingly difficult to adaptively change as a function of SNR, the benefits of optimization would be quite limited in practice.

## References


[1] "Chirp or FSK answer to multipath problem in digital communications," *Commun. Des. Dig.*, pp. 30–31, Sept./Oct. 1967.

[2] D. S. Dayton and W. H. Smith, "FM chirp communications: An easily-instrumented multiple access modulation form for dispersive channels," presented at the IEEE Int. Conf. Communications, 1967.

[3] M. R. Winkley, "Chirp signals for communications," presented at IEEE WESCON, 1962.

[4] V. A. Kotelnikov, *The Theory of Optimum Noise Immunity.* New York: McGraw-Hill, 1960.

[5] D. Middleton, *An Introduction to Statistical Communication Theory.* New York: McGraw-Hill, 1960.

[6] H. L. Van Trees, *Detection, Estimation, and Modulation Theory,* p. 2. New York: Wiley, 1968.

[7] M. Abramowitz and I. A. Stegun, Ed., *Handbook of Mathematical Functions,* Nat. Bur. Stand., U.S. Gov. Print. Off., Washington, D.C., June 1964.

[8] C. E. Cook and M. Bernfeld, *Radar Signals.* New York: Academic, 1967.

[9] A. J. Viterbi, "Optimum detection and signal selection for partially coherent binary communication, *IEEE Trans. Inform. Theory,* vol. IT-11, pp. 239–246, Apr. 1965.

[10] J. I. Marcum, "Table of Q functions," Rand Corp., Calif., Rep. RM-339, 1950.

[11] G. L. Turin, "Error probability for binary symmetric ideal reception through nonselective slow fading and noise," *Proc. IRE,* vol. 46, pp. 1603–1619, Sept. 1958.

[12] W. Magnus and F. Oberhettinger, *Formulas and Theorems for the Functions of Mathematical Physics.* New York: Chelsea, 1954, p. 96.

# Part III
# Coding

No subject is of more interest or has more facets than that of coding in a spread spectrum system. The system cannot work, whether it is intended for communication, navigation, or whatever, unless the code sequence used for spreading the spectrum has the proper qualities. (This is not necessarily true for chirp systems, which in their simplest form can operate quite handily without any code sequence at all.) The qualities in a code that are necessary are

1) good autocorrelation and cross-correlation properties;
2) sufficient length to support maximum-distance ranging;
3) sufficient length to support the expected jamming margin;
4) a large family of sequences having all of the preceding qualities available;
5) ready implementability.

The codes that have been employed most often to satisfy these demands are the maximal linear codes, or *m*-sequences, although it must be said that their greatest advantage is in their ease of implementation and the degree of understanding of these codes by workers in the field. In their defense, however, the *m*-sequences cannot be bettered when only a few code sequences are needed.

So far we have only spoken of those codes that are used for spectrum spreading (for direct carrier modulation in the direct sequence modulated systems or for carrier frequency control in the frequency hoppers). There are other codes that are also used to great advantage in spread spectrum systems, just as they are in other types of systems, although in the spread spectrum systems they are called upon to contribute more to the operation of the overall system than in some other applications. Error detecting and correcting codes, for instance, are often employed in spread spectrum systems in the data channel to protect the information from interference-induced errors. The correlation process in a spread spectrum system receiver acts to whiten any incoming interference and thus to optimize it from the standpoint of its effect on the decoder. The decoder, on the other hand, must work as near its threshold as possible because the system as an overall entity must work in the poorest signal-to-noise ratios possible (in fact, when the interference is much larger than the desired signal). Golay codes, Reed–Solomon codes, convolutional codes, and may others have been employed in spread spectrum systems to provide the error detection and correction function.

Unfortunately, the error detection and correction encoding methods available all increase the number of bits that must be sent to get a given amount of information across to a desired receiver. Since the process gain and jamming margin of any spread spectrum system are functions of the data rate and vary inversely with it, it is seen that one must trade off the amount of error detection and correction provided against the degree that the encoding process increases the data rate. That is, unless an encoding process produces a greater gain in signal-to-noise ratio than is lost in increasing the data rate, then it is of no use to a spread spectrum system. For example, if a rate one-half code is employed that does not permit the receiver to operate in a signal-to-noise environment that is at least 3 dB worse than it is capable of with unencoded data, then the difference is a direct loss in antijamming performance to the receiver. Among the best results to date have been those encountered with the Reed–Solomon codes, where a block of 6 (binary) bits are encoded as a block of 7 (octal) octits, with the resulting block tolerant of up to two (and for some blocks three) errors. This is a significant improvement over the unencoded information, with only a modest increase (7/6) in data rate.

Of course, there are other reasons for encoding, such as protection of the data sent, and this is also encountered in spread spectrum systems. Such protection may be provided by making the spectrum-spreading code an encryption-type code or by encrypting the baseband information prior to the spreading operation.

Spread spectrum systems of the direct sequence type are very similar to pulse code modulation (PCM) systems, except the usual PCM codes are replaced by very long code sequences. The code sequences employed usually vary in length, depending on their application. Some codes are used only for synch acquisition, and their length is usually on the order of a few thousand bits, with the length being bounded by the system's specific requirements for minimum correlation properties, on the short side. At the other end, synchronization codes, or preambles, are usually limited in length by the need to process them in a receiver in a minimum amount of time. Codes used for information transfer often have periods such that they cannot be expected to repeat for many years.

Three papers are included in this part. The first is on codes that are intended for ranging. The codes that are described by Titsworth have been employed successfully to range over interplanetary distances. Their prime advantage is that they facilitate a synchronization process that does not force a search over a code length commensurate with the distances involved, even though the codes themselves (which are "product" or "composite" codes) are of such length that they do not repeat within the range to be measured. That is, the period of the codes employed is greater than the propagation time of the signals employed at the greatest distance over which range is to be measured.

Gold's paper on sequences for spread spectrum multiplexing describes another type of composite sequence, devised by him, that has large sets of useful code sequences available and yet is readily and simply constructed. These codes are useful for communication as well as for ranging, and have bounded autocorrelation and cross-correlation values for all members of the set generated by a particular generator configuration. These codes are employed where a large number of code-division multiplexed system users are anticipated. They offer no particular advantage for synch processing (other than the cited correlation properties) over the $m$-sequences.

Forney's paper discusses most of the different types of coding that are in common use, and the applications for which they are useful, including the $m$-sequences. This paper was included to give a general survey of the code types that are available for spread spectrum application.

## OTHER PAPERS OF INTEREST


1) R. B. Blizard, "Quantizing for correlation decoding," *IEEE Trans. Commun. Technol.*, Aug. 1967.
2) L. J. Bluestein, "Interleaving of pseudo-random sequences for synchronization," *IEEE Trans. Aerosp. Electron. Syst.*, July 1968.
3) R. H. Braasch, "The distribution of ($n$-$m$) terms for maximal length linear pseudo-random sequences," *IEEE Trans. Inform. Theory*, July 1968.
4) S. C. Gupta and J. H. Painter, "Correlation analyses of linearly processed pseudo-random sequences," this reprint volume.
5) J. H. Lindholm, "An analysis of the pseudo-randomness properties of long $m$-sequences," *IEEE Trans. Inform. Theory*, July 1968.
6) J. H. Painter, "Designing pseudo-random coded ranging systems," this reprint volume.
7) W. C. Lindsey, "Coded noncoherent communications," *IEEE Trans. Space Electron. Telem.*, March 1965.
8) G. D. O'Clock, Jr., G. L. Grasse, and D. A. Gandolfo, "Switchable acoustic surface wave sequence geneator," *Proc. IEEE*, Oct. 1972.
9) R. C. Titsworth, "Optimal ranging codes," this reprint volume.
10) S. Wainberg and J. K. Wolf, "Subsequences of pseudo-random sequences," *IEEE Trans. Commun. Technol.*, Oct. 1970.
11) R. C. White, Jr., "Experiments with digital computer simulation of pseudo-random noise generators," *IEEE Trans. Electron. Comput.*, June 1967.
12) J. K. Wolf, "On the application of some digital sequences to communication," *IEEE Trans. Commun. Syst.*, Dec. 1963.
13) P. A. DeVito, P. H. Carr, W. J. Kearns, and J. H. Silva, "Encoding and decoding with elastic surface waves as 10 megabits per second," *Proc. IEEE*, Oct. 1971.
14) I. M. Jacobs, "Practical applications of coding," *IEEE Trans. Inform. Theory*, May 1974.
15) J. Lee and D. R. Smith, "Families of shift-register sequences with impulsive correlation properties," *IEEE Trans. Inform. Theory*, Mar. 1974.

# Optimal Ranging Codes

ROBERT C. TITSWORTH, MEMBER, IEEE

*Summary*—This paper provides an analysis of a continuous, coded ranging scheme. By the use of a Boolean function, several "component" sequences are encoded into a transmitted signal. The receiver correlates the delayed return signal with different Boolean combinations of delayed replicas of the components to determine separately the time delay of each component sequence. From these delays, the total delay is computed.

By proper choice of encoding logic, number and type of components, and the decoding logics and procedure, the range can be found in a relatively short time. Optimal parameters of this ranging device are derived.

## I. INTRODUCTION

A RANGING system [1], [2] is a radar device which can transmit a coded signal continuously and receive the delayed return signal continuously. Such a system is feasible whenever it is possible to isolate the transmitter from the receiver by distance, terrain, sufficient Doppler shift, rebroadcast at a different frequency from a transponder on the target, or a combination of these. The advantages of continuous operation include maximum average-to-peak power ratios, variable integration time, continuous range measurement and tracking, and extreme accuracy.

One feature that must be incorporated into such a system is quick and easy initial range determination. Continuous operation will often require quite long codes, if no range ambiguity is to exist, especially when the range is hundreds of millions of kilometers as one might encounter ranging a planetary spacecraft.

In the unconstrained channel with white, additive Gaussian noise, it has long been recognized that the optimum receiver is a set of correlators, or filters matched to each possible (assumed discrete) time-shifted return of the transmitted code [3]. For a long code, this requires a prohibitive amount of receiver equipment, and with only one correlator, serial operation requires an extremely long time to determine the range.

When the amount of receiver equipment is limited, matched filtering is thus no longer the optimal detection scheme. A better scheme, as is shown here, is one which, by the use of a Boolean function, combines several "component" sequences to generate the transmitted signal. The receiver quickly acquires the phase of each component and computes the range from this. This method was first suggested by Golomb [4], and an operational model, built by Easterling [5], has had amazing success ranging the planet Venus [6].

Manuscript received August 12, 1963.
The author is with the Jet Propulsion Laboratory, California Institute of Technology, Pasadena, Calif.

This Report presents a general method for treating Boolean functions of component sequences. The optimal logics, component sequences, and number of components can be found by using the method.

## II. COMPONENT-CODED RANGING CODES

### A. The Acquisition Ratio

Suppose that a signal $x(t)$, generated by modulating a carrier by a sequence $\alpha = \{\alpha_n\}$ having period $p$, is sent through a simple continuous channel with white, additive Gaussian noise of zero mean as shown in Fig. 1. The time series $y(t)$ presented to the receiver is

$$y(t) = x(t - \tau) + n(t).$$

Here we assume no attenuation in the channel; we do this without loss in generality by assuming that the receiver is capable of amplifying $y(t)$ to recover any channel loss. The noise is, of course, also amplified, and this must be taken into account.

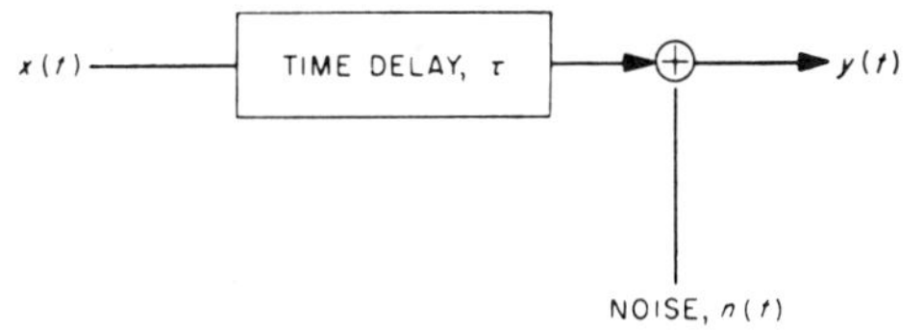


Fig. 1—The continuous channel.

If $t_0$ represents the clock rate of the modulating sequence $\alpha$, then the channel delay $\tau$ is, for some integer $k$,

$$\tau = kt_0 + \tau_0, \ (0 \leq \tau_0 < t_0).$$

Once $\tau_0$ is found, the receiver "locks" this quantity out of the measurement on $\tau$. We will assume, for the present, that such an *initial synchronization* or *clock lock* is in effect, and first consider cases with $\tau = kt_0$.

The optimum receiver to estimate $k$ for the Gaussian channel is shown in Fig. 2. This receiver minimizes the error probability for a given detection time, or, equivalently, the detection time for a given probability of error. It consists of filters (or correlators) matched to each possible transmitted signal, and this, as indicated previously, generally requires a large amount of equipment. Sometimes we are limited to a certain amount of equipment or receiver complexity, and we must operate on the incoming signal accordingly.

For example, by using $p$ correlators, we are able to estimate or "acquire" the time shift, or "phase" of the received signal with a certain probability of error after

Reprinted from *IEEE Trans. Space Electron. Telem.*, vol. SET-10, pp. 19–30, Mar. 1964.

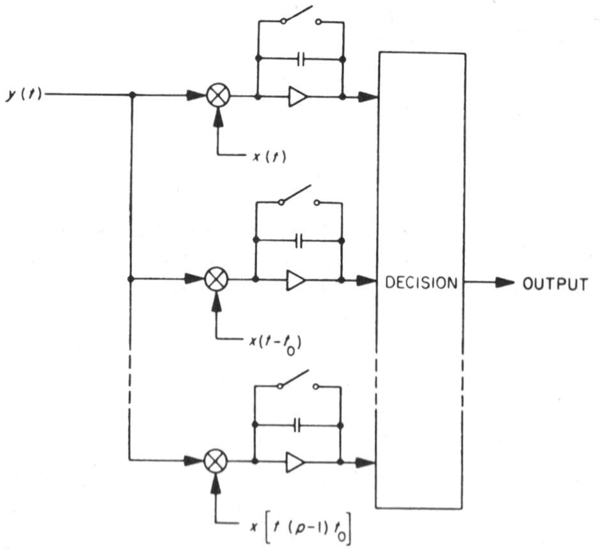


Fig. 2—The optimum receiver for the white-noise Gaussian channel.

integrating for, say, $T$ sec. This is the least $T$ giving this probability of error. However, when limited to *one* correlator in the receiver, we must correlate the incoming signal serially against every phase shift of the incoming signal, which requires $pT$ sec to achieve the same probability of error. There is thus a trade-off between receiver complexity and acquisition time:

$$T_{acq} = \frac{\text{time for a one-correlation receiver to acquire } \alpha}{\text{number of correlators in receiver}}.$$

Now, as an alternative, suppose our scheme is to cross-correlate $\alpha$ against several locally generated sequences, say $\gamma_1, \gamma_2, \cdots, \gamma_n$. The cross-correlation function $C_{\alpha\gamma_i}(m)$ repeats itself cyclically with period

$$v_i = (p, u_i)$$

if $\gamma_i$ has period $u_i$. That is, $C_{\alpha\gamma_i}(m + v_i) = C_{\alpha\gamma_i}(m)$.

Knowing the vector $\mathbf{m} = (m_1, m_2, \cdots, m_n)$ containing the delays $m_i$ (reduced modulo $v_i$) at which each of the $C_{\alpha\gamma_i}(m)$ is a maximum, we must be able to decide the most probable value of $k$ uniquely. The number of different vectors encountered must thus be greater than the number of phases of $\alpha$, so

$$p \leq [v_1, v_2, \cdots, v_n].$$

Second, the period $u_i$ of $\gamma_i$ cannot be relatively prime to $p$, for if it were, $C_{\alpha\gamma_i}(m)$ would be the same for all $m$ [because $v_i = (u_i, p)$]. Every $v_i$, therefore, divides $p$, and hence

$$p \geq [v_1, v_2, \cdots, v_n].$$

These last two inequalities indicate that

$$p = [v_1, v_2, \cdots, v_n].$$

With one integrator observing $T'$ seconds per step, the time required serially to perform all correlations of $\alpha$ with the $\gamma_i$, phase-by-phase and sequence-by-sequence, is $(v_1 + v_2 + \cdots + v_n)T'$. We choose $T'$ sufficiently long that the confidence limits in this scheme are the same as the previous ones using integration time $T$. The *acquisition ratio*, defined as

$$(T'_{acq})/(T_{acq}) = [(v_1 + v_2 + \cdots + v_n)T']/(pT)$$

represents the relative saving, if any, between the two schemes, each with the same specified number of integrators.

If it were possible to pick $\gamma_i$, $n$, and $T'$ in such a way that the ratio is less than unity, the alternate scheme would prove a more desirable receiver in that for a *given receiver complexity and error probability*, the *total time to acquire is less* in the second method. We will not only show that this is possible, but we will also give a way by which a great saving can be achieved.

## B. Correlation Time as a Function of Distinguishability

We now wish to compare the integration time $T$ required to give a constant probability of error as a function of correlation separation. Suppose a unit-power signal $x(t)$ is transmitted, $y(t) = x(t - m) + n(t)$ is received, and the receiver correlates $y(t)$ against a unit-power waveform $z(t)$ for a time $T$. The output $\Lambda(m, T)$ of the integrator is then

$$\begin{aligned}\Lambda(m, T) &= \int_0^T y(t)z(t)\,dt \\ &= \int_0^T x(t - m)z(t)\,dt + \int_0^T n(t)z(t)\,dt \\ &= TC_{xz}(m) + N(T).\end{aligned}$$

We allow $m$ to be any one of a discrete number of values, and we assume the noise is white, with zero mean. The noise term at the termination of integration has variance

$$\begin{aligned}\sigma_N^2 = \mathcal{E}(N^2) &= \int_0^T \int_0^T (N_0)/(2)\,\delta(t - s)z(t)z(s)\,dt\,ds \\ &= (N_0)/(2) \int_0^T z^2(t)\,dt = \tfrac{1}{2}N_0T.\end{aligned}$$

Let $\Delta C_{xz}$ represent the *distinguishability* of the normalized cross-correlation values $C_{xz}(m)$:

$$\Delta C_{xz} = |C_{xz}(m') - C_{xz}(m'')|,$$

where $|C_{xz}(m')| \geq |C_{xz}(m)|$ for all $m$, and $m''$ is chosen to minimize the difference above. The distinguishability-to-noise ratio limits the error probability; that is, two correlation detectors will have approximately the same probability of error if they have the same distinguishability-to-noise ratio, $\mathcal{E}(\Delta\Lambda)/\sigma_N$:

$$\begin{aligned}[\mathcal{E}(\Delta\Lambda)]/(\sigma_N) &= [T\Delta C_{xz}]/[(\tfrac{1}{2}N_0T)^{1/2}] \\ &= [(2T)/(N_0)]^{1/2}\,\Delta C_{xz}.\end{aligned}$$

As a result, the integration time for a given probability of error [more precisely, for a given $\mathcal{E}(\Delta\Lambda)/(\sigma_N)$] increases as the inverse-square of distinguishability of cross-correlation values.

$$T = \frac{N_0}{2}\left[\frac{\mathcal{E}(\Delta\Lambda)}{\sigma_N}\right]^2 [\Delta C_{xz}]^{-2}.$$

The ratio of the times $T'$ and $T$ for two such systems is hence

$$\frac{T'}{T} = \left(\frac{\Delta C_{xz}}{\Delta C_{x'z'}}\right)^2.$$

### C. Minimum Acquisition-Time Receivers

To minimize the acquisition ratio

$$\frac{T'_{\text{acq}}}{T_{\text{acq}}} = \frac{(v_1 + v_2 + \cdots + v_n)T'}{pT}$$

$$= \frac{(v_1 + v_2 + \cdots + v_n)}{[v_1, v_2, \cdots, v_n]}\left(\frac{\Delta C_{xz}}{\Delta C_{x'z'}}\right)^2$$

for a fixed $n$, by choosing $\alpha$ and $\gamma_i, \cdots, \gamma_n$ properly, we must first make the distinguishabilities $\Delta C_{x'z'}$ as large as possible, and second, minimize $(v_1 + \cdots + v_n)/[v_1, \cdots, v_n]$.

Recall that for each $i$ and $j$, $v_i$ and $v_j$ must have some nonunity relative prime factors. There will always exist $v'_i$, $i = 1, \cdots, n$, relatively prime in pairs (assuming $p \neq v_1 v_2 \cdots v_n$) with

$$p = v'_1 v'_2 \cdots v'_n$$

such that $(v'_1 + v'_2 + \cdots + v'_n) \leq (v_1 + v_2 \cdots + v_n)$. To demonstrate that this is possible, we proceed as follows: stepwise, consider all pairs $v_i, v_j$, and arbitrarily set $v_i = v'_i$ and $v'_j = v_j/(v_i, v_j)$ at each step. The final set $\{v'_i\}$ is pairwise relatively prime and $v'_1 v'_2 \cdots v'_n = p$, with either $v'_i < v_i$ or $v'_i = v_i$. Hence

$$(v_1 + v_2 + \cdots + v_n) \geq (v'_1 + v'_2 + \cdots v'_n).$$

Since we wish to pick $v_i$ to minimize the acquisition ratio, we must let the $v_i$ be relatively prime, for otherwise we could follow the procedure above to pick a relatively prime set of $v'_i$ giving a smaller acquisition ratio.

It is a well-known result that $(v_1 + \cdots + v_n)$ is minimized, relative to the constraint that $p = v_1 v_2 \cdots v_n$, by choosing each $v_i$ equal to $\sqrt[n]{p}$. Of course, the distinctness of each $v_i$ makes this impossible. We must, in consolation, group the $v_i$ as close to $\sqrt[n]{p}$ as possible, keeping them relatively prime.

In summary, for a minimum acquisition-time receiver, we seek $n$ well-chosen sequences whose correlations $C_{\alpha\gamma_i}(m)$ have periods $v_i$ which are relatively prime and close to $\sqrt[n]{p}$ and which have a maximum distinguishability $\Delta C'$ between phases. Over all such schemes, we then choose $n$ to further minimize the acquisition ratio, approximately

$$\frac{T'_{\text{acq}}}{T_{\text{acq}}} \simeq np^{1-n/n}\left(\frac{\Delta C}{\Delta C'}\right)^2.$$

## III. Boolean Combination of Component Sequences

It has been shown elsewhere [7] that the distinguishability of an autocorrelation function can always be made greater than that of a cross-correlation function. We may attempt to minimize this effect by defining $\alpha$ as a combination of "component" sequences $\xi_i$. That is, we would like to be able to combine the $\xi_i$ in some way to produce $\alpha$, choosing this function to maximize the distinguishability. We are dealing with binary sequences, and it is thus natural to use a Boolean function. We will assume that, for an arbitrary Boolean function $f$, the function is applied termwise, as though $\alpha$ were the output of a switching network when the inputs are the $\xi_i$ (see Fig. 3).

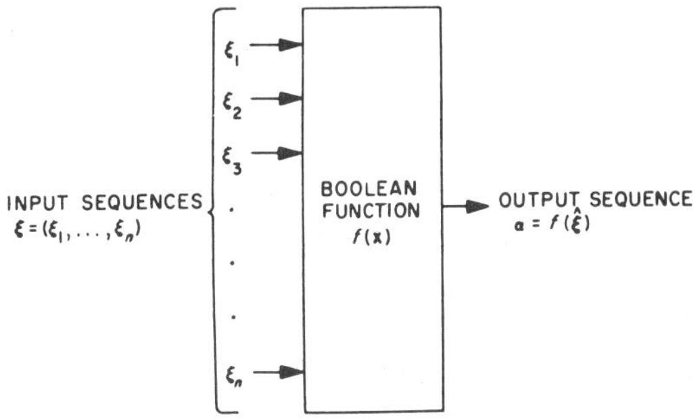


Fig. 3—Sequence generation by logical combination of component sequences.

We assume $\alpha$ and $\xi_i$ are binary ($\pm 1$) sequences, so that $f$ is a ($\pm 1$) Boolean function. Define $\hat{\alpha}$, $\hat{\xi}_i$, and $\hat{f}$ on (0, 1):

$$\alpha_i = (-1)^{\hat{\alpha}_i}$$

$$\xi_{ij} = (-1)^{\hat{\xi}_{ij}}$$

$$f = (-1)^{\hat{f}}.$$

As a convention, we will assume $f$ is a ($\pm 1$) function of (0, 1) variables $x_i$.

Since the transmitted sequence $\alpha = f(\boldsymbol{\xi})$ is a function of component sequences, we will correlate $\alpha$ at the receiver against sequences $\gamma_i = g_i(\boldsymbol{\xi})$, also made by forming Boolean functions of stored replicas of the same component sequences. When correlating $\alpha$ against $\gamma_i$, we agree to vary only the phase $m_i$ of $\xi_i$ at the receiver to compute $C_{\alpha\gamma_i}(m)$. Then $C_{\alpha\gamma_i}(m)$ has period $v_i = (p, u'_i)$, where $u'_i$ is the period of $\xi_i$. By our reasoning in Section II-A, we see that $u'_i$ must equal $v_i$ and satisfy all the previously stated conditions.

To optimize the set of $\xi_i$, we thus must choose the $v_i$ relatively prime in pairs, and each approximately $\sqrt[n]{p}$, where $p = v_1 v_2 \cdots v_n$ is the period of $\alpha$. Then we must choose $f$ and the $g_i$ to make the $\Delta C_{\alpha\gamma_i}$ as large as possible.

### A. The Boolean Transform

Let $f(\mathbf{x})$ be a $\pm 1$-valued Boolean function of (0, 1) variables $x_1, \cdots, x_n$. For any $\mathbf{s} = (s_1, s_2, \cdots, s_n)$, $s_i = 0$

or 1, define

$$\phi(\mathbf{s}, \mathbf{x}) = 2^{-n/2}(-1)^{s_1x_1+\cdots+s_nx_n}.$$

These $2^n$ functions of $\mathbf{x}$, the Rademacher-Walsh functions, form an orthonormal basis for $2^n$-space. Since $f(\mathbf{x})$ is completely specified by the values it assumes on each of the $2^n$ different $\mathbf{x}$, $f$ can be treated as a member of $2^n$-space. Relative to the basis $\phi(\mathbf{s}, \mathbf{x})$, $f(\mathbf{x})$ has components $F(\mathbf{s})$ given by

$$F(\mathbf{s}) = 2^{-n/2} \sum_{\text{all } \mathbf{x}} f(\mathbf{x})\phi(\mathbf{s}, \mathbf{x}).$$

That is, $F(\mathbf{s})$ is the projection of $f(\mathbf{x})$ on $\phi(\mathbf{s}, \mathbf{x})$, normalized so that

$$\sum_{\mathbf{s}} F^2(\mathbf{s}) = 1.$$

Similarly,

$$f(\mathbf{x}) = 2^{n/2} \sum_{\text{all } \mathbf{s}} F(\mathbf{s})\phi(\mathbf{s}, \mathbf{x}).$$

$F(\mathbf{s})$ can also be viewed as the correlation between the *truth table* of $f(\mathbf{x})$ and that of $s_1x_1 \oplus \cdots \oplus s_nx_n$.

### B. The Correlation Function

Consider the effect of putting binary sequences $\xi_i$ into the logic $f(\mathbf{x})$. The value of the $i$th sequence at time $k$ is $\xi_{ik}$, and the vector giving the input variables to $f$ at time $k$ is $\boldsymbol{\xi}_k$; the output is then $f(\boldsymbol{\xi}_k)$. This can also be expressed, by using the Kronecker delta, as

$$\alpha_k = f(\hat{\boldsymbol{\xi}}_k) = \sum_{\text{all } \mathbf{x}} f(\mathbf{x})\ \delta(\mathbf{x}, \hat{\boldsymbol{\xi}}_k),$$

$$\begin{aligned}\alpha_k &= 2^{n/2} \sum_{\text{all } \mathbf{s}} F(\mathbf{s})\phi(\mathbf{s}, \hat{\boldsymbol{\xi}}_k)\\ &= \sum_{\text{all } \mathbf{s}} F(\mathbf{s})(-1)^{s_1\hat{\xi}_{1k}+\cdots+s_n\hat{\xi}_{nk}}\\ &= \sum_{\text{all } \mathbf{s}} F(\mathbf{s})\xi_{1k}^{s_1}\xi_{2k}^{s_2} \cdots \xi_{nk}^{s_n}.\end{aligned}$$

Note in the above that the $F(\mathbf{s})$ are properties of the logic alone and do not involve the form of the input sequences.

Let $\gamma$ be another sequence made by inserting the $n$ component sequences $\xi_i$ into a logic $g(\mathbf{x})$:

$$\gamma_k = g(\hat{\boldsymbol{\xi}}_k) = \sum_{\mathbf{s}} G(\mathbf{s})\xi_{1k}^{s_1}\xi_{2k}^{s_2} \cdots \xi_{nk}^{s_n}.$$

At the receiver, we correlate the incoming sequence $\alpha$ against this locally generated one, choosing the logic $g(\mathbf{x})$ to maximize the distinguishability among phases. We allow different logics at the receiver for each component to be acquired; that is, while $\xi_1$ is being acquired, use $g_1(\mathbf{x})$, and while $\xi_2$ is being acquired, use $g_2(\mathbf{x})$, etc. This cross-correlation takes the form

$$C_{\alpha\gamma}(m) = \sum_{\mathbf{s}} \sum_{\mathbf{w}} F(\mathbf{s})G(\mathbf{w}) \cdot\left[\frac{1}{p} \sum_{k=0}^{p-1} \xi_{1,k}^{s_1}\xi_{1,k+m}^{w_1} \cdots \xi_{n,k}^{s_n}\xi_{n,k+m}^{w_n}\right].$$

The fact that the $\xi_i$ all have relative prime periods means that they are independent to the degree that the correlation of products is the product of the correlations. Because of this product rule and because

$$\frac{1}{v_i}\sum_{k=0}^{v_i-1} \xi_{i,k}^{s_i}\xi_{i,k+m}^{w_i} = \begin{cases} 1 & \text{if } s_i = w_i = 0\\ d_i & \text{if } s_i \neq w_i\\ C_i(m) & \text{if } s_i = w_i = 1,\end{cases}$$

where we introduce the notation

$$d_i = \frac{1}{v_i}\sum_{k=0}^{v-1} \xi_{ik}$$

$$C_i(m) = \frac{1}{v_i}\sum_{k=0}^{v-1} \xi_{i,k}\xi_{i,k+m},$$

we can then write the following expression for the cross-correlation function:

$$C_{\alpha\gamma}(m) = \sum_{\mathbf{s}} \sum_{\mathbf{w}} F(\mathbf{s})G(\mathbf{w}) \prod_{i=1}^{n} d_i^{|s_i-w_i|}\ [C_i(m)]^{s_iw_i}.$$

(Here we adopt $[\cdot]^0 = 1$ purely as convention.) If we denote the product term as $C(m; \mathbf{s}, \mathbf{w})$,

$$C_{\alpha\gamma}(m) = \sum_{\mathbf{s}} \sum_{\mathbf{w}} F(\mathbf{s})G(\mathbf{w})C(m; \mathbf{s}, \mathbf{w}).$$

This formula is of fundamental importance in finding the minimum acquisition-time receiver. Note that by using it, one may express the cross-correlation between any two Boolean functions of the $\xi_i$ as a sum of transform coefficients of the two functions weighted by autocorrelation properties of the $\xi_i$. Also note in the equation $C(m; \mathbf{s}, \mathbf{w})$ that when $s_i \neq w_i$,

$$|C(m; \mathbf{s}, \mathbf{w})| \leq d_i,$$

and when both $s_j \neq w_j$ and $s_i \neq w_i$,

$$|C(m; \mathbf{s}, \mathbf{w})| \leq d_i\, d_j, \text{ etc.}$$

From these considerations, when the $d_j$ are sufficiently small, we may often omit the terms with $\mathbf{s} \neq \mathbf{w}$ from the correlation equation. This is generally the case, for as we shall see, the $\xi_i$ must have maximally distinguishable correlation functions, a condition requiring small $d_i$, [7].

## IV. Minimum Acquisition-Time Systems

In this section we treat two ranging systems. The first is the optimal configuration assuming that symbol synchronization between transmitter and receiver is achieved through some external source. The second relaxes this condition, but instead uses one of the components as a "clock" sequence, locking a phase-locked loop to the incoming symbol rate.

Not only are the encoding logics $f$ different for these types of systems, but also the decoding logics $g_i$.

We assume that the transmitter codes are displaced from the receiver codes by $m_1, m_2, \cdots, m_n$ steps, or an equivalent shift of $m$ steps,

$m = m_i \pmod{v_i}$
$v_i$ = period of sequence at input $x_i$.

We step each component at the receiver until we have moved the locally generated components by an amount equivalent to $m$ and thereby determine the "distance" $m$ from transmitter to receiver.

If the $\alpha$ received is delayed by $m$ steps, our decoding scheme is also clear: after having found the delays $m_i$ giving maximum cross-correlations of $\alpha$ with each of $\xi_i$, we declare that $m$ is that integer such that, for each $i$,

$$m = m_i \pmod{v_i}$$

which has a unique solution modulo $p$ by the "Chinese" remainder theorem [8] of number theory.

### A. The Synchronous Receiver

This first system, as we have indicated above, is based on the assumption that initial synchronization or clock-lock is in effect so that the received sequence is symbol-wise in-step with the locally generated ones. The decoding procedure is based on the following criteria:

1) The order of component acquisition is immaterial, provided the proper decoding logic corresponding to that component is used.
2) Acquisition of any component does not rely on prior acquisition of any other component.

Consider the terms in $f(\hat{\xi})$ involving $\xi_i$; *i.e.*, the contribution of the $i$th input to the total output. Call this part of the signal $f_i(\hat{\xi})$. For example,

$$f_1(\hat{\xi}) = F(1, 0, \cdots, 0)\xi_1 + F(1, 1, 0, \cdots 0)\xi_1\xi_2 + \cdots.$$

Those terms of $f_1$ in which $\xi_2, \cdots, \xi_n$ appear can be viewed as "cross-talk," which can be a degrading factor in determining the shift of $\xi_1$ if no knowledge of $\xi_2, \cdots, \xi_n$ is assumed.

The receiver must thus either minimize this cross-talk and/or try to estimate what the cross-talk will be and use this information to further enhance reception.

If the signals in each channel are independent, or if we do not allow estimation of one component to influence the estimation of another, we have no other course than to minimize cross-talk. We desire, then, to separate from $f(\hat{\xi})$ only that component carrying the information we want. This is accomplished most effectively by correlating $\alpha = f(\hat{\xi})$ against $\xi_1$. We desire to pick $f$ and the $\xi_i$, $i = 1, 2, \cdots, n$, in such a way that the cross-correlations of $\alpha$ with each $\xi_i$ have maximum distinguishability. By choosing $g_i(\mathbf{x}) = (-1)^{x_i}$, we can write $\xi_i$ as

$$\xi_i = g_i(\hat{\xi}).$$

The transform of $g_i$ is easily computed, for we note that $g_i(\mathbf{x}) = 2^{n/2}\phi(\mathbf{x}, \mathbf{e}^i)$, defining $\mathbf{e}^i$ to be the $i$th unit vector having a single one, in the $i$th place.

$$\mathbf{e}^i = (0, 0, \cdots, 0, 1, 0, \cdots, 0).$$

The transform of $g_i$ is then

$$G_i(\mathbf{s}) = \delta(\mathbf{s}, \mathbf{e}^i).$$

Consequently, the cross-correlation equation reduces to

$$C_{\alpha\xi_i}(m) = \{[\sum_{\mathbf{s},\, s_i=1} F(\mathbf{s}) \prod_{j\neq i} (d_j)^{s_j}]C_i(m) + [\sum_{\mathbf{s},\, s_i=0} F(\mathbf{s}) \prod_{j\neq i} (d_j)^{s_j}]\, d_i\}.$$

For any two values $m'$ and $m''$ of $m_i$, the difference in correlation values $C_{\alpha\xi_i}(m)$ (and specifically the distinguishability) is dependent separately on the autocorrelation of $\xi_i$ and the Boolean function.

$$C_{\alpha\xi_i}(m') - C_{\alpha\xi_i}(m'') = [\sum_{\mathbf{s},\, s_i=1} F(\mathbf{s}) \prod_{j\neq i} (d_j)^{s_j}] \times [C_i(m') - C_i(m'')].$$

Our course to optimize the acquisition receiver is now clear. First, each $\xi_i$ is to have minimum out-of-phase autocorrelation values so that $C_i(m)$ has maximum distinguishability, and second, $f$ is to be chosen such that

$$|\sum_{\mathbf{s},\, s_i=1} F(\mathbf{s}) \prod_{j\neq i} (d_j)^{s_j}|$$

is maximized—also for each $i$. Further, we can always choose the sum to be *positive* by proper choice of $f$. Suppose the sum were negative. By choosing $g_i'(\mathbf{s}) = (-1)^{x_i+1}$, we correlate $\alpha$ against $\xi_i'$, given by

$$\xi_i' = g_i'(\hat{\xi}) = -\xi_i$$

and have $C_{\alpha\xi_i'}(m) = -C_{\alpha\xi_i}(m)$, which has the sum in question positive. By duality, we can thus always complement $x_i$ in $f(\mathbf{x})$, if need be, to make

$$\sum_{\mathbf{s},\, s_i=1} F(\mathbf{s}) \prod_{j\neq i} (d_j)^{s_j} \geq 0.$$

Now, consider the sum to be maximized,

$$\sum_{\mathbf{s},\, s_i=1} F(\mathbf{s}) \prod_{j\neq i} (d_j)^{s_j}.$$

One of the terms in the sum is $F(\mathbf{e}^i)$, but the remainder have products of $d_j$ as factors. Denote

$$d' = \max_{i\neq j} \{|d_j|\}$$

$$F_M = \max_{\substack{\mathbf{s},\, s_i=1 \\ \mathbf{s}\neq\mathbf{e}^i}} \{|F(s)|\}.$$

Using the triangle inequality, we bound the sum of remaining terms, calling it $F_i$ as follows:

$$|F_i| = \left|\sum_{\substack{\mathbf{s},\, s_i=1 \\ \mathbf{s}\neq\mathbf{e}^i}} F(\mathbf{s}) \prod_{j\neq i} (d_j)^{s_j}\right| \leq \sum_{\substack{\mathbf{s},\, s_i=1 \\ \mathbf{s}\neq\mathbf{e}^i}} |F(\mathbf{s})| \prod_{j\neq i} |d_j|^{s_j}$$

$$|F_i| \leq F_M \sum_{\substack{\mathbf{s},\, s_i=1 \\ \mathbf{s}\neq\mathbf{e}^i}} \prod_{j\neq i} (d')^{s_j} \leq F_M\left[\sum_{k=0}^{n-1} \binom{n-1}{k}(d')^k - 1\right].$$

The binomial theorem applied to the inequality gives

$$|\sum_{\mathbf{s},\, s_i=1} F(\mathbf{s}) \prod_{j\neq i} (d')| \leq F_M[(1 + d')^{n-1} - 1].$$

Note that when $d'$ is small this upper bound can be replaced by $nd'F_M$:

$$|F| \leq nd'F_M.$$

We recognize that by using nearly balanced sequences for the $\xi_i$ (which we want to do to optimize distinguishability [7]), it is highly efficient to maximize $F(\mathbf{e}^i)$ by proper choice of $f(\mathbf{x})$. In fact, any time that $nd' < 1$, this is the course we *must* follow to insure the largest possible $F(\mathbf{e}^i) + F$. When we use nearly balanced sequences, we can approximate

$$C_{\alpha\xi_i}(m) \simeq F(\mathbf{e}^i)C_i(m).$$

So that all channels are identical, let us set all $F(\mathbf{e}^i) = F(\mathbf{e}^1)$. We can then prove that *if* $f(\mathbf{x})$ *is a Boolean function such that* $F(\mathbf{e}^i) = F(\mathbf{e}^1)$ *for all* $i$, *and* $F(\mathbf{e}^1)$ *is maximal over all Boolean functions, then* $f(\mathbf{x})$ *is a strict majority logic*:

$$f(\mathbf{x}) = \begin{cases} 1 & \text{if } \mathbf{x} \text{ has less than } n/2 \text{ one's} \\ -1 & \text{if } \mathbf{x} \text{ has more than } n/2 \text{ one's.} \end{cases}$$

To show that this is true, note that

$$F(\mathbf{e}^1) = \frac{1}{n}\sum_{i=1}^{n} F(\mathbf{e}^i) = \frac{2^{-n}}{n}\sum_{i=1}^{n}\sum_{\mathbf{x}} f(\mathbf{x})(-1)^{x_i}$$

$$= \frac{2^{-n}}{n}\sum_{\mathbf{x}} f(\mathbf{x})\sum_{i=1}^{n}(-1)^{x_i}$$

$$= \frac{2^{-n}}{n}\sum_{\mathbf{x}} f(\mathbf{x})[n - 2\,||\mathbf{x}||]$$

where $||\mathbf{x}||$ denotes the number of *one's* in $\mathbf{x}$. To maximize $F(\mathbf{e}^1)$, if $||\mathbf{x}|| > n/2$, we must make $f(\mathbf{x}) = -1$, and if $||\mathbf{x}|| < n/2$, we must make $f(\mathbf{x}) = 1$. Those $\mathbf{x}$ with $||\mathbf{x}|| = n/2$, if $n$ is even, may be placed arbitrarily in the truth-table of $f$ without affecting $F(\mathbf{e}^i)$. If $n$ is odd, $f$ is a symmetric Boolean function; that is, we may permute the $x_i$ without changing $f$. And if $n$ is even, we can make it symmetric by symmetric placement of those $\mathbf{x}$ with $||\mathbf{x}|| = n/2$ in the truth table. Then, if $[y]$ denotes the integer part of the number $y$,

$$F(\mathbf{e}^i) = \frac{2^{1-n}}{n}\sum_{k=1}^{[n/2]}\binom{n}{k}[n - 2k]$$

$$= 2^{1-n}\binom{n-1}{\left[\frac{n}{2}\right]}.$$

For moderately large $n$, this is approximately

$$F(\mathbf{e}^i) \simeq [(\pi/2)(n - 1)]^{-1/2}$$

by the Stirling formula [2].

Into the acquisition ratio we insert the distinguishability for the cross-correlations $C_{\alpha\xi_i}(m)$ and the distinguishability of $C_{\alpha'}(m)$ if $\alpha'$ were an optimal sequence from the autocorrelation viewpoint. Whenever the $v_i$ are much larger than unity, both $\Delta C_i$ and $\Delta C_\alpha$ are approximately one. The acquisition ratio to be minimized is, then, approximately given by

$$\frac{T'_{\text{acq}}(n)}{T_{\text{acq}}} \simeq np^{1-n/n}\left[2^{1-n}\binom{n-1}{\frac{n-1}{2}}\right]^{-2}.$$

(As shown in Appendix II, we need consider only *odd n*.)

Use of the Stirling approximation reduces the approximate acquisition ratio to

$$\frac{T'_{\text{acq}}}{T_{\text{acq}}} \simeq \left(\frac{\pi}{2p}\right)n(n - 1)p^{1/n}.$$

To find the optimum value of $n$, the derivative of $T'_{\text{acq}}/T_{\text{acq}}$,

$$\frac{d(T'_{\text{acq}}/T_{\text{acq}})}{dn} \simeq \left(\frac{\pi}{2p}\right)\left(\frac{p^{1/n}}{n}\right)[2n^2 - n - (n - 1)\ln p]$$

goes to zero only when the term in brackets is zero; this occurs at those values of $n$, such that

$$\ln p = [(2n - 1)n]/[n - 1],$$

$$p = e^{n(2n-1)/(n-1)}$$

$$v_i \approx \sqrt[n]{p} = e^2e^{1/(n+1)}.$$

Upon insertion of this value into the acquisition ratio, we find the optimal ratio:

$$\left(\frac{T'_{\text{acq}}}{T_{\text{acq}}}\right)_{\text{opt}} \simeq \frac{\pi}{2}n(n - 1)e^{-2n+1}.$$

This ratio above is tabulated in Table I. Note that since the ratio is less than unity, the minimal acquisition-time receiver is better than matched filters.

TABLE I
OPTIMAL ACQUISITION RATIO AND PERIODS FOR GIVEN $n$, SINGLE CORRELATOR CASE

| $n$ | $p$ | $(T'_{\text{acq}}/T_{\text{acq}})$ |
|---|---|---|
| 1 | any | $1.0 \times 10^{0}$ |
| 3 | $1.8 \times 10^{3}$ | $6.4 \times 10^{-2}$ |
| 5 | $7.6 \times 10^{4}$ | $3.9 \times 10^{-3}$ |
| 7 | $3.8 \times 10^{6}$ | $1.5 \times 10^{-5}$ |
| 9 | $2.0 \times 10^{8}$ | $4.7 \times 10^{-6}$ |
| 11 | $1.0 \times 10^{10}$ | $1.3 \times 10^{-8}$ |
| 13 | $5.7 \times 10^{11}$ | $3.4 \times 10^{-9}$ |
| 15 | $3.1 \times 10^{13}$ | $8.4 \times 10^{-11}$ |
| 17 | $1.6 \times 10^{15}$ | $2.0 \times 10^{-12}$ |
| 19 | $9.1 \times 10^{16}$ | $4.6 \times 10^{-14}$ |

Hence, the minimal acquisition-time receiver, given an $\alpha$-period $p$, would ideally combine $n$ optimal binary sequences with

$$p \simeq e^{n(2n-1)/(n-1)}$$

using component sequences $\xi_i$ of periods $v_i$ relatively prime in pairs and near to $9(\simeq e^2)$.

### *B. Modified Synchronous Receivers*

Suppose, as an alternative, we are willing to make a receiver which has one correlator for each of the components $\xi_i$ of $\alpha$. What is the best receiver? Just as in the constant-equipment case, we define an acqusition ratio:

$$\frac{T'_{\text{acq}}}{T_{\text{acq}}} = \frac{\text{time for } n\text{-component acquisition}}{\text{time for 1-component acquisition}}$$

The time for a 1-component code $\alpha$ to be acquired is merely its period $p$ times the integration time $T$ per phase, or $pT$. On the other hand, with $n$ correlators working simultaneously, the time to be acquired is the new integration time per step $T'$ times the number of phases, or $\max_i \{v_i\}T'$,

$$\frac{T'_{acq}}{T_{acq}} = \frac{\max \{v_i\}}{[v_1, v_2, \cdots, v_n]} \frac{T'}{T}.$$

To minimize this ratio, we may argue as before: the $v_i$ must be relatively prime, for if they were not, we could pick a relatively prime set with the same least common multiple but having a smaller maximum component. Next, to further minimize the ratio, we want to make $(v_i)_{max}$ as close to the average $v_i$ as possible

$$(v_i)_{max} \simeq (v_1 + \cdots + v_n)/(n).$$

The best acquisition ratio is thus given by

$$\frac{T'_{acq}}{T_{acq}} \simeq \frac{v_1 + \cdots + v_n}{nv_1v_2 \cdots v_n} \frac{T'}{T}.$$

This equation is exactly the same form as that for the minimum-equipment receiver described previously except for a factor of $1/n$. The same technique for obtaining $\alpha$ from the components $\xi_i$ (which must be optimum binary sequences) must be applied in both cases, that is, $\hat{\alpha} =$ maj $(\hat{\xi})$. Further,

$$v_i \simeq \sqrt[n]{p}.$$

With a majority logic, optimum components, and $v_i \simeq \sqrt[n]{p}$, the acquisition ratio is approximately $1/n$ times that found in Section IV-A:

$$\frac{T'_{acq}}{T_{acq}} \simeq p^{-1+1/n} \left[ 2^{-n+1} \binom{n-1}{\frac{n-1}{2}} \right]^{-2}.$$

Upon setting the derivative of this ratio to zero, we find

$$p \simeq e^{n^2/(n-1)}$$

$$v_i \simeq e^{n/(n-1)} \simeq e$$

$$\left(\frac{T'_{acq}}{T_{acq}}\right)_{opt} \simeq \frac{\pi}{2}(n-1)e^n.$$

This is tabulated in Table II. Although if each $v_i$ were about $3(\simeq e)$ in length, the analysis above, based upon the assumptions that the $d_i$ are small and $n$ is large, may not be strictly valid because the relative prime condition on $\{v_i\}$ may carry $(v_i)_{max}$ far from $e$. However the analysis is indicative of the action to be taken in the design of such a receiver; after an approximate choice of $p$, choose $n$ such that

$$p \simeq e^{n^2/(n-1)}.$$

Having this $n$, choose $n$ relatively prime optimal components $\xi_i$ whose periods are as *small* as possible, but greater than one. Then modify the choice of $p$ to

$$p = v_1v_2 \cdots v_n.$$

The approximations certainly establish a lower bound on the acquisition ratio, in any case, since optimal conditions were assumed at all times.

TABLE II

Optimal Acquisition Ratio and Periods for Given $n$, $n$-Correlator Case

| $n$ | $p$ | $(T'_{acq}/T_{acq})$ |
|---|---|---|
| 1 | any | $1.0 \times 10^0$ |
| 3 | $9.0 \times 10$ | $1.5 \times 10^{-1}$ |
| 5 | $5.2 \times 10^2$ | $4.2 \times 10^{-2}$ |
| 7 | $3.5 \times 10^3$ | $8.6 \times 10^{-3}$ |
| 9 | $2.5 \times 10^4$ | $1.6 \times 10^{-3}$ |
| 11 | $1.8 \times 10^5$ | $2.6 \times 10^{-4}$ |
| 13 | $1.3 \times 10^6$ | $4.3 \times 10^{-5}$ |
| 15 | $9.5 \times 10^6$ | $6.7 \times 10^{-6}$ |
| 17 | $7.0 \times 10^7$ | $1.0 \times 10^{-6}$ |
| 19 | $5.1 \times 10^8$ | $1.6 \times 10^{-7}$ |

### C. Optimal Clock-Component Codes

We have previously assumed an initial synchronization or clock-lock condition in finding optimal codes. However, we now relax this condition so that the receiver must not only determine the proper integral number of phase steps separating the incoming and local codes, but it must also acquire the incoming symbol rate and lock its code generators to it.

Easterling's single-channel ranging receiver is shown in Fig. 4 (p. 26). The inner loop, or clock-loop, is synchronized to the symbol rate of the incoming code $\alpha$ by the presence of a "clock component" in $\alpha$, and the locally generated code $\gamma$ is slaved to the output of this clock-loop.

Whenever the clock-loop is locked to the clock component of $\alpha$, the local code $\gamma$ is stepwise synchronized to $\alpha$.

Both $\alpha$ and $\gamma$ are logical combinations of a clock sequence

$$+ - + - + - + - + - \cdots$$

and $n - 1$ other sequences, whose properties we shall describe in more detail later. The transmitter logic we take, for convenience, to be of the form

$$x_1 \oplus \hat{f}(x_1, x_2, \cdots, x_n)$$

and, similarly, those at the receiver to be

$$x_1 \oplus \hat{g}_i(x_1, x_2, \cdots, x_n).$$

In these functions, $x_1$ is the clock input and $x_2, \cdots, x_n$ are the other sequence inputs; $\oplus$, as usual, indicates modulo 2 addition. We have indexed the $g$'s with an $i$ to denote that we are willing to use different logics in the decoding procedure, perhaps a different logic for each component.

The correlation meter reads the normalized cross-correlation $C(m)$ between the incoming and local codes. The clock-loop is held in lock according to the normalized slope of $C(m)$, defined as

$$\Delta C(m) = \tfrac{1}{2}[C(m) - C(m')]$$

where $m'$ is the effect of stepping the clock phase one step forward, *i.e.*, from $m_1$ to $m_1 + 1$. We shall refer to $\Delta C(m)$ as the *clock-lock correlation*.

The optimal codes to use in the above scheme must have the following properties: 1) a specified initial clock-

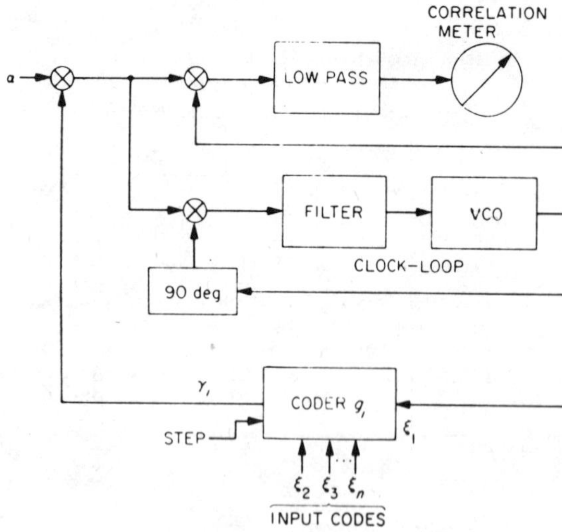


Fig. 4—The single channel ranging receiver with clock-acquiring loop.

lock correlation; 2) maximum increase in clock-lock correlation as components are acquired; and 3) no more than a specified percentage drop in clock-lock during the search.

Besides these obvious requirements, it is advantageous to adopt the following philosophy in choosing the logics:

1) Acquisition of $k$th component does not *rely* on the fact that any of the $k - 2$ previously considered non-clock components have been acquired.
2) The fact that previously considered components *are* acquired shall enhance acquisition of the component under present scrutiny.
3) Components not yet considered, whether such components happen to be already in-phase or not, shall not affect the acquisition.

In previous analysis, we have seen that the components $\xi_i$ must have relative prime periods, have small out-of-phase correlation, and a balance of one's and minus one's. To simplify calculations, we make the following assumptions concerning the $\xi_i$:

1) Independence, *i.e.*, the correlation between the $i$th and the $j$th input sequence $|C_{ij}(m)| = 0$ for all $m$, every $i \neq j$ and $i, j \neq 1$.
2) Perfect autocorrelation of input sequences, *i.e.*, $C_i(m) = 0$ for all $m \not\equiv 0 \bmod v_i$, all $i \neq 1$.
3) Balance, *i.e.*, equal number of *one's* and *zero's* in each component sequence, per period.

For the type of sequences we must use as components (pseudonoise or near-pseudonoise), none of the above assumptions strictly applies. In fact, 1) and 2) cannot occur simultaneously. However, each "$=0$" above can be replaced by "$<\epsilon$" for some appropriate $\epsilon$, so that the results are essentially the same whenever $\epsilon$ is small.

Based on these criteria, the optimum coding and decoding functions are found by the following rules:

1) *Encoding Function*: transmit $x_1 \oplus f(x_1, x_2, \cdots, x_n)$, where $f$ has $w$ one's in its truth table,

$$w = 2^{n-1}(1 - C_0)$$
$$C_0 = \text{initial clock-lock correlation.}$$

These $w$ one's are put in $f$ in a modified majority logic:

*if* $f(x_1, x_2, \cdots, x_n) = 1$
*and* $(x_2, \cdots, x_n)$ has fewer one's than some $(y_2, \cdots, y_n)$
then $f(y_1, y_2, \cdots, y_n) = 1$.

2) *Decoding Functions*: decode by correlating with $x_1 \oplus g_i(x_1, x_2, \cdots, x_n)$ where each $g_i$ has $u$ one's in its truth table,

$$u = 2^{n-1}(1 - K_0)$$
$$K_0 = \text{fractional drop in clock-lock from } C_0.$$

a) *Clock-component acquisition:* $g_i(x_1, x_2, \cdots, x_n) = 0$
$\Delta C = C_0$.

b) $k$th-*component acquisition*: first list the $w$ vectors on which $f(x_1, x_2, \cdots, x_n) = 1$ and calculate the numbers

$$F'(s_2, \cdots, s_n) = 2^{1-n}\left\{\begin{array}{l}\text{difference between number of times} \\ s_2x_2 \oplus \cdots \oplus s_nx_n = 1 \text{ and} \\ s_2x_2 \oplus \cdots \oplus s_nx_n = 0\end{array}\right\}$$

for every binary vector $(s_2, s_3, \cdots, s_n)$. Now choose the $u$ vectors on which $g_k(x_1, \cdots, x_n) = 1$ as follows:

*Step* 1) $x_k = 1$ for each of the $u$ vectors

*Step* 2) if for any $(s_2, \cdots, s_n)$ having all $s_j = 0$, $j > k$, and $F'(\mathbf{s}) \neq 0$, make the number

$$G_k'(s_2, \cdots, s_n) = 2^{1-n}\left\{\begin{array}{l}\text{difference between number of times} \\ s_2x_2 \oplus \cdots \oplus s_nx_n = 1 \text{ and} \\ s_2x_2 \oplus \cdots \oplus s_nx_n = 0\end{array}\right\}$$

have the same sign as $F'(\mathbf{s})$ and be as large in magnitude as possible. If it is not possible to make them have the same sign, make $G_k'(\mathbf{s})$ as near to zero as possible.

*Step* 3) If any $\mathbf{s}$ has $s_j = 1$, $j > k$, and $F'(\mathbf{s}) \neq 0$, make $G_k'(\mathbf{s})$ equal to zero if possible, and if not, preferably $F'(\mathbf{s})$ and $G_k'(\mathbf{s})$ should have the same sign.

The reasons for the above steps are based on the fact that, according to the assumptions, it follows that

$$\Delta C_{\alpha\gamma_k}(m) = C_0K_0 + \sum_{\mathbf{s}\neq 0} F'(\mathbf{s})G_k'(\mathbf{s}) \prod_{i=2}^{n} [C_i(m)]^{s_i}.$$

Step 1) makes the principal jump as large as possible, step 2) asks that the previously acquired components enhance acquisition when possible, and step 3) insures that the effect of unacquired components is minimized.

## Appendix I

### Example of an Optimal Clock-Component System

Consider a five-component (four-component plus clock) system with the following constraints:

1) Initial clock-lock, $C_0 = 0.625$
2) Drop in clock-lock, $K_0 = 0.625$.

These numbers fix the number of one's in the truth tables of $\hat{f}$ and $\hat{g}_i$:

$$w = u = 2^4(1 - 0.625) = 6.$$

The six one's of $\hat{f}$ are then placed on the following vectors, in accordance with the modified majority logic:

$$\hat{f}: \begin{cases} (1\ 1\ 1\ 1\ 1) \\ (1\ 1\ 1\ 1\ 0) \\ (1\ 1\ 1\ 0\ 1) \\ (1\ 1\ 0\ 1\ 1) \\ (1\ 0\ 1\ 1\ 1) \\ (0\ 1\ 1\ 1\ 1) \end{cases}.$$

The 16 numbers $F'(\mathbf{s})$ are easily calculated:

$$\begin{aligned} F'(1\ 0\ 0\ 0) &= F'(0\ 1\ 0\ 0) = F'(0\ 0\ 1\ 0) \\ &= F'(0\ 0\ 0\ 1) = 0.25 \\ F'(1\ 1\ 0\ 0) &= F'(1\ 0\ 1\ 0) = F'(1\ 0\ 0\ 1) \\ &= F'(0\ 1\ 1\ 0) = F'(0\ 1\ 0\ 1) \\ &= F'(0\ 0\ 1\ 1) = -0.125 \\ F'(1\ 1\ 1\ 0) &= F'(1\ 1\ 0\ 1) = F'(1\ 0\ 1\ 1) \\ &= F'(0\ 1\ 1\ 1) = 0 \\ F'(1\ 1\ 1\ 1) &= 0.125. \end{aligned}$$

To design an optimal clock-component system, we utilize the rules stated in Section IV-C:

1) *Clock acquisition*: $\Delta C_1 = C_0 = 0.625$
2) *Second component*: We choose six vectors which satisfy the rules 1), 2) and 3):

By 1): (– 1 – – –)
(– 1 – – –)
(– 1 – – –)
(– 1 – – –)
(– 1 – – –)
(– 1 – – –).

By 2): no constraint

By 3): columns 3, 4, and 5 must be balanced. Modulo 2 sum of columns 3, 4, and 5 should have balance or excess of one's.

Since there are six vectors, it is not possible to have rows 3, 4, and 5 balanced *and* the modulo 2 sum of any two columns also balanced. Hence, we seek to have more zero's in the modulo 2 sums of any two columns.

$$\hat{g}_2: \begin{cases} (0\ 1\ 0\ 0\ 0) \\ (1\ 1\ 0\ 0\ 1) \\ (0\ 1\ 0\ 1\ 0) \\ (0\ 1\ 1\ 1\ 1) \\ (1\ 1\ 1\ 1\ 1) \\ (1\ 1\ 1\ 0\ 0) \end{cases}$$

$$\begin{aligned} &G_2'(1\ 0\ 0\ 0) = 0.375 \\ &G_2'(0\ 1\ 0\ 0) = G_2'(0\ 0\ 1\ 0) = G_2'(0\ 0\ 0\ 1) = 0 \\ &G_2'(1\ 1\ 0\ 0) = G_2'(1\ 0\ 1\ 0) = G_2'(1\ 0\ 0\ 1) = 0 \\ &G_2'(0\ 1\ 1\ 0) = G_2'(0\ 0\ 1\ 1) = G_2'(0\ 1\ 0\ 1) = -0.125 \\ &G_2'(1\ 1\ 1\ 0) = G_2'(1\ 0\ 1\ 1) = G_2'(1\ 1\ 0\ 1) = 0.125 \\ &G_2'(0\ 1\ 1\ 1) = 0.25 \\ &G_2'(1\ 1\ 1\ 1) = -0.25. \end{aligned}$$

The only $G_2'(\mathbf{s})$ not satisfying 3) is $G_2'(1111)$. But we reason that this is acceptable because its contribution is detrimental only when all components are already in lock, a likelihood of only one chance per total period.

The clock-lock correlation equation is

$$\begin{aligned} \Delta C_2(m) = 0.391 &+ 0.094 C_2(m) + 0.015 \\ &\cdot [C_3(m)C_4(m) + C_3(m)C_5(m) + C_4(m)C_5(m)] \\ &- 0.031 C_2(m)C_3(m)C_4(m)C_5(m). \end{aligned}$$

Note from this that even if all components were in-phase, the net result would be an enhancement of 1.5 per cent.

3) *Third component*: Again choose six vectors:

By 1): (– – 1 – –)
(– – 1 – –)
(– – 1 – –)
(– – 1 – –)
(– – 1 – –)
(– – 1 – –).

By 2): $G_3'(--0\ 0)$ is to have the same sign as $F'(--0\ 0)$ and be as large as possible:

(– 1 1 – –)
(– 1 1 – –)
(– 1 1 – –)
(– 1 1 – –)
(– 1 1 – –)
(– 1 1 – –).

By 3): Again, columns 4 and 5 must be balanced. This again means their modulo 2 sum cannot be balanced.

Since $F'(0\ 0\ 1\ 1)$ is negative, we must have a majority of zero's in $x_4 \oplus x_5$:

$$\hat{g}_3 : \begin{cases} (0\ 1\ 1\ 0\ 0) \\ (1\ 1\ 1\ 0\ 0) \\ (0\ 1\ 1\ 0\ 1) \\ (0\ 1\ 1\ 1\ 1) \\ (1\ 1\ 1\ 1\ 1) \\ (1\ 1\ 1\ 1\ 0) \end{cases}$$

$$G_3'(1\ 0\ 0\ 0) = G_3'(0\ 1\ 0\ 0) = 0.375$$

$$G_3'(0\ 0\ 1\ 0) = G_3'(0\ 0\ 0\ 1) = 0$$

$$G_3'(1\ 1\ 0\ 0) = -0.375$$

$$G_3'(1\ 0\ 1\ 0) = G_3'(1\ 0\ 0\ 1)$$

$$= G_3'(0\ 1\ 1\ 0) = G_3'(0\ 1\ 0\ 1) = 0$$

$$G_3'(1\ 1\ 0\ 1) = G_3'(1\ 1\ 1\ 0) = 0$$

$$G_3'(0\ 0\ 1\ 1) = G_3'(1\ 1\ 1\ 1) = -0.125$$

$$G_3'(1\ 0\ 1\ 1) = G_3'(0\ 1\ 1\ 1) = 0.125.$$

The clock-lock correlation equation is:

$$\Delta C_3(m) = 0.391 + 0.094C_2(m) + 0.094C_3(m)$$
$$+ 0.047C_2(m)C_3(m) + 0.015C_4(m)C_5(m)$$
$$- 0.015C_2(m)C_3(m)C_4(m)C_5(m).$$

Again, the effect of components 4 and 5 being in-phase is nullified.

4) *Fourth component*: The six vectors on which $\hat{g}_4 = 1$ must have:

By 1): (– – – 1 –)
(– – – 1 –)
(– – – 1 –)
(– – – 1 –)
(– – – 1 –)
(– – – 1 –).

By 2): $G_4'(- - - 0)$ are to have the same sign as $F'(- - - 0)$ and be as large as possible,

(– 1 1 1 –)
(– 1 1 1 –)
(– 1 1 1 –)
(– 1 1 1 –)
(– 1 0 1 –)
(– 1 0 1 –).

By 3): Column 5 is to be balanced, and since $F'(0\ 1\ 0\ 1)$ is nonzero, we make $G_4'(0\ 1\ 0\ 1) = 0$:

$$\hat{g}_4 : \begin{cases} (0\ 1\ 1\ 1\ 0) \\ (0\ 1\ 1\ 1\ 1) \\ (1\ 1\ 1\ 1\ 0) \\ (1\ 1\ 1\ 1\ 1) \\ (0\ 1\ 0\ 1\ 0) \\ (1\ 1\ 0\ 1\ 1) \end{cases}$$

$$G_4'(1\ 0\ 0\ 0) = G_4'(0\ 0\ 1\ 0) = 0.375$$

$$G_4'(1\ 0\ 1\ 0) = -0.375$$

$$G_4'(0\ 1\ 0\ 0) = G_4'(1\ 1\ 1\ 0) = 0.125$$

$$G_4'(1\ 1\ 0\ 0) = G_4'(0\ 1\ 1\ 0) = -0.125$$

$$G_4'(0\ 0\ 0\ 1) = G_4'(1\ 0\ 0\ 1) = G_4'(0\ 0\ 1\ 1)$$
$$= G_4'(1\ 0\ 1\ 1) = 0$$

$$G_4'(0\ 1\ 0\ 1) = G_4'(1\ 1\ 0\ 1) = G_4'(0\ 1\ 1\ 1)$$
$$= G_4'(1\ 1\ 1\ 1) = 0.$$

Clock correlation is now:

$$\Delta C_4(m) = 0.391 + 0.094C_2(m) = 0.031C_3(m)$$
$$+ 0.094C_4(m) + 0.015C_2(m)C_3(m)$$
$$+ 0.047C_2(m)C_4(m) + 0.015C_3(m)C_4(m).$$

5) *Fifth component*: The last six vectors must satisfy only 1) and 2):

By 1): (– – – – 1)
(– – – – 1)
(– – – – 1)
(– – – – 1)
(– – – – 1)
(– – – – 1).

By 2):

$$\hat{g}_5 : \begin{cases} (0\ 1\ 1\ 1\ 1) \\ (1\ 1\ 1\ 1\ 1) \\ (0\ 1\ 0\ 1\ 1) \\ (1\ 1\ 0\ 1\ 1) \\ (0\ 1\ 1\ 0\ 1) \\ (1\ 1\ 1\ 0\ 1) \end{cases}$$

$$G_5'(1\ 0\ 0\ 0) = G_5'(0\ 0\ 0\ 1) = 0.375$$

$$G_5'(0\ 1\ 0\ 0) = G_5'(0\ 0\ 1\ 0) = G_5'(1\ 1\ 0\ 1)$$
$$= G_5'(1\ 0\ 1\ 1) = 0.125$$

$$G_5'(1\ 1\ 0\ 0) = G_5'(1\ 0\ 1\ 0) = G_5'(0\ 1\ 0\ 1)$$
$$= G_5'(0\ 0\ 1\ 1) = -0.125$$

$$G_5'(1\ 0\ 0\ 1) = -0.375$$

$$G_5'(0\ 1\ 1\ 0) = G_5'(1\ 1\ 1\ 1) = 0.125$$

$$G_5'(1\ 1\ 1\ 0) = G_5'(0\ 1\ 1\ 1) = -0.125.$$

Clock correlation is then:

$$\Delta C_5(m) = 0.391 + 0.094C_2(m) + 0.31C_3(m)$$
$$+ 0.031C_4(m) + 0.094C_5(m) + 0.015C_2(m)C_3(m)$$
$$+ 0.015C_2(m)C_4(m) + 0.047C_2(m)C_5(m)$$
$$- 0.015C_3(m)C_4(m) + 0.015C_3(m)C_5(m)$$
$$+ 0.015C_4(m)C_5(m) + - 0.015C_2(m)C_3(m)C_4(m)C_5(m).$$

Once the calculations are made, the logics given in Table III are established. The decoding proceeds as follows (see Fig. 5):

TABLE III

RANGING ENCODING AND DECODING FUNCTIONS

| $x_1$[a] | $x_2$ | $x_3$ | $x_4$ | $x_5$ | $\hat{g}_2$ | $\hat{g}_3$ | $\hat{g}_4$ | $\hat{g}_5$ | $\hat{f}$ |
|---|---|---|---|---|---|---|---|---|---|
| 0 | 0 | 0 | 0 | 0 | 0 | 0 | 0 | 0 | 0 |
| 0 | 0 | 0 | 0 | 1 | 0 | 0 | 0 | 0 | 0 |
| 0 | 0 | 0 | 1 | 0 | 0 | 0 | 0 | 0 | 0 |
| 0 | 0 | 0 | 1 | 1 | 0 | 0 | 0 | 0 | 0 |
| 0 | 0 | 1 | 0 | 0 | 0 | 0 | 0 | 0 | 0 |
| 0 | 0 | 1 | 0 | 1 | 0 | 0 | 0 | 0 | 0 |
| 0 | 0 | 1 | 1 | 0 | 0 | 0 | 0 | 0 | 0 |
| 0 | 0 | 1 | 1 | 1 | 0 | 0 | 0 | 0 | 0 |
| 0 | 1 | 0 | 0 | 0 | 1 | 0 | 0 | 0 | 0 |
| 0 | 1 | 0 | 0 | 1 | 0 | 0 | 0 | 0 | 0 |
| 0 | 1 | 0 | 1 | 0 | 1 | 0 | 1 | 0 | 0 |
| 0 | 1 | 0 | 1 | 1 | 0 | 0 | 0 | 1 | 0 |
| 0 | 1 | 1 | 0 | 0 | 0 | 1 | 0 | 0 | 0 |
| 0 | 1 | 1 | 0 | 1 | 0 | 1 | 0 | 1 | 0 |
| 0 | 1 | 1 | 1 | 0 | 0 | 0 | 1 | 0 | 0 |
| 0 | 1 | 1 | 1 | 1 | 1 | 1 | 1 | 1 | 1 |
| 1 | 0 | 0 | 0 | 0 | 0 | 0 | 0 | 0 | 0 |
| 1 | 0 | 0 | 0 | 1 | 0 | 0 | 0 | 0 | 0 |
| 1 | 0 | 0 | 1 | 0 | 0 | 0 | 0 | 0 | 0 |
| 1 | 0 | 0 | 1 | 1 | 0 | 0 | 0 | 0 | 0 |
| 1 | 0 | 1 | 0 | 0 | 0 | C | 0 | 0 | 0 |
| 1 | 0 | 1 | 0 | 1 | 0 | 0 | 0 | 0 | 0 |
| 1 | 0 | 1 | 1 | 0 | 0 | 0 | 0 | 0 | 0 |
| 1 | 0 | 1 | 1 | 1 | 0 | 0 | 0 | 0 | 1 |
| 1 | 1 | 0 | 0 | 0 | 0 | 0 | 0 | 0 | 0 |
| 1 | 1 | 0 | 0 | 1 | 1 | 0 | 0 | 0 | 0 |
| 1 | 1 | 0 | 1 | 0 | 0 | 0 | 0 | 0 | 0 |
| 1 | 1 | 0 | 1 | 1 | 0 | 0 | 1 | 1 | 1 |
| 1 | 1 | 1 | 0 | 0 | 1 | 1 | 0 | 0 | 0 |
| 1 | 1 | 1 | 0 | 1 | 0 | 0 | 0 | 1 | 1 |
| 1 | 1 | 1 | 1 | 0 | 0 | 1 | 1 | 0 | 1 |
| 1 | 1 | 1 | 1 | 1 | 1 | 1 | 1 | 1 | 1 |

[a] $x_1$ is the clock component.

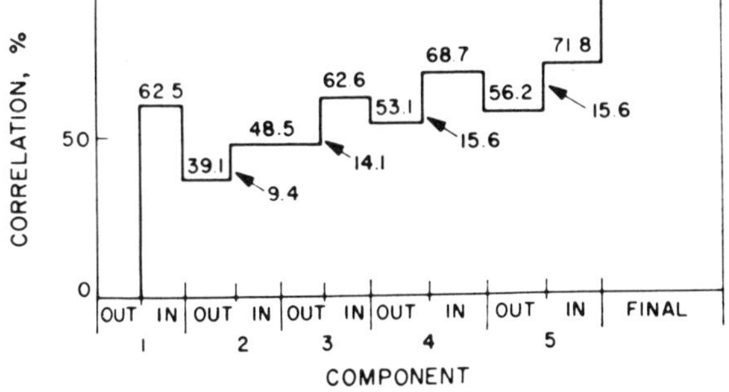


Fig. 5—Acquisition diagram.

1) *First component*: clock-locks, 62.5 per cent correlation.

2) *Second component*: with clock in lock, using $g_2$, correlation is 39.1 per cent until the second component is acquired when correlation jumps 9.4 per cent to 48.5 per cent. If any of components 3, 4, or 5 are in lock, the initial clock-lock at this point may be 1.5 per cent higher.

3) *Third component*: using $g_3$, assuming clock and second-component lock, the clock-lock correlation is 48.5 per cent until third component acquisition, when correlation jumps 14.1 per cent to 62.6 per cent. Components 4 and 5 have no effect.

4) *Fourth component*: using $g_4$ and assuming components 2 and 3 are acquired the clock correlation stands at 53.1 per cent and jumps 15.6 per cent to 68.7 per cent as component 4 is locked. Component 5 does not affect the reading.

5) *Fifth component*: using $g_5$, assuming components 2, 3, and 4 are in lock, the clock-lock is initially 56.2 per cent, jumping 15.6 per cent to 71.8 per cent as component 5 is stepped into phase.

6) *Final combination*: when all components are locked, the decoder logic is changed to $f$, and the correlation jumps to 100 per cent.

## APPENDIX II

### CALCULATION OF $F(s)$ FOR MAJORITY LOGIC

Let $n$ be odd and let $f$ be the unique majority logic. We consider only odd $n$, because if $n$ were even, then

$$\frac{F_n(\mathbf{e}^1)}{F_{n+1}(\mathbf{e}^1)} = \frac{2^{1-n}\begin{pmatrix} n-1 \\ \frac{n}{2} \end{pmatrix}}{2^{-n}\begin{pmatrix} n \\ \frac{n}{2} \end{pmatrix}} = 1.$$

We could thus increase $n$ by one without affecting the correlation value (or the correlation time) but decreasing the ratio $(\Sigma v_i)/(\Pi v_i)$.

We wish to calculate the transform of $f(\mathbf{x})$. Since $f$ is a symmetric function, if $\mathbf{s}$ has $k$ one's (*i.e.*, $\mathbf{s} = k$), then for some permutation $\pi$

$$F(\mathbf{s}) = F(\pi\mathbf{u}^k) = F(\mathbf{u}^k)$$
$$\mathbf{u}^k = (1, 1, \cdots, 1, 0, \cdots, 0),$$

and by this symmetry of $f$, we need to calculate only these $F(\mathbf{u}^k)$.

$$F(\mathbf{u}^k) = 2^{-n/2} \sum_{\mathbf{x}} (-1)^{x_1+\cdots+x_k} f(\mathbf{x})$$
$$= 2^{n/2}\Bigg[ \sum_{\mathbf{x}, ||\mathbf{x}|| < (n/2)} (-1)^{x_1+\cdots+x_k} - \sum_{\mathbf{x}, ||\mathbf{x}|| > (n/2)} (-1)^{x_1+\cdots+x_k} \Bigg].$$

Define the two sums above as

$$A(k) = \sum_{\mathbf{x},\,||\mathbf{x}||<(n/2)} (-1)^{x_1+\cdots+x_k}$$

$$B(k) = \sum_{\mathbf{x},\,||\mathbf{x}||>(n/2)} (-1)^{x_1+\cdots+x_k}.$$

Suppose that vector $\mathbf{x}$ has $i$ one's in it, $j$ of which lie in $x_1, \cdots, x_k$, and $i - j$ in $x_{k+1}, \cdots, x_n$. There are $\binom{k}{j}\binom{n-k}{i-j}$ such vectors $\mathbf{x}$, and thus

$$A(k) = \sum_{i=0}^{(n-1)/2} \sum_{j=0}^{\min(k,i)} \binom{k}{j}\binom{n-k}{i-j}(-1)^j$$

$$= \sum_{i=0}^{(n-1)/2} \sum_{j=0}^{\infty} \binom{k}{j}\binom{n-k}{i-j}(-1)^j.$$

By similar reasoning,

$$B(k) = \sum_{i=(n+1)/2}^{n} \sum_{j=0}^{\infty} \binom{k}{j}\binom{n-k}{i-j}(-1)^j.$$

Let $\mathfrak{a}(t)$ be the generating function

$$\mathfrak{a}(t) = \sum_{i=0}^{\infty}\sum_{j=0}^{\infty} \binom{k}{j}\binom{n-k}{i-j}(-1)^j t^i$$

$$= \sum_{j=0}^{\infty} \binom{k}{j}(-1)^j t^j \sum_{i=0}^{\infty} \binom{n-k}{i-j} t^{i-j}$$

$$= \sum_{j=0}^{\infty} \binom{k}{j}(-1t)^j \sum_{m=0}^{\infty} \binom{n-k}{m} t^m$$

$$= (1-t)^k(1+t)^{n-k}.$$

Note that the sum of the coefficients of $t^0, t^1, \cdots, t^{(n-1)/2}$ is precisely $A(k)$, that is,

$$A(k) = \text{coeff. of } t^{(n-1)/2} \text{ in } (1-t)^k(1+t)^{n-k} \cdot (1+t+\cdots+t^{(n-1)/2})$$

$$= \text{coeff. of } t^{(n-1)/2} \text{ in } (1-t)^{k-1}(1+t)^{n-k} \cdot (1-t^{(n+1)/2})$$

$$= \text{coeff. of } t^{(n-1)/2} \text{ in } (1-t)^{k-1}(1+t)^{n-k}$$

$$= \text{coeff. of } t^{n-1} \text{ in } (1-t^2)^{k-1}(1+t^2)^{n-k}$$

$$= \text{coeff. of } t^{-1} \text{ in } \frac{(1-t^2)^{k-1}(1+t^2)^{n-k}}{t^n}.$$

By this procedure, we reduce $A(k)$ to the residue of a rational function, to be calculated by the Cauchy residue theorem:

$$A(k) = \frac{1}{2\pi j}\oint \frac{(1-t^2)^{k-1}(1+t^2)^{n-k}}{t^n}\,dt \qquad (j = \sqrt{-1})$$

integrating along any simple closed path containing the origin.

$$A(k) = \frac{1}{2\pi j}\oint \left(\frac{1}{t} - t\right)^{k-1}\left(\frac{1}{t} + t\right)^{n-k} \frac{dt}{t}.$$

Choose the integration path to be unit circle, $t = e^{iz}$

$$A(k) = \frac{2^{n-2}(-j)^{k-1}}{\pi}\int_0^{2\pi} \sin^{k-1} z \cos^{n-k} z\, dz.$$

Because $A(k)$ must be real, we may limit our attention to the real part of the equation (*i.e.*, to odd $k$). This integral is one which can be reduced by a standard table of integrals (*e.g.*, see Burington [9]) to

$$A(k) = \Re e\left\{(-j)^{k-1} \frac{(k-1)!\left(\frac{n-k}{2}\right)!}{\left(\frac{n-1}{2}\right)!\left(\frac{k-1}{2}\right)!}\binom{n-k}{\frac{n-k}{2}}\right\}.$$

By a similar procedure, or by invoking symmetry of the majority function, we compute

$$B(k) = A(k).$$

The final result for $F(\mathbf{s})$ is, then

$$F(\mathbf{u}^k) = 2^{1-n}\Re e\left\{(-j)^{k-1} \frac{(k-1)!\left(\frac{n-k}{2}\right)!}{\left(\frac{n-1}{2}\right)!\left(\frac{k-1}{2}\right)!}\binom{n-k}{\frac{n-k}{2}}\right\}$$

which, for $k = 1$, gives the result obtained previously for $F(\mathbf{e}^1)$:

$$F(\mathbf{e}^1) = 2^{1-n}\binom{n-1}{\frac{n-1}{2}}.$$

## References


[1] M. Easterling, "Long Range Precision Ranging System," Jet Propulsion Lab., Pasadena, Calif., Rept. No. 32-80, pp. 1-7; 1961.

[2] M. Easterling, *et. al.*, "The Modulation in Ranging Receivers," Jet Propulsion Lab., Pasadena, Calif., Research Summary, No. 36-7, vol. 1, pp. 62-65; 1961.

[3] W. B. Davenport, and W. L. Root, "Random Signals and Noise," McGraw-Hill Book Co., Inc., New York, N. Y.; 1958.

[4] S. W. Golomb, "Deep Space Range Measurement," Jet Propulsion Laboratory, Pasadena, Calif., Research Summary, No. 36-1, pp. 39-42; 1960.

[5] M. Easterling, "Acquisition Ranging Codes and Noise," Jet Propulsion Lab., Pasadena, Calif., Research Summary, No. 36-2, pp. 31-36; 1960.

[6] W. K. Victor, R. Stevens, and S. W. Golomb, "Radar Exploration of Venus," Jet Propulsion Lab., Pasadena, Calif., Rept. No. 32-132; 1961.

[7] R. C. Titsworth, "Correlation Properties of Cyclic Sequences," Jet Propulsion Lab., Pasadena, Calif., Rept. No. 32-388; July, 1963.

[8] G. Birkhoff, and S. MacLane, "A Survey of Modern Algebra," The Macmillan Co., New York, N. Y.; 1953.

[9] R. S. Burington, "Mathematical Tables and Formulas," Handbook Pub., Inc., Sandusky, Ohio; 1933.

# Optimal Binary Sequences for Spread Spectrum Multiplexing

## I. Introduction

Linear shift register sequences (see Zierler[1] and Gold[2]) have found extensive applications in spread spectrum communication systems. The binary sequences generated by shift register devices serve as the encoding mechanism of such systems which, when added to the baseband information, results in a wideband low-power-density signal which has statistical properties similar to noise. The casual listener is thus denied access to the baseband information which can be recovered from the wideband signal only through correlation with a stored reference sequence in the receiver which is an exact replica of the original encoding sequence.

The usefulness of the maximal linear sequences in spread spectrum communications depends in large part on their ideal autocorrelation properties. The autocorrelation function of a binary sequence $h$ is defined as $\theta_h(\tau)$ = (number of agreements − number of disagreements) when the sequence $h$ is compared with a cyclic shift of itself. It is well known that for maximal linear sequences $\theta_h(0)$ = period of the sequence and $\theta_h(\tau) = -1$ for $\tau \neq 0$. The detection by the receiver of the high in-phase correlation value $\theta_h(0)$ determines the synchronization between transmitter and receiver necessary for the removal of the encoding sequence and the recovery of the baseband information. In multiplexing applications many systems will be operating in the same neighborhood and each communication link will employ a different maximal encoding sequence. In general, the cross-correlation function between different maximal sequences may be relatively large. Thus different systems operating in the same environment can interfere with the successful attainment and maintenance of proper synchronization by having the receiver of one communication link lock onto the cross-correlation peaks obtained by correlating with the encoding sequence of a different communication link. Thus the successful use of spread spectrum communication systems in multiplexing applications depends upon the construction of large families of encoding sequences with uniformly low cross-correlation values. In this paper we present an analytical technique for the construction of such families of linear binary encoding sequences.

## II. Notation

Following the notation of Zierler[1] we denote by $V(f)$ the vector space of linear sequences generated by the recursion relation corresponding to the polynomial $f$ of degree $n$ and further identify the members of $V(f)$ with binary $2^n - 1$ tuples. If $f$ is a primitive polynomial over the field $K = \{0, 1\}$ then $h \in V(f)$ implies $h$ is a maximal linear sequence. We denote by $||h||$ the number of ones in the sequence $h$ and by $\bar{h}$ the sequence such that $\bar{h}(i) = h(i) + 1$. The correlation function $\theta$ of two binary sequences $a$, $b$ has been defined as

$$\theta(\tau) = \sum_{i=0}^{2^n-1} \chi a(i) \chi b(i + \tau)$$

where $\chi$ is the unique isomorphism of the additive group $\{0, 1\}$ onto the multiplicative group $\{1, -1\}$. We note that $\theta(a, b)(\tau)$ is simply described as the number of agreements − number of disagreements of the sequences $a$ and $b$ for each $\tau$ and that

$$\theta(a, b) = 2^n - 1 - 2\,||a + b||.$$

In what follows $\alpha$ will always denote a primitive $2^n - 1$ root of unity in a splitting field of $x^{2n-1} + 1$ and the minimal polynomial of $\alpha^i$ will be denoted by $f_i$. Finally, we note the following result of Bose and Chaudhuri.[3]

*Theorem 1*

Let $\alpha$ be any primitive element of the splitting field of $x^{2n-1} + 1$. Let $f_i$ be the minimal polynomial of $\alpha^i$. Let

$$g = \frac{x^{2^n-1} + 1}{\operatorname{lcm}\{f_1, f_2, \cdots f_{2k}\}}$$

Then $a, b \in V(g)$ implies $||a + b|| > 2k$.

## III. Statement and Proof of Result

Our techniques for the construction of large families of encoding sequences with uniformly low cross-correlation values is based on the following result.

*Theorem 2*

Let $\alpha$ be any primitive element of $GF(2^n)$. Let $f_1$ be the minimal polynomial of $\alpha$. Let $f_t$ be the minimal polynomial of $\alpha^t$ where

$$t = \begin{cases} (2^{(n+1)/2}) + 1 & (n \text{ odd}) \\ (2^{(n+2)/2}) + 1 & (n \text{ even}). \end{cases}$$

Then $a \in V(f_1)$ and $b \in V(f_t)$ implies $|\theta(a, b)| \leq t$.

The significance of this theorem is that it tells how to select shift register tap connections which will generate maximal linear sequences with a known bound on the cross-correlation function. Since $\alpha$ is primitive, the sequence generated by the shift register corresponding to $f_1$ is maximal. Since

$$2^{(n+1)/2} + 1 \quad \text{and} \quad 2^{(n+2)/2} + 1$$

are both relatively prime to $2^n - 1$ for $n \not\equiv 0$ mod the 4 sequence corresponding to the polynomial $f_t$ is also maximal in these cases. Theorem 2 thus permits the selection of pairs of maximal sequences with known bound on the cross-correlation function. This result is of practical importance since, for example, for $n = 13$ there are 630 maximal sequences and there exist pairs of these sequences

Manuscript received July 22, 1966; revised February 4, 1967.

Reprinted from *IEEE Trans. Inform. Theory*, vol. IT-13, pp. 619–621, Oct. 1967.

whose correlation values are as high as $\theta = 703$ while Theorem 2 guarantees the selection of pairs of sequences such that $|\theta| \leq 129$.

This result is a special case of the more general theorem stated in the following which has been obtained independently by Gold[5] and Kasami,[4] and is related to the weight distribution of error-correcting codes.

*Theorem*

Let $a$ and $b$ be maximal linear sequences given by

$$a(i) = T(\alpha^{-i}) \quad \text{and} \quad b(i) = T((\alpha^{2^l+1})^{-i})$$

where $\alpha$ is a primitive $2^n - 1$ root of unity ($n$ odd), $l$ is any integer such that $(l, k) = 1$, and $T$ is the trace of $GF(2^n)$. Then $\theta(a, b)(n) = -1$ when $a(\tau) = 0$ and

$$\theta(a, b)(\tau) = \begin{cases} -(2^{(n+1)/2} + 1) \\ \quad \text{or} & \text{when} \quad a(\tau) = 1. \\ (2^{(n+1)/2} - 1) \end{cases}$$

The proof of this theorem is contained in Gold[5].

In the remainder of this section, we proceed to the proof of Theorem 2 by means of a series of lemmas.

*Lemma 1*

Let $\alpha$ be any primitive $2^n - 1$ root of unity in a splitting field of

$$x^{2^n-1} + 1.$$

Let

$$g_k = \frac{x^{2^n-1} + 1}{\text{lcm}\ \{f_1, f_2, \cdots f_k\}}$$

where $f_i$ is the minimal polynomial of $\alpha^i$. Let $f$ be an irreducible polynomial of degree $n$. Let $A_f$ be the conjugate class of roots of $f$. Let $m_f = \min \{i \mid \alpha^i \varepsilon A_f\}$, the class leader of $A_f$. Then $m_f > k$ implies $f$ is a factor of $g_k$.

*Proof*: $f$ irreducible of degree $n$ implies $f \mid x^{2^n-1} + 1$ implies $f \mid g_k$ lcm $\{f_1, f_2, \cdots f_k\}$, and $m_f > k$ implies $f_i \mid \text{lcm}\ \{f_1 \cdots f_k\}$ implies $f \mid g_k$.

*Lemma 2*

Let $\alpha$ be any primitive $2^n - 1$ root of unity in a splitting field of

$$x^{2^n-1} + 1.$$

Let $u = 2^{n-1} - 1$. Let

$$v = \begin{cases} 2^{n-1} - 1 - 2^{n-1/2} & \text{for } n \text{ odd} \\ 2^{n-1} - 1 - 2^{n/2} & \text{for } n \text{ even.} \end{cases}$$

Let $f_u$ be the minimal polynomial of $\alpha^u$. Let $f_v$ be the minimal polynomial of $\alpha^v$. Then $m_{f_u} = u$ and $m_{f_v} = v$.

*Proof*: $\alpha^r$ and $\alpha^s$ belong to the same conjugate class of $GF(2^n)$ if, and only if, there exists an integer $k$ such that $\alpha^r = (\alpha^s)^{2^k}$ if, and only if, $r = s \cdot 2^k$ modulo $2^n - 1$ if, and only if, there exists a cyclic permutation $p$ such that $[r(0), r(1), \cdots r(n-1)] = [s(p(0)), s(p(1)) \cdots s(p(n-1))]$ where

$$r = \sum_{i=0}^{n-1} r(i)2^i \quad \text{and} \quad s = \sum_{i=0}^{n-1} s(i)2^i.$$

Now $u = 2^n - 1 = \sum_{i=0}^{n-1} u(i)\, 2^i$ where $[u(0), u(1), \cdots u(n-1)] = [1\ 1 \cdots 1\ 0]$. Clearly any permutation of $[1\ 1 \cdots 1\ 0]$ corresponds to a larger integer and hence $m_{f_u} = u$. Now

$$v = 2^{n-1} - 1 - 2^{n-1/2} = \sum_{i=0}^{n-1} v(i)2^i$$

where

$$\left[v(0), v(1), \cdots v\left(\frac{n-3}{2}\right), v\left(\frac{n-1}{2}\right), \cdot v\left(\frac{n+1}{2}\right) \cdots v(n-2)v(n-1)\right] = [\underbrace{1, 1, \cdots 1}_{n-1/2 \text{ ones}}, 0, \underbrace{1 \cdots 1}_{n-1/2 \text{ ones}}, 0].$$

Again it is clear that any cyclic permutation of $[v(0), \cdots v(n-1)]$ will result in a larger integer and hence $m_{f_v} = v$. A similar argument holds when $v = 2^{n-1} - 1 - 2(n/2)$.

*Lemma 3*

$f_u$ and $f_v$ are factors of $g_{v-1}$ where $u$ and $v$ are as in Lemma 2 and

$$g_{v-1} = \frac{x^{2^n-1} + 1}{\text{lcm}\ \{f_1, f_2, \cdots f_{v-1}\}}$$

then $f_v \mid g_{v-1}$.

*Proof*:

$$m_{f_u} = u \text{ (by Lemma 2)} = 2^n - 1$$

$> 2^{n-1} > v - 1$ implies $f_u \mid g_{v-1}$ (by Lemma 1)

$$m_{f_v} = v \text{ (by Lemma 2)} > v - 1 \text{ implies } f_v \mid g_{v-1}.$$

*Lemma 4*

Let $f_i$ denote the minimal polynomial of $\alpha^i$. Let

$$g_k = \frac{x^{2^n-1} + 1}{\text{lcm}\ \{f_1, f_2, \cdots f_k\}}.$$

Then $a, b \ \varepsilon\ V(g_k)$ implies $|\theta(a, b)| < 2^n - 1 - 2k$.

*Proof*: $a, b \ \varepsilon\ V(g_k)$ implies $a + b \ \varepsilon\ V(g_k)$ implies $||a + b|| > k$ by Theorem 1. Since 1 is not a primitive root of unity, $1 + x$ is clearly a factor of $g$, and hence $V(1 + x) \subset V(g_k)$. Thus the constant sequence of ones is a member of $V(g_k)$, and hence $V(g_k)$ is closed with respect to the operation of complementation, i.e., $h \ \varepsilon\ V(g_k)$ implies $\bar{h} \ \varepsilon\ V(h_k)$ where $\bar{h}(i) = 1 + h(i)$.

Thus $a, b \ \varepsilon\ V(g_k)$ implies $a + b \ \varepsilon\ V(g_k)$ implies $\widetilde{a + b} \ \varepsilon\ V(g_k)$ implies $||\widetilde{a + b}|| = 2^n - 1 - ||a + b|| > k$ implies $k < ||a + b|| < 2^n - 1 - k$ implies $|\theta(a, b)| < (2^n - 1) - 2k$.

*Proof of Theorem 2*: Let $\beta = \alpha^{-2}$. Then $\beta$ is clearly a primitive $2^n - 1$ root of unity and

$$\alpha = \alpha^{-2}(2^{n-1} - 1) = \beta^{2^{n-1}} - 1 = \beta^u$$

$$\alpha^t = \begin{cases} \alpha^{(2^n+1)/2} + 1 & (\text{for } n \text{ odd}) = \\ \alpha^{(2^n+2)/2} + 1 & \text{for } n \text{ even;} \end{cases}$$

$$\left. \begin{matrix} \alpha^{-2}[2^{n-1} - 1 - 2^{(n-1)/2}] = \beta^{2^{n-1}} - 1 - 2^{n-1/2} \\ \alpha^{-2}[2^{n-1} - 1 - 2^{n/2}] = \beta^{2^{n-1}} - 1 - 2^{n/2} \end{matrix} \right\} = \beta^v.$$

Now $f_1$ is the minimal polynomial of $\alpha = \beta_u$ and $f_t$ is the minimal polynomial of $\alpha^t = \beta_v$. By Lemma 2 $m_{f_1} = u > v - 1$ and $m_{f_t} = v > v - 1$. Thus by Lemma 1 $f_1$ and $f_t$ are factors of $g_{v-1}$. Hence, $V(f_1) \subset V(g_{v-1})$ and $v(f_t) \subset V(g_{v-1})$. Thus $a \ \varepsilon\ V(f_1)$ and $b \ \varepsilon\ V(f_t)$ implies $a$ and $b \ \varepsilon\ (g_{v-1})$. Thus by Lemma 4

$$|\theta(a, b)| < 2^n - 1 - 2(v - 1) =$$

$$\begin{cases} 2^n - 1 - 2[2^{n-1} - 2 - 2^{n-1/2}] = 2^{(n+1)/2} + 3 \\ 2^n - 1 - 2[2^{n-1} - 2 - 2^{n/2}] = 2^{(n+2)/2} + 3. \end{cases}$$

Since the value of the cross-correlation function is always odd we have

$$|\theta(a, b)| \leq 2^{n+1/2} + 1 \quad \text{for} \quad n \text{ odd}$$

$$|\theta(a, b)| \leq 2^{n+2/2} + 1 \quad \text{for} \quad n \text{ even}.$$

For 13-stage shift registers there are pairs of maximal sequences with cross-correlation peaks as high as $\theta(\tau) = 703$ while proper selection of shift registers in accordance with the above theorem guarantees sequences whose cross correlation satisfies the inequality

$$|\theta(\tau)| \leq 2^{(13+1)/2} + 1 = 129.$$

We note further that for purely random sequences of length $2^{13} - 1 = 8191$ we would expect the cross-correlation function to exceed $2\sigma = 2\sqrt{8192} \sim 180$ for 5 percent of the correlation values and hence linear sequences chosen in accordance with our technique perform better with respect to their cross-correlation properties than purely random sequences.

## IV. Construction of Encoding Families

In this section we show how to provide large families of encoding sequences each of period $2^n - 1$ and such that the cross-correlation function of any pair of sequences of the family has a cross-correlation function $\theta$ which satisfies the inequality

$$|\theta(\tau)| \leq 2^{(n+2)/2} + 1.$$

In a spread spectrum multiplexing application such families form ideal codes which minimizes interlink interference. Instead of having each communication link employ a different maximal sequence we assign to each link a member of the encoding family to be constructed below. These are nonmaximal linear sequences, and hence their autocorrelation function will not be two-valued; however, the out-of-phase value of the autocorrelation function will satisfy the above inequality. Thus by slightly relaxing the conditions on the autocorrelation function we obtain a family of encoding sequences with the high cross-correlation peaks eliminated.

The procedure for generating these encoding families is embodied in the following theorem.

*Theorem*

Let $f_1$ and $f_t$ be a preferred pair of primitive polynomials of degree $n$ whose corresponding shift registers generate maximal linear sequences of period $2^n - 1$ and whose cross-correlation function $\theta$ satisfies the inequality.

$$|\theta| \leq t = \begin{cases} 2^{(n+1)/2} + 1 & \text{for} \quad n \text{ odd} \\ 2^{(n+2)/2} + 1 & \text{for} \quad n \text{ even} \quad n \not\equiv \text{mod } 4. \end{cases}$$

Then the shift register corresponding to the product polynomial $f_1 \cdot f_t$ will generate $2^n + 1$ different sequences each period $2^n - 1$ and such that the cross-correlation function $\theta$ of any pair of such sequences satisfies the above inequality.

*Proof*: $a \in V(f_1 \cdot f_t) = V(f_1) + V(f_t)$ implies $a = b + c$ where $b \in V(f_1)$ and $c \in V(f_t)$. Period $(b + c) = \text{lcm}\,\{\text{period } b, \text{period } c\} = 2^n - 1$. Since degree $f_1 \cdot f_t = 2n$, there are $(2^{2n} - 1)/(2^n - 1) = 2^n + 1$ essentially different sequences in $V(f_1 \cdot f_t)$. Finally $a, b \in V(f_1 \cdot f_t)$ implies

$$\begin{cases} a = a_1 + a_t \\ b = b_1 + b_t \end{cases}$$

where $a_1, b_1 \in V(f_1)$, and $a_t, b_t \in V(f_t)$. $|\theta(a, b)| = |\theta(a_1 + b_1, a_t + b_t)| \leq t$ by Theorem 2 since $a_1 + b_1 \in V(f_1)$ and $a_1 + b_1 \in V(f_t)$.

Thus, by way of illustration, if we consider the pair of polynomials, $f_1(x) = 1 + x + x^2 + x^3 + x^7$ and $f_t(x) = 1 + x + x^2 + x^3 + x^4 + x^5 + x^7$ then the product polynomial is $f_1(x) f_2(x) = 1 + x^2 + x^6 + x^8 + x^{11} + x^{12} + x^{14}$ and the corresponding 14-stage shift register will generate 129 different linear sequences of period 127. The cross-correlation function $\theta$ of any pair of such sequences will satisfy the inequality $|\theta(\tau)| \leq 17$.

Robert Gold
Magnavox Research Laboratories
Torrance, Calif. 90503

### References

[1] N. Zierler, "Linear recurring sequences," *J. SIAM*, vol. 7, March 1959.
[2] R. Gold, "Characteristic linear sequences and their coset functions," (accepted for publication *J. Soc. Ind. Appl. Math.*, May 1965).
[3] W. W. Peterson, *Error Correcting Codes*. New York: Wiley, 1961.
[4] T. Kasami, "Weight distribution formula for some class of cyclic codes," University of Illinois, Urbana, Rept. R-265, April 1966.
[5] R. Gold, "Maximal recursive sequences with 3-valued recursive cross-correlation functions" (submitted for publication, January 1967).

# Coding and its application in space communications

*Once regarded as purely academic, coding theory has turned out to be eminently practical for the modern applications of space channels*

**G. David Forney, Jr.** Codex Corporation

*Between 1948—when Shannon first proposed his basic theorems on information theory—and the start of the space age, little practical application developed from the lessons of coding theory. This article presents an overview of the Shannon theorem, interesting practical codes, and their application to the space channel. It turns out that a simple encoder in combination with a decoder of modest complexity placed into an uncoded communications system can increase the data rate by a factor of four or more depending on the coding scheme and the allowable error rate. Use of a convolutional code with sequential decoding has proved to be the outstanding scheme for these applications. It appears that, in the future, coding will find a place in most new digital space communication systems.*

Coding theory has a history no doubt unique among engineering disciplines: the ultimate theorems came first, practical applications later. For many years after Shannon's announcement of the basic theorems of information theory in 1948, the absence of any actual realization of the exciting improvements promised by the theory was a source of some embarassment to workers in the field. A standard feature of IEEE Conventions in this period was a session entitled "Progress in Information Theory," or something similar, in which the talks purporting to show that the theory was approaching practical application tended instead to confirm the prejudices of practical men that information theory would do nothing for them.

In retrospect, there were two principal reasons for this lag. First, Shannon's coding theorems were existence theorems, which showed that within a large class of coding schemes there existed some schemes—nearly all, actually—that could give arbitrarily low error rates at any information rate up to a critical rate called channel capacity. The theorems gave no clue to the actual construction of such schemes, however, and the search for coding techniques capable of remotely approaching the theoretical capacity proved so difficult that a folk theorem was proposed: "All codes are good, except those we can think of."

Second, the channels of practical interest—telephone lines, cable, microwave, troposcatter, and HF radio—proved not to have anything like the statistical regularity assumed in the proof of the coding theorems. In fact, most theorems are based on the assumption of statistical independence in the noise affecting each transmitted symbol, whereas on the channels just cited disturbances tend to be manifested in bursts spanning many bits. This is to say nothing of other anomalies that arise in practice, such as a channel described at a recent information theory symposium as "a very good channel, with errors predominantly due to a noisy Coke machine near the receiver."

Over the past decade, the situation has improved tremendously. The problem of finding workable coding schemes has been recognized to be fundamentally a problem of finding decoders of reasonable complexity. The solution has been sought in considering classes of

Reprinted from *IEEE Spectrum*, vol. 7, pp. 47–58, June 1970.

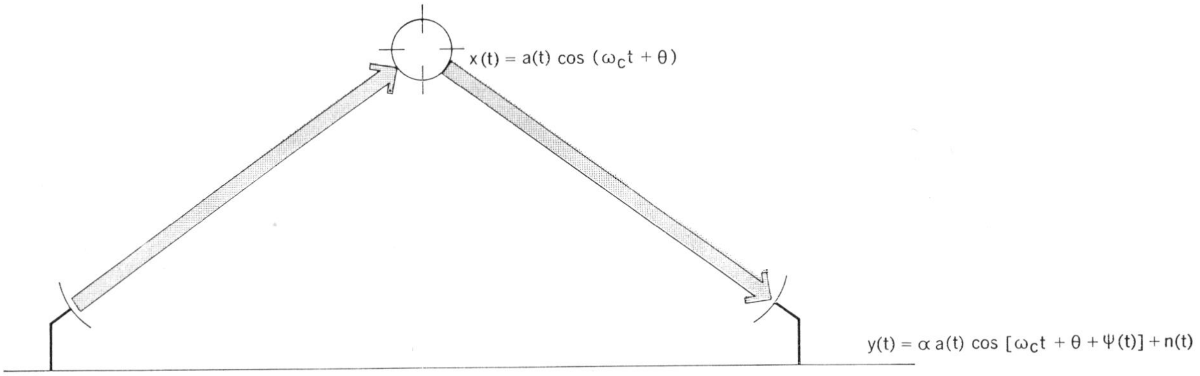


**FIGURE 1. Amplitude modulation on a satellite channel.**

**FIGURE 2. Discrete-time channel model.**

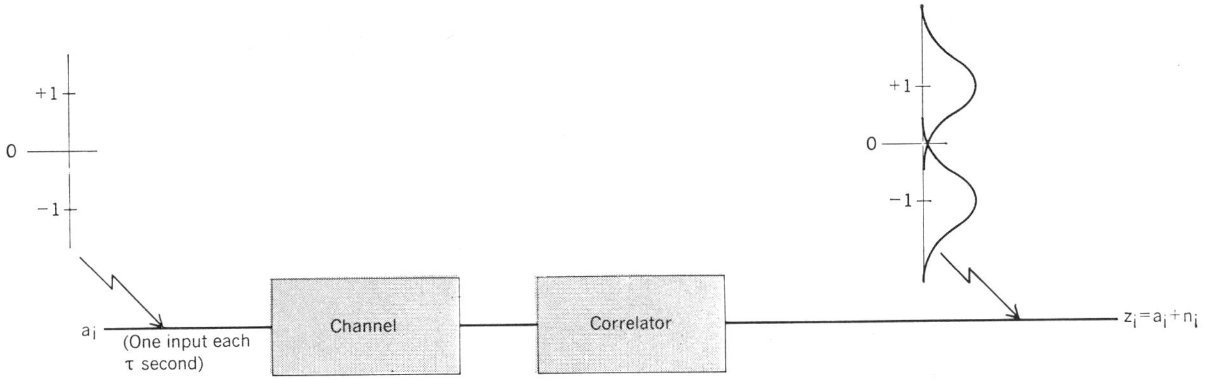


codes so structured that efficient decoding becomes feasible (but not so much structured that the codes themselves are no good). The most popular approach has been to use the structures of abstract algebra to generate classes of good, decodable block codes. A second approach uses linear sequential circuits to generate a class of codes that are called convolutional; at least for the applications to be discussed here, convolutional codes seem to have better balance between structure and randomness than is capable with the perhaps too-structured block codes.

A second major development of the last decade has been the emergence of the space channel into practical importance, both in the requirements of NASA for efficient transmission from deep-space probes, and in the proliferation of earth-orbiting communications satellites. The remarkable characteristic of the space channel is that, within the sensitivity of tests performed to date, it appears to be accurately modeled as a white-Gaussian-noise channel. Anyone who has ever taken a statistical subject knows that white Gaussian noise is the archetype of statistically regular, nonbursty noise, and as such is the theorist's dream. Consequently, in considering possible schemes for the space channel, one may use the most profound theorems, the most subtle analyses, and the most accurate simulations. One is also able to propose the most sophisticated and powerful decoding procedures, and predict performance to the accuracy of a fraction of a decibel. The initial successes of coding on the space channel have led to its incorporation in all space-system designs (of which the author is aware) in the last two years or so. For this reason, as well as the pedagogical neatness of the white-Gaussian-noise channel, this article uses the space channel for both orientation and motivation. We shall say little about the literally more mundane channels mentioned earlier, for although applications of coding have also been increasing in those environments, the schemes used are much more *ad hoc*, and more than qualitative predictions about behavior on real channels rarely can be made.

## The space channel

The model of the space channel that we shall use reflects all the significant characteristics of the channel, without some details important only in practice; it is illustrated in Fig. 1. An amplitude-modulated carrier

$$x(t) = a(t) \cos (\omega_c t + \theta)$$

is generated aboard a satellite and transmitted to an earth antenna. (Frequency and phase modulation are also used, but not as often as AM, and offer no advantage in principle.) The model still applies when the signal actually originates at another ground station and the satellite is only a repeater, since the power available on the ground is so much greater than that aboard the satellite that the uplink may be considered perfect in most cases. The received signal

$$y(t) = \alpha a(t) \cos [\omega_c t + \theta + \psi(t)] + n(t)$$

is subject to several principal disturbances:

1. Simple attenuation $\alpha$ due to distance (assumed perfectly linear). The received signal power is denoted $P$.

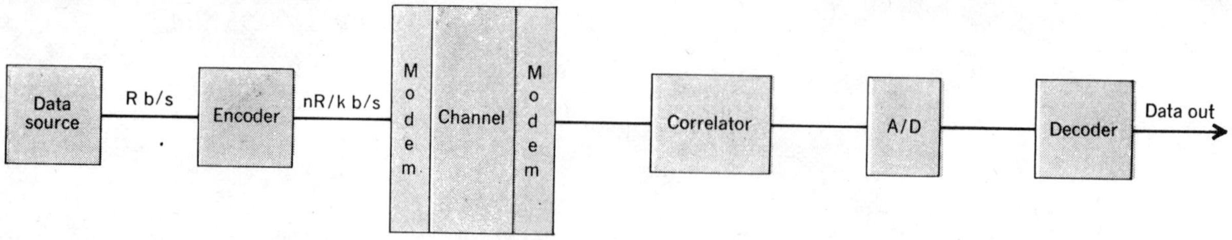


**FIGURE 3. System block diagram.**

2. Additive white Gaussian noise $n(t)$ arising in the receiver front end, with single-sided spectral density $N_o$.

3. Phase variations $\psi(t)$ due to imperfect tracking, uncompensated Doppler shifts, an unstable carrier oscillator, and so forth. In the applications with which the author is familiar, with the carrier $\omega_c$ in S band, the phase variations are the only important departure from the ideal white-Gaussian-noise model, and make themselves felt at low data rates by frustrating perfectly coherent demodulation. On a NASA mission with a terminal of the Goldstone type, phase variations can be kept to a few hertz or less, and are unimportant unless the bit rate is of the order of 10 bits per second or less. However, in some military applications where the receiver is aboard a plane, ship, jeep, or other moving platform, "low" data rates may be as high as 75 to 2400 b/s. We shall assume hereafter that we are at high enough rates that essentially perfect phase tracking and coherent demodulation can be maintained.

It will also be assumed that the information to be transmitted is already in digital form, leaving totally aside the kind of coding (source coding) that is concerned with efficient representation of the information in bits. (The gains from efficient source coding may be expected to equal or exceed those claimed in the following for efficient channel coding. The best techniques of the infant field of data compression are, however, even more *ad hoc* than those for channel coding on bursty channels.) The information rate will be denoted as $R$ b/s.

When a communications system can pass $R$ information bits per second over a white Gaussian channel on which the received power is $P$ and the noise density $N_o$, with some acceptable quality, we say that the system is operating at a *signal-to-noise ratio per information bit* $E_b/N_o = P/N_oR$. This dimensionless parameter then serves as a figure of merit for different coding and modulation schemes. Note that it incorporates any effective power loss due to coding redundancy. A system designer who simply wants to select a communications scheme to get the most data rate for a given power and receiver noise temperature, or to use the least power for a fixed data rate, will pick the scheme that can operate at the lowest $E_b/N_o$ with adequate quality (if he can possibly afford it).

An appropriate modulation technique, and the only one we shall consider, is pure time-discrete, $N$-level amplitude modulation. By this we mean that the modulating waveform $a(t)$ can only change at discrete intervals $\tau$ seconds apart, and during any $\tau$-second period, sometimes called a baud, it can take on one of $N$ discrete values, usually equally spaced. We let $a_i$ be the value in the $i$th interval. If $N$ is a power of two, say $2^m$, then the *signaling rate* is $1/\tau$ symbols (bauds) per second, and the *transmitted rate* $m/\tau$ bits per second. Ideally, the bandwidth occupied is $W = \frac{1}{2}\tau$ hertz, but this is only an approximation (and a lower bound) to the practical bandwidth. By far the most common scheme of this class is the binary ($N = 2$) case, with $a(t) = \pm 1$; this is commonly called PSK or phase-shift keying, the terminology arising from a viewpoint in which $a(t)$ has constant magnitude 1 and the phase $\theta$ is modulated to the two values $\pm \pi/2$.

With white Gaussian noise, and perfect phase tracking, it is appropriate to use a correlation or matched filter receiver. Mathematically, in the $i$th baud such a receiver forms the integral

$$z_i = \int_{i\tau}^{i\tau+\tau} y(t) \cos [\omega_c t + \theta + \psi(t)]\, dt$$

It is easily shown that $z_i = a_i + n_i$, where $a_i$ is the modulation amplitude (scaled) in the $i$th baud and $n_i$ is the noise, a Gaussian random variable centered on 0 and independent from baud to baud. (This assumes perfect synchronization of the timing intervals, which can be approached as closely as desired in practice.) Furthermore, no information is lost in the correlation operation, in the sense that any decision on what was sent that is based on the correlator outputs $z_i$ can be just as good as the information based on the complete received waveform. Thus we have replaced our continuous-time model with a discrete-time model, illustrated in Fig. 2 for PSK. Every $\tau$ seconds, a level $a_i$ (one of $N$) is sent, and a correlator output $z_i$ is received.

In the absence of coding, a *hard decision* is made on the correlator output as to which level was actually sent. For example, with binary PSK, a positive $z_i$ leads to a decision of +1, and negative to −1. With coding, it is usually desirable to keep an indication of how reliable the decision was; this can range from establishing a null zone around 0, which is treated as no decision or an *erasure*, to retaining essentially all the information in the correlator output by sufficient finely quantized analog-to-digital conversion (normally three bits), called a *soft* (or *quantized*) *decision*. Schematically, any of these possibilities will be represented by a box following the correlator output labeled A/D.

We can now lay out the complete block diagram of a system that includes coding (Fig. 3). Information bits arrive at a rate of $R$ b/s. An encoder of code rate $k/n$ inserts $n - k$ redundant bits for every $k$ information bits, giving a transmitted bit rate of $nR/k$ b/s. These bits are taken $m$ per baud into the modulator; at the receiver, a noisy correlator output is developed for each baud and A/D converted. The resulting hard decisions, soft decisions, or whatever, enter the decoder, which uses the redundancy in the data as well as (with soft decisions) the reliability of the received information to estimate which information bits were actually sent. When the signal-to-noise ratio is specified, this is a well-defined mathematical model, and it makes sense to ask the question: How much information can we transmit through this channel, and what do we put in the encoder and decoder boxes to do it? The surprising fact upon which we commented at the beginning of this article is that the answer to the first question was announced long before anyone had the remotest idea how to answer the second.

### Channel-capacity statements

Shannon's original work[1] showed that the capacity of the communication system blocked out in Fig. 3 is

$$C = \tfrac{1}{2} \log_2 (1 + P/N_o W) \quad \text{bits/baud}$$

$$\text{or } W \log_2 (1 + P/N_o W) \quad \text{bits/second}$$

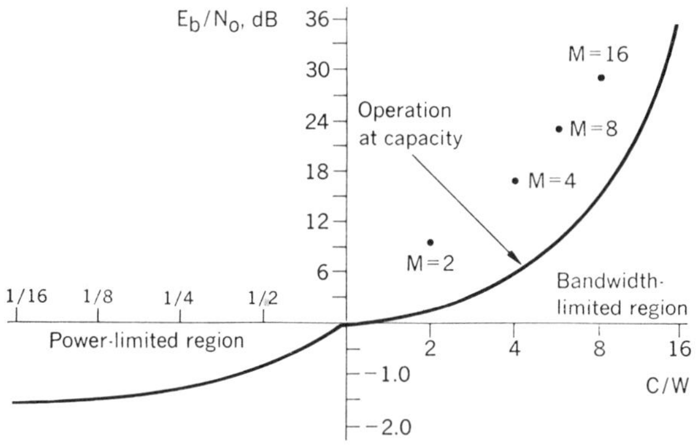


**FIGURE 4. $E_b/N_o$ as a function of C/W in bandwidth-limited and power-limited regions (note change of scale), with operation at capacity contrasted with M-level amplitude modulation [Pr ($\mathcal{E}$) = $10^{-5}$].**

**FIGURE 5. Bit-error probability as a function of signal-to-noise ratio per information bit for situations involving no coding and coding at capacity.**

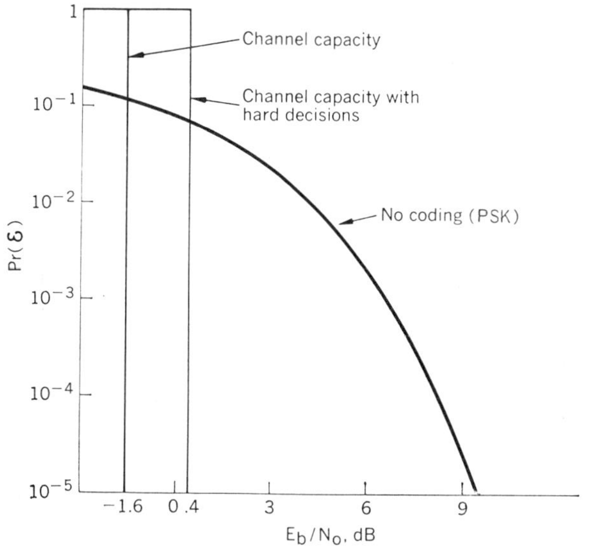


where $P$ is the received signal power, $N_o$ the single-sided noise spectral density, and $W$ the nominal bandwidth $\tfrac{1}{2}\tau$. Shannon showed that whenever the information rate $R$ is less than $C$, then there exists some coding and modulation scheme with as low a decoded error probability as you like; whereas if $R > C$, then the error probability cannot approach zero and more coding generally only makes things worse. Finally, it can be shown that the same results apply when the special modulation assumptions of Fig. 3 are removed, and any signaling scheme whatsoever is allowed.

At one time, this classic formula fell into disrepute, after it had been used loosely by all sorts of coarse fellows who applied it promiscuously to channels not remotely characterized by the white-Gaussian-noise model. With the advent of the space channel, however, it is time to rehabilitate it for the insight it provides.

Suppose we could actually transmit at capacity; the signal-to-noise ratio per information bit would then be $E_b/N_o = P/N_oC$. The number of bits per cycle of bandwidth under the same conditions would be $C/W$. The capacity formula is usefully rewritten as a relation between these two dimensionless parameters:

$$C/W = \log_2 [1 + (P/N_oC)(C/W)]$$

This relation is plotted in Fig. 4. We see that, for a fixed power-to-noise ratio $P/N_o$, more and more efficient communication is possible as the bandwidth is increased, and that with no bandwidth limitations, $E_b/N_o$ approaches a limit of ln 2 ($\approx$0.69, or $-1.6$ dB), called the Shannon limit. To date, space communication has been characterized by severe power limitation and bandwidth to burn, so that this so-called power-limited case has been the regime of interest. We note that, although the $E_b/N_o$ limit is reached only for infinite bandwidth, at ½ bit per cycle of bandwidth (or a code rate of about ¼ with PSK) we are practically there.

Let us now see what coding has to offer in the power-limited case. Figure 5 is a more standard curve of error probability versus $E_b/N_o$ in decibels. The no-coding curve is that for ideal PSK, which is representative of what was in fact used in the years B.C. (before coding), as in the Mariner '64 system that returned the first pictures from Mars. We see that an $E_b/N_o$ of 6.8 dB is required to obtain a bit error probability of $10^{-3}$ and 9.6 dB to obtain $10^{-5}$. On the other hand, the capacity theorem promises essentially zero error probability whenever $E_b/N_o$ exceeds $-1.6$ dB. This means that potential coding gains of 8 to 11 dB (a factor of 6 to 12) are possible, which is rather exciting in an environment where the cost of a decibel is frequently measured in millions of dollars. Since, in the power-limited region, $R$ is directly proportional to $P$, this gain may be taken either as reduced power or as increased data rate.

Another curve of parenthetical interest is included in Fig. 5, the capacity curve when the A/D box of Fig. 3 makes hard decisions. It turns out that this costs a factor of $\pi/2$ or 2 dB. We remark on this loss here because it seems to be one of the universal constants of nature: regardless of the coding scheme, use of hard decisions rather than soft in the power-limited region always costs about 2 dB.

The situation is quite different when the channel is bandwidth-limited rather than power-limited. The following simple argument shows that, in this region, coding no longer offers such dramatic gains. Referring back to the capacity formula, we see that for $P/N_oW \gg 1$, with fixed $N_o$ and $W$, each increase by a factor of four in $P$ leads to an increase of 1 bit/baud in channel capacity. On the other hand, consider what is required to increase the transmission rate in conventional multilevel amplitude modulation by 1 bit/baud. To double the number of signal levels while maintaining the same level separation and therefore the same probability of error requires increasing the amplitude span of the levels by a factor of two, as in Fig. 6, or the average power $P$ by a factor of about four (this rapidly becomes exact as $N = 2^m$ increases). Thus, if $R_{AM}$ is the rate achievable with amplitude modulation and $C$ the capacity for some power $P$, then as $P$ increases by $k$ factors of four, we have

$$P \rightarrow 4^k P$$

$$R_{AM} \rightarrow R_{AM} + k$$

$$C \rightarrow C + k$$

$$\frac{R_{AM}}{C} \rightarrow \frac{R_{AM} + k}{C + k} \rightarrow 1 \quad \text{as } k \rightarrow \infty$$

Thus we can nearly achieve capacity without coding as we get deeper into the bandwidth-limited region. In Fig. 4, we plotted the first few AM points for $\Pr(\mathcal{E}) = 10^{-5}$ to show how rapidly $R_{AM}$ approaches $C$. It therefore may be anticipated that as communications satellites achieve greater and greater effective radiated power the attractiveness of coding will diminish. One also suspects that this argument partially explains why, despite the fact that much outstanding early work on coding, including Shannon's, came out of the Bell Telephone Laboratories, to date there has been negligible operational use of coding on telephone circuits, which are engineered to be high signal-to-noise ratio, narrow-bandwidth lines. Comsat, by inheriting telephone-type tariffs that require its bandwidth to be offered in narrow slices, has been hobbled in the same way.

## Maximum-length shift-register codes

In the remaining sections, we will discuss different types of codes and decoding methods, in an attempt to give an impressionistic feel for what they involve, with particular reference to performance on the power-limited space channel. We begin with block codes, which were the first to be studied and have the most well-developed theory. The maximum-length shift-register (or pseudorandom or simplex) codes are a class of codes that make a good introduction to algebraic block codes. Their properties are interesting and easy to derive, and serve as an easy entrée to the mysteries of finite fields, upon which further developments in block codes depend. Furthermore, they are actually useful in space applications and in noncoding areas as well. The number and quality of the pictures of Mars returned from the recent Mariner probes depended on the use of codes like these.

Consider first a digital feedback circuit such as the one depicted in Fig. 7; i.e., an $m$-bit shift register whose serial input is the modulo-2 (exclusive-or) sum of two or more of the bits in the shift register. In Fig. 7, $m = 4$ and the two bits are the rightmost $b_1$ and the leftmost $b_4$, so that the input $b_{in}$ is expressed mathematically as

$$b_{in} = b_1 + b_4 \quad \text{modulo 2} \tag{1a}$$

or, using the notation $\oplus$ for modulo-2 addition,

$$b_{in} = b_1 \oplus b_4 \tag{1b}$$

When we say "shift register," we imply that whenever the circuit is pulsed by a clock pulse (not shown), $b_{in}$ enters the left end, all other bits shift one place to the right, and the rightmost bit $b_1$ is lost.

It is well to be absolutely solid on the properties of modulo-2 arithmetic before striding off into the woods of algebraic coding theory.* Only two quantities occur in the arithmetic, 0 and 1. They may be added and multiplied as though they were ordinary integers, except that $1 \oplus 1 = 0$. This leads to the curious property that any number (0 or 1) added to itself in this arithmetic "cancels," i.e., equals zero, so that each number can be regarded as the negative of itself, and addition and subtraction are indistinguishable. (For example, if $a = b \oplus c$, then $b =$

* In general, the operations of modulo-$N$ arithmetic ($N$ equal to any integer) are the same as those of ordinary arithmetic after every number is reduced to its remainder when divided by $N$. For example, 8 modulo 3 is 2.

**I. Modulo-2 arithmetic**

Addition

| + | 0 | 1 |
|---|---|---|
| 0 | 0 | 1 |
| 1 | 1 | 0 |

Multiplication

| × | 0 | 1 |
|---|---|---|
| 0 | 0 | 0 |
| 1 | 0 | 1 |

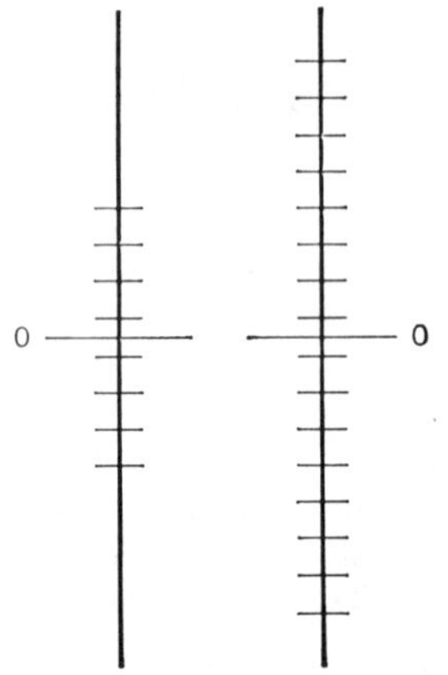


**FIGURE 6. Doubling the number of levels with the same level spacing requires quadrupling the power in pulse amplitude modulation.**

**FIGURE 7. Maximum-length shift-register sequence generator with m = 4 stages.**

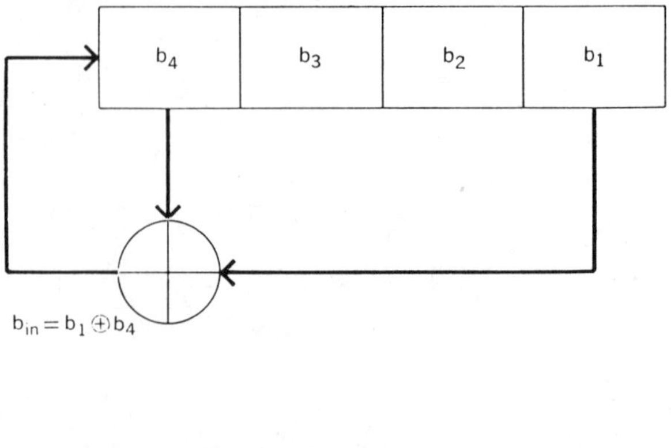

$a \ominus c = a \oplus c$.) Addition and multiplication tables are given explicitly in Table I. It is easy to verify that all the ordinary rules of arithmetic—i.e., $a + b + c = c + b + a$, $a(b + c) = ab + ac$, etc.—apply in modulo-2 arithmetic, so that we can manipulate symbolic expressions freely, just as though they involved ordinary numbers, with the additional rule that $a + a = 0$.

Return now to the feedback circuit of Fig. 7. What happens when it is shifted a number of times? The answer clearly depends on what its initial contents are. If all stages initially contain zeros, then the input will be zero, so that a shift will leave the register in the all-zero state. There are 15 other initial states; if we pick one of them, say 0001, and use Eq. (1), we find that 15 shifts cycle the register through all nonzero states and return the register to the starting point. The state diagram is shown in Fig. 8; it consists of two cycles: the one-state all-zero cycle, and the 15-state nonzero cycle. The name "maximum-length shift register" is given to this circuit since, given that 0000 must go to 0000, the 15-state cycle is the maximum length possible.

It is a nontrivial result of algebra that for any number of stages $m$ we can always find a circuit like Fig. 7 with a state diagram like Fig. 8. The input is always a modulo-2 sum of certain stages of the register, so the all-zero state always gives a zero input, and the zero state always goes into the zero state on a shift. The remaining $M - 1$ states form a maximum-length cycle, where $M = 2^m$. Table II specifies input connections to the modulo-2 adder that will give a maximum-length shift register for $1 \leq m \leq 34$.

A block code using the circuit of Fig. 7 as an encoder operates as follows: The message to be transmitted, assumed to be a sequence of bits, is segregated into 4-bit segments. Each segment is loaded into the 4-bit shift register, and the register is shifted 15 times. The 15 bits coming out of the rightmost stage of the register are transmitted as a block, or code word. Table III gives the 15-bit code words corresponding to each 4-bit information segment.

This code is called a (15, 4) code, since code words have 15 bits for each 4 information bits. By using registers of different lengths $m$, we can create $(M - 1, m)$ codes. Since $M = 2^m$, as $m$ gets large, the ratio of information bits to transmitted bits (the code rate) becomes very small, which limits the usefulness of these codes for coding purposes; in other applications, however, the fact that a very long nonrepeating sequence can be generated with a short register is the feature of interest.

We can quickly determine some properties of the $(M - 1)$-bit sequences generated by these registers. First, the bits in these sequences are the rightmost bits of the $M - 1$ nonzero state sequences of length $m$. Since exactly half of all $m$-bit sequences end in "1," precisely $M/2$ 1's occur in any maximum-length sequence (for example, 8 bits out of the 15 in the sequence of the example). In a long sequence, if we look at the output at a random time, the probability of seeing a "1" is $(M/2)/(M - 1)$, or just

**FIGURE 8. State diagram of feedback circuit in Fig. 7.**

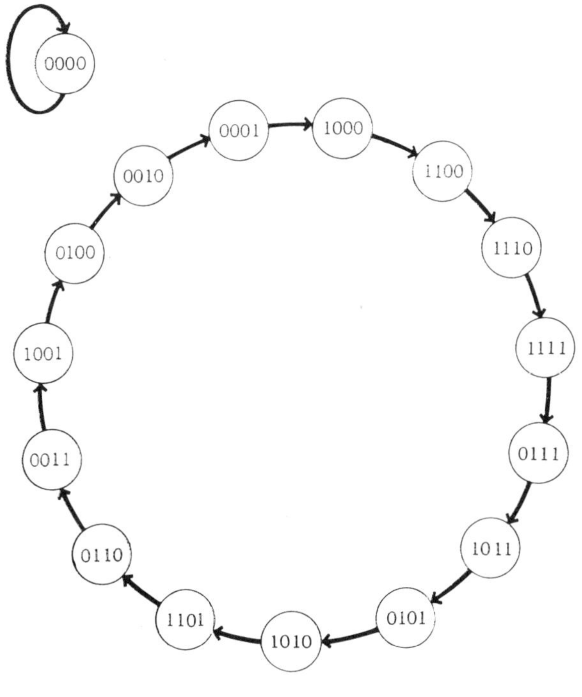


**II. Connections for MLSR generators**

| m | Stages Connected to Modulo-2 Adder | m | Stages Connected to Modulo-2 Adder |
|---|---|---|---|
| 1 | 1 | 18 | 1, 12 |
| 2 | 1, 2 | 19 | 1, 15, 18, 19 |
| 3 | 1, 3 | 20 | 1, 18 |
| 4 | 1, 4 | 21 | 1, 20 |
| 5 | 1, 4 | 22 | 1, 22 |
| 6 | 1, 6 | 23 | 1, 19 |
| 7 | 1, 7 | 24 | 1, 18, 23, 24 |
| 8 | 1, 5, 6, 7 | 25 | 1, 23 |
| 9 | 1, 6 | 26 | 1, 21, 25, 26 |
| 10 | 1, 8 | 27 | 1, 23, 26, 27 |
| 11 | 1, 10 | 28 | 1, 26 |
| 12 | 1, 7, 9, 12 | 29 | 1, 28 |
| 13 | 1, 10, 11, 13 | 30 | 1, 8, 29, 30 |
| 14 | 1, 5, 9, 14 | 31 | 1, 29 |
| 15 | 1, 15 | 32 | 1, 11, 31, 32 |
| 16 | 1, 5, 14, 16 | 33 | 1, 21 |
| 17 | 1, 15 | 34 | 1, 8, 33, 34 |

**III. Code words in a (15, 4) code**

| Information Bits | Code Word |
|---|---|
| 0000 | 000000000000000 |
| 0001 | 000111101011001 |
| 1000 | 100011110101100 |
| 0100 | 010001111010110 |
| 0010 | 001000111101011 |
| 1001 | 100100011110101 |
| 1101 | 110010001111010 |
| 0110 | 011001000111101 |
| 1011 | 101100100011110 |
| 0101 | 010110010001111 |
| 1010 | 101011001000111 |
| 1101 | 110101100100011 |
| 1110 | 111010110011001 |
| 1111 | 111101011001000 |
| 0111 | 011110101100100 |
| 0011 | 001111010110010 |

about ½. Furthermore, since all $m$-bit sequences except the all-zero sequence occur somewhere in the maximum-length sequence, the probability of seeing a "1" given any $m - 1$ or fewer preceding bits is still nearly one half. These and other statistical properties make a maximum-length sequence difficult to distinguish from a sequence generated truly randomly, as by flipping a coin, yet these sequences are easy to generate and repeatable. Thus they are commonly used to generate pseudorandom bits.

The class of maximum-length shift-register codes is representative of the major classes of algebraic block codes, in that such codes have the properties of being

1. Systematic; that is, the information bits are transmitted unchanged as part of the code word. In the example (Table III), the first four bits of each code word are the information bits.

2. A parity-check code; that is, each of the noninformation (parity) bits is a parity check on (modulo-2 sum of) certain information bits. This can be proved inductively; for example, in the example code, the fifth bit is the modulo-2 sum of the first and fourth; the sixth is the sum of the second and fifth, but this is the same as the second plus the first plus the fourth; in general, the $n$th bit is some modulo-2 sum of previous bits, which are themselves each modulo-2 sums of information bits, so the $n$th bit is also some modulo-2 sum of information bits. (In fact, in the maximum-length shift-register codes, the parity bits consist of all possible different parity checks on the information bits.)

3. Cyclic; that is, the end-around shift of any code word is another code word.

The parity-check property can be used to prove the most important single result concerning parity-check codes (the group property), which is that if we form the modulo-2 sum of two code words, we get another code word.

The modulo-2 sum of two $n$-bit code words is defined as the bit-by-bit modulo-2 sum; that is, if $x_i$ and $y_i$, $1 \leq i \leq n$ are the bits in the two original code words, then the bits $z_i$ in their sum are

$$z_i = x_i \oplus y_i$$

Thus the information bits in $z$ are the modulo-2 sum of the information bits in $x$ and $y$. The parity bits in $z$ are what we get when we put the modulo-2 sum of the information bits in $x$ and $y$ into our 4-bit register and shift 15 times; it is not hard to see that they are the modulo-2 sum of the parity bits in $x$ and $y$, since the shift-register connection is itself a modulo-2 sum. In other words, the two circuits in Fig. 9 have identical outputs.

This can be verified also by taking any two of the words in Table III and forming their modulo-2 sum; the result will be another one of the cyclic shifts of the basic sequence.

The group property gives immediate answers to questions about distance or correlation between code words. The distance (Hamming distance) between two code words is defined as the number of places in which they differ. If we form the modulo-2 sum of two code words, the resulting word will have zeros in the positions in which the two code words agree, and ones where they differ; thus the distance between two code words is exactly the number of ones in their sum. But, from the group property, their sum is another code word; and in the maximum-length shift-register codes all words have the same number of ones,* namely $M/2$ (eight in our example). Thus the distance between any two words in these codes is $M/2$, or about half the code length.

The equidistant property of maximum-length shift-register codes makes them an optimum solution to the following problem in signal design: How can one construct $M$ equal-energy signals to minimize the cross-correlation between any two signals, with no bandwidth limitations? Let us suppose that a code word is sent by PSK, so that a 0 is sent as a baud of amplitude $-1$ and a 1 as amplitude $+1$. The $M$-code words then correspond to $M$ vectors in $M - 1$ dimensions, all of equal energy (autocorrelation) $M - 1$. The cross-correlation (inner product) of any two vectors is a sum of baud-by-baud correlations, equal to $+1$ if the vectors agree in that place, and $-1$ if they disagree. But we have just proved that the Hamming distance between any two code words is $M/2$, so that any two vectors disagree in $M/2$ places and agree in the remaining $M/2 - 1$. Consequently, any two vectors are anticorrelated with cross-correlation $-1$. This implies that as vectors in $(M - 1)$-space, the code words form a geometrical object called a simplex, which is universally believed (though it has never quite been proved) to be the distribution of equal-energy signals in signal space that minimizes the probability of in-

* Except the all-zero word, of course; this is the code word we get when we sum any code word with itself.

**FIGURE 9. Two equivalent linear circuits.**

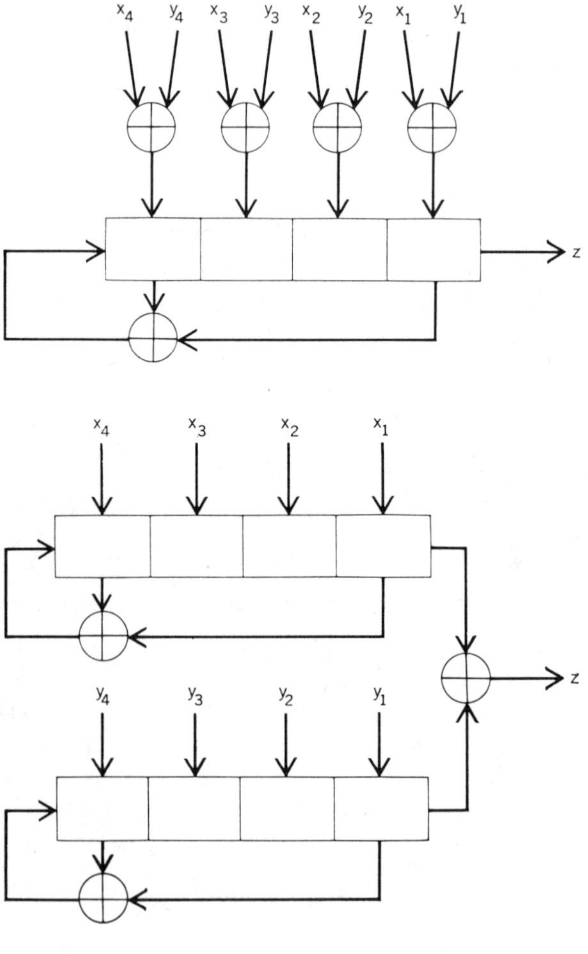

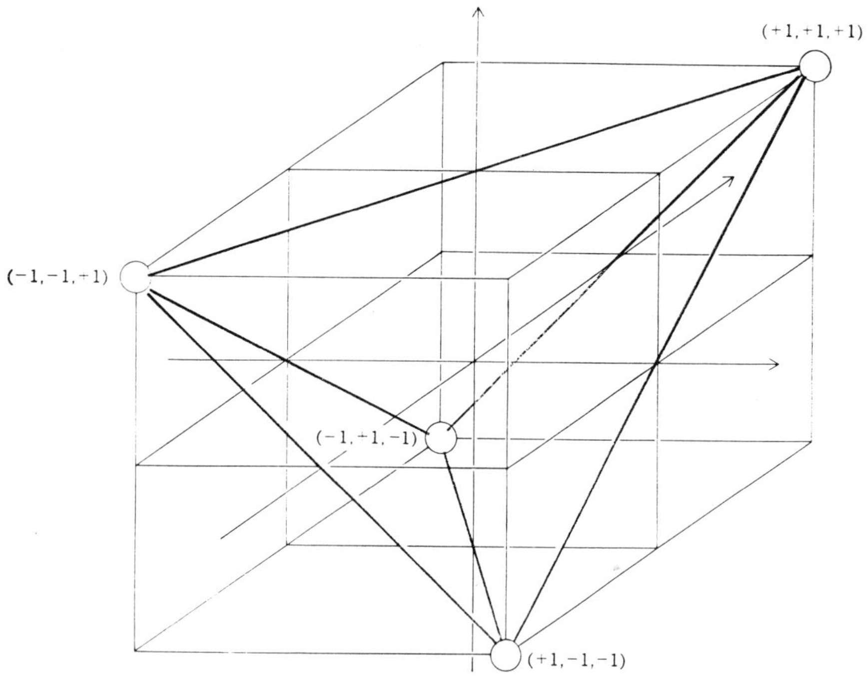


**FIGURE 10. Simplex (tetrahedron) formed by m = 2, (3, 2) code in three dimensions.**

**FIGURE 11. Performance of various block codes.**

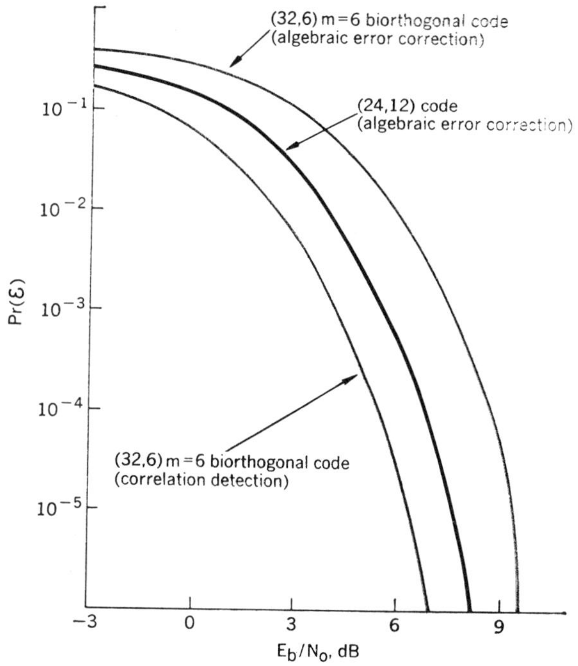


correct detection. Figure 10 shows the simplex corresponding to the $m = 2$ maximum-length shift-register code, which takes the form of a tetrahedron in three dimensions. Here is an intriguing contact between algebraic coding theory and the geometry of $N$ dimensions.

Suppose now that we use such a binary code with PSK modulation; how shall we decode it at the receiver? As in Fig. 3, we assume that we start with the $M - 1$ correlator outputs $z_i$ that correspond to the $M - 1$ bauds required to send a code word. For definiteness, we use the code of our example in which $m = 4$ and $M - 1 = 15$. Here we shall see a distinction between the viewpoints of the signal designer and of the algebraic coding theorist. The signal designer would take the attitude that what we have here is a way of sending one of 16 signals through a white Gaussian channel, where each possible signal is made up of 15 binary chips, and thus is a vector in 15 dimensions. As in the pure binary case, the optimum detection method is to correlate the received signal against all the 16 possible transmitted signals, which can be done by simply summing the correlator outputs $z_i$ multiplied by $\pm 1$ according to the code word amplitude in the corresponding baud. Thus 16 computations followed by a selection of the largest correlation must be performed. (It turns out that the correlations can be done simultaneously in a special-purpose computer—called the "Green machine" at Jet Propulsion Laboratory[2] as an $M$-point fast Hadamard transform, which is structurally very similar to a fast Fourier transform.) The computational load remains manageable for $m$ less than eight or so, which is also where the bandwidth occupied by these codes begins to be absurdly large. A modified (biorthogonal) $m = 6$ code was used in the Mariner '69 expedition; its performance curve is shown in Fig. 11.[3]

An alternate approach is usually taken by the algebraic coding theorist. The first step is to make a hard decision on each correlator output to obtain a 15-bit digital word called the received word. Now we are back in the realm of modulo-2 arithmetic, Hamming distance, and so forth. In the hard-decision process, a number of bit errors will usually be made. From the distance properties of the original code, one can determine that if fewer than some maximum number of errors occur, then correct decoding is guaranteed. In the example, where the Hamming distance between any two words is eight, it is easy to see that if three errors occur in the reception of any code word, then the received word will differ in three places from the correct word, but in at least five places from any other word, so that in principle decoding should be correct. In

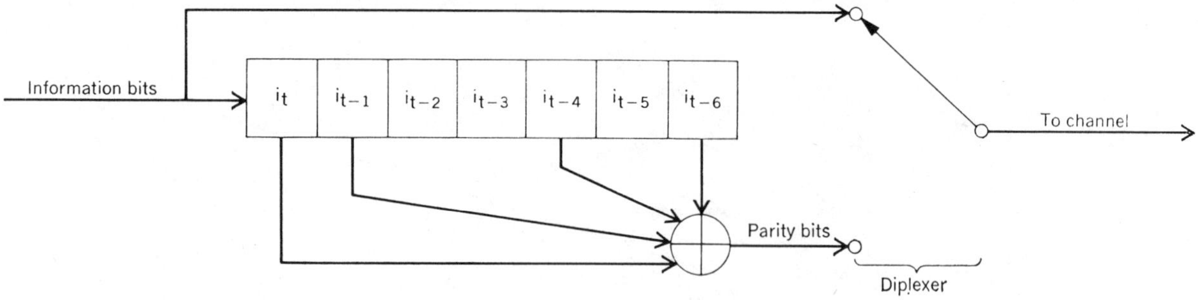


**FIGURE 12. Convolutional encoder.**

general, a number of bit errors equal to the greatest integer less than half the Hamming distance is guaranteed to be correctable.

One decoding method suitable for the (15, 4) example code is permutation decoding.[4] From the distance properties of this code, we know that if we can find some code word within Hamming distance three of the received word, then we should assume that word was sent, since all other code words must be at least distance five from the received word. To find such a word, we can start by simply reencoding the four received information bits, and checking whether the reencoded parity bits agree with the received parity bits in all but three or fewer places. If so, we are done. If not, then because of the cyclic property of the code, we can take any other four consecutive received bits, treat them as information bits, and generate the rest of the cycle (end-around) that makes up the code. (If this is not immediately clear, try taking any four consecutive positions of any code word in Table III, loading them into the encoder shift register, and shifting 15 times to generate the whole code word, starting at that point and cycling around past the beginning.) If there are actually three or fewer bit errors, at least one set of four consecutive positions will be received correctly, so by taking each set of four in turn, reencoding, and comparing, we will eventually find the correct code word. (This cyclic permutation scheme is also used to correct burst errors, since a correctable burst of errors will not affect at least one set of $k$ consecutive bits.[5])

The performance of hard decisions followed by algebraic error correction is also shown in Fig. 11, for the same (32, 6), distance-16 code as in the correlation detection curve. We see that it is more than 3 dB worse for the lower error probabilities. It might therefore seem that the correlation technique is the better one; however, algebraic decoding remains feasible for much longer code lengths and numbers of information bits, where correlation detection is computationally infeasible. A curve for the (24, 12) (minimum distance eight) extended Golay code is also shown in Fig. 11; with longer codes, the hard-decision disadvantage can eventually be overcome.

Ideally, one would like a scheme whose computational complexity was like that of the algebraic decoding schemes, but would make use of all the information in the correlator output and thus achieve performance like that of correlation detection. At least two approaches (orthogonal equation decoding[6,7] and generalized minimum-distance decoding[8]) with these features are known, but they have not been extensively studied due to the existence of superior convolutional coding schemes (to be described in the next section).

Although we have studied only the maximum-length shift-register codes here, more advanced algebraic block codes involve quite similar ideas. Peterson[9] and Berlekamp[10] are the standard references of the field.

## Convolutional codes

Historically, the coding world has been divided between block-code people and convolutional-code people. Although relations between these groups are perfectly amicable, block-code types tend to harp on the relatively primitive theoretical understanding and development of convolutional codes vis-à-vis block codes, whereas convolutional-code types point out that in all respects in which convolutional codes can be compared with block codes they are essentially as good in theory, and in some major respects better, while in practice they are typically simpler. The correctness of both these viewpoints will be illustrated in this section. Whereas we have considered an infinite class of good block codes, we cannot now consider such a class of convolutional codes, since classes of reasonably good codes in the block-code sense are unknown. Instead we shall consider a simple typical code and some reasonable ways of decoding it. The best of these methods will be seen to give better performance on the space channel than any block-code techniques.

Consider the linear sequential circuit illustrated in Fig. 12. Like the maximum-length shift-register generator of Fig. 7, it consists of a shift register and a modulo-2 adder connected to several shift-register stages. In this case, however, information bits are continuously entered into the left end of the register, and for each new information bit a parity bit (a parity check on the current bit and three of those in the past) is computed according to the formula

$$p_t = i_t \oplus i_{t-1} \oplus i_{t-4} \oplus i_{t-6}$$

Information and parity bits are transmitted alternately over the channel. The code generated by this encoder is called a rate-½ convolutional code: rate ½ because there are two transmitted bits for every information bit, convolutional because the parity sequence is the convolution of the information sequence with the impulse response 1,1,0,0,1,0,1, modulo-2. Like the block codes considered earlier, the code is systematic (information bits are transmitted), and is a parity-check code; therefore, it has the group property (the modulo-2 sum of two encoded sequences is the encoded sequence corresponding to the modulo-2 sum of the information sequences).

We shall now suppose that the encoded sequence is sent over a binary channel and that hard decisions are made at the receiver output. How do we decode? First, the decoder must establish which received bits are information and which parity, but as there are only two possibilities, trial and error is a feasible procedure. (For block codes, the comparable problem involves a choice between $n$ phases, where $n$ is the block length, and some special synchronization means may be required.) This done, we shall let the decoder form *syndromes*, which are defined as follows:

Take the received information sequence, and from it recompute the parity sequence with an encoder identical to that of Fig. 12. Compare these recomputed parity bits with the parity bits actually received; the outputs from the comparator (another modulo-2 adder) are called the syndromes (see Fig. 13). (The syndrome idea is equally useful with block codes.)

It is evident that if no errors occur in transmission over the channel, the recomputed parity bits will equal the received parity bits and all syndromes will be zero. On the other hand, if an isolated error occurs in the parity sequence, then a single syndrome will be equal to one at the time of the error. If an isolated error occurs in the information sequence, then the syndromes will equal one at all times when the incorrect bit is at a tapped stage of the shift register, so the syndrome sequence will be 1,1,0,0,1, 0,1,0,0 . . . , starting at the time of the error. The syndrome pattern for more than one error is just the linear superposition (modulo-2) of the syndrome patterns for each of the individual errors. Thus do the syndromes indicate the nature of the disease.

An obvious technique for correcting single isolated errors now suggests itself. Such an error will manifest itself as a syndrome pattern of 1100101 or 1000000, depending on whether it is in an information or a parity bit. The first time we see a 1 in the syndrome sequence, we know that an error has occurred; the value of the following syndrome tells us whether it was an information or parity error. Since only information errors need be corrected, an AND gate looking for two successive syndrome "ones" suffices, as illustrated in Fig. 14(A).

One can correct double errors with the hardly more complicated circuit of Fig. 14(B). Here the syndromes are fed into a 7-stage shift register; a threshold circuit fires if three or four of four selected places contain ones. The selected places are those that would contain ones if there were only a single information error. A single parity error, in addition, can only disturb one input to the threshold circuit; similarly, it can be verified that with this particular code a second information error can only interfere with one input, so that if only two errors occur the threshold circuit will certainly fire at the right time. On the other hand, it can also be verified that under the assumption of only two errors the circuit will never fire at the wrong time. Finally, the complement line is included to take out the effect of a corrected error in those syndrome bits that were inverted by it, so that the decoder can handle all error patterns that do not have more than two errors in any seven consecutive pairs of received bits.

Both these decoders are examples of threshold decoders[7] (working on a self-orthogonal code[11]). Threshold

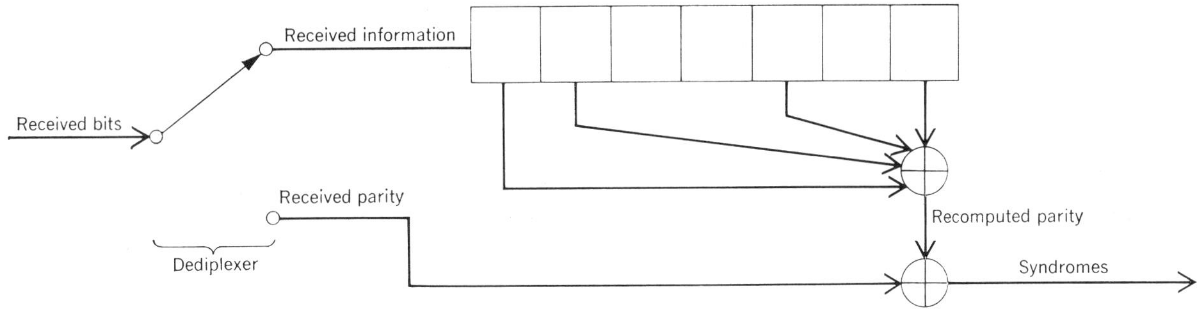


**FIGURE 13. Syndrome formation at the receiver.**

**FIGURE 14. Simple single- and double-error-correcting threshold decoders.**

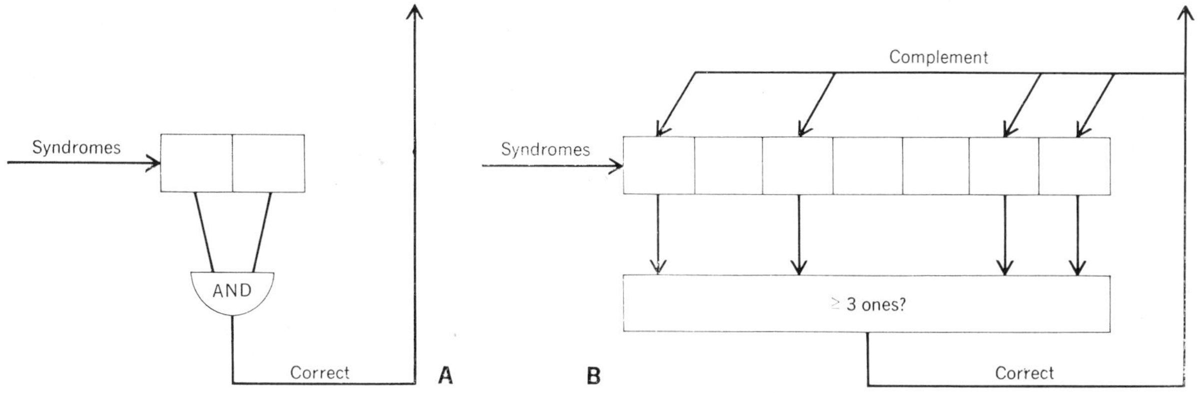

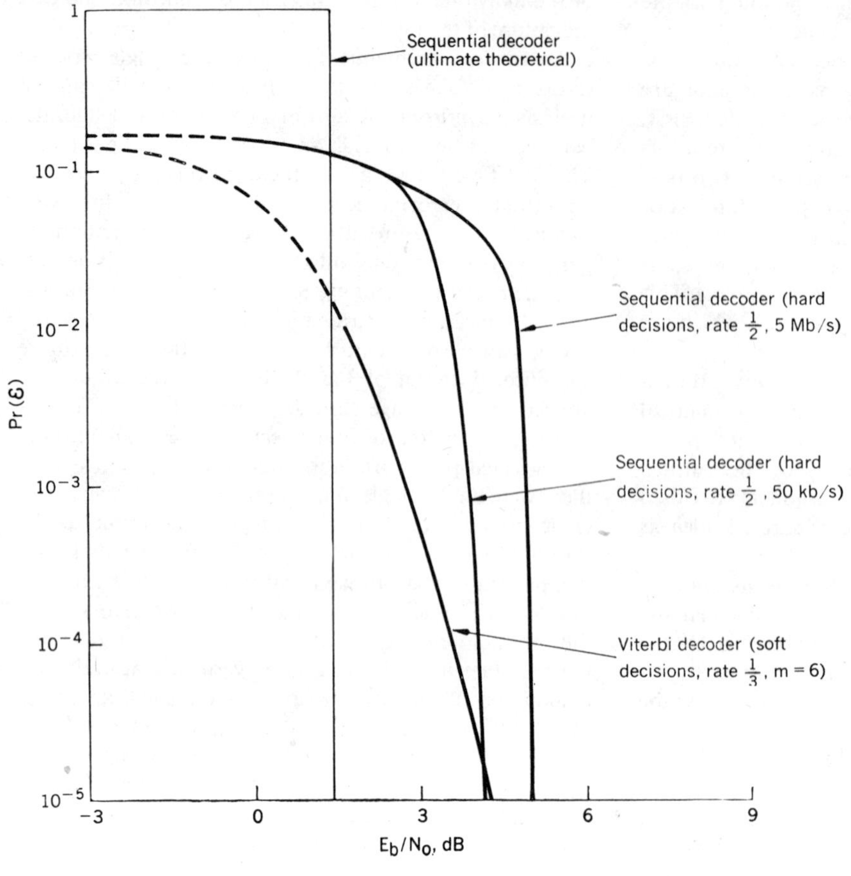


**FIGURE 15. Performance of convolutional decoders.**

decoding is an extremely simple technique that applies to many short codes correcting a few errors, and that is easily extended to correct bursts of errors. Its efficiency diminishes as the number of errors to be corrected becomes large, and for this reason it is not an outstanding performer on the space channel. With hard decisions, the performance of the three-error-correcting (24, 12) convolutional code (shift register length 12) is about the same (to within 0.2 dB) as that of the (24, 12) block code of Fig. 11.

Sequential decoding was invented by Wozencraft[12] in about 1957. Through a decade of improvement, analysis, and development, it has become the best-performing practical technique known for memoryless channels like the space channel, and will probably be the general-purpose workhorse for these channels in the future. Like much else in the convolutional-coding domain, it is hard to explain and analyze, but relatively easy to implement. Very crudely, a sequential decoder works by generating hypotheses about what information sequence was actually sent until it finds some that are reasonably consistent with what was received. It does this by a backward and forward search through the received data (or through syndromes). It starts by going forward, generating a sequence of hypotheses about what was sent. It checks what was received against what would have been transmitted given the hypotheses, and according to the goodness of the agreement updates a measure of its happiness called the metric. As long as it is happy, it goes forward; when it becomes unhappy, it turns back and starts changing hypotheses one by one until it can go forward happily again. A simple set of rules for doing this is called the Fano algorithm.[13–15]

It is evident even from this meager description that sequential decoding involves a trial-and-error search of variable duration. When reception is perfect, the decoder's first guess is always correct, and only one "computation" (generation of a hypothesis) is required per bit. The more noise, the more hypotheses must be generated, up to literally millions to decode a single short segment. Because of the variability of the computational load, buffer storage of the received data must be provided to permit long searches. Whenever this buffer overflows, the decoder must jump ahead and get restarted, leaving a section of data undecoded. This overflow event therefore leads to a burst of output errors; its frequency generally dominates the probability of decoding error, since the code can be made long enough that the probability the decoder is actually happy with incorrect hypotheses can be made negligible.

Sequential decoding is outstandingly adaptable; it can work with soft or hard decisions and PSK, or with any modulation and detection scheme. In the four implementations for the space channel to date, the Lincoln Experimental Terminal decoder[16] works with 16-ary frequency-hopping modulation and incoherent list detection; the NASA Ames decoder for the Pioneer satellites[17] and the JPL general-purpose decoder[18] work with PSK and soft (eight-level) decisions; and the Codex decoder, built for the U.S. Army Satellite Communication Agency,[19] works with PSK (or DPSK or QPSK) and hard decisions, the choice in every case being based on system considerations. Sequential decoding can even make efficient use of known redundancies in the data, as was done for some preexisting parity checks in the Pioneer data format. The one thing a sequential decoder cannot tolerate is bursts of errors, which will cause excessive computation; therefore, it cannot be applied without modification to any channel but the space channel.

The performance of sequential decoding depends both on the modulation and detection scheme with which it is used, and on the data rate relative to the internal computation rate. The theoretical limit of any sequential decoder on a white Gaussian channel is $E_b/N_o = 1.4$ dB, exactly 3 dB above the Shannon limit; this limit can be approached with PSK, soft decisions, and low-rate codes. The simplest possible sequential decoder working with rate-½ codes, PSK, and hard decisions has a theoretical limit of $E_b/N_o = 4.5$ dB; 2 dB of this loss is due to hard decisions, 1 dB to the choice of rate ½ rather than a lower rate. Actual performance depends on the data rate as well as the error rate desired, although the curves are very steep; Fig. 15 shows measured curves at 50 kb/s and 5 Mb/s for the Codex decoder,[20] which has an internal computation rate of 13.3 Mb/s.

Somehow the idea that sequential decoding is complicated to implement has achieved considerable circulation. This is undoubtedly partly due to the difficulty of the literature. Also, the first sequential decoder (SECO[21]), built at Lincoln Laboratory for telephone lines with the technology of an earlier day, was an undoubted monster, due in part to large amounts of auxiliary equipment such as equalizers. It should be emphasized that three of the four implementations just mentioned involve only a drawer of electronics with a core memory system for the buffer storage; the fourth, the Pioneer system, was actually done in software because of the low maximum bit rate (512 b/s).

We conclude by mentioning two more classes of schemes of current interest. One, the Viterbi algorithm,[22] performs optimum correlation detection of short convolutional codes much as the Green machine does of block codes. Figure 15 shows the performance of this algorithm[23] with soft decisions when the decoding complexity is comparable to that of the $m = 6$ block decoder of Fig. 11; performance is uniformly superior. This algorithm is competitive in performance with sequential decoding for moderate error rates, but cannot achieve very low error rates efficiently. On the other hand, it can be implemented in a highly parallel pipe-lined decoder capable of extremely high speeds (tens of megabits) where sequential decoders become uneconomic. It therefore may find application in high-data-rate systems with modest error requirements, such as digitized television.

The second class represents attempts to bridge the final 3-dB gap between the sequential decoding limit and the Shannon limit by combining sequential decoding with algebraic block code constraints. Recent unpublished work of Jelinek gives promise of performances between 1 and 2 dB from the Shannon limit without excessive computation. At the moment, all schemes in this class seem most suited for software implementation, and will probably be used only for low-data-rate applications where the ultimate in efficiency is desired, as in deep-space probes.

Thus do we near practical achievement of the goal set by Shannon 20 years ago.

REFERENCES


1. Shannon, C. E., "A mathematical theory of communication," *Bell System Tech. J.*, vol. 27, pp. 379–423, 623–656, 1948.
2. Green, R. R., "A serial orthogonal decoder," Jet Propulsion Lab. Space Programs Summary 37-39, vol. 4, pp. 247–252, 1966.
3. *Digital Communications with Space Applications*, appendix 4, S. Golomb, ed. Englewood Cliffs, N.J.: Prentice-Hall, 1964.
4. MacWilliams, J., "Permutation decoding of systematic codes," *Bell System Tech. J.*, vol. 43, pp. 485–506, 1964.
5. Gallager, R. G., *Information Theory and Reliable Communication.* New York: Wiley, 1968, pp. 291–297.
6. Gallager, R. G., *Low-Density Parity-Check Codes.* Cambridge, Mass.: M.I.T. Press, 1963, pp. 42–52.
7. Massey, J. L., *Threshold Decoding.* Cambridge: M.I.T. Press, 1963, pp. 59–63.
8. Forney, G. D., "Generalized minimum distance decoding," *IEEE Trans. Information Theory*, vol. IT-12, pp. 125–131, Apr. 1966.
9. Peterson, W. W., *Error-Correcting Codes.* Cambridge: M.I.T. Press, 1961.
10. Berlekamp, E. R., *Algebraic Coding Theory.* New York: McGraw-Hill, 1968.
11. Robinson, J. P., and Bernstein, A. J., "A class of binary recurrent codes with limited error propagation," *IEEE Trans. Information Theory*, vol. IT-13, pp. 106–113, Jan. 1967.
12. Wozencraft, J. M., and Reiffen, B., *Sequential Decoding.* Cambridge: M.I.T. Press, 1961.
13. Fano, R. M., "A heuristic discussion of probabilistic decoding," *IEEE Trans. Information Theory*, vol. IT-9, pp. 64–74, Apr. 1963.
14. Wozencraft, J. M., and Jacobs, I. M., *Principles of Communication Engineering.* New York: Wiley, 1965.
15. Gallager, R. G., *op. cit.*, pp. 263–286.
16. Lebow, I. L., and McHugh, P. G., "A sequential decoding technique and its realization in the Lincoln Experimental Terminal," *IEEE Trans. Communication Technology*, vol. COM-15, pp. 477–491, Aug. 1967.
17. Lumb, D. R., "Test and preliminary flight results on the sequential decoding of convolutionally encoded data from Pioneer IX," 1969 IEEE Internat'l Communications Conf. Record, Boulder, Colo., pp. 39/1–8.
18. Lushbaugh, W., "Multiple-mission sequential decoder," Jet Propulsion Lab. Space Programs Summary 37-58, vol. 2, pp. 33–36, 1969.
19. Forney, G. D., Jr., and Langelier, R. M., "A high-speed sequential decoder for satellite communications," *1969 IEEE Internat'l Communications Conf. Record*, Boulder, Colo., pp. 39/9–17.
20. "High-speed sequential decoder," Codex Corp. final rept., Contract DAAB07-69-C-0051, U.S. Army Satellite Communication Agency, Ft. Monmouth, N.J., June 6, 1969.
21. Lebow, I. L., *et al.*, "Application of sequential decoding to high-rate data communication on a telephone line," *IEEE Trans. Information Theory*, vol. IT-9, pp. 260–269, Apr. 1963.
22. Viterbi, A. J., "Error bounds for convolutional codes and an asymptotically optimum decoding algorithm," *IEEE Trans. Information Theory*, vol. IT-13, pp. 260–269, Apr. 1967.
23. Heller, J., "Improved performance of short constraint length convolutional codes," Jet Propulsion Lab. Space Programs Summary 37-56, vol. 3, pp. 83–84, 1969.

# Part IV
# Chirp Techniques

The best known spread spectrum technique was originally intended for use in radar systems to increase the effective power of the radar transmitters by allowing them to transmit a longer pulse while retaining the desirable characteristics of a narrow pulse. This was accomplished by transmitting a frequency modulated pulse that is time compressed in the receiver into a much narrower pulse with correspondingly higher effective power.

Early chirp systems were hampered by the physical constraints of building delay lines that had dispersion characteristics sufficient to provide high TW products. In recent years, new techniques have been developed to overcome these difficulties, with surface wave delay lines being at the forefront, and other types of dispersive elements also being developed. Some of these newer types of devices can provide TW products of 1000 or more, in small packages similar to those employed for semiconductors.

In light of such developments, it was inevitable that great interest should be generated in using chirp waveforms in communications and ranging systems as well as radars. Current development programs promise to show that chirp is an effective tool for producing small, low cost, and lightweight spread spectrum systems for communications and control in hostile interference environments.

The three papers included here are intended to give an introduction of the workings of chirp, and an overview of the possibilities using current technology. Cook's paper, written in 1958, describes pulse compression or chirp signals and the lumped constant networks used as dispersive filters for signal compression at that time. The second paper, by Millet, shows the result of using a nonlinear FM waveform to suppress the sidelobes produced in time compressing a chirp signal. This paper is included here because of its unusual nature in that there are few references in the literature that cover anything other than linearly swept signals.

The third paper, by Gerald *et al.*, is a very good survey of current applications, coupled with a discussion of the techniques required to produce 1000:1 compression ratios with acoustic surface wave filters. Although this paper was written in 1972, compression ratios (*TW* products) for such devices have not increased a great deal since that time. Current compression ratios for the very best devices that can be constructed are estimated to be about 10 000:1, which is an improvement of 10 dB.

It is expected that future spread spectrum systems will employ the chirp techniques to a greater extent than they have been used in the past, because of the great reduction in size and the improvement in performance that has been recently achieved.

## OTHER PAPERS OF INTEREST


1) G. A. Coquin and R. Tsu, "Theory and performance of perpendicular diffraction delay lines," *Proc. IEEE*, June 1965.
2) C. L. Grasse and D. A. Gandolfo, "400 MHz acoustic surface-wave pulse expansion and compression filter," *IEEE Trans. Microwave Theory Tech.*, June 1971.
3) J. H. Eveleth, "A survey of ultrasonic delay lines operating below 100 Mc/s," *Proc. IEEE*, Oct. 1965.
4) T. A Martin, "The IMCON pulse compression filter and its applications," *IEEE Trans. Microwave Theory Tech.*, Apr. 1973.
5) G. S. Kino, S. Ludvik, H. J. Shaw, W. R. Shreve, J. M. White, and D. K. Winslow, "Signal processing by parametric interactions in delay line devices," *IEEE Trans. Microwave Theory Tech.*, Apr. 1973.
6) A. G. Bert, B. Epsztein, and G. Kantorowicz, "Signal processing by electronbeam interaction with piezoelectric surface waves," *IEEE Trans. Microwave Theory Tech.*, Apr. 1973.
7) D. T. Bell Jr., J. D. Holmes, and R. V. Ridings, "Application of acoustic surface-wave technology to spread spectrum communications," *IEEE Trans. Microwave Theory Tech.*, Apr. 1973.
8) J. Burnsweig and J. Wooldridge, "Ranging and data transmission using digital encoded FM—"chirp" surface acoustic wave filters," *IEEE Trans. Microwave Theory Tech.*, Apr. 1973.
9) P. M. Grant, J. H. Collins, B. J. Darby, and D. P. Morgan, "Potential applications of acoustic matched filters to air-traffic control systems," *IEEE Trans. Microwave Theory Tech.*, Apr. 1973.
10) P. J. Hagon, F. B. Micheletti, R. N. Seymour, and C. Y. Wrigley, "A programmable surface acoustic wave matched filter for phase-coded spread spectrum waveforms," *IEEE Trans. Microwave Theory Tech.*, Apr. 1973.
11) D. P. Morgan and J. G. Sutherland, "Generation of pseudonoise sequences using surface acoustic waves," *IEEE Trans. Microwave Theory Tech.*, Apr. 1973.
12) A. J. Berni and W. D. Gregg, "On the utility of chirp modulation for digital signalling," this reprint volume.

# Pulse Compression—Key to More Efficient Radar Transmission*

CHARLES E. COOK†, SENIOR MEMBER, IRE

*Summary*—**Increased demand for greater detection ranges in radar systems is often thwarted by the transmitting tube peak power limitation which, for narrow pulse operation, is usually reached before the full average power capability of the tube is realized. The technique of pulse compression offers a means of increasing the average power available to illuminate radar targets without any loss at the receiver of the resolution needed for the tactical requirements of the system. This is accomplished by transmitting a wide pulse in which the carrier is frequency modulated and then, by proper signal processing methods, causing a time compression of the received signal to a much narrower pulse of high effective peak power. The spectra and time functions of a particular class of pulse compression signals are analyzed and the basis for compression filter design is derived. Test waveforms demonstrate the resolving capability of the pulse compression technique.**

## Introduction

Since the inception of the military applications of radar techniques, emphasis has been placed on extending the ranges at which objects may be detected. In most instances, the demand for increased detection range has not been at the expense of normal tactical requirements for a certain minimum amount of range resolving capability. Faced with this situation, radar tube designers have been forced to concentrate on stepping up the peak powers of their tubes, since the tactical considerations have not permitted extending detection ranges by increasing average power by means of a wider transmitted pulse. As a consequence, in many situations high-powered tubes are being used inefficiently as far as average power is concerned. To compensate for this inefficiency, engineers have developed post-detection integration techniques to extend the radar detection range. These techniques also lead to further inefficiencies as far as the use of total available average power is taken into consideration. It will be the purpose of this paper to study a technique for increasing the average power capability of a pulse radar so that there is neither an increase in peak power nor a degradation of pulse resolution.

## Pulse Compression Evolution

Several individuals have been concerned with the problem outlined above and have sought means for solving the problem of increasing radar detection range when the pulse width must be kept fixed and peak power limitations control the average power that may be used.[1–3] R. H. Dicke and S. Darlington in the United States have proposed more or less identical approaches, but on the basis of patent applications Dicke would appear to have priority of conception as far as the ideas discussed here are involved.

Dicke reasoned that if the carrier frequency of a transmitted pulse were linearly swept, as shown in Fig. 1(b), a pulse compression filter with the time-delay vs frequency characteristic of Fig. 1(c) could be used to delay one end of the pulse relative to the other. This would produce, at the filter output, a narrower pulse [Fig. 1(d)] which would be of greater peak amplitude. The linear time-delay characteristic of the filter would act to delay the high-frequency components at the start of the input pulse more than the low-frequency components at the end of the pulse, with frequency components in between experiencing a proportional delay. The net result would be a time compression of the pulse. Since a passive linear filter is postulated, the principle of the conservation of energy applies and the buildup in peak power of the compressed pulse would be proportional to the ratio of the widths of the filter input and output pulses. Thus

$$\frac{\hat{P}_0}{\hat{P}_i} = \frac{T}{\tau} \tag{1}$$

where

$\hat{P}_i$ = peak power input pulse,
$\hat{P}_0$ = peak power compressed pulse.

If the pulse width $\tau$ represents the desired resolution, it can be seen that if this technique is feasible a pulse of width $T$, representing an increase in average power, may be transmitted with an associated frequency modulation that contains the information necessary to construct the desired compressed pulse of greater effective peak power. However, the actual peak power limitations of a pulse radar system are by-passed, thus opening another avenue for extending radar performance.

## Heuristic Analysis of Linear FM Pulse Compression

The basis for undertaking investigation of the type of system postulated by Dicke stemmed from the heuristic reasoning given below. The more rigorous analysis is

* Original manuscript received by the IRE, July 7, 1958; revised manuscript received May 28, 1959 and November 23, 1959.
† Air Armament Division, Sperry Gyroscope Co., Great Neck, N. Y.

[1] R. H. Dicke, "Object Detection Systems," U. S. Patent No. 2,624,876; January 6, 1953.
[2] S. Darlington, "Pulse Transmission," U.S. Patent No. 2,678,997; May 18, 1954.
[3] W. Cauer, German Patent No. 892,772; December 19, 1950.

Reprinted from *Proc. IRE*, vol. 48, pp. 310–316, Mar. 1960.

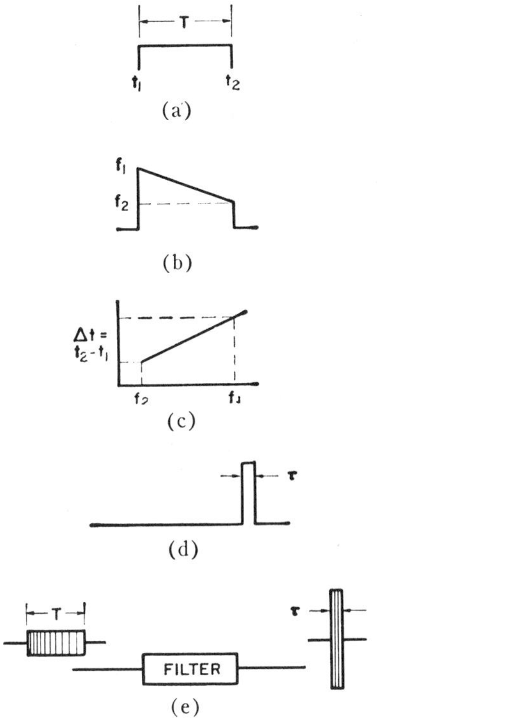


Fig. 1—Idealized pulse compression characteristics. (a) Wide-pulse envelope. (b) Carrier-frequency modulation. (c) Filter time-delay characteristic. (d) Compressed-pulse envelope. (e) Input-output wave forms of compression filter.

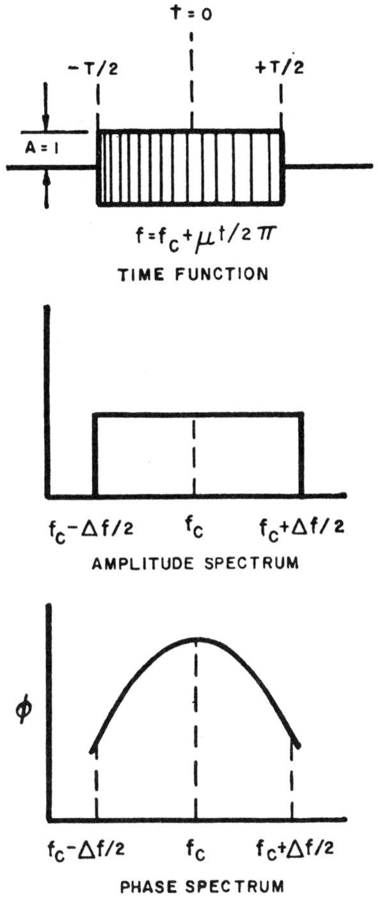


Fig. 2—Wide-pulse waveform parameters and assumed amplitude and phase spectra.

supplied in the next section and in the Appendix.

The transmitted pulse is to have a rectangular envelope and a carrier frequency that is of the form

$$\omega = \omega_c + \mu t \qquad |t| < \frac{T}{2}. \tag{2}$$

The phase angle of the transmitted frequency becomes, when envelope contributions are ignored,

$$\phi = \int \omega dt = \omega_c t + \tfrac{1}{2}\mu t^2 + C_1. \tag{3}$$

Thus, the phase angle $\phi$ is seen to contain a square-law term

$$\tfrac{1}{2}\mu t^2. \tag{4}$$

Further, if the product of the transmitted pulse width $T$ and the frequency deviation $\Delta f = \Delta\omega/2 = f_2 - f_1$ is large, the linear progression of the carrier frequency between $f_2$ and $f_1$ should result in an essentially rectangular spectrum-amplitude distribution. Fig. 2 plots the essential features of the pulse derived by this method of reasoning.

The compression filter is to have a linear time-delay vs frequency characteristic of opposite sense to the linear frequency sweep. Functionally, this may be expressed as

$$t_d = 2K(\omega - \omega_1) + b. \tag{5}$$

Since the filter is being used in a band-pass application, the associated filter phase shift is

$$\beta_f = \int t_d d\omega = K(\omega - \omega_1)^2 + b\omega + C_2. \tag{6}$$

It must be realized that in a practical filter design only that portion of the phase function which corresponds to a positive time delay can be synthesized. The relationships of (5) and (6) are plotted in Fig. 3.

If the constants $\mu$ and $k$ are properly matched, the spectrum at the compression-filter output is assumed to consist of a rectangular amplitude distribution and a flat or linear phase component. The time function of the compressed pulse is easily recognized from the spectrum parameters as having a $(\sin x)/x$ envelope, the pulse width being $\tau = 1/\Delta f$ when measured 4 db down from the peak amplitude. The spacing between the first zeros of this envelope is $2/\Delta f$. The carrier frequency under the above assumptions is a constant, $f_c$, and the peak amplitude is, of course, $\sqrt{T\Delta f}$ (Fig. 4).

No loss of generality will result if the compression filter is assumed to have a bandwidth $\Delta f$ and a rectangular amplitude response centered at $f_c$. This reduces the operation to matched filtering in the North sense if the second-order effects are ignored in this type of analysis.

The results obtained above confirm the earlier assumption that such a pulse compression system would

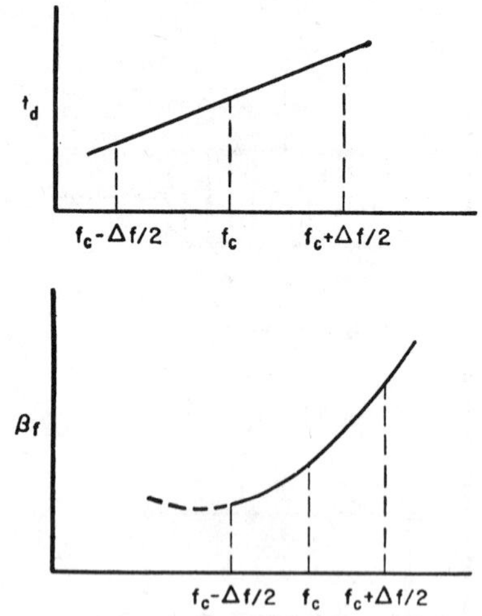


Fig. 3—Compression filter time-delay and phase shift.

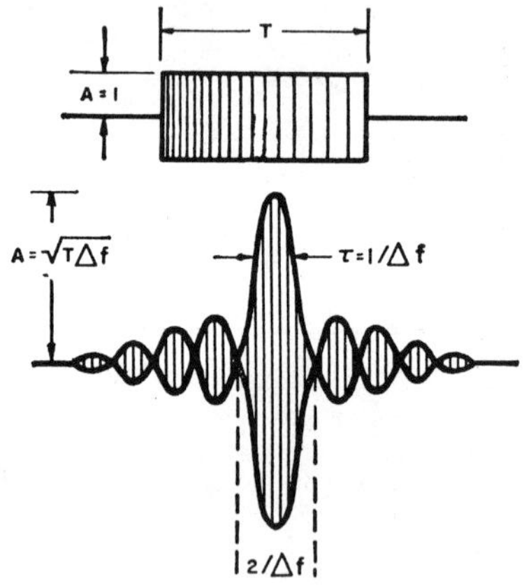


Fig. 4—Wide-pulse and compressed-pulse waveforms derived by heuristic analysis.

yield an output pulse of width $\tau = 1/\Delta f$ (measured at the appropriate point) having an increased peak power ratio

$$\frac{\hat{P}_0}{\hat{P}_i} = \frac{T}{\tau} = T\Delta f.$$

The less obvious result was that the shape of the compressed pulse would be $(\sin x)/x$ and not rectangular. This may not be the most desirable pulse waveform for some radar applications because of the high sidelobe levels. Reducing these unwanted signals is entirely analogous to antenna-pattern sidelobe reduction, and some useful efforts in this area have been reported.[4,5]

## Derivation of Linear FM Pulse Compression Spectra

For the system under study, the transmitted signal function is

$$f(t) = A \cos\left(\omega_c t + \tfrac{1}{2}\mu t^2\right), \quad -\frac{T}{2} < t < \frac{T}{2}, \tag{7}$$

where the carrier frequency is

$$\omega = \omega_c + \mu t.$$

If the constant $A$ is neglected, the spectrum of this signal is

$$\begin{aligned} F(\omega) &= \int_{-T/2}^{T/2} \cos\left(\omega_c t + 1/2\mu t^2\right) e^{-j\omega t} dt \\ &= \frac{1}{2}\left[\int_{-T/2}^{T/2} \exp j\left[(\omega_c - \omega)t + \tfrac{1}{2}\mu t^2\right] dt \right. \\ &\quad \left. + \int_{-T/2}^{T/2} \exp -j\left[(\omega_c + \omega)t + \tfrac{1}{2}\mu t^2\right] dt\right]. \end{aligned} \tag{8}$$

The second integral essentially defines the spectrum at negative frequencies and has a negligible contribution at positive frequencies, provided the ratio $f_c/\Delta f$ is sufficiently large, which would be the case in any practical application of pulse compression.

The spectrum expression, after a suitable change of variables, becomes

$$F(\omega) = \frac{1}{2}\sqrt{\frac{\pi}{\mu}}\, e^{-j(\omega_c-\omega)^2/2\mu} \int_{\sqrt{\pi/\mu}\,(-T/2+(\omega_c-\omega)/\mu)}^{\sqrt{\pi/\mu}\,(T/2+(\omega_c-\omega)/\mu)} e^{j(\pi/2)x^2} dx. \tag{9}$$

The above integral yields

$$\begin{aligned} F(\omega) &= \frac{1}{2}\sqrt{\frac{\pi}{\mu}}\, e^{-j(\omega_c-\omega)^2/2\mu} \\ &\cdot \left[ C\left(\frac{\frac{\mu T}{2} + (\omega_c - \omega)}{\sqrt{\pi\mu}}\right) + jS\left(\frac{\frac{\mu T}{2} + (\omega_c - \omega)}{\sqrt{\pi\mu}}\right) \right. \\ &\left. + C\left(\frac{\frac{\mu T}{2} - (\omega_c - \omega)}{\sqrt{\pi\mu}}\right) + jS\left(\frac{\frac{\mu T}{2} - (\omega_c - \omega)}{\sqrt{\pi\mu}}\right) \right] \end{aligned} \tag{10}$$

where

$$C(x) = \int_0^x \cos\frac{\pi}{2} y^2 dy \tag{11a}$$

and

$$S(x) = \int_0^x \sin\frac{\pi}{2} y^2 dy \tag{11b}$$

are the Fresnel integrals.

Expressing the spectrum function in the form

$$F(\omega) = e^{-\alpha_S - j\beta_S},$$

then the spectrum amplitude-function is

$$e^{-\alpha_S} = \frac{1}{2}\left(\frac{\pi}{\mu}\right)^{1/2} \left\{\left[C(x_1) + C(x_2)\right]^2 + \left[S(x_1) + S(x_2)\right]^2\right\}^{1/2} \tag{12a}$$

[4] T. T. Taylor, "Design of Line Sources for Narrow Beamwidth and Low Side Lobes," Hughes Aircraft Co., Culver City, Calif., Tech. Memo No. 316; July, 1953.

[5] C. E. Cook, "Modification of Pulse Compression Waveforms," presented at Natl. Electronics Conf., Chicago, Ill.; October 15, 1958.

and the spectrum phase-function is

$$\beta_s = (\omega_c - \omega)^2/2\mu - \tan^{-1}\left[\frac{S(x_1) + S(x_2)}{C(x_1) + C(x_2)}\right] \quad \text{(12b)}$$

where

$$x_1 = \frac{\frac{\mu T}{2} + (\omega_c - \omega)}{\sqrt{\pi\mu}} \quad \text{and} \quad x_2 = \frac{\frac{\mu T}{2} - (\omega_c - \omega)}{\sqrt{\pi\mu}}.$$

If, as implied in the previous section, matched filtering is attempted, the filter transfer characteristics $e^{-\alpha_f - j\beta_f}$ must be conjugate to the spectrum function derived above, that is

$$e^{-\alpha_S} = e^{-\alpha_f}$$

and

$$\beta_S = -\beta_f.$$

In practice, the phase characteristic of the compression filter is made to match only the imaginary square-law spectrum component, assuming that the residual phase term

$$-\tan^{-1}\left[\frac{S(x_1) + S(x_2)}{C(x_1) + C(x_2)}\right]$$

will not prove harmful. The consequences of this assumption are shown in the results of the Appendix.

The Fresnel functions do not represent a closed-form solution, and the spectrum functions must be derived from tables of Fresnel integrals.[6,7] The Fresnel function argument is

$$y = \left[\frac{\frac{\mu T}{2} \pm (\omega_c - \omega)}{\sqrt{\pi\mu}}\right]. \quad \text{(13)}$$

By making the substitutions

$\mu = \Delta\omega/T$, $\Delta\omega$ = frequency deviation within wide pulse,

$\Delta\omega = 2\pi/\tau$, $\tau$ = narrow pulse width,

$\omega_c - \omega = n\Delta\omega/2$,

then

$$y = \sqrt{\frac{T}{\tau}}\left(\frac{1 \pm n}{\sqrt{2}}\right). \quad \text{(14)}$$

The argument, $y$, appears as a function of the compression ratio $T/\tau$, and is seen to be independent of the absolute amount of the frequency deviation, $\Delta\omega$.

Fig. 5 illustrates the shape of the spectrum components for various values of compression ratio. As this ratio increases, the amplitude distribution becomes more nearly rectangular and the residual phase component flat over the band of frequencies of major interest. The derivation of pulse shapes for these spectra made use of numerical summation. In each instance, the combination of the real and imaginary spectrum components produced a wave-form arbitrarily close to the $(\sin x)/x$ function and of the prescribed peak amplitude. As this study program developed, a closed-form solution for this method of pulse compression (linear frequency sweep within a rectangular pulse and a square-law phase compression filter) was obtained by J. E. Chin of the Sperry Gyroscope Co., and is given in the Appendix. This analysis showed that the filter-output pulse envelope is precisely of the $(\sin x)/x$ form. Moreover, it was shown that the carrier of the filter output pulse is frequency swept at the same rate as the input pulse but in the opposite direction. However, the total frequency deviation between the first zeros of the compressed pulse is given by

$$2\frac{\Delta\omega\tau}{T}. \quad \text{(15)}$$

Whether this represents a serious problem or not will depend on the particular application and the compression ratio involved. Physically, the presence of this residual frequency modulation may be explained as arising from the frequency components introduced by the rise and fall portions of the wide-pulse envelope. These frequency components do not occur at the times dictated by the linear sweep of the carrier frequency. The resultant effect of the compression filter is to disperse these components in a manner to produce the reverse frequency sweep cited above. (This explanation results from the additional analysis of linear FM pulse-com-

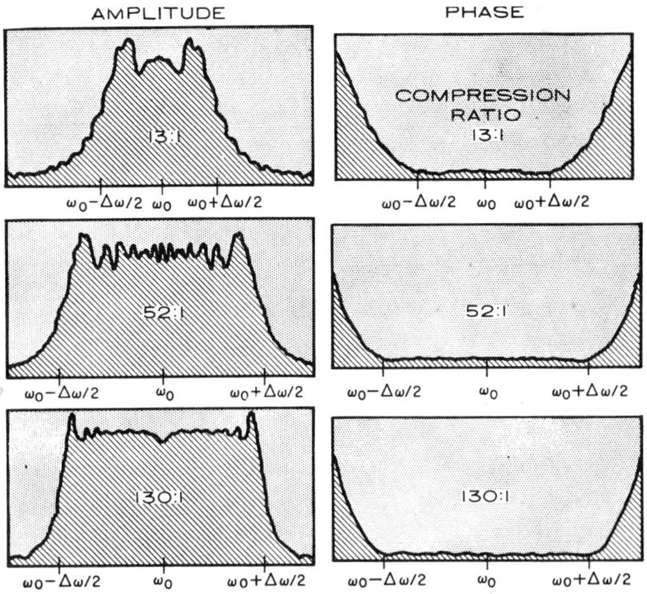

Fig. 5—Postcompression amplitude and phase spectra for various compression ratios.

[6] E. Jahnke, and F. Emde, "Table of Functions," Dover Publications, Inc., New York, N. Y.; 1945.

[7] A. Van Wijngaarden and W. L. Scheen, "Tables of Fresnel Integrals," Computation Dept. of the Mathematical Center, Amsterdam, The Netherlands, Rept. No. R49; 1949.

pression performed by B. L. Hulland of the Sperry Gyroscope Co.)

The foregoing analysis showed that the compression filter would require a square-law phase characteristic of the form

$$\beta_f = -(\omega_c - \omega)^2/2\mu;$$

the associated time delay is then

$$t_d = \frac{d\beta_f}{d\omega} = (\omega_c - \omega)/\mu.$$

This characteristic is physically unrealizable since it yields negative time delays over half the frequency band. This objection is met by adding a sufficiently large constant delay so that the filter time-delay is positive at all frequencies of interest. The modified filter time-delay is then

$$t_d' = (\omega_c - \omega)/\mu + k$$

and the phase characteristic to be approximated by the filter design is

$$\beta_f' = -(\omega_c - \omega)^2/2\mu + k\omega + C_2.$$

The type of network chosen for the filter design was the bridged-T equivalent (see Fig. 6) of the all-pass constant-resistance lattice network. Design techniques for all-pass networks are well covered in the literature,[8–10] and the minute design details of a particular application need not be examined here. As the name implies, all-pass networks theoretically have no losses. Network purists will insist, and rightly so, that this characteristic cannot be obtained in practice, especially at frequencies in the IF range. However, judicious use of phase and amplitude compensating networks will provide the necessary engineering approximation for a system application.

Fig. 7 indicates a possible laboratory arrangement to test the pulse compression characteristics of a particular filter design. Increased compression ratios may be obtained by cascading additional sections of the designed filter. Figs. 8 and 9 indicate the type of test results that may be expected. Fig. 8 shows a representative compressed pulse, this being an IF waveform in which the lower half has been masked out to reveal the signal sidelobe detail more clearly. Fig. 9 shows the uncompressed pulses from two inputs and their respective video detected outputs from the compression filter for several degrees of overlap of the input signals. This demonstrates the linear operation of this technique in

[8] O. J. Zobel, "Distortion correction in electrical networks with constant resistance recurrent networks," *Bell Sys. Tech. J.*, vol. 7, pp. 438–534; July, 1928.

[9] E. A. Guillemin, "Communications Networks," John Wiley and Sons, Inc., New York, N. Y., vol. 2; 1935.

[10] J. C. Pinson, "Transient Correction by Means of All-Pass Networks," Ph.D. dissertation, Mass. Inst. Tech., Cambridge; June, 1957.

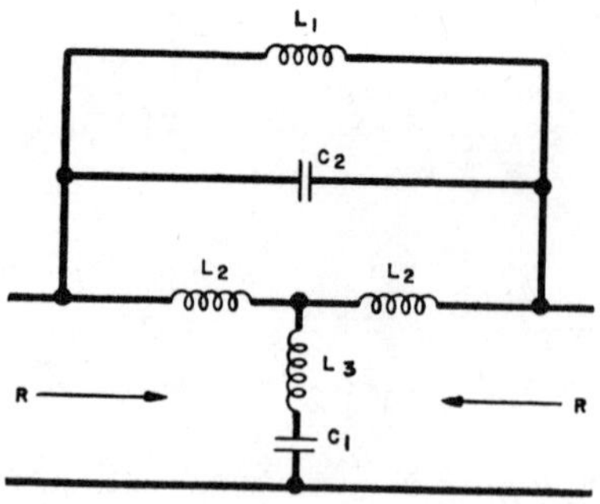


Fig. 6—General form of bridged-T all-pass network.

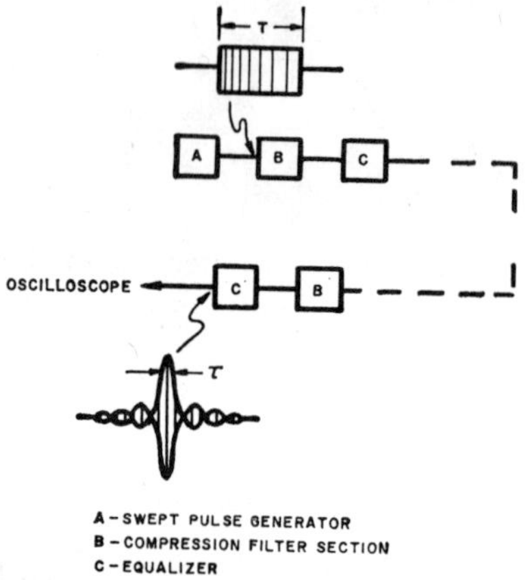


Fig. 7—Compression-filter laboratory test equipment.

that the output response for broad overlapping pulses from multiple inputs will be precisely the superposition of the responses from each input when the others are absent. The amplitude ripples on the wide pulses illustrate the effect of the compression-filter delay line on the frequency-swept input signals.

## Conclusion

A technique for increasing the average power capability in peak power limited pulse-transmission systems has been analyzed. The theoretical aspects are closely allied to matched-filter and cross-correlation methods. The derived pulse shape for this technique is $(\sin x)/x$, but the waveform may be modified by approaches that are analogous to the reduction of antenna-pattern sidelobes.

## Appendix

The following closed-form solution of linear FM rectangular-envelope pulse compression is the result of the contributions of J. E. Chin to this study program.[11]

$$\begin{aligned} f(t) &= \exp\left[j(\omega_c t + \tfrac{1}{2}\mu t^2)\right] \qquad -T_0 \le t \le T_0 \\ f(t) &= 0 \qquad |t| > T_0. \end{aligned} \tag{16}$$

[11] J. E. Chin and C. E. Cook, "The mathematics of pulse compression—a problem in systems analysis," *Sperry Engrg. Rev.*, vol. 12, pp. 11–16; October, 1959.

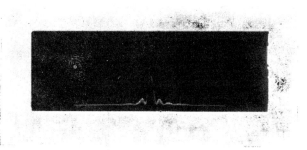

Fig. 8—Compression-filter IF waveform (lower half of waveform masked to reveal greater sidelobe detail).

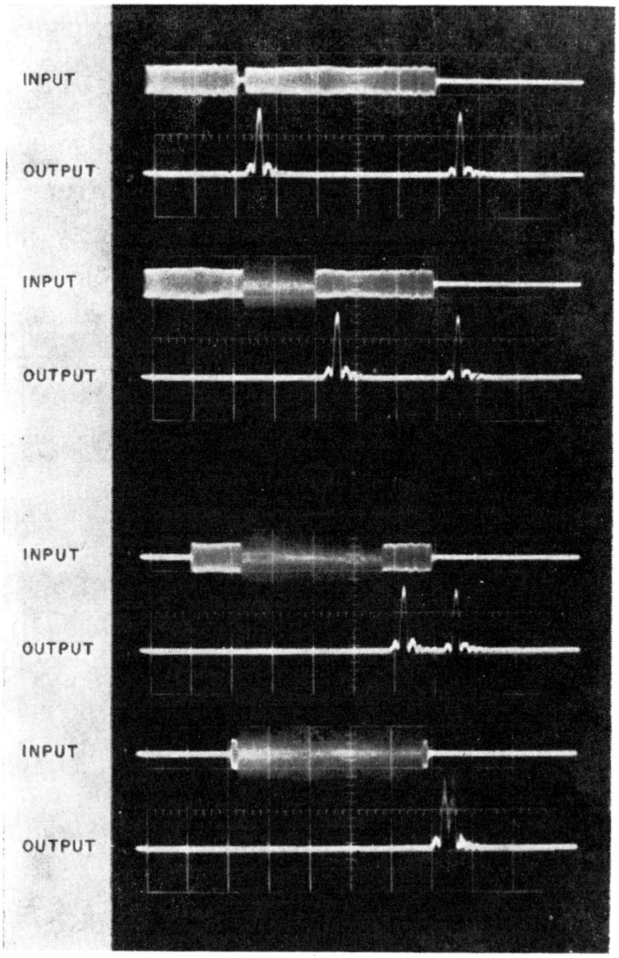


Fig. 9—Multiple inputs and detected outputs of a pulse compression filter illustrating principle of superposition.

The pulse spectrum is

$$F(\omega) = \int_{-\infty}^{\infty} f(t)e^{-j\omega t}\,dt$$

$$= \int_{-T_0}^{T_0} \exp\left\{j\left[(\omega_c - \omega)t + \tfrac{1}{2}\mu t^2\right]\right\} dt. \tag{17}$$

The generalized compression-filter function is

$$H(\omega) = \exp\left[j\,\frac{(\omega_c - \omega)^2}{2\mu}\right] \tag{18}$$

and the filter-output spectrum $G(\omega) = F(\omega)H(\omega)$

$$\therefore\ G(\omega) = \exp\left[j\,\frac{(\omega_c - \omega)^2}{2\mu}\right]$$

$$\int_{-T_0}^{T_0} \cdot\exp\left[j(\omega_c - \omega)t + \tfrac{1}{2}\mu t^2\right]dt. \tag{19}$$

The term $g(t)$ represents the output time function where

$$g(t) = \frac{1}{2\pi}\int_{-\infty}^{\infty} G(\omega)e^{j\omega t}d\omega. \tag{20}$$

Thus,

$$g(t) = \frac{1}{2\pi}\int_{-\infty}^{\infty}\left(\exp\left[j\,\frac{(\omega_c - \omega)^2}{2\mu}\right]\right.$$

$$\left.\int_{-T_0}^{T_0}\cdot\exp\left[j(\omega_c - \omega)\tau + j\,\frac{\mu}{2}\tau^2\right]d\tau\right)e^{j\omega t}d\omega. \tag{21}$$

This rearranges to

$$g(t) = \frac{1}{2\pi}\int_{-T_0}^{T_0}\left[\exp j\left\{\tfrac{1}{2}\mu\tau^2 + \omega_c\tau + \frac{\omega_c^2}{2\mu}\right.\right.$$

$$\left.\left. - (\omega_c + \mu\tau - \mu t)^2/2\mu\right\}\right]$$

$$\cdot\left[\int_{-\infty}^{\infty}\exp\left[j(\tfrac{1}{2}\mu)\{\omega - (\omega_c + \mu\tau - \mu\tau)\}^2\right]d\omega\right]d\tau \tag{22}$$

letting

$$u = \frac{\omega - (\omega_c + \mu\tau - \mu t)}{\sqrt{2\mu}}$$

$$g(t) = \frac{\sqrt{2\mu}}{2\pi}\int_{-T_0}^{T_0}\left[\exp j\left\{\frac{\mu\tau^2}{2} + \omega_c\tau + \frac{\omega_c^2}{2\mu}\right.\right.$$

$$\left.\left. - (\omega_c + \mu\tau - \mu t)^2/2\mu\right\}\right]\left[\int_{-\infty}^{\infty}\exp(ju^2)du\right]d\tau, \tag{23}$$

but

$$\int_{-\infty}^{\infty} e^{ju^2}du = \int_{-\infty}^{\infty}(\cos u^2 + j\sin u^2)du = \sqrt{\pi}e^{j\pi/4}$$

and

$$g(t) = \sqrt{\frac{\mu}{2\pi}}\,e^{j(\omega_c t - 1/2\mu t^2 + \pi/4)}\int_{-T_0}^{T_0} e^{j\mu t\tau}\,d\tau$$

$$= \sqrt{\frac{2\mu}{\pi}}\exp\left[j\left(\omega_c t - \frac{1}{2}\mu t^2 + \frac{\pi}{4}\right)\right]\int_0^{T_0}\cos\mu t\tau\,d\tau$$

$$= \sqrt{\frac{2\mu T_0^2}{\pi}}\ \frac{\sin\mu t T_0}{\mu t T_0}$$

$$\cdot\exp\left[j\left(\omega_c t - \frac{1}{2}\mu t^2 + \frac{\pi}{4}\right)\right]. \tag{24}$$

Now

$$\mu = \frac{2\pi\Delta f}{2T_0}$$

where $\Delta f$ = swept-frequency deviation. The output-input peak power ratio is derived by squaring the amplitude of the output pulse, the input amplitude having been taken as unity. This yields

$$\frac{2\mu T_0^2}{\pi} = \left(\frac{4\pi\Delta f}{2T_0}\right)\left(\frac{T_0^2}{\pi}\right) = 2T_0\Delta f. \tag{25}$$

If the wide pulse width assumes the same dimensions as in the section on spectra derivation

$$2T_0 = T,$$

then the output-input pulse width and peak-power ratios become $T\Delta f$, if the convention is adopted that the output pulse is measured at the points $t = \pm\frac{1}{2}\Delta f$.

## Acknowledgment

The investigation reported herein is part of the general program of the Sperry Gyroscope Co., for studying advanced techniques. W. W. Mieher and C. E. Brockner were chiefly responsible for the guidance and support necessary to provide program continuity. The author is also indebted to J. E. Chin, L. R. Sadler, and J. Cerar, who have made substantial contributions to the progress of the project.

# A Matched-Filter Pulse-Compression System Using a Nonlinear FM Waveform

ROBERT E. MILLETT, Member, IEEE
Hazeltine Corporation
Plainview, N. Y.

Abstract

**The realization of a rectangular pulse-compression waveform having low time sidelobes and zero mismatch loss due to spectral weighting is discussed. The theoretical aspects of the design of such a waveform are presented with particular reference to frequency modulated, rectangular pulses. The design and performance of a matched-filter pulse-compression system having essentially zero mismatch loss are presented. The system discussed has a time–bandwidth product of 22 and time sidelobes suppressed at least 27 dB; the measured mismatch loss is 0.1 dB. The difficulty of achieving the required nonlinear time delay dispersion is overcome by synthesizing the dispersive network as a cascade of all-pass networks.**

Manuscript received April 28, 1969.

## I. Introduction

The advantages of pulse-compression techniques for simultaneously providing high maximum radar range and range resolution are well-known [1]. The attendant disadvantage of time sidelobes associated with the compressed pulse is usually minimized by applying spectral weighting in the radar receiver. In the conventional linear frequency modulated (LFM) pulse-compression system, in which a rectangular LFM pulse is transmitted, the spectral weighting applied in the receiver results in a *mismatched filter* with an unavoidable degradation of signal-to-noise ratio (SNR).

This report describes a pulse-compression waveform in which the frequency modulation is nonlinear over the expanded-pulse duration. It is shown that this modulation results in a nonuniform spectral amplitude, while the rectangular time envelope is retained. Application of equal nonuniform weighting in the receiver then results in a *matched filter* with *time sidelobes lower than those associated with a uniform spectrum.*

The design of a pulse-compression system utilizing nonlinear FM is described and the performance achieved is discussed in the concluding sections. The design requires a dispersive filter having nonlinear dispersion; the usual difficulty of achieving such dispersion has been avoided by realizing the dispersive filter as a cascade of all-pass networks.

## II. Principles of Matched-Filter Pulse Compression

The criterion for a matched filter has been shown by Klauder *et al.* [1] to be

$$H(\omega) = F^*(\omega),$$

where $H(\omega)$ is the transfer function of the filter, $F(\omega)$ is the spectrum of the input signal, and $*$ denotes the complex conjugate. That is, a filter is matched to the input signal when its transfer function is equal to the complex conjugate of the signal spectrum. Under such circumstances, the peak signal to rms noise ratio at the output of the filter is maximized (for white Gaussian noise at the input). For a LFM pulse-compression waveform, the matched-filter criterion requires that the compression channel response have a uniform amplitude (assuming a rectangular expanded pulse) and a time delay dispersion which is equal, but of opposite slope to the dispersion which generates the expanded pulse.

The uniform amplitude predicated by the matched-filter requirement is in conflict with the desirability of low time sidelobes since it would result in a maximum sidelobe level of $-13$ dB. Generally, in making a tradeoff between low sidelobes and minimum SNR degradation, the former is more significant; consequently, the compression channel response is designed to weight the signal spectrum to achieve low sidelobes. The mismatch loss which results is from 1 to 2 dB, depending on the particular weighting function chosen [2]; since this loss can only be compen-

Reprinted from *IEEE Trans. Aerosp. Electron. Syst.*, vol. AES-6, pp. 73–78, Jan. 1970.

sated by increased transmitter power or lower receiver noise figure, it is often desirable to eliminate it.

However, it has been shown [3], [4] that it is possible to achieve low sidelobes with a matched filter by equally dividing the spectral weighting between the expansion channel and the compression channel. The required weighting of the expanded pulse spectrum is approximately realized for a rectangular pulse envelope by utilizing nonlinear FM. The time-delay dispersion of the expansion network and the amplitude of the expanded pulse spectrum are related by

$$-\frac{dT_d(\omega)}{d\omega} = C \mid F(\omega) \mid^2 \qquad (1)$$

for a rectangular pulse of large time–bandwidth product. In (1), $T_d(\omega)$ is the group time delay as a function of angular frequency.

For "cosine squared on a pedestal" weighting

$$\mid F(\omega) \mid^2 = k + (1 - k) \cos^2 (\omega - \omega_0)/2\Delta, \qquad (2)$$

in which $k$ is the amplitude of the pedestal and $\Delta$ is the signal bandwidth. Substituting (2) into (1) and integrating, the expression for $T_d(\omega)$ is found to be

$$T_d(\omega) = -\frac{T}{2\pi}\left(\frac{\bar{\omega}}{\Delta} + \frac{(1 - k)}{(1 + k)} \sin \frac{\bar{\omega}}{\Delta}\right). \qquad (3)$$

In (3), the constant $C$ has been evaluated such that the total dispersion over the bandwidth $\Delta$ is $T$. Also, $\omega - \omega_0$ has been replaced by $\bar{\omega}$. A plot of (3) is shown in Fig. 1 in which the various parameters are defined.

With the prescribed dispersion applied in the pulse expansion network, a rectangular output pulse of large time–bandwidth product will have a spectral amplitude,

$$\mid F(\omega) \mid = \sqrt{k + (1 - k) \cos^2 \frac{\bar{\omega}}{2\Delta}} \cdot$$

If the pulse-compression channel amplitude response has the same variation with frequency, and if the dispersion is of the opposite sense as that in the expansion channel, then the compression channel is a *matched filter* and the total spectral weighting is "cosine squared on a pedestal."

The realization of a matched-filter, low sidelobe pulse-compression system is achieved at the expense of an increased Doppler sensitivity relative to a LFM system. For target returns with nonzero Doppler shifts the nonlinearity in the time delay dispersion of the compression network does not completely cancel that in the expansion channel. The resulting distortion sidelobes can be predicted by means of Fig. 2, reprinted from [2]. This shows the distortion sidelobe as a function of Doppler shift and the magnitude of sinsusoidal deviations from linear time-delay dispersion. For example, a pulse-compression waveform which has 4 $\mu$s dispersion and spectral weighting for 36 dB sidelobe suppression would have a time delay nonlinearity of about $\frac{1}{2}$ $\mu$s. From Fig. 2, target returns with 10 kHz Doppler shifts would have distortion sidelobes equal to the design sidelobe level, $-36$ dB. Since the maxima of the distortion sidelobes fall within the main pulse, their effect is not severe; for example, 36 dB distortion sidelobes would distort the main pulse by $\pm\frac{1}{2}$ dB.

## III. System Design

A pulse-compression system, having low time-sidelobes and no theoretical mismatch loss, has been designed in accordance with the principles of Section II. The system has a time–bandwidth product of 22, an expanded pulsewidth of 4 $\mu$s and a compressed pulsewidth of less than $\frac{1}{4}$ $\mu$s. Due to the low time–bandwidth product, gating sidelobes, which are associated with a rectangular expanded pulse, limit the achievable sidelobe suppression to approximately 28 dB [2]. In order to achieve as low sidelobes as possible, the spectral weighting is designed

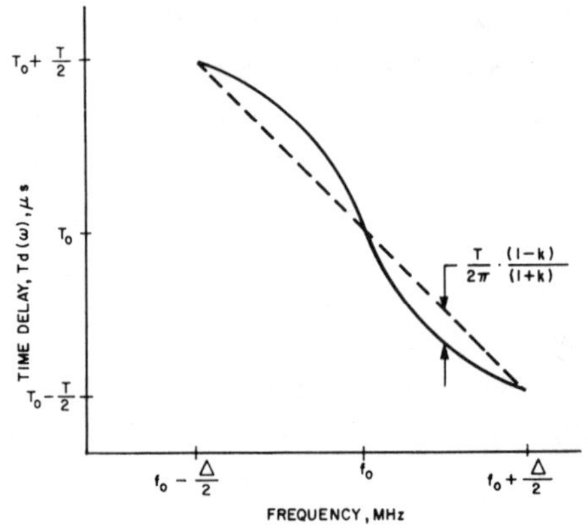


Fig. 1. Nonlinear dispersion for the control of spectral amplitude.

Fig. 2. Doppler sensitivity of cancellation of time delay nonlinearities.

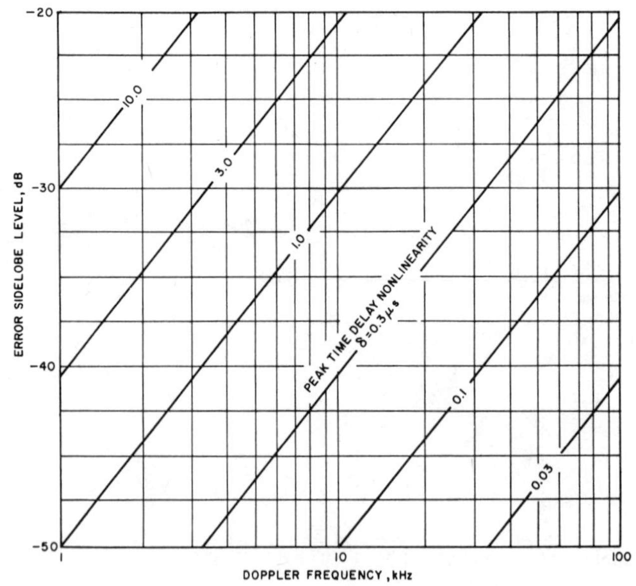

for −36 dB sidelobes so that the effects of gating primarily determine sidelobe level.

For spectral weighting of this nature, the constant in (3), $k=0.14$. Thus, the nonlinear dispersion of the expansion channel is of the shape shown in Fig. 1, and $T=4$ μs, $\Delta=5.5$ MHz, and the peak time delay nonlinearity is 0.48 μs. The required dispersion is achieved in two identical dispersive filters of the form described, one for the expansion channel and one for the compression channel. An effective opposite slope is obtained for compression by spectrum inversion about the center frequency of the dispersive filter.

Each dispersive filter is synthesized as a cascade of bridged-tee networks which are, assuming lossless components, all-pass networks. Since they have constant amplitude response with frequency, an array of bridged tees can be combined to synthesize an arbitrary group delay function. A schematic diagram of a bridged-tee network is shown in Fig. 3(A), and its time delay function is shown in Fig. 3(B).

The delay function of the tee can be expressed approximately in terms of its center frequency $\omega_0$ and its peak delay $2/\sigma$. The function shown in Fig. 3(B) approaches the exact delay function asymptotically as $\sigma/\omega_0$ approaches zero. The parameters $\omega_0$ and $\sigma$ can be expressed in terms of the circuit elements as

$$\omega_0^2 = \frac{2}{L_1C_1} - \frac{1}{(2R_0C_1)^2},$$

and

$$\sigma = \frac{1}{2R_0C_2}$$

where $R_0$ is the characteristic impedance of the bridged tee.

Fig. 4 illustrates one method of cascading several bridged tees to obtain the desired linear time-delay function. The ratio of $\omega_0$ to $\sigma$ is constant for all networks, and the center frequencies of the tees are more heavily concentrated at the low end of the band. The exact center frequencies of the tees are determined by an iterative solution obtained on a digital computer. The ratio $\omega_0/\sigma$ is chosen to result in realizable circuit elements.

In order to minimize the network loss and the number of tees required to synthesize the dispersive filter, it should be centered at the lowest possible frequency. In general, operation at or near a center frequency which results in a 100 percent bandwidth is an acceptable compromise between narrow-band operation and low network loss. In the present design, the center frequency of the dispersive network is 6.5 MHz.

The complete compression filter is shown in Fig. 5; it

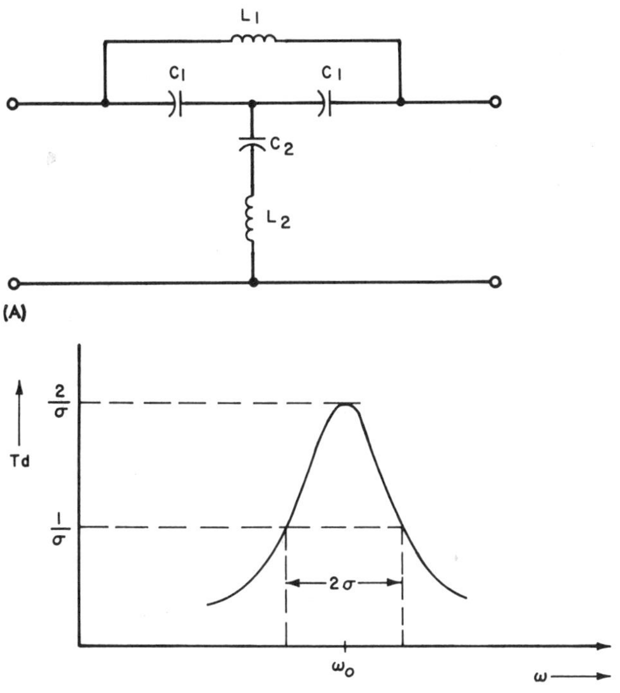

Fig. 3. Bridged-tee network. (A) Schematic diagram. (B) Delay function.

Fig. 4. Synthesis of linear delay dispersion.

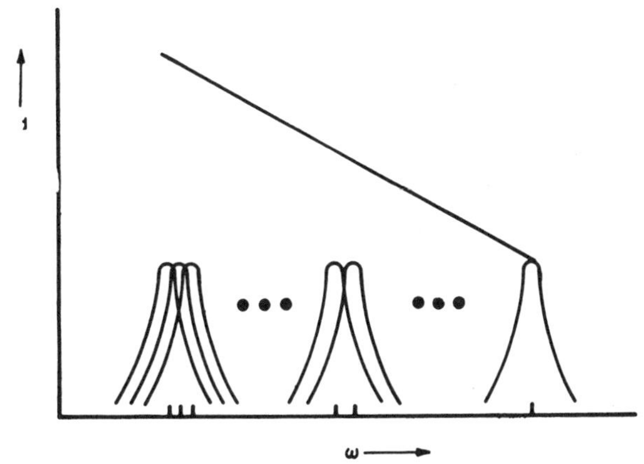


Fig. 5. Compression channel dispersive filter.

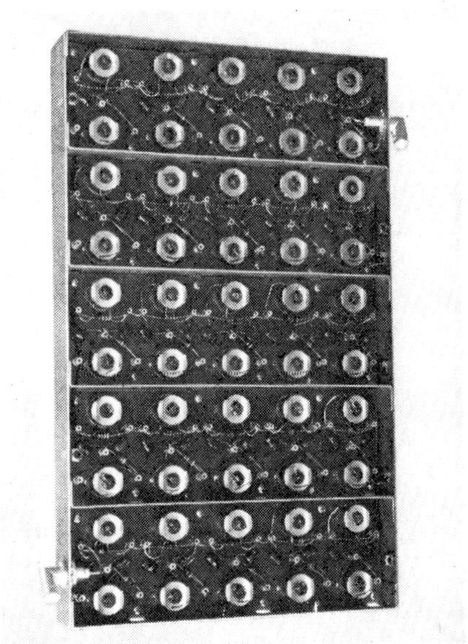

comprises 25 tees. The center frequencies of the tees range from 3.6 to 9.3 MHz. Inductance values range between $\frac{1}{2}$ and $10\frac{1}{2}$ $\mu$H; coil $Q$s are approximately 150. The capacitors in the networks are between 36 and 1200 pF.

A simplified block diagram of the pulse expansion channel is shown in Fig. 6. When triggered by a timing pulse, the impulse generator and spectrum shaping filter provide a video signal of the appropriate bandwidth with which to modulate the CW carrier (which is a coherent reference signal if the radar uses coherent processing). The spectrum shaping filter is designed so that the expanded pulse is approximately rectangular. The signal spectrum is down-translated from 1-F (30 MHz) to the center frequency of the expansion filter (6.5 MHz). Following expansion, the pulse is up-translated to the 1-F and final shaping of the rectangular, expanded pulse is provided by a limiter and a gated amplifier.

Fig. 7 shows the pulse compression channel in which all processing is done at the center frequency of the dispersive network. After down-translation, the pulse is compressed and applied to the weighting filter. (In the compression channel, the local oscillator frequency is above the input spectrum, thus providing the spectrum inversion necessitated by the use of two identical dispersive filters.) As discussed in Section II, the weighting filter amplitude response is equal to the signal spectral amplitude. That is,

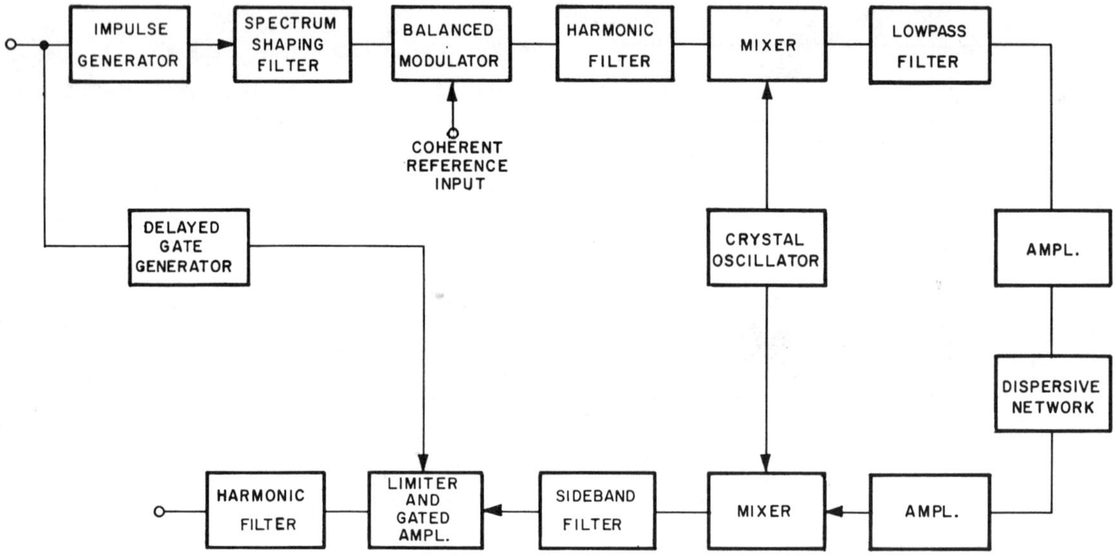


Fig. 6. Block diagram of the pulse expansion channel.

Fig. 7. Block diagram of the compression channel.

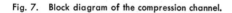

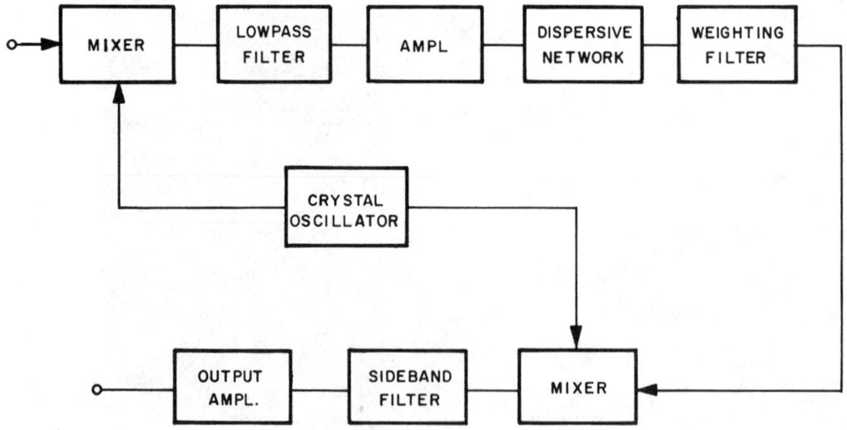

$$|H(\omega)| = \sqrt{k + (1-k)\cos^2 \frac{\bar{\omega}}{2\Delta}}$$

where, in this system, $k=0.14$ and $\Delta=5.5$ MHz.

Following up-translation, the compressed, low-sidelobe pulse is amplified to the desired output level.

## IV. Results

The expansion channel and four identical compression channels just described have been fabricated and their performance evaluated. The implementation of four compression channels is intended to demonstrate the repeatability of performance from unit to unit.

The output of the expansion channel is shown in Fig. 8. Fig. 8(A) shows the signal in the time domain and it is seen to be very nearly rectangular. The rise and fall times are about 100 ns and the pulse amplitude is flat within $\pm 0.3$ dB. Fig. 8(B) shows the expanded pulse spectrum which, in contrast to that of an LFM pulse, is not rectangular. The nonuniform spectral amplitude which is a consequence of the nonlinear FM is shaped in accordance with the discussion in Section II. The ripples about a smooth taper which appear in Fig. 8(B) are the characteristic "Fresnel" ripples inherent in a low time–bandwidth system with a rectangular pulse.

Fig. 9 shows the compressed pulse output on both a normal and a magnified scale. The 3 dB pulsewidth is about 220 ns. The maximum sidelobe level is $-28$ dB. The sidelobes on the right side of the main pulse in Fig. 9(B) clearly display the typical structure of gating sidelobes [2]; the maximum level is about $-30$ dB, which is somewhat lower than would be predicted for an LFM pulse compression system. Although it has not been verified in general, the nonlinear FM approach employed here appears to offer the added advantage of being less affected by the gating sidelobe phenomenon than an LFM system is.

In comparing the outputs of the four compression channels, it is found that the pulsewidths are identical within $\pm 5$ ns and the maximum sidelobe level is between $-27$ and 28.5 dB, indicating a high degree of repeatability of the dispersive network characteristic.

The mismatch loss was determined in each compression channel by comparing the theoretical and measured processing gain. This was done by first measuring the signal gain experienced by the expanded pulse input and then the noise gain experienced when the input is a noise source. The signal gain less the noise gain is the processing gain. The amount that the latter varies from the matched filter gain $G_m$, where

$$G_m = 10 \log_{10} T\Delta,$$

is the mismatch loss. In this manner, *the measured mismatch loss for the four compression channels is found to be*

Fig. 8. Expanded pulse waveform and spectral amplitude. (A) Waveform: 0.2 volts/div; 1 µs/div. (B) Spectral amplitude: 1 MHz/div.

(A)

(B)

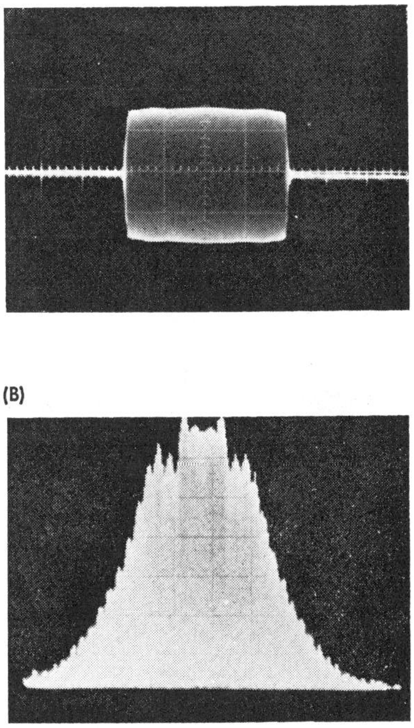

Fig. 9. Compressed pulse waveform. (A) Normal scale: 0.5 volts/div; 0.5 µs/div. (B) Magnified scale: 2 div=25 dB; 0.5 µs/div.

(A)

(B)

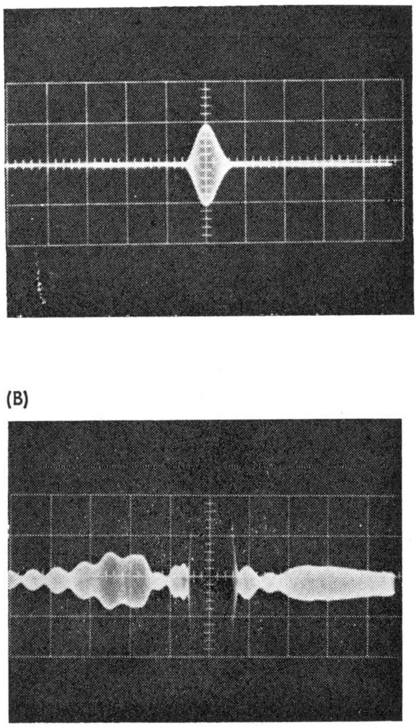

*between 0.1 and 0.2 dB, compared with the theoretical value of 1.09 dB for an LFM system.*

The Doppler sensitivity of the nonlinear FM system has been measured by varying the local oscillator frequency in the expansion channel; this effectively shifts the signal away from the center frequency of the dispersive filter. For Doppler shifts of 45 kHz, the maximum range sidelobes increase about 1 dB.

The effect of temperature on the pulse compression system has also been evaluated. Over a temperature range from 0° to 50° C, the variation of compressed pulsewidth for each channel is less than $\pm 15$ ns; sidelobe suppression remains 26 dB or better.

In summary, the feasibility of a matched-filter pulse compression system with low time sidelobes has been demonstrated. In the system described, a 1.1 dB mismatch loss has been substantially reduced by utilizing the nonlinear FM waveform. The difficulty generally associated with achieving the necessary dispersive characteristic has been avoided by using a cascade of all-pass networks to realize the dispersive filters.

**Acknowledgment**

The development of the matched-filter system described was performed under a contract with Compagnie Francais Thomson Houston, Bagneux, France; their permission to publish the material is gratefully acknowledged. At Hazeltine, F. G. Herring was responsible for the system design and J. J. Strong provided general direction. Others who contributed significantly to the program include J. Crush, L. E. Foley, S. J. Kerbel, and P. M. Krencik.

**References**

[1] J. R. Klauder, A. C. Price, S. Darlington, and W. J. Albersheim, "The theory and design of chirp radars," *Bell Sys. Tech. J.*, vol. 39, pp. 745–808, July 1960.

[2] R. E. Millett, "Limitations on range sidelobe reduction in chirp type pulse compression radar," to be published.

[3] E. L. Key, E. N. Fowle, and R. D. Haggarty, "A method of pulse compression employing non-linear frequency modulation," M.I.T. Lincoln Laboratory, Lexington, Mass., Tech. Rept. 207, September 1959.

[4] C. E. Cook and M. Bernfeld, *Radar Signals*. New York: Academic Press, 1967, ch. 7.

# The Design and Applications of Highly Dispersive Acoustic Surface-Wave Filters

HENRY M. GERARD, W. RICHARD SMITH, WILLIAM R. JONES, AND J. BENJAMIN HARRINGTON

*Invited Paper*

*Abstract*—**The development of a low-loss broad-band linear FM dispersive filter having a time–bandwidth (TB) product of 1000 is discussed. Two systems applications for highly dispersive linear FM filters—pulse compression radar and a microscan receiver—are discussed with emphasis on filter performance requirements. The principal factors which influence the design of surface-wave filters are reviewed and theoretical design procedures are outlined. The 1000:1 filters, which are implemented on strong-coupling *YZ* lithium niobate, typically meet the design goal of a 100-MHz rectangular passband and have a CW insertion loss of less than 35 dB. Measured data are presented for the filter performance in a pulse-compression loop and in a prototype broad-band microscan (compressive) receiver.**

## I. Introduction

THEIR SIZE, design flexibility, and reproducibility make acoustic surface-wave devices excellent candidates for many important applications in radar and communication systems. This paper discusses applications, design, and fabrication of highly dispersive filters (HDF's) as a specific class of surface-wave devices.

A dispersive filter is a delay line whose group delay is a nonconstant function of the instantaneous frequency of the input signal, and whose amplitude response is generally shaped for its specific application. In particular, a linear FM dispersive filter is designed to have a linear group delay versus frequency. Because of their importance, we will concentrate our attention on linear FM dispersive filters; however, the basic concepts apply equally well to the broader class.

For the purpose of this paper, we arbitrarily define a *highly dispersive* filter as one with a time–bandwidth (TB) product of $\Delta\tau\Delta f \gtrsim 1000$, where $\Delta\tau$ is the differential time delay and $\Delta f$ is the filter bandwidth.

Although there are many applications for dispersive filters, the discussion in Section II is confined to pulse-compression radar and the microscan, or compressive, receiver. This section emphasizes the importance of highly dispersive pulse-compression filters for meeting the present-day requirements of these systems. Section III continues with an overview of the design considerations for a highly dispersive filter. Such factors as insertion loss, bandwidth, and time dispersion are herein related to the transducer geometry and choice of substrate. This is followed by a review of the design theory, which demonstrates the extent to which current transducer circuit models may be employed in the design and analysis of complex dispersive filters.

In Section V the performance of a low-loss 100-MHz bandwidth 1000:1 linear FM dispersive filter is presented with filter errors treated in detail.

In the final section, some new techniques are discussed which promise to extend the realm of acoustic surface-wave filter capabilities to meet future requirements.

## II. Applications

### *Pulse-Compression Radar*

HDF's are of special interest for application to large TB pulse-compression radars. The purpose of using large TB dispersive filters is to implement long-range high-range resolution radar systems for the detection, identification, and tracking of high-speed airborne objects.

The linear FM dispersive filter is by far the most extensively studied and widely used in radar applications [1]. This may be traced to the simplicity of linear FM filter design and the inherent tolerance of the linear FM waveform to Doppler-shifted returns from high-velocity targets.

A pulse-compression radar system may generate the frequency-modulated pulse by applying a short pulse to the input of a dispersive filter. The "chirped" output pulse is spread in time and peak-power reduced by a factor equal to the TB product of the filter. This stretched pulse is frequency-converted to the radar RF, amplified, and transmitted. The received target returns are amplified, down-converted to the receiver IF, and compressed in a matched dispersive filter. This compression increases the peak amplitude of the returning signals and reduces their time duration by the TB product, i.e., the compression ratio. Spreading the signal in time upon transmission increases the radar range by permitting the peak power-limited transmitter to radiate more energy per pulse. However, the signal sensitivity and dynamic range thus gained are decreased by the insertion loss incurred during pulse expansion. Thus the dispersive-filter insertion loss is a critical factor in determining the maximum dynamic range of a chirp radar system.

Detecting, identifying, and tracking high-speed airborne objects require range resolution of 1–2 m and velocity resolution on the order of 1000 m/s. Range resolution $\Delta R$ and Doppler velocity resolution $\Delta V$ are related to signal bandwidth $\Delta f$ and pulse duration $\Delta\tau$ as

$$\Delta R \simeq \frac{c}{2\Delta f} \tag{2-1}$$

and

$$\Delta V \simeq \frac{c}{2f_0\Delta\tau} \tag{2-2}$$

Manuscript received September 15, 1972; revised October 16, 1972. This work was supported in part by the U.S. Army Electronics Command, Fort Monmouth, N. J., under Contract DAAB-07-71-C-0046, and in part by the Rome Air Development Center, Griffiss Air Force Base, Rome, N. Y., under Contract F30602-71-C-0347.

The authors are with the Hughes Aircraft Company, Ground Systems Group, Fullerton, Calif. 92634.

Reprinted from *IEEE Trans. Microwave Theory Tech.*, vol. MTT-21, pp. 176–186, Apr. 1973.

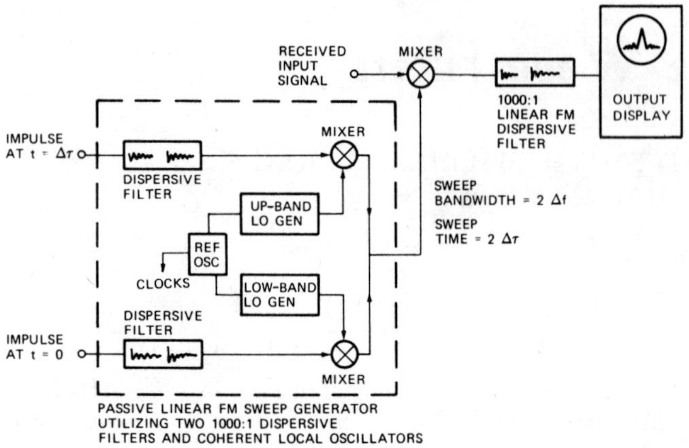


Fig. 1. Block diagram of microscan or compressive receiver, utilizing large TB product linear FM dispersive filters and passively generated sweep.

where $f_0$ is the radar carrier frequency and $c$ is the speed of light.[1] For a typical 3-GHz radar, the above resolutions require $\Delta f \simeq 100$ MHz and $\Delta\tau \simeq 50$ μs. From this example, it is clear that TB products ($\Delta f\Delta\tau$) of several thousand are needed. Consequently, we have chosen to define a highly dispersive filter as one having a TB product in excess of 1000.

### *Microscan (Compressive) Receiver*

The microscan receiver, sometimes referred to as a compressive receiver, is used to detect and instantaneously measure the frequencies of unknown signals. This type of receiver is essentially a fast spectrum analyzer equivalent to a contiguous filter bank of up to several thousand filters.

The basic design, Fig. 1, differs from a conventional receiver in that the center frequency is controlled by a sweeping local oscillator (dashed box in Fig. 1). The LO sweep, which may be generated by a linear FM dispersive filter, produces a signal whose frequency sweeps linearly over a band $B$ in time $T$. In the specific implementation, two 1000:1 dispersive filters are combined (with appropriate frequency translation) to generate a sweep having $B=2\Delta f$ and $T=2\Delta\tau$. Since the dispersive filter following the mixer acts as a matched filter by compressing the signal that was modulated by the sweeping LO, the frequency versus time slope of this compression filter must match the sweep rate of the local oscillator.

The receiver operation may be clarified using the sweep-intercept diagram shown in Fig. 2, in which the mixer output frequency is plotted as a function of time. A typical displayed output, as shown at the bottom of Fig. 2, contains one compressed pulse for each received frequency. The time delay of the compressed output pulse is determined by the specific portion of the LO sweep that is mixed down to the compression filter band. Thus the frequency of the received signal, which controls the frequency translation of the sweep, also controls the time of the output pulse. That is, two signals differing in frequency by $\delta f$ produce displayed pulses that are separated in time by $\delta t=(\Delta\tau/\Delta f)\delta f$.

The two intercepted CW signals superimposed on the response diagram represent the highest and lowest frequencies ($f_{s\max}$ and $f_{s\min}$) that can be resolved using the full bandwidth of the compression filter. The criterion for full resolution is that the mixer output signal for the received frequency completely span the frequency range $|f-f_0| \leq \Delta f/2$, which defines the passband of the compression filter. If the mixer output signal does not cover the full band of the compression filter, the effective compression ratio is reduced, and the output corresponding to that frequency will not have the full-time (hence frequency) resolution.

[1] For a more general treatment of range and velocity resolution see [16].

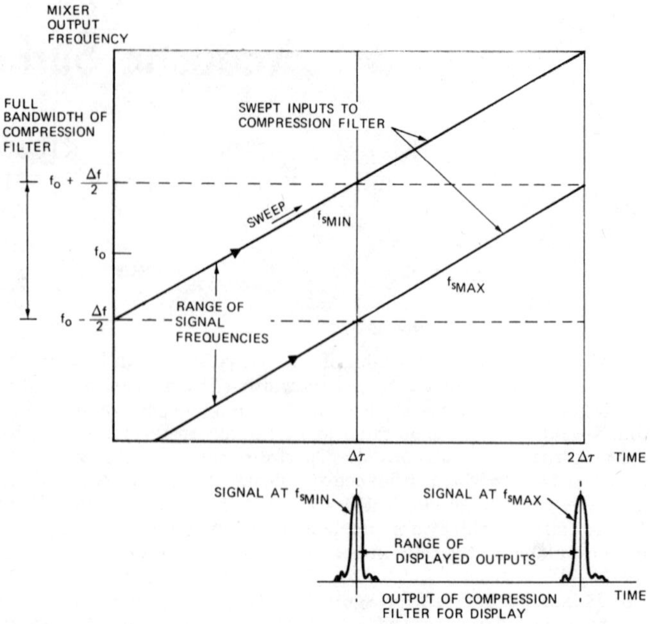


Fig. 2. Sweep diagram for sweep range, $B=2\Delta f$, and sweep time, $T=2\Delta\tau$, showing compressed outputs for two input frequencies.

The range of signal frequencies $f_s$ over which full resolution occurs is shown in Fig. 2 for the particular receiver described above, in which the local oscillator frequency ($f_{LO}$) sweeps over the range $|f_{LO}-f_0| = \Delta f$. In general, it can be shown that the range of full-frequency resolution is equal to the sweep range minus the compression-filter bandwidth.

After compression, the time resolution is

$$\Delta t \simeq \frac{1}{\Delta f} \tag{2-3}$$

which gives a frequency resolution of

$$\delta f_r \simeq \Delta t\left(\frac{\Delta f}{\Delta\tau}\right) = \frac{1}{\Delta\tau}\,. \tag{2-4}$$

To achieve high-frequency resolution, large dispersion is required in the compression filters. Moreover, high sweep rates $\Delta f/\Delta\tau$ are required to cover large bandwidths in minimum time. Since the compression filter requires a large TB product, highly dispersive filters are an attractive candidate for this application.

## III. Overview of Design Considerations

The dispersive filter design requires determining a surface-wave filter with an impulse response specified in the time domain as

$$h(t) = e(t)\exp\left[j\phi(t)\right] \tag{3-1}$$

or in the frequency domain as

$$H(f) = E(f)\exp\left[j\Phi(f)\right]. \tag{3-2}$$

This paper concentrates on a linear FM waveform of center frequency $f_0$, pulse length $\Delta\tau$, chirp bandwidth $\Delta f$, and an impulse response

$$h(t) = \begin{cases} \exp\left[j2\pi\left(f_0 t + \frac{\Delta f}{\Delta\tau}\frac{t^2}{2}\right)\right], & |t| < \frac{\Delta\tau}{2} \\ 0, & |t| > \frac{\Delta\tau}{2}. \end{cases} \quad (3\text{-}3)$$

The surface-wave filter is treated as a two-port network whose terminal pairs are the electrical terminals of the two surface-wave transducers. The voltage transfer function $T(f)$ of this network, when loaded, is required to be

$$T(f) = A \exp\left[-j2\pi f\tau\right]H(f) \quad (3\text{-}4)$$

i.e., $T(f)$ must be made equal to the desired spectrum to within a nondispersive delay $\tau$ and a constant $A$. The constant $A$ is maximized when the transducer and external circuit are matched for minimum insertion loss.

Important limitations which influence the construction of a highly dispersive surface-wave filter satisfying (3-4) are enumerated below.

1) The pulse length $\Delta\tau$ of a single filter is limited by the length of the piezoelectric crystal. The length is also limited by the increase in acoustic propagation loss proportional to the number of electrodes ($N \simeq 2f_0\Delta\tau$).

2) The center frequency ($f_0$) is limited to about 300 MHz by the state of the art in photolithography.

3) The fractional bandwidth ($\Delta f/f_0$) limitation depends on whether the filter is configured with one dispersive transducer and one nondispersive transducer or with two dispersive transducers. Ordinary periodic nondispersive transducer fractional bandwidths are limited to about 0.25, with new types of nondispersive transducers showing promise for fractional bandwidths up to 0.4. Using a pair of dispersive transducers divides the total pulse length between two transducers, requiring that their *combined* response satisfy (3-4). The fractional bandwidth of dispersive transducers is limited to less than 1.0 to prevent the low-frequency electrodes, synchronous at $f_0-(\Delta f/2)$, from generating interfering third harmonic signals at $f_0+(\Delta f/2)$. If no special bulk wave suppression techniques are employed, the fractional bandwidth should be somewhat smaller than 1.0 to prevent the low-frequency electrodes from generating bulk waves when operated at $f_0+(\Delta f/2)$.

4) The apodization (acoustic aperture tapering) required to produce the desired amplitude response $E(f)$ can complicate the design theory. When both transducers are apodized, the circuit model [2] may fail, since it does not model the complicated double sum required to account for the response of each electrode in the receiving transducer to the acoustic waves from each electrode in the launching transducer [3]. Designs with only one apodized transducer circumvent this problem.

5) The low ($<50\ \Omega$) transducer impedance requires the use of low-loss broad-band matching networks. The transducer impedance is low because large numbers of electrodes lead to a large capacitance and radiation conductance, which cannot be reduced by use of a narrow aperture because of diffraction limitations.

6) A compression filter with temporal amplitude weighting for compressed-pulse sidelobe suppression is subject to acoustic diffraction problems. This is because highly tapered transducer apertures are needed to implement amplitude weighting directly into the acoustic filter via the function $e(t)$ in (3-1). An external weighting filter eliminates this problem.

7) Large acoustic multiple-transit echoes can occur in highly dispersive filters implemented on strong-coupling piezoelectric materials (such as *YZ* lithium niobate) which are attractive for low insertion-loss applications. The strong coupling causes a relatively large perturbation in the acoustic-wave impedance under the metal electrodes. The resultant small acoustic reflections from each electrode can add in phase to give large multiple-transit echoes [2]. The "double electrode" technique [4] eliminates this problem, but the required fabrication process becomes intractable at high frequencies. Fortunately, the problem is ameliorated in large TB filters inasmuch as the multiple-transit echoes undergo a large decorrelation suppression relative to the desired signal and are also attenuated by propagation loss.

## IV. Filter Design and Analysis

In order to implement a surface-wave filter it is necessary to choose a scheme for employing *two* transducers which together produce the desired frequency response. Specifically, it is necessary to find two new signals from which the two individual transducers are to be designed. One method is to use a short unapodized nondispersive transducer[2] whose spectral amplitude response is nearly constant over the desired bandwidth $\Delta f$. Such a transducer launches a straight-crested wave whose transverse energy distribution is uniform (ignoring diffraction effects in the near field). In this case the filter transfer function $T(f)$ assumes the product form

$$T(f) = T_1(f) \cdot T_2(f) \quad (4\text{-}1)$$

where $T_1(f)$, the electroacoustic transfer function of the nondispersive transducer, is approximately

$$T_1(f) \cong A_1 \exp\left[-j2\pi f\tau_1\right] \quad (4\text{-}2)$$

and $T_2(f)$, associated with the dispersive transducer, is to be designed from the relation

$$T_2(f) = (A/A_1) \exp\left[-j2\pi f(\tau - \tau_1)\right]H(f). \quad (4\text{-}3)$$

Thus one transducer has a transfer function of the same form (3-4) as specified for the entire filter. The main disadvantage of this configuration is the inherent bandwidth limitation of the nondispersive transducer. Broad bandwidth operation can be achieved by dividing the differential time delay $\Delta\tau$ between two identical apodized transducers each having bandwidth $\Delta f$. Reference [3] shows that the transfer function of a filter employing two apodized transducers, in general, cannot be described by the product of the individual transducer transfer functions. However, the product form (4-1) is a good approximation if the apodized transducers are identical and the compression ratio is very large.

The desired impulse response can be synthesized by using two identical apodized transducers whose common electroacoustic transfer function is $\sqrt{H(f)}$, where $H(f)$ is given by (3-2). The desired filter impulse response is the linear FM waveform given by (3-3). If we denote the Fourier transform by $F$, the resulting time signal for each transducer is $h_1(t) = F^{-1}\{\sqrt{F[h(t)]}\}$. For large $\Delta\tau\Delta f$, $h_1(t)$ is approximately a

[2] A periodic transducer or any transducer with a plane of symmetry normal to the propagation direction is nondispersive.

linear FM waveform given by

$$h_1(t) \cong \begin{cases} \exp\left[j2\pi\left(f_0 t + \frac{\Delta f}{\Delta\tau}t^2\right)\right], & |t| < \frac{\Delta\tau}{4} \\ 0, & |t| > \frac{\Delta\tau}{4}. \end{cases} \quad (4\text{-}4)$$

The filter-synthesis problem is thus reduced to designing a transducer which produces the impulse response $h_1(t)$ given by (4-4).

According to the naive linear FM prescription, the transducer electrodes should be placed at temporal positions given by

$$2\left(f_0 t_n + \frac{\Delta f}{\Delta\tau}t_n^2\right) = \left(n - \frac{N_1}{2}\right) \quad (4\text{-}5)$$

where $N_1 = f_0\Delta\tau + 1$ is the number of electrodes in each transducer. Reference [2] shows that (4-5) must be modified because of the interaction between the acoustic waves and electric load. The modified equation is

$$2\left(f_0 t_n + \frac{\Delta f}{\Delta\tau}t_n^2\right) + \tan^{-1}\left\{\frac{Q_L}{f_0}\left(f_0 + \frac{2\Delta f}{\Delta\tau}t_n\right)\right\} = \left(n - \frac{N_1}{2}\right). \quad (4\text{-}6)$$

The parameter measuring the interaction is the "load $Q$," defined by

$$Q_L = 2\pi f_0 C_T R_L \quad (4\text{-}7)$$

where $R_L$ is the load resistance and $C_T$ is the transducer capacitance.

There are at least two additional effects which require further modification of the electrode-positioning law (4-6). One is the difference in the surface-wave velocity in the metallized electrode regions compared to that in the gaps between electrodes. If the transducer is constructed with the electrode width being a constant fraction of the spacing between adjacent line centers, (4-6) remains valid provided that an "effective" surface-wave velocity [5] is used in converting from temporal electrode positions to spatial positions ($x_n = v_{eff}t_n$). However, common techniques for fabrication of high-frequency transducer patterns generally dictate a constant electrode width. The required modification to the spatial electrode positions is described in [5] for the case corresponding to $Q_L = 0$. Another effect is velocity dispersion due to finite-thickness electrodes. This problem becomes increasingly serious as the design frequency of the filter is increased.

Completion of the transducer design consists of specifying the acoustic apertures ($w_n$) of the electrodes; that is, the length of overlap of adjacent electrodes measured in the direction transverse to acoustic propagation. For linear FM transducers of large compression ratio, the apertures are given to an excellent approximation by [2]

$$w_n \propto \left(\frac{f_n}{f_0}\right)^{-3}\left[1 + Q_L\left(\frac{f_n}{f_0}\right)^2\right] \quad (4\text{-}8)$$

where $f_n$ is the synchronous frequency defined by $f_n = (t_{n+1} - t_n)^{-1}$. Note that the apertures are wider at the low-frequency end than at the high-frequency end of the transducer, and for

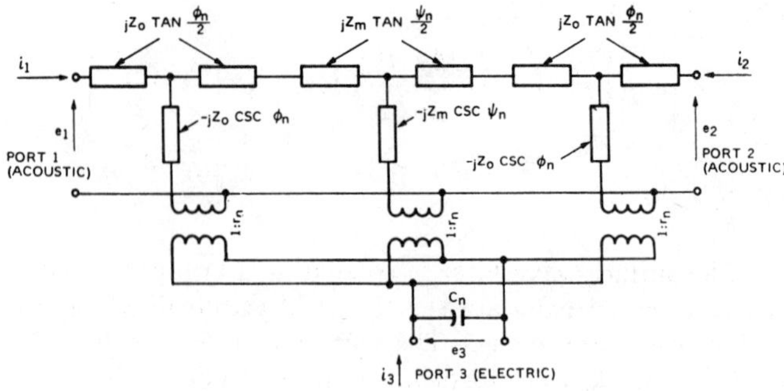


Fig. 3. Mason equivalent circuit for the crossed-field model of one electrode including an acoustic impedance discontinuity.

weak coupling to the load ($Q_L \to 0$), the apertures vary as $f_n^{-3}$. Slight modifications to (4-8) are required to compensate for electrostatic electric field variations if all transducer electrodes have the same width.[3]

The 1000:1 linear FM transducer design incorporated the modifications outlined above and was implemented using an iterative numerical procedure to derive the electrode pattern.

Detailed calculations of filter performance are carried out by use of the crossed-field Mason circuit model [6], modified to include acoustic-propagation loss, velocity dispersion under the metal electrodes, and different acoustic-wave impedances in the electrode and gap regions. The three-port circuit for one electrode plus half of each adjacent gap is shown in Fig. 3. The metallized region has an acoustic impedance $Z_m$ and transit angle $\psi_n = 2\pi f L_{sn}/v_m$, where $L_{sn}$ is the width of the $n$th electrode and $v_m$ is the acoustic velocity in the metallized region. In general, $v_m$ is taken to be a frequency-dependent function of the form $v_1 - khf$, where $k$ is a constant of the materials, $h$ is the electrode thickness, and $f$ is the operating frequency. The gap region consisting of half of each gap adjacent to the $n$th electrode has length $L_{gn}$, and is represented by two transmission lines, each of impedance $Z_0$ and transit angle $\phi_n = \pi f L_{gn}/v_0$, where $v_0$ is the surface-wave velocity of the unmetallized region. Evaluation of the effect of acoustic-propagation loss requires the inclusion of imaginary parts of $Z_0$, $Z_m$, $\phi_n$, and $\psi_n$. Reference [2] gives further details of the electrode capacitance $C_n$, electroacoustic transformers, and interconnection of the single-electrode networks into a transducer circuit.

The computer program which utilizes the above model for transducer analysis also combines transducers to find the frequency-domain response of a dispersive filter. In addition, it finds the response of a pulse-compression loop (expansion and compression filters with optional spectral weighting filter), giving frequency-domain amplitude and phase information as well as compressed pulses in the time domain.

The analytical model confirms the effectiveness of designing the transducers to account for a reduced, dispersive velocity under metal electrodes and for coupling to the electric load. When these effects are not taken into account in the transducer design, the result is phase errors which in turn cause severe distortion of the recompressed pulse and associated sidelobes. Fig. 4 is a plot of the computed phase error for a pulse-compression loop in which the expanded pulse is spectrally inverted and compressed in the same filter used for expansion. The associated recompressed pulse shown in Fig.

[3] Details of this modification are described in [2].

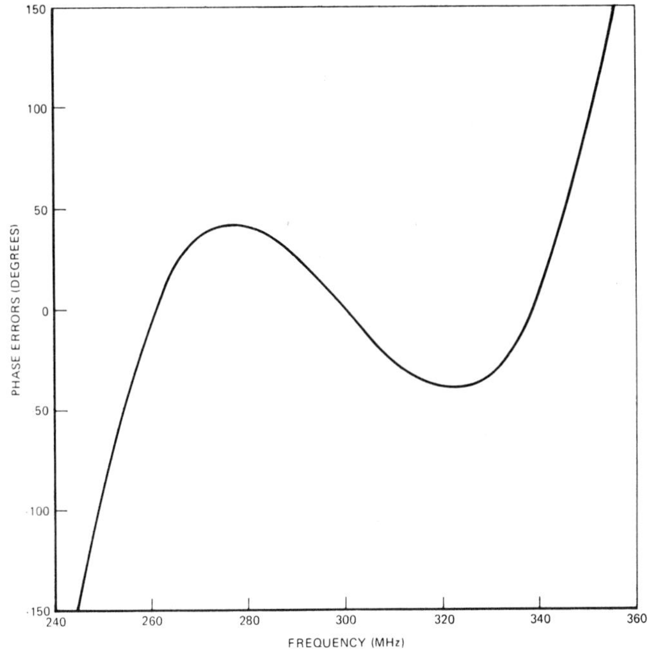


Fig. 4. Phase error caused by neglecting electric load interactions and acoustic velocity reduction in electrode regions in a 1000:1 filter used for both pulse expansion and compression.

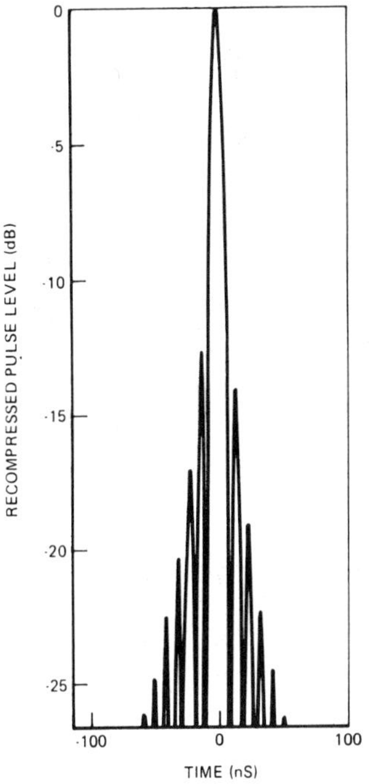


Fig. 6. Compressed pulse from a 1000:1 filter designed to account for electric-load interactions and acoustic velocity reduction in electrode regions.

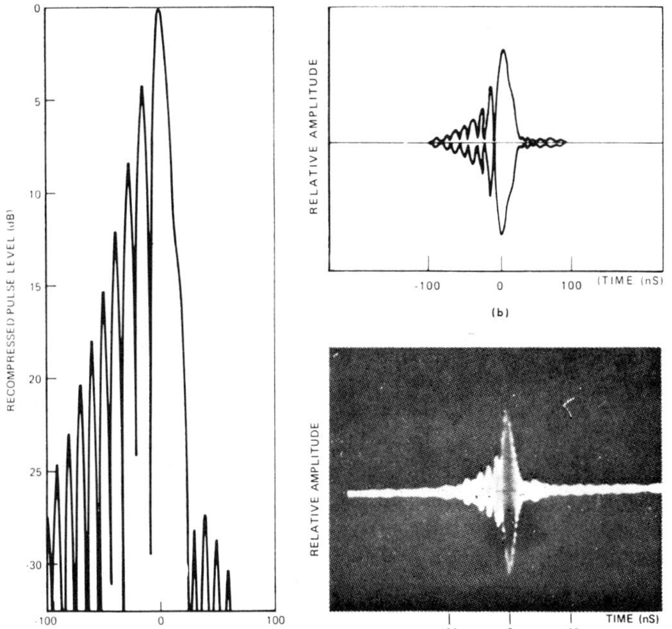


Fig. 5. Compressed pulse from a 1000:1 filter without correction for electric-load interactions and acoustic velocity reduction in electrode regions. (a) Calculated. (b) Calculated amplitude. (c) Observed amplitude.

5(a) and (b) is severely distorted from the desired sin $x/x$ shape, with the largest leading sidelobe being only 4 dB below the main recompressed pulse. This result is essentially confirmed by the experimental data of Fig. 5(c), although the largest leading sidelobe is somewhat lower ($-8$ dB) than predicted.

When the transducer design is modified to account for coupling to the load and the electrode-region velocity reduction, the phase errors are reduced to less than 4° in the operating band of 250–350 MHz. The recompressed pulse (Fig. 6) very nearly conforms to a sin $x/x$ shape. The 1-dB difference between the levels of the largest leading and trailing sidelobes is a consequence of additional load-interaction effects which are discussed in [2], but were not accounted for in the present design.[4] The acoustic-wave impedance discontinuities caused by the metal electrodes as well as acoustic-propagation loss have been neglected in the calculations described above, inasmuch as the purpose was to verify the value of the lossless discontinuity-free circuit-model analysis for transducer design. The circuit model is presently being used to investigate the combined effects of the impedance discontinuities, propagation loss, and matching circuits in order to further optimize transducer design. Insertion-loss data calculated with and without the impedance–discontinuity effect, but without considering acoustic propagation loss, are presented in [2, fig. 10].

## V. 1000:1 Dispersive-Filter Performance

The performance of a large compression-ratio broad bandwidth dispersive filter designed for 100-MHz bandwidth at a center frequency of 300 MHz is discussed in this section. To obtain broad-band operation with low CW insertion loss, strong-coupling *YZ* lithium niobate was used. For the required bandwidth, insertion losses of less than 40 dB cannot be realized with a weak-coupling substrate such as quartz. The use of lithium niobate led to the unveiling of several interesting complications associated with the strong piezoelec-

[4] See [2, p. 463] for the discussion of the "radiation admittance" term which causes this effect.

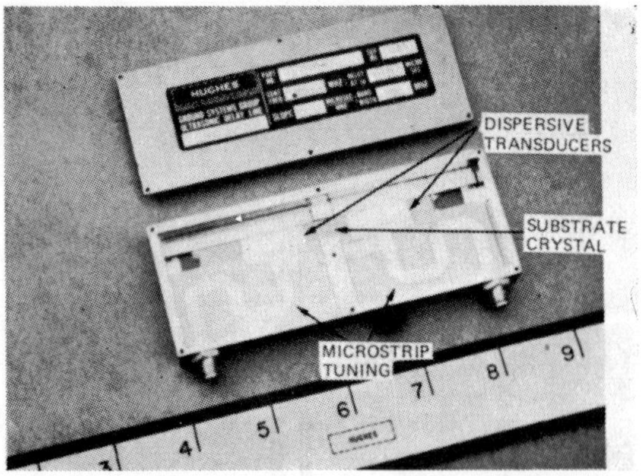


Fig. 7. Prototype 1000:1 dispersive filter with microstrip tuning circuits.

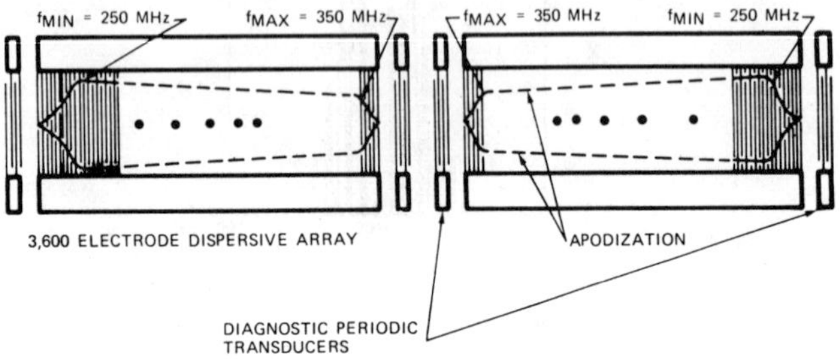


Fig. 8. 1000:1 dispersive-filter transducer geometry.

tric coupling. With appropriate compensations, however, the excellent observed performance demonstrates that strong-coupling materials are extremely valuable for complex pulse-compression filter applications. Moreover, the study of strong coupling effects has given valuable insights into similar effects that can cause problems in all extremely long dispersive filters, even when weak-coupling materials are used.

The prototype 1000:1 dispersive filter, shown in Fig. 7, includes the delay crystal with interdigital transducer arrays and the microstrip impedance matching transformers. The tapping electrodes in the input and output arrays are located on the acoustic substrate to yield a "down-chirp" linear FM waveform.

The transducer structures are fabricated from 750-Å aluminum, deposited using the "lift-off" or expendable-mask lithography technique [7]. This technique has proved most valuable in achieving uniform 2.5-$\mu$m widths for the required 7200 electrodes which are spaced over a pattern area of more than 2 in. The transducer geometry used in the 1000:1 design is shown schematically in Fig. 8. The choice of a down-chirp configuration is essential for the following reason. The metal electrodes on the surface of a strongly piezolectric substrate cause wave-impedance discontinuities, resulting in undesirable surface-wave reflections [2], [8]. These reflections are of critical importance in the 1000:1 filter design since their magnitude is comparable to that for a periodic array of nearly 140 electrodes [5]. In linear FM transducers, these reflections introduce high directivity, enhancing the coupling of acoustic waves directed toward the high-frequency end and suppressing those directed toward the low-frequency end. The down-chirp configuration is therefore most desirable for low filter insertion loss.

Theoretical design considerations show that favorable source and load impedances for efficient operation of the transducers are considerably less than 50 Ω. The microstrip circuits provide an impedance reduction of approximately 17:1, thereby improving the efficiency of the dispersive filter. These circuits are composed of a quarter wavelength transmission line with a shorted stub, and are similar to those described in [15].

The measured CW insertion-loss spectrum of a typical tuned 1000:1 dispersive filter, shown in Fig. 9, exhibits a rectangular passband which conforms closely to the ideal shape for an unweighted expansion (transmitter) filter. The realization of insertion loss as low as 30 dB is very encouraging for a filter of such complexity, although the measured amplitude ripple of approximately $\pm 0.8$ dB is slightly larger than predicted by the lossless transducer circuit model [2]. Triple-transit echoes, spurious signals, and direct electromagnetic feedthrough are typically suppressed by more than 50 dB. The departure of the measured phase response from an ideal quadratic phase function is also shown in Fig. 9. The dispersive filters were thermally insulated in order to prevent drifts during the 15 min required to complete the phase and amplitude measurement on a computer-controlled network analyzer.

Fig. 10 shows the impulse response, or expanded pulse, of the 1000:1 dispersive filter and the recompressed pulse envelope using the same filter to both expand and compress. Spectral inversion was employed prior to compression in order to transform the down-chirp linear FM into its matched "up-chirp" waveform. The nearly rectangular impulse response is consistent with the flat insertion-loss spectrum shown in Fig. 9. The sin $x/x$ form of the recompressed pulse envelope is evidence that the amplitude and phase performance of the 1000:1 dispersive filter is nearly ideal. Some departure from a perfect sin $x/x$ shape is, however, apparent in the more distant time sidelobes. The measured null width of 20 ns, Fig. 11(a), is in accord with the 100-MHz bandwidth.

The deviation of the recompressed waveform from a perfect sin $x/x$ shape indicates that high time sidelobe suppression may be difficult to achieve. This conjecture is supported by the comparison of recompressed pulses for both unweighted and Hamming-weighted cases. The same dispersive filters were used for both measurements with the Hamming weighting implemented by means of a coaxial transmission-line transversal filter. Fig. 11(b) shows that Hamming weighting increases the null width of the recompressed pulse from 20 ns (unweighted) to 38 ns, and the time sidelobe suppression, from 13 dB (unweighted) to 27 dB. Theoretically, for a 1000:1 linear FM design, the use of Hamming spectral weighting is capable of 42-dB time sidelobe suppression with null width broadening by a factor of 2 [1], [9]. This discrepancy results from the amplitude and phase errors in the dispersive-filter response. Since the phase and amplitude variations (which are discussed in more detail below) are largely random, it does not seem likely that extending the design-compression ratio by increasing bandwidth or time dispersion will lead to further reduction in the achievable sidelobe suppression. While designs having compression ratios of more than 1000:1 are realizable, some question remains as to whether time sidelobe suppression in excess of about 30 dB can be achieved without the use of external equalization to compensate for the small variations in each filter response.

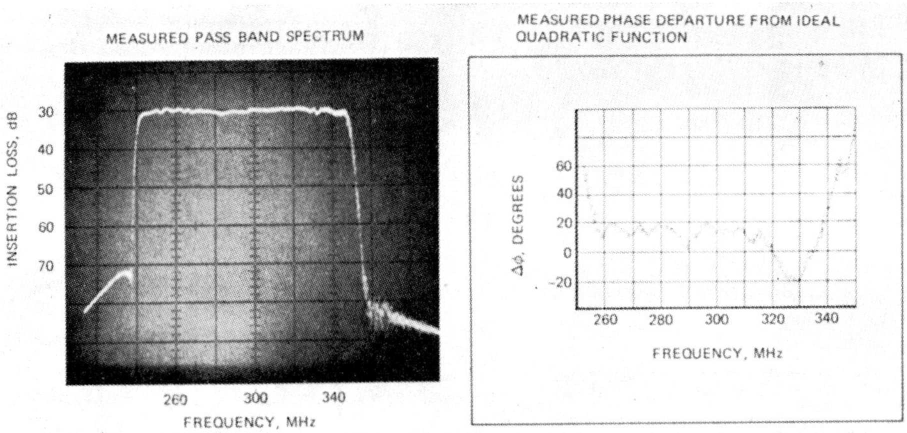


Fig. 9. Measured insertion-loss spectrum and phase deviation from a quadratic for 1000:1 linear FM dispersive filter.

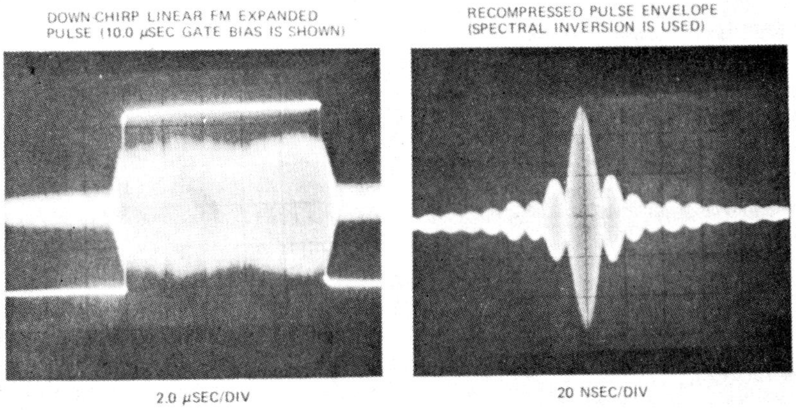


Fig. 10. Expanded and compressed pulse envelopes for unweighted 1000:1 linear FM dispersive filter.

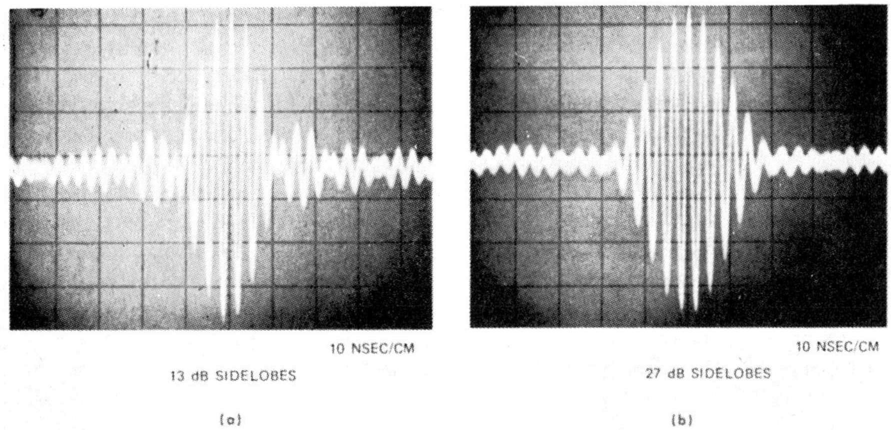


Fig. 11. Recompressed pulse waveforms. (a) With no spectral weighting. (b) With Hamming weighting.

A prototype compressive receiver which utilizes three 1000:1 linear FM dispersive filters has been assembled and tested. Two of these filters generate the sweeping local oscillator signal while the third is utilized to compress the IF mixer-output waveform (see Fig. 1). The operation of the microscan receiver was discussed in Section II. The necessity of maintaining high signal-to-noise ratios requires that all filters have low insertion loss. Specifically, the signal from the sweeping local oscillator into the mixer should be at least 10 dB above the maximum received signal to avoid degradation of the receiver performance.

Typical measured results are shown in Fig. 12(a) and (b). Fig. 12(a) shows the detected output of the compression filter for two equal-amplitude CW signals separated by 1 MHz. Fig. 12(b) shows the same situation with 400-kHz separation between signals. During these tests equal amplitude signals of −95 dBm were resolved down to a separation of 200 kHz. These encouraging results were obtained in spite of using dispersive filters which had small differences in chirp slope. The use of adjustable temperature-controlled ovens to achieve matching chirp slopes in the dispersive filters is expected to improve the resolution to 100 kHz.

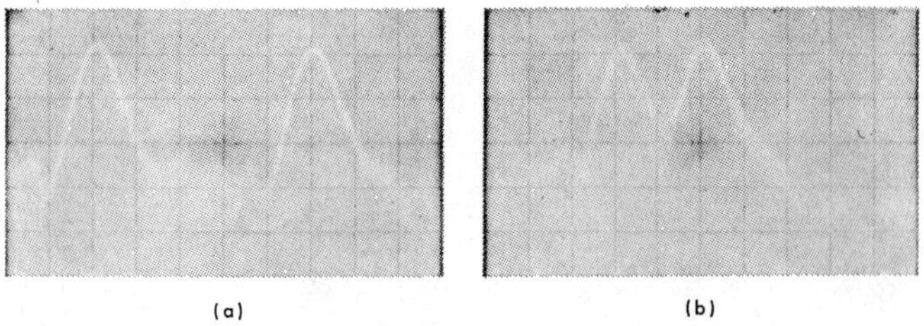


Fig. 12. Compressive receiver output pulses for CW signals separated by (a) 1 MHz. Time scale: 20 ns/div. Receiver units are −95 dBm. (b) 400 kHz. Time scale: 20 ns/div.

The foregoing discussion demonstrates that high-performance 1000:1 dispersive filters with low insertion loss can be realized. We now focus on the finer details of the filter behavior, with particular emphasis placed on the explanation of the losses and the factors which lead to errors and variations in the filter response.

Electrical impedance data have been used to estimate the conduction losses in an untuned dispersive transducer in the following manner. Within the range of 250–350 MHz, the total series resistance measured 1.8 Ω. Since circuit-model predictions indicate an acoustic radiation resistance of 0.62 Ω, the remaining resistance of approximately 1.2 Ω therefore corresponds to nonacoustic losses within the transducer. We can calculate the total loss for an untuned dispersive transducer. The transducer efficiency in terms of the generator impedance, $R_G$, the radiation resistance $R_a$, the conduction loss $R_c$, and the array capacitance $C_T$, is given by

$$E_T \simeq \frac{4R_G R_a}{(R_G + R_a + R_c)^2 + (1/\omega C_T)^2}. \qquad (5\text{-}1)$$

For $R_G = 50$ Ω, $R_c = 1.2$ Ω, $R_a = 0.6$ Ω, and $C_T = 160$ pF, the transducer loss is 14 dB. Of this, roughly 9 dB corresponds to electrical mismatch loss, and the remainder to conduction losses within the transducer. A 3-dB loss, which is commonly included to account for the bidirectional loss in conventional interdigital transducers, has not been included here because of the highly directional nature of the long transducers.

The microstrip networks are designed to reduce $R_G$ to approximately 3 Ω, thereby improving the impedance match of the transducers. As a result, the tuning circuits provide a reduction in the filter insertion loss by approximately 15 dB. The realization of this large improvement required careful attention to the minimization of conduction losses in the microstrip circuits, since a circuit resistance of only a few ohms could easily negate any advantage gained by tuning.

The typical insertion loss for a tuned 1000:1 dispersive filter ranges between 30 and 35 dB. With transducer mismatch and conduction losses accounting for typically 13 dB, the remaining loss arises principally from the propagation loss of the acoustic wave within the electroded regions. Since long dispersive gratings are nearly periodic, they produce an almost perfect acoustic reflection (i.e., the reflection loss is very small). The triple-transit suppression in the 1000:1 dispersive filter is therefore approximately equal to twice the propagation loss between the points of reflection. Thus the propagation loss in the 1000:1 filter can be measured across the passband by simply observing the frequency-dependent time-delay characteristics of narrow-band tone pulses and measuring triple-transit echo suppression. The measured triple-transit suppression data, shown in Fig. 13, indicate that the propagation

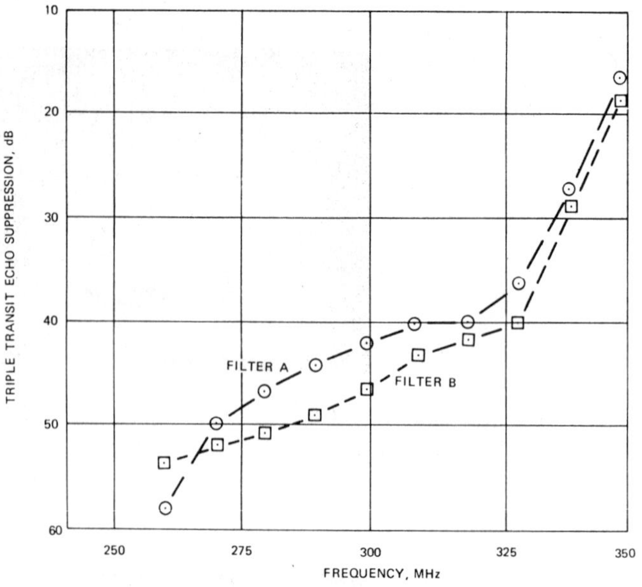


Fig. 13. Triple-transit echo suppression versus frequency measured in two different 1000:1 linear FM dispersive filters.

loss varies by about 5 dB over the passband. The relatively high measured midband propagation loss of 22–25 dB may indicate appreciable scattering of the surface wave into bulk waves within the arrays. The propagation loss is seen to decrease sharply at the upper edge of the passband where the distance of propagation within the electroded regions becomes small. Combining the propagation loss from Fig. 13 with the 13-dB total-tuned transducer loss, gives reasonably good agreement with the measured insertion loss. The corresponding loss for an untuned dispersive filter, in which the transducer loss is approximately 28 dB, also agrees well with measured values of typically 50 dB. The overall measured loss, as well as the details of the passband shape, have been found to vary by several decibels as a consequence of differences in the propagation loss within the electroded regions. The frequency dependence of the propagation loss appears to be intimately related to the nature of the metal electrodes. Anomalies in the passband shape, such as small peaks and valleys and the "non-Fresnel" shaped ripple may, therefore, be eliminated by improved fabrication uniformity.

Since the filter-loss characterization presented above does not shed much light on the nature of the filter-phase response, it yields little information about the pulse-compression performance of the 1000:1 dispersive filters. The factors which determine the filter-phase characteristics are the phase shifts associated with the transducer capacitance and matching circuits and the frequency dependence of the acoustic phase delay. The circuit effect is far smaller than the acoustic phase delay which contributes $2\pi$ for each acoustic wavelength in the delay path. For this reason, variations in the acoustic delay properties are the principal cause of the phase deviations observed in 1000:1 filters.

It is important to distinguish between "errors" and "variation" in the phase response. Errors are departures from quadratic frequency dependence of the phase, while variations refer to differences in the constants used to describe the quadratic phase functions of different filters. In general, small phase errors produce time sidelobes in the recompressed pulse whose size and position depend on the nature of the error [1]. The presence of these phase errors defeats the effectiveness of con-

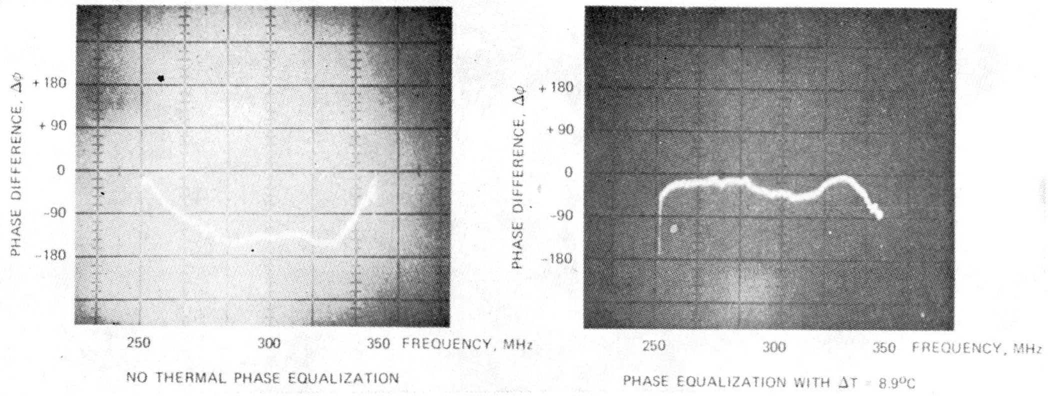


Fig. 14. Phase difference versus frequency between two 1000:1 linear FM dispersive filters before and after thermal chirp-slope equalization ($\Delta T = 8.9°C$).

ventional spectral weighting techniques for suppressing the 13-dB time sidelobes which are characteristic of a pair of perfect (error-free) matched linear FM filters.

Since accurate phase behavior is of primary importance in large compression-ratio dispersive filters, factors which lead to errors merit special attention.

Provided electrode positions are corrected to account for the constant width electrodes and other strong coupling effects discussed in Section IV, accurate phase response depends on transducer fabrication. Improper photoresist exposure, for example, may cause the actual electrode width to be in error by an amount $\Delta W$. This causes the acoustic phase from the region of excitation to the high-frequency end of the array to change by

$$\Delta\phi(f) = 2\pi f\left\{\left[\frac{\Delta\tau}{\Delta f}\right][f - f'] + \left[\frac{\Delta W}{v_0}\right]\left[\frac{\delta v}{v_0}\right]\eta(f')\right\} \tag{5-2}$$

where

$$f' \simeq f\left\{1 + 2f\left[\frac{\Delta W}{v_0}\right]\left[\frac{\delta v}{v_0}\right]\right\}$$

and $v_0$ is the unmetallized surface-wave velocity, $\delta v$ is the change in velocity resulting from shorting, and $\eta(f)$ is the number of electrodes between the point of excitation and the high-frequency end of the array. In the constant electrode-width arrays, the corrected electrode positions do not differ appreciably from the linear FM law; therefore,

$$\eta(f) \simeq 2\Delta\tau\left\{f_0 + \frac{[f_{\min}^2 - f^2]}{2\Delta f}\right\} \tag{5-3}$$

where $f_{\min}$ is the minimum frequency in the filter band and $\Delta\tau$ is twice the time dispersion for a single array. Since the dispersive filters are operated using spectral inversion to invert the passband about the center frequency $f_0$, the phase error is expressed with reference to the midband frequency. Of particular interest are the phase error terms in $(f-f_0)^2$ and $(f-f_0)^3$, which correspond to the changes in chirp slope and delay linearity, respectively. These terms are given by

$$\Delta\phi_2 \simeq 2\pi[f - f_0]^2\left[\frac{\Delta W}{W}\right]\left[\frac{\delta v}{v_0}\right]\left[\frac{9f_0}{4f_{\max}}\right]\left[\frac{\Delta\tau}{\Delta f}\right] \tag{5-4}$$

and

$$\Delta\phi_3 \simeq 2\pi[f - f_0]^3\left[\frac{\Delta W}{W}\right]\left[\frac{\delta v}{v_0}\right]\left[\frac{\Delta\tau}{\Delta f}\right]\left[\frac{3}{4f_{\max}}\right] \tag{5-5}$$

where $f_{\max}$ is the highest frequency in the filter band. The design electrode width $W$ equals a quarter wavelength at $f_{\max}$. Thus the error in the phase response is proportional to both the fabrication tolerance $\Delta W/W$ and to $\delta v/v_0$.

Measurements of the phase response of the 1000:1 dispersive filters indicate that it can generally be fitted to within 20° of a quadratic curve centered at $f_0$. The constants defining the "best-fit" quadratics for different filters, however, vary over a range of almost 0.5 percent. Therefore, when two filters are operated as a matched pair they often exhibit a phase mismatch of several hundred degrees over the 100-MHz band.

From (5-4), the predicted chirp-slope error is related to $\Delta W/W$ by

$$\frac{\Delta \text{ chirp slope}}{\text{chirp slope}} = \frac{9}{2}\frac{f_0}{f_{\max}}\left[\frac{\delta v}{v_0}\right]\left[\frac{\Delta W}{W}\right]. \tag{5-6}$$

With $\delta v/v_0 \simeq 2.2 \times 10^{-2}$ for $YZ$ $LiNbO_3$ [10], the observed chirp-slope variations of 0.5 percent correspond to $\Delta W/W \simeq 6$ percent. This is reasonable for the large number of filters tested with the substantial evolution of the fabrication processes. In the most recent filters, fabricated in pairs using identical photoresist exposures, the chirp-slope variations were found to correspond to electrode-width variations of less than 1.0 percent. This demonstrates that careful controls on fabrication can substantially overcome the phase mismatch problem.

Unless the phase discrepancies are corrected, the recompressed waveform may bear little resemblance to the desired $\sin x/x$ shape. Small differences in chirp slope $\Delta\tau/\Delta f$ can be corrected relatively easily by using broad-band electromagnetic dispersive networks, for example, which have quite modest compression ratios [9], [11]. An alternate approach to matching the phase responses utilizes the temperature dependence of the acoustic velocity. With the filters in separate ovens, the temperatures are adjusted until the quadratic phase difference is cancelled. Fig. 14 shows the measured phase difference as a function of frequency for two dispersive filters before and after temperature compensation. The temperature difference,

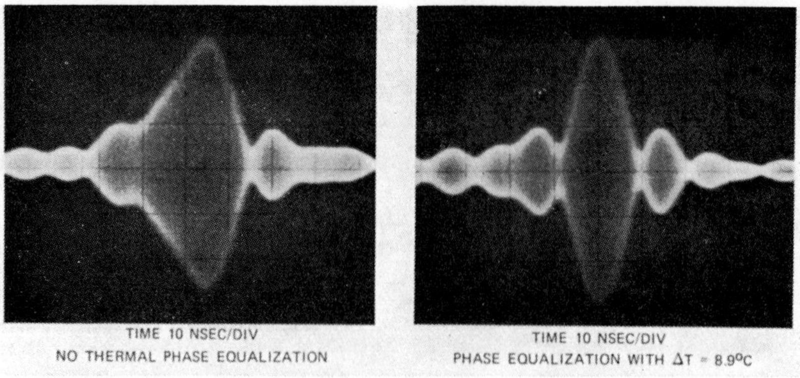


Fig. 15. Compressed pulse envelope for a pair of 1000:1 linear dispersive filters before and after thermal chirp-slope equalization ($\Delta T = 8.9°C$).

$\Delta T$, to offset the chirp-slope difference is

$$\Delta T = -\frac{1}{2K}\left\{\frac{\Delta(\text{chirp slope})}{(\text{chirp slope})}\right\} \tag{5-7}$$

where $K$ is the temperature coefficient of delay for the substrate material. For $YZ$ $LiNbO_3$ with $K = -85\times10^{-6}/°C$, [12], chirp-slope variations of as much as 0.5 percent can be equalized with temperature differences of less than 30°C. Fig. 15 shows the improvement in the shape of the recompressed pulse of the two filters in Fig. 14 using temperature-controlled ovens.

Examination of the cubic-phase error term in (5-5) shows that, although its magnitude is smaller than the quadratic term by almost a factor of 20, it may cause serious problems when the fabrication errors are large.

In addition to the smooth phase variations described above, small random departures (errors) of the phase data from a quadratic-frequency dependence have been observed. Because these errors are not reproduced in different filters fabricated from the same mask, it is unlikely that they result from errors in the design or fabrication of the photomask. It is more plausible that the errors are caused by nonuniformities in the metal electrode structure. The dependence of phase error on electrode width, derived from (5-2) and (5-3), indicates that only a few percent change in $W$ can produce an error of many degrees. In view of the magnitude of the measured phase errors of $\simeq 20°$, and the estimated fabrication tolerances, random variations in $W$ offer a plausible explanation for these errors. When the variation in $W$ is not uniform, the exact characterization of $\Delta\phi$ depends on the detailed nature of the variation and is not attempted here. The mathematical analysis of the consequences of a 20° nonperiodic phase error over the filter bandwidth has not been performed. However, experimental implementation of Hamming spectral weighting produced sidelobe suppression varying from 21 to 27 dB for different dispersive filters rather than the theoretical value of 42 dB.

In addition to reducing these errors by improved fabrication accuracy, a second approach may be to utilize a weaker coupling substrate to decrease $\delta v/v_0$. In so doing, the filter insertion loss is generally increased. Thus, for each specific application there is a tradeoff between the advantages of improved signal-to-noise ratio due to low loss and the disadvantages of poor time sidelobe suppression due to phase errors.

## VI. Conclusions

Acoustic surface-wave technology has for several years promised to revolutionize the design of complex filters at IF and high IF frequencies. The realization of a 100-MHz bandwidth, low insertion-loss dispersive filter indicates that these expectations are well on their way to being realized. This is not to imply that all the problems have been solved, but rather that continued effort in characterizing acoustic losses and improving fabrication controls will be rewarded.

We have shown that present phenomenological computer models are sufficiently versatile to cope with the second-order effects encountered with strong-coupling piezoelectrics. However, considerable work remains to be done in treating conduction and propagation losses in complex acoustic surface-wave filters.

The performance of the 1000:1 dispersive filter was shown to be highly encouraging with the remaining problems stemming primarily from fabrication variations. These difficulties might be substantially reduced with improvement of photolithography procedures, such as the use of flexible glass photomasks [13]. The use of a weak-coupling substrate can effect a reduction in errors in the filter response; however, this approach may increase the filter insertion loss.

The development of accurate and reproducible dispersive filters having compression ratios on the order of 1000 is the first step toward meeting future dispersive-filter requirements of TB's > 10 000. The passive chirp-sweep generator in the compressive receiver demonstrates that identical 1000:1 filters may be used to provide an increased compression ratio. This general technique of using $N$ linear FM dispersive filters to enhance the compression ratio by a factor of $N^2$, has been proven at low frequencies using 100:1 filters with $N = 10$ [14]. From the performance of the two 1000:1 filters in the compressive receiver (which were not phase compensated in ovens), the prospects seem excellent for combining several of the 1000:1 components to achieve TB = 10 000 or more.

Finally, it should be mentioned that a novel transducer geometry employing eighth wave or "double" electrodes has recently been reported in conjunction with the suppression of electrode reflections. It was demonstrated that transducers utilizing this geometry exhibit strong responses at their third harmonic. This double-electrode geometry may be utilized to great advantage in the design of highly dispersive filters since the suppression of electrode reflections helps to improve the triple-transit echo rejection. Even more significant is the fact that harmonic operation permits the upper frequency range of fabrication to be extended for most dispersive-filter designs [4].

In view of the wide utility of large TB dispersive filters having high compression ratios and the degree of success in present development efforts, the outlook is extremely bright for continued progress in the field of acoustic surface-wave dispersive filters.

## Acknowledgment

The authors wish to thank R. L. Lanphar for his assistance in the computational work and W. K. Masenten for his critical reading of the manuscript.

## References

[1] J. R. Klauder, A. C. Price, S. Darlington, and W. J. Albersheim, "The theory and design of chirp radars," *Bell Syst. Tech. J.*, vol. 34, pp. 745–808, July 1960.
[2] W. R. Smith, H. M. Gerard, and W. R. Jones, "Analysis and design of dispersive interdigital surface-wave transducers," *IEEE Trans. Microwave Theory Tech.*, vol. MTT-20, pp. 458–471, July 1972.
[3] R. H. Tancrell and M. G. Holland, "Acoustic surface wave filters," *Proc. IEEE*, vol. 59, pp. 393–409, Mar. 1971.
[4] T. W. Bristol, W. R. Jones, G. W. Judd, and W. R. Smith, "Further applications of double electrodes in acoustic surface wave device design," presented at the 1972 IEEE G-MTT Int. Microwave Symp.
[5] E. K. Sittig and G. A. Coquin, "Filters and dispersive delay lines using repetitively mismatched ultrasonic transmission lines," *IEEE Trans. Sonics Ultrason.*, vol. SU-15, pp. 111–119, Apr. 1968.
[6] W. R. Smith, *et al.*, "Analysis of interdigital surface wave transducers by use of an equivalent circuit model," *IEEE Trans. Microwave Theory Tech.*, vol. MTT-17, pp. 856–864, Nov. 1969.
[7] M. K. Stelter, "Chrome etching and relief deposition," *J. Photochem. Etching*, vol. 1, pp. 4–6, Dec. 1966.
[8] W. S. Jones, C. S. Hartman, and T. D. Sturdivant, "Second order effects in surface wave devices," *IEEE Trans. Sonics Ultrason.*, SU-19, pp. 368–377, July 1972.
[9] C. E. Cook and M. Bernfeld, *Radar Signals.* New York: Academic Press, Inc., 1967.
[10] J. J. Campbell and W. R. Jones, "A method for estimating optimal crystal cuts and propagation directions for excitation of piezoelectric surface waves," *IEEE Trans. Sonics Ultrason.*, vol. SU-15, pp. 209–217, Oct. 1968.
[11] T. R. O'Meara, "The synthesis of 'band pass' all-pass time delay networks with graphical approximation techniques," Hughes Res. Lab., Malibu, Calif., Rep. 114, 1962.
[12] J. D. Maines, E. G. S. Paige, A. F. Saunders, and A. S. Young, "Simple technique for the accurate determination of delay-time variations in acoustic-surface-wave structures," *Electron. Lett.*, vol. 5, pp. 678–680, Dec. 1969.
[13] H. I. Smith, F. J. Bachner, and N. Efremow, "A high-yield photolithographic technique for surface wave devices," *J. Electrochem. Soc.*, vol. 118, pp. 821–825, May 1971.
[14] R. D. Haggarty, L. A. Hart, and G. C. O'Leary, "A 10,000:1 pulse compression filter using a tapped delay line linear filter synthesis technique," in *EASCON Rec.*, pp. 306–314, 1968.
[15] T. M. Reeder and W. R. Sperry, "Broad-band coupling to high-$Q$ resonant loads," *IEEE Trans. Microwave Theory Tech.*, vol. MTT-20, pp. 453–458, July 1972.
[16] H. Urkowitz, "Ambiguity and resolution," in *Modern Radar*, R. S. Berkowitz, Ed. New York: Wiley, 1965, pp. 197–203.

# Part V
# Direct Sequence

Although there have been a number of direct sequence systems built, only two papers are included in this part. This is not because there are not many papers available; in fact, most of those that have been written in the spread spectrum area are concerned with direct sequence techniques. Most of the papers included in this volume are concerned with a direct seuqence system directly, or are at least applicable to such a system. Tausworthe's paper on ranging codes, for instance, was intended to describe codes used on Jet Propulsion Laboratories/NASA deep space probes, and those were and are direct sequence systems. Twenty-three out of the total of 43 papers reprinted here are directly applicable to direct sequence, which should give the reader some idea of the relative emphasis that has been placed on the various spread spectrum techniques over the years.

Ward's paper could just as well have been included in Part II, Applications, or in Part VII, Information Transmission. It describes the most prevalent method for transmitting information on a direct sequence or pseudonoise carrier: sequence inversion modulation, or in other words, biphase phase shift keying (PSK) of the code sequence. Since the code sequence is usually used to biphase or quadriphase modulate the RF carrier, then sequence inversion modulation is seen to add phase shifts to those that occur due to the unmodulated code sequence. This paper addresses the effects of adding a communications channel, by sequence inversion modulation, to a tracking system. The usual approach has been to add tracking to an existing communication link. The results given are generally not readily available elsewhere, and a good overview of direct sequence system design is included.

The second paper, by Blasbalg *et al.*, could well have been placed in Part II, Applications, as an example of considerations for design of a system compatible with satellite communications parameters. It also includes considerations of the problems encountered in employing spread spectrum systems in air-to-ground (and vice versa) links. It is included here because of its wide scope, and because it gives the reader a good grasp of the problems that he might encounter in links such as those that are contemplated.

Direct sequence systems have been and will continue to be the favored spread spectrum systems for many applications because of their relative simplicity, at least as compared with frequency hopping systems. Compared to chirp systems, direct sequence systems are usually more complex, but outperform the chirp systems in interference rejection. One recent competition between direct sequence, frequency hopping, and chirp techniques found the chirp system winning out because it was projected to be "smaller, lighter, and less expensive" than either direct sequence or frequency approaches. Then, to increase the interference rejection capability of the chirp system that won out because of its simplicity, direct sequence modulation was added.

This brings up the point that quite often in a spread spectrum application it is necessary to employ more than one kind of modulation (i.e., a "hybrid" spread spectrum form is used). In many of these applications it is found necessary to employ direct sequence modulation as one of those making up the overall waveform, since no other type of spread spectrum technique is as insensitive to as many different kinds of interference.

All things considered, direct sequence systems have been in the past, and will continue to be in the future, the standard against which all other anti-interference and ranging systems will be measured.

## OTHER PAPERS OF INTEREST

1) G. F. Sage, "Serial synchronization of pseudonoise systems," *IEEE Trans. Commun. Technol.*, Dec. 1964.
2) R. B. Ward, "Acquisition of pseudonoise signals by sequential estimation," *IEEE Trans. Commun. Technol.*, Dec. 1965.
3) L. E. Zegers, "Common bandwidth transmission of information signals and pseudonoise synchronization waveforms," *IEEE Trans. Commun. Technol.*, Dec. 1968.

# Digital Communications on a Pseudonoise Tracking Link Using Sequence Inversion Modulation

ROBERT B. WARD, MEMBER, IEEE

REFERENCE: Ward, R. B.: DIGITAL COMMUNICATIONS ON A PSEUDONOISE TRACKING LINK USING SEQUENCE INVERSION MODULATION,[1] Lockheed Missiles and Space Co., Palo Alto, Calif. Rec'd 3/25/66; revised 8/29/66. Paper 19TP67-907. IEEE TRANS. ON COMMUNICATION TECHNOLOGY, 15-1, February 1967, pp. 69–78.

ABSTRACT: The factors which enter into digital communication over a pseudonoise tracking link are developed. The deterioration of tracking quality due to simultaneous use of the tracking link for communication is shown to be small. The communication bit error probability is shown to be the same as that for coherent phase shift keying of a sine wave carrier when the tracking link uses biphase carrier modulation and the receiver uses balanced demodulators. In addition, the pseudonoise link supplies the necessary data bit synchronization. Experimental results are presented from laboratory equipment where data rates up to 47 000 b/s were transmitted over a pseudonoise tracking signal suitable for high accuracy range measurement to 3300 km.

*KEYWORDS:* Broadband, Communication Theory, Data Transmission Systems, Digital Signals, Modulation, Pseudonoise.

## Introduction

Ranging systems using pseudonoise modulation can provide highly accurate range measurement to large unambiguous range. Tracking links of such systems frequently operate between terminals which also have the need to communicate. For example, commands may be sent to a transponder, or identification and telemetering data may be returned from a transponder. When a correlation type of tracking receiver is used, there is available, as a result of the tracking operation, a noisefree synchronized pseudonoise signal. It appears reasonable, therefore, to attempt to use this reference signal to obtain very efficient digital communication.

This paper discusses the factors which enter into digital communications over a pseudonoise tracking link. In particular, a delay-lock tracking link and data transmission by sequence-inversion modulation are considered. Experimental results are presented from a video delay-lock system operating with a pseudonoise signal generated by a 15-stage shift register using a 1.5-MHz clock. Such a pseudonoise signal is suitable for highly accurate and unambiguous range measurement to 3300 km.

The techniques described here are also applicable to straight communication (nontracking) links where it is desirable to employ a wideband carrier for reasons of security, to enable multiple random access, etc.

## Background

A delay-lock pseudonoise tracking loop is shown in Fig. 1(a). Such a loop is used in a receiver to track the ranging

[1] This work was supported by Marshall Space Flight Center under Contract NAS8-11498.

Reprinted from *IEEE Trans. Commun. Technol.*, vol. COM-15, pp. 69–78, Feb. 1967.

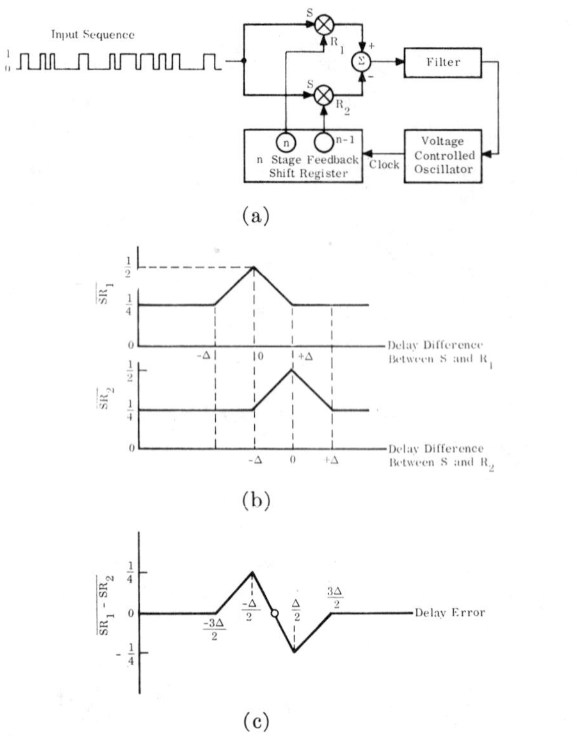


Fig. 1. Delay-lock loop. (a) Block diagram of delay-lock loop. (b) Average multiplier outputs. (c) Delay-lock discriminator curve.

modulation on an incoming signal. For the purposes of this paper the input to the delay-lock loop is presumed to be a *video* pseudonoise sequence, i.e., the modulation has already been obtained from the carrier by other means.

Operation of the delay-lock loop was first discussed by Spilker [1]. Described simply, its operation is as follows. The input signal is multiplied by each of two time-displaced pseudonoise signals identical in form to the input pseudonoise signal. The difference of the multiplier outputs is filtered in a low-pass filter and the voltage so obtained is used to control the frequency of a variable-frequency oscillator. The oscillator serves as the clock for a feedback shift register (FSR) which generates the reference pseudonoise signals used by the multipliers.

The average output of each multiplier as a function of the phase (or delay) error between the input and reference sequences to the multiplier is shown in Fig. 1(b). These functions are simply time-displaced autocorrelation functions of the pseudonoise signal. Since the filter is low pass, it tends to obtain the average of the differenced multiplier outputs. If the loop is opened at the VCO input and the static delay error is varied slowly by other means, the average filter output is the difference of the curves in Fig. 1(b) and is shown in Fig. 1(c). This is the delay-lock discriminator curve. If the loop is closed and the reference sequence is somehow brought into time synchronism with the input sequence, the loop will lock on and track.

## Digital Communication Modulation Types

The types of communications modulation which might be used with a pseudonoise ranging system can be grouped into three main categories:

1) communications modulation directly on RF carrier
2) communications modulation on a subcarrier
3) communications modulation on the pseudonoise ranging signal.

In any of these cases, the data bits are synchronized with the ranging sequence. That is, data bits always begin as certain states of the transmitter feedback shift register occur. A receiver, therefore, uses the identical state of its tracking feedback shift register to indicate when to perform integrate and dump decision operations for optimum recovery of data.

If the communications modulation is placed either directly on the carrier or on the ranging signal, special precautions are generally required in the receivers so that the data modulation does not affect tracking. This is not so when a subcarrier is used if the subcarrier and its sidebands are well separated from the ranging sidebands. Of course, this requires additional bandwidth.

Communications modulation, either on the carrier or a subcarrier, can be accomplished by the usual methods of phase shift keying, frequency shift keying, or amplitude modulation.

Some ways to data modulate a pseudonoise signal are the following:

1) frequency shift keying (FSK) of the clock
2) delay shift keying (DSK) of the pseudonoise signals
3) sequence inversion keying (SIK).

FSK is accomplished in the usual way by switching between different oscillators. DSK is accomplished by selecting the sequence to be transmitted either directly from the sequence generator or delayed an amount less than a tracking bit period. SIK is accomplished by selecting between a direct or complemented output from the sequence generator, or alternately by modulo 2 adding the data and the ranging sequence.

Both FSK and DSK produce errors in range tracking to the extent that the range loop bandwidth allows the loop to follow as the data perturbs it. Also, neither method is basically bipolar, the most efficient means for transmitting binary data. SIK is bipolar, and does not produce a range error for the tracking loop to follow. Therefore, this is the method of modulation considered in detail here.

## Effects of SIK on Delay-Lock Operation

First, we consider what modifications are required to a delay-lock tracking system to permit its operation when SIK is being used.

### *Transmitter Modifications*

Sequence inversion keying is performed in the transmitter as shown in Fig. 2. Data bits are synchronized by recognizing the all 1's state of the FSR and starting a data bit at that time. The clock is counted to determine the start of subsequent data bits. For example, a 15-stage shift register produces a ranging sequence whose length is $2^{15} - 1 = 32767$ tracking bits. The data-bit length may be chosen to

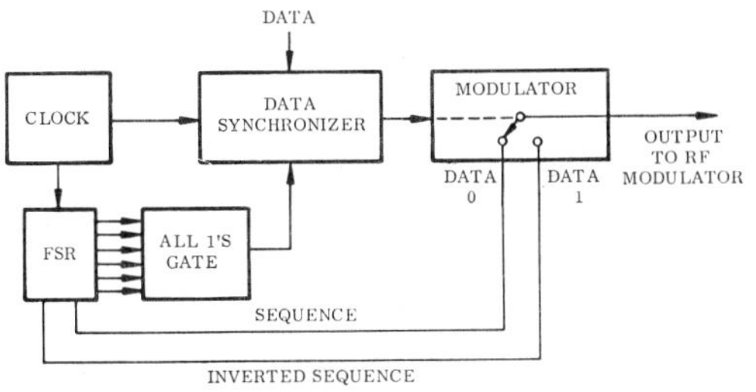


Fig. 2. Transmitter, sequence inversion keying.

be a factor of 32 767 in which case all data bits are the same length.

Alternatively, because the length of the ranging sequence is $2^n - 1$ bits, it may be divided into $2^{(n-p)}$ data bits where $2^{(n-p)} - 1$ data bits are of length $2^p$ and 1 data bit is of length $2^p - 1$. For example, if $n = 15$, $p = 7$, the sequence length $= 2^n - 1 = 32767$; the data bits per sequence $= 2^{(n-p)} = 256$. The breakdown of data bits per sequence is tabulated as follows:

| Length of Data Bit | Number of Data Bits | Totals |
|---|---|---|
| 128 | 255 | 32 640 |
| 127 | 1 | 127 |
| | | 32 767 |

In this case, the data synchronizer consists of a 128-bit clock pulse counter which is reset once per sequence by the all 1's gate. This second method of dividing the ranging sequence into data bits must be used when the FSR length $n$ results in a sequence length which is prime.

*Receiver Modifications to Permit Tracking*

Modifications to a delay-lock receiver to permit usage of SIK data modulation fall in two categories: 1) modifications to the delay-lock loop to permit tracking to take place and 2) additions needed for data readout (see the section *Receiver Modifications to Obtain Data Readout*).

First, consider what would happen to the delay-lock loop of Fig. 1(a) with SIK data modulation on the input. The average multiplier outputs appear in Fig. 3. If data *zeros* are being transmitted, the multiplier output is, of course, as before. However, transmission of data *ones* results in anticorrelation at the multiplier. For zero delay difference, the multiplier inputs are always opposite so that one factor is always zero and the multiplier output is always zero. The average multiplier outputs for data *ones* are shown dashed as a function of delay difference. The resulting delay-lock discriminator curve is also dashed and may be seen to produce the opposite sense control voltage.

In practically all cases it will turn out that the data-bit rate will be much higher than the bandwidth of the delay-lock tracking loop filter. Therefore, under these conditions, the filter would average the solid and dashed discriminator curves to produce zero. Therefore, tracking would not take place if the simple delay-lock circuit of Fig. 1(a) were used with SIK having equally probable data *zeros* and *ones*.

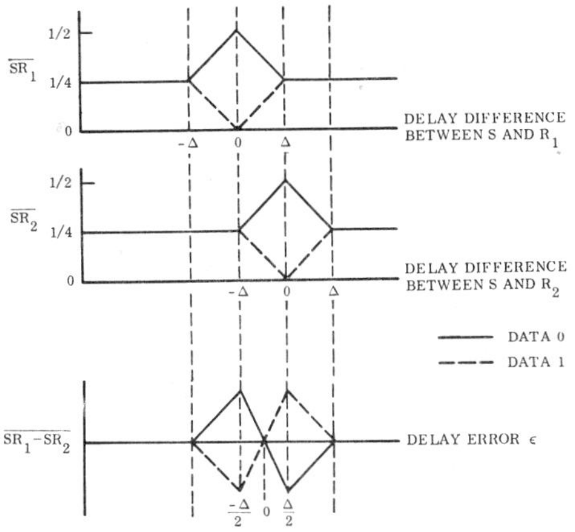


Fig. 3. Unmodified delay-lock loop with sequence inversion keying data modulation.

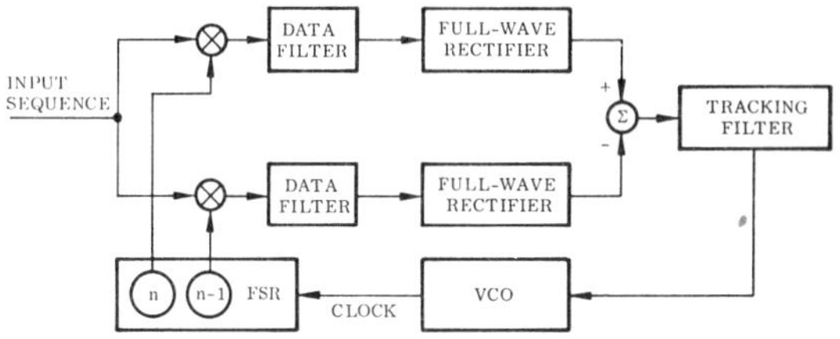


Fig. 4. Delay-lock loop for use with sequence inversion modulation.

This points out a method of operating with SIK that requires no change to the delay-lock loop. Suppose a fraction $k$ of the sequence is transmitted normally while the remaining portion $1 - k$ is devoted to transmission of data using SIK. Now, only the portion transmitting data is not effective in producing a discriminator characteristic. If equally probable data *zeros* and *ones* are assumed, the amplitude of the resultant discriminator curve is proportional to $k$. The disadvantage of this method, of course, is that a smaller amount of power is devoted to data transmission and, thus, the full data capability of the link is not used.

If the full sequence is to be devoted to data transmission, the delay-lock loop must incorporate rectifiers which change the multiplier output polarity so that regardless of whether a data *zero* or data *one* is being transmitted the control voltage will always be of the proper polarity for the tracking. This is shown in Fig. 4. Tracking performance of this delay-lock configuration has been analyzed by Gill [2]. The rectifiers are actually biased about the level 1/4 so that either correlation or anticorrelation at a multiplier produces equal outputs from the rectifier.

Data filters are placed between the multipliers and the rectifiers to prevent small signal suppression. Usually, pseudonoise tracking systems operate with signal-to-noise ratios in the intput bandwidth much less than unity. While multiplication by a reference signal is a linear operation as far as the input signal is concerned, rectification is not. Therefore, in order to prevent worsening of the SNR in the rectifier, the data filter is inserted to narrow the bandwidth enough so that the SNR at the rectifier is greater than unity. To accomplish this the filter bandwidth must be smaller than $P_s/N_o$ where $P_s$ is the signal power and $N_o$ is the noise power density.

Because the tracking error information exists as sidebands on the data signal, the filter bandwidth must also be large enough to pass the data signal so that the tracking information reaches the rectifier. This requires the filter bandwidth to be larger than $1/\delta$ where $\delta$ is the data bit period. The bandwidth requirements on the data filter do not conflict in a system design. Regardless of what may be the design minimum input SNR to the delay-lock loop, the data-bit period must be chosen to provide an improvement of SNR to at least +8 to +10 dB in the data bandwidth in order to obtain a sufficiently low data error rate. Therefore, as long as communications and tracking are desired to the same range, a filter bandwidth just large enough to pass the data will always result in greater than unity SNR at the rectifier.

The delay tracking error [2], [3] for a $(+\sqrt{P_s}, -\sqrt{P_s})$ input and (+1, −1) references is

$$\frac{\sigma_T}{\Delta} = \sqrt{\frac{p_o}{4P_s/N_o}\left(1 + \frac{8B_{\ell p}}{3P_s/N_o}\right)} \tag{1}$$

for a tracking loop damping factor of 1/2. Here

$\sigma_T \triangleq$ standard deviation of delay error
$\Delta \triangleq$ FSR clock period in the same time units as $\sigma_T$
$P_s \triangleq$ input signal power, watts
$N_o \triangleq kT$ = single-sided noise power spectral density, WHz
$B_{\ell p} \triangleq$ data filter equivalent noise bandwidth, Hz
$p_o \triangleq$ tracking loop undamped natural frequency, rad/s.

For the same delay-lock loop without the communications feature, the delay tracking error is

$$\frac{\sigma_T}{\Delta} = \sqrt{\frac{p_o}{4P_s/N_o}}. \tag{2}$$

The maximum effect on the tracking error can be computed from (1) and occurs when the communications bit rate is chosen to be the maximum possible. Then

$$\left.\frac{P_s}{N_o B_{\ell p}}\right|_{\min} \cong 8 \tag{3}$$

$$\left.\frac{\sigma_T}{\Delta}\right|_{\max} = \sqrt{\frac{p_o}{4P_s/N_o}\left(1 + \frac{1}{3}\right)} \tag{4}$$

and the tracking error is larger by 15.5 percent than if the communications link were not included. If a smaller communications data rate is chosen, the effect on the tracking error is even less.

## Receiver Modifications to Obtain Data Readout

Figure 5(a) shows the receiver modifications needed to read out the data. The input signal plus noise is multiplied by the $\Delta/2$ delayed output of the $n-1$ tap of the tracking feedback shift register. Since the delay-lock loop closely tracks the incoming sequence, the input and reference to the data multiplier are very nearly synchronous and either

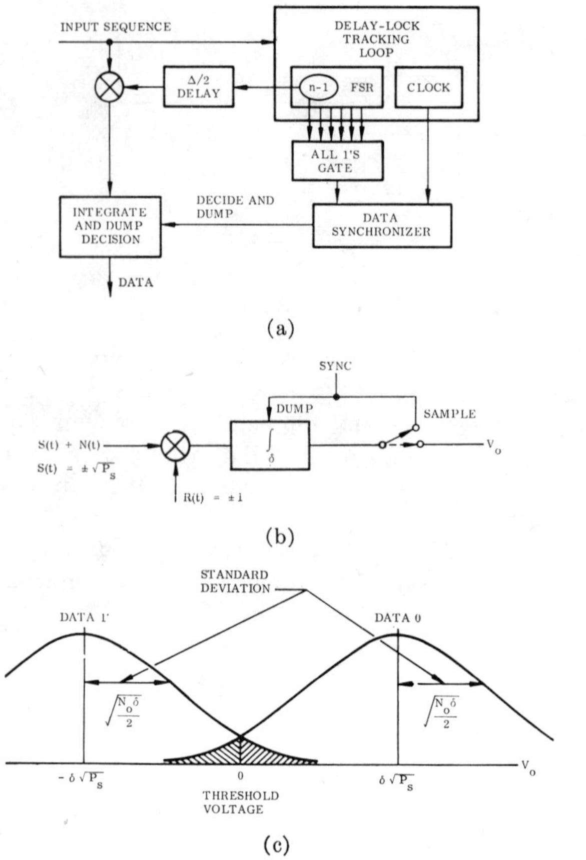


Fig. 5. Data readout for sequence inversion keying. (a) Block diagram. (b) Mathematical model. (c) Output voltage characteristics for $R = -1, +1$, $S = -\sqrt{P_s}, +\sqrt{P_s}$.

correlate or anticorrelate depending on whether a data 0 or 1 is being received. The data synchronizer operates in the same way as that of the transmitter and causes the integrate and dump operations to be performed at the correct time with respect to the data bits.

The model for the data readout circuit is shown in Fig. 5(b). The input noise $N(t)$ is assumed to be white and Gaussian with power spectral density $N_o/2$ where $N_o = kT$. The sampled output voltage is

$$V_o = \int_0^\delta R(t)[S(t) + N(t)]dt$$

$$V_o = \int_0^\delta R(t)S(t)dt + \int_0^\delta R(t)N(t)dt = V_{os} + V_{on}. \tag{5}$$

Two different possibilities exist for the form of the input signal and the reference. Each may be either unipolar or bipolar. A unipolar reference has the values 0, +1 whereas a bipolar reference has the values −1, +1. Likewise the input signal has the values 0, $+\sqrt{2P_s}$ when unipolar and the values $-\sqrt{P_s}$, $+\sqrt{P_s}$ when bipolar.

The best results are obtained when both the signal and the reference are bipolar. That case will be analyzed here. The signal component is then $V_{oso} = +\delta\sqrt{P_s}$ when a data *zero* was transmitted and $V_{os1} = -\delta\sqrt{P_s}$ when a data *one* was transmitted. Since $N(t)$ has zero mean and $N(t)$ and $R(t)$ are independent, the noise input to the integrator is white Gaussian noise with power spectral density $N_o/2$ and $V_{on}$ has zero mean. The variance of $V_{on}$ is

$$\overline{V^2_{on}} = \int_{-\infty}^{\infty} |H(f)|^2 \frac{N_o}{2}\, df \tag{6}$$

where

$$H(f) = \frac{1 - \exp(-j\omega\delta)}{j\omega} \tag{7}$$

is the transfer function of a finite time integrator. Therefore, the standard deviation of $V_{on}$ is

$$\sigma = \sqrt{\overline{V^2_{on}}} = \sqrt{\frac{N_o\delta}{2}} \tag{8}$$

The output voltage characteristics are shown in Fig. 5(c). The threshold is set at zero and the conditions under which bit errors occur are indicated by the shaded areas.

The same analysis when applied to other combinations of the input signal and reference gives values to complete Table I.

The bit error probability is obtained from the normal distribution and is shown as a function of $P_s\delta/N_o$ in Fig. 6. The best choice for the input signal is $\sqrt{P_s}, -\sqrt{P_s}$. This is natural since half the power in a 0, $\sqrt{2P_s}$ sequence is contained in the dc component which is not modulated by SIK, whereas the $\sqrt{P_s}, -\sqrt{P_s}$ sequence has no dc component so that all its power is modulated by data.

The results for $S = +\sqrt{P_s}, -\sqrt{P_s}$ and $R = -1, +1$ are identical with the results for coherent phase shift keying (Martin [4], Fig. 25) of a sine-wave carrier. The pseudonoise carrier, in addition, has provided the necessary data-bit synchronization.

TABLE I

CHARACTERISTICS OF VARIOUS DATA DEMODULATION SYSTEMS

| Input Signal | Reference 0, 1 | Reference −1, 1 |
|---|---|---|
| $\sqrt{2P_s}, 0$ | $\frac{V_{oso} - V_{osl}}{2} = \delta\sqrt{P_s}/2\sqrt{2}$<br>$\sigma = \frac{1}{2}\sqrt{N_o\delta}$<br>$\frac{V_{oso} - V_{osl}}{2\sigma} = \sqrt{P_s\delta/2N_o}$ | $\frac{V_{oso} - V_{osl}}{2} = \delta\sqrt{P_s}/2$<br>$\sigma = \sqrt{N_o\delta/2}$<br>$\frac{V_{oso} - V_{osl}}{2\sigma} = \sqrt{P_s\delta/N_o}$ |
| $+\sqrt{P_s}, -\sqrt{P_s}$ | $\frac{V_{oso} - V_{osl}}{2} = \frac{\delta}{2}\sqrt{P_s}$<br>$\sigma = \frac{1}{2}\sqrt{N_o\delta}$<br>$\frac{V_{oso} - V_{osl}}{2\sigma} = \sqrt{P_s\delta/N_o}$ | $\frac{V_{oso} - V_{osl}}{2} = \delta\sqrt{P_s}$<br>$\sigma = \sqrt{N_o\delta/2}$<br>$\frac{V_{oso} - V_{osl}}{2\sigma} = \sqrt{2\delta P_s/N_o}$ |

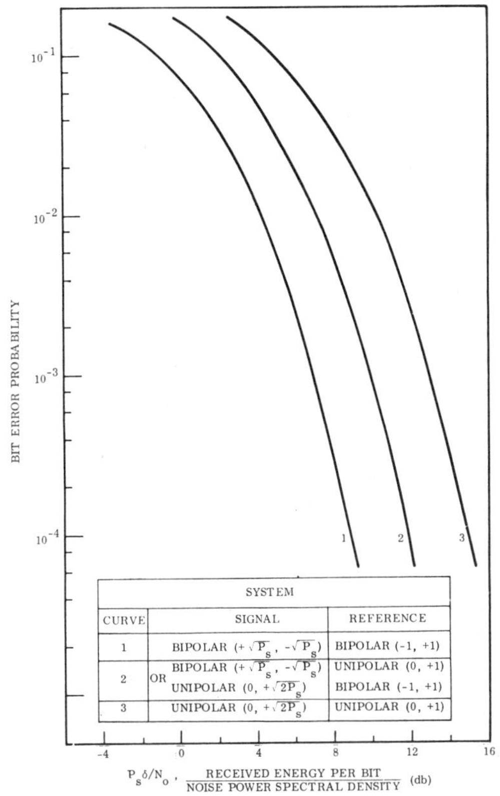


Fig. 6. Bit error probabilities for various modulation-demodulation systems.

## SOME OTHER CONSIDERATIONS

### *The Effects of Tracking Errors on Data Readout*

Tracking errors result in nonexact alignment of the input and reference sequences at the multiplier of the data readout system, Fig. 5(a). This may come about, for example, through noise-induced jitter, target dynamics, or equipment limitations. The result of such tracking errors is mainly that the signal component at the multiplier output is smaller and that a form of self-noise appears there. These effects have been analyzed by Gill [5], who obtained the following formula for the multiplier output when the sequences are long.

$$\frac{\text{signal power}}{\text{self-noise power}} = \frac{1}{2B_{LP}\,\Delta}\left(\frac{\Delta}{|\epsilon|} - 1\right)^2. \tag{9}$$

Here $\epsilon$ is the error in synchronism between the input and reference sequences to the multiplier. Figure 7 is based on (9) and shows how the data filter output signal to self-noise power ratio is affected by various tracking errors and data filter bandwidths. It is apparent that only for quite large data bandwidths and quite large tracking errors is the signal-to-noise ratio small enough to significantly affect the data bit error probability. The thermal noise errors of a delay-lock loop operating above threshold ($\sigma_\epsilon \leq 0.15\Delta$) will essentially not affect the data readout error. However, it is possible that if the design of the tracking loop allowed large transient or bias errors that small data errors could result.

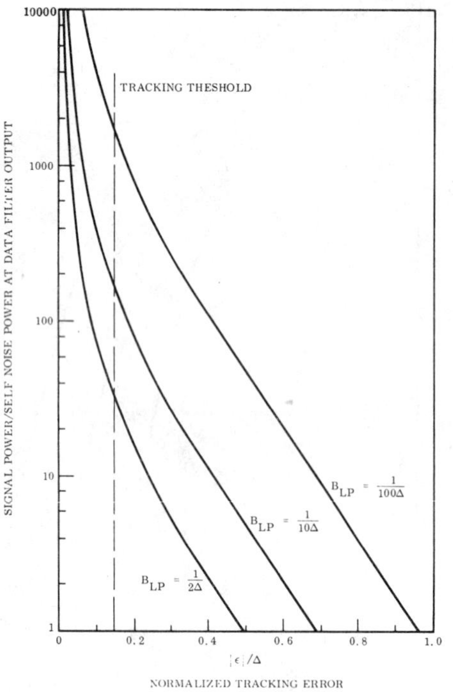


Fig. 7. Effect of tracking error on signal to self-noise power ratio.

### *Acquisition*

When the ranging or communicating link is first established or after a loss of contact, an acquisition process must take place. In this process, the receiver sequence generator is brought into synchronism with the incoming sequence and the tracking loop is locked in. The effect of SIK on this process is of interest.

Several methods of acquisition are in use. The sweeping acquisition method [1] causes the frequency of the receiver VCO to be offset slightly from the clock frequency of the incoming sequence. The reference sequence therefore drifts with respect to the incoming sequence until the point of synchronism is reached where control voltage is developed to cause lock-on. This method works with a delay-lock receiver modified to track SIK modulation because such a receiver provides the correct discriminator curve with or without modulation.

The stepping correlation [6] and sequential estimation [7] methods both require that a cross correlation be performed after each trial to determine whether or not synchronization has been achieved. These methods can be used without modification to achieve synchronization before data modulation is applied and then be disabled during communications modes. Since this is not convenient for reacquisition after an unscheduled dropout, it may be necessary to modify the cross correlators of such systems to indicate lock-on for either correlation or anticorrelation. Even then some deterioration will result. For example, the sequential estimation system depends on estimating $n$ (the number of shift-register stages) sequential bits of the incoming signal and loading them into the receiver shift register in order to obtain an estimate of the present state of the input. If a data *one* is being transmitted or if a data transition occurs during the $n$-bit estimate, an incorrect estimate will be obtained. These effects will be more detrimental when higher data-bit rates are being used.

## Experimental Results

The equipment designed for experimental verification of the principles of the preceding sections is not necessarily optimum or in a form desirable for an operational system. Generally, the designs were made on the basis of simplicity or convenience.

Also, for ease of understanding, the diagrams included here generally omit many necessary circuit details.

### *Delay-Lock Tracking in the Presence of SIK Modulation*

Circuits used for generation and tracking of SIK modulated signals are shown in block diagram form in Fig. 8. A 1.5-MHz crystal oscillator provides clock pulses at 667 ns intervals to step a 15-stage FSR and a 9-stage serial shift register. An all *ones* gate operated from the FSR resets the serial register to the all *zeros* position. The ripple-carry serial register then counts clock pulses to provide square waves at data bit rates of $F_c/256$, $F_c/128$, $F_c/64$, or $F_c/32$ as selected by the data rate switch. With the modulation switch in the square-wave position, these square waves are used in the modulator to gate either the sequence or the inverted sequence to the output. The transmission of alternate 0's and 1's of data is thus provided. The last data 1 in a sequence is one tracking bit short because the length of the tracking sequence is not divisable by 256.

Random data modulation is obtained by the use of a noise generator. A differentiating network operating from the data square waves provides sampling pulses at both positive and negative transitions of the data square waves. These pulses sample the noise voltage and cause the flip-flop to change state if the noise voltage is positive and to keep the same state if the noise voltage is negative. Since the noise voltage has zero mean, the probability of a data transition is 1/2 and the transitions always occur at the beginning of data bits. The transmission of bit-synchronized random data is thus provided.

In the delay-lock tracking receiver the multiplier references are obtained from the main and complementary outputs of the 14th- and 15th-stage flip flop of the receiver FSR. The input signal plus noise is limited to provide 0 and $-4$ volt levels. Since the reference sequences are also at these levels, simple OR circuits provide the multiplication function. The multiplier output is zero if either or both of the inputs is zero. Therefore, if the inputs are synchronous and anticorrelated, the multiplier output is a constant zero voltage. If the inputs are synchronous and correlated, the output is the 0, $-4$ volt sequence, the average value of which is $-2$ volts. If the inputs are not synchronous, the output is a 0, $-4$ volt sequence with average value $-1$ volt.

The data filters are low-pass 2-pole RC filters with four selectable bandwidths chosen to be in the range of data rate provided in the transmitter. Since the filters tend to obtain the average of their inputs, the filter output tends to be $-2$ volts correlated, 0 volt anticorrelated, and $-1$ volt

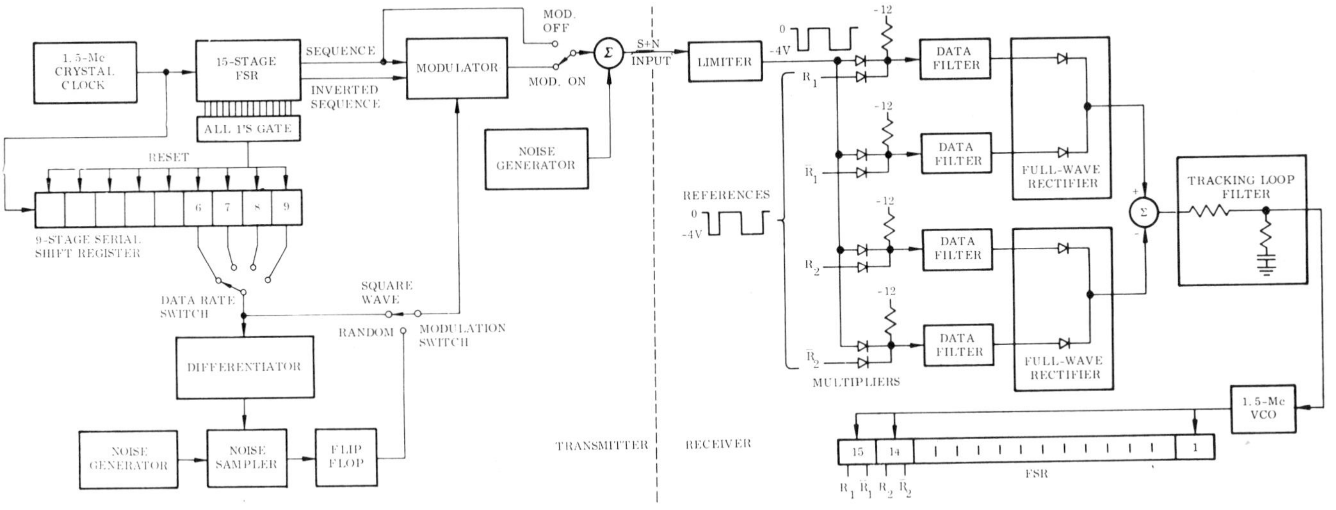


Fig. 8. Block diagram, sequence inversion keyed transmitter and delay-lock tracking receiver.

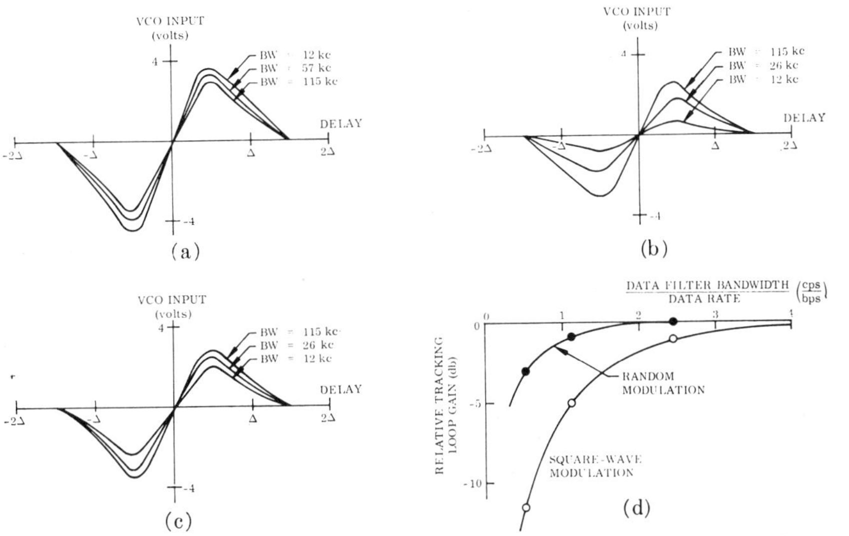


Fig. 9. Discriminator characteristics. (a) No modulation. (b) Square-wave modulation at 23.44 kb/s. (c) Random modulation at 23.44 kb/s. (d) Relative tracking-loop gain.

uncorrelated. The rectifier always selects the more positive of its two inputs so that whether data 0's or 1's are received, the rectifier output is 0 volt when the reference and signal are synchronous, and $-1$ volt when they are not synchronous. An autocorrelation is thus formed by the $R_1$ channel and a one-delta displaced autocorrelation function formed by the $R_2$ channel. The rectifier outputs are subtracted and the result filtered and used as the VCO control voltage. Figure 9 shows the discriminator curves measured to demonstrate the delay-lock discriminator characteristics. These experiments were performed by opening the loop at the VCO output and using the transmitter clock for both the transmitter and receiver. A variable delay-line in the clock line to the receiver allowed the sequences to be positioned with various relative delays.

Figure 9(a) was taken with no data being transmitted and shows that suitable control characteristics are obtained in this case. Curves were taken for various data filter effective noise bandwidths and point out the interesting fact that the amplitude of the discriminator characteristic increases with decreasing filter bandwidth. This is due to the fact that the wider filter bandwidths pass more of the self-noise components from the multipliers. These noise components are rectified to reduce the amplitudes of the cross correlation functions and, consequently, of the discriminator curve.

Figures 9(b) and 9(c) show the discriminator characteristic obtained when data are being transmitted. Figure 9(b), for square wave data, can be compared to Fig. 9(c), for random data, to see that considerably narrower data bandwidths are allowable for random data. This is to be expected since the spectral density of the random wave extends to dc. In Fig. 9(f), the relative tracking loop gain is plotted, as determined from Figs. 9(b) and 9(c). These show, for example, that a data filter bandwidth equal to the data-bit rate results in only 1-dB change of loop gain for random data while the filter bandwidth must be 2.5 times the data rate for the same gain change with squarewave

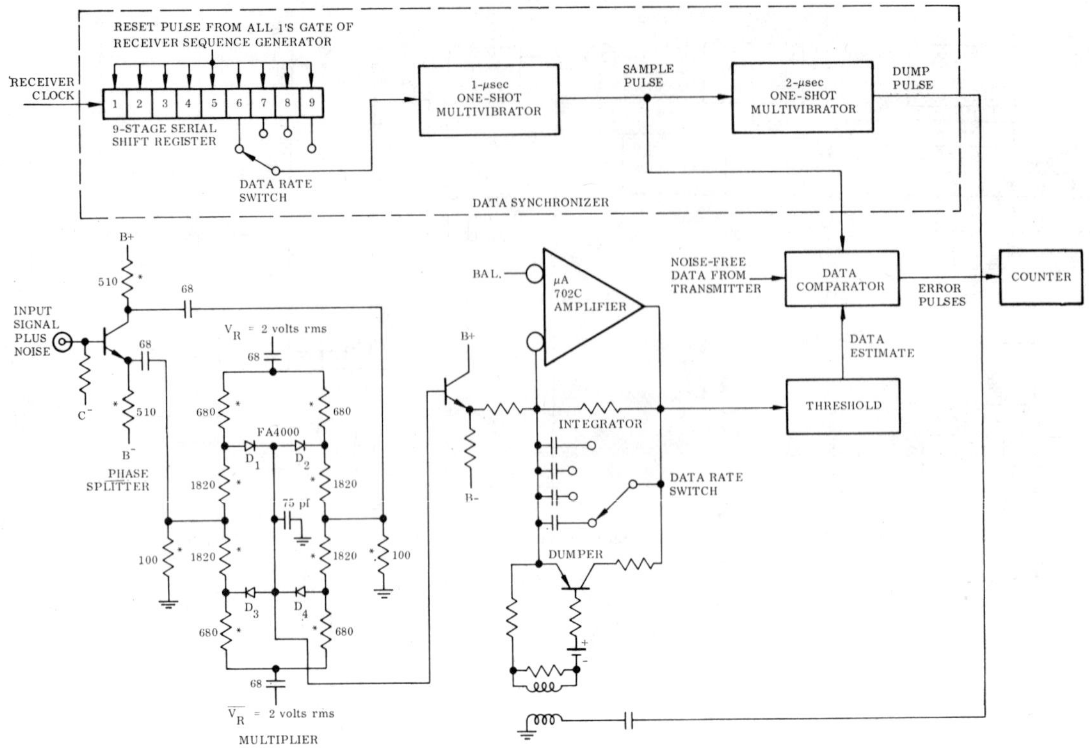


Fig. 10. Circuit diagram—data readout.

data. The usual case of data transmission is the random one so that normally the data filter would be designed to have a bandwidth about equal to the data-bit rate.

### *Data Readout*

The data readout and error rate circuitry constructed is shown in block diagram form in Fig. 10. The transmitter supplies the receiver with a data-modulated sequence to which noise has been added. The receiver tracks the incoming sequence using the delay-lock circuitry of Fig. 8 and also performs a synchronized integrate and dump data readout. A data sample pulse is generated at the end of each data period and is delivered to a data comparator circuit. If the data estimate at the receiver output is not the same as the data reference from the transmitter, the data sample pulse is gated to the output to represent an error. If the data estimate and reference are the same, no error pulse appears at the output. The multiplier is probably the most critical of the readout circuits because it must be linear to the input signal over a considerable dynamic range and, at the same time, be very well balanced so that the reference signal does not appear at the output.

Figure 11 presents oscillograms taken at various points of the data readout circuitry. Figure 11(a) is the waveform at the multiplier output and shows, by its ragged appearance, the effects of incomplete suppression of the reference signal. In this case the reference voltage was about 2-volt rms, the signal voltage about 0.1-volt rms, the multiplier output data voltage about 0.025-volt rms, and the multiplier output reference leakage voltage about 0.001-volt rms. This low leakage level was achieved by carefully balancing the multiplier reference voltages in isolation amplifiers and by using a matched quad diode, the FA4000, in the multiplier.

Figure 11(b) shows the integrator output and the received signal when all data *zeros* are being transmitted. In Fig. 11(c), alternate data *zeros* and *ones* are being transmitted and the same two waveforms are shown plus the receiver reference sequence. In Fig. 11(b) and 11(c) the data rate was set to be 5.84 kHz or 256 tracking bits per data bit. In Fig. 11(d) the data rate was 23.36 kHz or 64 tracking bits per data bit. Several things are evident from these photographs.

1) The time constants associated with the dump operation are quite adequate at the low data rate, but are becoming marginal at the high data rate.

2) The reference voltage leakage which appears at the multiplier output is not evident at the integrator output.

Figure 12 presents the results of error rate measurements. Error rates are plotted as a function of bit energy per unit noise density both for the case where the delay-lock tracking loop was operating and the case where the transmitter and receiver clocks were derived from the same oscillator. In the latter case, tracking jitter was not a factor. The data show about 1.5 to 2 dB more signal power required for a given error rate than theory predicts. The error rate with tracking is only about a half dB worse than for identical clocks, indicating that tracking jitter is not significant over the range of data taken.

The general 1.5 to 2 dB disagreement with theory is within the limits of accuracy which can be expected from a measurement of this sort. The measurements of both signal and noise power are difficult because of their broadband

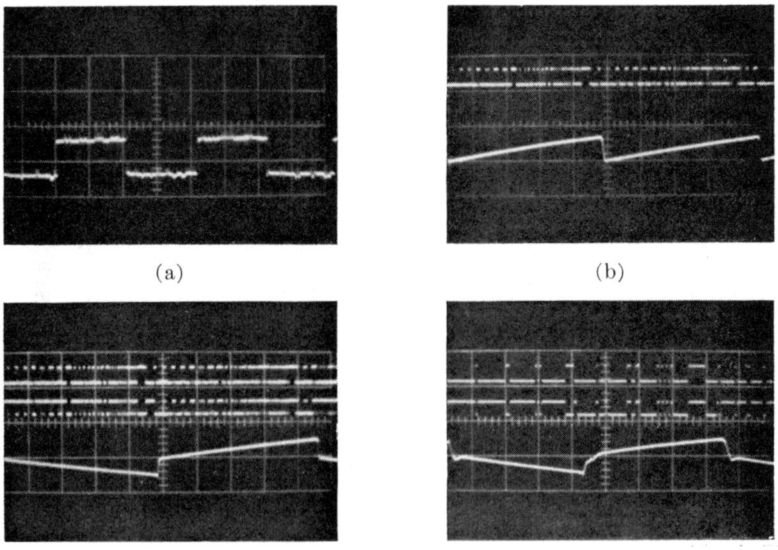

(a) (b) (c) (d)

Fig. 11. Data test circuit waveforms. (a) Multiplier output. (b) Integrator output—data *zeros*. (c) Integrator output—alternate data *zeros* and *ones*. (d) Data rate = 23.86 kHz.

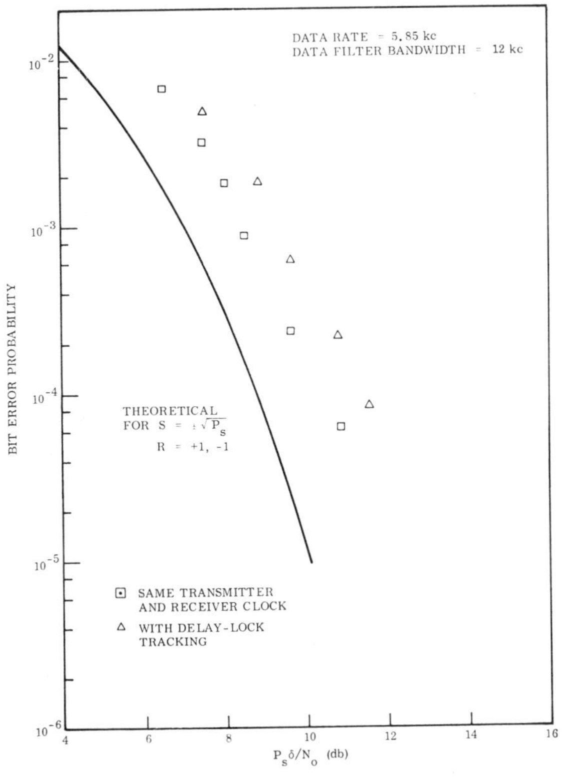


Fig. 12. Results of error rate experiments.

character and the desired white, Gaussian character of the noise is not easily obtained. Also, the circuitry is not perfect: a finite time is required for synchronized dumping, the dump is not complete, threshold circuits have some hysteresis, and so forth. Probably the most difficult circuit requirement to achieve is to prevent reference signal leakage from unduly appearing in the multiplier output. Although Fig. 11 does not include enough data bits to show the effect, it was observed that the integrated output amplitudes varied by about ±15 percent due to reference leakage. This causes additional errors.

## Conclusion

Communication using sequence inversion keying (SIK) of the pseudonoise modulation on a tracking link has been investigated. The effects on the tracking performance of the link have been examined and shown to be small. The changes to a delay-lock tracking circuit to accommodate SIK have been shown. Prediction of the theoretical error rate performance has shown it to be identical to that for coherent phase-shift keying of a sine wave. In addition, data-bit synchronization is provided.

Experimental results have been shown using a pseudonoise signal suitable for high accuracy (1 or 2 meters) range measurement with 3300 km ambiguity. Required signal power levels for given data error rates within 1.5 to 2 dB of theory have been experimentally achieved.

## Nomenclature

| *Symbol* | *Definition* |
|---|---|
| $V_{\ell_p}$ | data filter equivalent noise bandwidth |
| BW | also $B_{\ell_p}$ |
| DSK | delay shift keying |
| $f$ | frequency |
| $f_c$ | frequency of an FSR clock |
| FSK | frequency shift keying |
| FSR | feedback shift register |
| $H$ | transfer function |
| $j$ | $\sqrt{-1}$ |
| $k$ | fraction of a sequence transmitted without data |
| $n$ | number of stages in an FSR |
| $N$ | noise voltage |
| $N_o$ | single-sided noise power spectral density |
| $p$ | an integer related to the length of a data bit |

| | |
|---|---|
| $p_o$ | tracking loop undamped natural frequency |
| $P_s$ | power of the input binary signal |
| $R_1, R_2$ | reference voltages |
| $S$ | signal voltage |
| SIK | sequence inversion keying |
| SNR | signal-to-noise ratio |
| $t$ | time |
| $V_o$ | sampled data output voltage |
| $V_{on}$ | noise component of sampled data output voltage |
| $V_{os}$ | signal component of sampled data output voltage |
| $V_{oso}$ | signal component of sampled data output voltage with a *zero* transmitted |
| $V_{os1}$ | signal component of sampled data output voltage with a *one* transmitted |
| VCO | voltage controlled oscillator |
| $\delta$ | data integration time, data bit period |
| $\Delta$ | FSR clock period |
| $\epsilon$ | delay error |
| $\sigma$ | standard deviation of $V_{on}$ |
| $\sigma_T$ | standard deviation of delay error |
| $\omega$ | angular frequency |
| $(^-)$ | bar-average value. |

## References


[1] J. J. Spilker, Jr., "Delay-lock tracking of binary signals," *IEEE Trans. on Space Electronics and Telemetry*, vol. SET-9, pp. 1–8, March 1963.

[2] W. J. Gill, "A comparison of binary delay-lock tracking-loop implementations," *IEEE Trans. on Aerospace and Electronics Systems*, vol. AES-2, pp. 415–424, July 1966.

[3] R. B. Ward, "Tracking loop filter optimization study," Appendix H of "Delay-lock AROD system study, vol. 2-appendixes," LMS CEE Rept. 4-89-64-1, November 17, 1964.

[4] B. D. Martin, "The mariner planetary communication system design," *1962 Proc. Nat'l Telemetering Conf.*, pp. 1–26.

[5] W. J. Gill, "Effect ot synchronization error in the cross-correlation reception of binary pseudo-noise carrier communications," PHILCO(WDL) Palo Alto, Calif., Tech. Rept., May 20, 1965.

[6] G. F. Sage, "Serial synchronization of pseudonoise systems," *IEEE Trans. on Communication Technology*, vol. COM-12, pp. 123–127, December 1964.

[7] R. B. Ward, "Acquisition of pseudonoise signals by sequential estimation," *IEEE Trans. on Communication Technology*, vol. COM-13, pp. 475–484, December 1965.

# Air–Ground, Ground–Air Communications Using Pseudo-Noise Through a Satellite

HERMAN BLASBALG, Senior Member, IEEE
HANN F. NAJJAR, Member, IEEE
RENATO A. D'ANTONIO, Member, IEEE
IBM Center for Exploratory Studies
Rockville, Md.
RAYMOND A. HADDAD, Member, IEEE
IBM Space Systems Center
Rockville, Md.

Abstract

**An air–ground, ground–air communications system that utilizes a satellite and a central control facility is described. The double-hop pseudo-noise system advantages, including equal sharing of power, use of frequency translating repeaters, optimum multipath rejection, and acceptable power densities on the ground are discussed. The selection of code division is presented together with an analysis of signal-to-noise ratios with a varied input. Modulation schemes are discussed, pro and con, and the effective radiated power versus antenna sizes for several combinations are analyzed.**

Manuscript received June 12, 1967.
This paper was presented at the 1967 International Conference on Communications, Minneapolis, Minn., June 12–14, 1967.

## I. Introduction

In this paper, an air–ground, ground–air communication system using pseudo-noise through a satellite is presented. UHF transmissions arriving at the satellite repeater are translated up to SHF and routed through a ground based central control facility (CCF). After demodulation, processing, remultiplexing, and remodulation, the CCF retransmits the message to the satellite at SHF where the received signal is translated down to UHF and transmitted to the airborne terminal. A block diagram of such a link is shown in Fig. 1.

This double-hop pseudo-noise system has the following advantages over conventional single-hop satellite communications systems:

1) all transmitted signals take an equal share of the UHF repeater power, independent of terminal ERP;
2) a frequency translating satellite repeater is used, and signal processing in the satellite is not required;
3) airborne terminal is relatively simple;
4) airborne terminal requires minimum ERP;
5) optimum multipath rejection;
6) network traffic is inherently under control of CCF;
7) power density received at the ground is maintained at an acceptable level;
8) power density received by the satellite is maintained at a practical level.

The emphasis in this paper is on the use of code division as the optimum multiple access modulation technique for the transmission of vocoded voice messages.

A mathematical analysis is presented which obtains the signal-to-noise ratio at the output of a correlation receiver when the input is a mixture of pseudo-noise (PN) and multipath signals, and thermal noise. The optimum repeater bandwidth is obtained. A phase-lock loop pseudo-noise receiver is analyzed and a detailed block diagram is presented.

The air–ground link uses code division multiple access (CDMA). Here each terminal transmits a digital vocoded message by modulating a PN signal. The message is transmitted as a binary phase modulated signal alphabet onto a PN carrier. At the CCF, the messages are demultiplexed, demodulated, power-equalized, and finally remodulated for retransmission.

The retransmitted signal is always in digital form. In one form, the digital messages are time division multiplexed at the CCF, digitized, and modulated onto a PN carrier. In another useful form, the digital messages are code division multiplexed and retransmitted.

The pros and cons of the modulation schemes are dis-

Reprinted from *IEEE Trans. Aerosp. Electron. Syst.*, vol. AES-4, pp. 774–790, Sept. 1968.

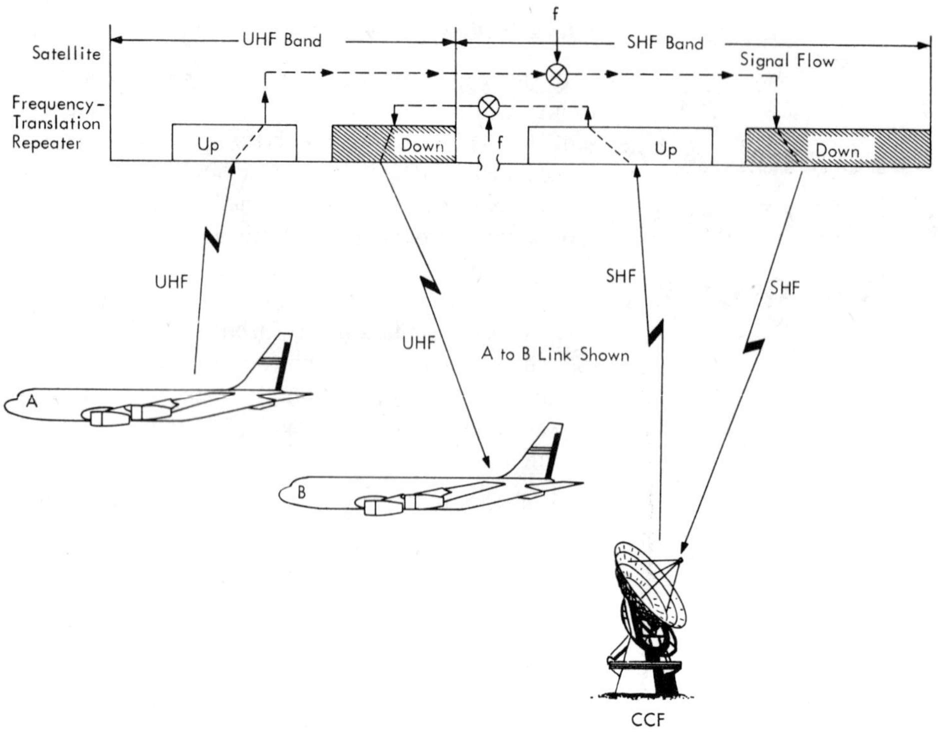


Fig. 1. Double-hop, wide-open repeater.

cussed. TDM makes optimum use of the UHF power in the satellite when the system is operating at full capacity. CDM takes advantage of the voice channel activity factor simply and naturally but suffers a 1–2 dB loss relative to TDM.

The tradeoffs between satellite ERP and satellite antenna size, and terminal ERP and satellite antenna size for several modulation schemes are presented along with sample calculations.

## II. Central Control Facility (CCF); Double-Hop Operation

Here, a small terminal satellite communication system using a wide-open linear repeater which routes all UHF signals through a large, ground based central control facility (CCF) is discussed. The UHF signals in the satellite are translated up to SHF and reradiated. These signals are received by the CCF, processed, and transmitted up to the satellite at SHF. In the satellite, the SHF signals are translated down in frequency to UHF and retransmitted to the small airborne terminal. This type of system has the advantage that the satellite repeater and the terminal are simple and that all processing is performed at the CCF. As long as the CCF link capacity is greater than the air-to-satellite capacity, operation is equivalent to processing onboard the satellite. In particular, the CCF can process out multipaths and unequal power users prior to retransmission.

Fig. 2 is an operational block diagram of the satellite system. In the diagram, code division multiple access (CDMA) is used. A terminal sends up a pseudo-noise PCM signal (i.e., PCM–PN) at UHF. Each terminal has a different PN code. The CDMA signals arriving in the satellite are translated up to SHF and repeated down to the CCF. The CCF demodulates the CDMA signals, processing out the multipaths and power variations, and the messages are then either time or code division multiplexed. The composite biphase signal modulates the SHF carrier and is transmitted back to the satellite. The satellite translates the signal down to UHF again and repeats it to the airborne terminal. Doppler correction is calculated at the CCF, and transmitted up, simplifying the operations of the airborne terminal.

The airborne terminal demultiplexes and demodulates the signal by means of coherent PSK (CPSK). In this mode, one time slot or PN code can be used to monitor channel activity and also to receive channel assignment and call up information. The CCF can therefore operate through this channel in the order wire mode.

Note that all traffic is under control of the CCF. This system can operate very easily in the push-to-talk mode where both users communicate on a single time slot or

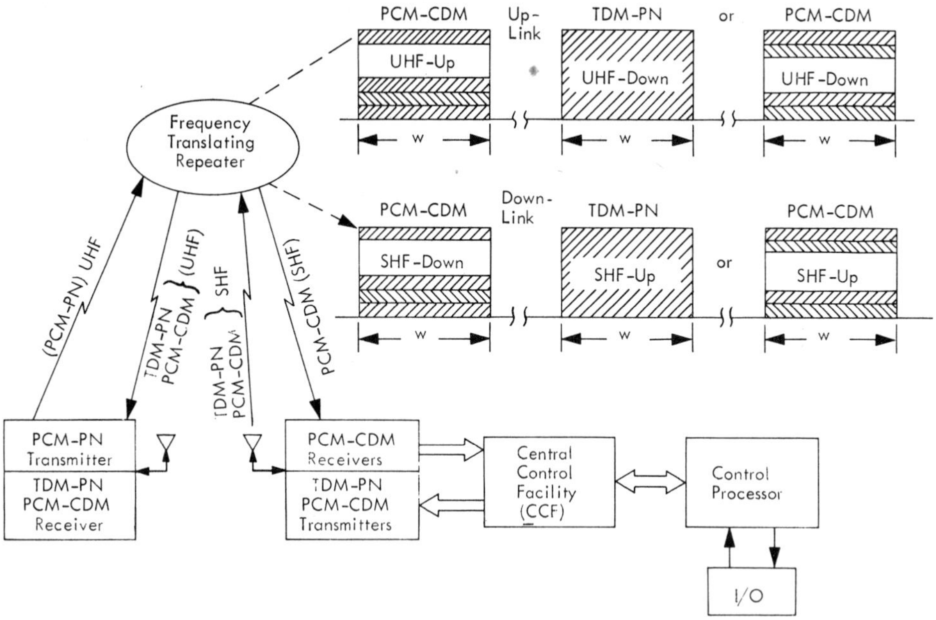


Fig. 2. Double-hop satellite repeater operating with central control facility (CCF), functional block diagram.

PN code in the down-link, which, of course, doubles the number of simultaneous talkers.

### A. Subscriber Set Transmitter [1]

A functional block diagram of the subscriber set is shown in Fig. 3. The vocoder message source biphase modulates the VCO which is also PN modulated and transmitted. The transmitted signal is PCM-PN. Clock is mixed with PN in order to perform signal tracking by means of a bandpass loop rather than a delay-lock discriminator, the former being easier to implement.

Fig. 3. PCM-PN ultra-high-frequency transmitter.

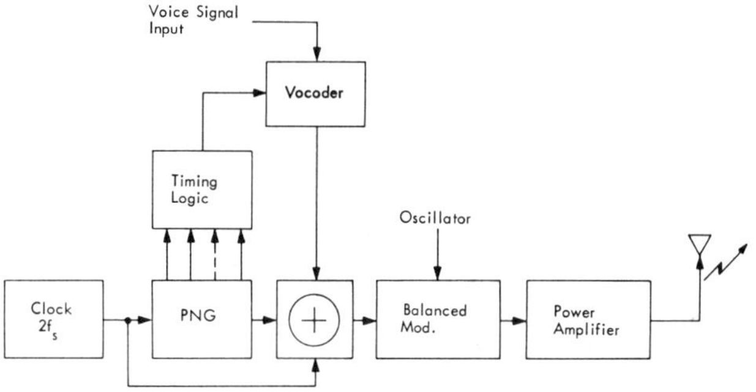


### B. CCF Receiver [1]

The CCF must demultiplex the received code division signal. It should be recognized that the CCF knows each code being received, since it assigns these to each user. Thus, once assigned, the terminal sends the PN signal and the CCF must acquire it. Each signal must be acquired and phase-locked independently; hence, a separate phase-lock loop (PLL) for each channel is required.

Fig. 4 is a typical CCF channel. There are two loops, one for tracking the RF carrier and one for tracking the PN clock. The digital data signal output is taken from the CPSK demodulator and data recovery circuits, and fed into the vocoder.

The input to the PN loop is the modulo-2 addition of clock and PN signal. This signal is fed into two mixers, one accepts PN as a reference input and the other $PN^* = PN \oplus f_s$. The output of one of the mixers is $2f_s$ and the other is $f_s$. These components are filtered and then fed into another mixer where the PN clock frequency $f_s$ is extracted. A conventional loop then tracks the PN signal.

The bandpass filters in the loop are sufficiently wide to pass the PN clock phase variations. When the reference PN signals are out of phase with the incoming signal, narrow-band noise is fed into both the RF and PN loops and, of course, neither will track under these conditions.

IBM is presently building this type of PN phase-lock demodulator for digital and analog transmissions to be used for code division multiple access (CDMA) and for pseudo-noise time division multiple access (PN-TDMA).

Fig. 5 shows a functional block diagram of the CCF multiple channel code division receiver. Each channel has a pseudo-noise PLL demodulator as shown in Fig. 4. The message outputs are processed, digitized, and then fed into the time division or code division multiplexers, whichever is the preferred scheme.

### C. CCF Multiplexers

Note that the CCF receiver is complex while the terminal transmitter is not. Thus the CCF performs the complex signal processing, acquisition, and PN tracking func-

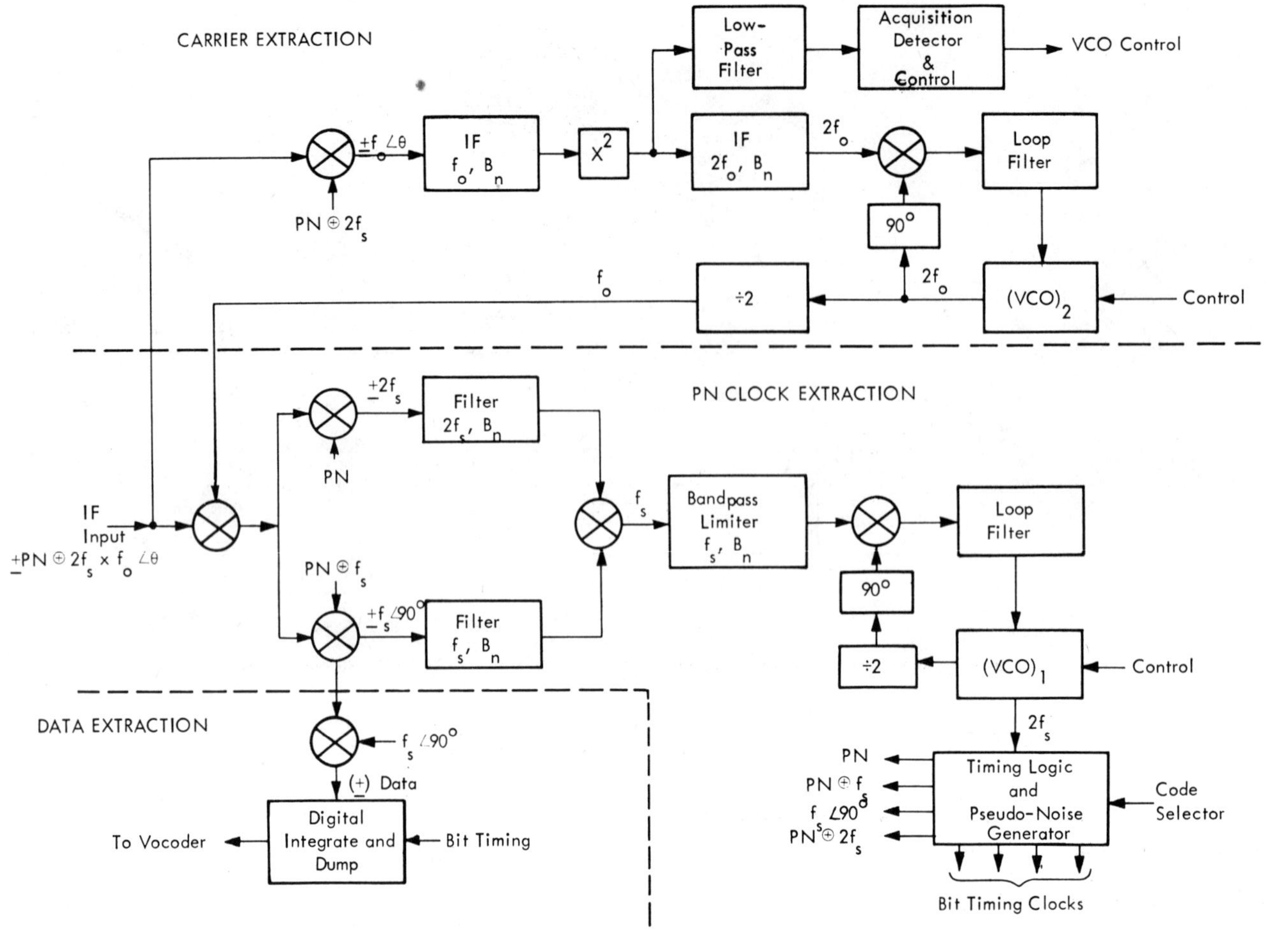


g. 4. Typical PCM-PN receiver channel of CCF (or user set).

g. 5. Code division receiver at CCF.

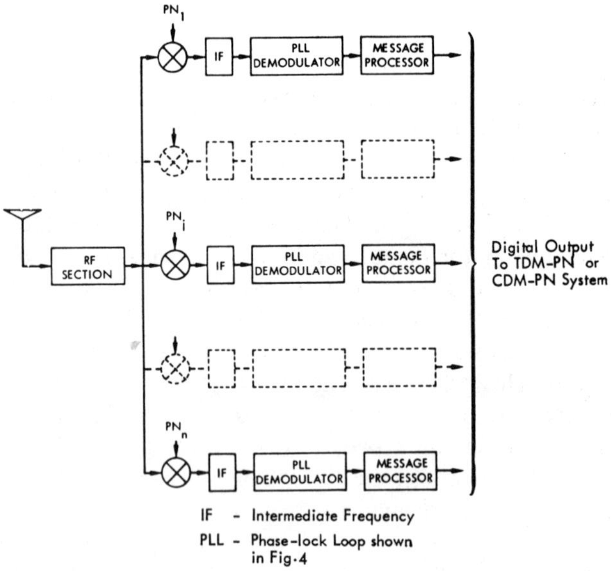

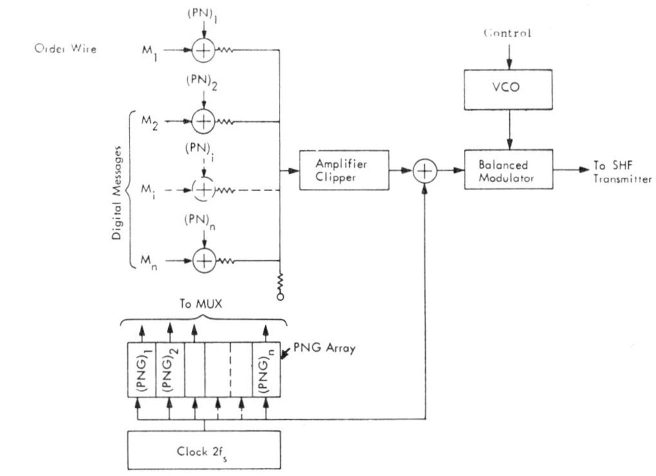


Fig. 6. CDM-PN CCF multiplexer.

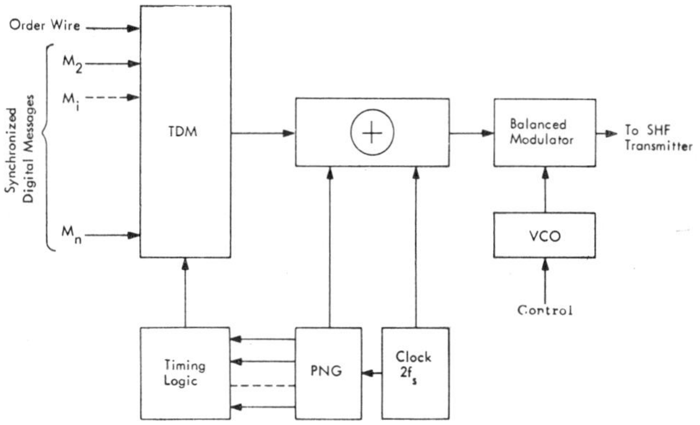


Fig. 7. TDM-PN CCF multiplexer.

tions, protecting the air-to-ground link against multipaths and against a strong signal taking an unequal share of the UHF satellite power. If we assume that the satellite–CCF and CCF–satellite link capacities exceed the total link capacity from air-to-satellite and satellite-to-air, then the CCF signal processing functions are equivalent to performing signal processing in the satellite. The complexity is, however, placed in the CCF, the satellite remaining a wide-open linear repeater. The CCF can be made into a high capacity link by using a large SHF antenna and low noise receiver. The SHF ERP in the satellite can also be made quite high by using a directional SHF antenna recognizing, however, that the cost of stabilizing the satellite will be a limiting factor on the size of the beam width that can be realized.

*Code Division Multiplexing:* Fig. 6 shows a block diagram of a code division multiplexer at the CCF. Each binary message biphase modulates a PN sequence addressed to a particular aircraft. The PN messages are added and fed into a video hard-limiter and then to a balanced modulator. This correction for Doppler is added to the data format and transmitted to the satellite at SHF. Thus, a constant envelope signal is transmitted, insuring that the peak-power limited UHF transponder in the satellite will be used efficiently. The video clipping at the multiplexer results in a 2 dB penalty.

The link from CCF to the terminal via the satellite can operate push-to-talk thereby doubling the number of users of the satellite. Here it is assumed that the UHF down-link sets the limit on the number of channels. That is, the CCF can switch a pair of talkers to time-share the same up-link channel. The system can also take full advantage of the voice channel activity factor by transmitting intermittent synchronizing information during conversation pauses, thereby reducing system activity. This can improve average performance by at least 3 dB.

*Time Division Multiplexing:* Here the received messages are multiplexed into a serial bit stream, i.e., each user is assigned a time slot while on the air. Since the messages are digital, then for TDM, stable clocks and possibly large buffers at the CCF may be required. The TDM system, from CCF to the satellite, is very attractive since it makes efficient use of the UHF transponder power. Performance is equivalent to TDMA without the difficulty of synchronizing the entire network.

Fig. 7 is a block diagram of the TDM-PN multiplexer at the CCF. The time division multiplexed digital messages are combined with a PN signal which recycles at the frame rate. The PN clock and digital messages are synchronized; when the terminal receiver is locked up, all synchronization information for recovering the digital messages is available. Thus, all the sideband power is used for message recovery and for extracting sync by means of signal processing at the terminal.

### III. Terminal Receiver

The terminal receivers for recovering CDM-PN and TDM-PN are essentially the same. In the former, the intended receiver locks to its PN signal while in the latter, all receivers lock to the same PN signal. Once locked, the receiver can select whichever time slot is meant for it.

The signal processing portion of the terminal receiver is identical to the block diagram shown in Fig. 4 with the appropriate timing suitable for TDM and CDM.

Both CDM and TDM make efficient use of the UHF transponder power. All timing is extracted from the PN signal, and as a result full sideband power is available for the data and for synchronization. In addition selective fading is eliminated provided the path delay exceeds a pseudo-noise bit duration. By processing out the multipaths at the CCF, UHF transponder power is not wasted on this type of interference; that is, all the UHF transponder power goes into the messages.

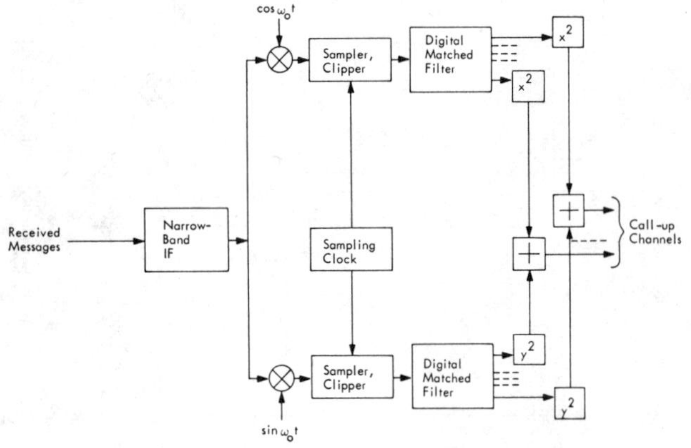


Fig. 8. RANSAC call-up receiver at CCF.

## IV. Call-Up Channel Monitoring and Assignment

In this system, all messages must be routed through the CCF. Thus the CCF accepts calls, transmits binary signals, assigns channels, and establishes connections and monitors traffic so as not to allow the network to overload. These functions are performed in addition to demultiplexing, demodulation, remodulation, and retransmission which optimize the overall communication channel efficiency.

Call-up is a low-data-rate short-duration asynchronous signaling procedure and can therefore be made very reliable. The call-up channel from terminal to CCF uses a random access noise-like signal address (RANSAC) technique developed by IBM just for such a purpose [2]. A call-up channel is defined as a PN-signal address which is used to transmit the called and calling parties' phone numbers. Of course, all parties in the network continuously monitor the order-wire channel to determine network and called party status. Thus, when a call is received, the CCF will assign a channel to the called and calling parties via the order wire. A channel is assigned by specifying the time slot which will be used for message reception. In addition, each party is assigned a distinct PN sequence for use in the terminal to CCF link. When this assignment is made, each party transmits the PN signal to the CCF. When the CCF acquires the signal, a code is transmitted via the assigned time slot indicating that message transmission can commence.

Fig. 8 is a block diagram of the RANSAC receiver [2]. The transmitter is essentially the same as Fig. 3 except that call-up data are transmitted at a much slower rate. The call-up message lies in the same band as the voice message, although it has a much narrower bandwidth. The narrow-band PN sequence is fed into a narrow-band IF which filters out a substantial portion of the broad-band PN signal energy. For example, if the ratio of message PNG rate to call-up PNG rate is 1000 to 1, then the broad-band signal is suppressed by 30 dB. This channel is therefore clear of message signal interference. Since the call-up channel has processing gain, several simultaneous calls can be accepted on different channels, at least. The output of the IF is quadrature demodulated, sampled, and clipped. This binary sequence is then fed into a digital matched filter (DMF), i.e., a digital tapped delay line, which drives an array of resistance matrices. A matrix of resistors is the linear weighting network, which is matched to a particular PN code. The calling party sends a burst of PN code followed by a digital message representing the called and calling parties' addresses. Each message "one" is transmitted as a PN code burst, and a "zero" by the absence of the code word. The initial code burst alerts the CCF to the fact that a call is coming in and generates sync information for the message bits that follow.

## V. Mathematical Analysis and System Design

### A. Signal-to-Noise Ratio Calculations and System Optimization

In the Appendix it is shown that the signal-to-noise ratio at the output of a correlation receiver when the input consists of a mixture of PN signals, discrete multipaths, and thermal noise is given by

$$\eta_i^2 = \frac{\dfrac{P_R T}{N_0}\left(\dfrac{P_i}{P_t}\right)}{\dfrac{P_R}{BN_0}\left(a + \dfrac{BN_w}{P_t} + \dfrac{P_t - P_i}{P_t}\right) + \left(1 + b\dfrac{P_R}{BN_0}\right)\left(1 + a + \dfrac{BN_w}{P_t}\right)} \tag{1}$$

where

$\eta_i^2$ = signal-to-noise ratio at the output of the $i$th receiver,

$P_R$ = power from satellite received by terminal,

$N_0$ = effective noise power density of terminal receiver,

$T$ = integration time for a received waveform,

$P_i$ = power received by satellite from $i$th terminal

$P_t = \sum_{i=1}^{k}, P_i$ = power received by satellite from all terminals

$B$ = PN signal bandwidth,

$N_w$ = effective noise power density of satellite receiver,

$a = J_w/P_t$ = ratio of multipath power to signal power at satellite receiver ($0 \leq a \leq 1$),

$b = J_0/P_R$ = ratio of multipath power to signal power at terminal receiver ($0 \leq b \leq 1$).

The RF bandwidth which maximizes the signal-to-noise ratio is

$$B = \left[\left(\frac{P_R}{N_0}\frac{P_t}{N_w}\right)((1+a)(1+b) - P_i/P_t)\right]^{1/2}. \qquad (2a)$$

Also,

$$B_0 = \left[\left(\frac{P_R^2}{N_0 N_w}\right)(1+a)(1+b)\right]^{1/2} \quad \begin{array}{l} P_R = P_t \\ P_i/P_t \ll 1. \end{array} \qquad (2b)$$

The optimum signal-to-noise ratio is

$$\eta_{i0}^2 = \frac{\dfrac{P_R T}{N_0}\left(\dfrac{P_i}{P_t}\right)}{1 + a + 2\left(\dfrac{P_R}{N_0}\dfrac{N_w}{P_t}\right)^{1/2}((1+a)(1+b) - P_i/P_t)^{1/2} + \dfrac{P_R}{N_0}\dfrac{N_w}{P_t}(1+b)} \qquad (3a)$$

$$= \frac{\dfrac{P_i T}{N_0}}{(1+a)\left[1 + \left(\dfrac{N_w}{N_0}\right)^{1/2}\left(\dfrac{1+b}{1+a}\right)^{1/2}\right]^2} \quad \begin{array}{l} P_R = P_t \\ P_i/P_t \ll 1. \end{array} \qquad (3b)$$

air-to-ground link which operates UHF air-to-satellite, and SHF satellite-to-ground, this assumption is also reasonable since the SHF power in the satellite is substantially less than the UHF power although the antenna gains in the SHF link are substantially greater. However, a large antenna in the satellite at SHF will require a complex stabilization system in order to avoid a pointing problem which will complicate the system substantially and could make the CCF mode of questionable value. Hence, we assume $P_R/P_t = 1$. This implies that the SHF link adds very little complexity to the satellite, although clearly we are willing to make the CCF reasonably complex.

The ratio of (1) and (3), under the assumption that $P_i/P_t \ll 1$, is

$$\left(\frac{\eta}{\eta_0}\right)^2 = \frac{1 + a + 2\left(\dfrac{P_R}{N_0}\dfrac{N_w}{P_t}\right)^{1/2}((1+a)(1+b))^{1/2} + \dfrac{P_R}{N_0}\dfrac{N_w}{P_t}(1+b)}{\left(1 + a + \dfrac{BN_w}{P_t}\right)\left(1 + \dfrac{P_R}{BN_0}(1+b)\right)}. \qquad (4)$$

Thus, when $P_t = P_R$,

$$\left(\frac{\eta}{\eta_0}\right)^2 = \frac{(1+a)\left[1 + \left(\dfrac{N_w}{N_0}\right)^{1/2}\left(\dfrac{1+b}{1+a}\right)^{1/2}\right]^2}{1 + a + \dfrac{P_R}{BN_0}(1+a)(1+b) + \dfrac{BN_w}{P_R} + \dfrac{N_w}{N_0}(1+b)}. \qquad (5)$$

Since $P_i/P_t \ll 1$ in all applications of interest, the bandwidth is for all practical purposes independent of the individual terminal power received by the satellite. The optimum signal-to-noise ratio is, for all practical purposes, directly proportional to the terminal power received by the satellite, as expected.

An important special case when small terminals are involved is to assume that the total power received by the satellite equals the total power received by the terminal. If we assume terminals having zero dB antenna gain at UHF, then this assumption implies that the total power on the ground equals the power in the satellite. For an

By interpreting the symbols correctly (5) can be used for the direct UHF–UHF link and for the UHF–SHF performance calculations.

We will now specialize (5) for the UHF–SHF and SHF–UHF and UHF–UHF links. We will assume a worst multipath situation, i.e., $a=1$, $b=1$.

*Case 1*—UHF–SHF; $a=1$, $b=0$:

$$\left(\frac{\eta}{\eta_0}\right)^2_{us} = \frac{\left[1 + \left(\dfrac{N_w}{2N_0}\right)^{1/2}\right]^2}{1 + \dfrac{P_R}{BN_0} + \frac{1}{2}\left(\dfrac{BN_w}{P_R} + \dfrac{N_w}{N_0}\right)}. \qquad (6)$$

When $N_w = 20N_0$, which is reasonable for this link,

$$\left(\frac{\eta}{\eta_0}\right)^2_{us} = 34.8 \frac{\rho}{\rho^2 + 22\rho + 40} \tag{7a}$$

where

$$\rho = \frac{BN_w}{P_R} = \frac{BN_w}{P_t} \tag{7b}$$

and $P_R$ is the SHF power received by the CCF which was assumed equal to the total UHF power received by the satellite.

The maximum of (7a), i.e., $(\eta/\eta_0)^2 = 1$, occurs when

$$\rho_0 = \sqrt{40}. \tag{7c}$$

From (3) and (7),

$$\eta_0^2 = 0.58 \left(\frac{PT}{N_w}\right) \tag{7d}$$

and from (7a),

$$\eta^2 = \left(\frac{20\rho}{\rho^2 + 22\rho + 40}\right)\frac{PT}{N_w} = \left(\frac{PT}{N_w}\right) D \tag{7e}$$

where

$$D = \frac{20\rho}{\rho^2 + 22\rho + 40} \tag{7f}$$

is the degradation from ideal up-link limited performance.

For this special case the optimum bandwidth is given by

$$B_0 = \sqrt{20}\frac{P_R}{N_w} = \sqrt{20}\frac{P_t}{N_w}. \tag{7g}$$

*Case 2—SHF–UHF Link; $a=0$, $b=1$*: The CCF-to-air link is assumed to be down-link or UHF power limited. The SHF up-link is assumed to be free of multipaths and having enough ERP to overcome satellite receiver noise. If TDM is used then the mutual interference is zero, and if code division is used at the CCF the TDM signal-to-noise ratio is reduced by $2/\pi$ (i.e., 2 dB). Thus for TDM with down-link multipaths at UHF,

$$\eta^2_{TDM} = \frac{P_R T}{KN_0(1 + P_R/BN_0)} \tag{8}$$

and for code division,

$$\eta^2_{CDM} = \frac{2}{\pi}\eta^2_{TDM} \tag{9}$$

where $K$ = number of channels and the other symbols refer to the UHF down-link. From (8) and (7b),

$$\eta^2_{TDM} = \frac{P_R T}{KN_0}\left(\frac{\rho}{\rho + N_w/N_0}\right). \tag{10}$$

For the UHF links it is reasonable to assume that if $N_w = N_0$, then

$$\eta^2_{TDM} = \frac{P_R T}{KN_0}\left(\frac{\rho}{1+\rho}\right) \tag{11a}$$

where

$$D = \frac{\rho}{1+\rho} \tag{11b}$$

is the degradation from ideal performance. When $\rho = \sqrt{40}$,

$$\eta^2_{TDM} = 0.86 \frac{P_R T}{KN_0}. \tag{11c}$$

By comparing (7d) with (11c), it is seen that performance is limited by the UHF–SHF link. The performance of the UHF–SHF link and the SHF–UHF link is, however, within 1.50 dB of each other.

*Case 3*—UHF–UHF; $a=1$, $b=1$: For direct air–air communications via a satellite, we have, from (5),

$$\left(\frac{\eta}{\eta_0}\right)^2 = \frac{\left[1 + \left(\frac{N_w}{N_0}\right)^{1/2}\right]^2}{1 + 2\frac{P_R}{BN_0} + \frac{1}{2}\frac{BN_w}{P_R} + \frac{N_w}{N_0}} \tag{12}$$

where $P_R$ is the UHF power received by the terminal and $P_R = P_t$.

If we assume $N_w = N_0$, then

$$\left(\frac{\eta}{\eta_0}\right)^2 = \frac{8\rho}{(\rho+2)^2}. \tag{13}$$

The maximum occurs when $\rho_0 = 2$.

The bandwidth is obtained from (2) as

$$B_0 = 2\frac{P_R}{N_0} = 2\frac{P_t}{N_w}. \tag{14}$$

From (3) and (13) we obtain the signal-to-noise ratio at the terminal receiver,

$$\eta^2 = \frac{PT}{N_w} D \tag{15a}$$

where

$$D = \frac{\rho}{(\rho+2)^2} \tag{15b}$$

is the degradation from ideal performance, and

$$\rho = \frac{BN_w}{P_R} \tag{15c}$$

where $P_R$ is the UHF power received by the terminal.

When $\rho_0 = 2$ (15a) becomes

$$\eta_0^2 = \frac{PT}{8N_w}. \tag{16}$$

Comparing the down-link performance of the double-hop system with the single-hop UHF–UHF system, for the same UHF channel parameters, shows that the former is superior by 8.30 dB. This is a substantial improvement, particularly since the SHF link was assumed unsophisticated although a good CCF receiver was selected. The optimum satellite bandwidth for the double-hop system

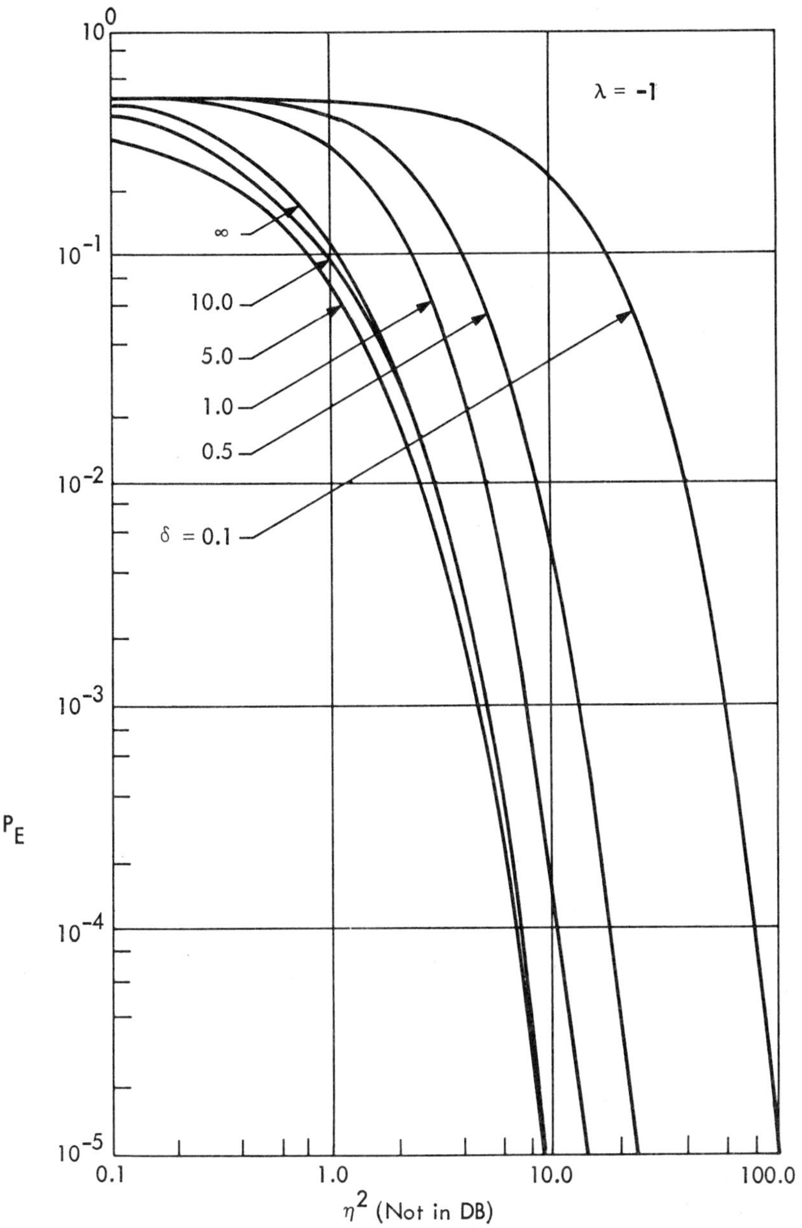


Fig. 9. Error probability curves for PN modem used in system.

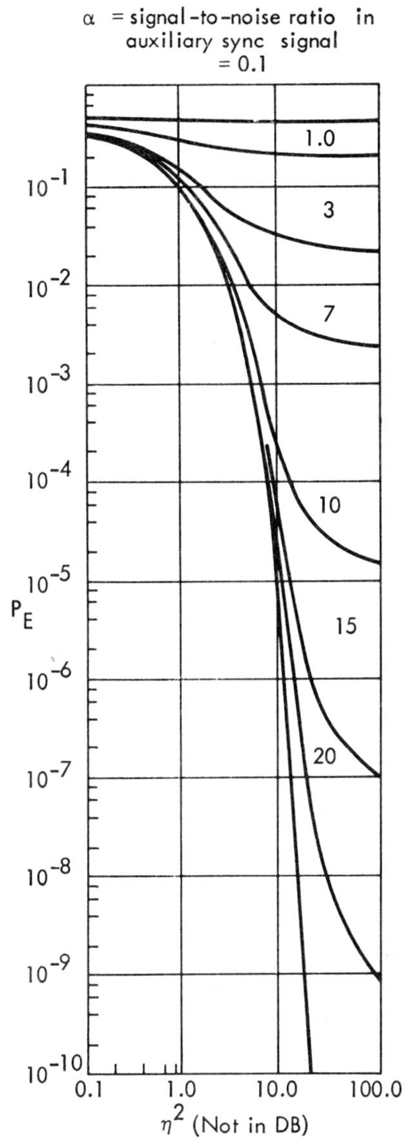


Fig. 10. Error probability for a system which uses an auxiliary carrier.

is twice as large as for the single-hop system. The double-hop system requires 6.70 dB less terminal power than the single-hop system.

*Case 4*—UHF–SHF; $a=b=0$: This is double-hop communications without the presence of multipaths. From (3), when $P_R=P_t$,

$$\eta_0{}^2 = \frac{PT/N_0}{[1+[N_w/N_0]^{1/2}]^2}\cdot \tag{17}$$

When $N_w=20N_0$,

$$\eta_0{}^2 = 0.67\frac{PT}{N_w}\cdot \tag{18}$$

The performance is only 0.60 dB better without multipaths than with multipaths. The double-hop system does effectively suppress multipaths. The effect of power fluctuations in the up-link is also processed-out by the CCF since the signal suppression parameters depend on the total power and not on the individual power. The optimum bandwidth (2) is, for all practical purposes, also dependent only on the total power.

*Case 5*—UHF–UHF; $a=b=0$: Here, we can use (17) and let $N_w=N_0$. Then

$$\eta_0{}^2 = \frac{PT}{4N_w}\cdot \tag{19}$$

Thus, multipaths degrade performance by 3 dB. Even without multipaths performance is 6 dB worse than ideal.

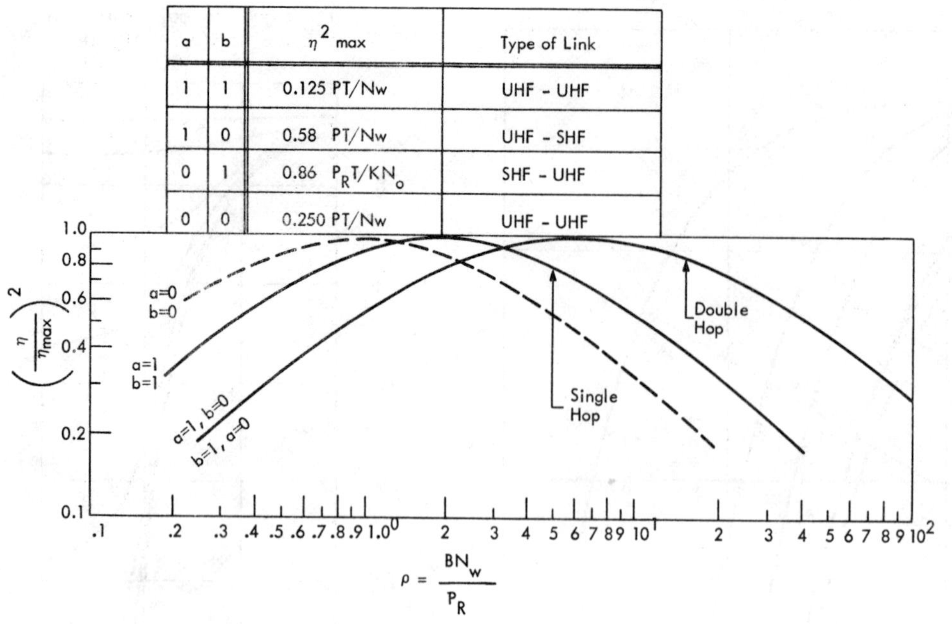


**Fig. 11. Signal-to-noise ratio versus RF bandwidth.**

From (2) the RF bandwidth is

$$B_0 = \frac{P_R}{N_0} = \frac{P_t}{N_w} \cdot \tag{20}$$

The 6 dB degradation from ideal performance is caused by the fact that the signal-to-noise ratio in the satellite receiver and in the terminal receiver is unity. There is a loss of 3 dB due to satellite receiver noise robbing half the repeater power and an additional 3 dB loss due to clutter generated by the PN signals. In order to reduce the clutter, it is necessary to widen the RF bandwidth so that $P_R/BN_0 \ll 1$, and to reduce the degradation caused by satellite receiver noise it is essential to increase the ERP of the terminals. The small airborne terminals are limited in up-link power and hence suffer a clutter penalty as well as a power penalty.

The CCF permits the use of a broad-band link since it has a link capacity which is greater than the up-link capacity. This operation is therefore equivalent to placing the CCF functions in the satellite receiver where the clutter would be processed out. The regenerated signal, free of thermal noise and clutter, is used in the down-link where now all the repeater power goes into the message signal.

*Case 6*—UHF–SHF; $a=1$, $b=0$, $P_R/P_t \gg 1$: Here we assume that the power received by the CCF is substantially greater than that received at UHF by the satellite receiver. From (3a),

$$\eta_0^2 = \frac{PT}{N_w(1+b)} \cdot \tag{21a}$$

When $b=0$,

$$\eta_0^2 = \frac{PT}{N_w} \cdot \tag{21b}$$

Comparing (18) and (21b) shows that $P_R \gg P_t$ gives almost the same performance as $P_R=P_t$ and $N_w=20N_0$. This indicates that selecting a good receiver at the CCF is sufficient to achieve a good SHF satellite–ground link.

### B. Error Probabilities [3]

Fig. 9 shows curves which describe the performance of the PN phase-lock loop digital receiver shown in Fig. 4. Fig. 10 shows the performance of a receiver which extracts a transmitted reference signal for performing coherent detection. The latter is less efficient since a portion of the available power is used for sync while in the former case all available power is put into the data and sync signal sidebands. Fig. 10 shows that no matter how much power is put into the data channel, performance is limited ultimately by jitter in the IF phase tracking loop.

### C. Degradation Caused by Suboptimum Bandwidth

The curves in Fig. 11 show how the signal-to-noise ratio degrades when the RF bandwidth is suboptimum. The double-hop system degrades about 1 dB if the RF bandwidth is reduced by a factor of two from its optimum value. A 3 dB loss is suffered if the up-link signal-to-noise ratio is unity, i.e., when $B=P_R/N_w$. At this point, double-hop operation is still 3 dB better than single-hop operation with multipaths.

It is emphasized that the RF bandwidth depends on the total average power received by the satellite and not on the power received from each terminal and as a result the bandwidth can be optimized for the case when the system is fully loaded and operating under maximum multipath degradation. Performance when operating below capacity and under improved propagation conditions will always be superior to the full capacity operation case.

Since the error probability curves depend exponentially on the signal-to-noise ratio and hence on $\rho$ (7), (11), and (15), small changes in $\rho$ will cause rapid changes in error probability. Ultimate performance is therefore a critical function of $\rho$.

## VI. System Performance and Comparisons

A very important characteristic for trade-off analysis at UHF is the satellite ERP-versus-satellite antenna size with weight as a parameter, shown in Fig. 12. This characteristic also influences the ground terminal transmitter power since the satellite antenna size is related to the performance of the up-link, particularly for small aircraft terminals. For small antenna sizes, a large amount of RF transmitter power is required in the satellite and, hence, the raw solar power must be large, which causes the satellite weight to be high. If the weight is held fixed, the RF power must be maintained sufficiently small; and hence the ERP is small.

The same ERP (Fig. 12) can be obtained by using a larger diameter antenna. At first, it may appear strange to observe that the increased antenna size does not increase the ERP at the specified weight. Upon reflection, it is recognized that the large array increases the weight of the satellite significantly more than the small antenna. This weight increase requires a decrease in the size of the solar cells; hence a corresponding decrease in the raw power of satellite which in turn causes a significant reduction in the RF power available to drive the antenna. This characteristic can be used for comparing various modulation schemes.

Also shown in Fig. 12 are curves of the terminal ERP-versus-antenna size. Here, the parameter is a given modulation scheme.

One operational limitation of the narrow-beam antenna is that only limited coverage is achieved and accurate stabilization is required. On the other hand, it has the advantage of placing a large amount of ERP in a localized region of interest. In some applications it may be operationally feasible to switch the beam to areas of interest. In this case full ERP is made available to each area on a time-shared basis.

### A. Budget Allotment for UHF Down-Link

| | |
|---|---|
| Effective noise-power density | $N_0 = -199.5$ dB/Hz |
| Error probability | $P_E = 10^{-3}$ |
| Signal-to-noise ratio per bit | $\eta^2 = 6.82$ dB |
| Carrier frequency | $f_c = 4 \times 10^8$ Hz |
| Total link losses at 400 MHz | $L_0 = 187$ dB |
| Number of simplex voice channels | $K = 32$ (15 dB) |
| Vocoder bit rate | $H = 2400$ bit/s (33.75 dB/Hz) |
| Terminal receiving antenna gain | $G_r = 0$ dB. |

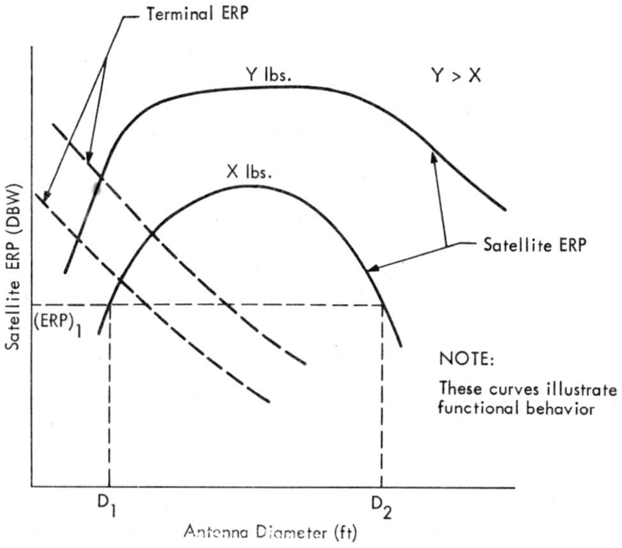


Fig. 12. Satellite and terminal ERP versus satellite antenna size for a given payload weight.

*Satellite ERP for Double-Hop System-UHF Down-Link:* The received power assuming a zero gain receiving antenna is

$$P_R = (\mathrm{ERP})_s - L_0 \tag{22}$$

where (11c) is used for the signal-to-noise ratio for TDM and hence for $P_R$. Then, from (22), and (11c) and from the budget allotment,

$$(\mathrm{ERP}_s) = 43.70 \text{ DBW} \rightarrow \text{TDM}. \tag{23}$$

For CDM the degradation is 2 dB, hence

$$(\mathrm{ERP})_s = 45.70 \text{ DBW} \rightarrow \text{CDM}. \tag{24}$$

If we now assume a 25 percent voice channel activity factor for CDM, then

$$(\mathrm{ERP})_s = 39.70 \text{ DBW} \rightarrow \text{CDM}. \tag{25}$$

The fact that there are pauses in speech, particularly when a push-to-talk system is used, should result in a 6 dB power improvement since on the average the repeater is only loaded 25 percent of the time. CDM takes instantaneous advantage of this fact while TDM does not. The CDM system, therefore, has 4 dB more margin than the TDM down-link.

*Single-Hop System*—UHF–UHF: From (16), the single-hop UHF–UHF system is approximately 8.30 dB worse than the double-hop TDM system, or

$$(\mathrm{ERP})_s = 52 \text{ dB}. \tag{26a}$$

Hard-limiting would increase this by about 1 dB. If we assume a 6 dB activity factor improvement, then

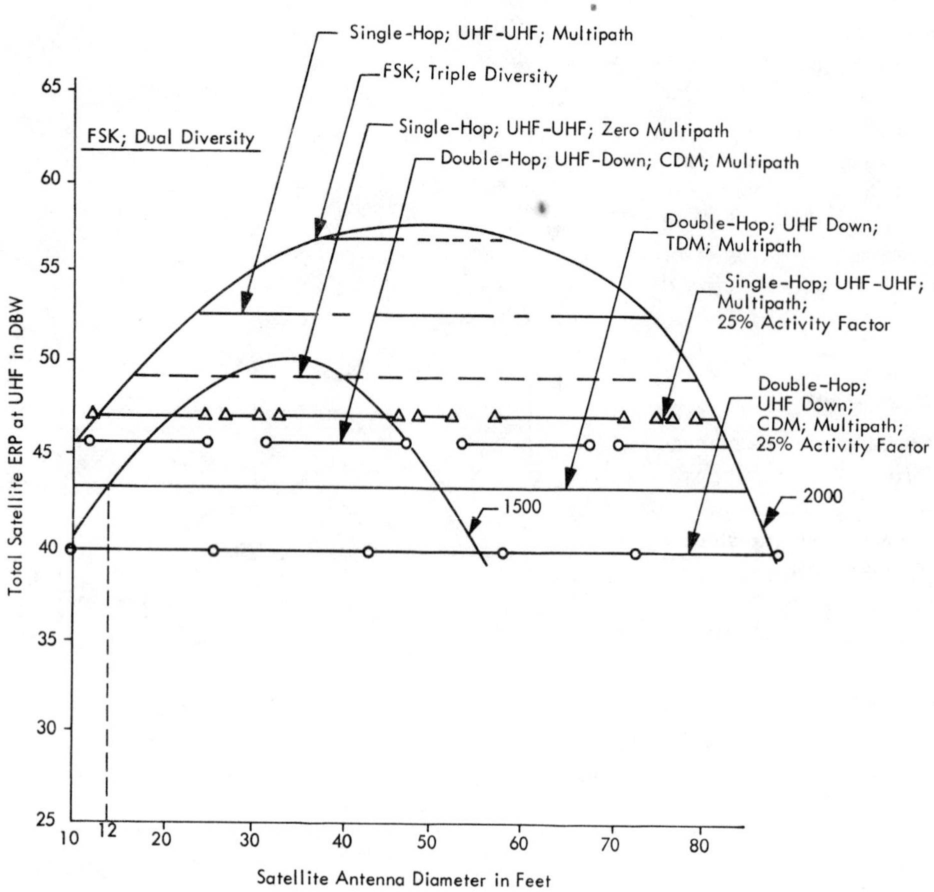


**Fig. 13.** Satellite-to-air performance characteristics.

$$(\text{ERP})_s = 47 \text{ dB}. \tag{26b}$$

The TDM double-hop system is therefore only 3.30 dB better, although the CDM system is over 7 dB better.

Fig. 13 shows lines of constant satellite ERP versus antenna diameter for the various system configurations considered. If a 1500-lb satellite is used, then all systems are admissible whose ERP and antenna diameters are in a region below the cap. All those systems which are above the cap will not "fly" since a sufficient amount of ERP cannot be achieved to support 32 vocoded channels. All PN systems can operate effectively with a 2000-lb satellite.

In Fig. 13 we also show the performance of FSK with diversity [4], i.e., a non-PN system. A 2000-lb satellite can support 32 vocoded voice FSK channels with triple diversity but only with 40- to 60-foot satellite antennas. The dual diversity FSK system will not fly.

The preferred system is, clearly, the double-hop system. The double-hop system will accommodate 32 channels of vocoded voice with various antenna sizes. In particular, the system will work with an antenna that covers the earth's disk as well as with a highly directional antenna. However, the TDM system does not provide sufficient margin for full-earth coverage. By using a bi-orthogonal alphabet of 16 levels, a 2-dB margin can be achieved. Since PN is used, there is adequate RF bandwidth to accommodate a 16 level bi-orthogonal alphabet [5].

The CDM system achieves sufficient margin provided a 6-dB activity factor improvement is assumed. The margin is therefore statistical and its validity can only be checked operationally.

It would appear that the preferred system is TDM since its performance can be safely predicted. Of course, the heavier satellite will allow full earth-disk coverage with approximately 4-dB margin.

### B. Terminal Transmitter Power

For a zero dB terminal antenna gain, the transmitter power is

$$P = P_{rs} + L_0 - G_{rs} \tag{27}$$

where

$G_{rs}$ = satellite antenna gain
$P_{rs}$ = power received by the satellite.

*Double-Hop System:* From (7d),

$$P_{rs} = \frac{\eta^2 H N_w}{0.58}. \tag{28}$$

Using the same budget for the UHF up-link as for the down-link, we have, from (27) and (28),

$$P = 30.20 - G_{rs}. \tag{29}$$

Equation (29) is graphed in Fig. 14. As the satellite antenna size increases the terminal power requirements are reduced monotonically. Even for a 10-foot diameter satellite antenna the terminal power is only 10 watts for double-hop operation and 100 watts for direct single-hop transmission. (When direct transmission is used the up-link ERP per channel is identical to the down-link ERP per channel.)

### C. Bandwidth Requirements

The double-hop system which uses TDM in the down-link has a different bandwidth requirement for the UHF–SHF up-link and for the SHF–UHF down-link. In practice, it is desirable to take advantage of this difference particularly since the frequency band allocated for the down-link is likely to be narrower than for the up-link. The up-link bandwidth is selected to minimize degradation caused by clutter and thermal noise. On the other hand, the down-link is clutter-free since TDM is used. The bandwidth is here determined by the data rate and the multipath rejection requirements. For example, a $\frac{1}{2}$-MHz PN bandwidth will completely reject paths separated by 2 $\mu$s or more. We will now calculate the up- and down-link bandwidth requirements for the double-hop system using the system design parameters which we have specified.

The bandwidth for the UHF to SHF link is obtained from (7d) and (7g):

$$B_0 = \sqrt{20}\,\frac{P_R}{N_0} = 7.70(\eta^2\,\mathrm{KH}). \tag{30}$$

Substituting in (30), $\eta^2 = 4.81$, $K = 32$, $H = 2400$ gives

$$B_0 = 2.84 \times 10^6 \text{ Hz}. \tag{31}$$

For the modem which we have proposed to use the actual bandwidth used will be twice the PN bandwidth. Therefore, $2B_0 = 5.68 \times 10^6$ Hz. The processing gain for a 2400-bit message is

$$B_0 T = 1180. \tag{32}$$

The SHF–UHF link uses TDM. The TDM link bandwidth is proportional to the total data rate and to the number of PN bits per message bit. Assume that the minimum path delay resolution is specified as $2 \times 10^6$ seconds. Then the PN bandwidth is

$$B = 0.50 \text{ MHz} \tag{33}$$

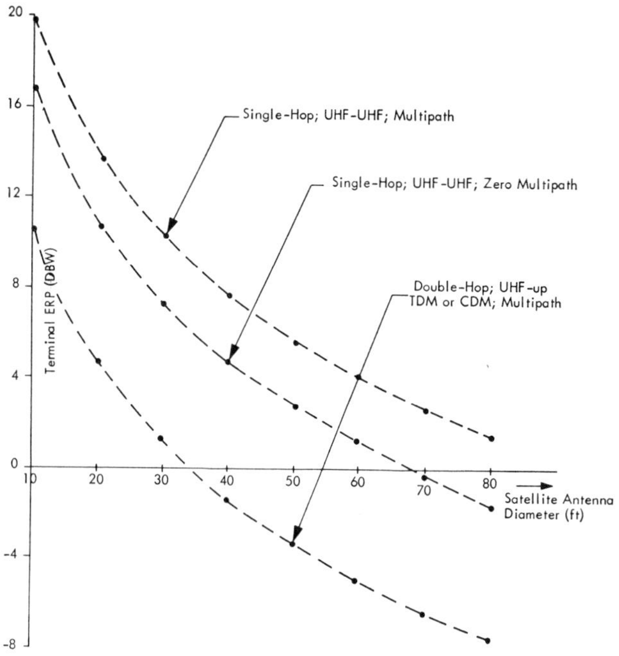


Fig. 14. Terminal ERP versus satellite antenna diameter.

and the processing gain per bit is

$$BT = 7.0. \tag{34}$$

Again for the modem, which we use, the actual RF band is doubled; therefore

$$2B = 10^6 \text{ Hz}. \tag{35}$$

Let us compare the bandwidth of the PN system to a frequency division system using binary FSK with triple diversity for each channel. Assume that the bandwidth for a single FSK channel is $3H$, where $H$ is the bit rate. Then, for triple diversity the band is $9H$. In addition, it seems reasonable to allow a guardband $3H$ cycles wide between adjacently transmitted channels. The overall FSK bandwidth is

$$B_{\mathrm{FSK}} = 12HK = 0.92 \times 10^6 \text{ Hz}. \tag{36}$$

Thus the PN down-link has essentially the same RF band as FSK with triple diversity. To some this may be a surprising result, since extremely wide bandwidth is associated with PN systems. However, any system which rejects multipaths by signal processing (rather than space diversity) must expand bandwidth. The PN system is much more efficient since multipath rejection is performed predetection; for example, coherently rather than incoherently.

### D. Power Density Receiver on the Ground

For radio frequency interference (RFI) purposes the power density received on the ground must be calculated.

TABLE I

Design Parameters For Several Systems

| System Type / Design System Parameters | ERP of Satellite (dBW) | ERP of Terminal (dBW) | RF Bandwidth (MHz) | | Power Density on Ground (dBW in 4 kHz band) | Power Density on Ground To Receiver Noise Density Ratio (dB) |
|---|---|---|---|---|---|---|
| | | | up | down | | |
| Double-Hop PN (TDM-PN Down) | 43.7 | 10.3 | 5.68 | 1.00 | −179.0 | −15.0 |
| Double-Hop PN (CDM-PN Down) | 45.7 | 10.3 | 5.68 | 5.68 | −184.8 | −18.5 |
| Single-Hop PN | 52.0 | 20.0 | 6.00 | 6.00 | −179.0 | −15.0 |
| FSK Triple Diversity | 56.9 | 23.9 | 0.92 | 0.92 | −165.0 | − 1.8 |

The power received on the ground from the PN system is −143.3 BW spread over a 1-MHz band. The power received in a 4 kHz band is therefore

$$P_{4\ \mathrm{kHz}} = -179\ \mathrm{DBW}. \tag{37}$$

Thus the interference-to-receiver temperature noise power ratio is

$$P_{4\ \mathrm{kHz}} - N_{4\ \mathrm{kHz}} = -15\ \mathrm{DBW}. \tag{38}$$

This shows that the additional noise generated by the satellite in terrestrial AM receivers is negligible. Equally important, the PN interference is not intermodulation distortion but more like thermal noise, which is preferred.

For FSK with triple diversity, the power received in a 4 kHz ground receiver is

$$P_{4\ \mathrm{kHz}} = -165.80\ \mathrm{DBW}. \tag{39}$$

Since FSK requires about 13.2 dB more ERP in the satellite than the TDM–PN and the same bandwidth, this result is expected. For FSK the margin below thermal noise is only 1.8 dB. The interference is now comparable to the receiver noise temperature and will therefore degrade AM performance by at least 1.2 dB. The degradation may even be greater since intermodulation distortion will probably be generated.

### E. Messages Other Than Vocoders

We have designed the system to accommodate 32 vocoded voice channels each 2400 bit/s. Since the system is digital, it will accommodate any set of digital messages as long as the total message capacity of the system is not exceeded. For example, for each voice signal, we can send 19 200 bit/s, log-differential delta; however, only four messages can now be accommodated. If a voice message is 38 400 bit/s delta, only two high-quality voice channels can be accommodated. The point to remember is that the double-hop PN system makes optimum use of satellite and terminal power, an important consideration when designing a small terminal–satellite communication system.

## VII. Summary and Conclusions

Table I is a summary of the calculated system design parameters for several systems which have been analyzed. We assume here that the satellite antenna has a 17 dB gain and that the activity factor is unity.

With regard to ERP, the double-hop PN systems using CDM in the UHF up-link are optimum and TDM–PN is optimum in the UHF down-link. FSK triple diversity is greatly inferior to the PN systems.

With regard to RF bandwidth the FSK system requires the least bandwidth, while the double-hop PN system with TDM–PN has a comparable down-link bandwidth. However, with respect to the power density received on the ground, the PN systems are far superior to FSK. From a technical point of view, the power density criterion is more important than the RF bandwidth in the down-link since the former determines the amount of interference generated in a 4-kHz AM voice channel. For all the PN systems studied, the power density received on the ground is substantially lower than the receiver noise density.

Our computations were based on a 2400-bit/s data rate per terminal. Clearly the bit rate/terminal can be increased to accommodate 19.2-kbit/s log-differential delta provided the number of voice channels is reduced by a factor of 8. Equivalently, if 75-bit/s teletype messages are used, the system will accommodate 1024 such channels.

The ERP in the PN terminal, even with a zero-dB antenna gain, is about 10 watts. This power can easily be generated across the required 6 MHz band with a solid-state transmitter. If a 3-dB antenna gain is used in the aircraft, all the ERP calculations are reduced by 3 dB or equivalently, for the same ERP, the number of channels can be doubled.

The double-hop TDM–PN down-link system can accommodate the specified traffic with an antenna which gives approximately full-earth-disk coverage with a 1500-lb satellite. The 2000-lb satellite gives this system more margin. On the other hand, FSK triple-diversity cannot achieve full-earth-disk coverage and can be accommodated only with a directional antenna mounted in a 2000-lb satellite. This, of course, means that the antenna beam must be time-shared among different earth locations. Furthermore, such an antenna must be an unfurlable phased array. We have also shown that the PN system requires a smaller terminal transmitter than conventional modulation.

In conclusion, pseudo-noise is by far the optimum modulation technique for air–ground, ground–air communications operating at UHF. It is far superior to FSK with diversity combining. The down-link power density is 13.2 dB lower than FSK and the down-link bandwidth is hardly greater than for triple-diversity FSK. This should remove the false image that PN always requires substantially more bandwidth than conventional methods. On the contrary we have shown that for air–ground, ground–air communications at UHF, pseudo-noise is optimum for commercial or military aircraft terminals.

The PN modem which we have proposed is no more complex than more conventional FMFB or FSK receivers. All components are state-of-the-art, off-the-shelf, small, compact, and requiring low power. A major portion of the circuitry consists of digital technology, and hence reliability is achieved with the use of integrated circuits. In fact, all the components used in the modem if necessary can be mil-qualified. The cost of such an airborne terminal should be lower than a triple-diversity FSK terminal since the terminal power requirements are substantially less. The PN modem cost, for large-quantity purchases, should be no greater than the cost of a triple-diversity FSK modem.

The PN modem which has been analyzed and proposed as an optimum solution to the air–ground, ground–air communications problem is presently being developed by the IBM Federal Systems Division at its Center for Exploratory Studies in Rockville, Md. This terminal will be tested over various satellite links shortly. It is expected that the measured performance will approximate closely the theoretical performance shown in this paper.

The calculations presented here strongly suggest that a comprehensive test program using various modulation techniques for aircraft terminals operating over VHF or UHF satellites, must include PN in its evaluation. Once an area of communications considered far-out and of value to the military only, PN modulation has now matured to the point where it may very well prove to be the most efficient and least expensive satellite communications technique in existence. A comprehensive experimental program is required to either prove or disprove this conjecture.

## Appendix

### Carrier-To-Noise Ratio Calculations

$P_t = \sum_i P_i =$ total signal power at satellite receiver,
$P_i =$ power received by satellite from $i$th transmitter,
$N_w =$ satellite receiver noise power density,
$N_{Jw} = J_w/B =$ noise power density in satellite receiver due to interference,
$N_0 =$ ground receiver noise power density,
$N_{J0} = J_0/B =$ noise-power density in ground receiver due to interference,
$P_R =$ satellite repeater power received by ground station,
$B =$ total RF bandwidth,
$\Delta T = 1/B =$ PN bit duration,
$T =$ integration time per message waveform.

Total noise-power density at satellite receiver:

$$N_w + N_{Jw}. \tag{40}$$

Total noise power density at ground receiver:

$$N_0 + N_{J0}. \tag{41}$$

Share of satellite repeater power in the $i$th message:

$$\frac{P_i P_R}{P_t + B(N_w + N_{Jw})}. \tag{42}$$

Share of satellite repeater power in up-link interference component:

$$\frac{B N_{Jw} P_R}{P_t + B(N_w + N_{Jw})}. \tag{43}$$

Share of satellite repeater power taken by onboard receiver noise:

$$\frac{B N_w P_R}{P_t + B(N_w + N_{Jw})}. \tag{44}$$

Share of satellite repeater power which goes into clutter:

$$\frac{(P_t - P_i) P_R}{P_t + B(N_w + N_{Jw})} = \frac{P_c P_R}{P_t + B(N_w + N_{Jw})} \tag{45}$$

where

$$P_c = P_t - P_i \tag{46}$$

is the clutter power.

The signal-to-noise power ratio in the desired channel is the ratio of the signal component (41) to the total interference equations (41), (43), (44), and (45). If $T$ is the duration of a message signal then the signal-to-noise ratio in the $i$th terminal is

$$\eta_i^2 = \frac{BT\left[\dfrac{P_i P_R}{P_t + B(N_w + N_{Jw})}\right]}{\dfrac{P_R}{P_t + B(N_w + N_{Jw})}\left[B(N_{Jw} + N_w) + P_c\right] + B(N_0 + N_{J0})}. \tag{47}$$

Equation (47) can be put in the form

$$\eta_i^2 = \frac{P_R T}{N_0}\left(\frac{P_i}{P_t}\right) D \tag{48a}$$

where

$$B = \left(\frac{P_t}{N_w}\right)^{1/2}\left[\frac{P}{N_0}\left(\frac{J_w + P_c}{P_t}\right) + \frac{J_0}{N_0}\left(1 + \frac{J_w}{P_t}\right)\right]^{1/2} \tag{49}$$

$$D = \frac{L}{\frac{P_R}{BN_0}\left[\frac{J_w}{P_t} + \frac{BN_w}{P_t} + \frac{P_c}{P_t}\right] + \left[1 + \frac{J_0}{BN_0}\right]\left[1 + \frac{J_w}{P_t} + \frac{BN_w}{P_t}\right]} \tag{48b}$$

where

$L$ = implementation losses in the system
$D \leq 1$ = degradation factor
$D = 1$ = ideal down-link limited performance.

Equations (48a) and (48b), properly interpreted, can be applied to the various satellite communications links which have been discussed in previous subsections. The signal-to-noise ratio can now be calculated for various channel parameters and used with the curves of the form shown in Section II-C for obtaining link performance.

The optimum bandwidth can be obtained by differentiating (47) with respect to $B$ and equating the derivative to zero; then

where

$$P_c = P_t - P_i.$$

In order to obtain the multipath performance relationships, let

$$a = \frac{J_w}{P_t} = \begin{cases}\text{ratio of multipath power to signal} \\ \text{power ratio at satellite receiver} \\ (0 \leq a \leq 1),\end{cases} \tag{50a}$$

$$b = \frac{J_0}{P_R} = \begin{cases}\text{ratio of multipath power to signal} \\ \text{power ratio at terminal receiver} \\ (0 \leq b \leq 1).\end{cases} \tag{50b}$$

We will assume that the discrete multipath delay is $\tau \geq \Delta T$ where $\Delta T$ is the duration of a PN bit. Then from (47) and (50)

$$\eta_i^2 = \frac{\frac{P_R T}{N_0}\left(\frac{P_i}{P_t}\right)}{\frac{P_R}{BN_0}\left(a + \frac{BN_w}{P_t} + \frac{P_t - P_i}{P_t}\right) + \left(1 + b\frac{P_R}{BN_0}\right)\left(1 + a + \frac{BN_w}{P_t}\right)}. \tag{51}$$

Similarly the PN bandwidth is

$$B = \left[\left(\frac{P_R}{N_0}\frac{P_t}{N_w}\right)((1 + a)(1 + b) - P_i/P_t)\right]^{1/2}. \tag{52}$$

From (51) and (52) the optimum signal-to-noise ratio is

$$\eta_{i0}^2 = \frac{\frac{P_R T}{N_0}\left(\frac{P_i}{P_i}\right)}{1 + a + 2\left(\frac{P_R}{N_0}\frac{N_w}{P_t}\right)^{1/2}((1 + a)(1 + b) - P_i/P_t)^{1/2} + \frac{P_R}{N_0}\frac{N_w}{P_t}(1 + b)}. \tag{53}$$

If we now take the ratio of (51) and (53), we have

$$\left(\frac{\eta}{\eta_0}\right)^2 = \frac{1 + a + 2\left(\frac{P_R}{N_0}\frac{N_w}{P_t}\right)^{1/2}((1 + a)(1 + b))^{1/2} + \frac{P_R}{N_0}\frac{N_w}{P_t}(1 + b)}{\left(1 + a + \frac{BN_w}{P_t}\right)[1 + P_R/BN_0(1 + b)]} \tag{54}$$

These equations describe the optimum behavior of the PN system. When $a=1$, $b=0$, we have maximum multipath degradation in the up-link and no degradation in the down-link. This describes the behavior of a UHF up-link and an SHF down-link. Similarly $a=0$, $b=1$ describes an SHF up-link and a UHF down-link. Since the CCF has an ERP which overrides satellite receiver noise we further assume $P_t \rightarrow \infty$. From these conditions we can calculate the behavior of a double-hop communication system. When an aircraft terminal operates at UHF over the ocean the direct and reflected rays have equal power, i.e., $a=1$ and $b=1$.

In (54) when $a=1$, $b=1$, we can calculate the performance of a single-hop PN system operating at UHF, over the ocean. The case $a=0$, $b=0$, is the same system with zero multipaths.

When the double-hop system is used the satellite receiver bandwidth from the airborne terminal to CCF (central control facility) is optimized so that the effects of thermal noise and PN clutter are minimized. When the CCF-terminal link is TDM clutter is nonexistent and hence the bandwidth can be reduced. Here PN is used only for the purpose of rejecting multipaths.

Further improvements in performance can be achieved by using multipath combining techniques. Since the multipaths can be resolved, they can be recombined at the receiver, thereby improving performance further. This may be a worthwhile approach since over the oceans one encounters two rays of approximately equal strength. Here it is required to lock up a PN loop to each path, demodulate the message, and combine coherently.

REFERENCES


[1] Springette, in *Advances in Communication Systems, Theory and Applications*, vol. 1, A. V. Balakrishnan, Ed. New York: Academic Press, 1965, pp. 108–112.

[2] F. Corr *et al.*, "A pulsed pseudo-noise UHF radio set," *IBM J. Res. Develop.*, vol. 9, pp. 256–263, July 1965.

[3] W. C. Lindsey, "Phase shift keyed signal detection with noisy reference signals," *IEEE Trans. Aerospace and Electronic Systems*, vol. AES-2, pp. 393–401, July 1966.

[4] F. E. Bond and H. F. Meyer, "Fading and multipath considerations in aircraft/satellite communications systems," presented at the 1966 AIAA Communications Satellite Systems Conf., Washington, D. C., AIAA paper 66-294.

[5] S. W. Golomb *et al.*, *Digital Communications with Space Applications.* Englewood Cliffs, N. J.: Prentice-Hall, 1964.

# Part VI
# Frequency Hopping

Although frequency hopping techniques have received a great deal of attention over the years, not many operational systems have been constructed. This is because until recently, the problem of building frequency synthesizers that could meet the stringent requirements for successful systems was beyond solution with the circuit technology that was available. At least a part of the problem having to do with those requirements was that of size and weight; early vintage frequency synthesizers were often large, heavy, and slow in tuning. Comparison of basic block diagrams of direct sequence and frequency hopping systems will show that on a block diagram basis a frequency hopping hopping system has an extra subsystem, the frequency synthesizer, and it is not justifiable in many instances to go to a frequency hopper because of this extra, complex, and expensive subsystem.

Frequency hopping systems have their advantages, however, and recent improvements in circuit technology, notably the integrated circuit area, have made synthesizers practical that have thousands of frequencies available, can be switched in less than a microsecond, and take up no more than one or two small printed circuit cards (excluding any frequency reference sources). The frequency synthesizers that have found most favor are the mix-and-divide type of Hastings and Stone (see the following listing, Other Papers of Interest) and the phase-lock-loop type with a variable divider in the feedback path (also the following listing, Other Papers of Interest). Here, the emphasis is not on frequency synthesis; one should bear in mind that a frequency hopping modulator is nothing but a code sequence generator similar to those employed in direct sequence systems, driving a frequency synthesizer that it commands to hop from frequency to frequency in a pattern that is determined by the code sequence being generated. A seeming preoccupation with frequency synthesis is at least partially justified in that the most critical part of any frequency hopping system's design is its synthesizer, and that will continue to be true for the foreseeable future.

It is worth noting that frequency hopping is often employed in conjunction with other forms of modulation, including other forms of spread spectrum modulation. One of the papers reprinted here is concerned with a hybrid frequency and time hopping system, where the composite signal is used to implement multiple access to a satellite communications link. Frequency hopping often finds application in such systems because it is in effect a kind of dynamic frequency-division multiplex technique in itself.

The second paper reprinted here is on the tactical transmission system (TATS), in which the frequency hopping technique was selected primarily to provide frequency diversity. The system does provide multiple access, however, making use of this capability. An interesting note on TATS is that the modulation employs 8-ary Reed–Solomon coding wherein binary data to be transmitted is encoded into octal Reed–Solomon data and the resulting eight-level signal is transmitted as one of a contiguous set of eight frequencies, with the set being hopped around. That is, each of the eight frequencies in the set corresponds to one of the eight levels, and the receiver demodulates the signal by detecting which of the eight was sent, converting this octal Reed–Solomon code back to its binary form and correcting errors in the process.

Schreiber's paper is an analysis of the noise generated in a frequency hopping receiver by phase shifts that occur due to the carrier hopping action, assuming that the carrier is simultaneously frequency modulated with the information being sent (i.e., a frequency modulated signal whose center frequency is being hopped). This paper very aptly shows the reason that information is almost always put into some digital format prior to being sent over a frequency hopping channel.

## OTHER PAPERS OF INTEREST


1) N. Abramson, "Bandwidth and spectra of phase-and-frequency-modulated waves," *IEEE Trans. Commun. Syst.*, Dec. 1963.
2) J. Noordanus, "Frequency synthesizers—A survey of techniques," *IEEE Trans. Commun. Tech.*, Apr. 1969.
3) Q. H. George, "Performance of noncoherent *M*-ary FSK systems with diversity under the influence of Rician fading," presented at the IEEE Int. Conf. Commun., June 1968.
4) F. G. Splitt, "Combined frequency and time-shift keyed transmission systems," *IEEE Trans. Commun. Syst.*, Dec. 1963.

# ANALYSIS OF A HYBRID FREQUENCY-TIME HOPPING RANDOM ACCESS SATELLITE COMMUNICATION SYSTEM+

John H. Wittman
Sylvania Electronic Systems
A Division of
Sylvania Electric Products Inc.
Williamsville, N.Y. 14221

Summary

This paper analyzes the multiple access performance of a satellite communications network, in which each subscriber employs a hybrid frequency time-hopping random access technique for the transmittal of binary information by means of a linear average power limited satellite repeater. The information is repetitively encoded into a number of binary chips. Individual MARK and SPACE chips are matched filter envelope detected and pairwise compared; the final binary decision is based upon a majority vote. The present analysis extends previous results by simultaneously taking into account RF phase cancellation effects at the satellite as well as up and down link noise. Some numerical results are presented using system parameters typical of a small subscriber net. The multiple access performance of the frequency-time hopping system is (for the assumed parameters and a bit error rate of $10^{-5}$) found to be about 6.6 dB poorer than that of a comparable orthogonal multiple access system.

## Introduction

The application of various pulse address techniques to facilitate multiple access to a satellite repeater is considered in several papers included in reference 1. In most of these papers the effect of phase cancellation caused by multiple pulse overlap is ignored; Doyle's paper, while considering phase cancellation, neglects the presence of additive noise. In a related paper by Cohen[2], the problem of phase cancellation of two sinusoidal signals in the presence of Gaussian noise is treated. In this paper, an analysis of the multiple access performance of a hybrid frequency-time hopping (pulse address) technique is presented which takes into account the simultaneous effects of RF phase cancellation and up and down link noise.

+ This work is extracted from a Sylvania internal research report of the same title, TR30-66.4, 9 May 1966.

++The concepts linear and average power limited are compatible only in the limit as the AGC time constant becomes much greater than a frame interval. For any given total input power, the repeater gain is assumed to have reached a steady state condition.

## System Model

### Link Parameters

A total of N average power limited ground transmitting terminals simultaneously access a single, wideband, frequency translating, satellite repeater. Communication system performance is to be quantitatively derived for a typical simplex link involving the $j^{th}$ transmitting terminal and the $k^{th}$ receiving terminal (see Figure 1). The desired signal of average power $S_j^s$, (N-1) interfering signals, the $i^{th}$ such signal having an average power of $S_i^s$, as well as additive white Gaussian noise of power spectral density $N_o^s$, arrive at the input to the satellite. The received signals are bandpass filtered (satellite bandwidth $W_S$) frequency translated, linearly amplified and retransmitted. The satellite incorporates an automatic gain control, having a time constant long compared to an information frame, for keeping the long term average satellite output power fixed.++ The desired signal, the (N-1) interfering signals, as well as the uplink noise relayed by the satellite, are received at the intended $k^{th}$ receiving site at a power level of $P_k^r$; in addition down-link noise, again additive white and Gaussian, of power spectral density $N_{ok}^r$ is added at the receiver input. The transmission media (both up- and down-links) is assumed to be time invariant, non-distorting and non-multiplicative.

To minimize the number of parameters against which performance might be measured the following quantities are defined,[1]

$$Q_{Uj} = \frac{S_j^s}{N_o^s} = \text{Up-link capacity quotient, referred to the } j^{th} \text{ transmitting terminal;} \quad (1)$$

$$Q_{Dk} = \frac{P_k^r}{N_o^r} = \text{Down-link capacity quotient, referred to the } k^{th} \text{ receiving terminal.} \quad (2)$$

### Modulation Parameters

The time-frequency plane (common to all subscribers in the net) is partitioned, as shown in Figure 2, into M distinct frequency channels each of bandwidth $W_S/M$ (where $W_S$ is the allocated

Reprinted from *IEEE Int. Conv. Rec.*, pt. 2, Mar. 20–23, 1967, pp. 61–68.

system bandwidth), and into K distinct time slots each of duration $T_F/K$ (where $T_F$ is the frame period and is equal to the reciprocal of the highest binary transmission rate). In effect the time-frequency plane is divided into a total of $MK=T_F W_s$ cells. The subscriber net is assumed to be synchronized in both time and frequency. Each subscriber transmits data at a sub-multiple of the highest rate, i.e., at a rate $R_{ip}=1/n_{ip} T_F$, where $n_{ip}$ is a positive integer. The double subscript notation is introduced to reflect the fact that data rate $R_{ip}$, established between the $i^{th}$ transmitter and the $p^{th}$ receiver may differ from link to link. For the particular link of interest to us (see Figure 1) the data rate is equal to $R_{jk}$. Each subscriber, independently and (pseudo) randomly, selects a set of r distinct cells from each of $n_{ip}$ successive frames to represent a MARK and a non-overlapping set of $n_{ip}r$ distinct cells to represent a SPACE. The number r (redundancy per frame) is assumed to be fixed throughout the network (although $n_{ip}$ is peculiar to each link). A particular cell is "occupied" by transmitting, during the applicable time slot, a constant amplitude plused sinusoid having a fixed carrier frequency characteristic of the cell. Phase coherence between the $n_{ip}r$ pulses (or chips) per bit is not maintained; in particular it is assumed that the phase angle of each chip is a random variable uniformly distributed between 0 and $2\pi$. Redundant frequency hopping (i.e., K=1), time hopping (i.e., M=1) as well at certain pulse address multiple access techniques are recognizable as limiting forms of this generalized hybrid.

The intended $k^{th}$ receiver is synchronized in both time and frequency to the desired signal. MARK and SPACE chips are individually matched filter envelope detected and pairwise compared to yield $n_{jk}r$ subdecisions. The final binary decision is based upon a majority vote.

## Performance Analysis

At the intended $k^{th}$ receiver, a total of $n_{jk}r$ subdecisions are made per information bit, with MARKS and SPACES assumed apriori equally probable. The channel is binary symmetric relative to each subdecision. Hence the probability of bit error is simply the probability of a MARK (or SPACE) error. A majority decision rule is assumed; it follows that for $n_{jk}r$ odd the probability of bit error, $P_e$, is given by

$$P_e = \text{Prob}\left[\begin{matrix}\text{that the number of} \\ \text{erroneous subdecisions}\end{matrix} > \frac{\eta_{jk}r}{2}\right] \qquad (3)$$

Since each subscriber transmits r pulses/frame independent of data rate, the total number of interfering pulses, i.e., $(N-1)r$, is constant from one frame to the next. Moreover, under the constraint that $r/MK \ll 1$, the average probability of subdecision error can be assumed to be independent from chip to chip. The bit error rate can then be related to the probability of chip error, $p_e$, through the expression

$$P_e = \sum_{\Delta = \frac{\eta r}{2} + \frac{1}{2}}^{\eta r} \binom{\eta r}{\Delta} p_e^{\Delta} (1-p_e)^{\eta r - \Delta} \qquad (4)$$

where, for notational simplicity, $n=n_{jk}$. It will be observed that the product, nr, can also be written in the form

$$\eta r = \frac{W_S}{R}\left(\frac{r}{MK}\right) \qquad (5)$$

The major analytical task is that of computing the average probability of chip error, $p_e$. This is accomplished as follows. Rigorous expressions are derived for the envelope distributions at the output of the MARK and SPACE matched filters given the input noise power and the exact condition of the interference (number and amplitude of interfering pulsed sinusoids) appearing at the input to each filter. The conditional probability of subdecision error is derived from these distributions. Under the added assumption of up-link balance (i.e., all signals appearing at the satellite input are equal in amplitude), this expression reduces to a single easily evaluated integral which depends only+ upon the number of interfering sinusoids, $(m_M-1)$, appearing in the MARK cell and the number of interfering sinusoids, $m_S$, appearing in the corresponding SPACE cell. The joint probability $P(m_M, m_S)$ is computed again invoking the assumption that $r/MK \ll 1$. The conditional probability of chip error is then averaged over all conditions of interference to yield the desired average probability of chip error.

### Conditional Probability of Chip Error

The probability of error associated with a particular chip will depend conditionally upon the ratio of chip energy-to-total up and down link noise power density, $E^r_{jk}/N^{tot}_{ok}$, measured at the intended receiver, as well as the exact condition of subscriber interference in the applicable pair of cells being compared. Interference in other cells, even if occuring at the same time, can be ignored for the following reasons:

(a) the entire system including the transponder is linear such that there are no intermodulation products;

(b) over time intervals of interest to us, the transponder appears to be a constant gain device; hence there is no signal suppression as a result of interference occuring in the same time slot but at a different frequency;

(c) the network is synchronized, so that interfering pulses occuring in different cells do not contribute anything to the detector output at the time of sampling.

The composite signal appearing in some arbitrary MARK cell, during the interval $0 < t < T_F/K$, can then be represented as

+Other system parameters being held fixed.

$$s_M(t) = \sqrt{2S_{jk}^r(K/r)}\cos(\omega_M t + \phi_{jk}) + \sum_{h=1}^{m_M-1}\sqrt{2S_{hk}^r(K/r)}\cos(\omega_M t + \phi_{hk}) + n_M^r(t). \quad (6)$$

where $\omega_M$ is the center frequency (angular) of the arbitrary MARK cell. The first term represents the desired signal, a pulsed sinusoid of power $S_{jk}^r(K/r)$, and random phase angle $\phi_{jk}$ uniformly distributed between 0 and $2\pi$. The second term represents the sum of $m_M$-1 statistically independent pulsed sinusoids the $h^{th}$ member having a power level $S_{hk}^r(K/r)$, and random phase angle $\phi_{hk}$ uniformly distributed between 0 and $2\pi$. The last term is the additive white Gaussian noise and includes both the up-link relayed noise as well as the ambient receiver noise. The composite signal appearing in the corresponding SPACE cell can be represented as

$$s_S(t) = \sum_{g=1}^{m_S}\sqrt{2S_{gk}^r(K/r)}\cos(\omega_S t + \phi_{gk}) + n_S^r(t). \quad (7)$$

The first term represents the sum of $m_S$ statistically independent interfering pulsed sinusoids each having a random phase angle uniformly distributed between 0 and $2\pi$. The second term consists of additive white Gaussian noise having the same power density as before.

Since the signals are matched filter, envelope detected, it is convenient to rewrite equations (6) and (7) in the form

$$\begin{aligned} s_M(t) &= A_M\cos(\omega_M t - \theta_M) + n_M^r(t), \\ &= B_M(t)\cos\left[\omega_M t + \psi_M(t)\right], \end{aligned} \quad (8)$$

and

$$\begin{aligned} s_S(t) &= A_S\cos(\omega_S t + \theta_S) + n_S^r(t), \\ &= B_S(t)\cos\left[\omega_S t + \psi_S(t)\right]. \end{aligned} \quad (9)$$

It suffices to derive expressions for the probability density function associated with the envelopes $B_M$ and $B_S$.+ The applicable pdf's shown as conditionally dependent upon the interference, are

$$W(B_M|m_M^*) = \int_0^{\sqrt{2S_{jk}^r(K/r)} + \sum_{h=1}^{m_M-1}\sqrt{2S_{hk}^r(K/r)}} W(B_M|A_M, m_M^*)\cdot W(A_M|m_M^*)\cdot dA_M, \quad (10a)$$

$$W(B_S|m_S^*) = \int_0^{\sum_{g=1}^{m_S}\sqrt{2S_{gk}^r(K/r)}} W(B_S|A_S, m_S^*)\ W(A_S|m_S^*)\ dA_S. \quad (10b)$$

+ Except for a scale factor these distributions will be the same as the distributions computed at the output of the envelope detectors.

Note that these conditional pdf's are dependent not just upon the value of the numbers $m_M$ and $m_S$, respectively, but upon the actual distributions of interfering pulse amplitudes as well. For notational simplicity, this is denoted by adding an asterisk to the quantities $m_M$ and $m_S$, wherever they are used to represent a particular set of amplitudes.

The conditional pdf $W(B_i|A_i, m_i^*)$ is clearly Rician, since $B_i$ represents the envelope of a signal consisting of a sinusoid of fixed amplitude $A_i$ (throughout the pulse interval) plus Gaussian noise. The conditional pdf $W(A_i|m_i^*)$ represents the envelope of a sum of sinusoids and is obtained from Kluyver's results.[3] Making use of these observations, and substituting $x_i = B_i/\sigma_n$, where $\sigma_n^2$ is the mean square noise power in the matched filter bandwidth $\Delta f = K/T_F$, it is shown in Appendix A that the equation (10) pdf's have the form

$$W(x_i|m_i^*) = x_i\int_0^\infty v\, e^{-v^2/2} J_o(x_i v)\prod_{l=1}^{m_i} J_o\left[\sqrt{\frac{2S_{lk}^r(K/r)}{\sigma_n^2}}\, v\right] dv, \quad (11)$$

Equation (11) gives the pdf for the envelope of $m_i$ statistically independent sinusoids, the $l^{th}$ sinusoid having a power level $S_{lk}^r(K/r)$ and a random phase angle (uniformly distributed between 0 and $2\pi$), plus Gaussian noise of mean square power $\sigma_n^2$. The result is similar to that of Kluyver's, excepting for the additional factor $e^{-\sigma_n^2 v^2/2}$; Kluyver considered only the noiseless case. Rice developed a similar expression for the case of two sine waves plus noise and suggested that his result could be extended by introducing additional Bessel factors inside the integral.[4]

The conditional probability of subdecision error $P(e|m_M^*, m_S^*)$ is just the probability that $B_S > B_M$, or equivalently, that $x_S > x_M$, i.e.,

$$P(e|m_M^*, m_S^*) = \int_0^\infty\int_{x_M}^\infty W(x_M, x_S|m_M^*, m_S^*)\, dx_S\, dx_M. \quad (12)$$

It will be noted, however, that

$$W(x_M, x_S|m_M^*, m_S^*) = W(x_M|m_M^*)\ W(x_S|m_S^*), \quad (13)$$

the last equality following since $x_i$ is dependent only upon the set of normalized amplitudes represented by $m_i^*$. Equation (12) can be written in the rather complex form:

$$P(e|m_M^*, m_S^*) = \int_0^\infty dx_M\left[x_M\int_0^\infty v\, e^{-v^2/2} J_o(x_M v)\prod_{l=1}^{m_M} J_o\left(\sqrt{\frac{2S_{lk}^r(K/r)}{\sigma_n^2}}\, v\right) dv\right] \int_{x_M}^\infty dx_S\left[x_S\int_0^\infty u\, e^{-u^2/2} J_o(x_S u)\prod_{g=1}^{m_S} J_o\left(\sqrt{\frac{2S_{gk}^r(K/r)}{\sigma_n^2}}\, u\right) du\right]. \quad (14)$$

This represents the probability of subdecision error given a particular set of ($m_M$-1) interfering pulsed sinusoids in the applicable MARK cell, and a particular set of $m_S$ interfering pulsed sinusoids in the applicable SPACE cell, plus white Gaussian noise. To compute the average probability of subdecision error it would be necessary to calculate $P(m_M^*, m_S^*)$, and to average $p_e$ over all possible combinations of the sets $m_M^*$ and $m_S^*$. It seems reasonable at this point to consider the somewhat more restricted case in which all the signal amplitudes (or powers) are equal.

Up-link Balance. The simplifying assumption is introduced that all of the signals arriving at the receiving terminal have the same amplitude as that of the desired signal. Since the satellite is linear, the same relationship holds at the input to the satellite; this condition is called up-link balance. As shown in Appendix A equation (14) reduces to

$$P(e|m_M, m_S) = \tfrac{1}{2} - \sqrt{\frac{2E}{N_0}}^{\frac{(m_M-m_S)}{2}} \int_0^{\infty} e^{-v^2} J_0^{m_S+m_M-1}\left(\sqrt{2E/N_0}\,v\right) J_1\left(\sqrt{\frac{2E}{N_0}}\,v\right) dv \qquad (15)$$

where $E/N_0$ is the ratio of chip energy-to-total (up- and down-link) noise power density and, as shown in Appendix B, is given by

$$\frac{E}{N_0} = \frac{E_{jk}^{r}}{N_{ok}^{tot}} = \frac{S_{jk}^{r}(K/r)}{\sigma_n^2} = \frac{\left(\frac{MK}{r}\right)\frac{Q_{Dk}}{W_S}}{N + \frac{Q_{Dk}}{Q_{Uj}}\left(1 + \frac{W_S}{Q_{Dk}}\right)} \, . \qquad (16)$$

When no sinusoidal interference is present, i.e., when $m_M=1$ and $m_S=0$, equation (15) reduces to

$$P(e|m_M=1, m_S=0) = \tfrac{1}{2} e^{-\frac{1}{2}(E/N_0)} \, , \qquad (17a)$$

the expected result for a non-coherent orthogonal system perturbed by white Gaussian noise only.[5] When up- and down-link noise are negligible, it can be shown that

$$P(e|m_M, m_S)\Big|_{\sigma_n^2 = 0} = m_S/(m_M + m_S) \, , \qquad (17b)$$

a surprisingly simple result originally derived by Doyle.[6]

Probability of Interference

From a strict viewpoint, the interference in one pair of cells is conditionally dependent upon the interference in other cells. However, under the assumption evoked earlier, i.e., $r/MK \ll 1$, this dependence can be ignored. It follows that

$$P(m_M, m_S) \doteq P(m_M) \cdot P(m_S) \, . \qquad (18)$$

The marginal pdf's are readily computed to yield

$$P(m_M, m_S) \doteq \binom{N-1}{m_M-1}\left(\frac{r}{MK}\right)^{m_M-1}\left(1-\frac{r}{MK}\right)^{N-m_M} \cdot \binom{N-1}{m_S}\left(\frac{r}{MK}\right)^{m_S}\left(1-\frac{r}{MK}\right)^{N-m_S-1} \, . \qquad (19)$$

Average Probability of Chip Error

Under the hypothesis that the signal is contained in the MARK cell, $m_M$ can take on values from 1 up to N; likewise, since by hypothesis the signal is not present in the SPACE cell, $m_S$ can take on values from 0 up to N-1. It follows that the average probability of chip error is given by

$$p_e = \sum_{m_M=1}^{N} \sum_{m_S=0}^{N-1} P(e|m_M, m_S) \; P(m_M, m_S) \, , \qquad (20)$$

where the quantities $P(e|m_M, m_S)$ and $P(m_M, m_S)$ are given by equations (15) and (19) respectively.

Analytical Summary

Equations (4), (15), (16), (19) and (20) collectively describe the error rate performance of the hybrid frequency-time hopping multiple access system. Although the required expressions are not amenable to grouping into a single equation, each is readily evaluated on a computer. It will be observed that performance depends upon the following ratios

$$N \, , \quad \frac{Q_{Dk}}{W_S} \, , \quad \frac{Q_{Dk}}{Q_{Uj}} \, , \quad \frac{W_S}{R} \quad \text{and} \quad \frac{r}{MK} \, .$$

Only the last parameter is unique to the hybrid modulation technique treated in this paper. Moreover, since performance depends only upon the area, $MK=T_F W_S$, of the time-frequency plane and not upon its dimensions, the results apply equally to the limiting forms of frequency and time-hopping.

Some Numerical Results

The above equations have been numerically evaluated for a number of different parameters. Some typical results derived under the assumption that up-link $Q_{Uj}=\infty$, are presented in Figures 3-7. In Figures 3-5 and Figure 7, the ratio $Q_{DK}/W_S$ is set equal to unity. The average chip error rate is plotted in Figure 3, as a function of number of simultaneous accesses for different values of the parameter r/MK. (Note this is actually a point curve, values of $p_e$ being calculated only for integer values of N.) For a fixed value of r/MK, it will be observed (from Figure 3) that the chip error rate increases monotonically with the number of users. This is a consequence of two factors, (1) the increased interference resulting from additional users and (2) the corresponding decrease in the $E/N_0$ ratio (as a result of the power sharing in the satellite). For N fixed, it will be noted that the probability of chip error increases monotonically with r/MK. This is a result of two factors, (1) the probability of encountering interference is increased and (2) the available energy/chip is decreased, both effects being a consequence of r increasing. In Figure 4, the probability of bit error is plotted against N for different values of frame redundancy r; in plotting these results the values MK=1000 and $n_{jk}=1$ (i.e., $R_{jk}=1/T_F$, the maximum rate) have been assumed. For no redundancy, i.e., r=1, the error rate performance is relatively poor, despite the large TW product (equal to 1000). This reflects the severe susceptibility of the multiple access technique to interference from like users. The susceptibility is quite analogous to that encountered with non-redundant frequency hopping systems in the face of tone jamming. As noted from Figure 4, the use of simple cell diversity, i.e., $r > 1$, results in a very significant improvement in performance, at least for smaller N. For fixed N, the bit error rate is however bounded from below as shown by the heavy dashed line. This behavior is illustrated somewhat more clearly in Figure 5; the bit error rate is plotted against r with N as a parameter. The existence of an optimum value of r which minimizes the bit error rate is evident in this figure. It will be noted that the optimum choice of r decreases as N increases. An analogous effect was first reported by Sommer in connection with the performance of a line-of-sight, asynchronous, random access discrete address (RADA) system incorporating binary on-off keying and pulse coincidence detection.[7] Chesler has reported similar results relating to the performance of a line-of-sight synchronous RADA system incorporating an M'ary FSK/TSK form of information modulation with coincidence detection.[8] For m=2 the method of modulation is identical to that described in this paper. Ignoring ambient noise and phase cancellation effects, Chesler derived the following relationship between the minimum bit (m=2) error rate and the optimum choice of r

$$P_e = \tfrac{1}{2}^{\,r_o+1} \qquad (21)$$

For comparison purposes, equation (21) is plotted as the dashed line in Figure 5; the agreement is quite good. By way of contrast, the probability of bit error vs r is plotted in Figure 6, for a $Q_{DK}/W_S$ value of .05, other parameters being the same as used in Figure 5. The significant point is that the optimum choice of r which minimizes the bit error rate is now 1, independent of either $P_e$ or N; this reflects the influence of down-link noise.

When numerical results similar to those plotted in Figures 3-5 are computed from other values of $n_{jk}$, i.e., for data rates less than maximum, it is possible to generate families of curves as illustrated in Figure 7, showing the relationship between number of accesses and binary data rate. For these curves, the binary error rate is fixed at $10^{-5}$ and $Q_{DK}=W_S=2.4\times10^6$Hz; since MK has already been fixed at 1000, this means that $R_{MAX}=2.4$ Kb/s. The envelope of the family of curves represents the best performance that can be achieved (for the given parameters) by optimally choosing r. It will be observed that from $R_{jk}=150$ b/s to $R_{jk}=2.4$ Kb/s the optimum choice of nr, i.e., the number of chips/bit, is about 15. Over this range of data rate the number of accesses is very nearly proportional to $R_{jk}^{-1}$, i.e., the optimized system degrades gracefully. Compared however to the performance that can be realized with an ideal orthogonal multiple access system (without bit splitting), the performance of the optimized hybrid frequency hopping system is about 6.6 dB poorer.

## Conclusions

A rigorous expression has been derived for the conditional probability of chip error in a synchronous frequency-time hopping type multiple access system; this expression takes into account the exact condition of interference in the MARK and SPACE cells, as well as the influence of up- and down-link noise and the system bandwidth. Under the assumption of up-link balance this expression has been reduced to a single easily evaluated integral. The probability of bit error was then computed under the added constraint that r/MK was much less than unity. The numerical results presented here indicate that the performance of the postulated hybrid system is substantially poorer than that realizable with a comparable ideal orthogonal multiple access technique. The use of a more optimum decision technique as well as more sophisticated coding of the binary information, such as suggested by Chesler,[8] can be expected to give improved performance.


## Acknowledgement

The author is indebted to Messr's R. Cyrulik and R. Fryer, of Sylvania Electronic Systems-Central, for the numerical computations.


## Appendix A

### Derivation of Equations (11) and (15)

The conditional pdf $W(B_i|A_i, m_i^*)$, contained in equations (10a) and (10b), is Rician and has the form

$$W(B_i|A_i,m_i^*) = \frac{B_i}{\sigma_n^2}\, e^{-(B_i^2+A_i^2)/2\sigma_n^2}\, I_o\left(\frac{A_iB_i}{\sigma_n^2}\right), \quad 0\le B_i\le\infty \qquad (A\text{-}1)$$

Using Kluyver's result,[3] the conditional pdf $W(A_i|m_i^*)$ is in turn given by

$$W(A_i|m_i^*) = \int_0^\infty A_i v\, J_o(A_i v) \prod_{l=1}^{m_i} J_o\left(\sqrt{2S_{lk}^r(K/r)}\; v\right) dv \,. \qquad (A\text{-}2)$$

Substituting equations (A-1) and (A-2) back into equation (10) (either a or b) and exchanging the order of the integration results in

$$W(B_i|m_i^*) = (B_i/\sigma_n^2)\, e^{-B_i^2/\sigma_n^2}\int_0^\infty v \prod_{l=1}^{m_i} J_o\left[\sqrt{2S_{lk}^r(K/r)}\; v\right] dv$$

$$\left[\int_0^{\sum_{l=1}^{m_i}\sqrt{2S_{lk}^r(K/r)}} A_i\, e^{-A_i^2/2\sigma_n^2}\, J_o(A_i v)\, I_o\left(\frac{A_iB_i}{\sigma_n^2}\right) dA_i\right] \cdot \qquad (A\text{-}3)$$

The argument inside the integral in brackets is zero for amplitudes greater than the upper limit; hence the upper limit can be increased to infinity and Weber's second exponential integral+ used to reduce the integral to the closed form

$$\sigma_n^2 \; e^{-(\sigma_n^2/2)\,(v^2 - B_i^2/\sigma_n^4)} \; J_o(B_i v) \; . \qquad (A\text{-}4)$$

Substituting this result into equation (A-3) yields

$$W(B_i|m_i^*) = B_i \int_0^\infty v \, e^{-\sigma_n^2 v^2/2} \prod_{l=1}^{m_i} J_o\left[\sqrt{2S_{lk}^r(K/r)}\; v\right] J_o(B_i v) dv \qquad (A\text{-}5)$$

Finally making the substitution $x_i = B_i/\sigma_n$, results in equation (11) in the text.

To derive equation (15), it will be observed that for a condition of up-link balance, equation (12) can be rewritten in the form

$$P(e|m_M, m_S) = \int_0^\infty D_{x_M}(x_s|m_M) \; W(x_S|m_S) \; dx_S \; , \qquad (A\text{-}6)$$

where $D_{xM}(x_S|m_M)$ is the conditional distribution function of $x_M$ and is given by

$$D_{x_M}(x_S|m_M) = \text{Prob}\left[x_M \leq x_S \mid m_M\right]$$

$$= x_s \int_0^\infty e^{-v^2/2} J_1(x_S v) \; J_o^{m_M}(\sqrt{2E/N_o}\; v)\; dv \qquad (A\text{-}7)$$

Substituting this result back into equation (A-6) and rearranging yields

$$P(e|m_M, m_S) = \int_0^\infty dx_S \int_0^\infty x_S \, e^{-v^2/2} J_1(x_S v) \; J_o^{m_M}(\sqrt{2E/N_o}\; v) dv$$

$$\int_0^\infty x_S \, u \, e^{-u^2/2} J_o(x_S u) \; J_o^{m_S}(\sqrt{2E/N_o}\; u) \; du \; . \qquad (A\text{-}8)$$

The integral on $x_S$ involves a unit doublet as shown by Doyle.[5] Using Weber's discontinuous integral,++ it is readily shown that for u and v positive

$$\int_0^\infty J_1(v x_S) \; u \; x_S^2 \; J_o(u x_S) \; dx_S = \delta_u'(u-v) \; . \qquad (A\text{-}9)$$

Substituting this result back into equation (A-8) results in

$$P(e|m_M, m_S) = -\int_0^\infty e^{-v^2/2} J_o^{m_M}(\sqrt{2E/N_o}\; v) \; \frac{d\left[e^{-v^2/2} J_o^{m_S}\left(\sqrt{\frac{2E}{N_o}}v\right)\right]}{dv} dv. \qquad (A\text{-}10)$$

Expanding the differential in equation (16) and integrating by parts yields equation (15).

---

+Watson, H.N., A Treatise on the Theory of Bessel Functions, Second Edition, Cambridge at the University Press, pg. 395, 1952.

++Ibid., pg. 406.

## Appendix B

### Derivation of Ratio of Energy Per Chip To Noise Power Density

The satellite is assumed to be linear and incorporates a long time constant AGC; by long, it is meant that the time constant is much greater than the duration of a frame period, $T_F$. Thus, from one pulse to the next the satellite appears to be a constant gain device. Transient effects resulting from occasional changes in the number of satellite users are ignored. The received energy/chip is given by

$$E_{jk}^r = S_{jk}^r \,(K/r)\;(T_F/K) = S_{jk}^r\,(T_F/r) \qquad (B\text{-}1)$$

whereas the total received noise power density can be expressed as the sum of two statistically independent noise power densities, i.e.,

$$N_{ok}^{tot} = N_{ok}^r + N_{ok}^{sr}, \qquad (B\text{-}2)$$

where $N_{ok}^{sr}$ is the noise power density received from the satellite, and $N_{ok}^r$ is the local noise power density added at the receiver. Since the satellite is linear it is readily shown that

$$\frac{S_{jk}^r\,(T_F/r)}{N_{ok}^{sr}} = \frac{S_j^s\,(T_F/r)}{N_{ok}^s} = Q_{Uj}\,(T_F/r), \qquad (B\text{-}3)$$

and

$$\frac{P_k^r}{N_{ok}^r} \; \frac{S_{jk}^r\,(T_F/r)}{P_k^r} = Q_{Dk}\,(T_F/r) \; \frac{S_{jk}^r}{P_k^r} \; . \qquad (B\text{-}4)$$

Again, since the satellite is linear and average power limited, it follows that

$$\frac{S_{jk}^r}{P_k^r} = \frac{S_j^s}{S_j^r + \sum_{i \neq j} S_i^s + N_o^s W_S} = \frac{1}{N_{eq}^j + \frac{W_S}{Q_{Uj}}} \qquad (B\text{-}5)$$

where

$$N_{eq}^j = \frac{\sum_{i=1}^{M} S_i}{S_j} \qquad (B\text{-}6)$$

Combining equations (B-3), (B-4) and (B-5) and assuming up-link balance, i.e., $N=(N_{eq})_j$, equation (16) is obtained.

### Bibliography

1. Aein, J.M., Kaiser, J. and Schwartz, J.W., Multiple Access to a Communication Satellite With a Hard-limiting Repeater, IDA/RESD, Washington, D.C., Report R-108, Volume I (ASTIA Document 457945) January 1965; Volume II (ASTIA Document 465789) April 1965.

2. Cohen, A.R., "Phase Cancellation in a Gaussian Noise Environment," IEEE Trans. on Communications Technology, Volume COM-14, pp 588-594, October 1966.
3. Kluyver, J.C., "A Local Probability Problem," Proceedings of the Royal Academy of Sciences, Amsterdam, Vol. 8, p 341, 1906.
4. Rice, S.O., "Mathematical Analysis of Random Noise. II," Bell System Tech. J., Vol. 24:46, 1945.
5. Lawton, John G., "Comparison of Binary Data Transmission Systems," Proc. 2nd National Conference on Military Electronics, pp 54-61, 1958.
6. Doyle, W., "An Asynchronous Pulse-Address Scheme Using Binary FSK," Multiple Access to a Communication Satellite Using a Hard Limiting Repeater, IDA/RESD, Washington, D.C., Report R-108, Volume II (ASTIA Document 465789) Appendix VC, pp 141-145, April 1965.
7. Sommer, R.C., "On the Optimization of Random Access Discrete Address Communications," Proc. IEEE (Correspondence), Vol. 52, pp 255, October 1964.
8. Chesler, D., "M'ary RADA System," Proc. IEEE (Correspondence), Vol. 53, pp 390-391, April 1965.


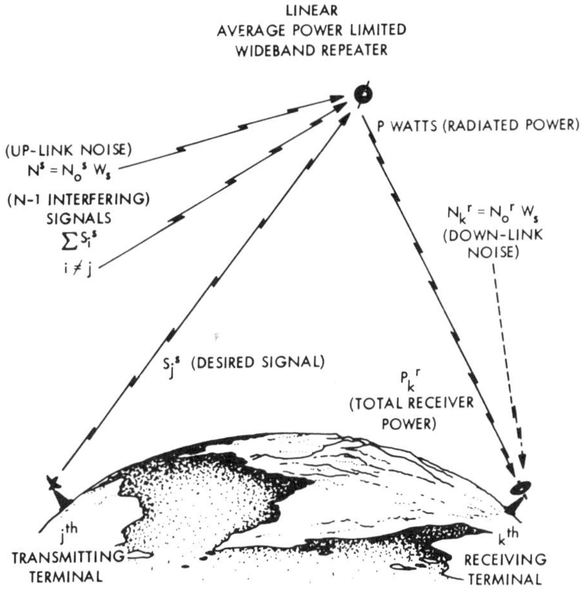


Figure 1. Typical Communication Link

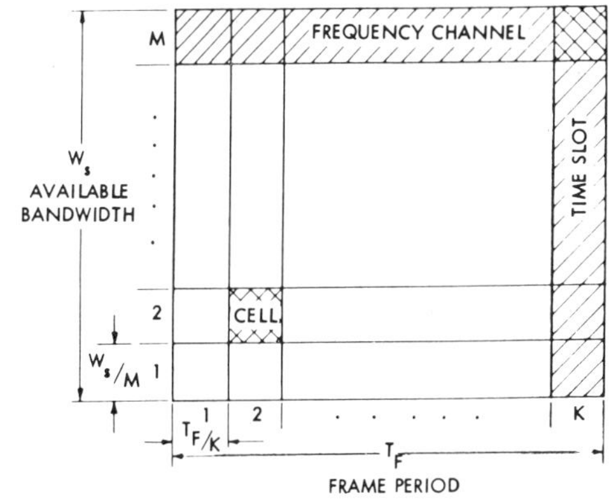


Figure 2. Partitioning of the Time-Frequency Plane

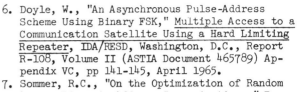

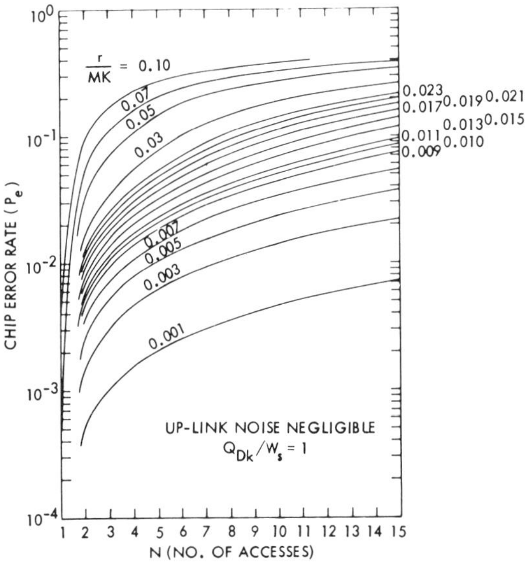


Figure 3. Chip Error Rate Vs. Number of Accesses

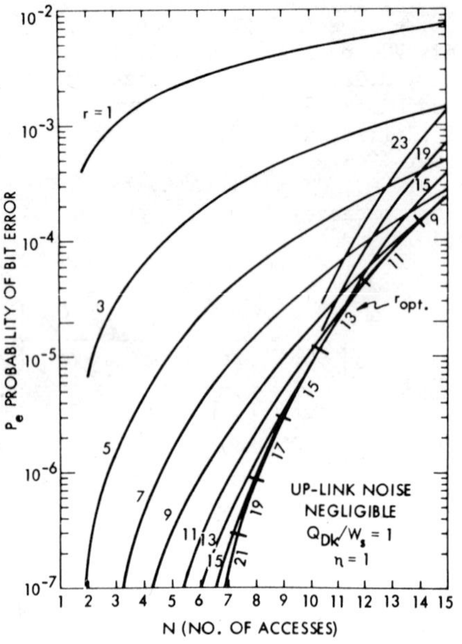


Figure 4. Bit Error Rate Vs. Number of Accesses

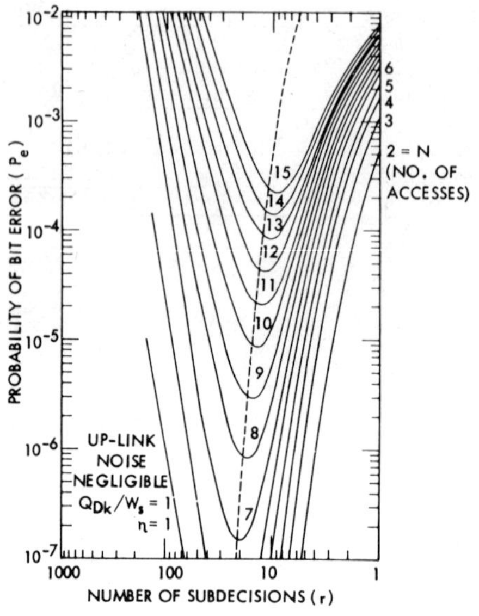


Figure 5. Bit Error Rate Vs. Number of Chips/Bit

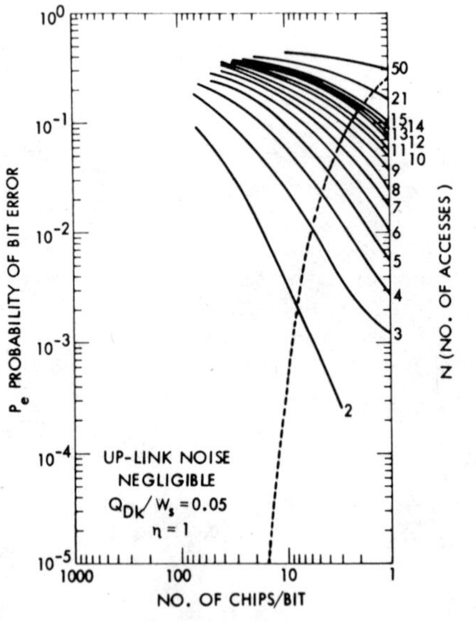


Figure 6. Bit Error Rate Vs. Number of Chips/Bit

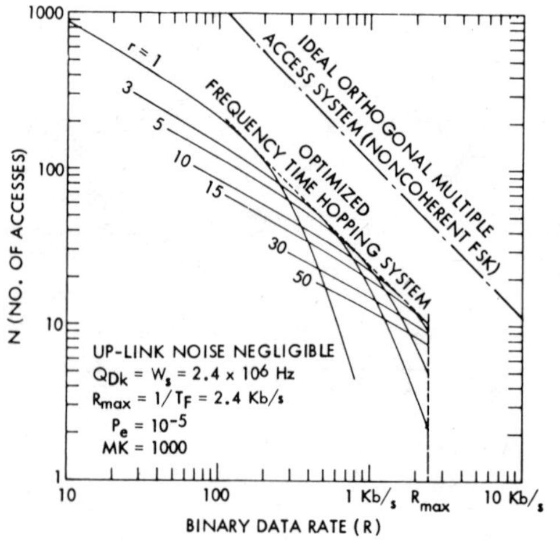


Figure 7. Number of Accesses Vs. Binary Data Rate

# Self-Noise of Frequency Hopping Signals

HEINZ H. SCHREIBER, MEMBER, IEEE

REFERENCE: Schreiber, H. H.: SELF-NOISE OF FREQUENCY HOPPING SIGNALS, Grumman Aerospace Corporation, Bethpage, N. Y. 11714. Rec'd 6/25/68; revised 1/27/69. Paper 69TP43-COM, approved by the IEEE Communication Theory Committee for publication without sponsored presentation. IEEE TRANS. ON COMMUNICATION TECHNOLOGY, 17-5 October 1969, pp. 588–590.

ABSTRACT: The self-noise of a system that uses frequency hopping for channel coding is determined for the limiting case of no receiver noise. The noise output is found to be a semirandom sequence of "clicks." Adjacent clicks are correlated, and the power density spectrum is of the form $\sin^2 x$.

## Introduction

The frequency hopping (FH) waveform has been suggested as a channel modulation technique that allows multiple access to hard-limiting and linear wide-band satellite repeaters [1], [2]. This constant envelope waveform may be designed to have a large time-bandwidth product and is classified as a spread spectrum signal. The spread spectrum signal is of general interest for multiple access to a hard-limiting wide-band repeater; the mutual interference effects produced by hard limiting a sum of spread spectrum signals can be approximated by an equivalent Gaussian noise source. Pseudonoise-phase shift keyed (PN-PSK) and linearly frequency swept (chirp) waveforms have also been suggested as spread spectrum multiple access waveforms. However, the FH waveform enjoys an advantage over these because large time-bandwidth products are more readily achieved. In addition, at the receiver the FH waveform is more readily acquired than the PN-PSK signal.

This paper considers the case of FH used primarily as a method of channel coding for privacy. The equation for the irreducible noise of this system is derived for the limiting case of no receiver noise or interfering signals. The derivation is based upon the following assumptions: 1) information modulation is analog FM, 2) the hopping codes in the receiver and the transmitter are synchronized, and 3) the transmitter carrier and receiver local oscillator frequencies are coherent.

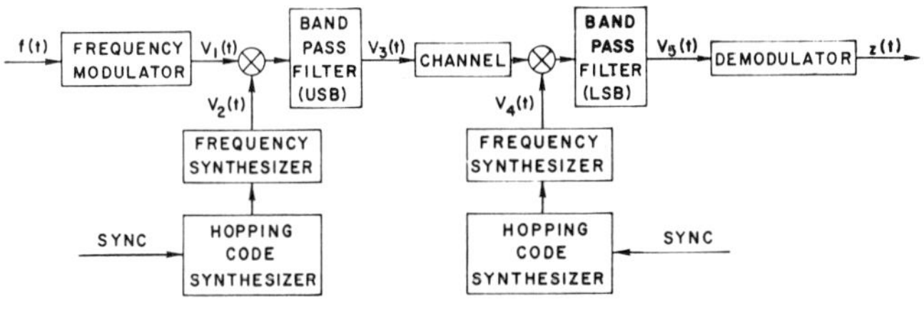


Fig. 1. System block diagram.

## System Description

Fig. 1 is a block diagram of the system. The transmitter and receiver each contain a mixer, a frequency synthesizer, and a hopping code generator. In addition, the transmitter contains a frequency modulator and the receiver a frequency discriminator. The channel and receiver are assumed noiseless.

Available channel bandwidth $W$, starting at $f_1$ Hz and extending to $(f_1 + W)$ Hz, is divided into $M$ narrower channels, each with bandwidth $W/M$ Hz and center frequency given by the following:

$$f_i = f_1 + (2i - 1)/2(W/M),$$

where $i$ is the channel number $(1 \leq i \leq M)$. In the transmitter the frequency synthesizer output $V_2(t)$ is changed every $\tau$ seconds (chip time) to one of the $M$ center frequencies, according to the hopping code. The sequence of frequencies repeats every $T$ seconds; thus, there are $K = T/\tau$ chips per hopping code word. This frequency hopped signal is mixed with the modulator output $V_1(t)$ to obtain the channel waveform $V_3(t)$. At the receiver the intermediate frequency (IF) signal $V_5(t)$ is obtained by mixing the channel waveform with the receiver frequency synthesizer output $V_4(t)$. The transmitter and receiver synthesizer outputs are assumed coherent, i.e., identical frequency but random phase. The frequency discriminator output $z(t)$ contains the original modulation.

## Analysis

Referring again to Fig. 1, it can be shown that the argument of the signal applied to the discriminator $V_5(t)$ is given by the following:

$$\psi(t) = \theta(t) + \omega_0 t + \sum_{k=-\infty}^{\infty} [\mathbf{a}_k \oplus \mathbf{b}_k] P_{\tau/2}\left(t - \frac{2k+1}{2}\tau\right) \quad (1)$$

where

| | |
|---|---|
| $\dot{\theta}(t) = d\theta(t)/dt$ | original modulation signal |
| $\omega_0$ | IF frequency |
| $\mathbf{a}_k$ | phase of transmitter synthesizer output in the $k$th interval (a random variable) |
| $\mathbf{b}_k$ | phase of receiver synthesizer output in the $k$th interval (a random variable) |
| $P_{\tau/2}(t)$ | pulse function; unit amplitude over $(-\tau/2, \tau/2)$ and zero otherwise |
| $\gamma_k = \mathbf{a}_k \oplus \mathbf{b}_k$ | sum, taken modulo $2\pi$. |

Equation (1) is obtained in the following manner (see Fig. 1). The frequency modulator output $V_1(t)$, in response to the signal $f(t)$, is given by

$$V_1(t) = \cos[\omega_0 t + \theta(t)]$$

Reprinted from *IEEE Trans. Commun. Technol.*, vol. COM-17, pp. 588–590, Oct. 1969.

where $\theta(t) = \int f(t)\,dt$. The hopping code generator produces a sequence of numbers; these control the transmitter frequency synthesizer output which is given by the following:

$$V_2(t) = \cos\left[\sum_{k=-\infty}^{\infty} (\omega_k t + \mathbf{a}_k) P_{\tau/2}\left(t - \frac{2k+1}{2}\tau\right)\right].$$

$\omega_k$ is selected from $M$ possible values at every $t = k\tau$, according to the hopping code. The channel signal $V_3(t)$ is selected as the upper sideband (sum frequency) of the first mixer output, as shown in the following:

$$\cos\left[\omega_0 t + \theta(t) + \sum_{k=-\infty}^{\infty} (\omega_k t + \mathbf{a}_k) P_{\tau/2}\left(t - \frac{2k+1}{2}\right)\right].$$

The receiver frequency synthesizer output $V_4(t)$ which is the same as $V_2(t)$ except for the independent random phase term $\mathbf{b}_k$, is mixed with the channel signal $V_3(t)$; the lower sideband (difference frequency) is selected for the IF signal $V_5(t)$. Recognizing that $\omega_k$ is the same in each chip interval for both $V_3(t)$ and $V_4(t)$, the argument of $V_5(t)$, given by (1), is as follows. The random variables $\mathbf{a}_k$ and $\mathbf{b}_k$ are independent and uniformly distributed over $0,2\pi$. Their sum is associated with the argument of a sine (or cosine) function and must be taken modulo $2\pi$.

The random variables $\gamma_k$ which are given by the modulo $2\pi$ sum of the independent random variables $\mathbf{a}_k$ and $\mathbf{b}_k$ must also be independent (and uncorrelated); in addition, they are also uniformly distributed over $(0,2\pi)$ [3]. Their expected values are readily found [4, pp. 140, 147]:

$$E\{\gamma_k\} = \pi$$

$$E\{\gamma_k\gamma_l\} = \begin{cases} (4/3)\pi^2, & k = l \\ \pi^2, & k \neq l. \end{cases}$$

The phase noise term, due to system implementation only, is represented by the stochastic process:

$$\mathbf{X}(t) = \sum_{k=-\infty}^{\infty} \gamma_k P_{\tau/2}\left(t - \frac{2k+1}{2}\tau\right). \tag{2}$$

For future use, it should be noted that the expected value of $\mathbf{X}(t)$ at any time $t_1$ is simply

$$E\{\mathbf{X}(t_1)\} = E\{\gamma_k\} = \pi.$$

The discriminator output signal is obtained from the time derivative of (1) and subsequent low-pass filtering.

The noise term out of the discriminator, prior to low-pass filtering, is given by the time derivative of (2). In performing this operation, use is made of the fact that the impulse function $\delta(t)$ is the time derivative of the step function, and that its area is given by the jump at the discontinuity. Then the output self-noise can be given by the following:

$$\dot{\mathbf{X}}(t) = \sum_{k=-\infty}^{\infty} \boldsymbol{\varepsilon}_k \delta(t - k\tau) \tag{3}$$

where $\boldsymbol{\varepsilon}_k = \gamma_k - \gamma_{k-1}$ is the jump at $t = k\tau$. The term $\dot{\mathbf{X}}(t)$ is a train of impulses which are periodically spaced in time, somewhat similar to Rice's clicks [5]. The areas of adjacent impulses are correlated. Examples of $\mathbf{X}(t)$ and $\dot{\mathbf{X}}(t)$ are shown in Fig. 2.

To evaluate the power density spectrum of $\dot{\mathbf{X}}(t)$, it will be necessary to evaluate its autocorrelation and then to take the Fourier transform. However, it can be seen that the problem is complicated because $\dot{\mathbf{X}}(t)$ is not stationary, i.e., its first-order density is dependent upon $t$. As a result, the autocorrelation of $\dot{\mathbf{X}}(t)$ is a function of two variables $t_1$ and $t_2$ and, in order to apply transform techniques to the analysis, it will be necessary to utilize two-dimensional Fourier transforms and time averages [4, pp. 440–451]. However, a simpler approach is possible.

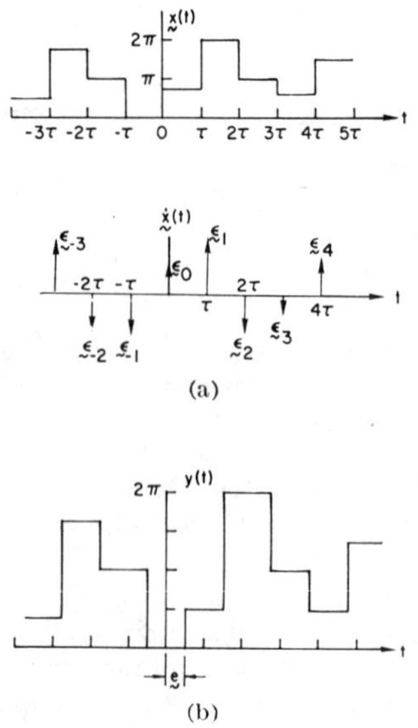


Fig. 2. Semirandom and random phase noise.

The basic problem is that the phase noise term has been defined as a semirandom signal; i.e., although its amplitudes are random, its points of discontinuity are known. Since the time reference for $\mathbf{X}(t)$ is somewhat arbitrary anyway, we could have initially formed the stochastic process $y(t)$ defined as

$$\mathbf{y}(t) = \mathbf{X}(t - \mathbf{e}) \tag{4}$$

where $\mathbf{X}(t)$ is defined in (2) and $\mathbf{e}$ is a random variable (see Fig. 2).

The value $\mathbf{e}$ is uniformly distributed over $(0,\tau)$ and is independent of $\mathbf{X}(t)$. The mean and autocorrelation of $y(t)$ are readily computed [4, pp. 294–296]:

$$E\{\mathbf{y}(t)\} = E\{\mathbf{X}(t)\} = \pi \tag{5}$$

$$R_y(t_1,t_2) = E\{\mathbf{y}(t_1)\mathbf{y}(t_2)\}$$

$$= \begin{cases} \pi^2, & |t_1 - t_2| > \tau \\ \pi^2 + (\pi^2/3)(1 - |t_1 - t_2|/\tau), & |t_1 - t_2| \leq \tau. \end{cases} \tag{6}$$

Time averages can be used to obtain the same results for the original function $X(t)$. However, the frequency interpretation of expected value must be utilized.

Let the demodulated output noise be denoted by $\mathbf{n}(t)$, so that

$$\mathbf{n}(t) = \dot{\mathbf{y}}(t). \tag{7}$$

Then the autocorrelation of the output noise $R_n(t_1,t_2)$, is related to the autocorrelation of the phase noise by the expression

$$R_n(t_1,t_2) = \frac{\partial^2 R_y(t_1,t_2)}{\partial t_1 \partial t_2}.$$

But $R_y(t_1,t_2)$ is a function only of $t_1 - t_2 = \alpha$. Thus the autocorrelation of the output noise may be written as

$$R_n(\alpha) = -(d^2/d\alpha^2)R_y(\alpha)$$

$$= (2\pi^2/3\tau)\delta(\alpha) - (\pi^2/3\tau)[\delta(\alpha + \tau) + \delta(\alpha - \tau)]. \tag{8}$$

Both $R_y(\alpha)$ and $R_n(\alpha)$ are plotted in Fig. 3.

As stated before the impulse function $\delta(t)$ is the derivative of the step function. The Fourier transform of (8) yields the power

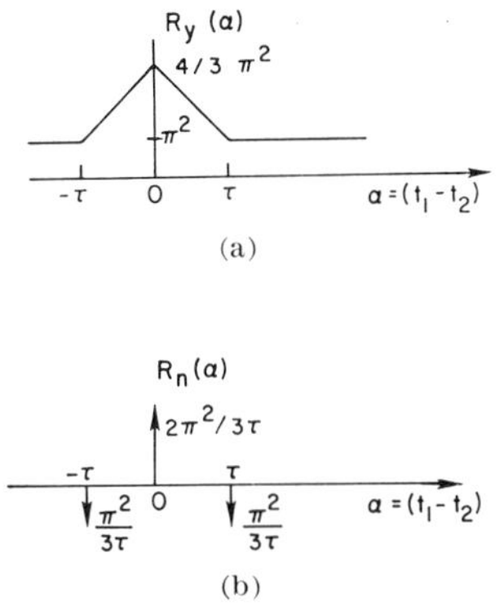


Fig. 3. Autocorrelation function of discriminator output.

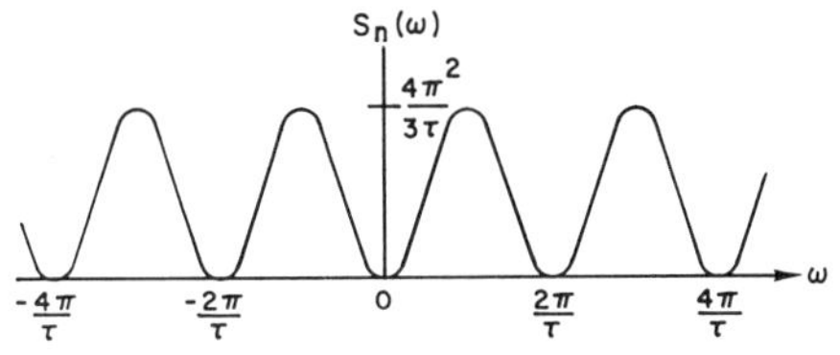


Fig. 4. Power density spectrum of discriminator output.

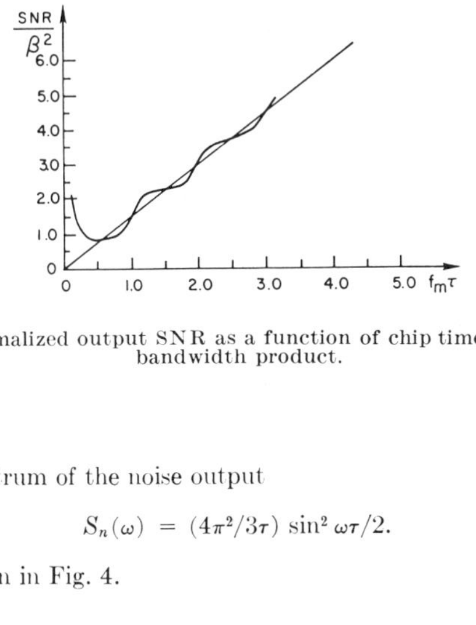


Fig. 5. Normalized output SNR as a function of chip time-information bandwidth product.

density spectrum of the noise output

$$S_n(\omega) = (4\pi^2/3\tau)\sin^2 \omega\tau/2. \quad (9)$$

This is shown in Fig. 4.

## Estimate of the Signal-To-Noise Ratio

Integration of (9) over the system information bandwidth $[\omega_m = 2\pi f_m]$ yields an expression for the output noise

$$N = (2\pi/3)(\omega_m/\tau)(1 - \sin \omega_m\tau/\omega_m\tau). \quad (10)$$

Let the modulation be sinusoidal, and select the index of modulation so that the channel bandwidth is equal to the Carson's rule bandwidth, i.e.,

$$W/M = 2(\beta + 1)f_m \quad (11)$$

where $\beta$ is the index of modulation. Then signal output power $P_s$ is given by

$$P_s = \tfrac{1}{2}(2\pi\beta f_m)^2 \quad (12)$$

and $(\mathrm{SNR})_0$ is given by

$$(\mathrm{SNR})_0 = \tfrac{3}{4}\beta^2(2f_m\tau)\left(1 - \frac{\sin 2\pi f_m\tau}{2\pi f_m\tau}\right)^{-1}. \quad (13)$$

It can be seen that $(\mathrm{SNR})_0$ is determined by the product of the FM index of modulation, the number of independent samples in $\tau$ for a signal of bandwidth $f_m$, and a correction factor due to nonflat noise, respectively. Fig. 5 is a plot of $(\mathrm{SNR})_0$, normalized to $\beta^2$, as a function of the chip time-information bandwidth product. For $f_m\tau > 2$, the $(\mathrm{SNR})_0$ is approximately $3\beta^2\ (f_m\tau/2)$. For very small $f_m\tau$, the SNR is approximately $\beta^2(4f_m\tau)^{-1}$; however, the model is not defined for the limiting case, where $\tau$ approaches zero. It should also be noted that the effect of bandpass filtering prior to demodulation has been neglected. This is valid if the bandpass filter is much wider than $f_m$.

An example will be used to demonstrate the significance of this hopping noise. Consider a frequency modulation system operating above the receiver threshold with a $\beta = 5$. Using extant results, it can be shown that, without hopping, the system will exhibit a demodulated SNR in excess of 36 dB. However, if the system is hopped, then the hopping noise will dominate for a large range of $f_m\tau$ values. For example, over the range of $f_m\tau$ from 0.5 to 16, the $(\mathrm{SNR})_0$ increases from 12.7 dB to only 27.7 dB. To match the receiver noise (at the threshold) requires $f_m\tau$ much greater. The hopping noise in this system dominates and it must therefore be considered.

## Summary

In the FH system channel modulation–demodulation operations introduce random phase discontinuities at the hopping rate in the IF (modem) output. These phase discontinuities are detected by a frequency discriminator as a semirandom sequence of impulses which cause an irreducible system output noise. It has been found that adjacent impulses have areas that are correlated random variables; as a result, the autocorrelation of the irreducible noise is not a single impulse, and the power density is not flat. It should be noted that adjacent pulse area correlation yields these characteristics and thus distinguishes this analysis from that of quantization noise in sampled data systems [6].

For analog FM it has been found that the signal-to- (irreducible) noise output ratio achieves a minimum at about one half for the chip time–information bandwidth product. This SNR may be improved by either increasing or decreasing the time–bandwidth product. In the former case the SNR improves (nearly) linearly with the time–bandwidth product whereas in the latter case the SNR improves as the reciprocal of the time-bandwidth product. However, the model used for this analysis breaks down as hopping time vanishes because the IF bandwidth $W/M$ is then too narrow to pass the demodulated signal $V_5(t)$ without excessive distortion. Therefore, the results of this analysis are valid for selecting the lower hopping rate required for a given SNR.

## Acknowledgment

The author wishes to thank Prof. A. Papoulis for his helpful discussions.

## References

[1] J. Kaiser, J. W. Schwartz, and J. M. Aein, "Multiple access to a communication satellite with a hard-limiting repeater," Institute for Defense Analysis, Arlington, Va., Rept. R-108, vol. 1, ASTIA Doc. AD 457945, January 1965.

[2] J. H. Wittman, "Analysis of a hybrid frequency–time hopping random access satellite communication system," *1967 IEEE Internatl. Conv. Rec.*, pt. 2, vol. 15, pp. 61–68.

[3] F. J. Scire, "A probability density function theorem for the modulo *y* values of the sum of two statistically independent processes," *Proc. IEEE* (Letters), vol. 56, pp. 204–205, February 1968.

[4] A. Papoulis, *Probability, Random Variables, and Stochastic Processes.* New York: McGraw-Hill, 1965.

[5] M. Schwartz, W. R. Bennett, and S. Stein, *Communication Systems and Techniques.* New York: McGraw-Hill, 1966, pp. 144–154.

[6] A. Papoulis, "Error analysis in sampling theory," *Proc. IEEE*, vol. 54, pp. 947–955, July 1966.

# TATS - A Bandspread Modulation - Demodulation System for Multiple Access Tactical Satellite Communication*

by
Paul R. Drouilhet, Jr.
Steven L. Bernstein

Lincoln Laboratory, Massachusetts Institute of Technology
Lexington, Massachusetts

ABSTRACT

TATS, a modulation - demodulation system for multiple access tactical satellite communication, is described. The modem utilizes coded MFSK message modulation and frequency-hopping for frequency diversity. The performance of the modem has been analyzed and measured in an extensive laboratory and field test program. Multiple access performance over channels disturbed by Gaussian noise, multipath propagation and RFI is discussed. It was found that interference to a TATS link caused by a large number of other users is approximately equivalent to that caused by Gaussian noise of the same power.

## I. INTRODUCTION

The distinguishing characteristics of tactical communication, at least as the term is used here, are that one or both of the terminals comprising a communication link are small mobile terminals, generally with the user located at or near the terminal rather than at a remote point, and that most circuits are intermittent (e.g., push-to-talk) rather than full-period. TATS, the Tactical Transmission System, is a modulation/demodulation system designed to provide reliable communication for such tactical circuits via a communications satellite. Of central consideration in its design have been certain problems unique to tactical circuits, particularly: (a) a very large number of low-duty cycle circuits and nets must efficiently share the limited available channel capacity afforded by the satellite; (b) much traffic will consist of short messages or interchanges interspersed between long periods of radio silence; (c) most terminals will be located on high-speed aircraft, ships, or small land vehicles; (d) the channel will often be disturbed by multipath propagation and RFI; and (e) the equipment must be simple to use, since its operation will often be a secondary duty for the operator.

*This work was sponsored by the Department of the Air Force.

## II. TATS MODEM DESCRIPTION

TATS employs frequency-hopping plus simple but efficient coding to generate a bandspread signal structure providing a high degree of multiple access (simultaneous use of single satellite channel by many users) and interference protection while retaining simple operating procedures and rapid synchronization. Two data rates are provided, 75 bits per second and 2400 bits per second.

### A. Signaling Technique

The design of the signaling (modulation-coding) system is the central factor in achieving the required multiple-access capability, interference resistance, and protection against the multipath experienced on satellite-to-aircraft links. Some form of bandspread signal structure is clearly indicated; the detailed implementation will, however, have a strong effect on both performance and system complexity. Particular attention must be given to the synchronization problem inherent in the use of bandspread signals in order to make this technique usable in the postulated tactical environment.

The signal structure chosen for TATS uses a Reed-Solomon code [1], multiple frequency-shift keying (MFSK), and bandspreading by means of fixed-pattern frequency hopping of the MFSK signal over the total transmitted bandwidth. Figure 1 depicts a functional block diagram of a TATS modem. The detailed structure can best be seen by considering

Reprinted from *IEEE Electron. Aerosp. Syst. Conv. Rec.*, Oct. 27–29, 1969, pp. 126–132.

separately the modulation-coding and the bandspreading.

1. Modulation-Coding

The basic signaling waveform is a $T_c$-second pulse of sine wave carrier (called a "chip") on one of eight frequencies spaced at $1/T_c$ -Hz increments. Sixty-four code words are generated as sequences of seven such pulses, with an additional fixed frequency pulse starting each code word to aid in time and frequency synchronization. Thus, the time required to transmit a code word is $8T_c$ sec. Since each code word carries six information bits, the data rate is $0.75/T_c$ bits per second. For a data rate of 75 or 2400 bits/sec, corresponding to synchronous transmission standards, $T_c$ is 10 msec or 312.5 $\mu$sec.

Figure 2 shows the frequency-time format for a typical code word ($f_c$, $f_c - 5\Delta$, $f_c + 7\Delta$, $f_c - 7\Delta$, $f_c - \Delta$, $f_c - 3\Delta$, $f_c + 5\Delta$, $f_c + \Delta$). The set of 64 code words has the property that any two of the code words use the same frequency in the same time slot at most once (not including the sync position); i.e., they differ in at least six slots. The set is generated from the (7, 2) octal Reed-Solomon code. The octal frequency commands generated from this block code are easily realized by two 3-bit shift registers.

An 8-channel receiver measures the amplitude of the envelope at the output of each of eight matched filters at the end of each $T_c$-sec pulse interval and quantizes each to 16 levels. The decoder uses these measurements to generate 64 numbers related to the likelihood that each of the code words is the one actually being received. This number, for a given code word, is equal to the sum of the quantized matched filter outputs corresponding to that code word. At the end of each code word interval, the code word having the highest likelihood is selected. This procedure is a nearly optimum realization of the maximum likelihood receiver for the Gaussian noise channel with or without random fading. Figure 3 is a functional block diagram of the decoding procedure.

2. Bandspreading

Bandspreading of the modulation format described above is accomplished by generating a new base or carrier frequency $f_c$ for each pulse, to which the selected frequency $-7\Delta$, $-5\Delta, \ldots, 7\Delta$ is added. Carrier frequencies are selected from a set of frequencies spaced equally over the available channel bandwidth. The hopping pattern of the carrier consists of a repetitive sequence of seven frequencies (a carrier frame); since the modulation frame contains eight chips, the carrier frequency for each chip position within the modulation frame is cycled through the pattern. This guarantees frequency diversity in the sync measurement in the presence of selective fading. A typical bandspread signal pattern for two modulation frames is shown in Fig. 4. The actual transmitted frequency is shown as a solid line; its frequency is that of the hopped carrier frequency, shown as the dashed line, with the modulation frequency added to it.

The set of hopping patterns was selected to have the following two properties: (1) each pattern uses the whole transmitted bandwidth, and (2) the number of overlaps between members of the set for all possible time shifts is small. The first property provides the diversity necessary to combat both frequency selective fading due to multipath and RFI. The second property minimizes the possibility of decoder error due to channel cross-talk. When a number of users are on the air, the frequencies used appear to be selected from a uniform probability distribution over the band.

The hopping patterns are chosen by a set of octal thumbwheel switches. These switches control shift registers similar to those used for encoding which, in turn, generate the carrier frequency in digital form. The data modulation is added to this. The table below shows the number of hopping patterns that can be generated and the number of possible carriers for each combination of data rate and satellite bandwidth.

| | Number of Hopping Patterns | Number of Possible Carriers |
|---|---|---|
| 500 kHz bandwidth | | |
| 75 b/s | 4096 | 256 |
| 2400 b/s | 64 | 16 |
| 10 MHz bandwidth | | |
| 75 b/s | 4096 | 4096 |
| 2400 b/s | 4096 | 256 |

B. Synchronization

To demodulate the received signal, the receiver must generate a local oscillator signal which frequency hops with the same time-frequency pattern as the received carrier, such that the difference frequency between the received carrier and the local oscillator is equal to the subsequent nominal intermediate frequency. Accurate time synchronization (within about 5% of a chip duration) is required between the received and the locally generated patterns and, in addition, the receiver local oscillator must be offset to compensate for any doppler shift or frequency translation error which occurs on the link. The receiver incorporates a synchronization system which continuously searches the initial time-frequency uncertainty region for a signal having the expected pattern and, on detecting such a signal, pulls in and tracks, i.e., establishes and maintains time and frequency synchronism between the received signal and the locally generated pattern. This preamble is followed by a four character start-of-message signal (without synch chips) which puts the modem into the data decoding mode. The data format is shown in Fig. 5.

The initial signal acquisition procedure is performed as a serial time search and a parallel (eight channel) frequency search. A time uncertainty of 7 chips and a frequency uncertainty of ±400 Hz (± 800 Hz in an extended Doppler mode) is covered. The length of preamble transmitted to allow for the search and pull-in is 490 chips in either data rate. This results in a 5 sec acquisition time in low rate and 5/32 sec in high rate.

Error signals for the pull-in and tracking loops are provided by the matched filter bank. Frequency errors are measured by finding the difference in output level of the two filters on either side of the nominal center. Time errors are obtained from the difference in center filter output between the first and second halves of the synchronization chips.

C. Hardware Realization

A number of prototype TATS modems were designed and constructed at Lincoln Laboratory. These modems consist of about 1000 packages of digital integrated circuits for the timing, control, interface and decoding logic along with the integrate and dump matched filter bank, mix and divide frequency synthesizers, and associated RF/IF circuitry. All circuits are miniaturized and are contained in two rack-mounted drawers.

Figure 6 is a picture of the inside of two drawers of equipment (one RF, one digital) and the control panel. These together with a power supply comprise one TATS modem. The two black boxes in the RF drawer are frequency synthesizers capable of producing $2^{20}$ frequencies in response to a 20 bit digital command. A standard data interface is provided for a variety of inputs at both 75 and 2400 b/sec including teletype, solid-state message composers and vocoders.

A pilot production run of the modem was undertaken by the Air Force Electronic Systems Division with an industrial contractor. This model has been reduced in size to one rack-mounted drawer including the power supply. It is being field tested extensively by the Services.

III. PERFORMANCE OF THE TATS MODEM

A. Approach to the performance analysis

As mentioned above, the TATS modem must be capable of efficient operation over a wide variety of channel conditions. Not all of the channels can be analyzed satisfactorily by mathematical computations. The case of strong RFI is an example where the details of the interference and of the receiver design (e.g. the AGC characteristic) are difficult to include in an accurate calculation of performance. In all cases it is impractical to attempt an exact evaluation of performance, whereas fairly tight bounds can be computed.

In view of the problems inherent in accurately modeling the channel and receiver, and in finding exact error expressions given a model, a three pronged approach to analyzing the TATS performance was undertaken.

First, computations of the theoretical behavior of the TATS code and similar codes [2] were performed. These yielded fairly tight bounds on the probability of error for various channels and code parameters. Also during this phase, synchronization algorithms were investigated by computer analysis.

Second, once the code parameters were chosen, computer simulations of various receivers were performed. These simulations gave close estimates of the theoretical modem performance for simple channels as well as some models of interference.

Third, a hardware link simulator was constructed. This facility, when used with a prototype modem, gave the actual modem performance over a wide range of channel conditions and allowed a comparison with the previous theoretical predictions.

The three phases of performance analysis are described below, followed by a summary of the results obtained.

B. Results obtained from computation

Computer results yielded information on the error rate performance, P(E) vs $E_B/N_0$, as a function of (1) code symbol alphabet size, (2) number of chips per code word, (3) matched filter output quantization (and AGC level settings) including the possibility of the list-of-L [3] block decoding. It was possible to obtain upper bounds (union bounds) on P(E) with the programs written for a variety of channels including additive Gaussian noise, Rayleigh faded multipath (the Rician channel) and some models of interference. Lindsey's derivations [4] were used extensively to find the bounds.

Other programs yielded predictions of how long a preamble would be needed to provide dependable synch acquisition as a function of the signal-to-noise ratio needed for reliable data transfer.

These computer results provided most of the design parameters for TATS. In particular, the following were determined on the basis of this phase of the analysis: (1) the code parameters (7 chips, 8 frequencies, 64 code words), (2) the matched filter output quantization (16 levels, yielding almost no degradation from continuous linear or square law), (3) the length of the preamble needed for reliable synch acquisition (294 chips with an extended Doppler search) and (4) the synch acquisition technique (16 half-chip summations done in parallel over eight frequency channels)

The performance predicted by computer showed that, with the parameters chosen: (1) the effects of multipath should be noticeable only at high signal-to-noise ratio, (2) the effect of multiple users was approximately the same as that of Gaussian noise of the same power, and (3) the effects of RFI on the error rate would be small.

C. Results obtained by computer simulation

Two computer simulations were performed to further define the TATS design and performance.

One simulated the pull-in loops used for fine time and frequency adjustments. The simulation showed that at the signal-to-noise ratios required by the decoder, final pull-in of the loops could be accomplished in less than 200 chips. The loop design used variable time constant, three level error signal, digital loops for both time and frequency. Once start-of-message is detected, the loops operate with an error signal obtained on every eighth chip. No more than 0.5 db degradation of the receiver performance occurs when the received signal has the maximum design range and doppler rates.

In the decoder simulation, a close estimate of the probability of error can be found instead of the union bounds discussed above. The estimates showed the union bound to be too conservative by about 1 db near $10^{-2}$ or $10^{-3}$ error rates for the Gaussian noise channel. Other channels, including RFI and multipath, were also investigated.

The simulation was useful as a design aid for certain receiver components such as the AGC. At the same time the degradation resulting from various non-ideal receiver components (e.g. limiters, gain imbalances) could be measured.

Concerning RFI, the results of the simulation showed that strong narrowband interference on one chip out of seven causes 0.75 db degradation in signal-to-noise ratio, and interference on two chips causes 1.5 db degradation. This excellent protection comes from three sources: (1) coding over a number of chips, (2) matched filter output limiting, so that a single or double hit does not greatly affect the decoder accumulators, and (3) an AGC that does not respond to one, two or three strong hits out of seven.

The simulation also indicated that downlink multipath either with independent Rayleigh fading from chip to chip or at a steady level (but random phase) would not degrade performance near error probabilities of $10^{-3}$. Multipath actually decreases the error rate if it is strong and steady.

D. Results obtained with the TATS link simulator.

For the last performance measuring phase, a hardware link simulator was constructed to be used with a prototype modem. Uplink and downlink multipath, multiple user signals, a hard limiting satellite, RFI, and noise can be simulated.

The first series of tests, on the additive Gaussian noise channel, yielded the dashed curve in Fig. 7. The ideal predicted values are shown as a solid curve. This was essentially a calibration run on the modem since this channel can be most accurately analyzed. High and low rate performance was nearly the same at the same $E_B/N_0$. (Of course a 15 db higher $P_r/N_0$ is required at high rate.)

The second series of tests, which served as a system calibration, included Gaussian noise added to the uplink of the hard-limiting repeater. In this case, the assumption that the satellite output consists of signal plus independent, flat Gaussian noise can be used to predict the probability of error very closely. The theory of signal-to-noise ratios in a bandpass limiter is well known [5, 6] and led to accurate results.

Next, mixtures of satellite users were simulated at various uplink power levels. It was found that over a wide range of conditions, the effect of other users on any given link is very nearly the same as Gaussian uplink noise of the same total uplink power.* This result greatly simplifies satellite capacity calculations. Figure 8 shows the number of equal power high or low rate TATS users that can be supported by a satellite of 500 kHz bandwidth as a function of the downlink signal-to-noise ratio in the 500 kHz band which is assumed the same for all terminals. A factor of 32 more users can be supported at the low data rate.

The results also showed the desirability of power control among mixtures of uplink transmitters. Maximum satellite channel capacity can be achieved only when users radiate power in proportion to their data rate; or, in particular, if all users at the same rate use equal ERPs.

The effects of multipath were then included with the simultaneous users. In this case it was found that as long as the differential path delay is at least 10 $\mu$sec there are no combinations of uplink and downlink multipaths that cause more than about 1 db degradation for a given direct ray $E_B/N_0$. (This degradation is the amount a transmitter would have to increase its power by to overcome the increase in error rate). The presence of multipath on only one of the two directions either reduces or has little effect on the error rate.

*An exception is limiter capture by a signal large compared to the sum of the other uplink powers.

E. Field Test Results

In addition to laboratory testing, TATS modems have been operated successfully for many hours over actual satellite links (LES-5, LES-6 and TACSAT) at both UHF and SHF. This operating time includes a number of airborne flight tests which were successful in establishing reliable, long range (e.g., Guam to Lexington, Mass.) air-to-ground communication. Airborne operations used both 2400 b/s vocoders for speech and TTY or message composers as low rate inputs. It is important to realize that this communication was accomplished with simple, low gain antennas (e.g., a blade) under less than ideal conditions which included multipath and RFI. Field tests are qualitatively in agreement with theory and laboratory experiments. Both ground and airborne tests are continuing.

F. Summary of Performance

Perhaps the single most important result obtained from the evaluation of performance concerned multiple access capacity. It was found that over a large range in satellite loading, the effect of other users on a given TATS link is the same as that of Gaussian uplink noise of the same total power in the satellite passband. Since the effects of Gaussian uplink noise were also measured (and correlated with theory), the system capacity can be predicted if the user terminal characteristics (ERP, antenna gain, etc.) are known.

Multipath propagation, causing frequency selective fading, is successfully combatted by the TATS modem through the use of coding and frequency diversity. Thus, the way is opened for UHF satellite communication from aircraft with simple antenna structures.

Frequency diversity, coding and matched filter output limiting combine to provide protection against sporadic RFI which is likely to be found in a tactical environment. Thus, shared allocations among conventional equipment and satellite users has been shown to be feasible.

## IV. ACKNOWLEDGMENT

Many people at Lincoln have participated in the design, implementation and testing of TATS. The authors would like to give much of this credit to: S. Russell, L. Goodman, B. Hutchinson, J. Atchison, R. Nickelson, J. Craig, P. Gendron and J. Siemasko.

The results quoted in this paper concerning the analysis and simulation of the acquisition and tracking loops are due to L. Goodman.

The link simulator was designed by D. Karp.

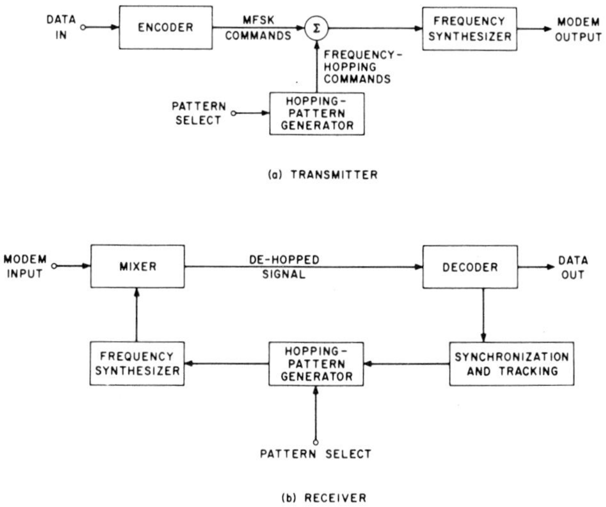


Fig. 1. TATS Functional Block Diagram

## BIBLIOGRAPHY


1. Peterson, W. W., Error-Correcting Codes, The M. I. T. Press, 1961.
2. Bluestein, L. and Greenspan, R., Efficient Approximation of Orthogonal Waveforms, Lincoln Laboratory Group Report 1964-48, 3 November 1964.
3. Wozencraft, J. and Jacobs, I., Principles of Communication Engineering, Pg. 481, John Wiley and Sons, 1965.
4. Lindsey, W., Error Probabilities for Rician Fading Multichannel Reception of Binary and N-ary Signals, PGIT, Vol. IT-10, October 1964.
5. Jones, J. J., Hard Limiting of Two Signals in Random Noise, PGIT, Vol. IT-9, January 1963.
6. Price, R., A Note on the Envelope and Phase Modulated Components of Narrowband Gaussian Noise, PGIT, September 1955.


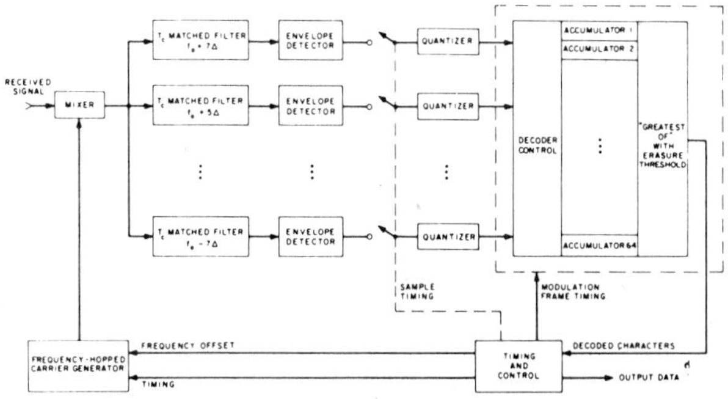


DECODING PROCEDURE FUNCTIONAL DIAGRAM

Fig. 3.

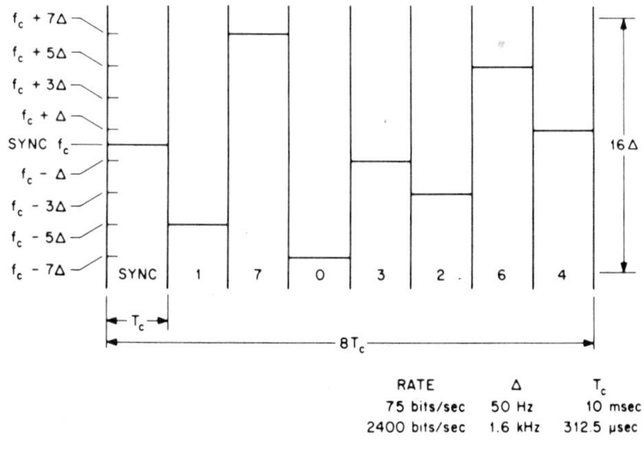


MODULATION FRAME

Fig. 2.

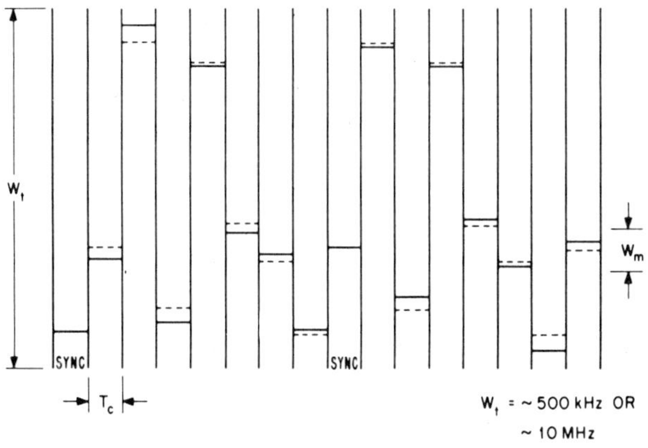


BANDSPREAD SIGNAL FORMAT

Fig. 4.

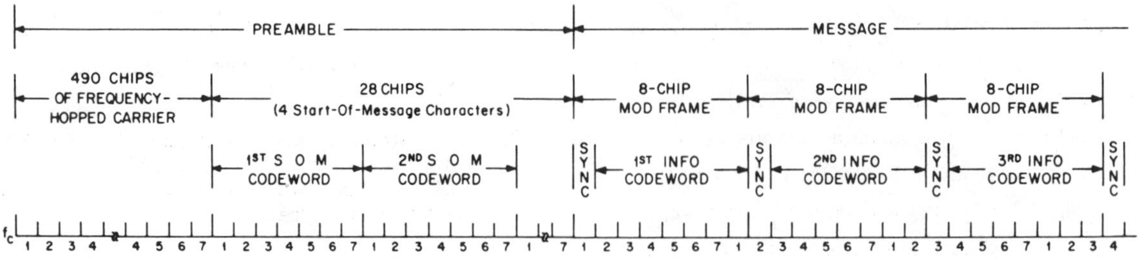


TATS TRANSMISSION FORMAT

Fig. 5.

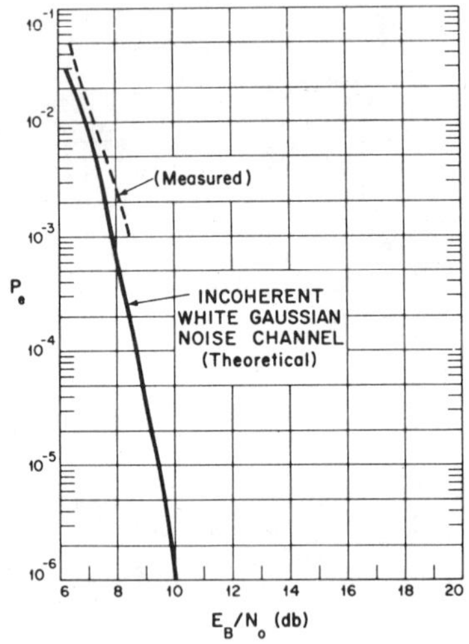


Fig. 7. Probability of Error vs. SNR

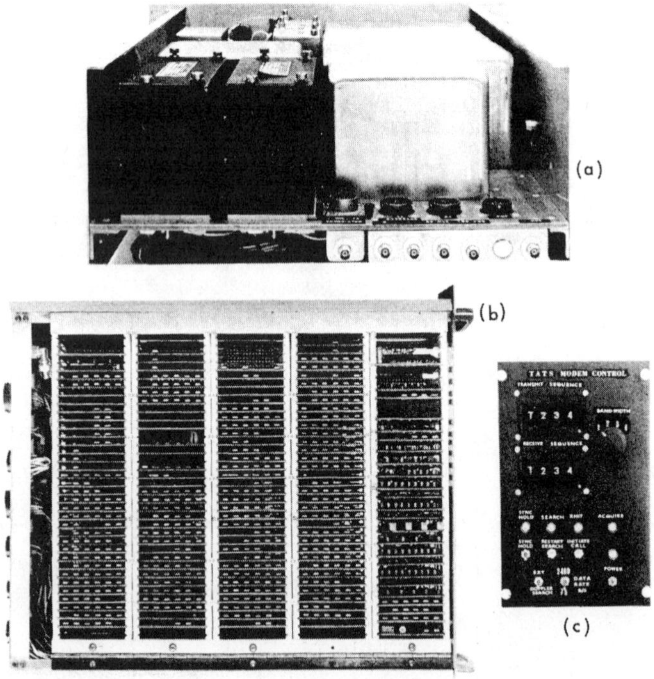


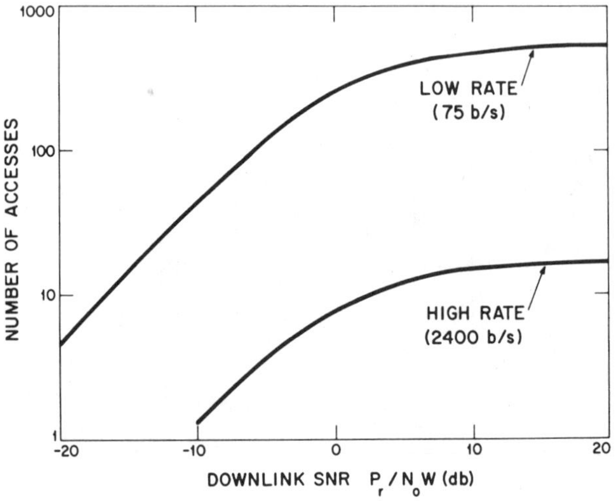


Fig. 8. Number of Accesses vs. Downlink SNR

Fig. 6. TATS Modem
(a) RF Drawer
(b) Digital Drawer
(c) Control Panel

# Part VII
# Information Transmission

In this part we are concerned with the information portion of spread spectrum systems. In an earlier part we talked about sequence inversion modulation (phase shift key of the pseudonoise carrier) and included Ward's paper on the subject. Other methods of embedding the information sent into the overall spread spectrum waveform exist (such as carrier frequency modulation), but the most often used method is that of inverting the code sequence with the information to be sent. A prime reason for the prominence of this method is that all one needs is a modulo-2 adder (assuming binary data and code) to perform the modulation function. The result of the modulo-2 addition is biphase modulation of the code sequence which in turn modulates the carrier. In a direct sequence system the modulated code sequence directly modulates the carrier. In a frequency hopper the modulated code sequence causes the frequency to shift according to the code pattern, and a chirp system chirps up or down depending on whether the code being applied is a one or a zero.

At the receiver, the story is quite different for these three basic spread spectrum techniques. The chirp signal is applied to a matched dispersive filter that outputs alternate pulses depending on whether a one or a zero was sent. The frequency hopping receiver usually compares alternate frequencies, since the code that goes to the frequency synthesizer in the transmitter is the pattern for a one or is the inverse pattern for a zero, and these two patterns cause different frequencies to be sent by the transmitter. The direct sequence receiver is more conventional and in fact is usually a little more difficult to build. This is because the signal produced by the sequence inversions turn out to be carrier phase modulation, which means that the signal appearing at a direct sequence demodulator is a double sideband suppressed carrier, usually either biphase or quadriphase modulated. Therefore, since this is the most difficult of the modulation/demodulation formats to implement, the technical papers have tended to concentrate in this area, so too does this part concentrate on coherence and phase shift modulation/demodulation.

The first reprinted paper in this part is included as a basic reference on phase lock theory. Phase lock loops and their double sideband suppressed carrier equivalent (the Costas loop) are used extensively in spread spectrum systems, and it is appropriate that such a basic paper be included here.

Cahn's paper on digital phase modulation defines the performance that one can expect for phase shift modulation of the type encountered in a direct sequence system, for various phase shifts (i.e., biphase, quadriphase, etc.), and for both coherent and differentially coherent signals. Although the same rules apply for spectrum-spreading modulation, this paper actually discusses phase shift keying for information. (The difference between phase shift keying for information and phase shift keying for spectrum spreading is that the spreading phase shifts occur at a much higher rate than the information shifts, and many can be misinterpreted without losing an information bit.)

Viterbi's paper is also concerned with coding for the information channel. As before, the results may be extrapolated for the spreading operation. The matched filter correlators shown are directly applicable to detection of either information bits or spread spectrum signal chips (with proper consideration for the large disparity in bit rates, of course). The information on coding and the comparisons given are directly applicable to either spread spectrum or any other type of information transmission system.

The remaining papers in this part concentrate on demodulation of double sideband suppressed carrier signals, and this is precisely the type of signal one encounters in many spread spectrum systems. Didday and Lindsey discuss and compare the various techniques that apply, while Lindsey and Simon extend the considerations, concentrating on two of the demodulator configurations (Costas and squaring loops) to cover the effects of frequency detuning such as might be encountered due to Doppler effects or oscillator drift. In practice, one rarely sees a spread spectrum carrier (or any other) that is at the exact design frequency, so considerations of the effects of operation under such conditions are most appropriate here.

## OTHER PAPERS OF INTEREST


1) D. T. Hess, "Equivalence of FM threshold extension receivers," *IEEE Trans. Commun. Technol.*, Oct. 1968.
2) L. A. Hoffman, "Receiver design and the phase-lock loop," *IEEE Electron. Space Exploration Ser.*, Aug. 1963.
3) R. Jaffe, and E. Rechtin, "Design and performance of phase-lock circuits capable of near-optimum performance over a wide range of input signal and noise levels," *IEEE Trans. Inform. Theory*, Mar. 1955.
4) N. S. Jayant, "Characteristics of a delta modulator," *Proc. IEEE*, Mar. 1971.
5) H. J. Landau, "Sampling, data acquisition, and the Nyquist rate," *Proc. IEEE*, Oct. 1967.
6) R. Lugannani, "Intersymbol interference and probability of error in digital systems," *IEEE Trans. Inform. Theory*, Nov. 1969.
7) H. T. McAleer, "A New look at the phase-locked oscillator," *IRE Trans.* June 1959.
8) B. M. Oliver, J. R. Pierce, and C. E. Shannon, "The philosophy of PCM," *Proc. IRE*, Nov. 1948.
9) R. W. Sanders, "Communications efficiency comparison of several communication systems," *Proc. IRE*, Apr. 1960.
10) L. Schuchman, "Dither signals and their effect on quantization noise," *IEEE Trans. Commun. Technol.*, Dec. 1964.
11) D. D. Weiner and B. J. Leon, "The quasistationary response of linear systems to modulated waveforms," *Proc. IEEE*, June 1965.
12) T. J. Tjhung, "Band occupancy of digital FM signals," *IEEE Trans. Commun. Technol.*, Dec. 1964.
13) J. W. Whelan, "Analog-FM versus digital-PSK transmission," *IEEE Trans. Commun. Technol.*, June 1966.
14) H. L. Van Trees, "Functional techniques for the analysis of the nonlinear behavior of phase-locked loops," *Proc. IEEE*, Aug. 1964.
15) A. J. Viterbi, "Phase-locked loop dynamics in the presence of noise by Fokker–Planck techniques," *Proc. IEEE*, Dec. 1963.

# Theory of AFC Synchronization*

WOLF J. GRUEN†, MEMBER, IRE

*Summary*—**The general solution for the important design parameters of an automatic frequency and phase-control system is presented. These parameters include the transient response, frequency response and noise bandwidth of the system, as well as the hold-in range and pull-in range of synchronization.**

## I. Introduction

Automatic frequency and phase-control systems have been used for a number of years for the horizontal-sweep synchronization in television receivers, and more recently have found application for the synchronization of the color subcarrier in the proposed NTSC color-television system. A block diagram of a general AFC system is shown in Fig. 1.

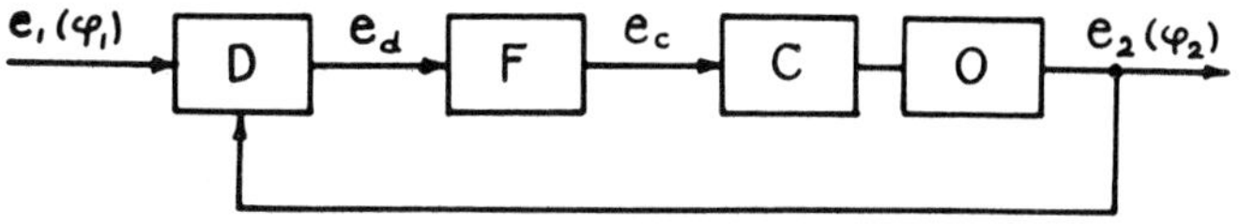


Fig. 1—Block diagram of A.F.C. loop.

The phase of the transmitted synchronizing signal $e_1$ is compared to the phase of a local oscillator signal $e_2$ in a phase discriminator D. The resulting discriminator output voltage is proportional to the phase difference of the two signals, and is fed through a control network F to a frequency-control stage C. This stage controls the frequency and phase of a local oscillator O in accordance with the synchronizing information, thereby keeping the two signals in perfect synchronism. Although in practice the transmitted reference signal is often pulsed and the oscillator comparison voltage non-sinusoidal, the analysis is carried out for sinusoidal signal voltages. The theory, however, can be extended for a particular problem by writing the applied voltages in terms of a Fourier series instead of the simple sine function. An AFC system is essentially a servomechanism, and the notation that will be used is the one followed by many workers in this field. An attempt will be made to present the response characteristics in dimensionless form in order to obtain a universal plot of the response curves.

## II. Derivation of the Basic Equation

If it is assumed that the discriminator is a balanced phase detector composed of peak-detecting diodes, the discriminator-output voltage can be derived from the vector diagram in Fig. 2. For sinusoidal variation with time, the synchronizing signal $e_1$ and the reference signal $e_2$ can be written

$$e_1 = E_1 \cos \phi_1 \tag{1}$$

and

$$e_2 = E_2 \sin \phi_2. \tag{2}$$

$\phi_1$ and $\phi_2$ are functions of time and, for reasons of simplicity in the later development, it is arbitrarily assumed that $\phi_1$ and $\phi_2$ are in quadrature when the system is perfectly synchronized, that is when $\phi_1 = \phi_2$.

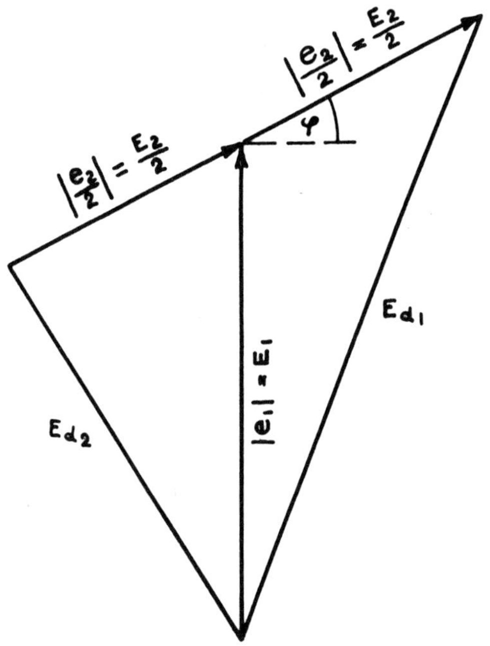


Fig. 2—Discriminator vector diagram.

While one of the discriminator diodes is fed with the sum of $e_1$ and $e_2/2$, the other is fed with the difference of these two vectors as shown in Fig. 2. The resulting rectified voltages $E_{d1}$ and $E_{d2}$ can be established by simple trigonometric relations. Defining a difference phase

$$\phi \equiv \phi_1 - \phi_2, \tag{3}$$

one obtains

$$E_{d1}^2 = E_1^2 + \frac{E_2^2}{4} + E_1E_2 \sin \phi \tag{4}$$

and

$$E_{d2}^2 = E_1^2 + \frac{E_2^2}{4} - E_1E_2 \sin \phi. \tag{5}$$

The discriminator output voltage $e_d$ is equal to the dif-

* Decimal classification: R583.5. Original manuscript received by the Institute, August 21, 1952; revised manuscript received February 25, 1953.
† General Electric Co., Syracuse, N. Y.

Reprinted from *Proc. IRE*, vol. 41, pp. 1043–1048, Aug. 1953.

ference of the two rectified voltages, so that

$$e_d = E_{d1} - E_{d2} = \frac{2E_1E_2}{E_{d1} + E_{d2}} \sin \phi. \tag{6}$$

If the amplitude $E_1$ of the synchronizing signal is larger than the amplitude $E_2$ of the reference signal, one obtains

$$E_{d1} + E_{d2} \cong 2E_1. \tag{7}$$

The discriminator output voltage then becomes

$$e_d = E_2 \sin \phi \tag{8}$$

and is independent of the amplitude $E_1$ of the synchronizing signal. As $\phi_1$ and $\phi_2$ are time-varying parameters, it should be kept in mind that the discriminator time constant ought to be shorter than the reciprocal of the highest difference frequency $d\phi/dt$, which is of importance for the operation of the system.

Denoting the transfer function of the control network $F$ as $F(p)$, the oscillator control voltage becomes

$$e_c = F(p)E_2 \sin \phi. \tag{9}$$

Assuming furthermore that the oscillator has a linear-control characteristic of a slope $S$, and that the free-running oscillator frequency is $\omega_0$, the actual oscillator frequency in operational notation becomes

$$p\phi_2 = \omega_0 + Se_c. \tag{10}$$

Substituting (3) and (9) into (10) then gives

$$p\phi + SE_2F(p) \sin \phi = p\phi_1 - \omega_0. \tag{11}$$

The product $SE_2$ repeats itself throughout this paper and shall be defined as the gain constant

$$K \equiv SE_2. \tag{12}$$

$K$ represents the maximum frequency shift at the output of the system per radian phase shift at the input. It has the dimension of radians/second.

Equation (11) can be simplified further by measuring the phase angles in a coordinate system which moves at the free-running speed $\omega_0$ of the local oscillator. One obtains

$$\boxed{p\phi + F(p)K \sin \phi = p\phi_1}. \tag{13}$$

This equation represents the general differential equation of the AFC feedback loop. $p\phi$ is the instantaneous-difference frequency between the synchronizing signal and the controlled-oscillator signal and $p\phi_1$ is the instantaneous-difference frequency between the synchronizing signal and the free-running oscillator signal.

Equation (13) shows that all AFC systems with identical gain constants $K$ and unity d.c. gain through the control network have the same steady-state solution, provided that the difference frequency $p\phi_1$ is constant. If this difference frequency is defined as

$$\Delta\omega \equiv p\phi_1 = \omega_1 - \omega_0, \tag{14}$$

the steady-state solution is

$$\sin \phi = \frac{\Delta\omega}{K} \cdot \tag{15}$$

This means the system has a steady-state phase error which is proportional to the initial detuning $\Delta\omega$ and inversely proportional to the gain constant $K$. Since the maximum value of sin $\phi$ in (15) is $\pm 1$, the system will hold synchronism over a frequency range

$$|\Delta\omega_{\text{Hold-in}}| \leqq K. \tag{16}$$

Equations (15) and (16) thus define the static performance limit of the system.

## III. Linear Analysis

An AFC system, once it is synchronized, behaves like a low-pass filter. To study its performance it is permissible, for practical signal-to-noise ratios, to substitute the angle for the sine function in (13). Then, with the definition of (3), one obtains

$$p\phi_2 + KF(p)\phi_2 = KF(p)\phi_1. \tag{17}$$

This equation relates the output phase $\phi_2$ of the synchronized system to the input phase $\phi_1$. It permits an evaluation of the behavior of the system to small disturbances of the input phase, if the transfer function $F(p)$ of the control network is specified.

### a. $F(p) = 1$

This is the simplest possible AFC system, and represents a direct connection between the discriminator output and the oscillator control stage. Equation (17) then becomes

$$p\phi_2 + K\phi_2 = K\phi_1. \tag{18}$$

If the initial detuning is zero, the transient response of the system to a sudden step of input phase $|\phi_1|$ is

$$\frac{\phi_2}{|\phi_1|}(t) = 1 - e^{-Kt}. \tag{19}$$

Likewise, the frequency response of the system to a sine-wave modulation of the input phase is

$$\frac{\phi_2}{\phi_1}(j\omega) = \frac{1}{1 + j\frac{\omega}{K}} \cdot \tag{20}$$

The simple AFC system thus behaves like an RC-filter and has a cut-off frequency of

$$\omega_c = K \text{ [radians/sec]}. \tag{21}$$

George[1] has shown that the m.s. phase error of the system under the influence of random interference is proportional to the noise bandwidth, which is defined as

[1] T. S. George, "Synchronizing systems for dot interlaced color TV," Proc. I.R.E.; February, 1951.

$$B = \int_{-\infty}^{+\infty} \left| \frac{\phi_2}{\phi_1} (j\omega) \right|^2 d\omega. \qquad (22)$$

The integration has to be carried out from $-\infty$ to $+\infty$ since the noise components on both sides of the carrier are demodulated. Inserting (20) into (22) then yields

$$B = \pi K \text{ [radians/sec]}. \qquad (23)$$

It was shown in (15) that for small steady-state phase errors due to average frequency drift, the gain constant $K$ has to be made as large as possible, while now for good noise immunity, i.e., narrow bandwidth, the gain constant has to be made as small as possible. A proper compromise of gain then must be found to insure adequate performance of the system for all requirements. This difficulty, however, can be overcome by the use of a more elaborate control network.

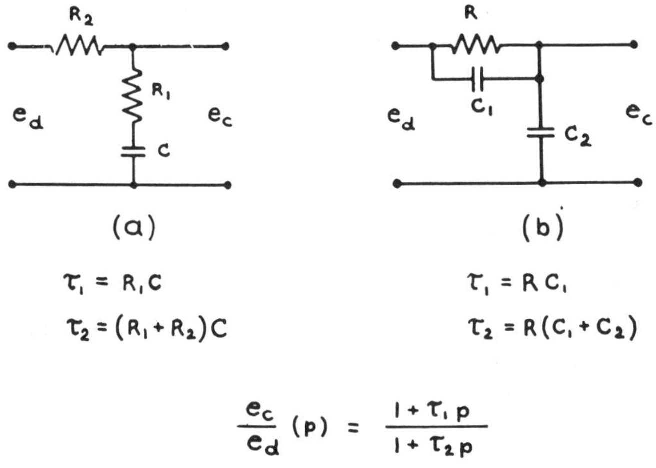


Fig. 3—Proportional plus integral control networks.

$$b. \; F(p) = \frac{1 + \tau_1 p}{1 + \tau_2 p}$$

Networks of this type are called proportional-plus integral-control networks[2] and typical network configurations are shown in Fig. 3. Inserting the above transfer function into (17) yields

$$p^2\phi_2 + \left(\frac{1}{\tau_2} + K\frac{\tau_1}{\tau_2}\right) p\phi_2 + \frac{K}{\tau_2}\phi_2 = K\frac{\tau_1}{\tau_2} p\phi_1 + \frac{K}{\tau_2}\phi_1. \qquad (24)$$

$\phi_1$ and $\phi_2$ are again relative phase angles, measured in a coordinate system which moves at the free-running speed of the local oscillator. To integrate (24), it is convenient to introduce the following parameters

$$\omega_n^2 \equiv \frac{K}{\tau_2} \qquad (25)$$

and

$$2\zeta\omega_n \equiv \frac{1}{\tau_2} + K\frac{\tau_1}{\tau_2} \cdot \qquad (26)$$

$\omega_n$ is the resonance frequency of the system in the absence of any damping, and $\zeta$ is the ratio of actual-to-critical damping. In terms of the new parameters the time constants of the control network are

$$\tau_1 = \frac{2\zeta}{\omega_n} - \frac{1}{K} \qquad (27)$$

and

$$\tau_2 = \frac{K}{\omega_n^2} \cdot \qquad (28)$$

With these definitions (24) becomes

$$p^2\phi_2 + 2\zeta\omega_n p\phi_2 + \omega_n^2\phi_2 = \left(2\zeta\omega_n - \frac{\omega_n^2}{K}\right) p\phi_1 + \omega_n^2\phi_1. \qquad (29)$$

The transient response of the system to a sudden step of input phase $|\phi_1|$ is found by integration of (29) and the initial condition for the oscillator frequency is obtained from (10). The transient response then is

$$\frac{\phi_2}{|\phi_1|}(t) = 1 - e^{-\zeta\omega_n t}\left[\cos\sqrt{1-\zeta^2}\,\omega_n t - \frac{\zeta - \frac{\omega_n}{K}}{\sqrt{1-\zeta^2}} \sin\sqrt{1-\zeta^2}\,\omega_n t\right]. \qquad (30)$$

For $\zeta < 1$ the system is underdamped (oscillatory), for $\zeta = 1$ critically damped and for $\zeta > 1$ overdamped (non-oscillatory). In order to avoid sluggishness of the system, a rule of thumb may be followed making. $4 < \zeta < 1^2$. The transient response of (30) can be plotted in dimensionless form if certain specifications are made for the ratio $\omega_n/K$. As the time constant $\tau_1$ of the control network must be positive or can at most be equal to zero, the maximum value for $\omega_n/K$ is found from (27), yielding

$$\left.\frac{\omega_n}{K}\right|_{\max} = 2\zeta. \qquad (31)$$

In this case the control network is reduced to a single time constant network ($\tau_1 = 0$). On the other hand, if for a fixed value of $\omega_n$ the gain of the system is increased towards infinity, the minimum value for $\omega_n/K$ becomes

$$\left.\frac{\omega_n}{K}\right|_{\min} = 0. \qquad (32)$$

Fig. 4 shows the transient response of the system for these two limits and for a damping ratio of $\zeta = 0.5$.

[2] G. S. Brown and D. P. Campbell, "Principles of Servomechanisms," John Wiley & Sons Publishing Co., New York, N. Y.; 1948.

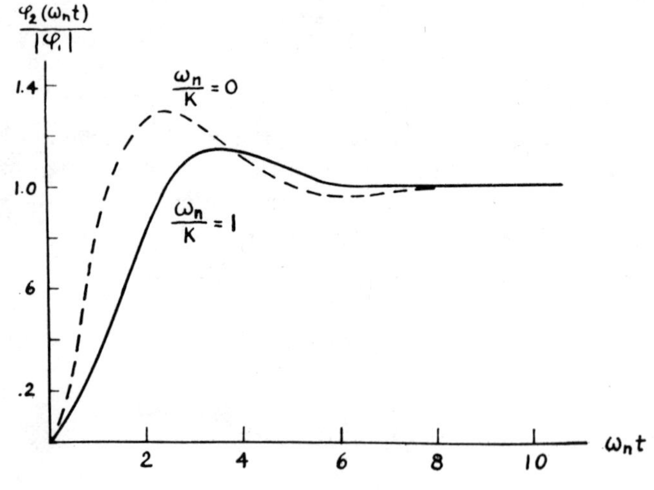


Fig. 4—Transient response for $\zeta = 0.5$.

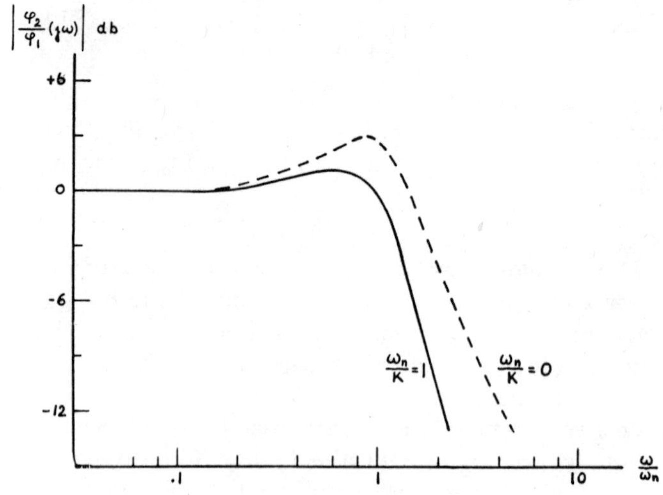


Fig. 5—Frequency response for $\zeta = 0.5$.

The frequency response of the system is readily found from (24) and one obtains

$$\frac{\phi_2}{\phi_1}(j\omega) = \frac{1 + j2\zeta\frac{\omega}{\omega_n}\left(1 - \frac{\omega_n}{2\zeta K}\right)}{1 + j2\zeta\frac{\omega}{\omega_n} - \left(\frac{\omega}{\omega_n}\right)^2}. \quad (33)$$

Its magnitude is plotted in Fig. 5 for the two limit values of $\omega_n/K$ and for a damping ratio $\zeta = 0.5$. The curves show that the cut-off frequency of the system, for $\zeta = 0.5$, is approximately

$$\omega_c \cong \omega_n \text{ [radians/sec.]}. \quad (34)$$

If $\phi_1$ and $\phi_2$ in (33) are assumed to be the input and output voltage of a four-terminal low-pass filter, the frequency response leads to the equivalent circuit of Fig. 6.

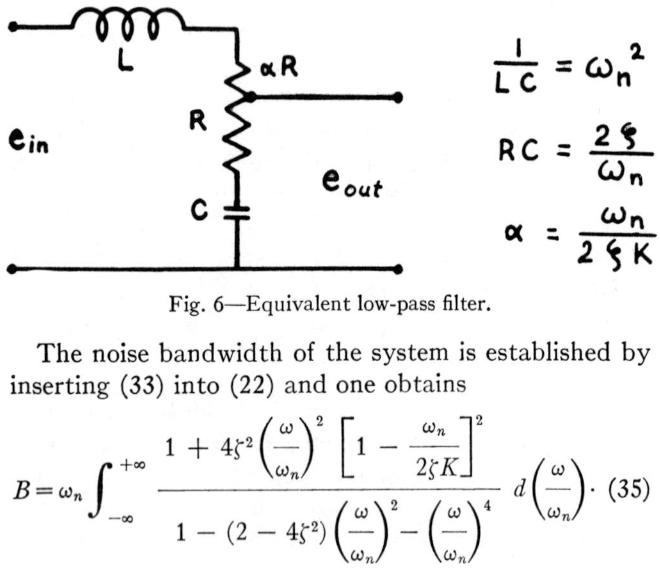


Fig. 6—Equivalent low-pass filter.

The noise bandwidth of the system is established by inserting (33) into (22) and one obtains

$$B = \omega_n \int_{-\infty}^{+\infty} \frac{1 + 4\zeta^2\left(\frac{\omega}{\omega_n}\right)^2\left[1 - \frac{\omega_n}{2\zeta K}\right]^2}{1 - (2 - 4\zeta^2)\left(\frac{\omega}{\omega_n}\right)^2 - \left(\frac{\omega}{\omega_n}\right)^4} d\left(\frac{\omega}{\omega_n}\right). \quad (35)$$

The integration, which can be carried out by partial fractions with the help of tables, yields

$$B = \frac{4\zeta^2 - 4\zeta\frac{\omega_n}{K} + \left(\frac{\omega_n}{K}\right)^2 + 1}{2\zeta}\pi\omega_n. \quad (36)$$

For small values of $\omega_n/K$, it is readily established that this expression has a minimum when $\zeta = 0.5$. Hence, the noise bandwidths for the limit values of $\omega_n/K$ and $\zeta = 0.5$ become

$$B\big|_{(\omega_n/K)\to 1} = \pi\omega_n = \pi K \text{ [radians/sec]} \quad (37)$$

and

$$B\big|_{(\omega_n/K)\to 0} = 2\pi\omega_n \text{ [radians/sec]}. \quad (38)$$

The above derivations, as well as the response curves of Figs. 4 and 5, show that the bandwidth and the gain constant of the system can be adjusted independently if a double time-constant control network is employed.

*c. Example*

The theory is best illustrated by means of an example. Suppose an AFC system is to be designed, having a steady state phase error of not more than 3° and a noise bandwidth of 1,000 cps. The local oscillator drift shall be assumed with 1,500 cps.

The required gain constant is obtained from (15), yielding

$$K = \frac{\Delta\omega}{\sin\phi} = \frac{2\pi \cdot 1{,}500}{\sin 3^\circ} = 180{,}000 \text{ radians/sec.}$$

Since $K$ is large in comparison to the required bandwidth, the resonance frequency of the system is established from (38).

$$\omega_n = \frac{B}{2\pi} = \frac{2\pi \cdot 1{,}000}{2\pi} = 1{,}000 \text{ radians/sec.}$$

The two time constants of the control network, assuming a damping ratio of 0.5, are determined from (27) and (28) respectively

$$\tau_1 = \frac{2\zeta}{\omega_n} - \frac{1}{K} = \frac{1}{1{,}000} - \frac{1}{180{,}000} \cong 10^{-3} \text{ sec},$$

and

$$\tau_2 = \frac{K}{\omega_n^2} = \frac{180{,}000}{1{,}000^2} = 0.18 \text{ sec.}$$

These values $K$, $\tau_1$, and $\tau_2$ completely define the AFC system. A proper choice of gain distribution and control-network impedance still has to be made to fit a particular design. For example, if the peak amplitude of the sinusoidal oscillator reference voltage is $E_2=6$ volts, the sensitivity of the oscillator control stage must be $S=30{,}000$ radians/sec/volt to provide the necessary gain constant of 180,000 radians/sec. Furthermore, if the capacitor $C$ for the control network of Fig. 3(a) is assumed to be 0.22 $uf$, the resistors $R_1$ and $R_2$ become 4.7 kΩ and 820 kΩ respectively, to yield the desired time constants.

## IV. Non-Linear Analysis

While it was permissible to assume small phase angles for the study of the synchronized system, thereby linearizing the differential (13), this simplification cannot be made for the evaluation of the pull-in performance of the system. The pull-in range of synchronization is defined as the range of difference frequencies, $p\phi_1$, between the input signal and the free-running oscillator signal, over which the system can reach synchronism. Since the difference phase $\phi$ can vary over many radians during pull-in, it is necessary to integrate the nonlinear equation to establish the limit of synchronization.

Assuming that the frequency of the input signal is constant as defined by (14), (13) can be written

$$p\phi + F(p)K \sin \phi = \Delta\omega. \tag{39}$$

Mathematically then, the pull-in range of synchronization is the maximum value of $\Delta\omega$ for which, irrespective of the initial condition of the system, the phase difference $\phi$ reaches a steady state value. To solve (39), the transfer function of the control network again must be defined.

*a.* $F(p) = 1$

The pull-in performance for this case has been treated in detail by Labin.[3] With $F(p)=1$ (39) can be integrated by separation of the variables and it is readily found that the system synchronizes for all values of $|\Delta\omega| < K$. The condition for pull-in then is

$$|\Delta\omega|_{\text{Pull-in}} < K. \tag{40}$$

Large pull-in range and narrow-noise bandwidth thus are incompatible requirements for this system.

*b.* $F(p) = \dfrac{1+\tau_1 p}{1+\tau_2 p}$

Inserting this transfer function into (39) and carrying out the differentiation yields

$$\frac{d^2\phi}{dt^2} + \left[\frac{1}{\tau_2} + K\frac{\tau_1}{\tau_2}\cos\phi\right]\frac{d\phi}{dt} + \frac{K}{\tau_2}\sin\phi = \frac{\Delta\omega}{\tau_2}\cdot \tag{41}$$

This equation can be simplified by inserting the coefficients defined in (25) and (26), and by dividing the resulting equation by $\omega_n^2$. This leads to the dimensionless equation.

$$\frac{d^2\phi}{\omega_n^2 dt^2} + \left[\frac{\omega_n}{K} + \left(2\zeta - \frac{\omega_n}{K}\right)\cos\phi\right]\frac{d\phi}{\omega_n dt} + \sin\phi = \frac{\Delta\omega}{K}\cdot \tag{42}$$

A further simplification is possible by defining a dimensionless difference frequency

$$y \equiv \frac{d\phi}{\omega_n dt} \tag{43}$$

and one obtains a first order differential equation from which the dimensionless time $\omega_n t$ has been eliminated. It follows

$$\frac{dy}{d\phi} = \frac{\dfrac{\Delta\omega}{K} - \sin\phi}{y} - \frac{\omega_n}{K} - \left(2\zeta - \frac{\omega_n}{K}\right)\cos\phi. \tag{44}$$

There is presently no analytical method available to solve this equation. However, the equation completely defines the slope of the solution curve $y(\phi)$ at all points of a $\phi-y$ plane, except for the points of stable and unstable equilibrium, $y=0$; $\Delta\omega/K=\sin\phi$. The limit of synchronization can thus be found graphically by starting the system with an infinitestimal velocity $\Delta y$ at a point of unstable equilibrium, $y=0$; $\phi=\pi-\sin^{-1}\Delta\omega/K$, and finding the value of $\Delta\omega/K$ for which the solution curve just reaches the next point of unstable equilibrium located at $y=0$; $\phi=3\pi-\sin^{-1}\Delta\omega/K$. The method is discussed by Stoker[4] and has been used by Tellier and Preston[5] to find the pull-in range for a single time constant AFC system.

To establish the limit curve of synchronization for given values of $\zeta$ and $\omega_n/K$, a number of solution curves have to be plotted with $\Delta\omega/K$ as parameter. The limit of pull-in range in terms of $\Delta\omega/K$ then can be interpolated to any desired degree of accuracy. The result, obtained in this manner, is shown in the dimensionless graph of Fig. 7, where $\Delta\omega/K$ is plotted as a function of $\omega_n/K$ for a damping ratio $\zeta=0.5$. Since this curve represents the stability limit of synchronization for the system, the time required to reach synchronism is infinite when starting from any point on the limit curve. The same applies to any point on the $\Delta\omega/K$-axis, with exception of the point $\Delta\omega/K=0$, since this axis describes a system having either infinite gain or zero bandwidth, and neither case has any real practical significance. The practical pull-in range of synchronization, therefore, lies inside the solid boundary. The individual points

[3] Edouard Labin, "Theorie de la synchronization par controle de phase," *Philips Res. Rep.*, (in French); August, 1941.

[4] J. J. Stoker, "Non-linear vibrations," *Interscience;* New York, 1950.

[5] G. W. Preston and J. C. Tellier, "The Lock-in Performance of an A.F.C. Circuit," Proc. I.R.E.; February, 1953.

entered in Fig. 7 represent the measured pull-in curve of a particular system for which the damping ratio was maintained at $\zeta = 0.5$. For small values of $\omega_n/K$ this

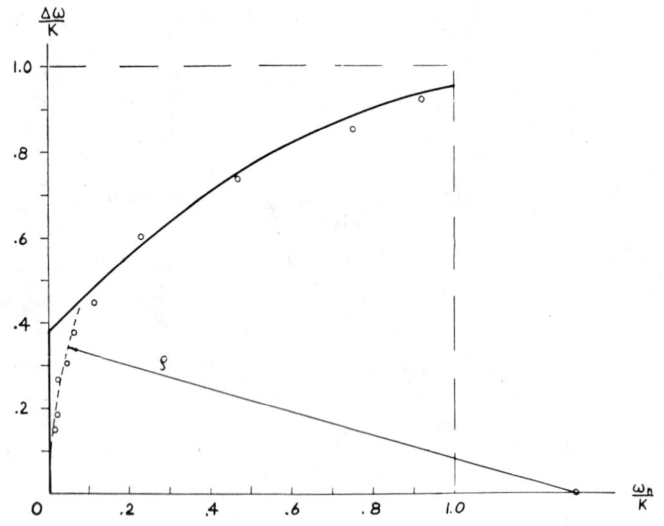


Fig. 7—Pull-in range of synchronization for $\zeta = 0.5$.

pull-in curve can be approximated by its circle of curvature which, as indicated by the dotted line, is tangent to the $\Delta\omega/K$-axis and whose center lies on the $\omega_n/K$-axis. The pull-in range thus can be expressed analytically by the equation of the circle of curvature. If its radius is denoted by $\zeta$, the circle is given by

$$\left(\frac{\omega_n}{K} - \zeta\right)^2 + \left(\frac{\Delta\omega}{K}\right)^2 = \zeta^2. \tag{45}$$

Hence, for $(\omega_n/K) \rightarrow 0$, the pull-in range of synchronization is approximately

$$\left| \Delta\omega_{\text{Pull-in}} \right|_{(\omega_n/K)\rightarrow 0} < \sqrt{2\zeta\omega_n K - \omega_n^2} \cong \sqrt{2\zeta\omega_n K}. \tag{46}$$

$\zeta$ can be interpreted as a constant of proportionality which depends on the particular design of the system, and which increases as the system gets closer to the theoretical limit of synchronization.

Equation (46) shows that the pull-in range for small values of $\omega_n/K$ is proportional to the square root of the product of the cut-off frequency $\omega_n$ and the gain constant $K$. Since the bandwidth of a double time constant AFC system can be adjusted independently of the gain constant, the pull-in range of such a system can exceed the noise bandwidth by any desired amount.

## V. Conclusions

The performance of an AFC system can be described by three parameters. These are the gain constant $K$, the damping ratio $\zeta$ and the resonance or cut-off frequency $\omega_n$. These parameters are specified by the requirements of a particular application and define the over-all design of the system. It has been shown that among the systems with zero, single and double time constant control networks, only the latter fulfills the requirement for achieving good noise immunity, small steady-state phase error and large pull-in range.

# Performance of Digital Phase-Modulation Communication Systems*

CHARLES R. CAHN†

*Summary*—**This paper analyzes the performance of digital phase modulation systems in Gaussian noise and determines required signal-to-noise ratio as a function of the number of discrete phases and the desired error rate, under conditions of no fading. Both coherent detection with a locally-derived reference carrier and phase comparison detection are considered. The calculations show that multiphase modulation provides an efficient trade of bandwidth for signal-to-noise ratio in comparison with multilevel amplitude modulation. It is also found that phase comparison detection introduces about a 3-db degradation over coherent detection except with binary modulation, for which the degradation is less than 1 db for error rates not exceeding about 0.001.**

## Introduction

THE need for efficient utilization of various media for transmission of digital data has stimulated the investigation of advanced coding and modulation techniques. Because highly stable oscillators are available for practical application, it is now possible to establish a phase reference in a receiver to detect digital phase-modulated signals, and a number of communication systems employing such signals have been developed.[1,2]

This paper determines the performance of such systems for the important case of signals corrupted by Gaussian noise and considers both coherent and phase-comparison detection schemes. A steady received signal is assumed in the analysis in accordance with the common procedure of adding fading allowances to the transmitter power calculated for median propagation and noise conditions. If an error rate averaged over a fading cycle is desired, a further graphical or analytical integration is necessary.[3]

## Optimum Detection

The signals of the type under consideration consist of phase-modulation pulses of specified width, transmitted at a known repetition rate. The signal is sampled in the receiver at the pulse peaks. Each sample has the form

$$s(t) = \sqrt{2S} \cos (\omega_0 t + \theta) \tag{1}$$

where $S$ is the received signal power, $\omega_0$ is the angular center frequency, and $\theta$ may have any value in the discrete set $2\pi k/m$, $0 \leq k \leq m - 1$. The detection problem is to determine $\theta$ when the signal is received under conditions of no fading and with additive Gaussian noise of the form

$$n(t) = x(t) \cos \omega_0 t + y(t) \sin \omega_0 t. \tag{2}$$

In (2), $x$ and $y$ are low-frequency random variables, each with zero mean and power $\overline{n^2} = N$. The bandwidth is assumed sufficient to resolve the individual pulses of the signal so that no overlap occurs at the sampled peaks.

Maximum likelihood detection is presumed for the theoretical analysis. With equal *a priori* probabilities for the possible phases, this type of detection corresponds to selection of that phase having the maximum *a posteriori* probability according to the particular processing scheme utilized in the receiver.

## Coherent Detection

The basic digital phase-modulation system provides a coherent phase reference in the receiver to facilitate signal processing. The set of $m$ possible transmitted signals may be described by a set of $m$ equally-spaced phasors in the complex plane, as shown in Fig. 1 for $m = 8$. Noise is

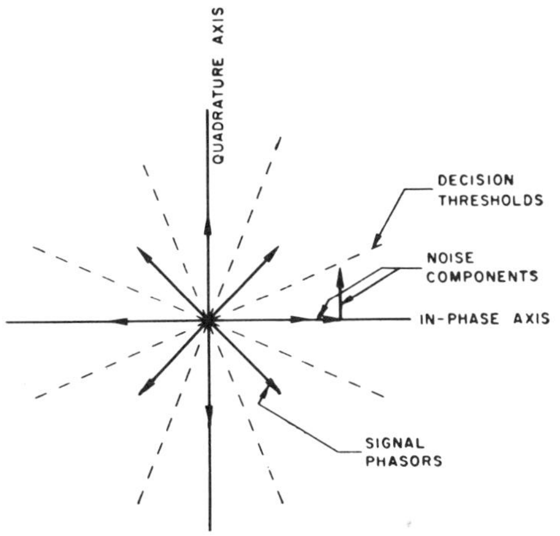


Fig. 1—Phasor representation of digital multiphase signals.

added in transmission and is indicated in Fig. 1 by the two quadrature components added to the zero-phase signal. These distort the signal, both in amplitude and in phase. The dotted lines placed symmetrically between the signal phasors indicate the optimum decision thresholds. The possible signal phase having maximum *a posteriori* probability is indicated by the sector in which the actual phase of signal-plus-noise falls.

* Manuscript received by the PGCS, December 12, 1958.
† Ramo-Wooldridge, a division of Thompson Ramo Wooldridge Inc., Los Angeles, Calif.

[1] M. L. Doelz, E. T. Heald, and D. L. Martin, "Binary data transmission techniques for linear systems," Proc. IRE, vol. 45, pp. 657–661; May, 1957.

[2] F. A. Losee, "A digital data transmission system using phase modulation and correlation detection," *Proc. Natl. Conf. on Aeronautical Electronics*, pp. 88–93; May, 1958.

[3] G. F. Montgomery, "A comparison of amplitude and angle modulation for narrow-band communication of binary-coded messages in fluctuation noise," Proc. IRE, vol. 42, pp. 447–454; February, 1954.

Reprinted from *IRE Trans. Commun. Syst.*, vol. CS-7, pp. 3–6, May 1959.

It is seen that the probability of an error due to noise is the probability that the phase of signal-plus-noise will be distorted outside the sector $-\pi/m < \theta < \pi/m$, where zero is the undistorted or true phase. This probability can be calculated by integration of the probability density of the phase of a steady signal plus Gaussian noise. The probability density of phase can be evaluated from the joint probability density of envelope and phase[4] by integrating over-all values of envelope from 0 to $\infty$ and is found to be

$$p(\theta) = \frac{1}{2\pi} e^{-S/N}[1 + \sqrt{4\pi S/N} \cos \theta e^{(S/N)\cos^2\theta} \cdot \Phi(\sqrt{2S/N} \cos \theta)] \quad (3)$$

where $\Phi(x)$ is the probability integral defined by

$$\Phi(x) = \frac{1}{\sqrt{2\pi}} \int_{-\infty}^{x} e^{-x^2/2}\, dx. \quad (4)$$

The probability density of phase is plotted in Fig. 2 for several values of signal-to-noise ratio, $S/N$.

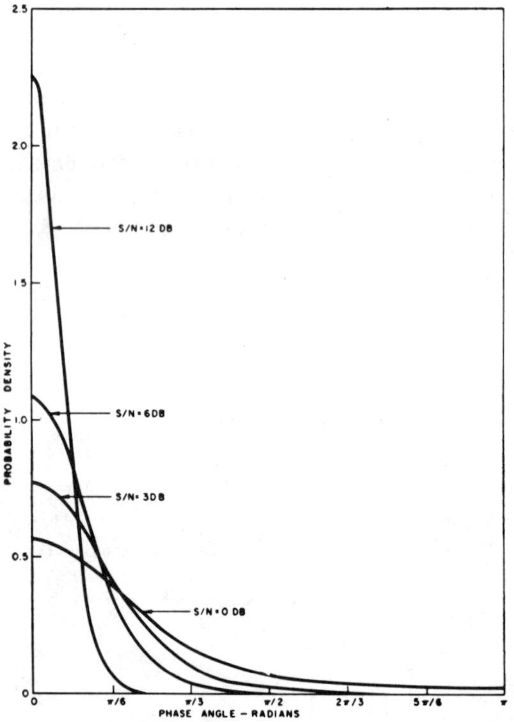


Fig. 2—Probability density of phase for sine wave plus Gaussian noise.

The probability of error $P_e$ as a function of the signal-to-noise ratio and the number of phase positions can be obtained by numerical or graphical integration of (3), according to

$$P_e = 1 - \int_{-\pi/m}^{\pi/m} p(\theta)\, d\theta. \quad (5)$$

[4] S. O. Rice, "Mathematical analysis of random noise," in "Noise and Stochastic Processes," Nelson Wax, ed., Dover Publications, Inc., New York, N. Y., p. 238; 1954.

From probability distributions previously presented in the literature,[5] a set of working curves has been drawn in Fig. 3. These curves indicate the required signal-to-noise ratio for a specified error rate and number of phase positions.

The information conveyed per pulse is $\log_2 m$ when multiphase modulation is used. Hence, for a fixed information rate, the signal bandwidth is reduced by this factor. A convenient normalization is the signal-to-noise ratio measured in the equivalent bandwidth, *i.e.*, the bandwidth necessary with binary phase modulation at the specified information rate. Assuming flat Gaussian noise over the frequency band of interest, the noise power is directly proportional to bandwidth, and the resulting curves are given in Fig. 4. The ordinate of these curves is directly proportional to required signal power and allows direct comparison of power requirements for communication systems with different numbers of phase positions. Note that biphase and quadriphase modulations are essentially equivalent, while triphase modulation requires slightly less signal power than biphase modulation.

## Phase-Comparison Detection

In certain cases of practical importance, obtaining and maintaining a coherent phase reference in the receiver is not feasible. In such cases, it may be possible to utilize phase comparison of successive samples for the detection process. Thus, the information is conveyed by the phase transitions between pulses rather than as the absolute phases of the pulses. It is apparent that this type of detection process is not as effective as coherent detection and will lead to a higher error rate for any specified signal-to-noise ratio.

For reasonably large positive values of $x$, the probability integral may be approximated by an asymptotic expansion such as

$$\Phi(x) \cong 1 - \frac{e^{-x^2/2}}{\sqrt{2\pi}\, x}. \quad (6)$$

If this expression is utilized in the probability density function (3) for the phase, the result is

$$p(\theta) \cong \frac{\cos\theta}{\sqrt{\pi N/S}} e^{-(\sin^2\theta)/N/S} \cong \frac{1}{\sqrt{\pi N/S}} e^{-(\theta^2)/N/S}, \quad |\theta| < \pi/2$$

$$\cong 0, \quad |\theta| > \pi/2 \quad (7)$$

with a smooth transition between the two expressions occurring at $\theta = \pm\pi/2$. That the probability density of the phase is approximately Gaussian for small angular deviations also may be seen from a formula previously derived by Rice.[6]

[5] K. A. Norton, E. L. Shultz, and H. Yarbrough, "The probability distribution of the phase of the resultant vector sum of a constant vector plus a rayleigh distributed vector," *J. Appl. Phys.*, vol. 23, pp. 137–141; January, 1952.

[6] S. O. Rice, "Statistical properties of a sine wave plus random noise," *Bell Sys. Tech. J.*, vol. 27, pp. 109–157; January, 1948.

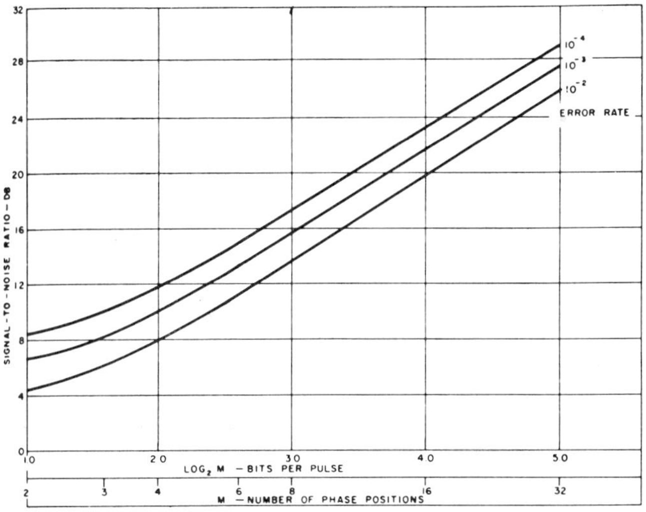


Fig. 3—Signal-to-noise ratio requirement for digital phase modulation.

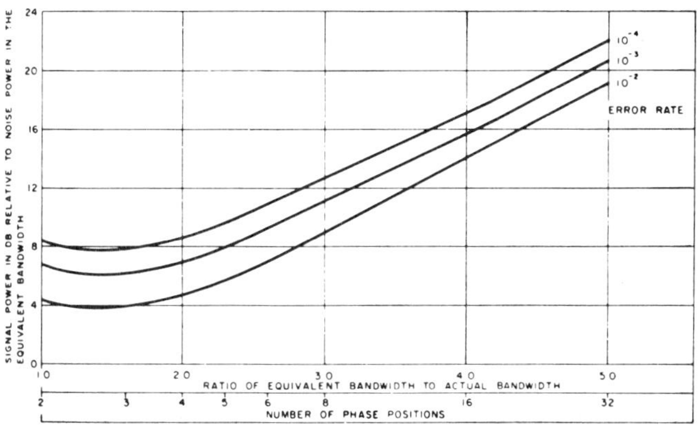


Fig. 4—Relative power requirement with digital phase modulation.

For phase comparison of successive samples with uncorrelated noise voltages, the resulting angle is a random variable defined by the difference of the phase angles of the two samples. For reasonably high signal-to-noise ratios and for small angular deviations, the difference phase has approximately a Gaussian distribution with twice the variance of the distribution for the phase of a single sample. Therefore, the degradation introduced by phase-comparison detection is essentially 3 db over coherent detection for a specified (low) error rate. This result applies, however, only with multiphase modulation for which the angular deviations of interest will be small.

For binary or phase-reversal modulation, the degradation at high signal-to-noise ratios is found to be less than 3 db. One method of calculating the error rate for a specified signal-to-noise ratio is to obtain the probability density function for the difference phase by graphical convolution of the density function for the phase of a single pulse.[7] The probability that the difference phase deviates by more than 90° from its proper value can then be obtained by graphical integration.

An alternate technique which gives a closed-form solution is now presented. Suppose that the phase of the noise-distorted first sample has the value $\theta$ with respect to its undistorted position. The conditional probability of error is then the probability that the phasor representing the noise-distorted second sample will cross the decision surface indicated in Fig. 5. Only the component of noise on the second sample parallel to the distorted position of the first sample can cause an error. The conditional probability of this is

$$p(\text{error} \mid \theta) = \frac{1}{\sqrt{2\pi N}} \int_{\sqrt{2S}\cos\theta}^{\infty} e^{-x^2/2N}\, dx$$
$$= 1 - \Phi(\sqrt{2S/N}\cos\theta). \qquad (8)$$

The total probability of error is the integral of the joint density function, $p(\theta)\, p(\text{error} \mid \theta)$, over all possible values of $\theta$, or

$$P_e = \int_{-\pi}^{\pi} p(\theta)[1 - \Phi(\sqrt{2S/N}\cos\theta)]\, d\theta. \qquad (9)$$

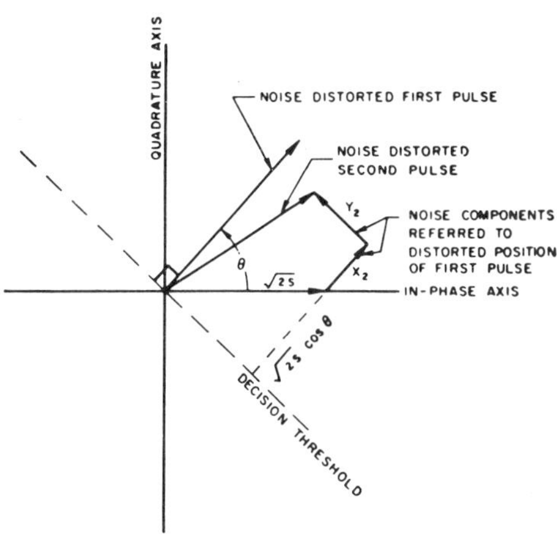


Fig. 5—Effects of noise on phase-comparison detection.

If the expression for $p(\theta)$ given in (3) is substituted into (9) and all functions expanded as (absolutely convergent) power series in $\sqrt{2S/N}\cos\theta$, it will be seen that all terms except a single constant term contain $\cos\theta$ raised to an odd power and will integrate to zero over a full cycle. The remaining constant term yields the probability of error,

$$P_e = \tfrac{1}{2}e^{-S/N}. \qquad (10)$$

The calculated probability of error for binary transmission with phase-comparison detection is presented in Fig. 6 along with the corresponding curve for coherent detection. It is seen that the degradation is indeed less than 3 db for high values of $S/N$.

In previous analyses[3,8] of binary transmission systems, a formula identical in form to (10) is derived for the error rate with frequency-shift modulation under nonfading

[7] J. L. Doob, "Stochastic Processes," John Wiley and Sons, Inc., New York, N. Y., p. 78; 1953.

[8] G. L. Turin, "Error probabilities for binary symmetric ideal reception through nonselective slow fading and noise," Proc. IRE, vol. 46, pp. 1603–1619; September, 1958.

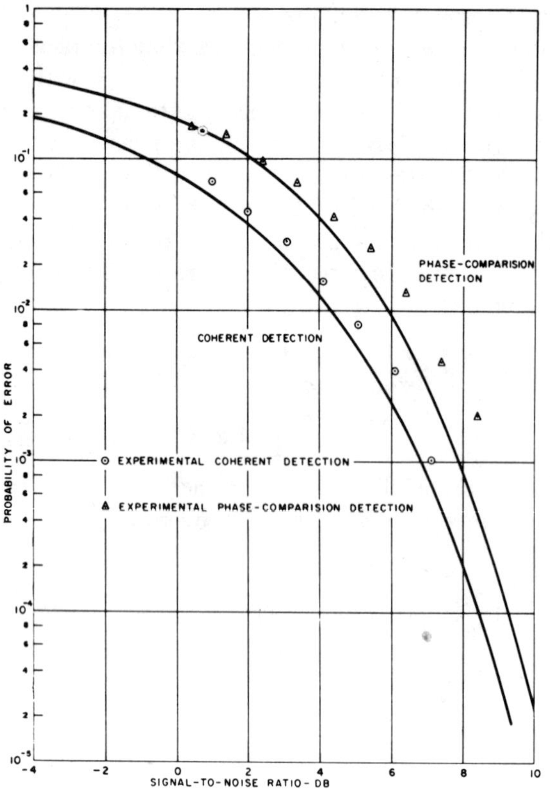


Fig. 6—Error rates with binary phase modulation.

conditions. This apparently is a coincidence, although not completely so, since phase transitions can be considered as the result of positive or negative shifts in the carrier frequency. It is important to note, however, that frequency-shift keying utilizes twice the bandwidth necessary with phase-reversal modulation and, therefore, requires 3 db more power for any specified error rate.

To verify the theoretical calculations for binary phase-modulated systems, experimental determinations of error rate vs signal-to-noise ratio were made with both coherent and phase-comparison detection. The results are shown along with the theoretical curves in Fig. 6. The agreement between theory and experiment regarding the relative performance of the two systems is excellent. The experimental curves show a small degradation with respect to the theoretical curves as may usually be expected due to non-ideal performance of practical phase detectors.

## Significance of Error Rate

The error rate given in (5) and in Fig. 6 is actually a character error rate. That is, the size of the alphabet is $m$ (number of phases), and $P_e$ is the probability that the transmitted character will be received incorrectly. In many cases, however, the information to be transmitted is in binary form and must be coded for an $m$-phase system. For example, three bits could be combined to give any of eight phases. The character error rate and the bit error rate are not usually equal under such circumstances.

As a simple illustration, suppose that the three bits select any of the eight phases by a Gray code, so that adjacent phase positions correspond to bit combinations differing in only one place. The large majority of transmission errors will cause the phase to fall in a sector adjacent to that of the correct signal, and only one bit will be in error. The average probability of error in the binary information is then about 1/3 of the value from (5).

Similar analyses can be made for other coding techniques that translate binary data into a set of $m$ characters for transmission over an $m$-phase system.

## Conclusions

Multiphase digital modulation proves to be an efficient technique for trading bandwidth for signal-to-noise ratio to reduce spectrum congestion. That is, as the number of phases is increased beyond two, the signal power required goes up slowly at first, particularly in comparison with the behavior for multilevel amplitude modulation.[9] In fact, no additional power is required until the number of phases exceeds four, when coherent detection is employed.

For high signal-to-noise ratios (low error rates), phase-comparison detection yields about a 3-db degradation over coherent detection, except in the binary case. In that special case, the degradation approaches zero with high signal-to-noise ratios and is less than about 1 db for error rates below 0.001. Therefore, multiphase modulation is not as efficient, relative to binary modulation, as was the case with coherent detection.

Although not considered in this paper, combinations of digital amplitude and phase modulation are also possible. When a large-size alphabet is contemplated, such combinations may make some efficient use of power than either amplitude or phase modulation used alone.

## Acknowledgment

The author wishes to thank J. Taber of Space Technology Laboratories, who suggested the approach used to calculate the probability of error for binary phase-comparison detection. Thanks are due also to B. Dell and H. Lee of Ramo-Wooldridge and to A. Gold of Space Technology Laboratories, who derived and plotted the probability density functions of phase and obtained the experimental data presented in Fig. 6.

[9] B. M. Oliver, J. R. Pierce, and C. E. Shannon, "The philosophy of pcm," Proc. IRE, vol. 36, pp. 1324–1331; November, 1948.

# On Coded Phase-Coherent Communications*

A. J. VITERBI†, MEMBER, IRE

*Summary*—The merits of phase-coherent communications are widely recognized for both discrete and continuous modulation systems [1]–[3]. The relative performances of phase-coherent and noncoherent transmission of binary data in the presence of additive white Gaussian noise have been analyzed and compared [1] and [2]. This paper considers the result of encoding independent equiprobable binary words or sequences of independent binary digits into sets of binary code words. These are transmitted over a channel perturbed by additive white Gaussian noise and detected by correlating them with their stored or locally generated replicas at the receiver.

The word error probabilities and bit error probabilities for low cross-correlation codes are determined as a function of the ratio

$$\frac{\text{(received signal energy)/bit}}{\text{(noise power)/(unit bandwidth)}}$$

The received information rate and the potential channel capacity are also computed. It is shown that in the limit as the code word length and the bandwidth approach infinity, the received information rate approaches the channel capacity for only one value of the above ratio.

## I. Basic Model

In ORDER to communicate $n$ bits of information, $2^n$ degrees of freedom must be available at the transmitter. These $2^n$ arbitrary messages or words are to be stored or generated at the transmitter. Depending on the information to be sent, one of the $2^n$ words is sent over a period of $nT$ seconds, $T$ being the transmission time alloted per bit. The communication channel is assumed to add an arbitrary disturbance to the transmitted signal (Fig. 1). The ideal receiver computes the conditional probability that each of the possible $2^n$ words was transmitted over the interval of $nT$ seconds, given the received word. It has been shown by Woodward [4], Davies [4] and [5], and Fano [6] that if the channel disturbance is white Gaussian noise, the probability computer consists of $2^n$ correlators which multiply the incoming signal by each of the $2^n$ stored or locally generated replicas of the possible transmitted words, integrate over the transmission interval, and are sampled at the end of this time. Thus the output of the $k$th correlator, which corresponds to the $k$th word $x_k$, is

$$\int_0^{nT} x_k(t)y(t)\,dt,$$

where $y(t) = x_m(t) + N(t)$, $x_m(t)$ is the received signal, and $N(t)$ is the channel noise. If the $2^n$ words were *a priori* all equally likely to be transmitted with equal energy, *i.e.*,

$$P(x_i) = P(x_j) \text{ and } \int_0^{nT} x_i^2(t)\,dt = \int_0^{nT} x_j^2(t)\,dt$$

for all $i$ and $j$, then the conditional probability that $x_k$ was sent, given that $y$ was received, is proportional to the exponential of the output of the $k$th correlator [6].

$$P(x_k \mid y) \sim \exp \int_0^{nT} x_k(t)y(t)\,dt. \qquad (1)$$

The decision device then examines all the correlator outputs and selects the waveform $x_k(t)$ corresponding to the maximum correlator output. This is known as maximum-likelihood detection and can be shown to minimize the probability of error when all the signals are equally likely and contain equal energies [7].

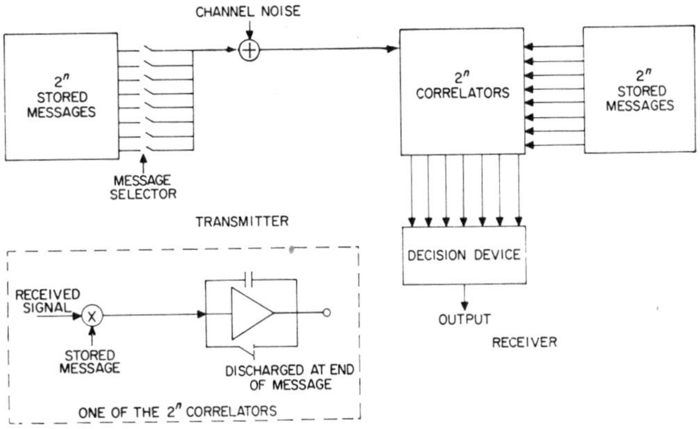


Fig. 1—Basic communications-system model.

It follows intuitively that in order to achieve low error probabilities, the waveforms should be as unlike as possible, such that in a noisy channel there will be the least possible chance to make the wrong selection of the word transmitted. More precisely, the cross-correlation coefficients among all pairs of words,

$$\rho = \frac{\int_0^{nT} x_i(t)x_j(t)\,dt}{\left[\int_0^{nT} x_i^2(t)\,dt \int_0^{nT} x_j^2(t)\,dt\right]^{1/2}}, \qquad (2)$$

should be made as low as possible. The least possible value of $\rho$ is $-1$. However, this value can be achieved only when the number of words in the set is two ($n = 1$). In this case, if $x_1(t) = -x_2(t)$, $\rho = -1$, and the words are said to be antipodal. In general, it is possible to make all the cross-correlation coefficients equal to zero. The set of words is then said to be orthogonal. Actually, it is possible to obtain sets of words for which some or all of the cross-correlations are negative (see Section III).

* Received by the PGSET, October 15, 1960. This paper presents the results of one phase of research carried out at the Jet Propulsion Lab., California Inst. Tech., under Contract NASw-6, sponsored by the National Aeronautics and Space Administration.

† Jet Propulsion Lab., California Inst. Tech., Pasadena, Calif.

Reprinted from *IRE Trans. Space Electron. Telem.*, vol. SET-7, pp. 3–14, Mar. 1961.

## II. Realization of the Model

The concepts discussed in the preceding section date back almost ten years. Little has appeared in the literature on the subject of coded phase-coherent communication since that time because of the difficulty in realizing the basic model with stored waveforms (other than for the case of binary waveforms in which one bit at a time is transmitted). The problem is greatly simplified by using binary sequences as the transmitted words, since these can be generated at both transmitter and receiver by relatively simple code generators.

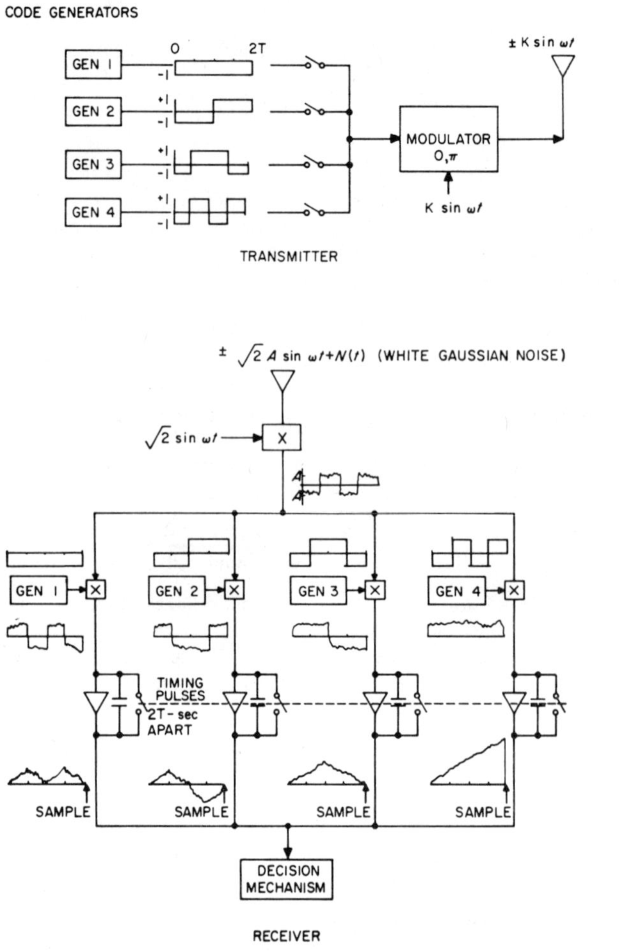


Fig. 2—Binary coded phase-coherent system for transmission of 2 bits per word.

Fig. 2 represents an example of such a binary coded phase-coherent system. The term "phase-coherent" refers not only to the coherence between the transmitted carrier and the locally generated carrier, but also to that between the transmitted and locally generated code words.

Blocks of two bits of information are transmitted by selecting one of a set of four binary code words. This set is orthogonal, since the words switch between $+1$ and $-1$, and it is easily verified that

$$\int_0^{2T} x_i(t)x_j(t)\,dt = 0$$

for $i \neq j$.

Phase modulation of $K \sin \omega t$ by $\pi$ rad when the word is at the $-1$ level is equivalent to amplitude modulation of the carrier by "$+1$'s" and "$-1$'s." At the receiver, the noisy signal is demodulated and fed to the four correlators. Only the low-frequency component of these inputs is shown in Fig. 2. Actually, the component centered at a frequency of $2\omega$ radians per second is eliminated by the integrator provided $\omega$ is a multiple of $\pi/2nT$, where $n$ is the number of bits per word.

Because the code words are orthogonal, the outputs of all correlators, except the one corresponding to the word sent, are zero in the absence of noise. If this were not the case, the noise-free output of the $i$th correlator would be proportional to

$$\int_0^{2T} x_i(t)x_j(t)\,dt$$

when the $j$th word was sent.

The properties and generation of the binary code words will be discussed in Section III. For the present, other characteristics of the model will be considered. It should be noted that multiplication of the additive noise by the locally generated words does not alter its white Gaussian statistics, since multiplying successive uncorrelated samples of noise arbitrarily by $+1$ and $-1$ does not alter the first-order distribution, nor does it render them correlated.

In general, if $n$ bits are transmitted as one word, the integrating time is $nT$. The integrate-and-discharge filter is assumed to produce an attenuation of $1/nT$. Thus, the signal will produce an output at time $nT$ of $e(nT) = A$, provided that $\omega nT$ is a multiple of $\pi/2$. The channel noise is white Gaussian with spectral density $N/2B$. (This input spectral density would produce a power of $N$ watts at the output of a band-pass filter of bandwidth $B$.) The variance at time $nT$ at the output of the integrate-and-discharge filter is[1]

$$\sigma^2 = E\left[\frac{1}{(nT)^2}\int_0^{nT} \sqrt{2}\,N(t)\sin\omega t\,dt \cdot \int_0^{nT} \sqrt{2}\,N(u)\sin\omega u\,du\right]$$

$$= \frac{1}{(nT)^2}\int_0^{nT}\int_0^{nT} E[N(t)N(u)]2\sin\omega t\sin\omega u\,dt\,du. \quad (3)$$

Since the noise is white with density $N/2B$,

$$E[N(t)N(u)] = \frac{N}{2B}\,\delta(t-u).$$

Therefore,

$$\sigma^2 = \frac{N}{2B(nT)^2}\int_0^{nT} 2\sin^2\omega t\,dt = \frac{N}{2BnT}, \quad (4)$$

[1] The noise contribution to the input of the integrate-and-discharge filter is $\sqrt{2}\,N(t)\sin\omega t$ multiplied by a binary code word. However, since this binary multiplication does not alter the statistics of the noise, it may be neglected.

provided that $\omega nT$ is a multiple of $\pi/2$. The ratio of peak output signal to the noise standard deviation is

$$\frac{e(nT)}{\sigma} = \frac{A}{\left(\frac{N}{2BnT}\right)^{1/2}} = \left(\frac{2A^2nT}{N/B}\right)^{1/2} = \left(\frac{2SnT}{N/B}\right)^{1/2}, \qquad (5)$$

where $S = A^2$ is the received signal power. Since $T$ is the transmission time per bit, the ratio

$$\frac{ST}{N/B} = \frac{\text{(received signal energy)/bit}}{\text{(noise power)/(unit bandwidth)}}$$

This is the basic parameter for communication in the presence of white Gaussian noise, for the numerator represents the parameters which may be varied by the communicator, while the denominator is the characteristic property of the channel.

It will be shown in Section III that if a set of $2^n$ code words is to be orthogonal, each word must contain $2^n$ symbols; that is, there are $2^n$ subintervals during which the word may be at either the $+1$ or $-1$ level. Each symbol is of duration $nT/2^n$ seconds. Since the carrier is the sinusoid $\sin \omega t$, it is possible to have other sinusoidal carriers at

$$\omega + \frac{2\pi\nu}{nT/2^n}, \qquad (\nu = \pm 1, \pm 2, \pm 3, \cdots)$$

without interfering with the given signal, provided $\omega$ is a multiple of $\pi/(nT/2^n)$, because over any given subinterval $nT/2^n$,

$$\int_0^{nT/2^n} \sin \omega t \sin\left[\left(\omega + \frac{2\pi\nu}{nT/2^n}\right)t + \phi\right] dt = 0$$

for $\nu = \pm 1, \pm 2, \pm 3, \cdots$. Thus, the effective bandwidth cocupied by the channel is $2^n/nT$ cps. If the sinusoidal carrier of the adjacent channel were constrained to alternate between $\phi = 0$ and $\phi = \pi$ relative to the given channel (*i.e.*, if it were modulated in the same way), then the adjacent sinusoid could be placed $\pi/(nT/2^n)$ radians per second away without interfering, thus making the effective bandwidth occupancy per channel only $2^{n-1}/nT$ cps.

Another characteristic of orthogonal code sets which is worth noting is that the noise components of the correlator outputs are mutually independent. Of course, the white noise input is the same for each correlator. However, during each of the $2^n$ code subintervals, the noise will be multiplied by $+1$ or $-1$. Thus, the cross-correlation between the noise components of any two correlators $i$ and $j$ is proportional to

$$\rho_N = E\left[\sum_{k=0}^{2^n-1} \int_{knT/2^n}^{[(k+1)nT]/2^n} x_i(t)N(t)\,dt\right] \times \left[\sum_{m=0}^{2^n-1} \int_{mnT/2^n}^{[(m+1)nT]/2^n} x_j(t)N(t)\,dt\right],$$

where $x_i(t)$ and $x_j(t)$ are $\pm 1$ during any given interval. Since the noise is white, the integral over one interval is independent of that over another. Thus,

$$E\left[\pm \int_{knT/2^n}^{[(k+1)nT]/2^n} N(t)\,dt\right]\left[\pm \int_{mnT/2^n}^{[(m+1)nT]/2^n} N(t)\,dt\right] = 0$$

for $k \neq m$, and

$$\rho_N = E\left\{\pm\left[\int_0^{nT/2^n} N(t)\,dt\right]^2 \pm \left[\int_{nT/2^n}^{2nT/2^n} N(t)\,dt\right]^2 \pm \cdots \pm \left[\int_{nT[1-(1/2^n)]}^{nT} N(t)\,dt\right]^2\right\}.$$

If the two codes $x_i$ and $x_j$ are to be orthogonal, however, there must be exactly as many subintervals during which $x_i$ and $x_j$ are of different signs as there are subintervals during which they are of the same sign (see Section III). Thus, for orthogonal codes, $\rho_N = 0$.

The optimal decision process and the error probabilities will be considered in Section IV. The next section will treat some basic properties of binary codes.

## III. Binary Codes

This section contains a brief description of the construction and basic properties of certain error-reducing codes. For a more thorough treatment, the reader is referred to the literature on coding[2] [8] and [9].

### A. Orthogonal Codes

A set of orthogonal codes has the property that the cross-correlation coefficients among all pairs in the set are zero. That is, for the code words

$$\{x_1, x_2, \cdots x_k\} \quad \text{and} \quad \{y_1, y_2, \cdots y_k\}$$

(where the $x_i$'s and $y_i$'s can take on the values $+1$ or $-1$), the sum of the products of corresponding symbols

$$\sum_{i=1}^{k} x_i y_i = 0.$$

It is sometimes more convenient to write the codes using the symbols 0 and 1 rather than $\pm 1$. The orthogonal property can then be stated as follows: Two code words are orthogonal if the number of symbol positions in which they are similar equals the number in which they are dissimilar.

Sets of orthogonal codes can be constructed in a multitude of ways, since the $2^n$ elements of any basis of a $2^n$-dimensional vector space over the field of two elements can be made orthogonal to one another [10]. A simple inductive construction of a set of orthogonal codes follows.

A single bit of information may be sent by selecting from a set of two orthogonal code words of two symbols

[2] It should be noted that these codes are usually classified in the literature as "error-correcting codes" because their redundancy permits correction of up to a given number of erroneous symbols after the message has been received and demodulated on a symbol-by-symbol basis. The present treatment differs from this in that the redundancy is utilized to decode the entire word in one operation rather than piecemeal. Hence, the property which is required of these redundant codes is a uniformly low cross-correlation coefficient.

each:

0 0
0 1 .

Two bits might be sent by using the code word set

0 0 0 0
0 1 0 1
0 0 1 1
0 1 1 0 .

It should be noted that this set can be constructed by extending the set for one bit both horizontally and vertically. The lower right-hand square is filled by the complements of these words. A code set for three bits may be constructed by extending the set for two:

| | |
|---|---|
| 0 0 0 0 | 0 0 0 0 |
| 0 1 0 1 | 0 1 0 1 |
| 0 0 1 1 | 0 0 1 1 |
| 0 1 1 0 | 0 1 1 0 |
| 0 0 0 0 | 1 1 1 1 |
| 0 1 0 1 | 1 0 1 0 |
| 0 0 1 1 | 1 1 0 0 |
| 0 1 1 0 | 1 0 0 1 . |

To prove that the construction yields an orthogonal code set at each step, assume that such a construction exists for $k$ bits. Then for $k + 1$ bits, extending the $2^k$ words vertically yields a set of $2^{k+1}$ words which are all orthogonal, except that each word in the top half is the same as one word in the bottom half. However, extending the words horizontally, the upper half of the extensions is the complement of the lower half. Again, all horizontal extensions are orthogonal, except that each word extension in the top half has as its complement in the bottom half the extension of that word for which the left halves are equal. Thus, each pair of words in the new set has as many similar symbols as it has dissimilar ones. Hence, the set is orthogonal.

### *B. Bi-Orthogonal Codes*

These codes were first discovered by Muller and Reed [8]. They can be generated by taking a set of orthogonal code words and adding to it the complements of each word. Thus, bi-orthogonal codes are really two sets of orthogonal codes which are mutually orthogonal, except that each code word in one set has its complement (or antipode) in the other set. A bi-orthogonal or Reed-Muller code for 4 bits can be constructed from the preceding orthogonal code for 3 bits:

| | |
|---|---|
| 0 0 0 0 0 0 0 0 | 1 1 1 1 1 1 1 1 |
| 0 1 0 1 0 1 0 1 | 1 0 1 0 1 0 1 0 |
| 0 0 1 1 0 0 1 1 | 1 1 0 0 1 1 0 0 |
| 0 1 1 0 0 1 1 0 | 1 0 0 1 1 0 0 1 |
| 0 0 0 0 1 1 1 1 | 1 1 1 1 0 0 0 0 |
| 0 1 0 1 1 0 1 0 | 1 0 1 0 0 1 0 1 |
| 0 0 1 1 1 1 0 0 | 1 1 0 0 0 0 1 1 |
| 0 1 1 0 1 0 0 1 | 1 0 0 1 0 1 1 0 . |

One advantage of this set over the corresponding orthogonal set is that it requires one-half as many symbols per code word. Thus, the bandwidth required to transmit the same number of bits per second is cut in half. Also, the average cross-correlation coefficient among all the codes in a set of $2^n$ words is $-1/(2^n - 1)$, as will now be shown. There are in all $(2^n - 1)2^{n-1}$ pairs. The cross-correlations are $-1$ for $2^{n-1}$ pairs, and zero for all the rest. Thus, the average correlation is

$$\frac{(-1)2^{n-1}}{(2^n - 1)2^{n-1}} = -\frac{1}{2^n - 1}.$$

Sets of bi-orthogonal codes have equal numbers of zeros and ones. This is a favorable property since, if all words are equally likely, this assures that the modulating signal will have zero mean; hence, all the power in the carrier will be modulated.

### *C. Shift-Register Codes*

It is known [11] that shift registers with linear modulo-2 feedback logic produce codes which have two-level autocorrelation functions. If the register has length $n$ and the code is of maximal length, $2^n - 1$, the lower level will be $-1/(2^n - 1)$ (see Fig. 3). Thus, a set of $2^n - 1$ codes with a uniform negative cross-correlation coefficient can be constructed by taking all shifted replicas of one maximal-length shift-register sequence. For example, a set of seven code words can be generated by taking all possible shifts of the sequence from a three-stage shift register with linear logic, as shown in Fig. 4. The eighth code word in this figure is the 0 vector (0 0 0 0 0 0 0). The cross-correlation coefficient among all possible pairs is $-1/(2^n - 1)$.

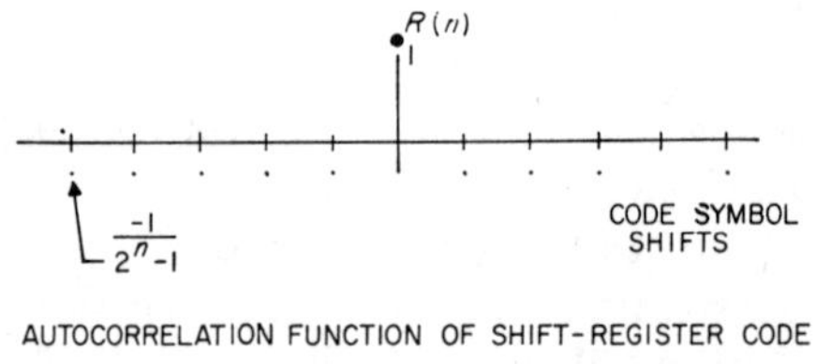


Fig. 3—Autocorrelation function of shift-register code.

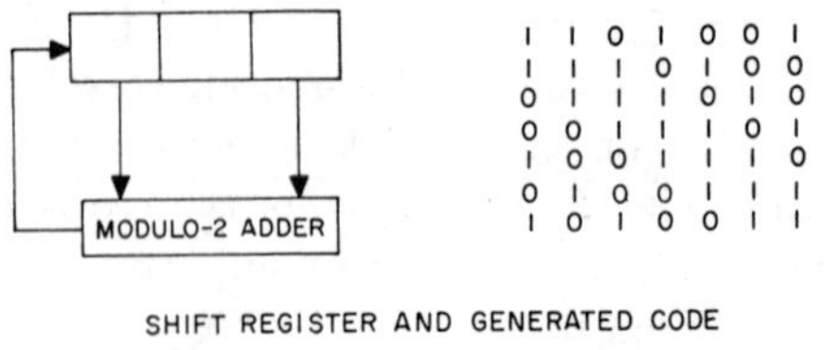


Fig. 4—Shift register and generated code.

Shift registers can be used to generate orthogonal or bi-orthogonal codes quite simply. For example, if a zero is added to every word of the set of Fig. 4 and to the 0 vector, a set of eight orthogonal code words is obtained. By taking the complemented output of the shift register, the complementary orthogonal set is also obtained:

| | |
|---|---|
| 0 1 1 0 1 0 0 1 | 1 0 0 1 0 1 1 0 |
| 0 1 1 1 0 1 0 0 | 1 0 0 0 1 0 1 1 |
| 0 0 1 1 1 0 1 0 | 1 1 0 0 0 1 0 1 |
| 0 0 0 1 1 1 0 1 | 1 1 1 0 0 0 1 0 |
| 0 1 0 0 1 1 1 0 | 1 0 1 1 0 0 0 1 |
| 0 0 1 0 0 1 1 1 | 1 1 0 1 1 0 0 0 |
| 0 1 0 1 0 0 1 1 | 1 0 1 0 1 1 0 0 |
| 0 0 0 0 0 0 0 0 | 1 1 1 1 1 1 1 1 . |

Note that this is not the same bi-orthogonal set as that generated in Section III-B. This example can be generalized to any number of bits.

To demonstrate how elegantly shift-register code generators can be used, consider the case in which the sequence 1 0 0 1 is to be transmitted by a bi-orthogonal code sequence. The first digit is transmitted immediately, while the digits 0 0 1 are loaded from right to left into the register of Fig. 4, which is made to circulate, and the complemented output digits of the shift register are transmitted. Thus, the whole transmitted sequence is 1 1 1 0 0 0 1 0, one of the words in the above set. If the first digit had been a zero, the uncomplemented output digits of the shift register would have been transmitted. Hence, each possible combination of four binary digits would generate a different word in the set.

## IV. Optimal Decision and Probability of Error

### A. Orthogonal Codes

The typical receiver for coded phase-coherent communication was shown in Fig. 2. The outputs of the correlators are fed into a device which determines the waveform most probably sent. If the *a priori* probabilities of the various code words are all equal, the disturbance is white Gaussian noise, and the energy in all transmitted words is the same, (1) indicates that the word which was most probably transmitted is that which corresponds to the maximum correlator output.

The probability that the word which was sent will be chosen correctly is equal to the probability that the output of all the other correlators will be smaller than the output of the given correlator. Assume that in the absence of noise, the output of the correlator corresponding to the word sent is $A$ and that the standard deviation of the output noise of any correlator is $\sigma$. For a set of $2^n$ code words, the probability that the correct one will be chosen is

$$P_C(n) = \int_0^\infty p(x_i)\,dx_i P(y_1, y_2, \cdots y_j \cdots y_{2^n-1} < x_i)$$
$$= \int_0^\infty p(x_i)\,dx_i \prod_{j=1}^{2^n-1} P(y_j < x_i), \tag{6}$$

where $p(x_i)$ is the probability density of the output of the correct correlator, and

$$P(y_j < x_i) = \int_{-\infty}^{x_i} p(y_j)\,dy_j$$

is the probability that the output of the $j$th incorrect correlator will be less than the correct correlator output. The second equality of (6) holds because the correlator noise outputs are mutually independent (see Section II).

Then, for the given parameter,

$$P_C(n) = \int_{-\infty}^{\infty} \frac{e^{-(x-A)^2/2\sigma^2}}{\sqrt{2\pi}\,\sigma}\,dx \left[\int_{-\infty}^{x} \frac{e^{-y^2/2\sigma^2}}{\sqrt{2\pi}\,\sigma}\,dy\right]^{2^n-1}. \tag{7}$$

Making the substitutions $z = y/\sigma$ and $u = (x - A)/\sigma$ yields

$$P_C(n) = \int_{-\infty}^{\infty} \frac{e^{-u^2/2}}{\sqrt{2\pi}}\,du \left[\int_{-\infty}^{u+(A/\sigma)} \frac{e^{-z^2/2}}{\sqrt{2\pi}}\,dz\right]^{2^n-1}. \tag{8}$$

The probability that a word is in error is

$$P_W(n) = 1 - P_C(n).$$

It was shown in (5) that the ratio of the output from the correct correlator to the standard deviation of the noise is

$$\frac{A}{\sigma} = \left(\frac{2nST}{N/B}\right)^{1/2}.$$

Then,

$$P_W(n) = 1 - \int_{-\infty}^{\infty} \frac{e^{-u^2/2}}{\sqrt{2\pi}}\,du \left[\int_{-\infty}^{u+[2nST/(N/B)]1/2} \frac{e^{-z^2/2}}{\sqrt{2\pi}}\,dz\right]^{2^n-1}. \tag{9}$$

This integral cannot generally be evaluated analytically. However, numerical integration by an IBM-704 computer yielded the results of Fig. 5 for code words containing up to 20 bits of information.

It is also of interest to investigate the behavior of (9) as $n$ tends to infinity. Taking limits and using the asymp-

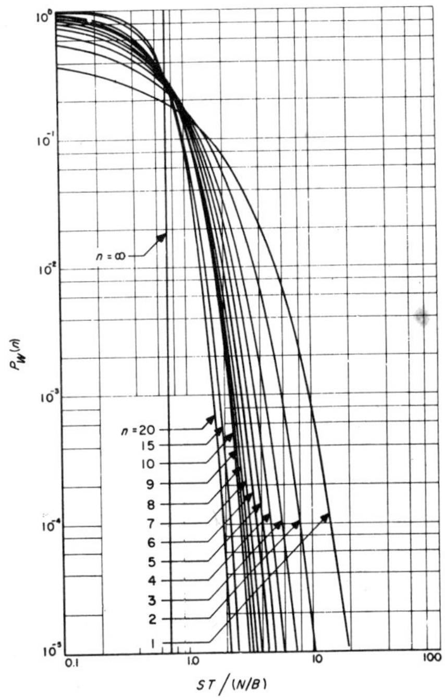


Fig. 5—Word error probability—orthogonal codes.

totic expression for the error function,

$$\lim_{n\to\infty} P_W(n) = 1 - \lim_{n\to\infty} \int_{-\infty}^{\infty} \frac{e^{-u^2/2}}{\sqrt{2\pi}} du \times \left[1 - \frac{e^{-nST/(N/B)}}{\sqrt{2\pi}\,[2nST/(N/B)]^{1/2}}\right]^{2^n-1}$$
$$= 1 - \lim_{n\to\infty}\left[1 - \frac{e^{-nST/(N/B)}}{\sqrt{2\pi}\,[2nST/(N/B)]^{1/2}}\right]^{2^n}.$$

To evaluate this limit, consider the limit of its logarithm:

$$\lim_{n\to\infty} \ln\left[1 - \frac{e^{-n\xi}}{\sqrt{2\pi}\,(2n\xi)^{1/2}}\right]^{2^n} = \lim_{n\to\infty} 2^n \ln\left[1 - \frac{e^{-n\xi}}{\sqrt{2\pi}\,(2n\xi)^{1/2}}\right]$$

where

$$\xi = \frac{ST}{N/B}.$$

Treating $n$ as a continuous variable and using l'Hospital's Rule,

$$\lim_{n\to\infty} \frac{\ln\left[1 - \dfrac{e^{-n\xi}}{\sqrt{2\pi}\,(2n\xi)^{1/2}}\right]}{2^{-n}}$$
$$= \lim_{n\to\infty} \frac{\left[1 - \dfrac{e^{-n\xi}}{2(\pi n\xi)^{1/2}}\right]^{-1}\left[\dfrac{e^{-n\xi}(2n^{1/2}\xi^{3/2} + n^{-1/2}\xi^{1/2})}{4\sqrt{\pi}\,n\xi}\right]}{-2^{-n}\ln 2}$$
$$= \lim_{n\to\infty} \frac{-(2e^{-\xi})^n \xi^{1/2}}{2(\pi n)^{1/2}\ln 2}.$$

If

$$2e^{-\xi} < 1 \quad \text{or} \quad \xi = \frac{ST}{N/B} > \ln 2,$$

this limit of the logarithm is zero; otherwise, it is unbounded negatively. Thus, for

$$\frac{ST}{N/B} > \ln 2, \qquad \lim_{n\to\infty} P_W(n) = 1 - e^0 = 0, \tag{10}$$

while for

$$\frac{ST}{N/B} \le \ln 2, \qquad \lim_{n\to\infty} P_W(n) = 1 - e^{-\infty} = 1; \tag{11}$$

that is, the error probability for an infinitely long word jumps from one to zero at the critical value

$$\frac{\text{(received signal energy)/bit}}{\text{(noise power)/(unit bandwidth)}} = \ln 2.$$

### *B. Bi-Orthogonal Codes*

To demodulate a set of $2^n$ bi-orthogonal code words carrying $n$ bits, only $2^{n-1}$ correlators are required. This is due to the fact that in the absence of noise any one correlator will produce a positive voltage $+A$ at time $nT$ for one code word, a negative voltage $-A$ for its complement, and zero voltage for all the rest. Thus, only one orthogonal code set need be generated at the receiver. The first step in the decision process is to establish whether the voltage at time $nT$ at the output of a given correlator is positive or negative; thereafter, the situation is the same as for orthogonal codes, and the optimal decision in the presence of white Gaussian noise is to choose the one corresponding to the greatest output.

The correct word will be selected if the absolute values of the outputs of all the other correlators are less than that of the given one, and furthermore, if the output of the correct correlator is of the right sign. Without loss of generality, assume that a word has been sent which produces a voltage $+A$ at time $nT$ on correlator $x_i$. The probability that it will be selected by the decision process is

$$P_C(n) = \int_0^{\infty} p(x_i)\,dx_i\left[\prod_{j=1}^{2^{n-1}-1} P(|\,y_j\,| < |\,x_i\,|)\right],$$

where

$$P(|\,y_i\,| < |\,x_i\,|) = \int_{-x}^{x} p(y_j)\,dy_j.$$

(This expression is valid because the noise outputs of the correlators are independent since the noise components are again multiplied by orthogonal words.)

In terms of the Gaussian densities,

$$P_C(n) = \int_0^{\infty} \frac{e^{-(x-A)^2/2\sigma^2}}{\sqrt{2\pi}\,\sigma}\,dx\left[\int_{-x}^{x} \frac{e^{-y^2/2\sigma^2}}{\sqrt{2\pi}\,\sigma}\,dy\right]^{2^{n-1}-1}.$$

Making the substitutions,

$$v = \frac{x - A}{\sigma} \quad \text{and} \quad z = \frac{y}{\sigma},$$

and recalling from (5) that

$$\frac{A}{\sigma} = \left(\frac{2nST}{N/B}\right)^{1/2},$$

the word error probability for bi-orthogonal coding is

$$P_W(n) = 1 - P_C(n) = 1 - \int_{-[2nST/(N/B)]1/2}^{\infty} \frac{e^{-v^2/2}}{\sqrt{2\pi}}\,dv \times \left[\int_{-\{v+[2nST/(N/B)]1/2\}}^{v+[2nST/(N/B)]1/2} \frac{e^{-z^2/2}}{\sqrt{2\pi}}\,dz\right]^{2^{n-1}-1}. \tag{12}$$

This expression was also evaluated, using an IBM 704, for various values of $n$ and the results plotted in Fig. 6. Its limit as $n$ approaches infinity can be computed in the same way as for orthogonal codes, and the result is the same.

### *C. Comparison of Coded and Uncoded Word Error Probabilities*

If a single bit were to be sent using a bi-orthogonal code, the code set would degenerate to two words of one symbol each. This is the special case of communication with two antipodal signals (such as $+1$ and $-1$). In this situation, to which we shall refer as uncoded, the probability that each bit is in error is obtained by letting

$n = 1$ in (12):

$$P_B = 1 - \int_{-[2ST/(N/B)]^{1/2}}^{\infty} \frac{e^{-v^2/2}}{\sqrt{2\pi}} dv = \int_{-\infty}^{-[2ST/(N/B)]^{1/2}} \frac{e^{-v^2/2}}{\sqrt{2\pi}} dv. \qquad (13)$$

If it is desired to transmit an $n$-bit word by sending one bit at a time by means of antipodal signals, the probability that the word will be received in error is one minus the product of the probabilities that each bit will be detected correctly. Thus,

$$P_W(n) = 1 - (1 - P_B)^n. \qquad (14)$$

This expression is plotted in Fig. 7. For the sake of comparison, Figs. 8 and 9 show the word error probabilities for coded and uncoded transmission, and, as might be expected, the two coding schemes produce almost identical results for large $2^n$. Also, the improvement due to coding for $n = 10$ is almost twice as great as for $n = 5$.

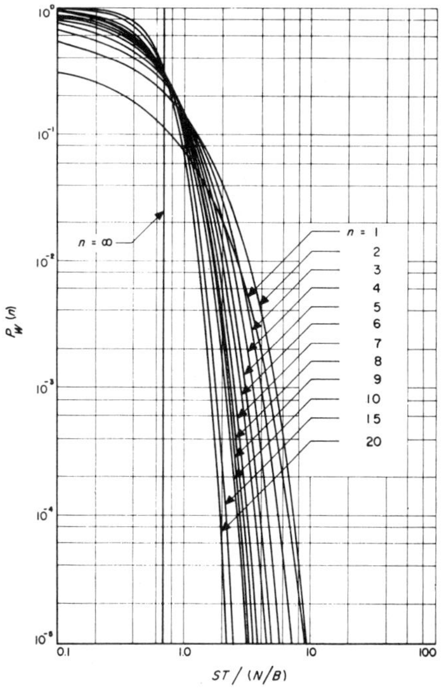


Fig. 6—Word error probability—bi-orthogonal codes.

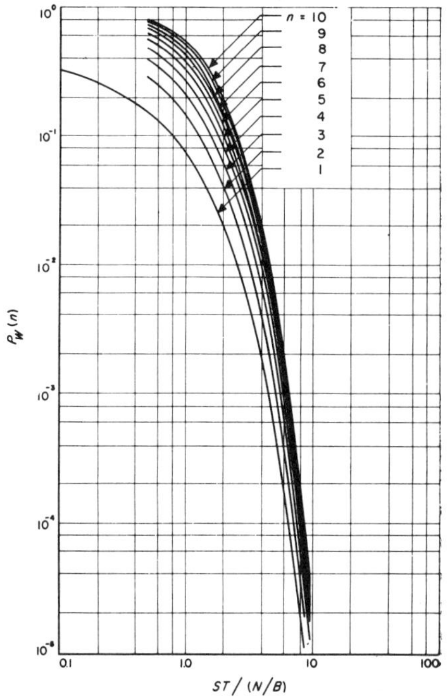


Fig. 7—Word error probability—uncoded.

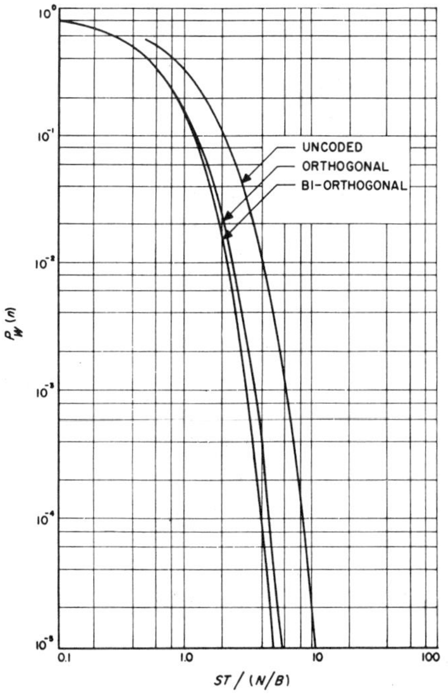


Fig. 8—Comparison of coded and uncoded word error probabilities; $n = 5$.

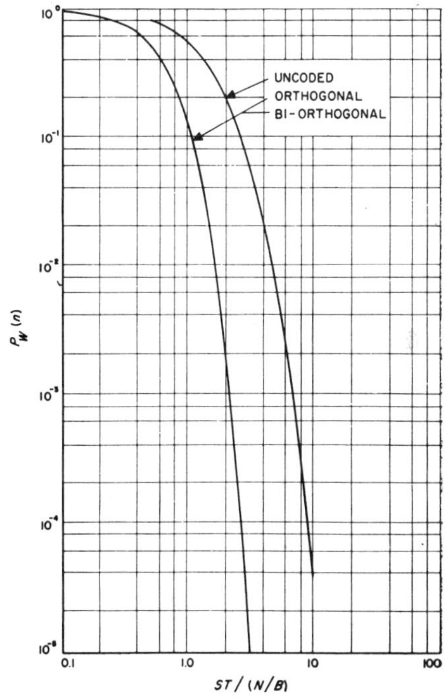


Fig. 9—Comparison of coded and uncoded word error probabilities; $n = 10$.

## V. Bit Error Probabilities

The significant measure of a communication system's performance depends upon its use. If a sequence of $n$-bit messages such as teletype or sampled data is to be sent, the word error probability is the important parameter. On the other hand, if a sequence of independent bits is sent, the bit error probability should be determined.

For orthogonal coding, since all errors are equally probable, the expected number of bits in error when an $n$-bit coded word has been detected incorrectly is

$$\frac{\sum_{i=1}^{n} i\binom{n}{i}}{\sum_{i=1}^{n}\binom{n}{i}} = \frac{n2^{n-1}}{2^n - 1}.$$

Thus, the conditional probability that a given bit is in error when the $n$-bit word within which it was encoded is incorrect is $2^{n-1}/(2^n - 1)$.

Then, in terms of the word error probability $P_W(n)$ for an $n$-bit orthogonal code word, the bit error probability is

$$P_B(n) = \frac{2^{n-1}}{2^n - 1} P_W(n). \tag{15}$$

Fig. 10 presents these probabilities for orthogonal codes.

For bi-orthogonal codes, the situation is somewhat more complicated. The probability of selecting the code word antipodal or complementary to the transmitted word is much lower than that of selecting a word orthogonal to it. Following the derivation of Section IV, this probability, which shall be termed an error of the first kind, is

$$P_1(n) = \int_{-\infty}^{-[2nST/(N/B)]^{1/2}} \frac{e^{-v^2/2}}{\sqrt{2\pi}}\,dv \times \left[\int_{-\{v+[2nST/(N/B)]^{1/2}\}}^{v+[2nST/(N/B)]^{1/2}} \frac{e^{-z^2/2}}{\sqrt{2\pi}}\,dz\right]^{2^{n-1}-1}. \tag{16}$$

The probability of selecting one of the $2^n - 2$ code words orthogonal to the transmitted word, which shall be termed an error of the second kind, is the total probability of error [$P_W(n)$ of (12)] less $P_1(n)$.

$$P_2(n) = P_W(n) - P_1(n). \tag{17}$$

It is assumed that complementary message words are coded into complementary code words so as to minimize the probability that a word error will cause all bits to be in error. Then, if an error of the first kind is made, the number of bits in error is exactly $n$; the conditional bit error probability, given that an error of the first kind was made, is 1. If an error of the second kind is made, the expected number of bits in error is

$$\frac{\sum_{i=1}^{n-1} i\binom{n}{i}}{\sum_{i=1}^{n-1}\binom{n}{i}} = \frac{(n-1)2^{n-2}}{2^{n-1} - 1}.$$

Thus, the bit error probability, given that an error of the second kind was made, is

$$\frac{(n-1)2^{n-2}}{n(2^{n-1} - 1)}.$$

The total bit error probability for bi-orthogonal codes is then

$$P_B(n) = P_1(n) + \frac{(n-1)2^{n-2}}{n(2^{n-1} - 1)} P_2(n). \tag{18}$$

Fig. 11 represents these results.

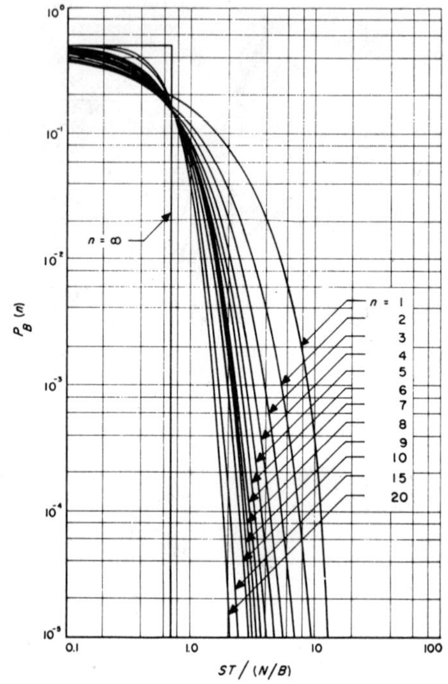


Fig. 10—Bit error probability—orthogonal codes.

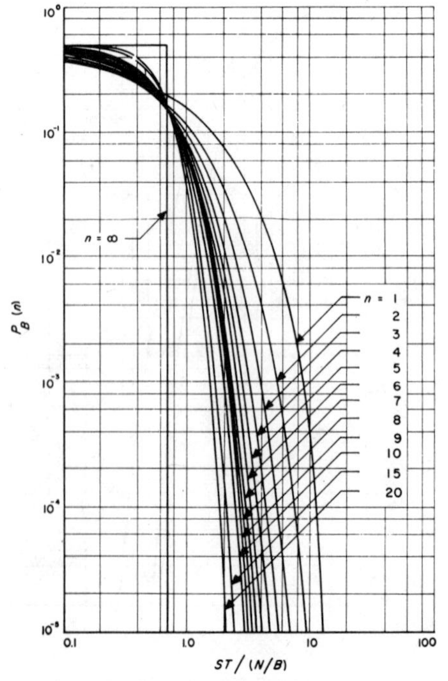


Fig. 11—Bit error probability—bi-orthogonal codes.

## VI. Information Rate and Channel Capacity

A measure of communication-system performance which transcends the subjective use of the received message is the channel information rate. Naturally, in the absence of noise, the information rate $H$ is equal to the transmission rate, $1/T$ bits per second. A noisy channel, however, increases the uncertainty of the received information and hence, decreases the rate of actual information received. This uncertainty or decrease in information, treated in the context of the definitions of information theory for a discrete channel [12], has been shown to be

$$H_x(y) = -\sum_i \sum_j P(x_i, y_j) \log_2 P(y_j \mid x_i), \tag{19}$$

where $x_i$ and $y_j$ are arbitrary transmitted and received signals, respectively; $H_x(y)$ is the uncertainty that $y$ was received when $x$ was sent; $p(x_i, y_j)$ is the joint probability that $x_i$ was sent and $y_j$ received; and $p(y_j \mid x_i)$ is the conditional probability that $y_j$ was received, given that $x_i$ was sent.

### *A. Orthogonal Codes*

The transition-probability diagram between transmitted and received words for codes having zero cross-correlation oefficients is shown in Fig. 12.c Only a portion of the diagram need be shown, since the pattern is repetitive.

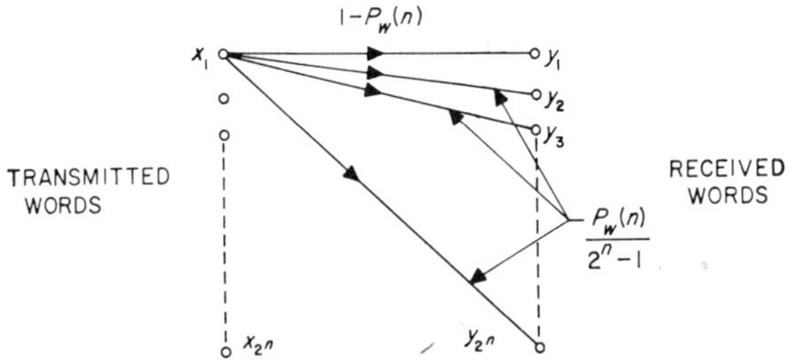


Fig. 12—Diagram of transition probabilities in the presence of noise—orthogonal codes.

The probability that the transmitted word was received correctly is $1 - P_W(n)$, while the probability that any one of the other $2^n - 1$ words was incorrectly chosen is $[P_W(n)]/(2^n - 1)$. Applying Bayes' Rule to (19),

$$\begin{aligned} H_x(y) &= -\sum_i P(x_i) \sum_j P(y_j \mid x_i) \log_2 P(y_j \mid x_i) \\ &= -\sum_j P(y_j \mid x_i) \log_2 P(y_j \mid x_i), \end{aligned}$$

since the errors are independent of the words sent. Then, with the transition probabilities of Fig. 12,

$$\begin{aligned} H_x(y) = &-[1 - P_W(n)] \log_2 [1 - P_W(n)] \\ &- P_W(n)[\log_2 P_W(n) - \log_2 (2^n - 1)] \end{aligned} \tag{20}$$

is the uncertainty per $n$-bit word.

Since the rate of transmission is $1/T$ bits per second or $1/nT$ words per second, the uncertainty rate is $[H_x(y)]/nT$. Subtracting this from the transmission rate[3] yields the received information rate:

$$H = \frac{1}{T}\left\{1 + \frac{[1 - P_W(n)] \log_2 [1 - P_W(n)] + P_W(n)[\log_2 P_W(n) - \log_2 (2^n - 1)]}{n}\right\} \frac{\text{bits}}{\text{sec}} \tag{21}$$

This measure is plotted in Fig. 13 as a function of the basic parameter $ST/(N/B)$. It is seen that as $n$ increases, the speed with which the information rate approaches $1/T$ increases. In the limit, as $n$ approaches infinity, $P_W(n)$ was shown to go from 1 to 0 stepwise at $ST/(N/B) = \ln 2$. Thus, the information rate also behaves stepwise in the limit going from 0 to $1/T$ at this value of the parameter.

Another important measure of information theory is the celebrated channel capacity. For our purposes, this may be defined as

$$C\left(\frac{ST}{N/B}\right) = \max_{\substack{\text{all possible}\\ \text{coding methods}}} \left[H\left(\frac{ST}{N/B}\right)\right]. \tag{22}$$

Shannon [12] has shown that this maximum can be achieved for continuous Gaussian-distributed signals and white Gaussian noise in the limit as the number of bits per message becomes infinite. It is given by the well-known formula,

$$C = B \log_2 \left(1 + \frac{S}{N}\right).$$

As was shown in Section III, the bandwidth occupancy of orthogonal codes is $B = (2^n/nT)$ cps. Thus,

$$\frac{S}{N} = \frac{ST}{N/B}\left(\frac{n}{2^n}\right)$$

and

$$C = \frac{1}{T}\left\{\frac{2^n}{n} \log_2 \left[1 + \frac{n}{2^n}\left(\frac{ST}{N/B}\right)\right]\right\} \frac{\text{bits}}{\text{sec}}. \tag{23}$$

In the limit, the capacity behaves as

$$\begin{aligned} \lim_{n\to\infty} C = &\frac{1}{T}\left(\frac{ST}{N/B}\right) \\ &\lim_{n\to\infty} \log_2 \left[1 + \frac{n}{2^n}\left(\frac{ST}{N/B}\right)\right]^{2^n/n[(N/B)/ST]} \\ = &\frac{1}{T \ln 2}\left(\frac{ST}{N/B}\right) \frac{\text{bits}}{\text{sec}}. \end{aligned} \tag{24}$$

Channel capacity is plotted in Fig. 14 as a function of $ST/(N/B)$ for several values of $n$.

It is of interest to determine how near to the absolute maximum an information rate can be achieved with a coded phase-coherent communication system. As has been noted, in the limit as the message length and bandwidth go to infinity, an information rate of $1/T$ can be achieved

[3] In general, the uncertainty $H_x(y)$ should be subtracted from the received entropy $H(y) = \sum_i P(y_i) \log P(y)$. However, in this case, since the transition probabilities due to noise are all the same, $[H(y)]/nT = [H(x)]/nT = 1/T$, the transmission rate.

with $ST/(N/B) = \ln 2$. Eq. (24) shows that for this value of $ST/(N/B)$, the channel capacity is, in fact, $1/T$; thus, in the limit of infinite coding, the channel capacity can be achieved. For higher values of $ST/(N/B)$, $\lim_{n\to\infty} H$ naturally remains constant at $1/T$ while $\lim_{n\to\infty} C$ increases linearly; thus, the efficiency $H/C$ decreases in inverse proportion to the parameter (Fig. 15).

Two observations with regard to these parameters are in order. When bandwidth is at a premium, channel capacity and channel efficiency are important parameters. However, when bandwidth is of secondary importance, and the basic purpose is only to transmit with as low an error probability or as high an information rate ($H$) as possible, the channel efficiency is not a significant measure of performance. Also, when reasonably error-free reception is required, it is not meaningful to speak of the information rate or channel efficiency. For example, it is seen in Fig. 13 that the received information rate is 82 percent of the transmission rate for a 10-bit word and a ratio of $ST/(N/B) = 1$. However, from Figs. 5 and 10, it is seen that the word error probability is 0.12 and the bit error probability is 0.06 for this case, which indicates rather poor reception.

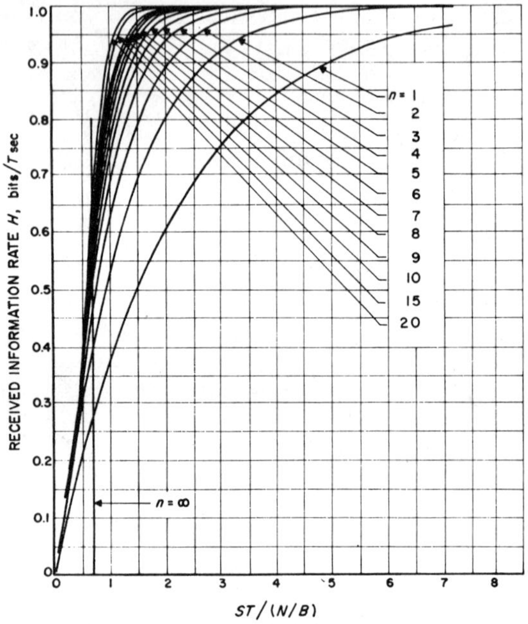


Fig. 13—Received information rate—orthogonal codes.

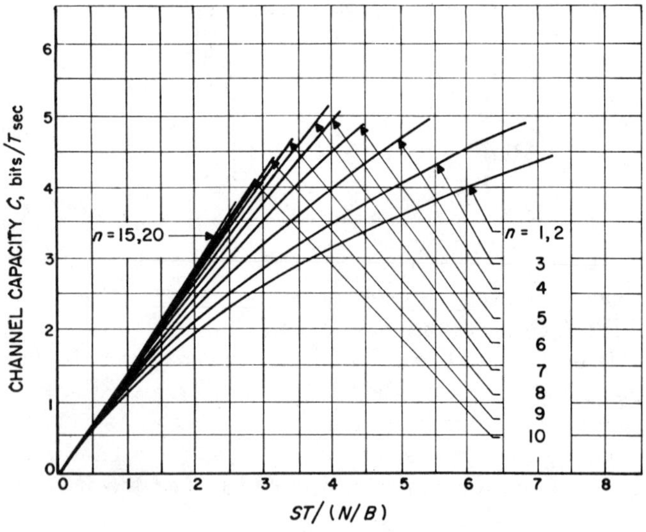


Fig. 14—Channel capacity—orthogonal codes.

### B. Bi-Orthogonal Codes

The transition probabilities for this type of coding were discussed in Section V. The transition diagram is shown in Fig. 16.

$$
\begin{aligned}
H_x(y) &= -\sum P(y_i \mid x_i) \log_2 P(y_i \mid x_i) \\
&= -[1 - P_W(n)] \log_2 [1 - P_W(n)] \\
&\quad - P_2(n)[\log_2 P_2(n) - \log_2 (2^n - 2)] \\
&\quad - P_1(n) \log_2 P_1(n),
\end{aligned}
\tag{25}
$$

and

$$
H = \frac{1}{T} - \frac{H_x(y)}{nT} \frac{\text{bits}}{\text{sec}}. \tag{26}
$$

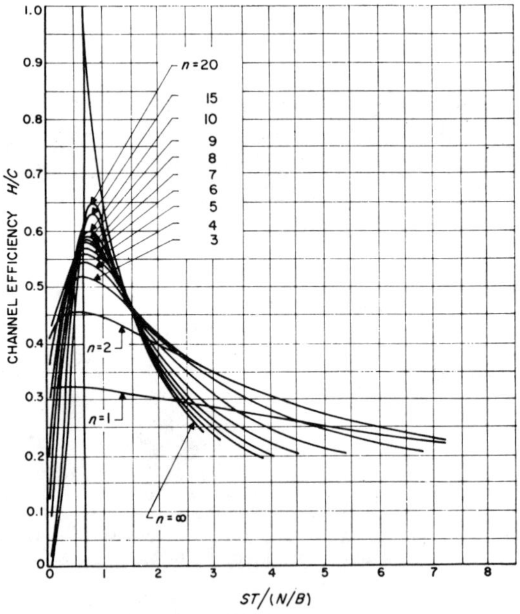


Fig. 15—Channel efficiency—orthogonal codes.

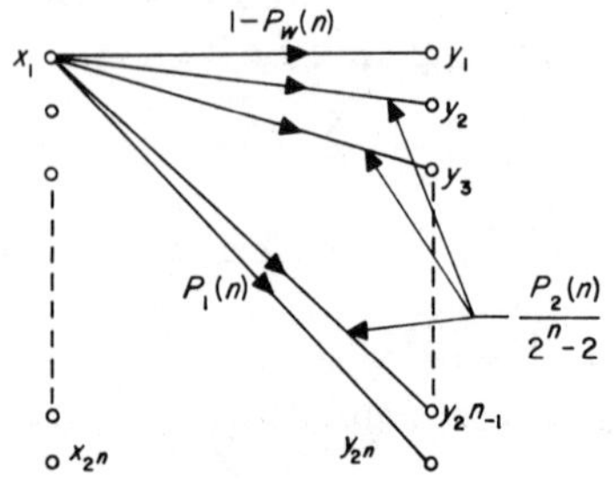


Fig. 16—Diagram of transition probabilities in the presence of noise—bi-orthogonal codes.

The bandwidth occupancy for bi-orthogonal codes is only $2^{n-1}/nT$, and half that for orthogonal codes. Thus,

$$C = \frac{1}{T}\left\{\frac{2^{n-1}}{n}\log_2\left[1+\frac{n}{2^{n-1}}\left(\frac{ST}{N/B}\right)\right]\right\}\frac{\text{bits}}{\text{sec}} \tag{27}$$

and

$$\lim_{n\to\infty} C = \frac{1}{T\ln 2}\left(\frac{ST}{N/B}\right)\frac{\text{bits}}{\text{sec}}.$$

Eqs. (26) and (27) and their ratio are plotted in Figs. 17–19, respectively. It is seen that the efficiency for small $n$ is greater than for orthogonal codes because of the lesser bandwidth occupancy. However, for large $n$, the received information rate and channel capacity, and hence the efficiency, are about the same for both types of coding.

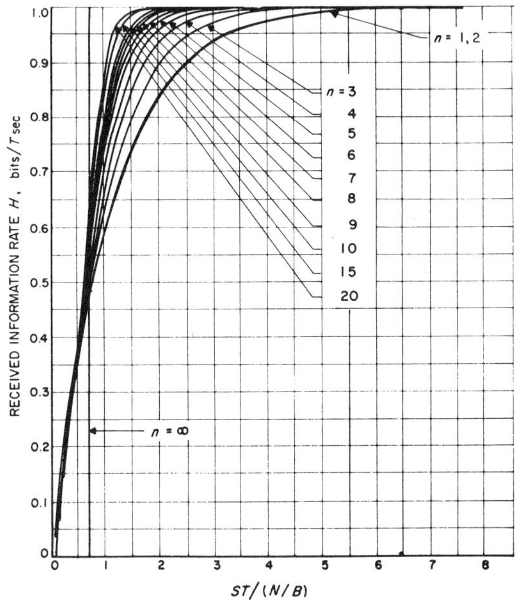


Fig. 17—Received information rate—bi-orthogonal codes.

## VII. Conclusions

Coding of information into sets of sequences characterized by low cross-correlation coefficients has the effect of reducing the error probabilities at the cost of expanding the bandwidth for a fixed rate of transmission. If the time alloted per bit is $T$ seconds and the number of bits per code words is $n$, the transmission rate is $1/T$ bits per second or $1/nT$ words per second, and the effective bandwidth is $2^n/nT$ cps for orthogonal codes and $2^{n-1}/nT$ cps for bi-orthogonal codes.

If five bits of information are to be sent with a word error probability of $10^{-3}$, the use of a bi-orthogonal code word will reduce the required

$$\frac{\text{(received signal energy)/bit}}{\text{(noise power)/(unit bandwidth)}}$$

ratio by 3 db under that required for similar performance with bit-by-bit detection. If ten bits are to be sent with the same word error probability, bi-orthogonal coding reduces the ratio required without coding by 5 db. Orthogonal codes are very nearly as effective as bi-orthogonal codes for $n$ greater than 5, but require twice as much bandwidth.

In the limit as the number of bits per code word and the bandwidth approach infinity, the error probability approaches zero for a

$$\frac{\text{(received signal energy)/bit}}{\text{(noise power)/(unit bandwidth)}}$$

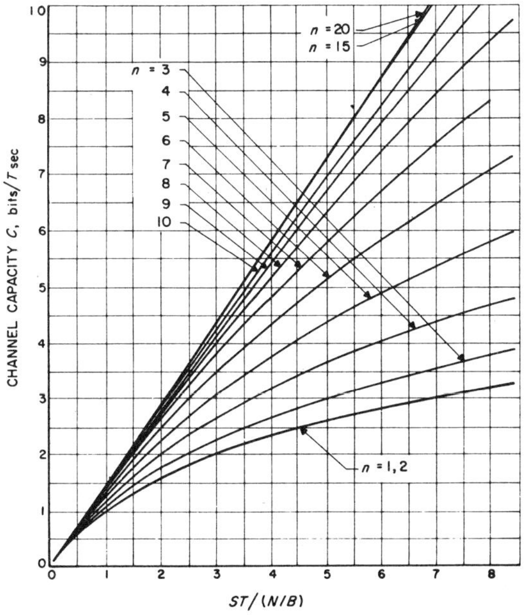


Fig. 18—Channel capacity—bi-orthogonal codes.

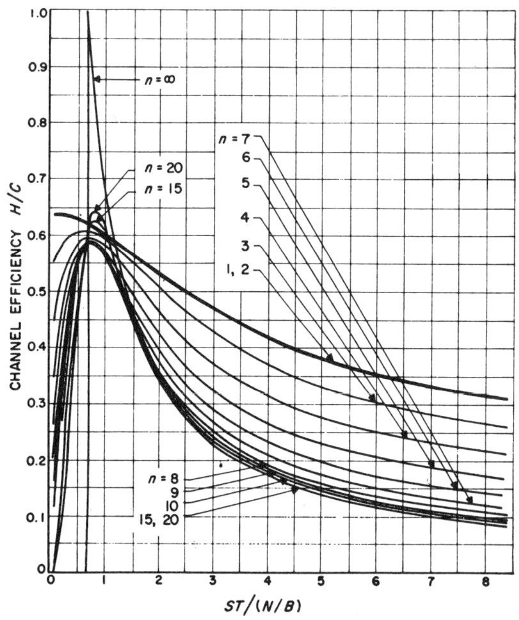


Fig. 19—Channel efficiency—bi-orthogonal codes.

ratio greater than $ln\ 2$, but it approaches one when the ratio is less than or equal to $ln\ 2$. Consequently, the received information rate goes stepwise from 0 to $1/T$ bits per second at this value of the ratio. In the limit, the channel capacity is a linear function of the above ratio. The

$$\frac{\text{received information rate}}{\text{channel capacity}},$$

or channel efficiency, is shown to approach one only when the ratio is $ln\ 2$. For lower values, the efficiency approaches zero, while for higher values the asymptotic behavior is inversely proportional to the ratio.

## Nomenclature

$A$ = received rms carrier amplitude
$B$ = effective signal bandwidth
$C$ = channel capacity
$e(nT)$ = peak filter output
$H$ = received information rate
$H_x(y)$ = uncertainty or decrease of information due to noisy channel
$i, j, k, m, \nu$ = indices
$N(t)$ = channel noise
$N/2B$ = channel white noise spectral density
$n$ = number of information bits per code word
$P$ = discrete probabilities
$P_B(n)$ = bit error probability for $n$-bit word
$P_C(n)$ = probability that $n$-bit word is correct
$P_W(n)$ = word error probability for $n$-bit word
$P(x_i)$ = probability that $i$th word was transmitted
$P(x_i, y_i)$ = joint probability that $i$th word was transmitted and $j$th word received
$P(y_i \mid x_i)$ = conditional probability that $j$th word was received given that $i$th word was transmitted
$p$ = probability densities
$S$ = received signal power
$s$ = Laplace operator
$T$ = transmission time per bit
$t$ = time variable
$u, v, z$ = variables of integration
$x, x_i$ = correlator output corresponding to transmitted word
$y, y_i$ = correlator output corresponding to other word
$\xi$ = $ST/(N/B)$
$\rho$ = correlation coefficient
$\sigma$ = noise variance at filter output at time $nT$.

## References


[1] C. W. Helstrom, "The resolution of signals in white Gaussian noise," Proc. IRE, vol. 43, pp. 1111–1118; September, 1955.
[2] J. G. Lawton, "Comparison of binary data transmission systems," Proc. 2nd Natl. Convention on Military Electronics, Washington, D. C., June 16–18, 1958; p. 54.
[3] R. M. Jaffe and E. Rechtin, "Design and performance of phase-lock circuits capable of near-optimum performance over a wide range of input signal and noise levels," IRE Trans. on Information Theory, vol. IT-1, pp. 66–76; March, 1955.
[4] P. M. Woodward and I. L. Davies, "Information theory and inverse probability in telecommunication," *Proc. IEE*, vol. 99, pt. 3, pp. 37–44; March, 1952.
[5] I. L. Davies, "On determining the presence of signals in noise," *Proc. IEE*, vol. 99, pt. 3, pp. 45–51; March, 1952.
[6] R. M. Fano, "Communication in the presence of additive Gaussian noise," in "Communication Theory," W. Jackson, Ed., Academic Press, Inc., New York, N. Y., pp. 169–182; 1953.
[7] D. Middleton and D. Van Meter, "Detection and extraction of signals in noise from the point of view of statistical decision theory," *J. Soc. Ind. and Appl. Math.* vol. 3, pt. 1, pp. 192–253; December, 1955; vol. 4, pt. 2, pp. 86–119; June, 1956.
[8] I. S. Reed, "A class of multiple-error-correcting codes and the decoding scheme," IRE Trans. on Information Theory, vol. IT-4, pp. 38–49; September, 1954.
[9] J. H. Green, Jr., and R. L. San Soucie, "An error-correcting encoder and decoder of high efficiency, " Proc. IRE, vol. 46, pp. 1741–1744; October, 1958.
[10] G. Birkhoff and S. MacLane, "A Survey of Modern Algebra," Macmillan Co., New York, N. Y.; 1953.
[11] S. W. Golomb, "Sequences With Randomness Properties," Glenn L. Martin Co., Baltimore, Md., Terminal Progr. Rept. under Contract Reg. No. 639498; June, 1955.
[12] C. E. Shannon, "The mathematical theory of communication," *Bell Sys. Tech. J.*, vol. 27, pp. 379–423, 623–656; July–October, 1948.

# Subcarrier Tracking Methods and Communication System Design

RICHARD L. DIDDAY, STUDENT MEMBER, IEEE, AND WILLIAM C. LINDSEY, MEMBER, IEEE

REFERENCE: Didday, R. L., and Lindsey, W. C.: SUBCARRIER TRACKING METHODS AND COMMUNICATION SYSTEM DESIGN,[1] Jet Propulsion Laboratory, California Institute of Technology, Pasadena, Calif. Rec'd 11/20/67. Paper 68TP43-COM, approved by the IEEE Communication Theory Committee for publication without oral presentation. IEEE TRANS. ON COMMUNICATION TECHNOLOGY, 16-4, August 1968, pp. 541–520.

ABSTRACT: It is advantageous from power considerations to allow suppressed-carrier coherently-detected communications. Two methods for generating a coherent reference for the demodulation of a suppressed-carrier signal, namely, the squaring loop and the mathematically equivalent Costas loop, are analyzed, including at some points the effects of VCO noise and initial frequency detuning. The steady-state phase error probability distribution is presented, as is the expected time to first loss of lock in the first-order loop. Probabilities of error in coded or uncoded telemetry systems which use a squaring loop to generate a coherent subcarrier reference are investigated, allowing appropriate values of system parameters to be chosen by system designers

## I. Introduction

VARIOUS communication systems, e.g., binary phase-shift keying (PSK), transmit information in the form $s(t) = \sqrt{2}\, Am(t) \sin(\omega_0 t + \theta)$. In order for the received signal to be demodulated coherently, it is necessary to determine or estimate the phase $\theta$ and frequency of the subcarrier $2 \sin(\omega_0 t + \theta)$ with as little error as possible. If the signal $s(t)$ contains a residual component of sufficient strength at the subcarrier frequency, this component could be tracked with a narrow-band phase-locked loop (PLL) and used to provide the desired reference signal. On the other hand, the power contained in the residual component does not convey any information other than the frequency and phase of the subcarrier. Thus, it represents power not available for the transmission of data and in practice it is always of interest to investigate techniques that conserve power.

Several practical methods are available that rely upon the transmission of a reference signal. For example, the phase reference may be transmitted along with a phase-shift keyed signal, and in order to maintain proper phase synchronization, the phase-keyed and reference signals must be close to each other in frequency and time such that any channel fluctuations along the propagation path effect both signals the same way. For completeness, we briefly discuss several methods of great practical importance.

First, we have differential phase-shift keying (DPSK). In a DPSK system, the PSK signal itself serves as the data signal and the reference signal. The phase of the signal received during one signaling interval serves as a reference for the next keying interval. The Kineplex [1] is an example of a system which has been mechanized.

Second, we have the so-called adjacent tone reference PSK system (AT-PSK). The reference signal for this system is transmitted at an adjacent frequency simultaneously with the keyed signal. At the receiver, the phase of the reference is adjusted to compensate for the frequency difference between the reference and phase-keyed signals. A practical system which employs this principal is illustrated by the DEFT system [2].

The third system is one referred to as the quadrature reference PSK system (Q-PSK). In this system, the phase of one quadrature component is modulated with the data stream while the phase of the in-phase component remains unkeyed. The Kathryn system is an example of this technique [3].

Finally, the so-called decision-directed measurement PSK (DDM-PSK) technique is employed. This system reconstructs a reference signal by estimating the modulation itself and using this estimate to eliminate it from the received signal. The decision directed system is, in essence, a generalization of the DPSK system which uses the previous signaling interval. A computer simulation of this type of system has been carried out by Proakis, Drouilhet, and Price [4]. More recently Bussgang and Leiter [5] derive the performance of a communication system in which a reference signal is transmitted at a frequency adjacent to the phase-keyed tone. Also Bussgang and Leiter report results pertinent to the problem of the joint occurrence of two character errors on a multiple phase-keyed signal.

A number of methods have been proposed for generating a reference subcarrier from the received signal even when the residual subcarrier component is not available. This paper analyzes and compares two methods of great practical interest in deep-space work. The results of the analysis are used to establish the performance of phase-coherent communication systems that utilize such subcarrier tracking methods. The first, the squaring loop method, has been numerously analyzed in the literature [6]–[9]. The second method, originally proposed by Costas, is the Costas loop [10]. This paper establishes the

[1] This paper represents the results of one phase of research carried out at the Jet Propulsion Laboratory, California Institute of Technology, Pasadena, under Contract NAS 7-100, sponsored by the National Aeronautics and Space Administration.

Reprinted from *IEEE Trans. Commun. Technol.*, vol. COM-16, pp. 541–550, Aug. 1968.

performance of these two subcarrier tracking methods using the Fokker–Planck apparatus as opposed to using linear tracking theory. The results are then used in predicting the performance of uncoded and block-coded communication systems. The theory developed is useful in the design and testing of subcarrier tracking loops and data detectors which are becoming common practice in deep-space telemetry systems.

## II. Squaring Loop Method

Our main concern here will be that of establishing a coherent subcarrier reference for demodulation of 180-degree PSK modulation. The mechanization of a typical squaring loop is illustrated in Fig. 1. The received signal $y(t)$ is bandpass filtered, squared to remove the modulation $m(t)$ and the resultant double frequency term is tracked by means of a conventional PLL whose noise bandwidth is $W_L$ cycles. When the output of the PLL is frequency divided by two, a coherent reference signal is available for demodulation purposes.

In deciding upon a method of determining the performance of the squaring loop, a significant parameter is the bandwidth of the bandpass filter whose transfer function is denoted by $H_i(p)$, where $p$ is the Heaviside operator. In fact, if the input is contaminated by white noise of spectral density $N_0$ W/Hz single-sided, and if the bandwidth of the filter is so large that the correlation time $\tau_i$ of its output noise is much smaller than the time constant $1/W_L$ of the PLL,[2] the squaring loop may be analyzed by using the mathematical techniques available from the theory of Markov processes, in particular, the Fokker–Planck equation [11].

As the bandwidth $W_i$ of the bandpass filter is narrowed, the correlation time $\tau_i$ of the output noise increases and may become equal or even greater than the time constant $1/W_L$ of the PLL. The cases when $\tau_i \geq 1/W_L$ are no less important in practice than the other extreme when $\tau_i < 1/W_L$. However, only the latter case is considered here.

Let the observed data $y(t)$ be denoted by

$$y(t) = \sqrt{2}\, Am(t) \sin(\omega_0 + \theta) + n(t) \tag{1}$$

where $m(t)$ is the signal envelope, i.e., the modulation, and let

$$n(t) = n_1(t) \cos(w_0 t + \theta) + n_2(t) \sin(\omega_0 t + \theta) \tag{2}$$

be a realization of a narrow-band noise process where $n_1(t)$ and $n_2(t)$ are statistically independent simple functions of a stationary jointly Gaussian process. We assume that the correlation time $\tau_n$ of the noise is small in comparison with the time constant of the PLL, i.e., $\tau_n \ll 1/W_L$.

[2] Correlation time of the random process $\{x(t)\}$ is defined by the relation $\tau = \int_0^\infty |R_x(\tau)| d\tau$ where $R_x(\tau)$ is the normalized correlation function of the process. The parameter $\tau$ gives some idea of the size of the time interval over which correlation extends between values of the process $x(t)$.

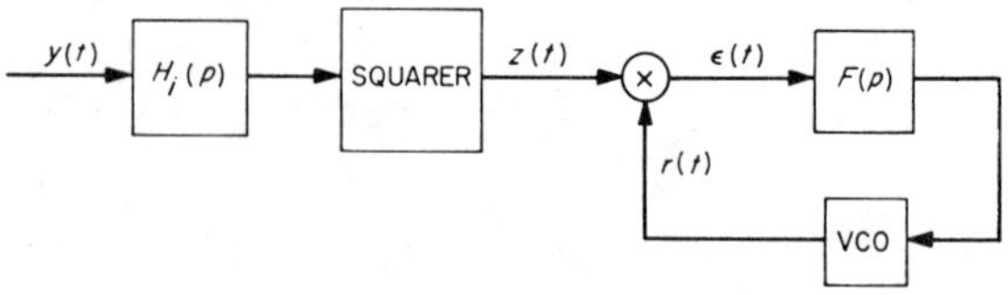


Fig. 1. Squaring loop.

Assuming a perfect square-law characteristic, the output process $z(t)$ is related to the input process $y(t)$ through

$$z(t) = [y(t)H_i(p)]^2 \tag{3}$$

where $H_i(p)$ is the transfer function of the bandpass filter and $p = d/dt$ is the Heaviside operator.

Substitution for $y(t)$ into (3) and taking only the terms around $2\omega_0$ yields, in operator form,

$$z(t) = H_i^2(p)\left\{\left[-A^2m^2(t) + \frac{n_1^2(t)}{2} - \frac{n_2^2(t)}{2} - \sqrt{2}Am(t)n_2(t)\right]\cos(2\omega_0 t + 2\theta) + [\sqrt{2}Am(t)n_1(t) + n_1(t)n_2(t)]\sin(2\omega_0 t + 2\theta)\right\}. \tag{4}$$

The output of the multiplier is $\epsilon(t) = K_m z(t) r(t)$ where $K_m$ is the multiplier constant. A convenient representation for $r(t)$ is

$$r(t) = \sqrt{2}\sin(2\omega_0 t + 2\hat{\theta}). \tag{5}$$

If one takes only those terms in the baseband frequency region, the product $r(t)z(t)$ becomes

$$z(t)r(t) = \frac{K_m H_i^2(p)}{2}\left\{\left[A^2m^2(t) - \frac{n_1^2(t) - n_2^2(t)}{2} + \sqrt{2}Am(t)n_2(t)\right]\sin[2(\theta - \hat{\theta})] + [\sqrt{2}Am(t)n_1(t) + n_1(t)n_2(t)]\cos[2(\theta - \hat{\theta})]\right\}. \tag{6}$$

The phase $\hat{\theta}(t)$ of the voltage control oscillator (VCO) output is related to its input through

$$\hat{\theta}(t) = \frac{K_{\text{VCO}}}{p}[z(t)r(t)F(p) + n_{\text{VCO}}(t)] \tag{7}$$

where $K_{\text{VCO}}$ is the VCO gain constant in rad/s·V and $n_{\text{VCO}}(t)$ is a noise process associated with the VCO. Assuming that the input phase $\theta(t)$ is $\Theta_0 + \Omega_0 t$, we have from (6) and (7) the following stochastic differential equation of operation of a squaring loop,

$$p\phi + \frac{K_m K_{\text{VCO}} A^2 m^2(t) H_i^2(p) F(p)\sin 2\phi}{2} - \Omega_0 = u(t, \phi) \tag{8}$$

where $\phi = \theta - \hat{\theta}$ and

$$u(t, \phi) = \frac{K_{VCO}K_m F(p) H_i^2(p)}{2}\left\{\left[\frac{n_1^2(t)}{2} - \frac{n_2^2(t)}{2} - \sqrt{2}Am(t)n_2(t)\right]\sin 2\phi - [\sqrt{2}\, Am(t)n_1(t) + n_1(t)n_2(t)]\cos 2\phi\right\} + K_{VCO}n_{VCO}(t). \quad (9)$$

If we let $\Phi = 2\phi$, $K = K_{VCO}K_m$, assume that over the bandwidth of significant interest the filter $H_i(p) = 1$, and consider a first-order PLL loop, i.e., $F(p) = 1$, we have

$$\dot\Phi + KA^2m^2(t)\sin\Phi = K\left\{\left[\frac{n_1^2(t)}{2} - \frac{n_2^2(t)}{2} - \sqrt{2}\, Am(t)n_2(t)\right]\sin\Phi - [\sqrt{2}\, Am(t)n_1(t) + n_1(t)n_2(t)] \times \cos\Phi\right\} + 2K_{VCO}n_{VCO}(t) + 2\Omega_0. \quad (10)$$

We may now determine the probability density of $\Phi$ using the Fokker–Planck method. The equation of operation is of the form $\dot\Phi = F[\Phi, u(\Phi, t)]$ for which the corresponding Fokker–Planck equation [11] is, in the stationary case,

$$\frac{1}{2}\frac{\partial^2}{\partial\Phi^2}[K_2(\Phi)p(\Phi)] - \frac{\partial}{\partial\Phi}[K_1(\Phi)p(\Phi)] = 0 \quad (11)$$

where

$$K_1(\Phi) = \overline{F[\Phi, u(\Phi, t)]}$$

$$K_2(\Phi) = \int_{-\infty}^{\infty}\overline{\{F[\Phi, u(\Phi, t)]F[\Phi, u(\Phi, t+\tau)] - K_1^2(\Phi)\}}d\tau$$

and the bar denotes statistical averaging over the ensemble. If we make the assumptions that $\Phi$ is a slowly varying process $m(t) = \pm 1$, we find from (10) and (11) that

$$K_1(\Phi) = -KA^2\sin\Phi + 2\Omega_0$$

$$K_2(\Phi) = K_2 = K^2\sigma^2\int_{-\infty}^{\infty}\left[\sigma^2R_{n_1}^2(\tau) + 2A^2R_{n_1}(\tau) + \frac{K_{VCO}^2}{K^2}R_{VCO}(\tau)\right]d\tau \triangleq K^2N_{sq} \quad (12)$$

where $\sigma^2$ and $R_{n_1}(\tau)$ are, respectively, the variance and the envelope of the correlation function of the noise component in (2). They correspond to the variance and correlation function of the independent processes $n_1(t)$ and $n_2(t)$ in (2). Substitution of (12) into the partial differential equation given in (11) and using the boundary conditions

$$\int_{-\pi}^{\pi}p(\Phi)d\Phi = 1$$

$$p(\Phi + 2\pi) = p(\Phi) \quad (13)$$

we have as a solution to (11)

$$p(\phi) = \frac{\exp(\pi\beta)}{4\pi^2 I_{j\beta}(\rho)}\exp(\beta\phi + \rho\cos\phi) \times \int_{\phi}^{2\pi+\phi}\exp(-\beta x - \rho\cos x)dx \quad (14)$$

where $\beta = 2\Omega_0/K_2(\phi)$ and $\rho = 2A^2K\, K_2$. When there is no initial detuning, $\Omega_0 = 0$ and we have

$$p(\Phi) = \frac{\exp\left\{\left[\frac{2A^2K}{K_2}\right]\cos\Phi\right\}}{2\pi I_0\left(\frac{2A^2K}{K_2}\right)}, \quad |\Phi| < \pi \quad (15)$$

where $I_0(x)$ is the modified Bessel function of zero order and of argument $x$. If we introduce the change of variable $\Phi = 2\phi$ and make use of the Jacobian of the transformation, we find that

$$p(\phi) = \frac{\exp[2A^2\, KN_{sq}\cos 2\phi]}{\pi I_0\left(\frac{2A^2}{KN_{sq}}\right)}, \quad |\phi| < \frac{\pi}{2}. \quad (16)$$

The density function is defined from only $-\pi/2$ to $\pi/2$ since the actual phase error being tracked is $\Phi = 2\phi$. Hence, we should not expect the input phase $\Phi$ to behave as in the usual PLL case.

A case of practical interest is a second-order loop with $F(p) = 1/(1 + \tau p)$. Substituting this form into (8), and taking $\Omega_0 = 0$, we find that [15]

$$\tau\ddot\phi + \dot\phi + KA^2\sin\phi = 2\,u(t, \phi). \quad (17)$$

The two-dimensional Fokker–Planck equation [11] is of the form

$$\frac{\partial^2}{\partial\dot\phi^2}\{p(\phi, \dot\phi)A_1\} - \frac{\partial}{\partial\dot\phi}\{A_2p(\phi, \dot\phi)\} - \dot\phi\frac{\partial p(\phi, \dot\phi)}{\partial\phi} = \frac{\partial p(\phi, \dot\phi)}{\partial t} = 0 \quad (18)$$

where

$$A_1 = \int_{-\infty}^{0}E\{[\ddot\phi(t) - \overline{\ddot\phi(t)}][\ddot\phi(t+\tau) - \overline{\ddot\phi(t+\tau)}]\}dt$$

$$A_2 = E(\ddot\phi) + \int_{-\infty}^{0}E\left\{\left[\frac{\partial\ddot\phi(t)}{\partial\dot\phi} - \overline{\frac{\partial\ddot\phi(t)}{\partial\dot\phi}}\right][\ddot\phi(t+\tau) - \overline{\ddot\phi(t+\tau)}]\right\}dt.$$

Making the assumptions that $m(t)$ and $\phi(t)$ are slowly varying so that $m(t) = m(t+\tau)$ and $E\phi(t)n(T+\tau) = 0$, the Fokker–Planck equation becomes

$$\frac{K^2N_{sq}}{2\tau^2}\frac{\partial^2p(\phi, \dot\phi)}{\partial\dot\phi^2} + \frac{1}{\tau}\frac{\partial}{\partial\dot\phi}(\dot\phi + A^2K\sin\phi)p(\phi, \dot\phi) - \frac{\dot\phi\,\partial p(\phi, \dot\phi)}{\partial\phi} = 0 \quad (19)$$

in the steady-state case, and where, as before,

$$N_{sq} = \sigma^2 \int_{-\infty}^{\infty} [\sigma^2 R^2(\tau) + 2A^2 R(\tau)] d\tau.$$

The solution is seen to be

$$p(\phi, \dot{\phi}) = \sqrt{\frac{\tau}{K^2 N_{sq}}} \frac{\exp\left[-\left(\frac{\tau}{K^2 N_{sq}}\right)\dot{\phi}^2 + \left(\frac{2A^2}{KN_{sq}}\right)\cos\phi\right]}{2\sqrt{\pi^3} I_0\left(\frac{2A^2}{KN_{sq}}\right)}. \tag{20}$$

If we integrate (20) to obtain $p(\phi)$, it is easily seen that the density is identical to that of the first-order case (see (16)).

As a first example of our results, assume that the normalized correlation function of the envelope of the input noise process possesses Markov-type power spectrum with variance $\sigma^2 = N_0 W_i$, i.e.,

$$R_{n_1}(\tau) = \exp(-2W_i|\tau|) = R_{n_2}(\tau) \tag{21}$$

where $W_i$ is the one-sided bandwidth of the noise $n_1(t)$ or $n_2(t)$. Physically, (21) represents a noise source that has been generated by passing white noise through an RC filter which possesses a 3-dB frequency of $W_i/2\pi$ Hz. Thus, $K_2(\phi)$ in (12) becomes

$$K_2 = 2K^2\sigma^2\left(\frac{\sigma^2}{4W_i} + \frac{A^2}{W_i}\right) \tag{22}$$

and the solution in (15) is given by

$$p(\phi) = \frac{\exp(D \cos 2\phi)}{\pi I_0(D)}, \quad |\phi| \leq \pi/2 \tag{23}$$

where

$$D = \frac{x}{2}\left(\frac{1}{1 + \frac{1}{4xy}}\right) \tag{24}$$

$$x = \frac{2A^2}{N_0 W_L}, \quad y = \frac{W_L}{W_i}.$$

Here $W_L$ is taken to be the bandwidth of the loop as defined from the linear PLL theory, i.e.,

$$W_L = 2B_L = \frac{1}{2\pi j}\int_{-j\infty}^{j\infty} |H(s)|^2 ds = \frac{A^2 K}{2} \tag{25}$$

where $H(s)$ is the closed-loop transfer function of the loop in linearized form. The square of the signal amplitude $A$ is present because of the squaring operation.

As a second example, assume that

$$R_{n_1}(\tau) = R_{n_2}(\tau) = \frac{\sin \pi W_i \tau}{\pi W_i \tau}. \tag{26}$$

Then it is easy to show that

$$D = x\left(\frac{1}{1 + \frac{1}{2xy}}\right) \tag{27}$$

where

$$x = \frac{2A^2}{N_0 W_L}, \quad y = \frac{W_L}{W_i}.$$

Examples for other noise envelopes, hence, other presquaring filters, may be easily evaluated. The two examples given represent results for the limiting cases of the class of Butterworth-type spectra.

If one assumes that $\phi$ is small, then the distribution of $\phi$ with the ideal bandpass presquaring filter becomes Gaussian with variance

$$\sigma_\phi^2 = \frac{1}{4}\sigma_\Phi^2 = \frac{1}{D} = \left(\frac{1 + \frac{1}{2xy}}{x}\right). \tag{28}$$

This result agrees with that obtained using linear PLL theory [1]–[4]. The variance of the phase error $\Phi$, as determined from (14), is

$$\sigma_\Phi^2 = \frac{\pi^2}{3} + 4\sum_{k=1}^{\infty} \frac{(-1)^k}{k^2} \frac{I_k(D)}{I_0(D)} \tag{29}$$

where $I_k(D)$ is the modified Bessel function of order $k$ and argument $D$. For large $D$, $\sigma_\Phi^2$ approaches $1/D$ as it should.

## III. Mean Time to First Cycle Slip

The evaluation of the mean first passage time of the phase error in the PLL has been performed analytically by two different methods. Both techniques, that presented by Viterbi [16] and that of Tausworthe [17], involve the use of Fokker–Planck methodology. We shall briefly retrace Viterbi's method as it applies to the squaring loop.

Viterbi's technique is, in a sense, the classical first passage time solution [11]. We shall be dealing with a function $f = f(\phi, t)$ that describes the probabilistic behavior of those sample functions that have not exceeded the boundary up to time $t$. We assume that the loop begins in lock, hence

$$f(\phi, 0) = p(\phi, 0) = \delta(\phi) \tag{30}$$

where $p(\phi, t)$ is the density function describing all sample functions of the process. We argue that, since after a long period of time all sample functions will have exceeded our limiting value $\pm\phi_l$,

$$f(\phi, \infty) = 0. \tag{31}$$

Additional considerations indicate that

$$f(\pm\phi_l, t) = 0. \tag{32}$$

Recognizing that $f(\phi, t)$ must satisfy the time-varying Fokker–Planck equation, we find that in the first-order case

$$f(\phi, \infty) - f(\phi, 0) = \frac{\partial}{\partial\phi} A^2 K \sin\phi\, F(\phi) + \frac{1}{2}\frac{\partial^2}{\partial\phi^2} \times K^2 N_{sq} F(\phi) \tag{33}$$

where we have integrated over time and let

$$F(\phi) = \int_0^\infty f(\phi, t)dt.$$

After making use of (30) and (31) and integrating over $\phi$, we have

$$c_1 - h(\phi) = A^2 K \sin\phi\, F(\phi) + \frac{1}{2}\frac{\partial}{\partial\phi} K^2 N_{sq} F(\phi) \quad (34)$$

where $h(\phi)$ is the unit step function. Equation (34) is easily solved to yield (after applying condition (32))

$$F(\phi) = \exp\left(\frac{2A^2}{KN_{sq}}\cos\phi\right)\int_{-\phi_l}^{\phi_l}\frac{2}{K^2N_{sq}} \times \exp\left[-(2A^2KN_{sq}\cos\xi)\right]\left[\frac{1}{2} - h(\xi)\right]d\xi. \quad (35)$$

Now we note that the expected time to first passage is

$$T(\phi_l) = \int_0^\infty t \Pr\ (t \text{ seconds until } |\phi > \phi_l)dt \quad (36)$$

and, as Viterbi shows, this is equivalent to

$$T(\phi_l) = \int_0^\infty \int_{-\phi}^{\phi_l} f(\phi, t)d\phi dt. \quad (37)$$

Finally,

$$T(\phi_l) = \frac{2}{K^2N_{sq}}\int_0^{\phi_l}\int_{-\phi_l}^{\phi_l}\exp\left(-\frac{2A^2}{KN_{sq}}\right)(\cos\xi - \cos\phi)d\xi d\phi \quad (38)$$

and setting $\phi_l = 2\pi$, we obtain the mean time to first skip.

$$T(2\pi) = \frac{2\pi^2}{K^2N_{sq}} I_0^2\left(\frac{2A^2}{KN_{sq}}\right) = \frac{2\pi^2}{K^2N_{sq}} I_0^2(D). \quad (39)$$

## IV. Costas Loop

In the Costas loop shown in Fig. 2, the phase of the data subcarrier is extracted from the suppressed carrier signal $s(t)$ plus noise $n(t)$ by multiplying the input voltages of the two phase detectors (multipliers) with that produced from the output of the VCO and a 90-degree phase shift of that voltage, filtering the results and using this signal to control the phase and frequency of the loop's VCO output.

If we denote the output of the upper loop multiplier by $z_c(t)$ and the output of the lower loop multiplier by $z_s(t)$ (see Fig. 2), then the output $z_c(t)$ is

$$z_c(t) = y(t)\sqrt{2}\cos(\omega_0 t + \hat{\theta}) \quad (40)$$

while the output of the low-pass filter becomes

$$y_c(t) = \left[Am(t) + \frac{n_2(t)}{2}\right]\sin\phi + \frac{n_1(t)}{\sqrt{2}}\cos\phi \quad (41)$$

when (1) is substituted into (24) and all double frequency terms neglected. Similarly, the output $y_s(t)$ is given by

$$y_s(t) = \left[Am(t) + \frac{n_2(t)}{\sqrt{2}}\right]\cos\phi - \frac{n_1(t)}{\sqrt{2}}\sin\phi. \quad (42)$$

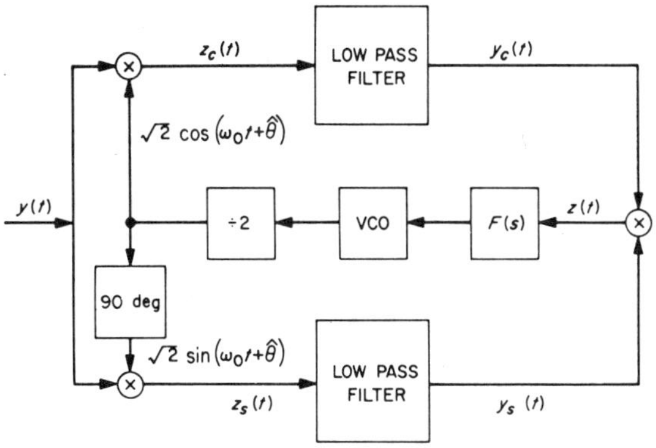


Fig. 2. Costas loop.

The control voltage $z(t) = y_c(t)y_s(t)$ becomes

$$z(t) = \frac{1}{2}\left[Am(t) + \frac{n_2(t)}{\sqrt{2}}\right]^2\sin 2\phi + \frac{n_1(t)}{\sqrt{2}}\left[Am(t) + \frac{n_2(t)}{\sqrt{2}}\right] \times\left(\frac{1+\cos 2\phi}{2}\right) - \frac{n_1(t)}{\sqrt{2}}\left[Am(t) + \frac{n_2(t)}{\sqrt{2}}\right] \times\left(\frac{1-\cos 2\phi}{2}\right) - \frac{n_1^2(t)}{4}\sin 2\phi. \quad (43)$$

Now

$$\hat{\theta} = K_{\text{VCO}}K_m F(p)\, z(t) \quad (44)$$

and if we omit all dc terms, the stochastic differential equation which governs the behavior of the Costas loop in the presence of noise reduces to

$$\dot{\Phi} + KA^2F(p)m^2(t)\sin\Phi = KF(p)\left\{\left[\frac{n_1^2(t)}{2} - \frac{n_2^2(t)}{2} - \sqrt{2}\,Am(t)n_2(t)\right]\sin\Phi - [\sqrt{2}An_1(t)m(t) + n_1(t)n_2(t)]\cos\phi\right\}. \quad (45)$$

If, as in the previous case, we ignore the effects of the filter $H_i(p)$, then the stochastic differential equation obtained for the squaring loop method and the stochastic differential equation for the Costas loop are identical. Thus, the solution for $p(\Phi)$ is identical and the noise behavior of the two circuits is the same. This, of course, assumes that the low-pass filter transfer functions can be obtained by simply translating, by $f_0$ Hz, the bandpass filter function of the squaring loop.

From this it may be concluded that the two approaches to subcarrier tracking yield equivalent results when the filters in the Costas loop are the low-pass equivalents of the bandpass filter in the squaring loop. The choice of which loop to use cannot be determined on theoretical grounds, and consequently, must be determined from an engineering hardware point of view, i.e., the relative ease with which the corresponding filters can be constructed. The Costas receiver has the disadvantage of requiring some form of power measurement to distinquish which of the signals $\sin(\omega_0 t + \theta)$ or $\cos(\omega_0 t + \theta)$ is actually in phase with the received carrier. Both methods of subcarrier tracking exhibit the usual 180-degree phase ambiguity inherent in all systems that attempt to recover the subcarrier phase from a modulated signal, i.e., changing the sign of the received signal leaves the sign of the recovered subcarrier unaltered.

One obvious question which comes to mind is to ask for the presquaring filter which maximizes the signal-to-noise ratio at the output of the PLL. This problem has been solved and the optimum filter, for the case where the modulating spectrum is narrow with respect to the carrier frequency, has been shown [12] to be given by

$$H_i(p) = k\left[\frac{S_s(p)}{S_s(p) + \frac{N_0}{2}}\right]^{1/2} \tag{46}$$

where $k$ is an arbitrary positive constant and $S_s(p)$ is the power spectrum of modulated signal $s(t)$. For large signal-to-noise conditions the optimum presquaring filter given by (30) becomes $H_i(s) \sim k$ while for small signal-to-noise conditions the optimum filter becomes

$$H_i(p) \sim \left[\frac{2S_s(p)}{N_0}\right]^{1/2} \tag{47}$$

This says that for small signal-to-noise conditions the optimum filter is matched to signaling spectrum. Arbitrarily setting $k = 1$ says that the optimum filter for large signal-to-noise ratios is an ideal bandpass filter, a case for which the performance is known. On the other hand, for small signal-to-noise ratios the performance of the two loops may be assessed once the spectrum of the modulated signal $s(t)$ is defined. It is the conjecture of the authors that the improvement over an ideal bandpass filter is negligibly small in the signal-to-noise ratio region where such synchronization techniques are useful in practice. In the next section we show that squaring or Costas loops are most useful in data detection systems where the ratio of data rate $R$ to the tracking loop bandwidth $W_L$ are large, i.e., high data rate systems.

Various other approaches to the problem of estimating the subcarrier phase when no residual component is present at the subcarrier frequency are available, and in some cases have been analyzed. Layland [9] and Proakis [4] analyze methods which essentially estimate the modulation itself. This estimate is used in an attempt to eliminate the modulation from the subcarrier. This, therefore, provides an unmodulated sinusoid which can be tracked by a PLL.

*Performance of Correlation Receivers*

Consider the situation where $[m(t)]$ represents the set of signals $[x_k(t),\ k = 1, \cdots, N]$. For the present we assume that each signal in the set occurs with equal probability, contains equal energies, exists for a time duration of $T$ seconds, and is orthogonal, i.e.,

$$\int_0^T x_k(t)x_j(t) = \delta_{jk} \tag{48}$$

where $\delta_{jk} = 1$ for $j = k$ and $\delta_{jk} = 0$ for $j \neq k$. In the presence of white Gaussian noise the optimum receiver, i.e., the one which minimizes the error probability, computes

$$C_k = \int_0^T y(t)x_k(t)dt \tag{49}$$

from all $k = 1, \cdots, N$ and makes its decision in favor of that signal which yields the largest $C_k$.

Of particular interest here is the case where the set of signals $[x_k(t)]$ are code words taken from an orthogonal code dictionary containing $N = 2^n$ code words, i.e., the signals are sequences of plus and minus ones. In this case the time duration $T$ becomes the product of the number of bits per code word multiplied by the time duration per bit, i.e., $T = nT_b$. If one assumes that word sync and symbol sync[3] (i.e., the instants in time where one word begins and another ends and the instants in time where the modulation may change states) are known exactly and that either the squaring loop method or Costas loop is used to provide subcarrier sync, the conditional probability that the data detector will err may be shown to be given by [13], [14]

$$P_E(\phi) = 1 - P_c(\phi) = 1 - \int_{-\infty}^{\infty} \frac{\exp\left(-\frac{y^2}{2}\right)}{\sqrt{2\pi}} \times \left[\int_{-\infty}^{y+\sqrt{2Rn}\cos\phi} \frac{1}{\sqrt{2\pi}} \exp\left(-\frac{x^2}{2}\right)dx\right]^{2^n-1} dy \tag{50}$$

where $R = A^2T_b/N_0$. The average word error probability is obtained from (34) by averaging over the distribution of $p(\phi)$, i.e.,

$$P_E = \int_{-\pi/2}^{\pi/2} p(\phi)P_E(\phi)d\phi. \tag{51}$$

Thus, from (23), (50), and (51) we have[4]

$$P_E = 1 - \int_{-\pi/2}^{\pi/2} \frac{\exp(D\cos 2\phi)}{\pi I_0(D)}\,d\phi \int_{-\infty}^{\infty} \exp\left(\frac{-\frac{y^2}{2}}{\sqrt{2\pi}}\right) \times \left[\int_{-\infty}^{y+\sqrt{2nR}\cos\phi} \frac{\exp(-x^2/2)}{\sqrt{2\pi}}\,dx\right]^{2^n-1} dy \tag{52}$$

where

$$D = \frac{\delta R}{2}\left(\frac{1}{1 + \frac{1}{4\delta yR}}\right) \tag{53}$$

[3] This assumption is not too restrictive since jitter on the phase of the subcarrier is more deleterious on system performance than jitter about the instants in time with which the modulation may change states. This, of course, is a consequence of coherent detection.

[4] In some cases the bit error probability is of interest. The ratio of the bit error probability to the word error probability is $2^{n-1}/2n - 1$ [14].

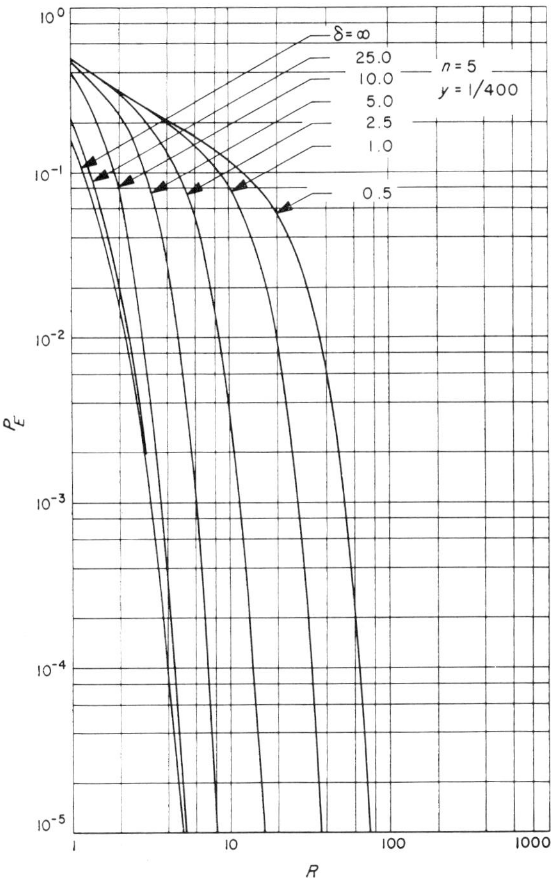


Fig. 3. Word error probability $P_E$ versus $R$ ($n = 5$).

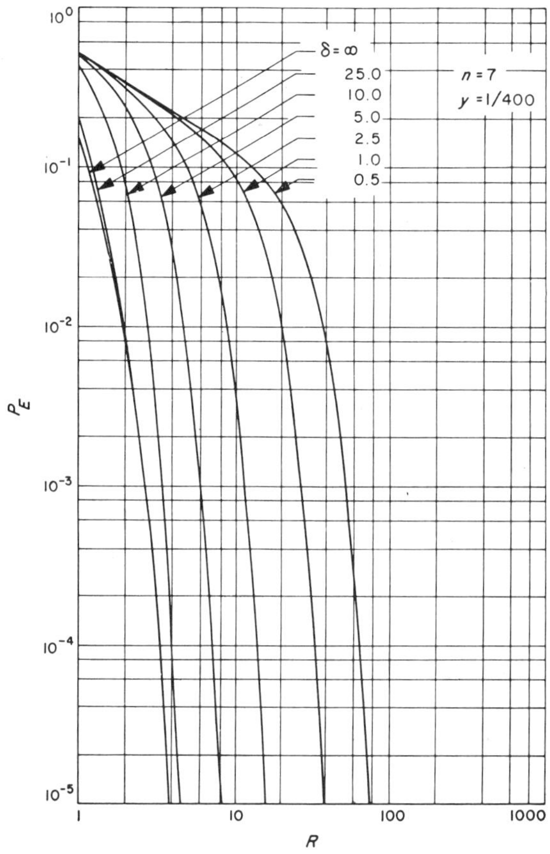


Fig. 4. Word error probability $P_E$ versus $R$ ($n = 6$).

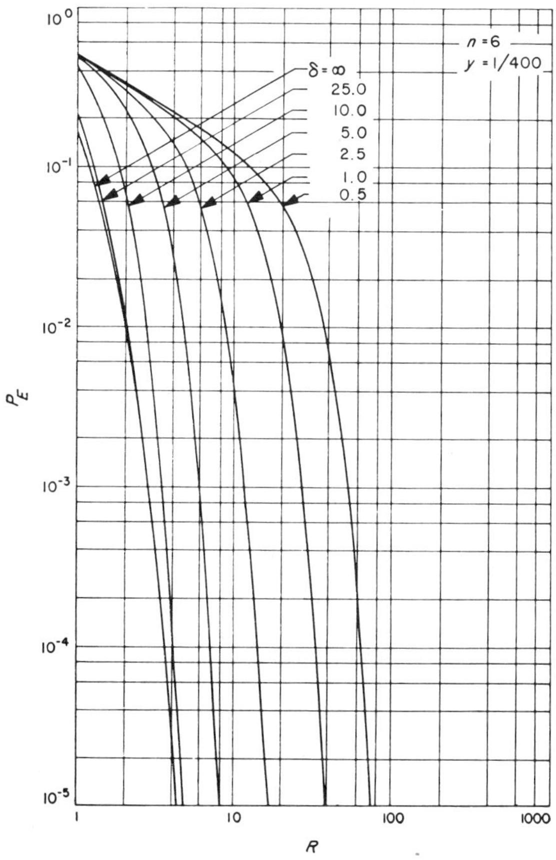


Fig. 5. Word error probability $P_E$ versus $R$ ($n = 7$).

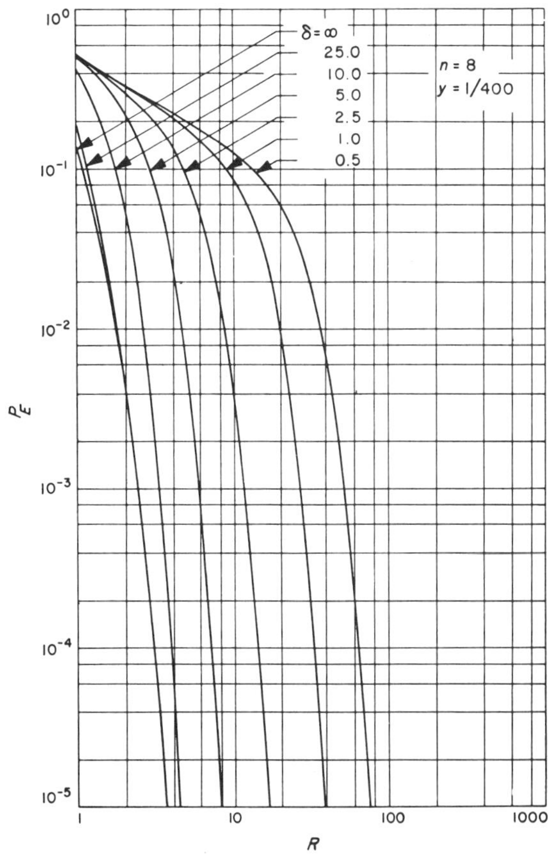


Fig. 6. Word error probability $P_E$ versus $R$ ($n = 8$).

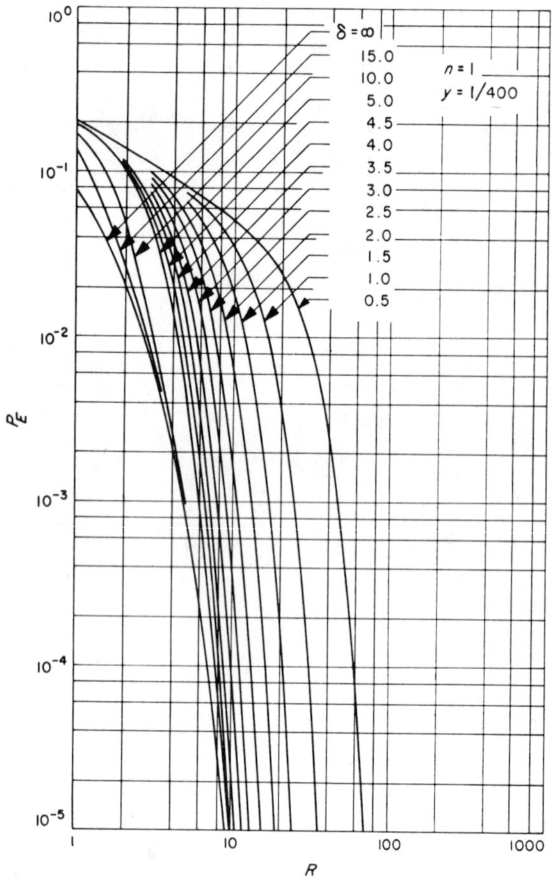


Fig. 7. Bit error probability $P_E$ versus $R$ ($n = 1$, $y = 1/400$).

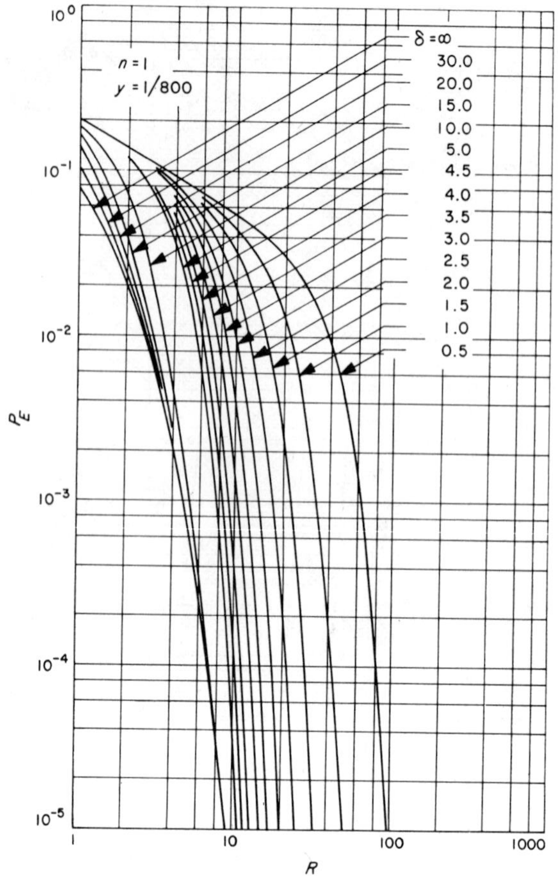


Fig. 8. Bit error probability $P_E$ versus $R$ ($n = 1$, $y = 1/800$).

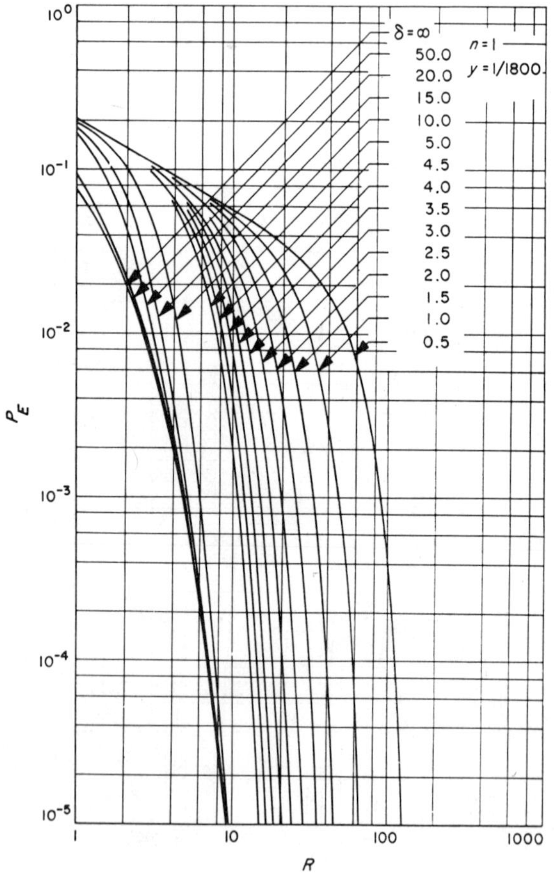


Fig. 9. Bit error probability $P_E$ versus $R$ ($n = 1$, $y = 1/1800$).

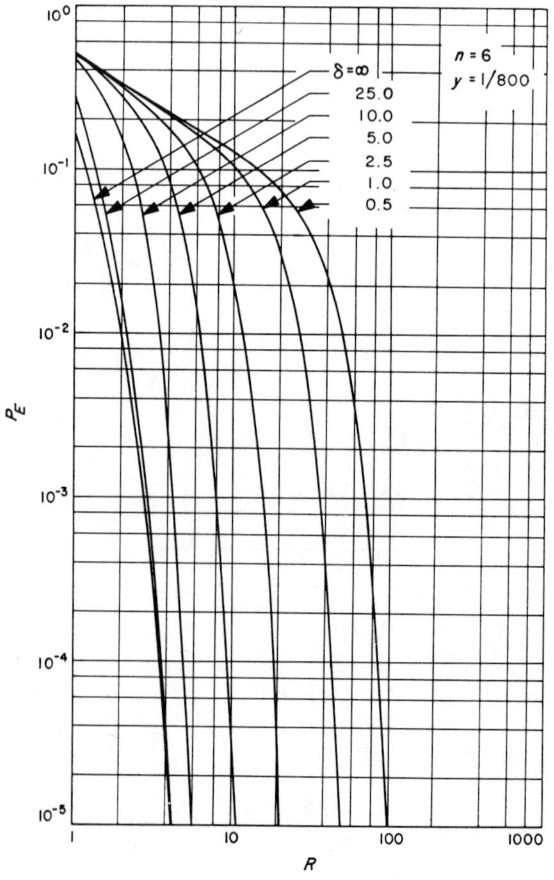


Fig. 10. Word error probability $P_E$ versus $R$ ($n = 6$, $y = 1/800$).

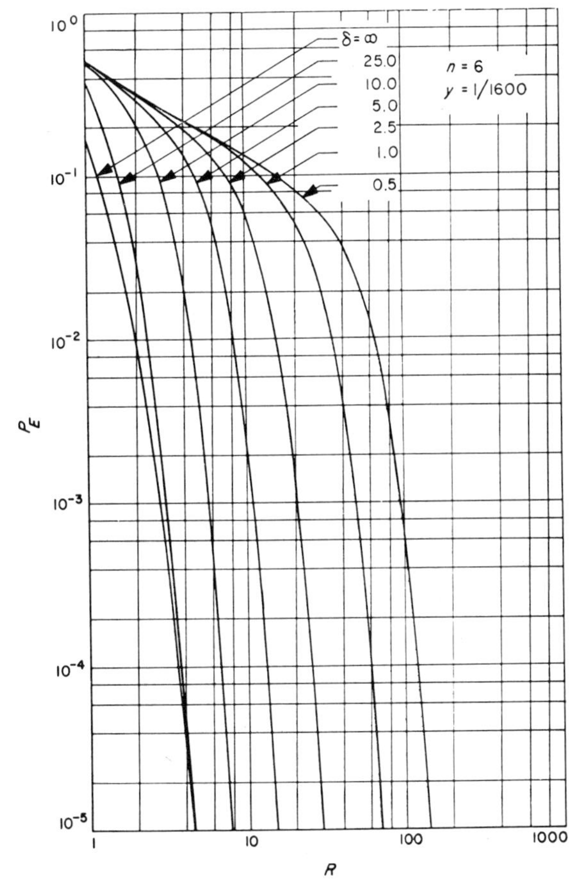


Fig. 11. Word error probability $P_E$ versus $R(n = 6, y = 1/1600)$.

if an ideal bandpass filter precedes the squaring loop or

$$D = \delta R\left[\frac{1}{1 + \dfrac{1}{2\delta y R}}\right] \tag{54}$$

if an RC filter centered around $\omega_0$ precedes the squaring loop. The parameters $R$, $\delta$, $y$, and $R$ are defined by

$$R = \frac{A^2 T_b}{N_0}, \quad \delta = \frac{2R}{W_L}, \quad y = \frac{W_L}{W_i}, \quad R = \frac{1}{T_b}. \tag{55}$$

We point out that the parameter $R$ is the data rate of the system.

Equation (52) has been integrated numerically using an IBM 704 computer for $n = 5, 6, 7$, and 8. The results of the numerical integration are illustrated in Figs. 3–6 for the situation where an ideal bandpass filter precedes the PLL. The parameter $y$ was set at 1/400 since this is typical of what might be encountered in practice. It is clear from these figures that obtaining subcarrier sync by the method outlined here is most beneficial in systems where $\delta = 2R/B_L \gg 1$, i.e., high data rate systems.

One may proceed to develop the performance of such a system for biorthogonal codes. However, if one recalls that for $n \geq 5$, the performance of systems that utilize orthogonal code dictionaries is approximately equal to systems that employ biorthogonal code dictionaries, then the results presented in Figs. 3–6 may be used in carrying out a particular design where biorthogonal codes are used. The performance of a block-coded system which uses biorthogonal codes is given by

$$P_E = 1 - \int_{-\pi/2}^{\pi/2} P_c(\phi)\,\frac{\exp(D\cos 2\phi)}{\pi I_0(D)}\,d\phi \tag{56}$$

where

$$P_c(\phi) = \int_{-\sqrt{2nR}\cos\phi}^{\infty} \frac{\exp\left(-\dfrac{y^2}{2}\right)}{\sqrt{2\pi}}\left[\int_{-y+\sqrt{2nR}\cos\phi}^{y+\sqrt{2nR}\cos\phi} \times \exp\left(\frac{-\dfrac{x^2}{2}}{\sqrt{2\pi}}\right)dx\right]^{2^{n-1}-1} dy. \tag{57}$$

For $n \geq 5$, numerical integration of (54) of the IBM 7090 produces results, for all practical purposes, equivalent to those shown in Figs. 3–6.

Finally, it is of interest to understand how the value of $y = W_L/W_i$ effects the performance of a particular design. This trend is best illustrated, for various values of $y$, in Figs. 7–9 for uncoded telemetry systems, and in Figs. 4, 10, and 11 for block-coded telemetry systems. The results given in Figs. 7–9 were obtained by numerical integration of (56) with $n = 1$ while the results given in Figs. 4, 10, and 11 are for all practical purposes valid for biorthogonal codes even though they were computed from (50). This is due to the fact, mentioned earlier, that for $n \geq 5$ the performance of telemetry systems that employ orthogonal codes is approximately equivalent to that of telemetry systems that employ biorthogonal codes [13], [14]. An obvious conclusion that may be reached here is that for a fixed $\delta$ and $R$, system performance improves as the ratio $y = W_L/W_i$ becomes larger. This result is comprehensible from a physical point of view.

## V. Conclusion

A model probability distribution for the phase error exhibited by the squaring or Costas loop has been derived using the Fokker–Planck equation. The parameters of this distribution are evaluated in terms of the covariance function of the input noise and, in particular, for two specific noise spectra. The steady-state probability density of the phase error coupled with the expected time to first cycle slip gives a fairly complete analytic description of the behavior of the process. The model distribution is then used to assess the degradation in performance of a coded or uncoded telemetry system which tracks the phase of the subcarrier using this method. If the phase of a suppressed carrier signal is derived from the modulated data subcarrier by means of a Costas or a squaring loop, the critical design parameter, which indicates the usefulness of such tracking loops in the demodulation process, is the ratio of the data rate to the bandwidth of the loop. In the case of coded systems, this implies high data rates for error rates less than $10^{-2}$.

## References


[1] M. L. Doelz, E. T. Heald, and D. L. Martin, "Binary data transmission techniques for linear systems," *Proc. IRE,* vol. 45, pp. 656–661, May 1957.

[2] T. deHass, "Statistics of the frequency-differential phase relationship of CW signals transmitted over a 4,000-mile ionospheric path," *Proc. 10th Nat'l Comm. Symp.*, pp. 398–406, October 1964.

[3] H. F. Kathryn, "Radio teletype and data system final report—phase I," General Atronics Corp., West Conshohocken, Pa., Rept. 938–203-14, Contract DA 36-039 SC-85192, September 1961.

[4] J. G. Proakis, P. R. Drouilhet, Jr., and R. Price, "Performance of coherent detection systems using decision-directed channel measurement," *IEEE Trans. Communication Systems,* vol. CS-12, pp. 54–63, March 1964.

[5] J. J. Bussgang and M. Leiter, "Phase shift keying with a transmitted reference," *IEEE Trans. Communication Technology,* vol. COM-14, pp. 14–22, February 1966.

[6] H. Van Trees, "Optimum power division in coherent communication systems," M.I.T. Lincoln Lab., Lexington, Mass., Tech. Rept. 301, February 1963.

[7] J. J. Stiffler, "On the allocation of power in synchronous binary PSK communication systems," *Proc. 1964 Nat'l Telemetering Conf.*, June 2–4.

[8] W. C. Lindsey, "Phase-shift-keyed signal detection with noisy reference signals," *IEEE Trans. Aerospace and Electronic Systems,* vol. AES-2, pp. 393–401, July 1966.

[9] J. W. Layland, "Signal design for communication with timing uncertainties," Ph.D. dissertation, Carnegie Institute of Technology, Pittsburgh, Pa., June 1965.

[10] J. P. Costas, "Synchronous communications," *Proc. IRE,* vol. 44, pp. 1713–1718, December 1956.

[11] R. L. Stratonovich, *Topics in the Theory of Random Noise,* vol. I. New York: Gordon and Breach, 1963.

[12] J. W. Layland, "An optimum squaring loop filter," Jet Propulsion Lab., Pasadena, Calif., Space Programs Summary 37-37, vol. IV, p. 290, February 28, 1966.

[13] W. C. Lindsey, "On the design and performance of frequency multiplexed, phase modulated, block coded communication systems," *IEEE Trans. Communication Technology,* (to be published).

[14] A. J. Viterbi, "On coded phase-coherent communications," *IEEE Trans. Space Electronics and Telemetry,* vol. SET-7, pp. 3–14, March 1961.

[15] V. M. Karshin, "Operation in noise: synchronous voltage generator circuits," *Telecommunications and Radio Engineering,* December 1965.

[16] A. J. Viterbi, "Phase-locked loop dynamics in the presence of noise by Fokker–Planck techniques," *Proc. IEEE,* vol. 51, pp. 1737–1753, December 1963.

[17] R. C. Tausworthe, "Cycle slipping in phase-locked loops," *IEEE Trans. Communication Technology,* vol. COM-15, pp. 417–421, June 1967.

# The Performance of Suppressed Carrier Tracking Loops in the Presence of Frequency Detuning

WILLIAM C. LINDSEY, MEMBER, IEEE, AND MARVIN KENNETH SIMON

**Abstract—The extraction of a coherent reference for purposes of demodulating double-sideband suppressed carrier (DSB-SC) signals can be accomplished using either a squaring loop or a Costas loop. By means of the Fokker–Planck equation, this paper establishes the tracking performance of these two circuits in the presence of frequency detuning, and then applies the results in evaluating the performance of coherent demodulators of digital (coded or uncoded) data. The results are sufficiently general to assess the effects of a broad class of prefiltering characteristics on tracking performance, as well as the effects due to various loop filter mechanizations. An expression for the moments of the time to first loss of synchronization is also given.**

## INTRODUCTION

THIS paper establishes the performance of two widely used circuits, viz., the squaring loop and the Costas loop, used in communications engineering for purposes of 1) demodulation of double-sideband suppressed carrier (DSB-SC) analog signals, and 2) extraction of a carrier or subcarrier reference for use in a phase-coherent receiver where digital modulation is transmitted. Previous work [1] established the nonlinear performance of these two circuits, shown in Figs. 1 and 2, for the case where the loop filters have unit gain, i.e., first-order loops. This paper extends these results to the case of higher order reference-extracting loops and, in particular, treats the case of greatest practical interest, viz., the second-order loop with frequency detuning. The results are sufficiently general to establish the so-called "squaring loss" for the various practical prefiltering selectivity characteristics, e.g., filters whose impulse response can be modeled as the Butterworth, Bessel, Laguerre, or Chebyshev type. The paper evaluates this loss analytically for several typical examples.

In the case of coherent demodulation of analog signals, the output low-pass filter characteristics of Figs. 1 and 2 are determined using Wiener filtering theory. This problem has been treated [2] for the case of linear modulation at the transmitter by one of two classes of modulation processes,

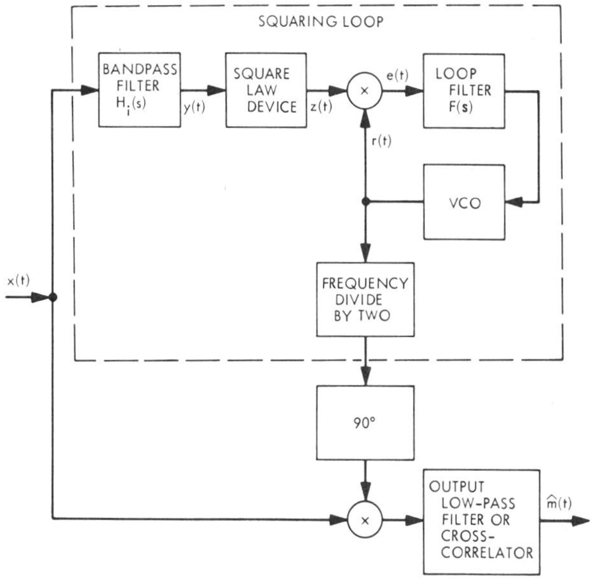


Fig. 1. Coherent demodulator with squaring loop reference extractor for suppressed carrier signals.

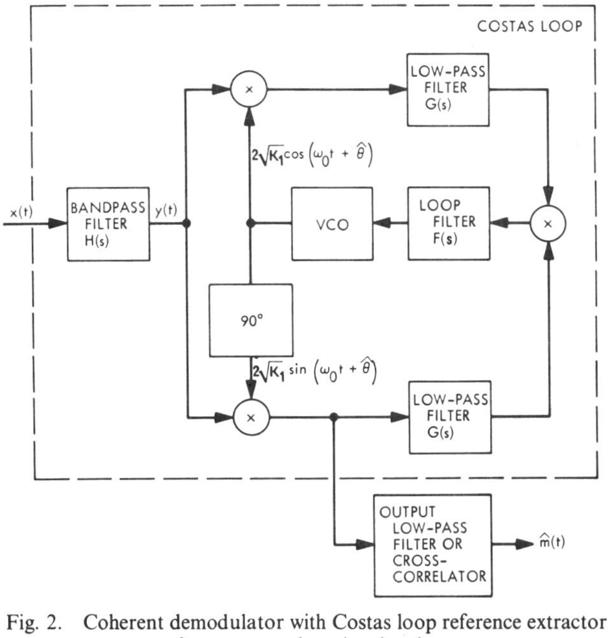


Fig. 2. Coherent demodulator with Costas loop reference extractor for suppressed carrier signals.

Manuscript received September 12, 1969; revised June 5, 1970. This paper presents results of one phase of research carried out at the University of Southern California under NASA Grant MGL-05-016-044 and the results of one phase of research carried out at the Jet Propulsion Laboratory, California Institute of Technology, under NASA Contract NAS 7-100.

W. C. Lindsey is with the University of Southern California, Los Angeles, and is a Consultant to the Jet Propulsion Laboratory, California Institute of Technology, Pasadena, Calif. 91103.

M. K. Simon is with the Jet Propulsion Laboratory, California Institute of Technology, Pasadena, Calif. 91103.

Reprinted from *Proc. IEEE*, vol. 58, pp. 1315–1321, Sept. 1970.

viz., the Butterworth and asymptotically Gaussian processes. In Figs. 1 and 2, $\hat{m}(t)$ represents the receiver's reconstruction of the transmitted message $m(t)$.

If the modulation consists of a sequence of equiprobable $\pm 1$'s, as in PCM telemetry, the output low-pass filter becomes a cross-correlator that is implemented by an integrate and dump circuit. The coherent reference for this filter is obtained via the squaring loop or Costas loop. This paper is primarily concerned with the problem of establishing a coherent reference for purposes of extracting digital data, as well as establishing the performance (error probability) of the data detector as a function of system parameters, e.g., frequency detuning, loop signal-to-noise ratio, etc. As previously mentioned, for the case where the modulation is a zero-mean stochastic process, the results given here and those presented in [2] can be used to establish system performance. In what follows, we draw heavily upon the notation introduced in [1]–[3].

## Coherent Demodulation of DSB Signals with a Squaring Loop or a Costas Loop

In this section, we establish the stochastic differential equation of operation of the squaring loop outlined in Fig. 1 and introduce notation that will be necessary in later analyses. As was previously shown [1], coherent demodulation of DSB-SC signals with a Costas loop (see Fig. 2) is mathematically equivalent to the circuit performance of Fig. 1, i.e., the circuits of Figs. 1 and 2 have the same stochastic differential equation of operation.[1] Thus, the choice of circuit to be used in a particular system design becomes entirely a problem of implementation.

Let the observed data $x(t)$ be given by

$$x(t) = \sqrt{2}\,Am(t)\sin\Theta(t) + n_i(t) = s(t) + n(t) \quad (1)$$

where $\Theta(t) = \omega_0 t + \theta(t)$, $m(t)$ is the signal modulation, $\omega_0$ is the nominal carrier frequency, and $\theta(t)$ is the random phase to be tracked by the squaring loop. The noise $n_i(t)$ is assumed white Gaussian with one-sided spectral density $N_0$ W/Hz. The received signal is then bandpass filtered by $H_i(s)$, with the resultant output $y(t)$ in the form

$$y(t) = \sqrt{2}Am(t)\sin\Theta(t) + n(t) \quad (2)$$

where $W_i$ is the equivalent two-sided noise bandwidth of $H_i(s)$. Note that $W_i/2$ represents the actual bandwidth (positive frequencies only) of the bandpass filter. We further assume that the transfer function $H_i(s)$ is symmetrical about $\omega_0$ and introduces no additional phase shift. Writing (2) in this form is equivalent to assuming that the filter $H_i(s)$ passes the signal component of $x(t)$ in (1) undistorted. In practical applications this assumption is justifiable. For the case of digital data transmission, the modulation will be in the form of a $\pm 1$ pulse train with period $T$. Furthermore, if $W_i < \omega_0/\pi$, then the noise $n(t)$ can be expressed in the form of a narrowband process [4] about the nominal center frequency of the bandpass filter, i.e.,

$$n(t) = \sqrt{2}\left[n_A(t)\cos 2\pi f_0 t - n_B(t)\sin 2\pi f_0 t\right] \quad (3)$$

where $n_A(t)$ and $n_B(t)$ are statistically independent Gaussian noise processes with identical symmetrical spectra corresponding to the low-pass equivalent of $n(t)$. Alternately, one can expand the noise $n(t)$ about the actual frequency of the input observed data by

$$n(t) = \sqrt{2}\left[n_1(t)\cos\Theta(t) - n_2(t)\sin\Theta(t)\right] \quad (4)$$

with $n_1(t)$ and $n_2(t)$ given by

$$n_1(t) \triangleq n_A(t)\cos\theta(t) + n_B(t)\sin\theta(t)$$
$$n_2(t) \triangleq -n_A(t)\sin\theta(t) + n_B(t)\cos\theta(t). \quad (5)$$

Assuming $\theta(t)$ is narrow-band relative to $W_i$ (e.g., $\theta(t) = \theta_0 + \Omega_0 t$; $\Omega_0 \ll \pi W_i$), then following arguments similar to those given by Viterbi [5] it can be concluded that $n_1(t)$ and $n_2(t)$ are approximately statistically independent Gaussian variables with spectra equivalent to those of $n_A(t)$ and $n_B(t)$, respectively. Hereafter, we use the expansion of $n(t)$ given in (4) under the above assumptions.

Assuming a perfect square-law device, the input to the phase-locked loop (PLL) part of the overall squaring loop is (keeping only the terms around $2f_0$)

$$z(t) = y^2(t) = \left[-A^2m(t) + n_1^2(t) - n_2^2(t) + 2Am(t)n_2(t)\right] \cdot\cos 2\Theta(t) + \left[2Am(t)n_1(t) - 2n_1(t)n_2(t)\right]\sin 2\Theta(t). \quad (6)$$

The reference signal $r(t)$ in Fig. 1 is represented by

$$r(t) = 2K_1\sin 2\hat{\Theta}(t) = 2K_1\sin\left[2(2\pi f_0 t) + 2\hat{\theta}(t)\right] \quad (7)$$

where $\hat{\theta}(t)$ is the PLL estimate of $\theta(t)$. The dynamic error signal then becomes (keeping only baseband frequency components)

$$e(t) = K_m z(t)r(t) = K_m K_1\{\left[A^2m^2(t) - n_1^2(t) + n_2^2(t) - 2Am(t)n_2(t)\right]\sin 2\phi(t) + \left[2Am(t)n_1(t) - 2n_1(t)n_2(t)\right]\cos 2\phi(t)\} \quad (8)$$

where $\phi(t) \triangleq \theta(t) - \hat{\theta}(t)$, and $K_m$ is the multiplier grain.

The instantaneous frequency at the VCO output is related to $e(t)$ by

$$\frac{2d\hat{\Theta}(t)}{dt} = K_V\left[F(p)e(t) + n_V(t)\right] + 2\omega_0 \quad (9)$$

where $K_V$ is the VCO gain constant in rad/s/V, $F(p)$ is the loop filter with $p$ the differential operator $d/dt$, and $n_V(t)$ is a noise process associated with the VCO. If the input phase process is now characterized by $\theta(t) = \theta_0 + \Omega_0 t$, then the stochastic differential equation of operation in Fig. 1 becomes

$$\frac{d\phi(t)}{dt} = 2\Omega_0 - KF(p)\left[A^2m^2(t)\sin\Phi(t) + v(t, \Phi(t))\right] - K_V n_V(t) \quad (10)$$

where $K = K_1 K_m K_V$, $\Phi(t) = 2\phi(t)$, and

[1] We assume here that the shaping of the noise spectrum produced by the cascade of $G(s)$ and $H(s)$ in Fig. 2 is equivalent to that produced alone by $H_i(s)$ in Fig. 1.

$$v(t, \Phi(t)) = \left[-n_1^2(t) + n_2^2(t) - 2Am(t)n_2(t)\right] \sin \Phi(t) + \left[2Am(t)n_1(t) - 2n_1(t)n_2(t)\right] \cos \Phi(t) \tag{11}$$

in which $\Phi(t)$ represents the actual phase error being tracked by the loop. In the case of digital modulation, $m(t) = \pm 1$ so that $m^2(t) = 1$. For the case where the message $m(t)$ is a zero-mean random process that is high pass relative to the equivalent loop bandwidth, we can replace $m^2(t)$ in (10) by its mean value. This rapidly becomes obvious if we decompose $m^2(t) \sin \phi(t)$ as

$$m^2(t) \sin \phi(t) = \overline{m^2(t)} \sin \phi(t) + \left[m^2(t) - \overline{m^2(t)}\right] \sin \phi(t)$$

where the second term is a zero-mean high-pass process and will be outside the bandwidth of the tracking loop. Furthermore, if $m(t)$ is not in itself high pass in nature, we can make it so by putting it on a subcarrier. Assuming that the process is normalized such that $\overline{m^2} = 1$, we have

$$\dot{\Phi}(t) = 2\Omega_0 - KF(p)\left[A^2 \sin \Phi(t) + v(t, \Phi(t))\right] - K_V n_V(t) \tag{12}$$

where the dot above $\Phi$ denotes differentiation with respect to $t$. To determine the steady-state probability density function (pdf) of $\Phi(t)$, we apply a procedure based upon the Fokker–Planck equation.

## The Fokker–Planck Equation for Approximately Markov Processes

The method used in determining the pdf of $p(\Phi)$ is based on the theory developed in [6] surrounding the use of the "fluctuation equation" approach. Basically, the method acknowledges the fact that under certain circumstances, a non-Markov process can be replaced or approximated by a Markov process. The validity of this replacement is discussed in detail in [6].

To begin the development, the loop filter $F(p)$ is expressed in terms of its Heaviside expansion:

$$F(p) = F_0 + \sum_{k=1}^{N} \frac{1 - F_k}{1 + \tau_k p}. \tag{13}$$

Substituting (13) into (12) and introducing the coordinates

$$y_0(t) \triangleq \Phi(t)$$

$$y_k(t) \triangleq -\frac{(1 - F_k)K}{1 + \tau_k p}\left[A^2 \sin \Phi(t) + v(t, \Phi(t))\right] \cdot k = 1, 2, \cdots, N \tag{14}$$

yields a set of $(N+1)$ first-order stochastic differential equations

$$\begin{aligned}\dot{\Phi}(t) &= 2\Omega_0 - KF_0\left[A^2 \sin \Phi(t) + v(t, \Phi(t))\right] - K_V n_V(t) + \sum_{k=1}^{N} y_k(t) \\ \dot{y}_k(t) &= -\frac{y_k(t)}{\tau_k} - \frac{(1 - F_k)K}{\tau_k}\left[A^2 \sin \Phi(t) + v(t, \Phi(t))\right] \qquad k = 1, 2, \cdots, N.\end{aligned} \tag{15}$$

The vector $y = [y_0, y_1, \cdots, y_N]$ represents, in an appropriate (N+1)-dimensional space, the state of the system at time $t$. If in fact $v(t, \Phi(t))$ and $n_V(t)$ were white Gaussian noise processes, then $y$ would be a Markov vector [6] and the Fokker–Planck equation could be applied directly. However, if the correlation time [6] of the processes $n_V(t)$ and $v(t, \Phi(t))$ is small in relation to the correlation time of the system, we can replace $y$ by an approximate vector Markov process and apply the "fluctuation equation" approach discussed by Stratonovich [6].

Each component of $y$ can be expressed as a generalized nonlinear function of $y$, $v(t, \Phi(t))$, and $n_V(t)$:

$$\dot{y}_k(t) = G_k\left[y, v(t, y_0(t))\right] \qquad k = 0, 1, \cdots, N \tag{16}$$

so that the steady-state solution for the joint pdf $p(y)$ satisfies, in the diffusion approximation, the equation of probability flow per unit time:

$$\nabla \cdot \mathscr{I}(y) = 0 \tag{17}$$

where

$$\nabla \triangleq \left[\frac{\partial}{\partial y_0}, \cdots, \frac{\partial}{\partial y_N}\right]$$

is the del operator.[2] Here the vector $\mathscr{I} = (\mathscr{I}_0, \mathscr{I}_1, \cdots, \mathscr{I}_N)$ is the probability current density [3] with projections $\mathscr{I}_k = \varepsilon_k \cdot \mathscr{I}$, in which $\varepsilon_k$ is a unit vector pointed in the positive direction of the $k$th coordinate axis. In the steady state, the $k$th projection of the probability current is defined by

$$\mathscr{I}_k(y) \triangleq \left[K_k(y) - \frac{1}{2}\sum_{l=0}^{N} \frac{\partial}{\partial y_l} K_{lk}(y)\right] p(y) \tag{18}$$

with intensity coefficients $K_k(y)$ and $K_{lk}(y)$ given by

$$\begin{aligned}K_l(y) &\triangleq \overline{G_l\left[y, v(t, y_0)\right]} \\ K_{lk}(y) &\triangleq \int_{-\infty}^{\infty} \overline{\{G_l[y, v(t, y_0)]G_k[y, v(t + \tau, y_0)] - K_l(y)K_k(y)\}}\, d\tau.\end{aligned} \tag{19}$$

In (19), the overbar denotes statistical average conditioned on a fixed $y$. Using (15) and (16), the intensity coefficients in

[2] Here we have tacitly assumed that a steady-state solution exists. For a first-order Markov process, Khasminskii [8] has indicated the conditions under which this assumption is valid, while Gray [9] has shown when the solution is unique.

(19) are evaluated by the following:

$$K_0(y) = 2\Omega_0 - F_0 A^2 K \sin\Phi + \sum_{k=1}^{N} y_k$$

$$K_l(y) = -\frac{y_l}{\tau_l} - \frac{(1-F_l)}{\tau_l} A^2 K \sin\Phi \quad l = 1, 2, \cdots, N$$

$$K_{00}(y) = K^2 F_0^2 \int_{-\infty}^{\infty} \left[ R_v(\tau) + \frac{K_V^2}{K^2 F_0^2} R_V(\tau) \right] d\tau$$

$$l = 1, 2, \cdots, N$$

$$K_{lk}(y) = \frac{K^2(1-F_l)(1-F_m)}{\tau_l \tau_m} \int_{-\infty}^{\infty} R_v(\tau) d\tau$$

$$l, k = 1, 2, \cdots, N \quad (20)$$

where $n_v(t)$ is assumed independent of the input noise $n_i(t)$, and

$$R_v(\tau) \triangleq \overline{v(t, \Phi) v(t+\tau, \Phi)}$$

$$R_V(\tau) \triangleq \overline{n_V(t) n_V(t+\tau)}. \quad (21)$$

*The Probability Density of the Phase Error*

Upon substitution of (20) into (17) and (18), the problem of finding the pdf of $p(\Phi)$ reduces to a special case of the solution given in [3]. Without belaboring the details, the pdf of the phase error can be approximated by

$$p(\Phi) = \frac{\exp[\beta\Phi + \alpha\cos\Phi]}{4\pi^2 \exp(-\pi\beta) |I_{j\beta}(\alpha)|^2} \int_{\Phi}^{\Phi+2\pi} \cdot \exp[-\beta x - \alpha \cos x] dx \quad |\Phi| \le \pi \quad (22)$$

where

$$\beta \triangleq \frac{4}{N_{sq} F_0^2 K^2} \left[ 2\Omega_0 - A^2 K \overline{\sin\Phi} \sum_{k=1}^{N} (1 - F_k) \cdot \left( 1 + \frac{N_{sq}}{4A^4 \tau_k \sigma_G^2} \right) \right]$$

$$\alpha \triangleq \frac{4}{N_{sq} F_0^2 K^2} \left[ A^2 K F_0 - \frac{K N_{sq}}{4A^2 \sigma_G^2} \sum_{k=1}^{N} \left( \frac{1 - F_k}{\tau_k} \right) \right]$$

$$\sigma_G^2 = \overline{\sin^2\Phi} - (\overline{\sin\Phi})^2$$

$$N_{sq} \triangleq 2 \int_{-\infty}^{\infty} \left[ R_v(\tau) + \frac{K_V^2}{K^2 F_0^2} R_V(\tau) \right] d\tau \quad (23)$$

and $I_v(x)$ is the modified Bessel function of imaginary order $v$ and of argument $x$. The circular moments of this pdf are given by [3], [7]

$$\overline{\cos n\Phi} = \mathrm{Re}\left[ \frac{I_{n-j\beta}(\alpha)}{I_{-j\beta}(\alpha)} \right];$$

$$\overline{\sin n\Phi} = \mathrm{Im}\left[ \frac{I_{n-j\beta}(\alpha)}{I_{-j\beta}(\alpha)} \right] \quad (24)$$

where Re [·] and Im [·] denote, respectively, the "real part of" and the "imaginary part of" the bracketed quantities. These moments are of interest when the circuits of Figs. 1 and 2 are used to demodulate analog signals.

With $v(t, \Phi)$ as defined in (11), it is relatively straightforward to show (see the Appendix) that

$$R_v(\tau) = 4[A^2 R_{n_1}(\tau) + R_{n_1}^2(\tau)] \quad (25)$$

where

$$R_{n_1}(\tau) = \overline{n_1(t) n_1(t+\tau)} \simeq \frac{N_0}{2} \int_{-\infty}^{\infty} |H_l(j2\pi f)|^2 e^{j2\pi f\tau} df \quad (26)$$

and $H_l(j\omega)$ is the low-pass equivalent of $H_i(j\omega)$.

In the derivation of (25), it is necessary to have $m(t) = m(t+\tau)$. This assumption is valid for all $\tau$ of interest since $T \gg \tau_n$ with $\tau_n$ the decorrelation time of the noise. Substitution of (25) into (23) gives[3]

$$N_{sq} = 4A^2 N_0 \mathscr{S}_L^{-1} \quad (27)$$

where

$$\mathscr{S}_L^{-1} \triangleq 1 + \frac{2}{A^2 N_0} \left\{ \int_{-\infty}^{\infty} \left[ R_{n_1}^2(\tau) + \frac{1}{4} \left( \frac{K_V}{K F_0} \right)^2 R_V(\tau) \right] d\tau \right\} \quad (28)$$

is defined to be the circuit "squaring loss."

*The nth Moment of the First Passage Time*

The $n$th moment of the first passage time is of interest since this parameter is directly related to the $n$th moment of the time to first loss of phase synchronization. Denoting the $n$th moment of the first passage time to the barrier $\Phi_l$ by $\tau^n(\Phi_l)$, and using a result given in [3], we have

$$\tau^n(\Phi_l) = \frac{4}{N_{sq} K^2 F_0^2} \int_{-\Phi_l}^{\Phi_l} \int_{-\Phi_l}^{\Phi} [C_0'(n-1) - \tau^{n-1}(x)] \cdot \exp[U_0(x, \bar{t}) - U_0(\Phi, \bar{t})] dx d\Phi \quad (29)$$

where $\tau^0(x) = u(x - \Phi_0)$, $u(x)$ is the unit step, and $\Phi = \Phi_0$ at the initial time $t = t_0$. The constant $C_0'(n)$ is determined from

$$C_0'(n) = \frac{\int_{-\Phi_l}^{\Phi_l} \tau^n(x) \exp[U_0(x, \bar{t})] dx}{\int_{-\Phi_l}^{\Phi_l} \exp[U_0(x, \bar{t})] dx} \quad (30)$$

with

$$U_0(x, \bar{t}) = -\frac{4}{N_{sq} K^2 F_0^2} \int^{x} \left[ 2\Omega_0 - A^2 K F_0 \sin\Phi + \sum_{k=1}^{N} E(y_k, \bar{t} | \Phi) \right] d\Phi \quad (31)$$

where $E(y_k, \bar{t}|\Phi)$ is the conditional expectation of $y_k$ at $\bar{t}$, given $\Phi$, and $\bar{t}$ is a point such that $\bar{t} \in [0, \infty]$. If the orthogonality principle is used to evaluate $E(y_k, \bar{t}|\Phi)$, then [3]

$$U_0(x, \bar{t}) = \beta x + \alpha \cos x \quad (32)$$

and $\bar{t}$ is taken as $\infty$.

At this point, our results are extremely general in that

[3] It is assumed here that $H_l(j\omega)$ is normalized such that $H_l(0) = 1$.

they hold for a broad class of loop filters as well as for prefilter characteristics. In the next section, several special cases of practical interest are considered.

## Tracking Performance of Second-Order Loop; $N=1$, $(F_0=F_1=\tau_2/\tau_1)$

### *The Phase Error Density $p(\Phi)$*

The quantities $\beta$ and $\alpha$ that characterize the probability distribution of $\Phi$ can now be related to an equivalent set of system parameters $\rho'$, $B_L$, and $r$ by

$$\beta=\left(\frac{r+1}{r}\right)^2\frac{\rho'}{2W_L}\left[2\Omega_0-A^2K\overline{\sin\Phi(1-F_1)}\cdot\left(1+\frac{F_1}{(r+1)\rho'\sigma_G^2}\right)\right] \quad (33)$$

$$\alpha=\left(\frac{r+1}{r}\right)\rho'-\frac{1-F_1}{r\sigma_G^2} \quad (34)$$

where

$\omega=$ actual received frequency
$\Omega_0=\omega-\omega_0=$ loop detuning, rad/s
$A^2K=$ open-loop gain
$r=$ loop damping coefficient $=A^2KF_1\tau_2$ ($r=2$ for for 0.707 damping, $r=4$ for critical damping)
$W_L=$ two-sided loop bandwidth $=(r+1)/(2\tau_2)$; $r\tau_1>>\tau_2$
$\rho'=$ effective signal-to-noise ratio in loop bandwidth $=(\rho/4)\mathscr{S}_L=(\rho_i/2\gamma)\mathscr{S}_L$
$\rho=$ equivalent signal-to-noise ratio in loop bandwidth of standard second-order PLL $=2A^2/N_0W_L$
$\rho_i=$ input signal-to-noise ratio in input bandwidth $=2A^2/N_0W_i$
$\gamma=$ ratio of two-sided noise bandwidth of loop to that of $H_l(\omega)=2W_L/W_i$.

### *The Mean Time to First Slip*

The $n$th moment of the first slip time is found from (29) and (30), with $N=1$ and $\Phi_l=2\pi$. Making use of linear tracking theory to establish a relationship for $E(y_1,\bar{t}|\Phi)$ [3], (31) becomes[4]

$$U_0(\Phi,\bar{t})\approx-\left(\frac{r+1}{r}\right)\rho'\cos\Phi-\frac{\rho'}{2r}\Phi^2-\frac{2\rho'\Omega_0}{A^2K}\Phi \quad (35)$$

and

$$W_L\tau^n(2\pi)\approx\left(\frac{r+1}{r}\right)^2\frac{\rho'}{2}\int_{-2\pi}^{2\pi}\int_{-2\pi}^{\Phi}\left[C_0'(n-1)-\tau^{n-1}(x)\right]\cdot\exp\left[\rho'\left(\frac{r+1}{r}\right)[\cos\Phi-\cos x]+\frac{\rho'}{2r}(\Phi^2-x^2)+\frac{2\rho'\Omega_0}{A^2K}(\Phi-x)\right]dx\,d\Phi. \quad (36)$$

[4] As discussed in [3], the linear PLL theory with $\bar{t}=\infty$ appears to give a better estimate of $E(y_1,\bar{t}|\Phi)$ than the estimate obtained using the orthogonality principle that produced (31). This fact has been justified on the basis of experimental work [3]. This also assumes that $\phi_0=0$ and $y_0=0$ at $t=0$.

TABLE I

$$\mathscr{S}_L=\left[1+\frac{K_L}{\rho\gamma}\right]^{-1}$$

| Prefilter Type | Equivalent Low-Pass Transfer Characteristic $\lvert H_l(j\omega)\rvert^2$ | $\dot{K}_L$ |
|---|---|---|
| 1) $n$th-order Butterworth | $\dfrac{1}{1+\left(\dfrac{\omega}{\omega_i}\right)^{2n}}$; $\omega_i=\dfrac{(2n-1)\pi W_i}{2\Gamma\left(\frac{1}{2n}\right)\Gamma\left(2-\frac{1}{2n}\right)}$ | $\dfrac{2n-1}{2n}$ |
| 2) Gaussian | $\exp\left[-2\left(\dfrac{\omega}{\omega_i}\right)^2\right]$; $\omega_i=\sqrt{2\pi}\,W_i$ | $\dfrac{1}{\sqrt{2}}$ |
| 3) Sinusoidal roll-off $(0\le\xi\le1)$ | $\dfrac{1}{4}\left[1-\sin\dfrac{\pi}{2}\left(\dfrac{\omega-\omega_i}{\xi\omega_i}\right)\right]^2$ for $\lvert\omega-\omega_i\rvert\le\xi\omega_i$ | |
| | $0$ for $\omega-\omega_i\ge\xi\omega_i$ | $\dfrac{1-\frac{29}{64}\xi}{1-\frac{1}{4}\xi}$ |
| | $1$ for $-\omega_i\le\omega-\omega_i\le-\xi\omega_i$ | |
| | $\omega_i=\dfrac{\pi W_i}{2\left(1-\frac{1}{4}\xi\right)}$ | |

### *Evaluation of the Squaring Loss for Various Prefiltering Characteristics; $H_l(s)$*

As a first example, consider a bandpass filter with an RC transfer function. Then the equivalent low-pass spectrum for $n_1(t)$ or $n_2(t)$ has a correlation function

$$R_{n_1}(\tau)=R_{n_2}(\tau)=\frac{N_0}{4}(W_i)\exp(W_i|\tau|) \quad (37)$$

where $W_i$ is again the two-sided noise bandwidth of the input filter $H_i(j\omega)$. If we neglect the effect of $n_V(t)$, then from (35) and (28),

$$\mathscr{S}_L=\frac{1}{1+\dfrac{1}{2\rho\gamma}}. \quad (38)$$

For an ideal bandpass filter (i.e., $H_l(j\omega)=1$; $|f|<W_i/4$, and zero otherwise),

$$\mathscr{S}_L=\frac{1}{1+\dfrac{1}{\rho\gamma}}. \quad (39)$$

We note that these are the two limiting cases of the Butterworth spectra [2]. Various other examples of prefiltering characteristics can easily be carried out. (See Table I for a partial list.)

## Receiver Performance for Digital Modulation

The output of the squaring loop (i.e., $r(t)$) is frequency divided by two to provide a noisy reference for demodulation of the data off the carrier. Thus, the effective phase error for purposes of computing the error probability performance of the data detector is $\phi=\Phi/2$. By simple transformation of variables, the density function for $\phi$ becomes

$$q(\phi) = 2p(\Phi)\Big|_{\Phi=2\phi} \qquad |\phi| \leq \frac{\pi}{2}. \tag{40}$$

If $P_e(\phi)$ is the conditional probability that the data detector will commit a bit (or word) error, then the average bit (or word) error probability is

$$P_e = \int_{-\pi/2}^{\pi/2} P_e(\phi)q(\phi)d\phi = \int_{-\pi}^{\pi} P_e\left(\frac{\Phi}{2}\right)p(\Phi)d\Phi. \tag{41}$$

We also note that polarity ambiguity is a problem in suppressed carrier systems and (41) in no way attempts to include this effect. Details on techniques to resolve the polarity ambiguity in practical applications are not given here. For a correlation-type receiver with perfect word and bit sync and an orthogonally coded transmitted signal set, the word error probability is given by [5]

$$P_{ew}(\phi)=1-P_{cw}(\phi) = 1-\int_{-\infty}^{\infty}\frac{e^{-z^2}}{\sqrt{\pi}}\left\{\frac{1}{2}\operatorname{erfc}\left[-z-\sqrt{R_d n}\cos\phi\right]\right\}^{2^n-1}dz \tag{42}$$

where $n$ is the number of symbols (binits) per code word, $R_d=A^2T_b/N_0$ is the energy per bit-to-noise spectral density ratio, $T_b$ is the bit time, and erfc $(y)$ is the complementary error function defined by

$$\operatorname{erfc}(y) = \frac{2}{\sqrt{\pi}}\int_y^{\infty} e^{-t^2}dt. \tag{43}$$

Note that $R_d$ can be related to $\rho$ by $\rho=R_d\delta$, where $\delta=2/W_LT_b$. The corresponding conditional bit error probability $P_{e_B}(\phi)$ for a $\pm 1$ transmitted signal set is given by

$$P_{e_B}(\phi) = 1 - \int_{-\infty}^{\infty}\frac{e^{-z^2}}{\sqrt{\pi}}\left\{\frac{1}{2}\operatorname{erfc}\left[-z-\sqrt{2R_d}\cos\phi\right]\right\}dz = \frac{1}{2}\operatorname{erfc}(\sqrt{R_d}\cos\phi). \tag{44}$$

Note that $P_{e_B}(\phi)$ is not obtained from $P_{ew}(\phi)$ for orthogonal codes by letting $n=1$. This is so since in an orthogonally coded system the words are 90° apart, whereas in a one-bit system ($\pm 1$) they are separated by 180°.

Fig. 3 plots $P_{e_B}$ as defined by (44) and (41) versus $\Omega_0/A^2K$ (frequency detuning/open-loop gain) with $R_d$ as a parameter for $F_1=0.002$, $\delta=25$, $\gamma=0.002$, $r=2$, and RC and ideal bandpass filter characteristics. This curve can also be used for

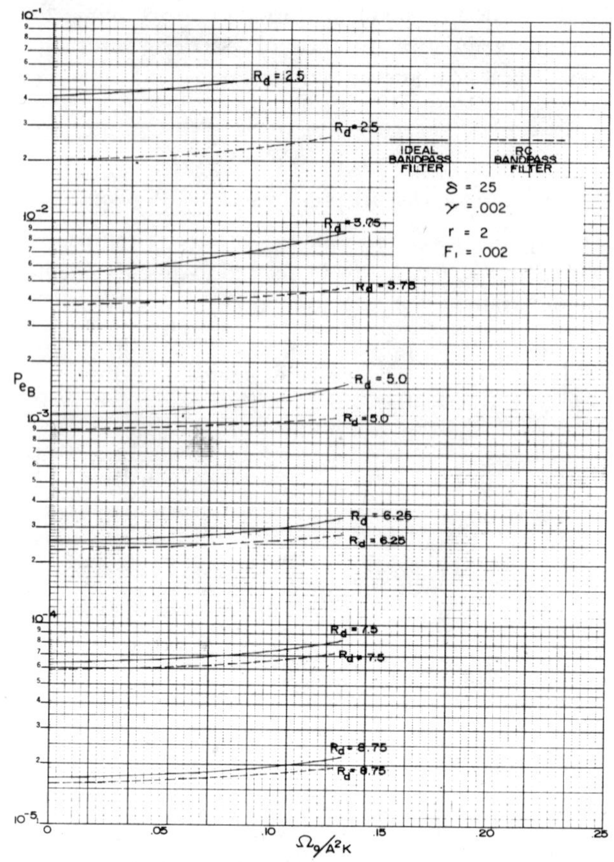


Fig. 3. Bit error probability as a function of normalized frequency detuning.

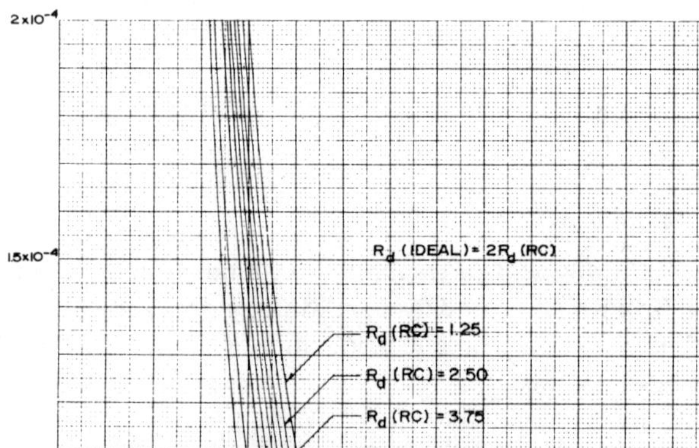

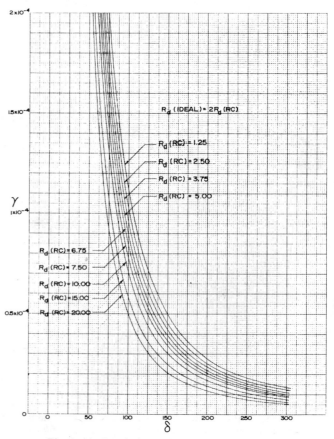

Fig. 4. A plot of $\gamma$ versus $\delta$ for various values of $R_d$.

other combinations of values $\gamma$ and $\delta$. To determine these, Fig. 4 plots $\gamma$ versus $\delta$ and $R_d$ as a parameter for RC and ideal bandpass filters. It is sufficient to note that the probability of slipping a half-cycle is much smaller than $P_{e_B}$ computed in Fig. 3.

## Conclusions

This paper has presented results that can be applied to the problem of designing and planning of coherent communications systems that transmit digital or analog data as double-sideband suppressed carrier signals. The demodulation of digital data has been discussed in detail. Coherent demodulation of analog signals can be treated using the results presented here in combination with those given in [2].

## Appendix

### Evaluation of the Autocorrelation Function of $v(t, \Phi)$

The autocorrelation function of $v(t, \Phi)$ is defined by

$$R_v(\tau) = E[v(t, \Phi)v(t + \tau, \Phi)] \tag{45}$$

with $v(t, \Phi)$ given by

$$v(t, \Phi) = [2Am(t)n_1(t) - 2n_1(t)n_2(t) \cos \Phi + [n_2^2(t) - n_1^2(t) - 2Am(t)n_2(t)] \sin \Phi \tag{46}$$

and $n_1(t)$ and $n_2(t)$ independent zero-mean Gaussian random variables.

Substituting (46) into (45) and assuming $m(t)=m(t+\tau)$ for all $\tau$ of interest gives, upon simplification,

$$\begin{aligned} R_v(\tau) = {} & [4A^2R_{n_1}(\tau) + 4R_{n_1}(\tau)R_{n_2}(\tau)] \cos^2 \Phi \\ & + [R_{n_1}^2(0) + 2R_{n_1}^2(\tau) + R_{n_2}^2(0) + 2R_{n_2}^2(\tau) \\ & - 2R_{n_1}(0)R_{n_2}(0) + 4A^2R_{n_2}(\tau)] \sin^2 \Phi. \end{aligned} \tag{47}$$

If $R_{n_1}(\tau)=R_{n_2}(\tau)$, then

$$\begin{aligned} R_v(\tau) &= [4A^2R_{n_1}(\tau) + 4R_{n_1}^2(t)] \cos^2 \Phi \\ &\quad + [4A^2R_{n_1}(\tau) + 4R_{n_1}^2(\tau)] \sin^2 \Phi \\ &= 4[A^2R_{n_1}(\tau) + R_{n_1}^2(\tau)]. \end{aligned} \tag{48}$$

## References


[1] R. L. Didday and W. C. Lindsey, "Subcarrier tracking methods and communication system design," *IEEE Trans. Commun. Tech.*, vol. COM-16, pp. 541–550, August 1968.

[2] W. C. Lindsey, "Optimum coherent linear demodulation," *IEEE Trans. Commun. Tech.*, vol. COM-13, pp. 183–190, June 1965.

[3] ——, "Nonlinear analysis of generalized tracking systems," *Proc. IEEE*, vol. 57, pp. 1705–1722, October 1969. Also, University of Southern California, Los Angeles, Calif., Rep. USC EE 317, December 1968.

[4] W. B. Davenport, Jr., and W. L. Root, *An Introduction to the Theory of Random Signals and Noise.* New York: McGraw-Hill, 1958.

[5] A. J. Viterbi, *Principles of Coherent Communication.* New York: McGraw-Hill, 1966.

[6] R. L. Stratonovich, *Topics in the Theory of Random Noise,* vol. 1. New York: Gordon and Breach, 1963, pp. 83–103.

[7] W. C. Lindsey and M. K. Simon, "The effect of loop stress on the performance of two-channel phase-coherent communication systems," to be published in *IEEE Trans. Commun. Technol.*, October 1970.

[8] R. Z. Khasminskii, "Ergodic properties of recurrent diffusion processes and stabilization of the Cauchy problem for parabolic equations," *Theory Probab. Its Appl. (USSR)*, vol. 5, pp. 179–196, 1960.

[9] A. H. Gray, "Uniqueness of steady-state solutions to the Fokker–Planck equation," *J. Math. Phys.* (Cambridge, Mass.), vol. 6, pp. 644–647, April 1965.

# Part VIII
# Ranging

Ranging with spread spectrum systems has been a *fait accompli* for at least 15 years, as the first real application of direct sequence modulation techniques. Tausworthe's paper in Part III, Coding, was concerned with coding specifically for ranging systems. Here four papers are reprinted that deal with the direct sequence techniques for ranging. A number of other papers are in existence in this area, and references to them may be found at the end of this introduction in the listing, Other Papers of Interest, as well as in this volume's bibliography.

The first paper reprinted here is a parallel to the direct sequence ranging systems and differs from them primarily in that the systems discussed employ random noise rather than pseudorandom noise for carrier modulation. No currect application of random noise modulated ranging is known to this editor, because of the ease with which a well-defined known pseudonoise signal can be generated, and random noise is neither so well behaved nor does it have the two-valued correlation functions of PN signals. Painter's paper, on the other hand, is specifically concerned with direct sequence ranging system design. Its stated purpose is to present a concise set of analytical tools for design or analysis of such systems, and as such is one of the earliest papers to do so.

The fourth paper is one of my own. I have included it here because it presents a modified (called hybrid) direct sequence ranging technique that can be used to advantage where distances are large and acquisition time is a factor. The technique employs the baseband channel to supplement the direct sequence RF coding, which makes it possible to employ short quickly searched code sequences over distances that would not be practical for a more conventional direct sequence system.

Richardson's paper, the fifth paper in this part, discusses the design of transponders for long distance ranging. It also compares limiting and linear transponders and their performance.

Frequency hopping systems are not usually employed for range measurement. This is because the code rates and the frequency hopping rates used in these systems are not normally commensurate with high range resolution. A possible exception is found in high speed coherent frequency hoppers, and a reference to such a hopper is found at the end of this introduction in the listing, Other Papers of Interest.

Chirp techniques have been employed in radar for some time, and since radar systems have ranging as one of their prime functions, it is suggested that those who are interested in employing chirp spread spectrum ranging see the wealth of material that is available in the radar area on such applications. For ranging purposes, chirp techniques are basically echo ranging techniques that use the *TW* product of the chirp waveform to advantage for reducing peak power requirements. Otherwise, there is little difference in a chirp ranging system and in a conventional radar ranging system.

## OTHER PAPERS OF INTEREST

1) A. W. Rihaczek and R. M. Golden, "Resolution performance of pulse trains with large time-bandwidth products," *IEEE Trans. Aerosp. Electron Syst.*, July 1971.

# Noise-Modulated Distance Measuring Systems*

B. M. HORTON†

*Summary*—**Distance-measuring systems using random noise as the modulating function are described. The distance measurement is accomplished by correlating the modulation on the transmitted and received signals. The spectrum of the modulating function determines the way in which this correlation, and hence system output, depends on distance to a reflecting target. Physical realizability of filters limits the output-to-distance behavior of linear, noise-modulated systems. Theoretically, either amplitude or frequency modulation can be used, but the latter has distinct advantages in overcoming incidental spurious signals generated within the system. Actual multiplication of signals is avoided through use of a conventional mixer. The resulting system is similar to existing altimeters but is free of the ambiguities inherent in periodically modulated systems, avoids the "fixed error," and is capable of measuring distances down to a few feet. This makes it particularly suited for use as an altimeter in blind landing systems.**

## INTRODUCTION

THE purpose of this paper is to discuss the general characteristics of distance-measuring, or ranging systems in which the transmitted energy is modulated with random noise. One reason for interest in this type of system is that it appears to be promising for use as an altimeter for blind landing. Discussion will primarily concern CW systems.

* Original manuscript received by the IRE, January 15, 1959.
† Diamond Ordnance Fuze Labs., Washington, D. C.

Distance-measuring systems which depend upon reflection of energy from a target usually are based on a predictable detailed relationship between the transmitted and returning signals. Pulse radar systems measure time delay,[1] and FM systems measure phase shift or frequency difference[2–9] to determine distance to the target. Those systems which are modulated with a periodic function are subject to ambiguities for targets whose time delay is greater than the repetition period. "Jitter" of the repetition period is often used to reduce

[1] L. N. Ridenour, ed., "Radar system engineering," M.I.T. Rad. Lab. Ser., McGraw-Hill Book Co., Inc., New York, N. Y., vol. 1; 1947.
[2] S. Matsuo, "A direct reading radio-wave-reflecting-type absolute altimeter for aeronautics," PROC. IRE, vol. 26, pp. 848–858; July, 1938.
[3] "FM radar altimeter," *Electronics*, pp. 130–134; April, 1946.
[4] D. G. C. Luck, "Frequency Modulated Radar," McGraw-Hill Book Co., Inc., New York, N. Y.; 1949.
[5] F. Penin and G. Phelizon, "Le mesureur de distance DME," *Onde Elect.*, vol. 33, pp. 309–318; January, 1953.
[6] A. Black, K. E. Buecks, and A. H. Heaton, "Improved radio altimeter," *Wireless World*, vol. 60, pp. 138–140; March, 1954.
[7] G. Collette and R. Labrousse, "Un altimetre radioelectrique a modulation de frequence," *Ann. Radioélec.*, vol. 10, pp. 387–398; January, 1955.
[8] H. Gutton, H. Familier, and B. Ginger, "Etude de la modulation de frequence appliquee a la mesure des distances," *Ann. Radioélec.* vol. 11, pp. 107–117; April, 1956.
[9] M. A. W. Ismail, "A Study of the Double Modulated FM Radar," Verlag Leeman, Zurich Switz., pp. 22–23; 1955.

Reprinted from *Proc. IRE*, vol. 47, pp. 821–828, May 1959.

the effect of this ambiguous response. When used in this way, the random variations are a perturbation to the orderly (and usually periodic) modulation of the transmitter.

In addition to the ambiguities arising from the repetition period, there is, in a periodic FM altimeter, a quantizing effect, sometimes called the "fixed error," which causes discrete changes in system output with changes in target distance. Although this quantizing effect can be avoided,[10,11] a system which is inherently free of such effects would be desirable.

Elimination of the inherent ambiguities and the quantizing effect in a distance-measuring system implies that the modulation is not periodic and hence the spectrum of the modulating signal is not a harmonic series. One way of insuring that the modulation is not periodic is to use random noise as the modulating function. It is the purpose of this paper to discuss the general characteristics of noise-modulated systems, to point out some of the novel features which can be achieved, to discuss some of their limitations, to describe several types of noise-modulated systems, and to report the successful operation of one type of system. The method of analysis gives opportunity, within the limits of realizability and practicality, to design a system with a particular desired output-vs-distance relation.

Recent investigations[12–14] of the power spectrum of a carrier which is modulated by random noise give pertinent information on the spectral characteristics of the signals in the systems to be described here. Although those results were not available at the time that the work being reported here was done, they are very useful in determining the relation between system parameters and the signal spectrum. Use of noise itself as the carrier has also been investigated,[15] but the results do not apply to the present system.

## Application of the Correlation Function to Distance Measurement[16]

Suppose a system radiates energy which is modulated in amplitude, phase, or frequency by a "random" function, *e.g.*, Gaussian noise. If a target very close to the transmitter reflects back some of the energy with a very short time delay, the transmitter will not have had sufficient time to make a very great change in amplitude (or phase, or frequency) during this short time. For a target at a greater distance, the time delay of the return signal will be greater, and there will be an increased probability of a large change in the signal which is being transmitted. If we now make a comparison between the outgoing and incoming signals, we have a result whose statistical properties depend upon distance. At zero distance (no time delay) the transmitted and return signals are identical, and we find perfect *correlation* between them. At very large distances, the return signal will seem to be almost completely unrelated to what is being transmitted, *i.e.*, the transmitted and return signals are *uncorrelated.*

The way in which correlation between the transmitted and return signals changes from perfect correlation at zero distance to lack of any correlation at very great distances depends upon the frequency components in the random function, *i.e.*, the spectrum of the noise. If only very-low-frequency components are present, then the transmitted signal cannot change rapidly in time, and the correlation between the outgoing and return signals changes very slowly with increasing distance. If, however, very-high-frequency components are present, the transmitter can make rapid changes in amplitude, phase, or frequency, and the correlation between the two signals goes rapidly toward zero as the time delay between transmitted and return signals increases.

It should be noted that if the modulating function is truly a random function, there is some probability that the outgoing and returning signals can be very different even for a very close target, but such large differences are not as likely as smaller ones. In the system being proposed here, only the average relationship between the outgoing and returning signals is used to determine distance. The accuracy with which the distance determination is made depends upon the length of time during which the relationship is measured as well as upon the accuracy of system parameters.

Correlation of a function with itself is called its "correlation function" or "autocorrelation" in communication theory, and "serial correlation" in the field of statistics. In an actual system, one of the signals can be modified by noise, Doppler effect, and other forms of interference, hence the correlation between the outgoing and return signals is not precisely its "autocorrelation" or "correlation function." However, since the system is based on the principle implied by these terms, they are appropriate, and departures from the principle will be treated as error signals.

The correlation-function principle has the possibility of being used in systems which employ radio waves, light, sound, or other effects as carrier. It is only necessary that the random function be impressed upon the

[10] H. P. Kalmus, J. C. Cacheris, and H. A. Dropkin, "Nonquantized frequency-modulated altimeter," IRE Trans. on Aeronautical and Navigational Electronics, vol. ANE-1, pp. 15–21; June, 1954.

[11] M. A. W. Ismail, "A precise new system of FM radar," Proc. IRE, pp. 1140–1145; September, 1956.

[12] J. L. Stewart, "The power spectrum of a carrier frequency modulated by Gaussian noise," Proc. IRE, vol. 42, pp. 1539–1542; October, 1954.

[13] R. G. Medhurst, "The power spectrum of a carrier frequency modulated by Gaussian noise," Proc. IRE, vol. 43, pp. 752–753; June, 1955.

[14] P. R. Karr has shown in unpublished reports the relation between the spectrum of a carrier which is frequency modulated with random noise and the spectrum of the modulating function. For a high modulation index, the resulting spectrum asymptotically approaches the probability density of instantaneous resulting frequency.

[15] A. A. Kharkevich, "The transmission of signals by modulated noise," in "Telecommunications," Pergamon Press, Inc., London, Eng., pp. 43–47; 1957.

[16] Material in this section was presented in Natl. Bur. Stand. Classified Rep. O.E.D. 13.4-205R, issued May 23, 1952, and reissued in a slightly shorter version as Natl. Bur. Stand. Classified Rep. 17–104, November 7, 1952.

outgoing energy and detected in that which is reflected back from the target.

In some applications it will be advantageous actually to measure, not the correlation function itself, but a closely related function which might be called the "anti-correlation" function. This will be discussed after some features of the correlation function principle have been presented.

*The Correlation Function*

Let $F(t)$ be a dimensionless continuous random-noise function with a Gaussian distribution of amplitudes and no dc component. The correlation function $\psi(\tau)$ of $F(t)$ is defined by [17,18]

$$\psi(\tau) = \left(\frac{1}{K}\right) \lim_{T\to\infty} \frac{1}{T}\int_0^T F(t)F(t-\tau)dt \tag{1}$$

where the normalizing factor $K$ is given by

$$K = \lim_{T\to\infty} \frac{1}{T}\int_0^T [F(t)]^2 dt. \tag{2}$$

The amplitude spectrum $S(f)$ of a function $G(t)$ which is equal to $F(t)$ in the interval $0 \leq t \leq T$ and zero outside the interval is:

$$S(f) = \int_0^T F(t)e^{-i2\pi f t}dt, \tag{3}$$

and the corresponding normalized "power" spectrum $w(f)$ is

$$w(f) = \left(\frac{1}{K}\right) \lim_{T\to\infty} \frac{2\,|\,S(f)\,|^2}{T}, \tag{4}$$

considering only positive frequencies. The correlation function is related to the power spectrum by the Wiener-Khintchine relation

$$\psi(\tau) = \int_0^\infty w(f) \cos 2\pi f\tau df, \tag{5}$$

and

$$w(f) = 4\int_0^\infty \psi(\tau) \cos 2\pi f\tau d\tau. \tag{6}$$

We see that a system which performs the operation of correlating $F(t)$ with $F(t-\tau)$, as indicated by (1), will behave in accordance with (5), *i.e.*, its distance dependence will be governed by the power spectrum $w(f)$ of the random noise. It can be seen from (6) that some desired system behavior $\psi(\tau)$ can be postulated, and the corresponding noise power spectrum determined. Many types of correlation function, however, lead to unrealizable, or impractical power spectra.

We now consider several special cases of noise spectra and give the corresponding correlation functions. In each case, we use a normalized power spectrum *i.e.*, a spectrum for which

$$\int_0^\infty w(f)df = 1, \tag{7}$$

and a normalized $\psi(\tau)$ in order that $\psi(0) = 1$.

*Case I—Ideal Band-Pass Filter:* Let

$$\begin{aligned} w_1(f) &= \frac{1}{f_2 - f_1} \text{ for } f_1 \leq f \leq f_2 \\ &= 0 \text{ for } f < f_1 \\ &= 0 \text{ for } f > f_2. \end{aligned} \tag{8}$$

Using (5) and integrating, we obtain

$$\psi_1(\tau) = \frac{1}{(f_2 - f_1)2\pi\tau}\left[\sin 2\pi f_2\tau - \sin 2\pi f_1\tau\right]. \tag{9}$$

When $f_1 = 0$, the low-pass filter case,

$$\psi_1(\tau) = \frac{1}{2\pi f_2\tau} \sin 2\pi f_2\tau. \tag{10}$$

Both of these functions oscillate, and thus have the disadvantage that a certain value of $\psi(\tau)$ may correspond to more than one value of $\tau$. When $f_1$ and $f_2$ are almost equal, $\psi_1(\tau)$ looks like a very slightly damped sine wave. As the bandwidth is increased, the "damping" increases. When $f_1 = 0$, $\psi_1(\tau)$ appears highly damped.

*Case II—Exponential Filter:* Now suppose

$$w_2(f) = ae^{-af} \tag{11}$$

where $a$ is a constant.

Again using (5) and integrating, we obtain

$$\psi_2(\tau) = \frac{1}{1 + \left(\dfrac{2\pi\tau}{a}\right)^2}. \tag{12}$$

Here we have a correlation function which decreases monotonically with increasing $\tau$ for $\tau > 0$, hence ambiguity in the relation between $\tau$ and $\psi_2(\tau)$ is avoided. It would be impossible, however, to obtain a noise spectrum conforming exactly to (11) and would be difficult to approximate.

*Case III—Low-Pass RC Filter:* In this case we assume that the noise spectrum is that which would be produced if "white" noise from a generator of zero output impedance is passed through the circuit of Fig. 1. The output power spectrum is

$$w_3(f) = \frac{4/\lambda}{(2\pi f)^2 + (1/\lambda)^2}, \tag{13}$$

where $\lambda = R_1R_2C/(R_1 + R_2)$ is the time constant of the noise-shaping network. If we substitute (13) into (5) and integrate, we obtain

$$\psi_3(\tau) = e^{-\tau/\lambda}. \tag{14}$$

[17] M. C. Wang and G. E. Uhlenbeck, "On the theory of the Brownian motion II," *Rev. Mod. Phys.*, vol. 17, pp. 323–342; April–July, 1945.

[18] S. O. Rice, "Mathematical analysis of random noise," *Bell Sys. Tech. J.*, vol. 23, pp. 282–332; July, 1944. For convenience in later use of this function, we have used $f(t-\tau)$ in place of Rice's $f(t+\tau)$, but the difference vanishes as $T\to\infty$ when $\tau$ is finite.

This correlation function, the inverse of Case II, is a monotonically decreasing function of delay time $\tau$, hence avoiding ambiguities in the relationship between $\psi(\tau)$ and $\tau$. It also has the advantage that the noise spectrum can be shaped with a simple circuit.

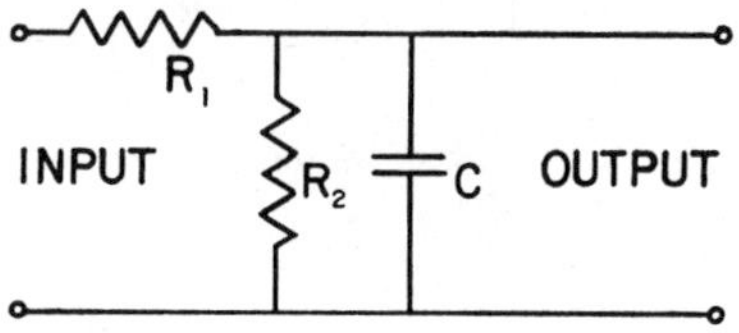


Fig. 1—Noise filter for Case III.

*Case IV—Gaussian Filter With Maximum at Zero Frequency:*

$$w_4(f) = \frac{1}{f_c}\sqrt{\frac{2}{\pi}}\, e^{-f^2/2f_c^2} \tag{15}$$

*i.e.*, the power spectrum follows a one-sided normal distribution with maximum density at zero. This leads to

$$\psi_4(\tau) = e^{-2\pi^2 f_c^2 \tau^2} \tag{16}$$

which also follows the normal distribution with maximum at zero. Such a correlation function may be especially adapted to some applications where, for example, greater range s nsitivity is desired at a particular range. The required power spectrum $w_4(f)$ would, as in Case II, however, be impossible to obtain exactly.

*Case V—Gaussian Filter With Maximum at $\bar{f}$:* In this case we assume that the noise power follows a normal distribution with mean value at $\bar{f}$, and has a standard deviation (in frequency) of $\sigma$, *i.e.*,:

$$w_5(f) = \frac{1}{\sigma\sqrt{\pi}}\, e^{-(f-\bar{f})^2/2\sigma^2}. \tag{17}$$

If we put (17) in (5) and integrate, we obtain an approximate expression for the corresponding correlation function $\psi_5(\tau)$, which is valid when $\bar{f} \gg \sigma$,

$$\psi_5(\tau) = [\cos 2\pi\tau\bar{f}]e^{-2\pi^2\tau^2\sigma^2}, \tag{18}$$

an oscillating function with a Gaussian envelope.

The required power spectrum of the noise may be obtained approximately with tuned circuits, but $\psi_5(\tau)$ has the disadvantage that it oscillates and hence has ambiguities in the relationship between $\psi(\tau)$ and $\tau$.

Of the several cases of noise spectrum which have been presented, three have led to correlation functions which give no ambiguities, but two of these may require a complex noise band-shaping network while the other requires only a resistance-capacitance network. Its correlation function $\psi_3(\tau)$, (14) is

$$\psi_3(\tau) = e^{-\tau/\lambda}. \tag{14a}$$

If one wants $\psi_3(\tau)$ to have the value $1/e$ (*i.e.*, $\tau = \lambda$) for a distance of 100 feet, then

$$\lambda = \frac{2 \times 100}{C} \approx 2 \times 10^{-7}$$

seconds, approximately. The corresponding half-power point frequency for the RC network is about 0.8 mc. This case has the property that a certain percentage change in range gives a constant percentage change in $\psi_3(\tau)$ for all ranges. This is shown by the fact that

$$\frac{\dfrac{d}{d(\tau/\lambda)}\psi_3(\tau)}{\psi_3(\tau)} = \frac{-e^{-\tau/\lambda}}{e^{-\tau/\lambda}} = -1. \tag{19}$$

A disadvantage of the correlation function is that it has its maximum value when $\tau = 0$. This means that a small amount of leakage from the transmitting antenna to the receiving antenna might obscure a return signal of greater strength but with a greater time delay. Similarly, a small return from a near target may obscure a large target farther out. This is discussed more fully in later sections. This property of the correlation function led to the search for a function which is complementary to the correlation function, *i.e.*, one which starts at zero for zero distance and increases monotonically to a maximum value at infinite distance.

### *"Anticorrelation" Distance Measurement*

In the correlation function system, a function was multiplied by its delayed version, and the average value of this product was obtained. [See (1).] The average value of this product is a maximum when the delay is zero. In the "anticorrelation" system to be discussed now, we find the mean square value of the difference between the value of a function and its delayed version. When the time delay $\tau$ is zero, the instantaneous difference is zero, hence the mean-square difference is zero, and the effect of leakage from transmitter to receiver is lessened.

The "anticorrelation" function $H(\tau)$ will be defined by

$$H(\tau) = \lim_{T\to\infty}\frac{1}{2T}\int_0^T [F(t) - F(t-\tau)]^2 dt \tag{20}$$

$$= \lim_{T\to\infty}\left[\frac{1}{2T}\int_0^T [F(t)]^2 dt + \frac{1}{2T}\int_0^T [F(t-\tau)]^2 dt - \frac{1}{T}\int_0^T F(t)F(t-\tau)dt\right].$$

If $(F(t)$ is normalized, *i.e.*, in (2), $K = 1$, then

$$H(\tau) = 1 - \lim_{T\to\infty}\frac{1}{T}\int_0^T F(t)F(t-\tau)dt \tag{21}$$

or

$$H(\tau) = 1 - \psi(\tau). \tag{22}$$

Thus we see that $H(\tau)$, defined as half the mean-square difference between normalized $F(t)$ and $F(t-\tau)$, is the complement of their mean product $\psi(\tau)$.

Using (22) and the correlation functions obtained in Cases I–V in the previous section, we have immediately, from (22), $H(\tau)$ for the noise spectra considered there.

For a noise band which is shaped by the RC network, (Case III)

$$H_3(\tau) = 1 - e^{-\tau/\lambda}. \tag{23}$$

If a response of

$$H_3(\tau) = 1 - \frac{1}{e}$$

is desired for a target at 100 feet, $\lambda$ must be approximately $2\times10^{-7}$ seconds, which again corresponds to a half-power frequency of about 0.8 mc.

At very small values of $\tau/\lambda$, $H_3(\tau)$ is approximately proportional to $\tau/\lambda$; thus the output of this system is, for near targets, nearly a linear function of distance.

The fractional range sensitivity is:

$$\frac{\frac{d}{d(\tau/\lambda)} H_3(\tau)}{H_3(\tau)} = \frac{e^{-\tau/\lambda}}{1 - e^{\tau/\lambda}} = \frac{1}{e^{\tau/\lambda} - 1} \cdot \tag{24}$$

When $\tau = 0$ this is unlimited, and as $\tau \to \infty$, it approaches the value zero. Thus the system has its highest sensitivity at the shortest distances.

When $\tau/\lambda = 1$, the fractional range sensitivity has the value 0.58.

## Practicality of Various Systems

The foregoing discussion shows that a system which impresses noise modulation on a carrier, and then correlates it with the modulation reflected from a target, is able to determine distance to the target. It has been shown that measurement of the mean-square difference between the modulation on the transmitted energy and the modulation on the received energy gives a system output which is the complement of the correlation function. Any type of system capable of performing the above operations can be used to measure distance.

Modulating a particular characteristic of the transmitted energy always involves some incidental modulation of other characteristics, and this leads to practical difficulties in achieving good system sensitivity. Some of the transmitted energy invariably arrives at the receiver input terminals with a very short time delay and tends to obscure small signals. Target signal levels vary over a very wide range, may obscure one another, may cause abnormal operation of parts of the system, or may require balancing or normalizing operations which are not practical to achieve.

Leakage from the transmitter to the receiver is conveniently avoided by operating the receiver at either different times and/or different frequencies from those being used by the transmitter. Pulse systems accomplish this in time by turning off the transmitter during signal receiving times. Conventional FM altimeters accomplish this by making the receiver very insensitive to frequencies in the modulation waveform, and thus they are insensitive to signals having a small time delay. Practical noise-modulated systems must deal with these same problems.

### *AM Systems*

An AM correlation-function system would give an output which would depend on signal strength as well as target distance, unless complete normalizing of the return signal were accomplished. This implies an essentially perfect automatic gain control in the receiver, if system output is to be dependent upon distance only. Thus such a system is not very practical.

In an AM correlation-function system, the response $\psi(\tau_a, \tau_b)$ to two signals of amplitude $a$ and $b$, having delay times $\tau_a$ and $\tau_b$ respectively, would be:

$$\psi(\tau_a, \tau_b) \equiv \frac{\lim_{T\to\infty} \frac{1}{T}\int_0^T F(t)\left[aF(t-\tau_a) + bF(t-\tau_b)\right]dt}{\sqrt{K}\left[aF(t-\tau_a) + bF(t-\tau_b)\right]_{\text{rms}}} \tag{25}$$

where the terms in the denominator of (25) serve to normalize $\psi(\tau_a, \tau_b)$. We can obtain from (25) and from the definition of (1), that

$$\psi(\tau_a\tau_b) = \sqrt{K}\,\frac{a\psi(\tau_a) + b\psi(\tau_b)}{\left[aF(t-\tau_a) + bF(t-\tau_b)\right]_{\text{rms}}}, \tag{26}$$

which is a weighted mean of $\psi(\tau_a)$ and $\psi(\tau_b)$ where $a$ and $b$ are the weighting factors. The contributions of signals $a$ and $b$ to $\psi(\tau_a, \tau_b)$ have the ratio,

$$R_{ab} = \frac{a\psi(\tau_a)}{b\psi(\tau_b)} \cdot \tag{27}$$

This result shows how a weak signal of strength $a$ can obscure a larger signal of strength $b$, if $\psi(\tau_a)$ is much larger than $\psi(\tau_b)$. In a radiating system where the strength of signal declines rapidly with distance, this may be a very objectionable property.

An AM anticorrelation system must obtain the difference between two normalized functions, otherwise system output will again depend upon signal strength as well as target distance. Normalizing the received signal is so difficult that such a system is not very practical.

Interference between two signals in an AM anticorrelation system is somewhat involved, and an analysis will not be given here because it is of no immediate practical interest.

### *FM Systems*

An FM correlation type system has the advantage that a comparison of the frequencies of the transmitted and returning signals can be made essentially independent of the signal level. The "capturing effect" of an FM receiver which greatly suppresses receiver output for all but the largest signal,[19] can either be beneficial or detrimental, depending on relative signal levels.

[19] J. Granlund, "Interference in Frequency Modulation Reception," Ph.D. dissertation, Mass. Inst. Tech., Cambridge, Mass.; 1950.

An FM correlation-function system must convert the frequency modulation on the returning signal to some convenient form, say voltage, in order to multiply it by the modulation being impressed on the transmitted signal. Such a conversion would involve either 1) a discriminator operating at the carrier frequency or 2) a mixer and local oscillator to heterodyne the signal to a lower frequency and a discriminator at the lower frequency. Such a system could be made, but like the AM systems, would be very sensitive to leakage from transmitter to receiver and would be substantially more complex than a conventional FM altimeter.

*Simple Noise-Modulated System*

A simpler system using noise modulation is an FM anticorrelation system. A sample of the transmitted signal is used as the local oscillator in a conventional mixer, as is done in conventional FM altimeters. The mixer output has an instantaneous frequency equal to the magnitude of the instantaneous frequency difference of the transmitted and received signals. Thus, direct conversion to a conveniently low frequency is accomplished without a separate local oscillator. The type of receiver best suited to handling the difference-frequency signal depends upon the application. If a wide-band limiting receiver is used, it will preserve the "zero crossings" of the mixer output. When the modulation index of the mixer output is high, the zero crossings give a good measure of the average magnitude of the instantaneous difference frequency.[20] This high modulation index corresponds to large phase excursions of the difference-frequency phasor between changes in sign of the instantaneous difference frequency. Large phase excursions occur when the transmitter is swept monotonically over a wide frequency range and/or when the time delay of the received signal is large. If the rate of zero crossing is converted to a fluctuating voltage, squared, and averaged, the system output will behave, to the extent that zero crossing rate is a good measure of instantaneous frequency, as an anticorrelation system.

We now take note of the fact that the random noise function $F(t)$ assumed has a Gaussian probability distribution of amplitudes. If the frequency-deviation characteristic of the transmitter is linear, the transmitted signal will have a Gaussian probability density with mean value at the carrier frequency. The returning signal will, for a noise-free, stationary target likewise have a Gaussian probability with the same mean value. Since the difference frequency,

$$\Delta\omega = \omega(t) - \omega(t - \tau) \tag{28}$$

is the difference of frequencies having a Gaussian distribution, it too will have a Gaussian probability distribution, but with zero mean. The mixer does not, however, preserve the algebraic sign of the difference frequency, so the mixer output is a signal whose probability distribution of instantaneous frequency is a one-sided Gaussian distribution, with its maximum at an instantaneous frequency of zero.

Since the instantaneous difference frequency follows a Gaussian distribution, the average squared difference frequency $\overline{\Delta\omega^2}$ is related to the average magnitude of the difference frequency $\overline{|\Delta\omega|}$ by

$$\overline{|\Delta\omega|} = \sqrt{\frac{2}{\pi}(\overline{\Delta\omega^2})}. \tag{29}$$

Because of this relationship, which holds as long as $\Delta\omega$ has a Gaussian probability distribution, the FM anticorrelation system can, by measuring the average magnitude of the difference frequency, determine through (29) the mean-square frequency difference which is in turn related to the correlation function and the noise power spectrum. This noise-modulated system is no more complex than a conventional altimeter.

The precise relationship between mean magnitude of the difference frequency and the noise power spectrum will now be obtained. Suppose the transmitter is frequency modulated so that the instantaneous frequency deviation of the transmitter is $\omega(t)$. Let

$$F(t) = \frac{\omega(t)}{\omega(t)_{\rm rms}}, \tag{30}$$

where

$$\lim_{T\to\infty} \frac{1}{T}\int_0^T \omega(t)dt = 0, \quad \text{and} \quad \omega(t)_{\rm rms} = \{\overline{\omega(t)^2}\}^{1/2}; \tag{31}$$

then

$$H(\tau) = \lim_{T\to\infty} \frac{1}{2T}\int_0^T \left[\frac{\omega(t)}{\omega(t)_{\rm rms}} - \frac{\omega(t-\tau)}{\omega(t)_{\rm rms}}\right]^2 dt \tag{32}$$

$$= \frac{1}{[\omega(t)_{\rm rms}]^2} \lim_{T\to\infty} \frac{1}{2T}\int_0^T [\omega(t) - \omega(t-\tau)]^2 dt \tag{33}$$

$$= \frac{1}{[\omega(t)_{\rm rms}]^2} \lim_{T\to\infty} \frac{1}{2T}\int_0^T [\Delta\omega]^2 dt. \tag{34}$$

Using (29)

$$H(\tau) = \frac{\pi\{\overline{|\Delta\omega|}\}^2}{4\omega(t)_{\rm rms}{}^2}. \tag{35}$$

But

$$H(\tau) = 1 - \psi(\tau)$$

$$= 1 - \int_0^\infty w(f)\cos 2\pi f\tau df.$$

Hence

$$\{\overline{|\Delta\omega|}\}^2 = \frac{4}{\pi}[\omega(t)_{\rm rms}]^2\left\{1 - \int_0^\infty w(f)\cos 2\pi f\tau df\right\}, \tag{36}$$

[20] P. R. Karr, "A Note on Zero Crossings and Average Frequency," Diamond Ordnance Fuze Labs., Washington, D. C., Tech. Rep. No. 133; October 25, 1954.

or

$$\overline{|\Delta\omega|} = \frac{2}{\sqrt{\pi}}\,\omega(t)_{\mathrm{rms}}\sqrt{1 - \int_0^\infty w(f)\cos 2\pi f\tau\, df}, \tag{37}$$

which shows the way in which this system depends upon the power spectrum $w(f)$ of the modulating noise.

If the RC filter of Case III is used to shape the noise spectrum, the mean magnitude of the difference frequency is

$$\overline{|\Delta\omega|} = \frac{2}{\sqrt{\pi}}\,\omega(t)_{\mathrm{rms}}\sqrt{1 - e^{-\tau/\lambda}}. \tag{38}$$

The normalized mean magnitude $m_1$ of the difference frequency for this case is

$$m_1 = \frac{\overline{|\Delta\omega|}}{\omega(t)_{\mathrm{rms}}} = \frac{2}{\sqrt{\pi}}\sqrt{1 - e^{-\tau/\lambda}}. \tag{39}$$

This theoretical behavior is plotted in Fig. 2. The system output changes most rapidly at short time delays.

A similar plot for the Gaussian filter of Case IV is also given in Fig. 2. In this case the normalized mean magnitude $m_2$ of the difference frequency is

$$m_2 = \frac{2}{\sqrt{\pi}}\sqrt{1 - e^{-2\pi^2 f_c^2 \tau^2}}. \tag{40}$$

*Test of Simple System*

A system, shown in the block diagram of Fig. 3, was built in accordance with the above description of the "Simple Noise-Modulated System." The results of tests with this system are shown in Fig. 4. The noise spectrum used was that provided by a commercial noise generator having a spectrum intermediate between the Cases III and IV. The receiver was of the broad-band limiting type with suppression of the low frequency response to avoid effects of the leakage signal. Only the zero crossings of the difference frequency signal (excluding the very low frequency portion of the spectrum) were preserved. A linear discriminator provided an average output voltage proportional to the average frequency of these zero crossings. With very short time delay or very low frequency deviations, the phase excursions of the difference frequency phases were insufficient to "capture" the receiver from its own noise, and this placed a lower limit on the system output. At the largest frequency deviations and longest time delays, the discriminator was driven out of its linear region part of the time, and this is indicated by the saturation effect in system output. It can be seen from the figure that the general behavior of system output does conform to expectations.

## Limitations, Errors, Modifications

*Limitations*

Since the Fourier transform exists for a wide class of functions, one might be tempted to expect that a system might be designed to give almost any desired output with distance. Suppose, for example, that a correlation function which is a step function is desired. The corresponding power spectrum is, according to (6), the Fourier transform of this step function and hence would involve *negative* power in some spectral regions. This, of course, is not even theoretically achievable.

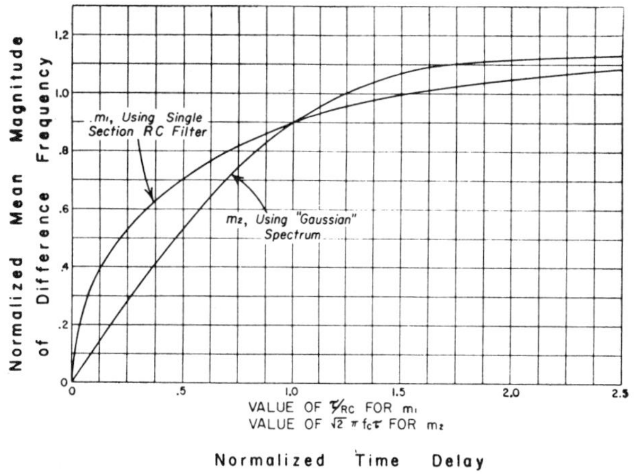


Fig. 2—Theoretical output for simple system.

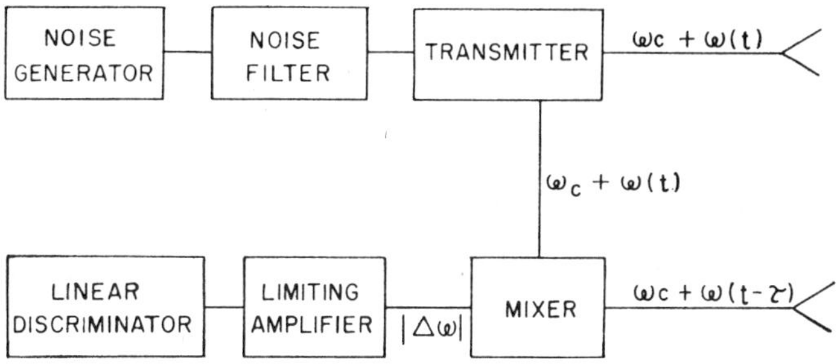


Fig. 3—Block diagram of simple noise-modulated system.

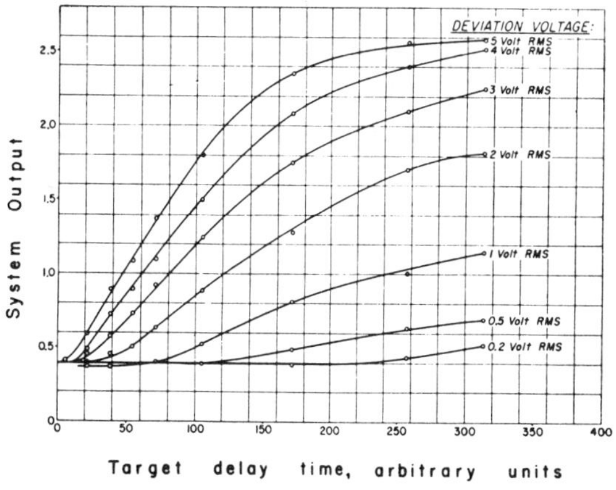


Fig. 4—Performance of simple noise-modulated system.

*Errors*

Certain errors are inherent in a noise modulated system because of the short term variability of the random noise and the fact that unlimited averaging time is not available. A complete analysis of this limitation has not been made, but in the case of an FM system which counts zero crossings of the difference frequency signal, an upper limit can be set. The individual zero crossings can be no more random than if they were completely independent, and in that case, the standard deviation of samples of zero crossings for which the average number is $\bar{n}$ would have the approximate value $\sqrt{n}$ and a *relative* standard deviation of $\sqrt{n}/\bar{n}=1/\sqrt{\bar{n}}$. Thus, if $\bar{n}$ were 1,000, the rms fluctuation would be approximately thirty-two and the root-mean-square relative fluctuation would be about 3 per cent.

If, in an FM system, the return signal is shifted by a fixed amount, as would occur by the Doppler effect, the resulting probability distribution of the magnitude of the instantaneous difference frequency will be that of a Gaussian distribution which is folded (by the mixer action) at a point other than its mean value. If the Doppler shift is small compared to the mean magnitude of the difference frequency brought about by the modulation, $\overline{|\Delta\omega(t)|}$, the effect on system output would be very small, since the fixed frequency shift would alternately add and subtract from $|\Delta\omega(t)|$.

### *Modifications*

Numerous variations to the basic system are possible, and no attempt will be made to list them all, but several have interesting possibilities and should probably be mentioned.

A system which provides for an internally delayed version of the transmitted signal (or of the modulation on it) could use this delayed signal for comparing with the received signal. In a correlation system, this would give maximum correlation for a signal delay equal to the internal delay. An anticorrelation system would yield a null at the same point.

The saturation effect at high difference frequencies and the small phase excursions at small time delays in the simple system suggest the desirability of maintaining an essentially constant difference-frequency spectrum by means of a servo system which would control the root-mean-square frequency deviations of the transmitter. The servo output could then be used to indicate range. This modification would make better use of receiver bandwidth and would tend to maintain constant relative statistical error.

## Summary

A new type of modulation function, random noise, has been introduced in distance-measuring systems. It makes possible a new class of system output-to-distance relations, and in particular, it is possible to have an average output which is an unambiguous function of distance. Systems having an output which is an arbitrary function of distance are not possible because of physical realizability and practicality considerations. System characteristics can easily be changed by switching filters for the modulating noise. Using simple filters, it is possible to make a system which has its highest sensitivity at the shortest ranges, and this makes such a system particularly suited for blind landing applications.

These systems do not depend upon the detailed relationship between transmitted and returning signals, hence some time averaging must be used for accuracy. Usually, however, the averaging time required is not large.

Many variations of the basic system are possible, for example a servo can be used to control some system parameter and thus maintain constant spectrum into the receiver. The simplest noise-modulated distance measuring system is frequency modulated, and is no more complex than a conventional FM altimeter.

# Designing Pseudorandom Coded Ranging Systems

JOHN H. PAINTER, Member, IEEE
Motorola, Inc.
Scottsdale, Ariz.

Abstract

**This paper develops a set of mathematical tools for system design or analysis of a type of pseudorandom coded ranging system used in several space programs. Certain probabilities of failure of the system to perform the ranging function and the times required for the system to perform prescribed ranging functions are defined and related to system parameters. A set of sample calculations is presented for clarification of the computational techniques.**

Key Words—**Digital signals, pseudonoise, ranging systems, spacecraft tracking, correlation detection.**

Manuscript received January 25, 1966; revised July 11, 1966.

## Introduction

Spacecraft tracking systems employing pseudorandom code (PN) ranging techniques [1] have been implemented for several space programs. Notable among these programs are Mariner, Lunar Orbiter, and Apollo [2]. PN ranging is also planned for the Manned Orbiting Laboratory and Voyager spacecraft. The PN ranging technique was developed at the Jet Propulsion Laboratory, Pasadena, Calif., and may be traced through many research and program progress reports published there [3].

The basic ranging technique is described as follows. In a base ranging subsystem, a PN code is digitally generated [4]. The code is phase modulated onto a radio frequency carrier and is transmitted to a transponder ranging subsystem which may be one of two types. If the transponder simply retransmits the received code and channel noise, using phase modulation, it is defined as a "turnaround" transponder. If the transponder "acquires" the received code and uses it to synchronize a code generator, thus regenerating the received code for retransmission, it is defined as a "regenerative" transponder. With either transponder type, the retransmitted code is acquired in the base ranging subsystem and is compared in time delay to the base transmitted code on a continuous basis. The time delay between codes is a measure of two-way range between the base subsystem and transponder subsystem.

Although much work has been done on PN ranging systems, to the best of the author's knowledge, a simple concise set of analytical tools for design or analysis of these systems is nonexistent. This paper attempts to provide such a set of tools. A secondary purpose of the paper is to show that with appropriate design and optimization such systems have the capability of ranging spacecraft anywhere in the solar system.

The base subsystem, which is treated first in the text, is represented in a diagram by only those idealized functions necessary for mathematical modeling. The methods used for generation of range codes and range measurements are not discussed, since they are documented [4]. In the analysis of the base subsystem, a probability that the base channel errs in "acquiring" the transponded code is defined, assuming that correct acquisition implies correct range measurement. This probability of error is then related to the system parameters, in particular, to the base channel signal-to-noise ratio (SNR). Additionally, the minimum theoretical time required for acquisition of the transponded code is developed.

The two types of transponder subsystems mentioned are treated in the text in a fashion analogous to that for the base, using one transponder model which employs both "turnaround" and "regenerative" functions. For the turnaround function, a transponder correlation loss is defined and derived. For the regenerative function, a probability of acquisition error is defined and related to system parameters. Further, the regenerative channel de-

Reprinted from *IEEE Trans. Aerosp. Electron. Syst.*, vol. AES-3, pp. 14–27, Jan. 1967.

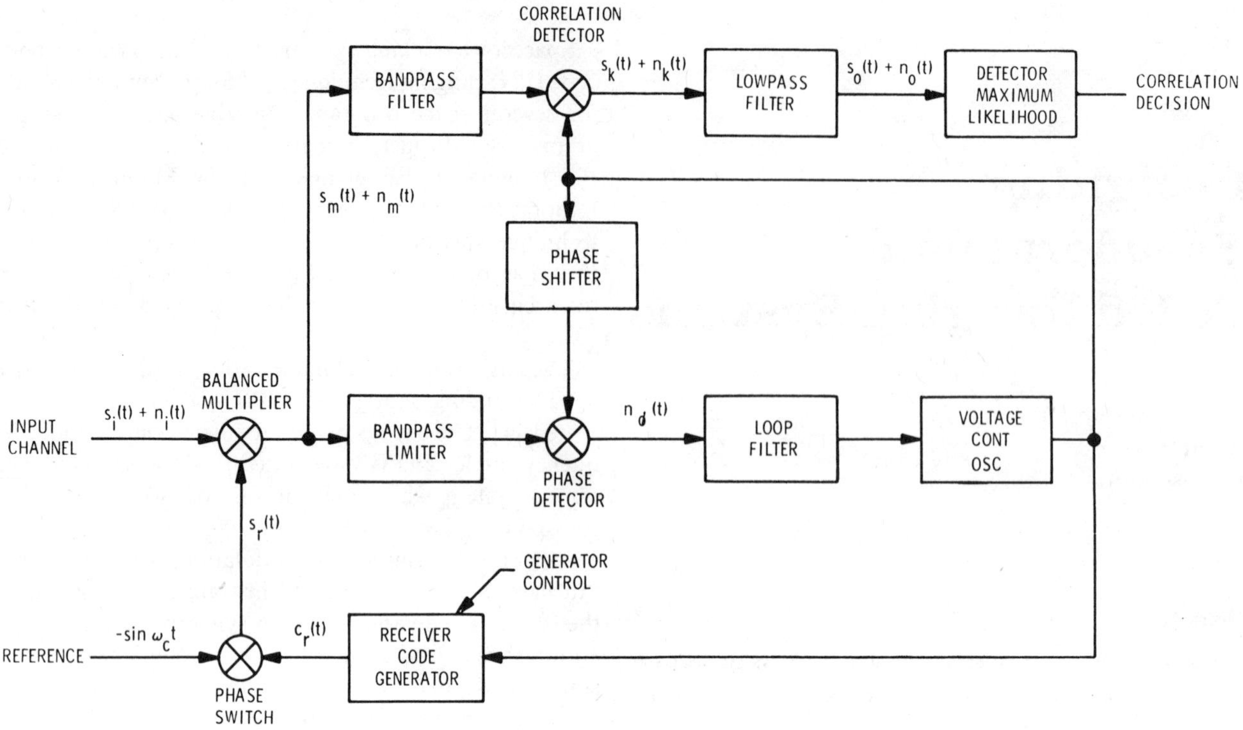


**Fig. 1. Base ranging channel.**

sign is optimized for acquisition error as a function of channel SNR.

The paper concludes with two sample calculations, using system parameters which represent a minimal extension of current state of the art. These parameters, in the author's opinion, are feasible for the early 1970's. One calculation is for a turnaround system; the other, for a regenerative system. The purposes of these calculations are to give insight into the use of the tools presented and to imply the capabilities of PN ranging systems.

The analytical content of this paper is necessarily terse, in order to concisely cover the amount of material presented. Although most analytical and computational steps are implied, sufficient development is presented to validate the final results to a reader familiar with the ranging technique. For the unfamiliar reader, sufficient references are given.

## The Base Ranging Channel

Figure 1 shows the base ranging channel with only those idealized functional elements necessary for mathematical modeling. The received signal is a phase modulated sinusoid taken as

$$s_i(t) = A \cos \left[\omega_c t + \Delta\phi_s c_s(t)\right] \tag{1}$$

where $A$ is peak sinusoid amplitude, $\omega_c$ is the unmodulated sinusoid radian frequency, $\Delta\phi_s$ is peak radian phase deviation, and $c_s(t)$ is the transponded ranging code. $c_s(t)$ takes only the values plus or minus one.

The input noise process is assumed as Gaussian, white, and bandlimited. It is modeled as an ergodic process by

$$n(t) = x(t) \cos \omega_c t - y(t) \sin \omega_c t. \tag{2}$$

The power spectral density of the input noise is specified as centered on $\omega_c$ with a physical bandwidth of $B_i$ c/s. The magnitude of the equivalent spectral density is defined as $|\Phi_n|$. Then, the spectral densities of the low-pass processes $x(t)$ and $y(t)$, in their nonzero frequency ranges, are related to the input density as

$$|\Phi_x| = |\Phi_y| = 2|\Phi_n|. \tag{3}$$

The input signal and noise are multiplied by a reference signal which is obtained by phase switching a coherent reference sinusoid by a locally generated "receiver code" $c_r(t)$. The reference signal is

$$s_{r(t)} = -c_r(t) \sin \omega_c t. \tag{4}$$

The signal and noise components out of the balanced multiplier are, respectively,

$$s_{m(t)} = \frac{A}{2} \sin (\Delta\phi_s) c_r(t) c_s(t) \tag{5}$$

and

$$n_m(t) = \frac{1}{2} c_r(t) y(t). \tag{6}$$

The multiplier noise process remains first-order Gaussian, though not white. From Appendix I, the spectral density of the multiplier noise is

$$\Phi_m(\omega) = \frac{1}{4}\left[\frac{1}{2\pi}\int_{-\infty}^{\infty}\Phi_{c_r}(y)\Phi_y(\omega - y)d_y\right] \tag{7}$$

$$= \left|\Phi_n\right|\frac{R}{2\pi}\left\{\frac{2\pi B_i}{\omega^2 - \pi^2 B_i^2} + \frac{\cos\left[\frac{\omega+\pi B_i}{R}\right]}{\omega + \pi B_i} - \frac{\left[\frac{\omega - \pi B_i}{R}\right]}{\omega - \pi B_i} + \frac{1}{R}\left[S_i\left(\frac{\omega + \pi B_i}{R}\right) - S_i\left(\frac{\omega - \pi B_i}{R}\right)\right]\right\} \tag{8}$$

where $R$ is the rate of signaling elements per second of the ranging code $c_r(t)$. $S_i$ is the "sine integral." Equation (8) employs the approximation that the code $c_r(t)$ is a random binary waveform with fixed element length $1/R$. The approximation is valid so long as the highest frequency nonnegligible fundamental component of the code is not commensurate with the spectral width of the input noise.

The bandpass filters at the multiplier output are very narrow and are centered on the clock frequency $\omega_{c1}$ of the code, where

$$\omega_{c1} = \pi R \tag{9}$$

The approximation is made that over the narrow filter passbands the noise spectral density is flat with a defined magnitude $|\Phi_{c1}|$. Also, the input bandwidth is fixed at

$$B_i = 5R. \tag{10}$$

Then

$$|\Phi_{c1}| = \Phi_m(\omega)\Big]_{B_i = 5R}^{\omega = \pi R} \tag{11}$$

$$\cong \tfrac{1}{2}|\Phi_n|. \tag{12}$$

For the ideal case of zero noise in the transponder ranging channel, the transponder output code $c_s(t)$ is a pseudorandom code which is formed from a Boolean combination of a clock sequence and pseudorandom sequences. The plus one and minus one states of the code correspond, respectively, to the Boolean ZERO and ONE states. The pseudorandom code sequence has the form

$$C_S = F[X, A, B, C \cdots H] \oplus CL \tag{13}$$

where $F$ is a combining function of the pseudorandom sequences $X$ through $H$ and $CL$ is a sequence of alternating ONES and ZEROS. The combining function employs "majority logic" and is

$$F[X, A, B, \cdots, H] = \overline{X}\cdot[(A\cdot B)\vee(B\cdot C)\vee \cdots \vee(H\cdot A)] \tag{14}$$

where "$\vee$" is the Boolean OR and "$\cdot$" is the Boolean AND.

With the correspondence employed between Boolean and analog states, the Boolean "modulo two" ($\oplus$) operation corresponds to analog multiplication.

Equation (5) shows that the multiplier output signal component contains a product of the transponder code and local receiver code. If, in the ideal case, the transponder code sequence has the form of (13) and the receiver code sequence has the form of (14), then the multiplier signal component is a clock square wave $c_1(t)$ when the two codes are synchronized. Under these conditions, the fundamental sinusoidal component of the multiplier signal is

$$s_{c1}(t) = 2\frac{A}{\pi}\sin(\Delta\phi_s)\cos\omega_{c1}t. \tag{15}$$

In the general case, $c_s(t)$ may or may not have the form implied by (13), because of noise. Likewise, $c_r(t)$ may or may not have the form implied by (14), because of different sequences used during code "acquisition." In general, the fundamental clock spectral component out of the multiplier is the term of frequency $\omega_{c1}$ existing in the cross power spectrum of $c_1(t)$ and $s_m(t)$. The reduction in amplitude of the clock sinusoid is predictable by use of the cross-correlation coefficient, $\sqrt{L_k}$, between $c_1(t)$ and $c_r(t)c_s(t)$. Then

$$s_{c1}(t) = 2\frac{A}{\pi}\sqrt{L_k}\sin(\Delta\phi_s)\cos\omega_{c1}t. \tag{16}$$

It has been shown [5] that the cross correlation, on a voltage basis, between two Boolean sequences or their corresponding waveforms is given by

$$\sqrt{L_k} = \frac{P(A) - P(D)}{P(A) + P(D)} \tag{17}$$

where $P(A)$ and $P(D)$ are the probabilities of agreement and disagreement, respectively, between the two waveforms. Since $c_1(t)$ and $c_r(t)c_s(t)$ each have only two states,

$$\sqrt{L_k} = 2P(A) - 1. \tag{18}$$

The probability of agreement is the cumulative probability of the "event" that "$c_1(t)$ equals $c_r(t)c_s(t)$."

$$P(A) = P[c_r(t)c_s(t) = c_1(t)]. \tag{19}$$

When the base ranging channel is used with a transponder ranging channel in the turnaround mode, the base ranging channel transmits a code $c_t(t)$ whose sequence is identically that of (13). By the use of $c_t(t)$, (19) may be written as

$$P(A) = P\{[c_r(t)c_t(t) = c_1(t)]\cdot[c_s(t) = c_t(t)] \vee [c_r(t)c_t(t) = \overline{c_1(t)}]\cdot[c_s(t) = \overline{c_t(t)}]\} \tag{20}$$

where "—" indicates the Boolean NOT.

Since the events $[c_s(t) = c_t(t)]$ and $[c_s(t) = \overline{c_t}(t)]$ are mutually exclusive and since the events $[c_r(t)c_t(t) = c_1(t)]$ and $[c_s(t) = c_t(t)]$ are statistically independent, we may write

$$L_k \triangleq L_{ks}L_{kb} \tag{21}$$

where the three $L$'s are power loss factors, with values between zero and unity due to partial correlation. Furthermore, $L_{ks}$ is a function only of the transponder channel, and $L_{kb}$ is a function only of the base channel.

$$L_{ks} = \{2P[c_s(t) = c_t(t)] - 1\}^2. \tag{22}$$

$$L_{kb} = \{2P[c_r(t)c_t(t) = c_1(t)] - 1\}^2. \tag{23}$$

The base channel "acquires" the transponded code by first sweeping the frequency of the VCO which controls the clock rate of the local receiver code. The receiver code sequence $C_R$ is initially all ZEROS or ONES. As the VCO sweeps into phase coherence with the clock component of the transponded code, the correlation coefficient increases from zero and the loop locks. Next, the structure of the receiver sequence is changed, as shown in Table I. The $X$ local sequence is shifted in time delay, element by element. An increase in correlation, $\sqrt{L_k}$, signals acquisition of the transponded $X$ sequence. The acquisition decision is made by recording the output of the correlation detector for each shift position of the local $X$ component and deciding, on a "maximum likelihood" basis [1], which shift gave the greatest correlation. This process is repeated for all code sequences, $X$ through $H$.

TABLE I

Base Receiver Code Sequences During Acquisition

| Mode | Receiver Code, $C_R$ | Correlation, $\sqrt{L_{kb}}$ | Remarks |
|---|---|---|---|
| $CL_0$ | 0 | 0 | Clock not acquired |
| $CL_1$ | 0 | $K_c$ | Clock acquired |
| $X_0$ | $\overline{X}\cdot A$ | $K_1$ | $\overline{X}$ not acquired |
| $X_1$ | $\overline{X}\cdot A$ | $K_2$ | $X$ acquired |
| $A_0$ | $\overline{X}\cdot A$ | $K_2$ | $A$ not acquired |
| $A_1$ | $\overline{X}\cdot A$ | $K_3$ | $A$ acquired |
| $B_0$ | $\overline{X}\cdot B$ | $K_2$ | $B$ not acquired |
| . | . | . | . |
| . | . | . | . |
| . | . | . | . |
| $H_1$ | $\overline{X}\cdot H$ | $K_3$ | $H$ acquired |
| Maj | $\overline{X}\cdot \mathrm{Maj}(A, B\cdots H)$ | 1.0 | All acquired |
| | | | $0<K_1<K_2<K_3<1.0$ |

Observation of Table I shows that minimum correlation occurs during acquisition of the $X$ component. From the standpoint of maintaining loop lock, acquisition of $X$ is the worst case.

The signal-to-noise ratio (SNR) at the input to the loop bandpass limiter, evaluated in the closed-loop noise bandwidth $B_n$ may be related to the channel input, using (12), (16), and (21), as

$$\left.\frac{S_{c1}}{N_{c1}}\right]_{B_n} = L_d L_m L_{kb} L_{ks} \left.\frac{S_i}{N_i}\right]_{B_n} \tag{24}$$

where

$$L_d = \frac{8}{\pi^2}; \quad \text{a detection loss} \tag{25}$$

$$L_m = \sin^2(\Delta\phi_s); \quad \text{a modulation loss} \tag{26}$$

and

$$\left.\frac{S_i}{N_i}\right]_{B_n}$$

is the channel input SNR computed in the loop bandwidth.

Inspection of Table I shows that acquisition of a code sequence is signaled by the voltage correlation $\sqrt{L_{kb}}$ increasing from $K_1$ to $K_2$ or from $K_2$ to $K_3$. The acquisition decision is made by integrating the output of the correlation detector for a set length of time for each code shift position, and then deciding on a maximum likelihood basis which code shift position gave the greatest correlation. A curve is available [6] which relates the integration time $T_L$ required for each information bit in the longest sequence having $N_L$ bits, and the ratio of signal power to one-sided noise spectral density, $|S_0/\Phi_0|$ at the decision device to the probability of a false decision, $P_L(FI)$. The curve is given as Fig. 2. The total integration time per trial correlation for a fixed sequence delay is the integration time per information bit times the number of information bits in the sequence. The integration time is fixed to accommodate the longest sequence and is kept constant during acquisition of the shorter sequences. The probability of false decision is greatest for the longest sequence.

The effective signaling voltage $s_0$ into the decision device is the change in correlation voltage $s_k$ which occurs at acquisition of a sequence

$$s_0 = (K_{n+1} - K_n)\frac{A}{\pi}\sqrt{L_m}\sqrt{L_{ks}}\,; \quad 1 \leq n \leq 2. \tag{27}$$

The magnitude of the noise spectral density is

$$|\Phi_0| = |\Phi_k| = \tfrac{1}{2}|\Phi_{c1}| = \tfrac{1}{4}|\Phi_n|. \tag{28}$$

The ratio of effective signaling power to noise spectral density into the decision device is then

$$\frac{S_0}{|\Phi_0|} = L_d L_m L_0 L_{ks} \frac{S_i}{|\Phi_n|} \tag{29}$$

where a correlation loss is defined as

$$L_0 \stackrel{\Delta}{=} (K_{n+1} - K_n)^2. \tag{30}$$

There are two most likely mechanisms by which the base ranging channel may err in acquiring the ranging code. One is a false decision that the longest sequence has been acquired. The other is if the clock loop becomes unlocked and slips one or more cycles during the time $\tau_x$ required to acquire $X$. The probability of loss of lock is denoted $P_x(LL)$. The probability of false decision indication is denoted $P_1(FI)$. The cumulative probability of error in acquisition is defined for the two mechanisms as

$$P_a(\epsilon) \stackrel{\Delta}{=} 1 - [1 - P_x(LL)][1 - P_1(FI)]. \tag{31}$$

The cumulative probability that a Type II second-order phase-locked loop loses lock in a time $\tau_x$ is treated by

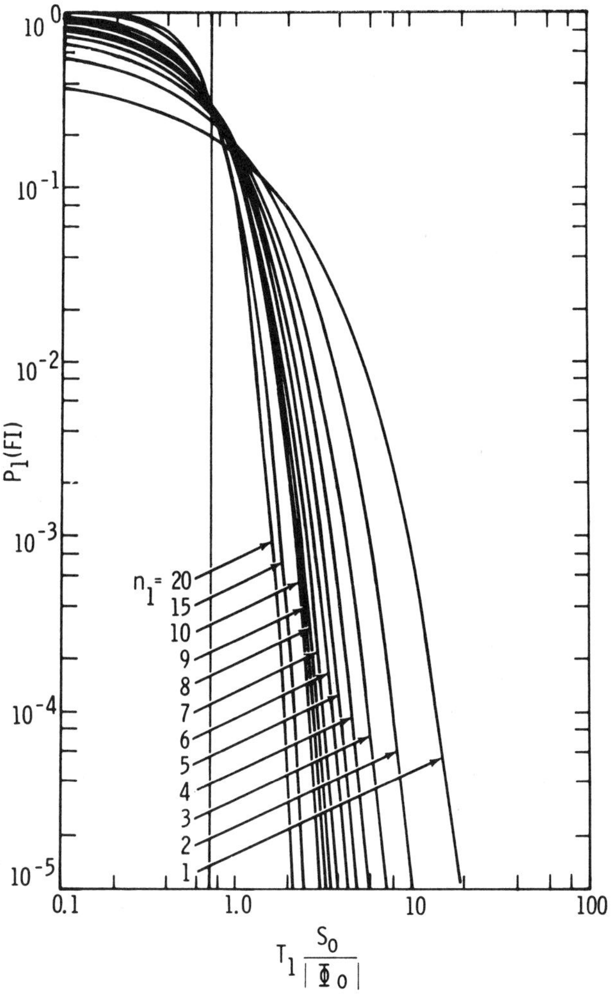


Fig. 2. Graph of probability of base channel false acquisition indication.

Sanneman and Rowbotham [7] and is well approximated by

$$P_x(LL) \cong 1 - \exp\left[-\frac{\omega_n \tau_x}{\omega_n \bar{\tau}}\right] \tag{32}$$

where $\omega_n$ is the loop undamped resonant frequency, and $\bar{\tau}$ is the mean time to loop loss of lock. For probabilities less than $10^{-1}$, (32) is well approximated by

$$\omega_n \tau_x \cong \omega_n \bar{\tau} P_x[LL]; \quad P_x(LL) < 10^{-1}. \tag{33}$$

Combining (24) and (29), the clock loop SNR is related to the correlator signal-to-noise spectral density as

$$\left.\frac{S_{c1}}{N_{c1}}\right]_{B_n} = \frac{L_{kb}}{L_0} \frac{S_0}{B_n |\Phi_0|} \tag{34}$$

where $|\Phi_0|$ is taken as "one-sided." During the "acquire $X$" mode,

$$\left.\frac{S_{c1}}{N_{c1}}\right]_{B_n}^{X} = \left.\frac{L_{kb}}{L_0}\right]^{X} \frac{S_0}{B_n |\Phi_0|}. \tag{35}$$

Figure 2 relates $P_1[FI]$ to the quantity $T_1(S_0/|\Phi_0|)$ where $T_1$ is the integration time per information bit of the longest sequence required to meet the specification on $P_1[FI]$. Then

$$\left.\frac{S_{c1}}{N_{c1}}\right]_{B_n}^{X} = \frac{1}{T_1 B_n} \left.\frac{L_{kb}}{L_0}\right]^{X} \left[T_1 \frac{S_0}{|\Phi_0|}\right]. \tag{36}$$

Now $T_1$ is related to $\tau_x$ as

$$T_1 = \frac{\tau_x}{N_1 \Sigma P_x} \tag{37}$$

where $N_1$ is the number of information bits in the longest sequence and $\Sigma P_x$ is the number of signaling elements in the $X$ sequence. Then

$$\left.\frac{S_{c1}}{N_{c1}}\right]_{B_n}^{X} = \frac{N_1 \Sigma P_X}{\omega_n \tau_x} \left.\frac{L_{kb}}{L_0}\right]^{X} \left[\frac{\omega_n}{B_n}\right] \left[T_1 \frac{S_0}{|\Phi_0|}\right]. \tag{38}$$

For a second-order phase-locked loop

$$\frac{\omega_n}{B_n} = \frac{8\delta}{1 + 4\delta^2} \tag{39}$$

where $\delta$ is loop damping ratio. Combining (33), (38), and (39),

$$\left[\frac{1}{8\delta} + \frac{\delta}{2}\right] \omega_n \bar{\tau} \left[\frac{S_{c1}}{N_{c1}}\right]_{B_n}^{X} = \left[\frac{N_1 \Sigma P_X}{P_x(LL)}\right] \left.\frac{L_{kb}}{L_0}\right]^{X} \left[T_1 \frac{S_0}{|\Phi_0|}\right]. \tag{40}$$

Viterbi [8] has derived an asymptotic expression for normalized time to unlock $\omega_n \bar{\tau}$, which agrees with Sanneman and Rowbotham for loop SNR greater than 3 dB [0 dB in $2B_N$]. It is given as

$$\omega_n \bar{\tau} = \left[\frac{\pi}{\frac{1}{\delta} + 4\delta}\right] \exp\left[2 \left.\frac{S_{c1}}{N_{c1}}\right]_{B_n}^{X}\right] \tag{41}$$

Then

$$\frac{\pi}{8} \left[\left.\frac{S_{c1}}{N_{c1}}\right]_{B_n}^{X}\right] \exp\left[2 \left.\frac{S_{c1}}{N_{c1}}\right]_{B_n}^{X}\right] = \left[\frac{N_1 \Sigma P_x}{P_x(LL)}\right] \left.\frac{L_{kb}}{L_0}\right]^{X} \left[T_1 \frac{S_0}{|\Phi_0|}\right]. \tag{42}$$

The left side of (42) is graphed in decibels ($10 \log_{10}$) vs. $S_{c1}/N_{c1}]_{B_n}^{x}$ in Fig. 3. For a given specification on range code structure and acquisition probabilities, the required value of clock loop SNR may be obtained by evaluation of the right side of (42) and inspection of Fig. 3.

## The Transponder Dual Ranging Channel

Figure 4 shows the transponder channel. The channel can function in two distinct modes. The regenerative mode is similar to that of the base channel wherein the received code is acquired and used to synchronize the transmitted code. The second mode is simply a turn-around mode wherein the received code plus noise are retransmitted.

The input signal and noise have the same forms as for the base channel and are given, respectively, as

$$s_i(t) = A \cos [\omega_c t + \Delta\phi_t c_t(t)] \tag{43}$$

$$n(t) = x(t) \cos \omega_c t - y(t) \sin \omega_c t. \tag{44}$$

In the turnaround mode, the local receiver code sequence $C_R$ is all zeros. The reference $s_r(t)$ is simply a sinusoid, $-\sin \omega_c t$. The signal and noise waveforms at the multiplier output are then, respectively,

$$s_m(t) = \frac{A \sin (\Delta\phi_t)}{2} c_t(t) \triangleq \frac{A}{2} \sqrt{L_m}\, c_t(t) \tag{45}$$

$$n_m(t) = \frac{y(t)}{2} \cdot \tag{46}$$

The limiter input physical bandwidth $B_1$ is assumed wide enough to pass $c_t(t)$ with negligible degradation but not wide enough to accept the entire spectrum of $y(t)$. The input noise function to the limiter $y_1(t)$ has a variance which is related to the input noise spectral density as

$$\sigma_{y1}^2 = \frac{|\Phi_y|}{4} B_1 = \frac{|\Phi_n|}{2} B_1 \tag{47}$$

where the spectral densities are one-sided.

The limiter output waveform $c_s(t)$ is a unit-peak rectangular wave which coincides exactly with $c_t(t)$ only in

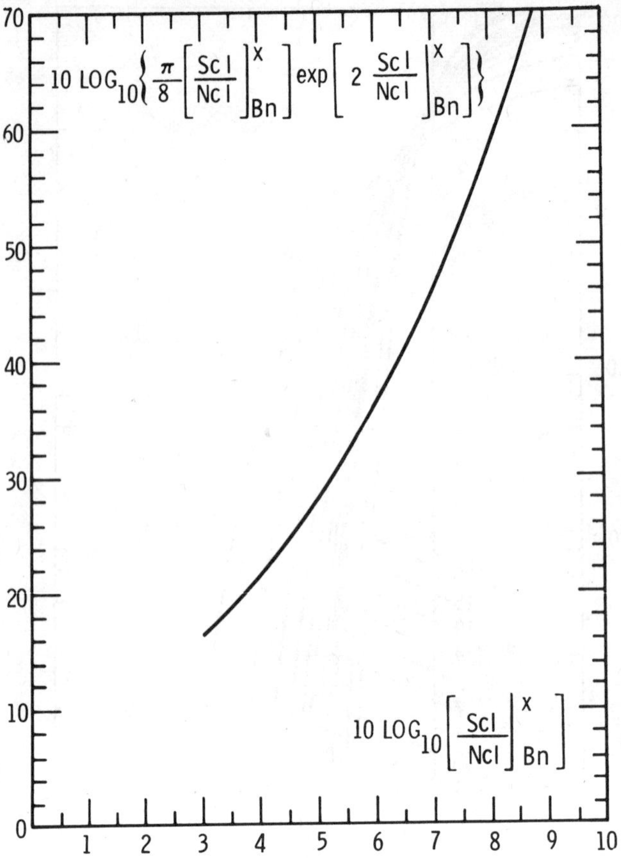


Fig. 3. Graph of (42) in decibels vs. clock-loop SNR.

Fig. 4. Transponder dual ranging channel.

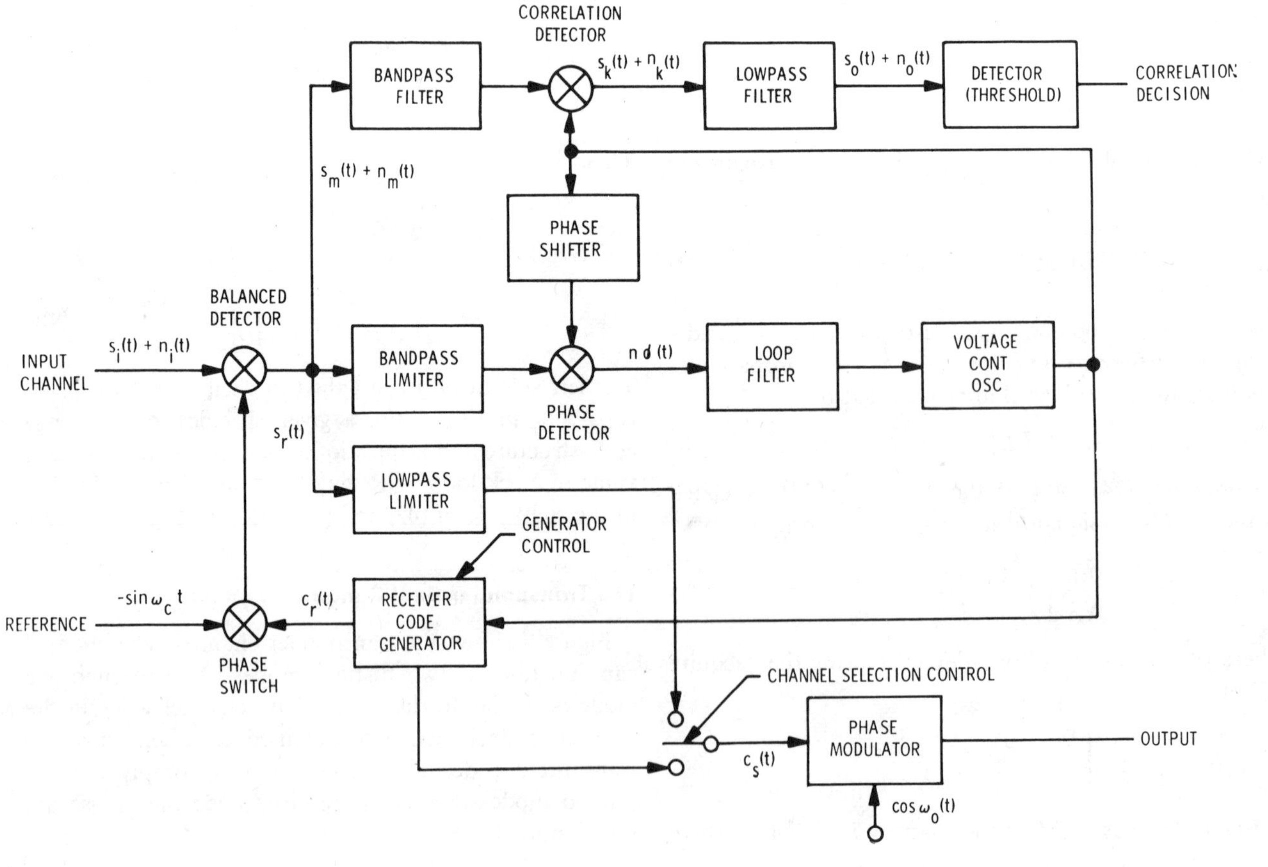

the no-noise case. The probability that $c_s(t)$ agrees with $c_t(t)$ is required for the evaluation of the transponder channel correlation loss $L_{ks}$, defined in (22). The probability is expressed as

$$P[c_s(t) = c_t(t)] = P\left\{\left[y_1(t) > \frac{A\sqrt{L_m}}{2}\right] \cdot [c_t(t) = +1] \vee \left[y_1(t) < \frac{A\sqrt{L_m}}{2}\right] \cdot [c_t(t) = -1]\right\}. \quad (48)$$

Since the events $[c_t(t)=+1]$ and $[c_t(t)=-1]$ are mutually exclusive, and the code and noise processes are statistically independent,

$$P[c_s(t) = c_t(t)] = P\left[y_1(t) > \frac{-A\sqrt{L_m}}{2}\right] P[c_t(t) = +1] + P\left[y_1(t) < \frac{A\sqrt{L_m}}{2}\right] P[c_t(t) = -1] \quad (49)$$

$$= \frac{1}{2}\left\{1 + \operatorname{erf}\left[\sqrt{\frac{L_m}{2}\frac{S_i}{N_i}}\right]_{B_1}\right\};$$

$$\operatorname{erf} z = \frac{2}{\sqrt{\pi}}\int_0^z e^{-x^2}dx \quad (50)$$

where "erf" denotes the "error function" and where $S_i/N_i\rfloor_{B_1}$ is the channel input SNR computed in the limiter bandwidth. Then from (22)

$$L_{ks} = \left[\operatorname{erf}\sqrt{\frac{L_m}{2}\frac{S_i}{N_i}}\right]_{B_1}^2. \quad (51)$$

When operated in the regenerative mode, the transponder channel is strongly similar to the base channel. The major difference is that a simple threshold detector makes the acquisition decision. Also, the form of the received code sequence is changed to insure that the ranging code is acquired in its entirety, rather than one sequence at a time. Using a priori trajectory information, the received code is positioned suitably close in delay to the local receiver code $c_r(t)$. Then the received code is swept past the receiver code at a sweep rate compatible to the clock loop and threshold detector. As the received code sweeps past the receiver code, maximum correlation occurs. The threshold detector senses correlation and enables the loop filter which is initially disabled. The loop then acquires the clock component of the received code and causes the receiver code to track the received code in clock rate and in delay.

The received code sequence $C_T$ has the same general form as (13). The combining function of the sequences has the form

$$F[X, A, B, \cdots, H] = \overline{X}\cdot[A \oplus B \oplus C \oplus \cdots \oplus H]. \quad (52)$$

The receiver code sequence has the form of (52).

The clock sinusoidal signal component may be written directly from (16) and (26) as

$$s_{c1}(t) = 2\frac{A}{\pi}\sqrt{L_k}\sqrt{L_m}\cos\omega_{c1}t. \quad (53)$$

$\sqrt{L_k}$ is the voltage correlation coefficient between the product $c_r(t)c_t(t)$ and $c_1(t)$, and is a function of the relative delay between $c_r(t)$ and $c_t(t)$. For a uniform sweep rate between codes, $\sqrt{L_k}$ is a triangular pulse with peak value of unity and base width, $2\tau$, the time required to sweep one signaling element of $c_t(t)$ completely past the corresponding element of $c_r(t)$. The peak correlation voltage $s_{kpk}$ and noise spectral density out of the correlation detector are, respectively,

$$s_{kpk} = \frac{A}{\pi}\sqrt{L_m} \quad (54)$$

$$|\Phi_k| = \frac{1}{4}|\Phi_n|. \quad (55)$$

The low-pass filter at the input to the threshold detector is a simple one-pole device with impulse response function

$$g(t) = K_f e^{pt} \quad (56)$$

where $K_f$ is an arbitrary gain constant and $p$ is the filter pole frequency, a real negative number. Since the correlation decision must be made no later than the time $\tau$ when the codes are exactly aligned, the filter response at time $\tau$ may be written as

$$s_0(\tau) = \frac{s_{kpk}K_f}{\tau\omega_p^2}[e^{-\omega_p\tau} + \omega_p\tau - 1] \quad (57)$$

where $\omega_p$ is the real radian frequency of the negative pole $p$. The filter response to the Gaussian noise process is obtained through use of the filter's equivalent noise bandwidth $B_f$ where

$$B_f = \frac{\omega_p}{4}\ \text{c/s}. \quad (58)$$

The variance of the output noise process $n_0(t)$ is then

$$\sigma_{n0}^2 = \frac{|\Phi_k|K_f^2}{4\omega_p} = \frac{K_f^2|\Phi_n|}{16\omega_p}. \quad (59)$$

The decision device is set to trigger on a voltage $s_0(\tau)$. It is assumed that the receiver driving this ranging channel has very good coherent AGC so that the signal is held essentially constant and only the noise changes in magnitude. The probability of failure to trigger at time $\tau$ which is equal to the probability of a false trigger due to noise is

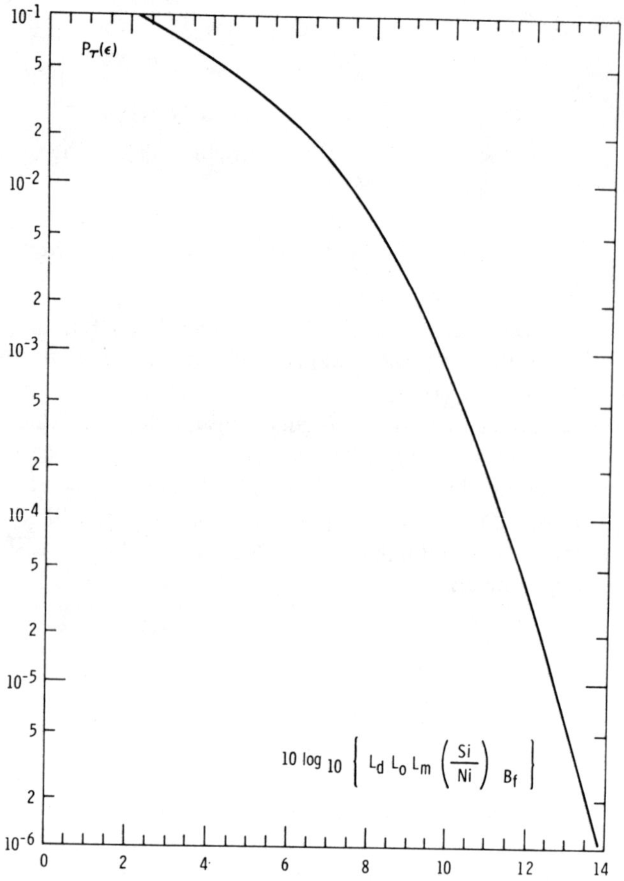


Fig. 5. Probability of error in acquisition for a transponder ranging channel. Graph of (62).

$$P_\tau(\epsilon) = P \mid n_0(\tau) < - s_0(\tau) \mid \tag{60}$$

$$= 1 - \Phi_u \left[ \frac{s_0(\tau)}{\sigma_{n0}} \right] \tag{61}$$

where $\Phi_u$ denotes the normalized Gaussian distribution function. Substituting (57) and (59)

$$P_\tau(\epsilon) = \frac{1}{2} \left[ 1 - \text{erf} \sqrt{\frac{L_d L_0 L_m}{2} \frac{S_i}{N_i}} \right]_{B_f}. \tag{62}$$

Equation (62) is graphed in Fig. 5.

$S_i/N_i \rfloor_{B_f}$ is the channel input SNR computed in the filter noise bandwidth and

$$L_d = \frac{8}{\pi^2}; \quad \text{a detection loss} \tag{63}$$

$$L_0 = \left[ \frac{1}{\omega_p \tau} (e^{-\omega_p \tau} - 1) + 1 \right]^2; \quad \text{a correlation loss.} \tag{64}$$

Figure 6 is a graph of (64). Inspection of the graph shows that for losses greater in magnitude than about 10 dB, the slope of the loss curve is constant at about $-17$ dB per decade of decreasing $\omega_p \tau$. For a fixed $\tau$, decreasing $\omega_p$ increases $S_i/N_i \rfloor_{B_f}$ but only at a 10 dB per decade rate. Hence, correlation loss overpowers increasing SNR in the region below the "knee" of the curve. The breakeven point occurs at approximately $\omega_p \tau = 2.15$ where $L_0 = -5.0$ dB. It is suggested that for this channel $\omega_p \tau = 2.15$ is optimum.

It is assumed that the loop is locked by the time $\tau$

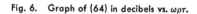

Fig. 6. Graph of (64) in decibels vs. $\omega_p \tau$.

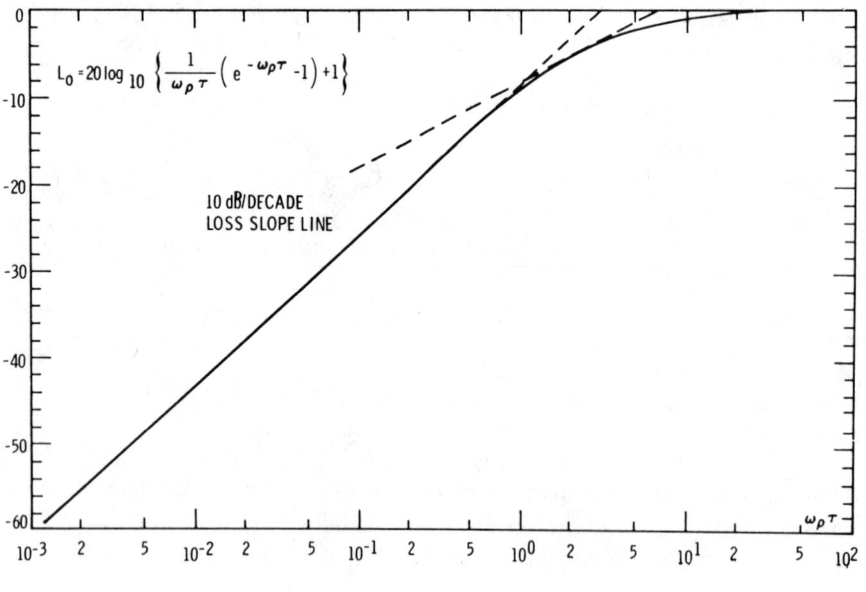

Since the received code is sweeping at a uniform rate, the loop is tracking a ramp function in phase with slope $\pi/\tau$. The error responses of the linearized loop for damping ratios less than or greater than unity, respectively, are

$$e_1(t) = \frac{\pi}{\tau}\left\{\frac{1+4\delta^2}{8B_n\delta\sqrt{1-\delta^2}}\exp\left[-\frac{8B_n\delta^2}{1+4\delta^2}\right]t \cdot \sin\left[\frac{8B_n\delta\sqrt{1-\delta^2}}{1+4\delta^2}\right]t; \quad \delta < 1. \right. \tag{65}$$

$$e_2(t) = \frac{\pi}{\tau}\left\{\frac{1+4\delta^2}{8B_n\delta\sqrt{\delta^2-1}}\exp\left[-\frac{8B_n\delta^2}{1+4\delta^2}\right]t \cdot \sin h\left[\frac{8B_n\delta\sqrt{\delta^2-1}}{1+4\delta^2}\right]t; \quad \delta > 1. \right. \tag{66}$$

Both error responses exhibit transient behavior which converges to zero for large time $t$. The times of maximum transient error are given implicitly as

$$\tan\left[\frac{8B_n\delta\sqrt{1-\delta^2}}{1+4\delta^2}\right]t = \sqrt{\frac{1}{\delta^2}-1}; \quad \delta < 1 \tag{67}$$

$$\tan h\left[\frac{8B_n\delta\sqrt{\delta^2-1}}{1+4\delta^2}\right]t = \sqrt{1-\frac{1}{\delta^2}}; \quad \delta > 1. \tag{68}$$

Maximum transient errors are given for damping ratios of 0.707 and infinity, respectively, as

$$e_{1\,\max} = 0.242\,\frac{\pi/\tau}{B_n}; \quad \delta = 0.707 \tag{69}$$

$$e_{2\,\max} = 0.25\,\frac{\pi/\tau}{B_n}; \quad \delta \to \infty. \tag{70}$$

If a total time could be specified during which the received code is sweeping, then the probability of the loop remaining locked during that time could be derived as was done for the base channel during the acquisition of the $x$ sequence. However, such a time is not readily specified. A simple approximation to the probability of loss of lock may be made, however, based on the linear loop model. The approximate loss-lock probability is that of the sum of the loop noise process $n_\phi(t)$ plus maximum transient error $e_{\max}$ exceeding $\pm\pi/2$ radians.

$$P[LL] \cong P[n_\phi(t) + e_{\max} \geq \pi/2] + P[n_\phi(t) + e_{\max} \leq -\pi/2]. \tag{71}$$

The loop noise process is approximated as Gaussian so that

$$P[LL] \cong 1 - \Phi_u\left[\frac{\pi/2 - e_{\max}}{\sigma_\phi}\right] + \Phi\left[\frac{-\pi/2 - e_{\max}}{\sigma_\phi}\right] \tag{72}$$

where $\Phi_u$ is the normalized Gaussian distribution function and $\sigma_\phi$ is the "rms loop phase noise." A worst case, or bounding approximation to (72) is

$$P[LL] \cong \left[1 - \operatorname{erf}\sqrt{\frac{L_dL_eL_m}{2}\,\frac{S_i}{N_i}\bigg]_{B_n}}\,\right] \tag{73}$$

where

$$L_e = [\pi/2 - e_{\max}]^2; \quad \text{a tracking error factor.} \tag{74}$$

Equation (73) which is identical to (72) for zero transient error and pessimistic by a factor of 2 for large transient error, is plotted in Fig. 7.

Equations (69) and (70) may be generalized for any case as

$$e_{\max} = K_{e_{\max}}\,\frac{\pi/\tau}{B_n} \tag{75}$$

where $K_{e_{\max}}$ is determinable from (65) through (68). An optimum choice may be made for $\omega_p\tau$ such that

$$\tau = \frac{[\omega_p\tau]_{\text{opt}}}{4B_f}. \tag{76}$$

From (75) and (76) then,

$$\frac{B_f}{B_n} = \frac{[\omega_p\tau]_{\text{opt}}\,e_{\max}}{4\pi K_{e_{\max}}}. \tag{77}$$

Now it is evident that

$$L_m\,\frac{S_i}{N_i}\bigg]_{B_n} \equiv \frac{B_f}{B_n}\,L_m\,\frac{S_i}{N_i}\bigg]_{B_f}. \tag{78}$$

From (76), (77), and (78), may be written

$$\frac{L_dL_eL_m\,\dfrac{S_i}{N_i}\bigg]_{B_n}}{L_dL_0L_m\,\dfrac{S_i}{N_i}\bigg]_{B_f}} = \frac{[\omega_p\tau]_{\text{opt}}}{L_0}\left\{\frac{e_{\max}\left[\dfrac{\pi}{2} - e_{\max}\right]^2}{4\pi K_{e_{\max}}}\right\}. \tag{79}$$

A total probability of error $P_A(\epsilon)$, in acquiring the received code and maintaining lock while the code is sweeping, is defined for the transponder channel as

$$P_a(\epsilon) \triangleq 1 - [1 - P_\tau(\epsilon)][1 - P(LL)]. \tag{80}$$

Given a specification on $P_a(\epsilon)$, the probability of error may be distributed in any desired manner between range code correlator and clock loop by proper choice of $P_\tau(\epsilon)$ and $P(LL)$. Then, using Figs. 5 and 7, the left-hand side of (79) may be evaluated. Next, an optimizing choice of $\omega_p\tau$ is made and $[\omega_p\tau]_{\text{opt}}/L_0$ evaluated using Fig 8. Finally, a value for $K_{e_{\max}}$ is selected and $e_{\max}$ is determined from (79). Using the values obtained for $K_{e_{\max}}$ and $e_{\max}$, a value for the product $\tau B_n$ is obtained from (75) as

$$\tau B_n = \pi\,\frac{K_{e_{\max}}}{e_{\max}}. \tag{81}$$

Using (76), a value for the product $\tau B_f$ is obtained as

$$\tau B_f = \frac{[\omega_p\tau]_{\text{opt}}}{4}. \tag{82}$$

Finally, a tradeoff is made between sweep time and filter bandwidths to obtain values for $\tau$, $B_n$, and $B_f$ from (81) and (82).

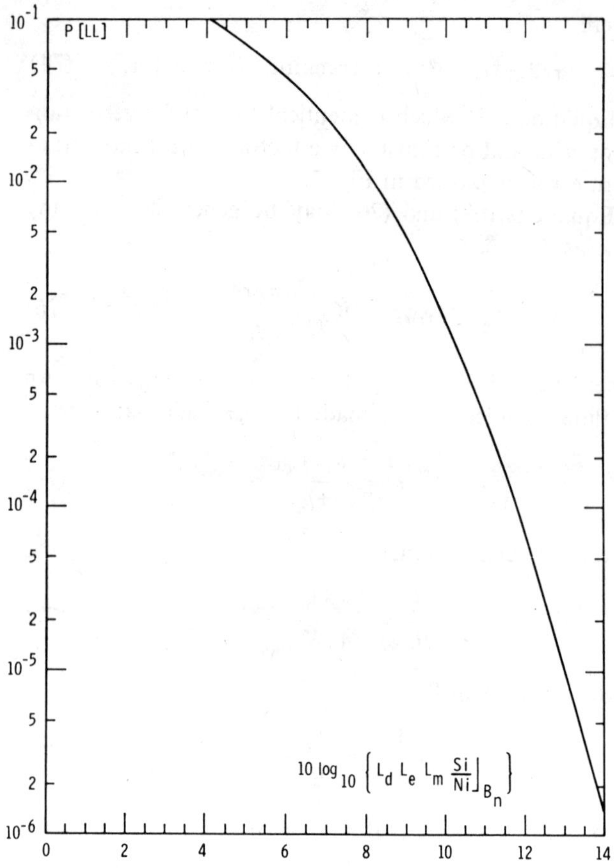


Fig. 7. Probability of loss of clock-loop lock for a transponder ranger channel. Graph of (73).

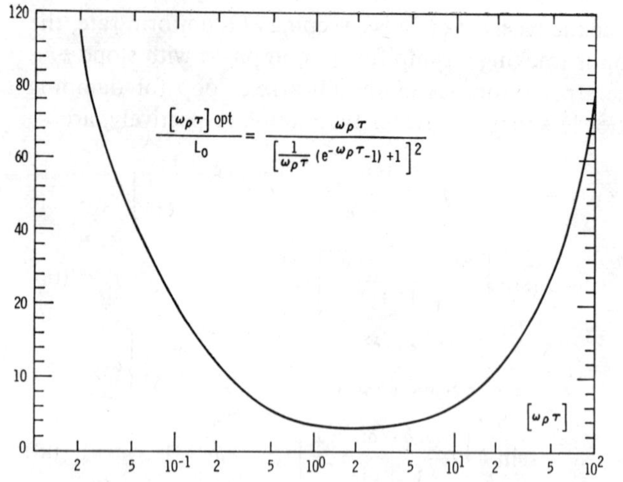


Fig. 8. Graph of $[\omega_\rho \tau]$ opt/$L_0$ vs. $[\omega_\rho \tau]$.

## Sample Calculations

For the purpose of demonstrating the use of the equations presented, consider a system with parameters as specified in Table II. A ranging code is chosen with one microsecond signaling elements and sequence lengths of 7, 83, and 127 elements. The first calculation is for a turnaround system.

As a starting point, specify the minimum acceptable cumulative probability of error in code acquisition for the base channel as

$$P_{ab}(\epsilon) = 10^{-3}. \tag{83}$$

Arbitrarily, the error probability is equally divided between probability of loss of clock loop lock and probability of false indication of acquisition.

$$P_x(LL) = P_1(FI) = 5 \times 10^{-4}. \tag{84}$$

The information content, in bits, of the longest sequence is

$$N_1 = \log_2 (127) = 7.0. \tag{85}$$

Interpolating from the graph of Fig. 2 gives

$$T_1 \frac{S_0}{|\Phi_0|} \cong 3.0. \tag{86}$$

Then, from (42)

$$\frac{\pi}{8}\left[\frac{S_{cl}}{N_{cl}}\right]_{B_n}^{x}\right] \exp\left[2\frac{S_{cl}}{N_{cl}}\right]_{B_n}^{x}\right]$$

$$= \left[\frac{7.0 \times 7}{5 \times 10^{-4}}\right]\left[\frac{0.25}{0.25}\right][3.0] = 54.7 \text{ dB}. \tag{87}$$

From the graph of Fig. 3 is obtained

$$\frac{S_{cl}}{N_{cl}}\bigg]_{B_n}^{x} = 7.7 \text{ dB}. \tag{88}$$

The clock loop threshold bandwidth (3 dB loop SNR) is taken as 0.4 c/s. At a loop SNR of 7.7 dB, $B_n$ is taken as

$$B_n = 0.7 \text{ c/s}. \tag{89}$$

During acquisition of $X$, the base channel correlation loss $L_{kb}$ is $-12$ dB. Then from (24) the input SNR required is

$$L_{ks}L_m \frac{S_i}{N_i}\bigg]_{B_n}^{\text{req}} = 7.7 + 0.9 + 12 = 20.6 \text{ dB}. \tag{90}$$

The signal-to-noise spectral density required is

$$L_{ks}L_m \frac{S_i}{|\Phi_n|}\bigg]_{B}^{\text{req}} = 19.1 \text{ dB}. \tag{91}$$

From (135) and Fig. 9 of Appendix II, the transponder correlation loss, which just causes the base-to-transponder and transponder-to-base ranging links to reach threshold, is determined to be

$$L_{ks} = -25.5 \text{ dB} \tag{92}$$

where the transponder limiter bandwidth and transmission frequencies are taken, respectively, as

$$B_1 = 2.5 \text{ mc/s} \tag{93}$$

$$\left\{\begin{array}{l} f_{bs} = 2113 \text{ mc/s} \\ f_{sb} = 2295 \text{ mc/s} \end{array}\right\}. \tag{94}$$

TABLE II

Ranging System Parameters

| Parameter | Remarks | Decibel Value |
|---|---|---|
| Base transmitter power | *400 kW | +56 dBW |
| Base transmission losses | | −0.5 dB |
| Base transmitting antenna gain | *210′ parabola | +60.3 dB |
| Polarization loss | | −0.4 dB |
| Transponder receiving antenna gain | "Omni" | +1.3 dB |
| Transponder receiving losses | | −2.5 dB |
| Modulation loss | 1 radian deviation | −1.6 dB |
| Transponder received ranging power | Normalized for space loss | +112.6 dBW |
| Transponder noise spectral density | *1300°K noise temperature | −197.5 dBW/cycle |
| Transponder received ranging Power-to-noise spectral density | Normalized for space loss | 310.1 dB/cycle |
| Transponder transmitter power | *50 watts | +17.0 dBW |
| Transponder transmission losses | | −3.0 dB |
| Transponder transmitting antenna gain | 7.5′ parabola | +32.5 dB |
| Polarization loss | | −0.1 dB |
| Base receiving antenna gain | *210′ parabola | +61.0 dB |
| Base receiving losses | | −0.2 dB |
| Modulation loss | 1 radian deviation | −1.6 dB |
| Base received ranging power | Normalized for space loss | +105.6 dBW |
| Base noise spectral density | *45°K noise temperature | −212.1 dBW/cycle |
| Base received ranging Power-to-noise spectral density | Normalized for space loss | 317.7 dB/cycle |

* These parameters represent an extension of the present state of the art. Feasibility of diplexing high-power transmission and low-noise reception channels through a common large antenna is being determined for the NASA Deep Space Network in relation to planetary missions of the 1970's [9].

Then from (132) the space loss on the trans-ponder-to-base link is found to be

$$L_{ssb} = 19.1 - 317.7 + 25.5 = -273.1 \text{ dB}. \quad (95)$$

The space loss corresponds to a threshold range of

$$R_{tt} = 4.68 \times 10^{8} \text{ km}. \quad (96)$$

From (29), the ratio of correlation signal-to-noise spectral density is

$$\frac{S_0}{|\Phi_0|} = -0.9 - 12.0 + 19.1$$
$$= 6.2 \text{ dB} = 4.18. \quad (97)$$

From (86), the theoretically required integration time per information bit of the longest sequence is

$$T_1 = \frac{3.0}{4.18} = 0.72 \text{ second}. \quad (98)$$

Now the threshold acquisition time $T_a$ for the code is essentially the integration time per bit, times the number of bits in the longest sequence, times the sum of signaling elements in all the sequences. Then

$$T_a = 0.72 \times 7.0[7 + 71 + 83 + 127]$$
$$= 1450 \text{ seconds} \quad (99)$$
$$= 24.2 \text{ minutes}. \quad (100)$$

The second calculation is for a regenerative system. As a starting point, specify the cumulative probability of error in code acquisition for the base channel as

$$P_{ab}(\epsilon) = 10^{-3}. \quad (101)$$

The base channel operates in this system as with a turn-around system except that there is zero transponder correlation loss $L_{ks}$. Hence, from (132), the space loss on the transponder-to-base link is

$$L_{sb} = 19.1 - 317.7 = -298.6 \text{ dB}. \quad (102)$$

The space loss corresponds to a threshold range of

$$R_{tr} = 8.82 \times 10^{9} \text{ km}. \quad (103)$$

The threshold acquisition time remains

$$T_a = 24.2 \text{ minutes}. \quad (104)$$

For the basc to transponder link, specify the cumulative probability of acquiring the received code and maintaining lock during code sweep as

$$P_{at}(\epsilon) = 10^{-3}. \quad (105)$$

The failure probability is arbitrarily divided between range code correlator and clock loop so that

$$P_{\tau}(\epsilon) = P(LL) = 5 \times 10^{-4}. \quad (106)$$

Optimize $\omega_p\tau$ so that

$$[\omega_p\tau]_{\text{opt}} = 2.15. \tag{107}$$

The channel is optimized for weak signal operation with

$$K_{e\,\max} = 0.242. \tag{108}$$

Now, from (79) determine

$$e_{\max} = 0.323 = 18.5°. \tag{109}$$

Then, from (81) and (82), respectively,

$$\tau B_n = \frac{0.242\pi}{0.323} = 2.35 \tag{110}$$

$$\tau B_f = \frac{2.15}{4} = 0.538. \tag{111}$$

Next it is assumed that the range uncertainty between the base and transponder channels at ranging system threshold is no more than about eleven hundred signaling elements. Arbitrarily, this length of the code is to be swept in an amount of time equal to the acquisition time of the base channel, or 1450 seconds. Then $\tau$, $B_n$, and $B_f$ are fixed at

$$\tau = 1.34 \text{ seconds} \tag{112}$$

$$B_n = 1.75 \text{ c/s} \tag{113}$$

$$B_f = 0.4 \text{ c/s}. \tag{114}$$

From (74), $L_e$ is determined:

$$L_e = +1.9 \text{ dB}. \tag{115}$$

Then from (106) and (73), the required input SNR is determined as

$$L_m \frac{S_i}{N_i}\bigg]_{B_n} = 9.8 \text{ dB}. \tag{116}$$

The required ranging power-to-noise spectral density is then

$$L_m \frac{S_i}{|\Phi_n|}\bigg]_S^{\text{req}} = 12.2 \text{ dB}. \tag{117}$$

The threshold space loss is obtained as

$$L_s = 12.2 - 310.1 = -297.9 \text{ dB}. \tag{118}$$

The space loss corresponds to a threshold range for the base-to-transponder link of

$$R_{\text{tr}} = 8.82 \times 10^9 \text{ km}. \tag{119}$$

Observation of the sample calculation results shows that the regenerative system capability exceeds that of the turnaround by a range factor of 18.8 for the particular assumptions employed. The question of whether or not the extra capability warrants the manifold complication of the transponder equipment is largely philosophical. For ranging inside the solar system, the question may be begged if the turnaround system is improved sufficiently. Possible improvements are: narrowing the clock loop bandwidth and going to a modulo-two code structure as in (52), or doing away with the transmitted clock component entirely. Such improvements are being investigated currently by the Jet Propulsion Laboratory [3].

## Conclusion

This paper has developed a set of mathematical tools which may be used to perform basic system design or analysis of pseudorandom coded ranging systems. Two sample calculations were presented using a hypothetical set of system parameters. The parameters were, in the author's opinion, entirely feasible by the early 1970's. The first calculation showed that a simple "turnaround" ranging system operates within specifications over a distance of $4.7 \times 10^8$ km, which is greater than the distance between Earth and Mars at superior conjunction. The second calculation showed that a more complex "regenerative" ranging system operates over a distance of $8.8 \times 10^9$ km, which is greater than the radius of the orbit of Pluto, the outermost planet in the solar system.

## Appendix I

In the treatment of the base ranging channel, a noise process is encountered which is the product of a low-pass Gaussian process and a pseudorandom binary waveform. The process is modeled as

$$n_m(t) = \tfrac{1}{2}c_r(t)y(t) \tag{120}$$

where $y(t)$ is a white, bandlimited Gaussian process with zero mean and $c_r(t)$ is a binary waveform taking on only the values plus or minus one in a pseudorandom sequence. It is known that the statistics of the process $n_m(t)$ remain first-order Gaussian [10].

The processes $c_r(t)$ and $y(t)$ are statistically independent. Therefore, the autocorrelation function of the product is the product of the autocorrelation functions of the processes. Now the spectral density of $y(t)$ is taken as

$$\begin{aligned}\Phi_y(\omega) &= 2|\Phi_n|; \qquad |\omega| < \frac{\Delta\omega_i}{2}\\ &= 0; \qquad \text{all other } \omega\end{aligned} \tag{121}$$

where $|\Phi_n|$ is the magnitude of the channel input noise density. The autocorrelation function of the noise process is [11]

$$R_y(\tau) = \frac{\Delta\omega_i}{\pi}|\Phi_n|\left[\frac{\sin\frac{\Delta\omega_i\tau}{2}}{\frac{\Delta\omega_i\tau}{2}}\right]. \tag{122}$$

$R_y(\tau)$ is aperiodic. The autocorrelation function of the pseudorandom code consists of periodic triangular pulses as shown in [1]. If the least period of the code autocorrelation function is so great that the product of autocorrelation functions only has appreciable value in the neighborhood of the origin, then the code may be approximated as truly random. This approximation requires that the highest first-order frequency component in the code be several times less than the highest frequency component of the noise

With the approximation, the spectral density of the product may be written as a frequency convolution

$$\Phi_m(\omega) = \frac{1}{4}\left[\frac{1}{2\pi}\int_{-\infty}^{\infty} \Phi_{cr}(y)\Phi_y(\omega - y)dy\right] \quad (123)$$

where $\Phi_{cr}(y)$ is taken as the spectral density of a random binary transmission

$$\Phi_{cr}(y) = \frac{1}{R}\,\frac{\sin^2\left(\frac{y}{2R}\right)}{\left(\frac{y}{2R}\right)^2} \quad (124)$$

where $R$ is the code element rate. Now

$$\Phi_y(\omega - y) = 2\,|\,\Phi_n\,|\,; \quad -\frac{\Delta\omega_i}{2} < \omega - y < \frac{\Delta\omega_i}{2}$$

$$= 0; \qquad |\,\omega - y\,| > \frac{\Delta\omega_i}{2}. \quad (125)$$

Then

$$\Phi_m(\omega) = \frac{1}{4\pi}\int_{\omega-\Delta\omega_i/2}^{\omega+\Delta\omega_i/2} \Phi_{cr}(y)\,|\,\Phi_n\,|\,dy \quad (126)$$

$$= \frac{|\,\Phi_n\,|}{4\pi R}\int_{\omega-\Delta\omega_i/2}^{\omega+\Delta\omega_i/2} \frac{\sin^2\left(\frac{y}{2R}\right)}{\left(\frac{y}{2R}\right)^2}\,dy \quad (127)$$

$$= |\,\Phi_n\,|\,\frac{R}{2\pi}\left\{\frac{\Delta\omega_i}{\omega^2 - \frac{\Delta\omega_i^2}{4}} + \frac{\cos\left[\frac{\omega + \frac{\Delta\omega_i}{2}}{R}\right]}{\omega + \frac{\Delta\omega_i}{2}} - \frac{\cos\left[\frac{\omega - \frac{\Delta\omega_i}{2}}{R}\right]}{\omega - \frac{\Delta\omega_i}{2}} + \frac{1}{R}\left[\mathrm{Si}\left(\frac{\omega + \frac{\Delta\omega_i}{2}}{R}\right) - \mathrm{Si}\left(\frac{\omega - \frac{\Delta\omega_i}{2}}{R}\right)\right]\right\} \quad (128)$$

where Si denotes the "sine integral."

## Appendix II

For a turnaround ranging system it is possible to determine, directly, the transponder channel correlation loss $L_{ks}$ which causes the base-to-transponder link and transponder-to-base link to reach "threshold" simultaneously. The determination requires knowledge of all the parameters of both channels except the range between them. Given the parameters, two ratios are defined.

$$\left.\frac{L_m S_i}{|\,\Phi_n\,|}\right]_S^{\text{avail norm}} \triangleq$$ The decibel ratio of available ranging power-to-noise spectral density at the transponder input, normalized to one unit distance.

$$\left.\frac{L_m S_i}{|\,\Phi_n\,|}\right]_B^{\text{avail norm}} \triangleq$$ The decibel ratio of available ranging power-to-noise spectral density at the base channel input, normalized to one unit distance.

Equation (51) of the text gives the equation for transponder channel limiter correlation loss as

$$L_{ks} = \left[\mathrm{erf}\sqrt{\left.\frac{L_m}{2}\,\frac{S_i}{N_i}\right]_{B_1}}\,\right]^2 \quad (129)$$

where $L_m$ is modulation loss and $S_i/N_i]_{B_1}$ is the channel input SNR computed in the limiter bandwidth, $B_l$. Equation (129) may be manipulated as

$$\left.\frac{L_m S_i}{|\,\Phi_n\,|}\right]_S^{\text{req}} = 10\log_{10} 2B_1\{[\mathrm{erf}^{-1}\sqrt{L_{ks}}\,]\}^2 \quad (130)$$

where $\mathrm{erf}^{-1}\sqrt{L_{ks}}$ is the argument of the error function which gives a value of $L_{ks}$ just causing the transponder channel to reach threshold.

$$\left.\frac{L_m S_i}{|\,\Phi_n\,|}\right]_B^{\text{req}} \triangleq$$ The decibel value of ranging power to noise spectral density at the input of the transponder channel which just gives threshold operation.

Now the space loss on the transmission link from base to transponder which just causes the transponder channel to reach threshold is

$$L_{sbs} = \left.\frac{L_m S_i}{|\,\Phi_n\,|}\right]_S^{\text{req}} - \left.\frac{L_m S_i}{|\,\Phi_n\,|}\right]_S^{\text{avail norm}} \quad (131)$$

For the base channel an equation analogous to (131) may be written as

$$L_{ssb} = \left.\frac{L_{ks} L_m S_i}{|\,\Phi_n\,|}\right]_B^{\text{req}} - \left.\frac{L_m S_i}{|\,\Phi_n\,|}\right]_B^{\text{avail norm}} - L_{ks}. \quad (132)$$

For (131) and (132) to be satisfied simultaneously, that is, at the same range, the difference in space loss on the two links is a function not of range, but only of carrier frequency. In general,

$$L_s\,\mathrm{dB} = K - 20\log_{10} F - 20\log_{10} R \quad (133)$$

where $F$ is carrier frequency, $R$ is range, and $K$ is a constant dependent on the system of measurement units.

Subtracting (131) from (132) gives

$$\frac{L_m S_i}{|\Phi_n|}\bigg]_S^{\text{req}} + L_{ks} = \frac{L_m S_i}{|\Phi_n|}\bigg]_S^{\text{avail norm}} - \frac{L_m S_i}{|\Phi_n|}\bigg]_B^{\text{avail norm}} + \frac{L_{ks} L_m S_i}{|\Phi_n|}\bigg]_B^{\text{req}} + 20 \log_{10}\left[\frac{f_{sb}}{f_{bs}}\right] \quad (134)$$

where $f_{sb}$ is the carrier frequency for the transponder-to-base link and $f_{bs}$ is the frequency for the base-to-transponder link.

Substituting (130) gives

$$20 \log_{10}\left[\operatorname{erf}^{-1}\sqrt{L_{ks}}\right] + L_{ks} = \frac{L_m S_i}{|\Phi_n|}\bigg]_S^{\text{avail norm}} - \frac{L_m S_i}{|\Phi_n|}\bigg]_B^{\text{avail norm}} + \frac{L_{ks} L_m S_i}{|\Phi_n|}\bigg]_B^{\text{req}} + 20 \log_{10}\left[\frac{f_{sb}}{f_{bs}}\right] - 10 \log_{10} B_1 - 3. \quad (135)$$

The terms on the left side of (135) are graphed vs. $L_{ks}$ in Fig. 9. The terms on the right side are all specifiable from requirements of system operation and knowledge of channel parameters. With the aid of the graph, the threshold value of $L_{ks}$ may be determined. From (132) the space loss and, hence, threshold range may be obtained.

*Author's Note:* In the intervening 18 months since the above material was produced, the author has done a little further work in the area of filtering effects on PN codes.[1] In particular, it appears that the bandwidth of the transponder turnaround ranging channel may be optimized to a lower value than that used in the sample calculation. An optimum bandwidth exists because of two opposite effects of reducing the bandwidth. One effect is to reduce the loss $L_{ks}$ due to the channel noise, defined by (51) above. A second, opposite, effect is to produce an increasing "correlation loss" due to filtering of the PN code itself. For the case of a one-pole low-pass filter, the optimum noise bandwidth appears to be in the neighborhood of $1.1/T$ c/s, where $T$ is code-element duration in seconds. This optimization is for very small-channel SNR and does not consider bandwidth tolerances due to aging or environment.

[1] S. C. Gupta and J. H. Painter, "Correlation analyses of linearly processed pseudo-random sequences," *IEEE Trans. on Communication Technology*, vol. COM-14, pp. 796–801, December 1966.

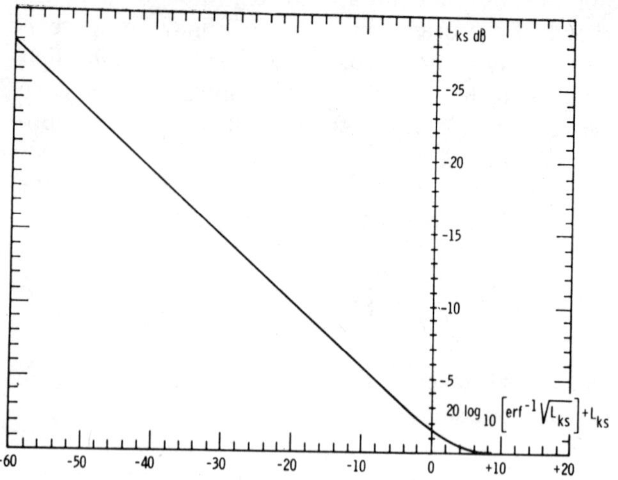


**Fig. 9. Graph of (135) vs. $L_{ks}$.**

REFERENCES


[1] S. W. Golomb et al., *Digital Communications.* Englewood Cliffs, N. J.: Prentice-Hall, 1964, pp. 85–105.

[2] J. H. Painter and G. Hondros, "Unified S-band telecommunications techniques for Apollo," vol. I, NASA, Washington, D. C., Tech. Note D-2208, p. 6, March 1965.

[3] (a) Jet Propulsion Laboratory (JPL), Pasadena, Calif., Research Summaries 36-1 through 36-14, vol. 1, for the period December 1, 1959 through April 1, 1962.
(b) JPL Space Program Summaries 37-11 through 37-14, vol. 1, for the period July 1, 1961 through March 1, 1962.
(c) JPL Space Program Summaries 37-15 through 37-33, vol. 3, for the period March 1, 1962 through May 1, 1965.

[4] Golomb et al. [1], chs. 2 and 6.

[5] Golomb et al. [1], p. 67.

[6] L. Baumert, M. Easterling, S. W. Golomb, and A. Viterbi, "Coding theory and its applications to communications systems," JPL, Pasadena, Calif., Tech. Rept. 32-67, p. 62, March 31, 1961.

[7] R. W. Sanneman, and J. R. Rowbotham, "Unlock characteristics of the optimum Type II phase-locked loop," *IEEE Trans. on Aerospace and Navigational Electronics*, vol. ANE-11, pp. 15–24, March 1964.

[8] A. Viterbi, "Phase-locked loop dynamics in the presence of noise by Fokker-Planck techniques, *Proc. IEEE*, vol. 51, pp. 1737–1753, December 1963.

[9] "Planned capabilities of the DSN for voyager," JPL, Pasadena, Calif., EPD-283, September 15, 1965.

[10] J. H. Painter, "On the statistics of the product of a Gaussian noise process and a pseudorandom binary code," *Proc. IEEE (Correspondence)*, vol. 53, pp. 2118–2119, December 1965.

[11] A. Papoulis, *Probability, Random Variables and Stochastic Processes.* New York: McGraw-Hill, 1965, p. 372.

# A SPREAD SPECTRUM RANGING TECHNIQUE FOR AEROSPACE VEHICLES

R. C. Dixon
Member of Technical Staff
TRW Systems Group
Redondo Beach, California

Abstract

This paper considers the factors affecting spread spectrum ranging and describes a non-ambiguous, fast operating "hybrid" system utilizing a combination of high rate pseudonoise modulation for fine range resolution and low rate modulation for coarse range resolution. This technique allows rapid distance measurement while maintaining the inherent accuracy of other pseudonoise ranging systems. The pseudonoise code sequences used are much shorter than those conventionally required for nonambiguous long distance ranging, which facilitates fast code phase acquisition. The low rate "range message" used to resolve any ambiguity due to repetition of the short code sequence is derived from the repetition of the pseudonoise ranging sequence itself.

## Introduction

Spread spectrum ranging systems offer an excellent means of long range distance measurement. The capabilities of these systems have been spectacularly demonstrated in space probes, supplying information required for course correction and operational timing with great accuracy. The inherent long range accuracy of spread spectrum ranging also makes it extremely attractive for navigational use in aircraft and manned space vehicles, but the relative size and complexity of first generation PN equipments has discouraged their use. Further, from an operational standpoint, spread spectrum systems have been impractical to use under rapidly changing conditions due to the fact that most practical systems require synchronous code sequence operation (that is, the signal seen by the receiver must be precisely correlated in time with a locally generated reference signal) and the time required to achieve the desired synchronism is often such that a high speed aircraft or other aerospace vehicle can obsolete a range reading before it is completed.

Because of the unique circumstances under which deep space systems are used, relatively long code sequence phase acquisition times are allowable. That is, the information required, while possibly critical to mission success, may be supplied by a lengthy, time-consuming process, without jeopardy to the mission itself, and synchronization times of up to several minutes have been common in space probe ranging systems. Therefore, deep space ranging techniques have not been directly applicable to highly manueverable vehicles. For aircraft use, where spread spectrum ranging offers its greatest utility, the implementation methods used for spacecraft ranging are not feasible, as a range measurement must be available whenever it is desired and with minimum waiting time.

One objection to spread spectrum systems, that of size, has been resolved by the introduction of integrated circuits. Both linear and digital integrated circuits are applicable to spread spectrum systems, but the advent of high speed digital integrated circuits has made possible small spread spectrum equipments capable of being carried by almost any aerospace vehicle. Digital circuits, such as shift registers, often make up major parts of spread spectrum equipments. High speed shift register implementation, for instance, has been improved over the years from the use, in 1959, of large lumped-constant delay networks to the present use of integrated logic circuits. A special integrated circuit capable of operation at bit rates in excess of 50 Mbps has been developed especially for code sequence generation in spread spectrum systems. This unit includes in one package both a flip-flop and a gated modulo-two adder, thus enabling construction of a shift register code sequence generator using only one package per stage, including all necessary feedback logic. In addition, for a given shift register length, every possible feedback combination is selectable. This makes selective range addressing through code assignment quite easy to implement.

Effort has also been expended in the area of building entire shift register sequence generators and other digital subsystems in a single integrated circuit package, through MOS techniques.

Though PN ranging systems have not been reduced in complexity, microminiaturization techniques have improved their reliability and reduced size to permit their use in both aircraft and space vehicles. Thus, time required for achieving synchronism between transmitting and receiving units has become the major factor limiting usage of pseudonoise ranging systems. Reduction of measurement time for ranging systems is the problem to which the hybrid ranging system described here is addressed.

## Factors Affecting Spread Spectrum Ranging

Pseudonoise Ranging. Several types of spread spectrum systems are in existence, each of which has its own particular advantages. All are characterized by the use of a much wider band of frequencies than is necessary for transmitting the basic information sent. Systems which hop from one frequency to another, or send short bursts of information at high rates, or simply modulate a carrier with a coded message, all are classed as spread spectrum systems. The type which has been used most often for ranging, however, is the direct sequence or pseudonoise (PN) modulated system. This is due to the relative simplicity of implementing PN systems (compared to other spread spectrum techniques) and to their inherent synchronous operation. For these reasons, only PN systems are considered in the following discussions, even though the basic ranging technique is applicable to other systems.

PN (pseudonoise) communications and navigations systems are characterized by their use of a pseudorandom code sequence to directly modulate an RF carrier. The codes used in PN systems generally have bit rates which are much higher than the bit rate of any information transmitted. (Typical bit rates for PN code sequences are in the one to ten Mbps region). Signals modulated by such sequences therefore are wideband and fit the general category of spread spectrum signals.

Reprinted from a paper in the *20th Annual Southwestern IEEE Conf. and Exhibition Rec.*, Apr. 17-19, 1968 and published by TRW.

PN codes vary in length from a few bits to billions of bits, depending on their use. The pattern of ones and zeros in such sequences does not repeat within this code length, and thus to an observer who views less than the entire sequence, the appearance is that of a random set of bits, such as might be produced by a noise generator. This noiselike stream of bits is actually a well defined signal whose short term properties resemble noise but which is repetitious and therefore quite predictable. (Hence the name "pseudo" noise). Signals such as these are simple to generate with shift register sequence generators, and these are used in almost all PN systems to construct the basic spectrum-spreading signal. The specific code sequence used, its length, and bit rate must be decided by overall system constraints of accuracy, bandwidth, and measurement time.

Figure 1 illustrates a typical PN ranging system. In the transmitter, a carrier is biphase modulated by the code sequence generator, which produces a wideband, suppressed carrier output signal, code modulated. The modulation spectrum produced by a PN code modulated transmitter is $\left(\frac{\sin x}{x}\right)^2$, with a main lobe bandwidth (null-to-null) equal to twice the code sequence's clock rate.

The receiver "decodes" a received signal by matching an internally generated sequence to the incoming signal. For ranging, the important point is that the receiver matches its internal sequence to the signal that it sees, and this signal is delayed by an amount of time equal to the propagation time from transmitter to receiver. The transmitter, then, is generating the same code sequence as the receiver, but is a number of code bits ahead of the receiver. This number of code bits depends on both distance and the rate of code generation.

Once the transmitting system has transmitted for a period long enough to allow the receiver to match its internal reference to the signal transmitted, the transmitter can send information, or instruct the receiver to transmit back to the original transmitter (called "interrogation" and "response"). Now, if the interrogating unit transmits a mark to the responder which causes the responder to switch to the transmit mode, and the interrogator goes into receive, the two are no longer synchronized. (Remember that the original receiver was "behind" the transmitter). The interrogator must now delay its code sequence so that it is "behind" the responder by the number of code bits equal to the propagation time. All that is now necessary to allow the interrogator to measure range is to count the number of bits that it must delay its code sequence to bring it back into synchronization with the unit now transmitting. (Note that the range measurement is made as a function of counting bits, and is a digital, discrete measurement accurate to within one bit period. Therefore, the accuracy of measurement is the same at any range, where the threshold of the system is exceeded).

Systems of this type have been implemented, and have been shown to be accurate and reliable. The limiting factor in the use of such a simple system is that the code sequences used must be long enough that they do not repeat over the maximum distance measured. (Otherwise, an ambiguity exists which is not resolvable from simple code sequence offset measurements). Thus, the number of bits to be searched is large, and search time becomes prohibitive at long range.

An alternative to the transmit-then-receive (interrogate-respond) technique uses two frequencies, in a duplex arrangement such as that shown in Figure 1b. Using this technique, only a frequency translation is necessary in the unit being ranged on. This unit retransmits the signal received (instead of a locally generated signal as in the responder) so that the unit measuring range receives a coded signal delayed by a number of code bits equivalent to twice the distance being measured. The ranging system must contain two code sequence generators-one for transmission, and the other for matching to the received signal. Once the received signal has been matched to the receive sequence generator, range measurements are made by simply counting the number of bits delay between the transmit and receive sequence generators in the ranging unit. Also, measurements may be continuous once system synchronization and an initial measurement occur. This is not true in the interrogate-respond system, as an interrogation and a response is necessary for each measurement. Again, the code sequence used must be longer than the number of bits delay at the longest range to be measured.

Chief drawbacks to the duplex measurement method are that two sequence and clock generators are required in the ranging unit and the frequency allocation problem is worsened because two channels are needed. For satellite applications, however, it is best because of the possible simplicity of the vehicle unit. The hybrid system developed is applicable to both interrogate-respond and duplex systems. In both systems, the code offset which must be searched out for synchronization is equal to twice the actual range. This is an important consideration, for it increases resolution, but also increases search time.

Code Sequence Bit Rates. The bit, or "clock," rate at which the PN code sequence is generated determines the basic resolution capability of a PN ranging system. In fact, resolution capability is limited only by the bandwidth required to support higher and higher bit rates. As bit rate is increased, range uncertainty is decreased, but at the cost of a wider band RF channel. High resolution ranging can be maintained, however, without transmitting the entire $\left(\frac{\sin x}{x}\right)^2$ spectrum, and many PN ranging systems transmit only the main lobe, or less, even though the biphase modulated RF signal's envelope may be seriously degraded by such narrow-banding.

The fact that basic resolution capability is not degraded by loss of bandwidth is due to the correlation properties of the code sequences. Synchronization between received and locally generated code sequences can be judged on the basis of correlation over the whole sequence length, rather than on a bit-by-bit basis. Therefore, a degradation in rise and fall time does not affect measurement accuracy, as long as the bandwidth is enough to reasonably reproduce the transmission of single code bits. Bandwidth loss effects on hybrid systems are identical to other PN systems.

PN code sequences have a correlation function which ideally is an isosceles triangle in which the base width is equal to twice the width of a single code bit. Exact code synchronization corresponds to the peak of this correlation function, while an advance or delay between received and reference sequences decreases correlation, which in effect is similar to raising the receiver threshold. The important point is that received and locally generated references must be within one bit before recognition of synchronization is possible. In fact, it is necessary in most systems for code synchronization to be within a small fraction of a bit of the maximum point of correlation before the code correlation circuit's output signal-to-noise ratio is sufficient to permit recognition of synchronization. For this reason, synchronous PN systems are inherently incapable of measurements in error by more than one bit. Narrowing of transmitter or receiver bandwidth tends to round the edges of the triangular correlation function as in Figure 3b, but this effectively raises receiver threshold rather than broadening the correlation area. Again, inherent accuracy is affected negligibly. What, then, does affect PN system ranging accuracy?

Selection of Clock Rate. Factors affecting the accuracy of a PN ranging system are chiefly clock rate, clock drift, and doppler shift of the clock rate. (Ignoring possible errors in the digital counting and readout circuits, which should be negligible).

Clock rates may be the same whether a ranging system is of the hybrid or conventional type. It is necessary to give some consideration to the combination of the clock rate in conjunction with the PN sequence length in a hybrid system, however, as the range message bit rate is the result of these parameters.

For example, let us assume that we wish to design a ranging unit capable of measuring range to within 0.1 nautical miles (one n.m. = 1852 meters), and that we want to count 10 bits per mile of propagation delay. 0.1 mile corresponds to a bit rate having a wavelength of 185.2 meters, or a repetition rate:

$$\frac{C}{R} = \frac{2.997925 \times 10^8}{1.852 \quad \times 10^2} = 1.618750 \text{ Mbps}$$

where C = speed of light
R = resolution

A PN system using a code sequence bit rate of 1.618750 MHz would therefore have a propagation delay of 10 bits per mile and a receiver 10 miles away would see a signal delayed by exactly 100 bits from the transmitter. That is, the signal appearing at the receiver was transmitted at a time which, on the transmitter's terms, was 100 bits earlier. Therefore, the receiver's sequence generator must be exactly 100 bits behind the transmitter to achieve maximum correlation, and between 99 and 101 bits behind the transmitter to be within the bounds of correlation. 1.618750 MHz is certainly not a standard frequency, but an accurate crystal stabilized source at this frequency is readily achievable. (As an aside, it should be noted that multiples of .161875 MHz may be used as clock rates to gain whatever resolution is desired, i.e. one-fiftieth mile would require a clock frequency of 50 x .161875 = 8.093750 Mbps. Of course, the number used for C, the speed of light, is that for light traveling in a vacuum, so that in any other medium some error will be seen. This is not significant, however, as long as all clocks operate at the same rate. 0.1 per cent range error limit due to common frequency offset would allow the clock rate to change up to 1618 bps). It is recalled that, in both the interrogate-respond and duplex ranging systems, the number of code bits of offset due to range is actually equivalent to twice the range being measured. Therefore, in these and similar systems, clock rate required to give a desired resolution is halved.

Once the nominal clock rate is chosen, both transmit and receive systems are expected to operate at the chosen frequency (within their error limits) except when a receiving unit is in the "search" mode, looking for correlation with an incoming signal.

Searching is accomplished by operating the receive unit clock at a rate slightly higher or lower than the nominal clock rate. This causes the receiver's code sequence to either advance or be retarded in phase with respect to the transmitted sequence, thus "sliding" the two sequences past one another comparing all possible code phase relationships until correlation occurs. In the interrogate-respond ranging system discussed previously, this search procedure occurs twice: first, when the initial transmission occurs, and second, when the responding unit replies.

Direction of search (forward or backward in code phase) is usually not important to a PN system, but in transmit-receive ranging systems it is important that the unit making the range measurement (the interrogator) search backward. That is, the interrogator's clock should run at a rate lower than the responder's clock, so that its code sequence is slipping backward with respect to the incoming signal. This is important, in that the responder's sequence generator is retarded with respect to the interrogator's sequence generator at the time of the transmit to receive switch, and the interrogator's code sequence must also be retarded to a number of bits equal to the propagation time in order to recorrelate. The period during which the interrogating unit is searching for recorrelation with the responding transmitter is the most vulnerable for error entry. During this time, any relative clock drift or doppler shift is accumulated by the bit search counter in the interrogator as a range error. This error is a function of relative clock difference, relative velocity, search time, and the difference between desired and actual clock rate. (Where actual operating rate is determined by crystal oscillators the clock can be held within a few cycles of the desired rate, so that errors due to systems operating at other than the desired nominal rate are negligible). On the basis of clocks operating near their design frequency, range error for an integral frequency clock system may be expressed by:

$$\text{Error (in bits)} = \left( |K_I - K_R| \pm 1.7\, V_R K_R \times 10^{-3} \right) T_S$$

where:
$K_I$ = receive unit clock rate (Bps)
$K_R$ = transmit clock rate (Bps)
$V_R$ = relative velocity (N.M.P.H.)
$T_S$ = correlation search time (seconds)

This expresses the errors accumulated due to a receive unit counting at an assumed clock rate $K_I$, while transmitter's reply actually is at a clock rate $K_R$ offset by the doppler frequency shift referred to transmitter clock signal. This is multiplied by search time, for the longer the time of the receive unit's search for correlation, the longer is the time that errors are accumulated at this rate. Doppler frequency errors may reduce errors due to clock differences or add to them, depending on the direction of errors and relative velocity.

Selecting the Ranging Code. Code sequences used in ranging should be chosen on the basis of considerations for their auto and cross correlation properties, and in most ranging systems, for sufficient length.

A code sequence such as the maximal linear type is an excellent choice for ranging. Not only are the properties of these codes well known, but the methods for generating them are straightforward and simple.

Where codes other than maximal are to be used, their auto-correlation and cross correlation properties should be carefully analyzed. Otherwise, interference between different sequences can nullify selective addressing, or minor correlation in a correct sequence can cause erroneous measurements due to falsely recognizing synchronization. Maximal codes are, by definition, the longest codes which can be generated by a given shift register, or a delay element of a given length. In the case of shift register sequence generators, which are the only type to be considered here, the maximum length sequence is $2^n - 1$ bits, where n is the number of stages in the shift register. A shift register sequence generator consists of a shift register working in conjunction with appropriate logic, which feeds back a logical combination of the state of two or more of its stages to its input. The output of such a sequence generator, and the contents of its n stages at any sample (clock) time, is a function of the outputs of the stages fed back at the previous sample time.

Basic properties of maximal codes are:[1,2]

1. The number of one's in a sequence equals the number of zero's to within one bit. For a 1023 bit code, there are 512 one's and 511 zero's. Therefore, any DC correlation term is negligible.

2. The distribution of one's and zero's is well defined and always the same. Relative positions of runs of one's and zero's vary from code sequence to code sequence, but the number of each run length does not. There are exactly $2^{n-(p+2)}$ runs of length p, for both one's and zero's, in every code sequence. (Except for n-1 zero's and n one's of which there is one run each. Also, n zero's and n-1 one's of which there are no runs.)[3]

3. Auto-correlation of a maximal linear code is such that for all values of phase shift, the correlation value is -1, except for the zero $\pm$ 1 bit phase shift area, where correlation varies linearly from the -1 value to $2^n-1$ (the sequence length). A 1023 $2^{10}-1$) bit maximal code therefore has a peak to average auto-correlation value of 1024, a range of 30.1 db in signal. It must be realized, however, that these values for auto correlation are valid only for averaging over the entire sequence length.

All of the properties of maximal sequences can be used to advantage in a ranging system. The question, then, in general, is not what type of code to use, but what length.

A ranging code used by a system which has no secondary resolving capability must be of sufficient length that it does not repeat over the maximum distance measured. That is, to measure a range of 1000 miles with a code giving 50 bits per mile resolution would require a code length of at least 50,000 bits. Otherwise, the code sequence would repeat, and the interrogator could recognize synchronization at more than one range. At the 8.093750 Mbps rate required to give 50 bit per mile resolution, the repetition period of the 65,535 $(2^{16}-1)$ bit code required would be $\frac{65,355}{8.093750} = 8.1$ milliseconds and the bandwidth of the correlation detector would be 43 Hz. If a 43 Hz recognition bandwidth is used, however, searching out a range at the maximum distance could require almost 20 minutes. Obviously, then in a simple ranging system, high resolution and long distance measurements must be traded off against measurement time.

The major problem in PN ranging for aircraft and maneuverable spacecraft has been the requirement for measurement at long range in a reasonably short period. Reduction of ranging time is limited by the maximum search rate a receiving unit is capable of achieving and the length of the code to be searched. Maximum search rate, in turn, is limited by the recognition time of the receiver's correlation detection circuits. (The receiver must be able to recognize correlation and stop the search process before the point of code synchronization is passed.) To complete the circle, the bandwidth of the correlation detectors must be commensurate with the auto correlation requirements of the codes used.

What techniques are available to reduce ranging time while maintaining accuracy? Much work has been performed in the area of developing special "acquirable" codes which have the required length for long range measurement, but which also have synchronization properties such that a range may be searched out without traversing the entire code length.[1] Jet Propulsion Laboratories has had great success with code sequences made up of three component codes assembled in such a way that the overall ranging sequence has a length which is the product of the three component code lengths. The search for correlation is done in parallel, in three correlation detectors, each of which compares an incoming product-code-modulated signal with one of the component codes. That is, all phases of each component code are searched for correlation.

Synchronization, in this process, is sequential, with a partial correlation occurring each time one of the component codes reaches its point of synchronization and complete correlation occurring when all three are synchronized. This technique can reduce range measurement time tremendously but suffers from threshold degradation due to partial correlation and attendant loss of correlator output signal-to-noise ratio when less than all of the component codes are synchronized.

## Hybrid Ranging System

A ranging technique which solves the problem of fast range measurement at long distances has been developed. This is a hybrid system approach in that more than one kind of modulation is used to measure range.* In this technique, a PN code, a few thousand bits long, and a digital "range message" (whose bit rate is the repetition rate of the PN sequence), simultaneously modulate the transmitter. The PN code does not determine maximum range so that its length is chosen short, to reduce search time. (The only bound on reducing code length is that any system crosscorrelation requirements be met.) Ambiguity in range caused by using a short PN code is resolved by the low rate digital message whose length is such that its repetition period is

*A similar technique was suggested by W. J. Judge of Magnavox Research Labs in an unpublished memo, in 1963.

longer than the propagation delay of the longest range to be measured. No separate search process is needed to synchronize this range message, however, as it is clocked by the PN code repetition and is therefore synchronized by the initial search process. All that is needed is a measurement of the relative phases of local or received range messages, which is as simple as counting the number of PN code repetitions between range message markers. Figure 2 illustrates the relationship between the PN code and the range message as they are used in the hybrid system. Each complete repetition of the high bit rate PN code sequence corresponds to one bit in the range message. The ratio of the bit rates is thus seen to be equal to the number of bits in the PN code.

The range message itself is the simplest kind of digital signal, made up of a number of square waves whose half-wave period is the PN code repetition rate, and which are inverted in phase after a time greater than the maximum expected propagation delay. This phase inversion is the marker which resolves the range ambiguity. If error correction capability is required, the range message can be structured to give the desired properties. The simple range message used was chosen to permit measurement without a separate message synchronization process.

Modulation is such that the PN code biphase modulates the transmitted carrier at its basic rate, permitting high resolution. The range message, however, is sent as a baseband signal, keying the same carrier that is modulated by the PN code. Composite transmitted output then is a $\left(\frac{\sin x}{x}\right)^2$ spectrum whose carrier shifts at the range message rate. Either frequency or phase shift keying is satisfactory for use in range message modulation. Phase shift keying is most optimum, and may be implemented by inverting the PN code at each range message one - zero transition. PSK demodulation is much more complex than FSK demodulation, however, as a simple phase-lock loop or a discriminator may be used for FSK detection. Signal-to-noise ratio at the demodulator in either the FSK or PSK case is excellent, since the PN code used is fully correlated by the synchronization process. Therefore, either modulation technique is satisfactory.

Timing, and a range unit block diagram, for a duplex hybrid ranging system is shown in Figure 3. A range measurement using this system would be made as follows:

1. At the initiation of the measurement, both transmit and receive PN generators are reset and started. The transmit generator PN modulates the transmitter at the nominal PN rate, and the receive PN generator searches backward.

2. As soon as the receive PN generator searches out the number of bits corresponding to range, synchronization occurs, and the number of bits searched is entered into a range counter.

3. At synchronization, the receiver sends a logic signal to the transmitter, which begins to generate the range message and to modulate the carrier with it. (Range message output from the receiver now delayed by the two-way propagation time between the transmitter and receiver, and can be compared with the transmitted message to resolve correct range).

4. The number of PN sequence repetitions between the occurrence of a phase reversal in the transmitted and received range message is counted, weighted, and added with the bits counted in the original search process. The measurement is complete.

   Subsequent measurements of range and range rate may be made by counting the number of PN code bits between the occurrence of all ones vectors in the transmit and receive PN generators.

Figure 4 shows simplified block diagrams and range message timing for a hybrid interrogate - respond ranging system which could be used where range readout is desired by both participants. It is recalled from Figure 2 that the entire PN sequence repeats once during each bit time in the range message, and is synchronous with it. Aircraft or manned space vehicles users might find the interrogate - respond technique best because it divides system complexity equally between identical systems.

One range cycle is described as follows (see timing diagram):

1. The interrogating unit transmits a PN modulated signal for a period long enough to assure that the intended responder has synchronized.

2. The range message, consisting of a series of one-zero bits (a square wave) at the PN code repetition rate, is sent, followed by a phase inversion of the range message. This information FSK modulates the PN modulated carrier.

3. At the PN code repetition marker following the phase inversion several things occur; (1) the responder starts generating an identical range message to that sent by the interrogator (i.e. a given number of square wave periods, an inversion, repeating), (2) the interrogator switches to receive, and (3) the responder switches to transmit.

   Search processing for resynchronization is delayed in the interrogator for a short period sufficient to exceed the T-R switching time. In this way, switching time in the two units is removed as a source of range error.

4. The responder now transmits a PN (only) modulated signal for a synchronization period, and the interrogator counts the number of bits searched to regain synchronization, storing the bit count in a range counter.

5. Responder modulates the PN modulated signal with the range message as it occurs. (Remember that it has been generating the range message since the T-R switch).

6. Interrogator receives the range message and counts the number of message bits between the first phase inversion in the received message and the next occurring in its own range message (which has also been generated since the T-R switch).

7. Each message bit counted is weighted, added to the PN bit count already entered, and read out as a range.

Selection of parameters used in hybrid systems is illustrated by the following example of a design for an interrogate-respond system:

Suppose (again) that it is desired that ranging be performed at distances up to 1000 miles, and with resolution of 0.1 mile but only one second is allowed for the measurement.

We wish to complete a range measurement in one second or less which means we must:

1. Interrogate, which consists of:

   a. transmitting a PN code sequence to allow the intended responder to synchronize.

   b. adding FSK or DSK information to the transmitted signal telling the responder to transmit.

   c. switching to receive and counting the number of bits necessary to search before synchronizing with the responder's PN signal.

   d. receiving and accumulating the range message information.

Since the two synchronization search processes (only one is required in a duplex system) consume most of the overall measurement time, let us allow 0.45 seconds for each synchronization. A 2047 bit PN code would have to be searched at a rate of approximately 4600 bits per second to assure recognition in this time.

A 4600 Bps search rate would require synchronization recognition in less than $\frac{1}{2300}$ second (since the correlation function is two bits wide). Therefore, the recognition bandwidth should be 805 Hz or greater.

Since:

$$\frac{\text{code length}}{\text{bit rate}} = \text{Repetition period} = \frac{.35}{\text{Recognition B.W.}}$$

then bit rate should be:

$$\frac{1}{\tau} = BW_R \times L$$

where:

$\tau$ = bit period

$BW_R$ = code length

and $.35 = \text{B.W.} \times T_R$ for the synchronization recognition circuit.

Code bit rate, using a 2047 bit code, searching 4600 bits per second, and using a synchronization recognition circuit 805 Hz wide, would be at least:

$$\frac{805 \times 2047}{.35} = 4.7 \text{ Mbps.}$$

The nearest multiple of .161875 is 30, and the clock rate used should be 4.856250 Mbps. (Resolution capability would be one-sixtieth mile).

Next, we construct the range message, which must have a period greater than the greatest propagation delay expected, or more than 6.3 msec. The repetition period of the code sequence is .42 msec., therefore, the code repeats almost fifteen times in this range. We use this repetition to generate a word made up of fifteen or more bits, having a bit period equal to the PN sequence repetition rate. This word is the "range message," and consists of a square wave (one-zero sequence) fifteen bits long, a phase reversal, fifteen bits, a phase reversal, etc.

In measurements using the range message, the phase reversal marks the beginning of a sequence, and each bit is weighted at $\frac{2047}{30} = 68.23$ miles. Therefore, for each bit of offset in the range message, the interrogator adds 68.23 miles to the range bits counted when searching for synchronization with the responder. (A duplex-hybrid system would weight its message at 34.115 miles per bit).

Overall range measurement time, then, using the parameters described, would be approximately 950 msec. Range resolution would be one-sixtieth mile, and maximum range would be 1091 miles. (Adding bits in the range message would increase maximum range capability at a rate of 68.25 miles per bit, and measurement time .42 msec. per bit). The design requirements are met.

## Summary

The hybrid ranging technique outlined may be used to reduce range measurement time in spread spectrum systems significantly, through reduction of synchronization search time.

Both duplex and interrogate - respond configurations are practical, each having its advantages. The interrogate - respond configuration allows identical units at all terminals and requires less channel space, while the duplex configuration permits shifting of complexity to one terminal, requires only one synchronization search, and therefore offers faster measurements than the I-R configuration.

By combining high rate PN modulation and low rate baseband modulation, ranging systems are possible which can furnish accurate range at long distances in minimum time.

## Acknowledgement

The hybrid ranging approach was developed while the author was employed at the Magnavox Research Laboratories in Torrance, California. The techniques described have been implemented and proven in actual ranging systems under field conditions.

## Bibliography

1. R. Gold. Study of Correlation Properties of Binary Sequences. Technical Report AFAL-TR-234. August 1966.

2. S. W. Golomb. Digital Communications with Space Applications. Prentice-Hall. 1964

3. J. B. Freymodsson. A Note on the Run-Length Distribution of Ones and Zeros in Maximal-Linear Shift Register Sequences. Magnavox Research Laboratories. November 1963

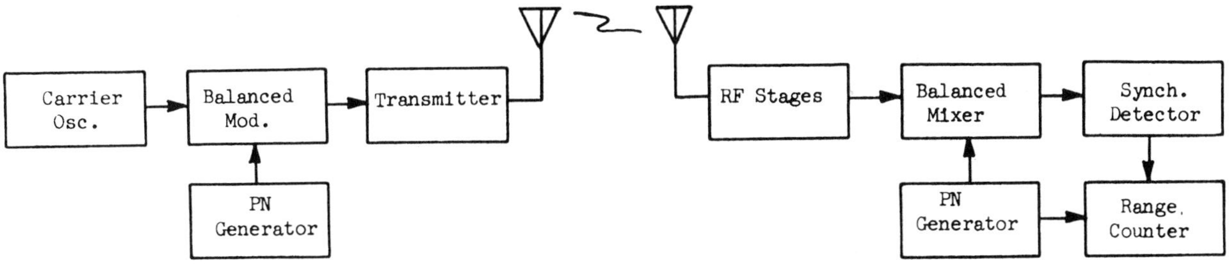


Figure 1a - Transmit-Receive Ranging System

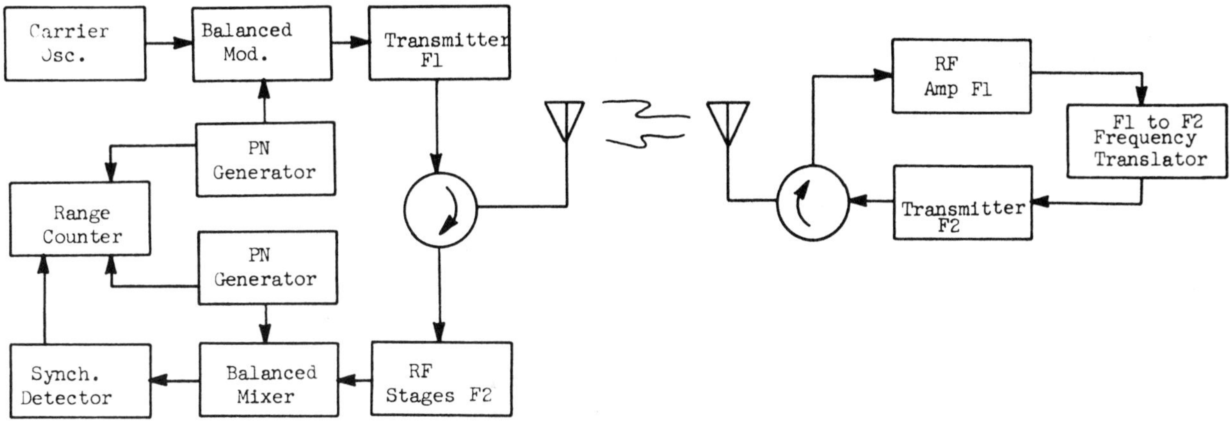


Figure 1b - Duplex Ranging System

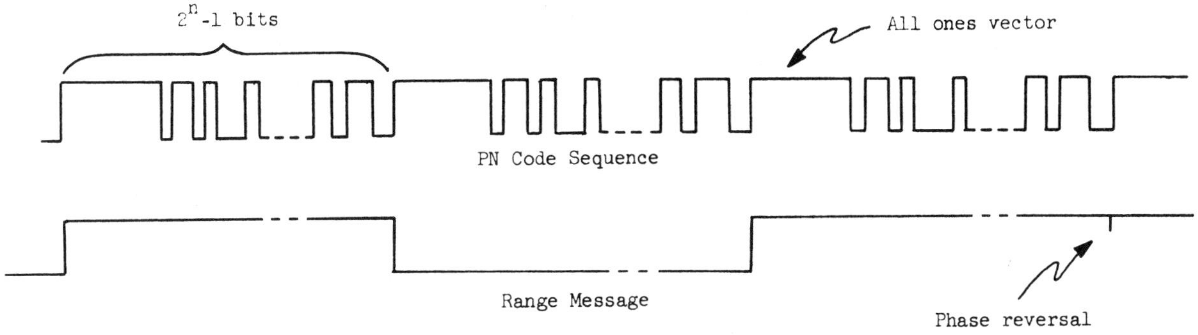


Figure 2 - Range Message - PN Sequence Relationship

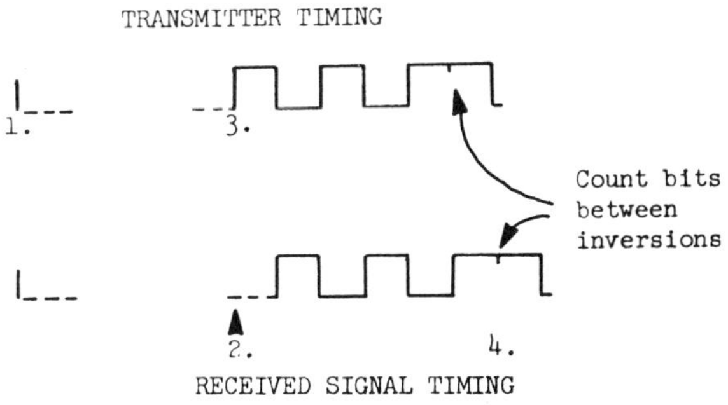


Figure 3a - Duplex Range Message Timing

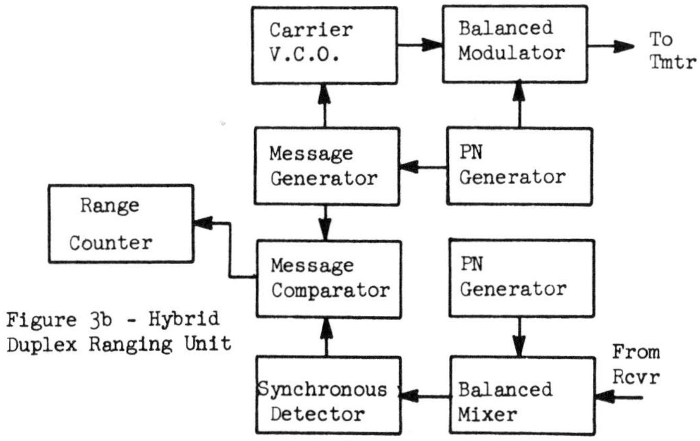


Figure 3b - Hybrid Duplex Ranging Unit

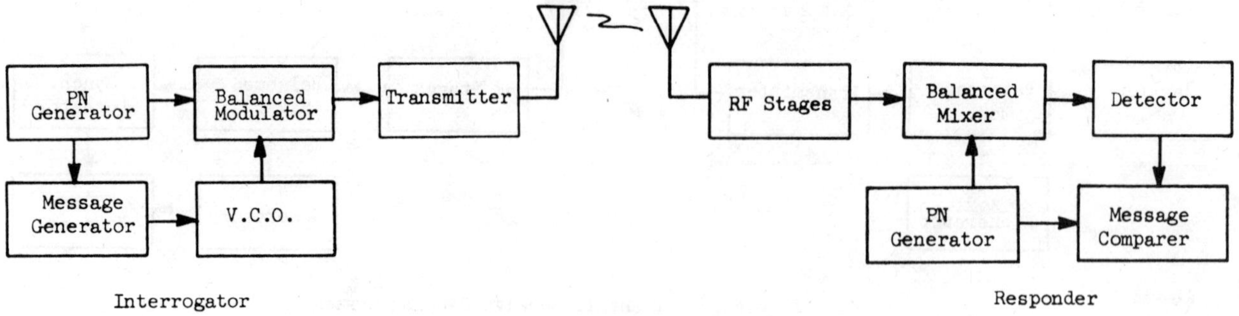


Figure 4a - Hybrid Ranging System - Interrogate Mode

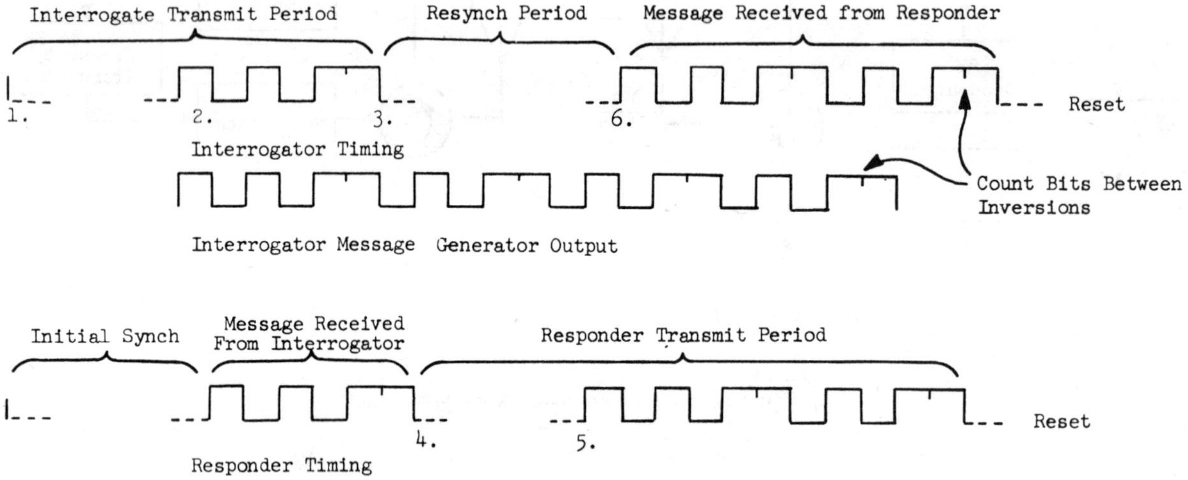


Figure 4b - Hybrid Ranging System Range Message Timing Diagram

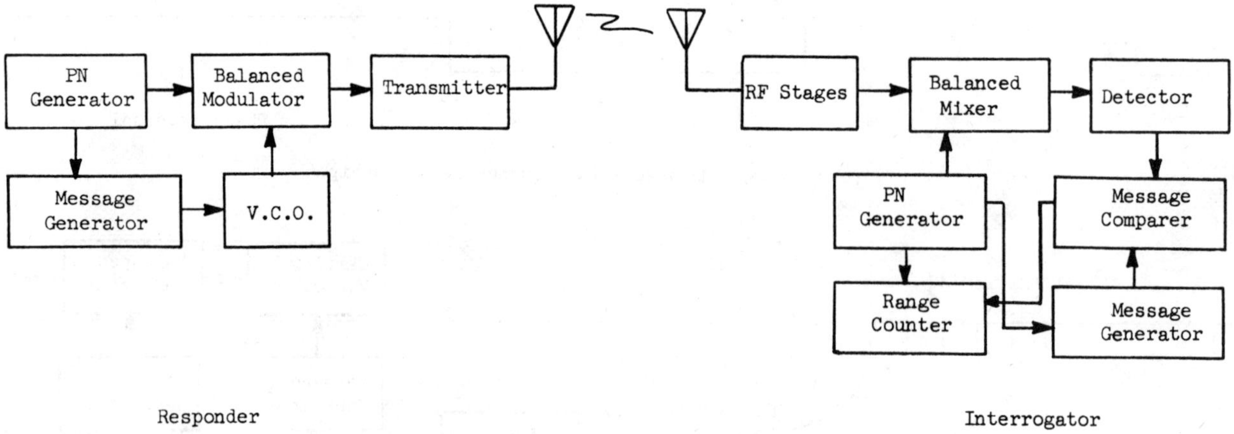


Figure 4c - Hybrid Ranging System - Respond Mode

# Optimum Transponder Design for Pseudonoise-Coded Ranging Systems, Weak Signals

ROBERT J. RICHARDSON, Member, IEEE
Martin Marietta Corporation
Denver, Colo. 80201

**Abstract**

**Optimization of the bandwidth of a turnaround transponder is carried out for weak signals at the transponder receiver. Optimum transponder bandwidth is found to be around $0.7T^{-1}$, where $T$ is the period of one element of the ranging code. Linear transponders are compared with transponders having baseband limiting. Phase modulation is assumed. It is shown that, for weak signals, linear transponders are preferable for a partitioning of the transponder transmitted power giving (carrier power)/(total power) > 0.43, while baseband limiters are preferred for (carrier power)/(total power) < 0.43.**

Manuscript received April 5, 1971; revised July 19, 1971.

**Symbols and Abbreviations**

| | |
|---|---|
| AGC | automatic gain control |
| $B_H$ | transponder filter noise bandwidth (two sided) |
| $c(t)$ | ranging code |
| FOM | transponder figure of merit |
| $G(s)$ | transfer function, ground station code filter |
| $H(s)$ | transfer function, transponder filter |
| IF | intermediate frequency |
| $K_m$ | scaling factor on modulator input signal |
| $L_{IM}$ | intermodulation loss |
| $L_L$ | limiter loss |
| $L_F$ | total system loss due to filtering |
| $N_M$ | noise power after transponder filtering |
| $N_{0G}$ | noise spectral density, ground receiver |
| $N_{0T}$ | noise spectral density, transponder receiver |
| $P_C$ | transponder transmitter power allocated to carrier |
| $P_R$ | relayed ranging signal power, not including noise |
| $P_{R1}$ | received signal strength at the transponder, ranging sidebands |
| $P_S$ | transponder transmitter power allocated to the ranging channel, including relayed noise |
| $P_T$ | total transponder transmitted power |
| PN | pseudonoise |
| PSK | phase-shift keying |
| $R_{\tilde{c}\hat{c}}(\tau)$ | cross-correlation function of filtered ranging sequence with filtered ground station sequence |
| $S_M$ | signal power after transponder filtering |
| SNR | signal-to-noise ratio |
| $T$ | period of one element of ranging code |
| $T_I$ | integration time, ground station correlator |
| $W_H$ | normalized transponder filter noise bandwidth (one sided), $\frac{1}{2} B_H T$ |
| $\phi$ | phase error, ground receiver coherent reference |
| $\sigma_m$ | rms value, signal plus noise, transponder modulator input. |

## Introduction

Spacecraft tracking with PN ranging is used in a number of tracking networks. Considerable analysis has been done on these systems [1]-[6], but the results given herein do not appear to have been published previously.

The two general types of transponders that have been considered are the turnaround transponder and the regenerative transponder. The former relays the noisy received uplink sequence using detection of the uplink baseband followed by low-pass filtering and remodulation onto the downlink carrier. Phase modulation is used on both the uplink and downlink. The latter locks a local sequence generator onto the received uplink sequence by correlation techniques and then transmits the regenerated sequence. While the regenerative approach gives improved performance, complexity of the transponder has discouraged its use.

Reprinted from *IEEE Trans. Aerosp. Electron. Syst.*, vol. AES-8, pp. 68–72, Jan. 1972.

This paper considers the optimization of a turnaround transponder. The objective of the optimization is to minimize the amount of time required to make a ranging fix, assuming fixed transponder transmitter power. The optimization consists of the selection of a transponder bandwidth and a comparison between three transponder receiver configurations, a linear receiver, a receiver with an IF limiter, and a receiver having a baseband hard limiter on its detected output. Uplink SNRs much smaller than unity are assumed. These very weak signals could be encountered on missions to the outer planets or on planetary entry, lander, or balloon missions where the vehicle does not have a high-gain antenna.

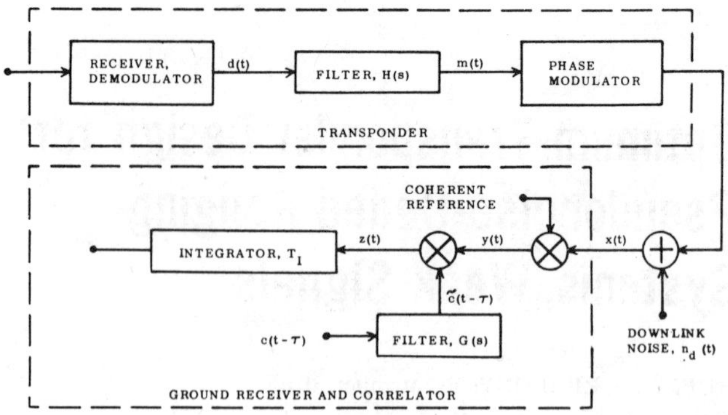

Fig. 1. Turnaround ranging system.

**Linear or AGC Receiver**

The effects of transponder filtering that must be evaluated include loss of signal power due to filtering, loss in performance due to the ground correlator mismatch with the filtered signal, and loss in resolution of the ranging waveform due to filtering of its high-frequency components. In general, however, these components of the system loss are not separable, but must be computed together.

Fig. 1 shows the assumed system. A binary PN ranging sequence $c(t)$ is assumed. The demodulated signal in the transponder is low-pass filtered by $H(s)$ prior to remodulation onto the downlink carrier. The ground station is modeled as demodulator followed by a correlator, with negligible precorrelator filtering. Filtering $G(s)$ of the locally generated binary sequence $c(t - \tau)$ used for correlation is allowed. If $G(s)$ is equal to $H(s)$, the ground receiver is matched to the incoming signal.

An expression for the performance figure of merit for this system, to be maximized by selection of $H(s)$ and $G(s)$, is derived in the Appendix. The result is given in (19). The derivation is due to Tausworthe [7]. It is valid for arbitrary $G$ and $H$ and for any transponder SNR. This paper considers only weak signals at the transponder and is further limited to the matched ground receiver case $G = H$. These two limitations permit a simplification of (19) to

$$\mathrm{FOM}_H = \frac{A\left[\frac{T}{2\pi}\int_{-\infty}^{\infty}\left(\frac{\sin(\omega T/2)}{(\omega T/2)}\right)^4\left(\frac{\omega T}{2}\right)^2 |H(j\omega)|^2\, d\omega\right]^2}{W_H\left[\frac{T}{2\pi}\int_{-\infty}^{\infty}\left(\frac{\sin(\omega T/2)}{(\omega T/2)}\right)^2 |H(j\omega)|^2\, d\omega\right]}. \tag{1}$$

$W_H$ is the one-sided transponder filter noise bandwidth normalized by $T^{-1}$,

$$W_H = \frac{T}{2\pi}\int_0^{\infty} |H(j\omega)|^2\, d\omega.$$

The normalizing constant

$$A = \frac{\frac{T}{2\pi}\int_{-\infty}^{\infty}\left(\frac{\sin(\omega T/2)}{(\omega T/2)}\right)^2 d\omega}{\left[\frac{T}{2\pi}\int_{-\infty}^{\infty}\left(\frac{\sin(\omega T/2)}{(\omega T/2)}\right)^4\left(\frac{\omega T}{2}\right)^2 d\omega\right]^2} \cong 0.421$$

is selected so that $\mathrm{FOM}_H$ is equal to $L_F W_H^{-1}$, where $L_F$ is the total system loss factor due to filtering and correlation distinguishability. This is done so that $L_F$, which is useful for link calculations, can be readily computed from the curves in Fig. 2. This normalization forces $\mathrm{FOM}_H$ to be asymptotic to $W_H^{-1}$ for large $W_H$, where $L_F$ approaches unity.

$\mathrm{FOM}_H$ has been computed versus $W_H$ for the following low-pass filters: rectangular, Gaussian, and single-pole RC. A calculation was also made for an unfiltered receiver, $G(s) = 1$, and a rectangular transponder filter. Results are shown in Fig. 2. Optimum noise bandwidth for these filters ranges from 0.61 to 0.76 $T^{-1}$. Relative performance of these filters, when optimized, is given by their peak values of $\mathrm{FOM}_H$. These values vary widely, with the rectangular filter giving the best performance and the single-pole the poorest.

The intermodulation loss given by a transponder using a linear receiver must be determined in order to compare this type of transponder with one employing baseband hard limiting of the detected and filtered signal at the downlink modulator input. It will be assumed that the downlink consists only of the carrier and the noisy ranging signal, and no other subcarriers.

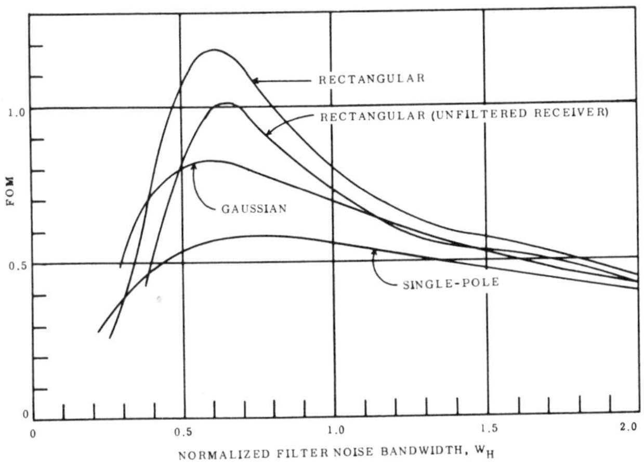


Fig. 2. Figure of merit for various filters.

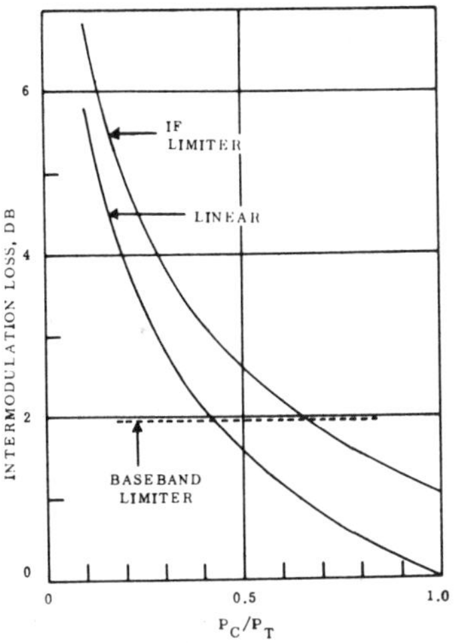


Fig. 3. Intermodulation loss, weak signals.

Given a premodulator SNR, $\text{SNR}_M = S_M/N_M \ll 1$, the modulator input $m(t)$ will have a Gaussian distribution. Its rms amplitude

$$\sigma_m = K_m(S_M + N_M)^{1/2} \tag{2}$$

is scaled by $K_m$ to give a specified partitioning of power between the carrier and the sidebands. The equations describing this partitioning for Gaussian modulating signals are

$$\frac{P_C}{P_T} = \exp(-\sigma_m^2) \tag{3a}$$

$$\frac{P_S}{P_T} = \sigma_m^2 \exp(-\sigma_m^2) \tag{3b}$$

where $P_C$ is carrier power, $P_S$ is signal power, and $P_T$ is total power (from [8, eq. (21)]).

The ranging signal power $P_R$ is $S_M/(S_M + N_M)$ of $P_S$, which gives

$$\frac{P_R}{P_T} = K_m^2 S_M \exp(-\sigma_m^2). \tag{4}$$

The intermodulation loss $L_{\text{IM}}$ is defined by

$$\frac{P_R}{P_T} = \left(1 - \frac{P_C}{P_T}\right)\left(\frac{S_M}{S_M + N_M}\right) L_{\text{IM}} \tag{5a}$$

$$\cong \left(1 - \frac{P_C}{P_T}\right) \frac{S_M}{N_M} L_{\text{IM}} \quad \text{(weak signal).} \tag{5b}$$

The carrier power will generally be fixed by the carrier-lock requirements of the ground receiver, so it is desirable to have an expression for $L_{\text{IM}}$ as a function of $P_C/P_T$. This is found by equating (4) and (5a) and substituting for $\sigma_m$ using (2), giving

$$L_{\text{IM}} = \frac{P_C}{P_T - P_C} \ln\left(\frac{P_T}{P_C}\right). \tag{6}$$

This is plotted versus $P_C/P_T$ in Fig. 3. The loss with IF limiting, 1.05 dB greater (from [9]), is also plotted in Fig. 3.

**Baseband Limiter Receiver**

Baseband limiting will cause some signal suppression for weak signals. On the other hand, it reduces the statistics of the modulating signal to those of a square wave, permitting a PSK modulation that is free of intermodulation loss. Therefore, for circumstances under which the intermodulation loss given by a nonlimited modulating signal is greater than the limiter loss, baseband limiting would be advantageous.

For baseband limiting,

$$\frac{P_S}{P_T} = \left(1 - \frac{P_C}{P_T}\right)\left(\frac{S_M L_L}{S_M L_L + N_M}\right) \tag{7a}$$

$$\cong \left(1 - \frac{P_C}{P_T}\right) \frac{S_M}{N_M} L_L \quad \text{(weak signals)} \tag{7b}$$

where $L_L$ is the limiter loss and $S_M$ and $N_M$ are now the signal and noise powers at the limiter input. It can be seen by comparing these to (5) that intermodulation loss and limiter loss are interchangeable only in the weak-signal limit. For stronger signals, the effects of limiter loss are suppressed.

Given a very weak baseband signal of arbitrary form in Gaussian noise at the input to a hard limiter, the signal or $S \times S$ component of the output will be an undistorted replica of the input signal, and the output SNR will be degraded by $2/\pi = 1.96$ dB below the input SNR. This can be inferred from results given in [10]. Therefore, in the weak-signal limit, the filtering and correlation losses used in the linear case can be retained, and the comparison between a linear and a hard-limiting receiver reduces to a comparison between the limiter loss of 1.96 dB and the intermodulation loss. For $P_C/P_T$ giving an intermodulation loss in the linear case greater than 1.96 dB, baseband limiting would be preferred. From Fig. 3, this occurs for downlink $P_C/P_T < 0.43$. Comparing baseband limiting with IF limiting, the former would be preferred for $P_C/P_T < 0.66$.

## Conclusions

Optimization of a turnaround ranging transponder has been examined in the limit of very weak received signal strength at the transponder. It is shown that the optimum transponder noise bandwidth is around 0.7 $T^{-1}$. System performance is dependent on the type of filter selected. Three types of filters, rectangular, Gaussian, and single-pole, were examined. The rectangular filter was found to give the best performance of the three filter types examined.

A comparison was also made between a linear transponder receiver, a receiver with an IF limiter, and a receiver having a baseband hard limiter on its detected output. These comparisons were made as a function of the ratio of carrier power to total power on the downlink $P_C/P_T$. It was found that a baseband limiter is preferred over an IF limiter for $P_C/P_T < 0.66$ and over a linear transponder for $P_C/P_T < 0.43$.

## Appendix

### Figure of Merit for Turnaround Transponder Filter

Given the system sketched in Fig. 1, it is desired to specify $\text{FOM}_{G,H}$ to be maximized by selection of $G(s)$ and $H(s)$. The binary PN ranging code is $c(t) = \pm 1$. The derivation of $\text{FOM}_{G,H}$ given herein is due to Tausworthe [7].

Following Fig. 1, the transponder demodulator output is $d(t) = \sqrt{P_{R1}}\, c(t) + n_1(t)$, where $P_{R1}$ is the received uplink power in the ranging sidebands. $n_1(t)$ is white, with a two-sided spectral density $N_{0T}$. $d(t)$ is filtered by $H(s)$, giving $m(t) = \sqrt{P_{R1}}\, \hat{c}(t) + \hat{n}_1(t)$. The post-filter noise power $N_M$ is

$$N_M = N_{0T} \int_{-\infty}^{\infty} |H(j\omega)|^2 \frac{d\omega}{2\pi} = B_H N_{0T} \tag{8}$$

where $B_H$ is the two-sided noise bandwidth of $H(s)$.

The post-filter signal power $S_M$ is

$$S_M = P_{R1} \int_{-\infty}^{\infty} S_{cc}(\omega)\, |H(j\omega)|^2\, d\omega \tag{9}$$

where $S_{cc}(\omega)$ is the spectrum of $c(t)$,

$$S_{cc}(\omega) = \frac{T}{2\pi}\left(\frac{\sin(\omega T/2)}{(\omega T/2)}\right)^2. \tag{10}$$

The assumption that $c(t)$ is of infinite duration, implicit in this spectrum, is justified because the ground station correlator integration time $T_I$ is much greater than $T$.

The premodulator scaling factor on $m(t)$, $K_m$ is selected to give a specified carrier power, using (2) and (3a). This gives

$$K_m = \frac{(\ln (P_T/P_C))^{1/2}}{(S_M + N_M)^{1/2}} \tag{11}$$

where $P_C/P_T$ is the desired power split.

The resulting modulated downlink signal plus the downlink noise $n_2(t)$ is the ground receiver input,

$$x(t) = \sqrt{2P_T}\, \cos\, [\omega_0 t + \theta + K_m m(t)] + n_d(t).$$

Sinusoidal phase demodulation by $\sqrt{2}\sin\,[w_0\, t + \hat{\theta}]$ gives

$$y(t) = \sqrt{P_T}\, \sin\, [K_m m(t) + \phi] + n_2(t)$$

where the phase error $\phi = \theta - \hat{\theta}$. $n_2(t)$ is white and has the same spectral density as $n_d(t)$, $N_{0G}$.

Multiplication by the filtered code $\tilde{c}(t-\tau)$ gives

$$z(t) = \tilde{c}(t-\tau)\left\{\sqrt{P_T}\, \sin\, [K_m m(t) + \phi] + n_2(t)\right\}.$$

Assuming that the phase error $\phi$ is small, that $n_2(t) \gg K_m \hat{n}_1(t)$, and that $K_m\sqrt{P_{R1}}\, \hat{c}(t)$ is small, the preceding equation reduces to

$$z(t) \cong K_m \sqrt{P_T P_{R1}}\, \tilde{c}(t-\tau)\hat{c}(\tau)(\cos\phi) + n(t).$$

$n(t) = n_2(t)\,\tilde{c}(t-\tau)$ is white, with spectral density

$$S_{nn}(j\omega) = N_{0G} \int_{-\infty}^{\infty} S_{cc}(\omega)\, |G(j\omega)|^2\, d\omega. \tag{12}$$

The integrator mean value is given by

$$\overline{z(\tau)} = K_m \sqrt{P_T P_{R1}}\ \overline{\tilde{c}(t-\tau)\hat{c}(\tau)}\ \overline{(\cos\phi)}. \tag{13}$$

The cross-correlation function

$$R_{\tilde{c}\hat{c}}(\tau) \triangleq \overline{\tilde{c}(t-\tau)\hat{c}(\tau)}$$

is equal to the transform of the cross-power spectrum of $\tilde{c}$ and $\hat{c}$,

$$R_{\tilde{c}\hat{c}}(\tau) = \int_{-\infty}^{\infty} S_{cc}(\omega)\, H(j\omega)\, G(-j\omega)\, e^{j\tau\omega}\, d\omega. \tag{14}$$

Substituting (11) and (14) into (13) gives

$$\overline{z(\tau)} = \frac{\sqrt{P_T P_{R1}}(\ln (P_T/P_C))^{1/2}\overline{(\cos\phi)}}{(S_M + N_M)^{1/2}} R_{\tilde{c}\hat{c}}(\tau). \tag{15}$$

Assuming clock synchronization, the code synchronization procedure uses sequential comparisons of the integrator outputs for values of $\tau$ separated by one clock period. The SNR for distinguishability of the correct value of $\tau(\tau = 0)$ is

$$\text{SNR}_D = \frac{(\overline{z(0)} - \overline{z(T)})^2\, T_I}{S_{nn}(j\omega)}. \tag{16}$$

We define

$$\Delta R \triangleq R_{\tilde{c}\hat{c}}(0) - R_{\tilde{c}\hat{c}}(T)$$

$$= \int_{-\infty}^{\infty} S_{cc}(\omega)\, H(j\omega)\, G(-j\omega)(1 - e^{jT\omega})\, d\omega. \tag{17}$$

Substituting (12), (15), and (17) into (16) gives

$$\mathrm{SNR}_D = \frac{P_T P_{R1} (\ln (P_T/P_C)) \overline{(\cos \phi)}^{\,2}\, T_I}{S_{nn}(j\omega)(S_M + N_M)} (\Delta R)^2 = \frac{P_T (\ln (P_T/P_C)) (\cos \phi)^{\,2}\, T_I}{N_{0G}} \mathrm{FOM}_{G,H}. \tag{18}$$

The figure of merit,

$$\mathrm{FOM}_{G,H} = \frac{\left[ \int_{-\infty}^{\infty} S_{cc}(\omega) H(j\omega) G(-j\omega)(1 - e^{jT\omega})\, d\omega \right]^2}{\left[ \int_{-\infty}^{\infty} S_{cc}(\omega) |G(j\omega)|^2\, d\omega \right] \left[ \int_{-\infty}^{\infty} S_{cc}(\omega) |H(j\omega)|^2\, d\omega + (B_H N_{0T}/P_{R1}) \right]} \tag{19}$$

is the quantity to be maximized by selection of $G$ and $H$.

### References


[1] "Transponder ranging system," Jet Propulsion Lab., California Institute of Technology, Pasadena, JPL Space Program Summary 37-14, vol. 1, pp. 75-99, January-February 1962.

[2] J.J. Spilker, "Delay-lock tracking of binary signals," *IRE Trans. Space Electron. Telem.*, vol. SET-9, March 1963.

[3] S.W. Golomb *et al., Digital Communications.* Englewood Cliffs, N.J.: Prentice-Hall, 1964, ch. 6.

[4] W.J. Gill, "A comparison of delay-lock tracking-loop implementations," *IEEE Trans. Aerospace and Electronic Systems*, vol. AES-2, pp. 415-424, July 1966.

[5] TRW Systems, Inc., Final Design Rept., SGLS, Contract AF04 (695)-610, February 1, 1967.

[6] J.H. Painter, "Designing pseudorandom coded ranging systems," *IEEE Trans. Aerospace and Electronic Systems*, vol. AES-3, pp. 14-27, January 1967.

[7] R.C. Tausworthe, personal communication.

[8] W.C. Lindsey, "Design of block-coded communication systems," *IEEE Trans. Communication Technology*, vol. COM-15, pp. 525-534, August 1967.

[9] W.B. Davenport, "Signal-to-noise ratios in bandpass limiters," *J. Appl. Phys.*, vol. 24, p. 720, June 1953.

[10] N.M. Blachman, "The signal X signal, noise X noise, and signal X noise output of a nonlinearity," *IEEE Trans. Information Theory*, vol. IT-14, pp. 21-27, January 1968.

# Part IX
# RF Effects

RF effects on spread spectrum systems are often not considered in an overall system design, on the basis that the systems are designed to operate in the presence of large interfering signals. "What could a little bit of nonoptimum signal path do to the operation?" is a question often asked. Unfortunately, the answer is "quite a lot." In fact, spread spectrum signals are probably much more vulnerable to the processes that occur within the systems that generate and process them than to anything that a deliberate jammer might do. Certainly, in some instances, the internal signal path can cause the system to be more vulnerable to outside interference, and many papers have been devoted to such an event. Three of the papers presented in this part are concerned with the effects of limiting on spread spectrum signals when they are to pass through the limiter along with a strong interference signal. Le Fande's paper discusses the effect of phase nonlinearities on spread spectrum systems.

Cahn's paper shows the important result that the interference-to-signal ratio experienced by a signal, when the interference is much larger than the signal, increases by 6 dB (to the detriment of the signal) when the two are passed through a bandpass limiter. Such bandpass limiters are often employed in satellite repeaters, and this is the problem addressed by Kwan's paper, which suggests an important form of quadriphase modulation (called double binary in Kwan's paper) to help in overcoming some of the probelms of such limiting. Kwan's primary emphasis is on bandlimiting the signal, but quadriphase modulation is also useful where the spread spectrum signal must pass through a limiting stage along with an interfering signal. For this reason, satellite spread spectrum signals are almost always quadriphase, as are other spread spectrum signals that are expected to be processed in an amplitude-nonlinear stage.

Anderson and Wintz's paper extends the analysis of limited spread spectrum signals to multiple access systems and discusses the effects of the codes used on the operation. It is worthwhile to note that those same communications satellite spread spectrum signals that pass through a limiting satellite are often also multiple access signals. Thus this paper is of significant interest.

Sevy also discusses signal processing that is of specific interest to spread spectrum system designers, extending his work to analysis of biphase or quadriphase signals when limited along with carrier coherent and noncoherent interference.

There are other effects that are of interest to the designer, though they are less well documented than the limiting effect. Doubling a biphase direct sequence signal wipes out the information, for instance, and one is left with nothing but a twice-frequency carrier. Such effects are documented in the papers listed.

## OTHER PAPERS OF INTEREST


1) J. M. Aein, "On the output power division in a captured hard-limiting repeater," *IEEE Trans, Commun. Technol.*, June 1966.
2) N. M. Blackman, "The output signal-to-noise ratio of a bandpass limiter," *IEEE Trans. Aerosp. Electron Syst.*, July 1968.
3) R. S. Elliott, Pulse waveform degradation due to dispersion in waveguide," *IRE Trans. Microwave Theory Tech.*, Oct. 1957.
4) I. Jacobs, "The effects of video clipping on the performance of an active satellite PSK communication system," *IEEE Trans. Commun. Technol.*, June 1965.
5) R. L. Kirlin, "Hard-limiter intermodulation with low input signal-to-noise ratio," *IEEE Trans. Commun. Technol.*, Aug. 1967.
6) P. D. Shaft, "Limiting of several signals and its effect on communication system performance," *IEEE Trans. Commun. Technol.*, Dec. 1965.
7) H. Staras, "The propagation of wide-band signals through the atmosphere," *Proc. IRE*, July 1961.
8) Kwon, S. Y. and R. S. Simpson "Effect of hard limiting on a quadrature PSK signal," *IEEE Trans. Commun. Syst.*, July 1963.

# A Note on Signal-to-Noise Ratio in Band-Pass Limiters*

CHARLES R. CAHN†, MEMBER, IRE

*Summary*—**A simplified analysis is presented to explain physically the change of signal-to-interference ratio which occurs in a band-pass limiter. The analysis utilizes the concept of sideband resolution into symmetric and anti-symmetric parts and considers only the asymptotic case where the signal-to-interference ratio is small in comparison with unity. Wide-band correlation-detection systems are discussed, as well as ordinary band-pass systems.**

**The important conclusion is reached that the degradation is highly dependent on the statistics of the interference amplitude fluctuations. However, when the signal is weak compared to the interference, the maximum possible degradation is 6 db and occurs for constant-amplitude interference.**

**Degradation with noise interference in a wide-band correlation-detection system has been obtained for arbitrary signal and noise bandwidths. It is found that the degradation ranges between 0.6 db and 1.0 db, the latter figure being for the case where the signal bandwidth is greater than approximately three times the noise bandwidth.**

## Introduction

THE EFFECT of an ideal band-pass limiter on signal-to-noise ratio has been rigorously analyzed[1] for the case of a sine wave in Gaussian noise interference. The results indicate that the input signal-to-noise ratio is degraded only by a numerical factor close to unity, the maximum degradation being $4/\pi$ (1.0 db) for signal-to-noise ratios much less than unity (0 db). This basic result has been extended[2] to allow calculation of the effect of the band-pass limiter on signal detectability, assuming a weak signal-to-noise ratio at the limiter input and Gaussian noise interference. The results show that the limiter produces a very small loss in signal detectability; for example, the factor is only 1.16 (0.6 db) for a wide-band rectangular noise spectrum.

The analyses referred to in the above paragraph do not admit an easily grasped physical picture which shows clearly why the desired signal in the presence of strong interference is not highly suppressed by the nonlinear action of the limiter. Furthermore, the analyses are valid only for Gaussian noise interference and do not present expected performance for arbitrary interference statistics. A further limitation is the restriction that the interference bandwidth be much wider than the signal bandwidth.

It is the purpose of this paper to present a simple analysis which, while applicable only for the case of a signal much weaker than the interference, does provide a simple physical picture and does not have the limitations mentioned above. The analysis will lead to a degradation factor which relates the output signal-to-interference ratio to the input ratio. However, as in the analyses mentioned,[1,2] only long-term averages are considered. It is, of course, recognized that short-term fluctuations can be significant in many practical situations where the application of a limiter might be considered. In addition, the interference is assumed noncoherent with the signal. A special analysis is required to treat coherent interference, which can greatly suppress the desired signal in certain cases.

The use of signal-to-interference ratio as an indication of system performance is common, in practice, for simplicity and is adopted here for this reason. It is, of course, true that the problem of signal detection has been studied extensively, and a more accurate and general statistical detection theory has been evolved to replace the simple criterion of signal-to-interference ratio.[3]

## Case of Two Sine Waves

The case which serves as the basis for simple analysis of more general inputs is that of two sine waves. For this case, the limiter input may be expressed as $A_1[\cos \omega_1 t + a \cos \omega_2 t]$, where $a$ denotes the amplitude ratio and is less than unity. The output of an ideal band-pass limiter, which removes the amplitude modulation without distorting the phase modulation,[4] is obtained by dividing the input by the instantaneous envelope, yielding

$$\frac{A_1[\cos \omega_1 t + a \cos \omega_2 t]}{A_1\sqrt{1 + a^2 + 2a \cos (\omega_1 - \omega_2)t}} = \cos \omega_1 t + \frac{a}{2} \cos \omega_2 t$$

$$- \frac{a}{2} \cos (2\omega_1 - \omega_2)t + \begin{array}{l}\text{terms proportional to}\\ \text{higher powers of } a.\end{array} \qquad (1)$$

It is seen from (1) that the limiter suppresses the weaker signal, relative to the stronger signal, by an amplitude factor of 2 (6db) and produces cross-modulation components, only one of which is of significant amplitude. In addition, the phase of each of the two signals is not affected by the limiter.

The above result, obtained by a series expansion method, is more easily established by considering the weaker signal as a sideband of the stronger signal and using the concept of symmetric and anti-symmetric sidebands.[5] It

* Received by the PGIT, May 3, 1960; revised manuscript received, July 19, 1960.

† Bissett-Berman Corp., Los Angeles, Calif. Formerly with Space Tech. Labs., Inc., Los Angeles, Calif.

[1] W. B. Davenport, "Signal-to-noise ratios in band-pass limiters," *J. Appl. Phys.*, vol. 24, pp. 720–727; June, 1953.

[2] R. Manasse, R. Price, and R. M. Lerner, "Loss of signal detectability in band-pass limiters," IRE Trans. on Information Theory, vol. IT-4, pp. 34–38; March, 1958.

[3] D. Van Meter and D. Middleton, "Modern statistical approaches to reception in communication theory," IRE Trans. on Information Theory, no. PGIT-4, pp. 119–145; September, 1954.

[4] W. B. Davenport and W. L. Root, "Introduction to the Theory of Random Signals and Noise," McGraw-Hill Book Co., Inc., New York, N. Y., p. 288; 1958.

[5] S. Goldman, "Frequency Analysis, Modulation and Noise," McGraw-Hill Book Co., Inc., New York, N. Y., pp. 167–181; 1948.

Reprinted from *IEEE Trans. Inform. Theory*, vol. IT-7, pp. 39–43, Jan. 1961.

is easily shown that the symmetric sidebands produce amplitude modulation only, and to a first approximation for weak sidebands, the anti-symmetric sidebands produce phase modulation only. Since the ideal band-pass limiter suppresses the amplitude modulation, only the carrier and the anti-symmetric sidebands are retained in the limiter output. The first-order terms on the right side of (1) are observed to be exactly these components. This approach may be generalized to include a multiplicity of frequency components about a single strong carrier. Each component is found to be independently affected by the limiter to the first approximation and, accordingly, is suppressed by an amplitude factor of 2 and is unchanged in phase.

Since the relative amplitudes and phases of the various frequency components of the desired signal are unchanged despite strong sine wave interference, the significant observation is made that the limiter output contains an undistorted replica of the desired signal. In fact, this conclusion applies even if the sine wave interference is phase modulated, and explains physically why the desired signal is not highly suppressed by the strong interference.

### Case of a Sine Wave and Strong Gaussian Noise Interference

If the interference is Gaussian noise and strong compared to the sine wave, it may be considered as a modulated carrier. The input to the limiter then may be expressed as

$$\text{input} = A_n \cos(\omega_1 t + \theta_n) + \sqrt{2S} \cos \omega_2 t, \tag{2}$$

in which the phase $\theta_n$ of the noise interference is random and the amplitude $A_n$ has a Rayleigh distribution. For simplicity, $\omega_1$ and $\omega_2$ are assumed unequal, although a more complicated argument can be used if $\omega_1 = \omega_2$ to yield the same result. For a fixed noise amplitude $A_n$, the sine wave, being a weak sideband, gives rise to two output sine waves of equal amplitude, one of which is at the frequency $\omega_2$ and in phase with the input sine wave. The other, at the frequency $2\omega_1 - \omega_2$, has the random phase of the noise. Although both output sine waves have the amplitude $\sqrt{S}/\sqrt{2}\,A_n$, there will be no average output at the frequency $2\omega_1 - \omega_2$, because of the random phasing.

The average amplitude (or steady component) of the sine wave output at the frequency $\omega_2$ is obtained by averaging over all possible noise amplitudes, as follows:

$$\text{Average sine-wave amplitude} = \sqrt{\frac{S}{2}}\,\overline{A_n^{-1}}$$

$$= \sqrt{\frac{S}{2}} \int_0^\infty \frac{1}{A_n} \frac{A_n}{N} e^{-A_n^2/2N}\, dA_n = \sqrt{\frac{\pi}{4}\frac{S}{N}} \tag{3}$$

where the bar denotes an ensemble average and $N$ is the average power of the interference. The output noise essentially has a power of $\frac{1}{2}$, since the limiter output is a phase-modulated sinusoid of unit amplitude and the desired signal component is much smaller than the noise component. Thus, the output signal-to-interference ratio is

$$\left(\frac{S}{N}\right)_{\text{out}} = \frac{\left(\sqrt{\frac{\pi}{4}\frac{S}{N}}\right)^2/2}{1/2} = \frac{\pi}{4}\left(\frac{S}{N}\right)_{\text{in}}, \tag{4}$$

which is identical with the result obtained by Davenport[1] by a rigorous treatment of this case.

It should be noted that with Gaussian noise interference, the average sine wave amplitude in the limiter output can be evaluated in closed form for an arbitrary signal-to-interference ratio directly from (2) divided by the instantaneous envelope.[6,7] Since the total output power from the limiter is always $\frac{1}{2}$, the output signal-to-interference ratio can also be expressed in closed form. However, a similar closed-form result for non-Gaussian interference does not appear to exist, in general.

### Case of a Sine Wave and Strong Non-Gaussian Interference

The calculation made for Gaussian noise (Rayleigh distribution of amplitude) can be generalized to include interference with an arbitrary amplitude distribution, on the assumption that the output interference power is much larger than the output signal power. From (3) and the fact that the output interference power is essentially $\frac{1}{2}$, the output signal-to-interference ratio is found to be

$$\left(\frac{S}{N}\right)_{\text{out}} = \frac{S}{2}\left(\overline{A_n^{-1}}\right)^2. \tag{5}$$

On the other hand, the input signal-to-noise ratio is

$$\left(\frac{S}{N}\right)_{\text{in}} = \frac{2S}{\overline{A_n^2}}. \tag{6}$$

Therefore, the degradation in signal-to-interference ratio due to the limiter is given by the factor

$$\Lambda = \frac{(S/N)_{\text{in}}}{(S/N)_{\text{out}}} = \frac{4}{\overline{A_n^2}\left(\overline{A_n^{-1}}\right)^2}. \tag{7}$$

As an example, (7) may be used to derive a closed-form expression for the degradation when the interference is a combination of a steady component and a Gaussian noise component. The amplitude of this combination has the probability density function

$$p(A_n) = A_n e^{-(A_n^2+2\gamma)/2} I_0(\sqrt{2\gamma}A_n) \tag{8}$$

where $\gamma$ is the power ratio of the steady component and the noise component. If the averages in (7) are evaluated, the result is obtained as follows:

$$1/\Lambda = \frac{\pi}{4}(\gamma + 1)[e^{-\gamma/2} I_0(\gamma/2)]^2, \tag{9}$$

which is graphed in Fig. 1.

[6] N. M. Blackman, "The output signal-to-noise ratio of a power-law device," *J. Appl. Phys.*, vol. 24, pp. 783–785; June, 1953.

[7] I. S. Reed, "An Approximation to the Output Signal-to-noise Ratio of a Signal, Passed through a Band-Pass Limiter, Followed by a Narrow-Band Filter," Lincoln Lab., Mass. Inst. Tech., Lexington, Group Rept. 47.17; June 2, 1958.

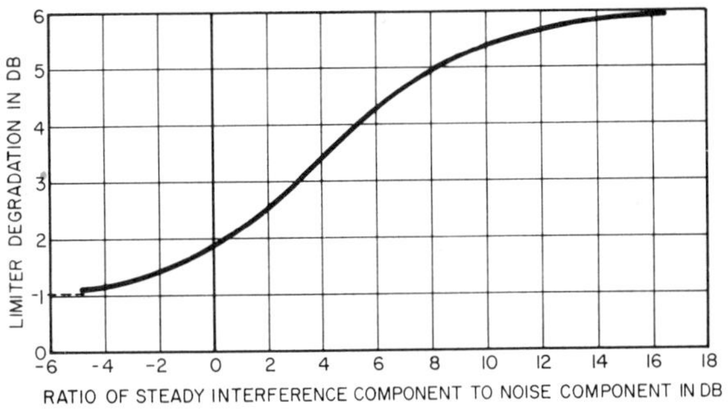


Fig. 1—Degradation for a combination of steady and Gaussian interference.

The graph in Fig. 1 shows how the degradation due to the limiter increases to a limiting value of 6 db as the fluctuation in the interference amplitude decreases. The worst possible degradation (6 db) actually occurs for interference with a constant amplitude, as may be verified by application of the Schwarz inequality.[8] The proof consists of verifying the successive inequalities,

$$\overline{A_n^2}(\overline{A_n^{-1}})^2 \geq (\overline{A_n}\,\overline{A_n^{-1}})^2 \geq 1. \tag{10}$$

The inequalities become equalities only if

$$\overline{A_n^2} = (\overline{A_n})^2, \tag{11}$$

which means that the variance of the probability distribution of amplitude is zero. This occurs only if the amplitude is constant. On the other hand, there is no lower limit; that is, probability distributions with the appropriate behavior at $A_n = 0$ render (7) arbitrarily small.[9] This nonmeaningful result arises from the approximation that the interference should always be strong compared to the sine wave. Furthermore, the signal-to-interference ratio is not an accurate criterion of system performance in such a case.

Since the interference is assumed to be noncoherent, no average output exists at the frequency $2\omega_1 - \omega_2$, and this term is not considered further in the discussion.

## Wide-Band Correlation Systems

A communication system can utilize a wide-band signal with a complex waveform, the objective being to trade bandwidth for interference reduction. Such a system may utilize correlation detection as an effective narrow-band reception technique.[10,11] While correlation detection with a matched reference is an optimal procedure for signals corrupted by additive white Gaussian noise,[12] it still often is used in practice when interference of a more general nature is present. For practical reasons related to gain control, a limiter can be incorporated in the receiver, as indicated in Fig. 2, which illustrates the basic coherent type of correlation processing. It is desired to calculate the degradation introduced by the limiter, determined by comparing the output signal-to-interference ratios obtained with and without the limiter. The restriction is made that the interference is much stronger than the signal, which is the case in practical situations where wide-band signals are used for interference reduction.

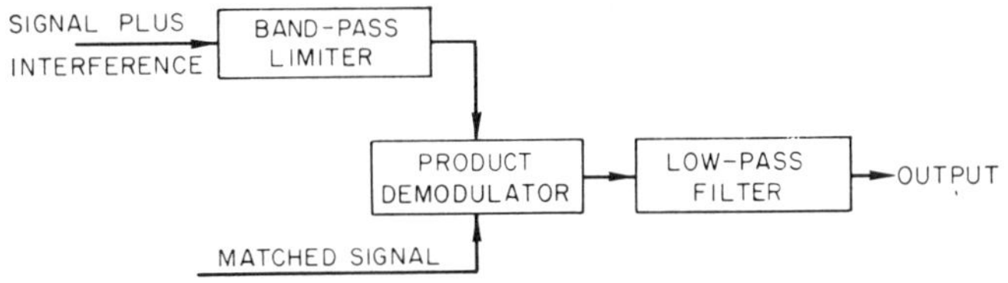


Fig. 2—Coherent correlation system.

Since the assumptions that the interference is strong and the signal is wide-band usually ensure that the output interference from the narrow-band low-pass filter is essentially Gaussian even when the limiter is used, the calculated signal-to-interference ratio degradation can be interpreted directly as a performance degradation.

The input to the receiver may be expressed as $s(t) + n(t)$, where $s(t)$ is the desired signal waveform and $n(t)$ is the interference waveform. The calculation of output signal-to-interference ratio will be performed first in the absence of limiting. Then the product demodulator output is $s^2(t) + s(t)n(t)$, the first term of which is the output signal and the second is the output interference. Thus, the average or dc output is

$$\text{dc output} = \overline{s^2(t)} = S, \tag{12}$$

using $S$ for the average power of the desired signal $s(t)$. The output interference term $s(t)n(t)$ is the product of two independent waveforms, so that its autocorrelation function is the product of the individual autocorrelation functions. The power spectral density of the output interference can therefore be obtained by convolution of the respective power spectral densities, $S(f)$ and $N(f)$, of the input signal and interference. Since the output interference spectrum is essentially constant over the significant passband of the low-pass filter, only the zero-frequency value $N_{out}(0)$ is needed and is given by

$$N_{out}(0) = \int_0^\infty S(f)N(f)\,df, \tag{13}$$

in which one-sided spectral densities are utilized.

[8] Birkhoff and MacLane, "A survey of Modern Algebra," The MacMillan Co., New York, N. Y., p. 183; 1948. The proof using the Schwarz inequality was initially developed by Dr. R. E. Graves, Space Tech. Labs.

[9] For example, distributions with a behavior at zero amplitude of the form $A_n^\alpha$, where $\alpha \leq 0$, cause the second average in (7) to be divergent.

[10] P. E. Green, Jr., "The output signal-to-noise ratio of correlation detectors," IRE Trans. on Information Theory, vol. IT-3, pp. 10-18; March, 1957.

[11] R. Price and P. E. Green, Jr., "A communication technique for multipath channels," Proc. IRE, vol. 46, pp. 555-570; March, 1958.

[12] P. M. Woodward, "Probability and information Theory with Applications to Radar," McGraw-Hill Book Co., Inc., New York, N. Y.; 1953.

The output interference power is equal to the product of $N_{out}(0)$ and the noise bandwidth $b$ of the low-pass filter.[13] Thus, the output signal-to-interference ratio is given by

$$\left(\frac{S}{N}\right)_{out} = \frac{S^2}{b\int_0^\infty S(f)N(f)\,df}, \tag{14}$$

which is a special case of (9) of Green's article.[10] In addition, fluctuations of the signal term $s^2(t)$ in the product demodulator output will also be present in the output of the low-pass filter. This fluctuation has been called self-noise, despite the fact that it is completely predictable from the wave-form $s(t)$.[10] However, when the interference is strong, the self noise is negligible, and for this reason has not been included in (14).

When the interference spectrum is uniform, $N(f) = N_0$, (14) may be shown to reduce to the well-known formula for the peak signal-to-noise ratio from a matched filter.[14] To demonstrate this, the low-pass filter is assumed to be an ideal integrator with a rectangular impulse response of duration $T$.[15] The noise bandwidth of this filter is easily calculated to be $1/2T$, so that (14) becomes

$$\left(\frac{S}{N}\right)_{out} = \frac{2TS^2}{N_0\int_0^\infty S(f)\,df} = \frac{2TS}{N_0} = \frac{2E}{N_0} \tag{15}$$

where $E = TS$ is the energy of the signal over the time interval $T$.

When limiting is performed on the input, the output signal-to-interference ratio becomes dependent on the amplitude distribution of the interference. Since the interference is strong, it is convenient to express the desired signal as a superposition of various frequency components and the interference as a modulated carrier with amplitude $A_n$, as in (2). Comparison of (2) with the first part of (3) shows that the limiter reduces the amplitude of each frequency component of the desired signal by the factor $\overline{A_n^{-1}}/2$, so that the useful dc output amplitude is also reduced by this factor. The output interference power has only a negligible contribution from the desired signal and may be evaluated from knowledge of the spectral density of the interference at the limiter output by an integral similar to (13). This distorted spectral density will be denoted by $N_L(f)$ and has a total power content of $\frac{1}{2}$. The degradation in output signal-to-interference ratio produced by the limiter then may be expressed as

$$\Lambda = \frac{(S/N)_{\text{no limiter}}}{(S/N)_{\text{limiter}}} = \frac{4\int_0^\infty S(f)N_L(f)\,df}{(\overline{A_n^{-1}})^2\int_0^\infty S(f)N(f)\,df}. \tag{16}$$

It should be emphasized at this point that the degradation $\Lambda$ defined by (16) is not, for general interference spectra, a degradation from an optimum detection process, but only an expression of the effect of a limiter in a system using correlation detection with a matched reference.

If $S(f)$ is essentially constant with the value $S(f_0)$ over the significant portions of $N(f)$ and $N_L(f)$ (narrow-band interference), (16) may be approximated as

$$\Lambda = \frac{4S(f_0)\int_0^\infty N_L(f)\,df}{(\overline{A_n^{-1}})^2 S(f_0)\int_0^\infty N(f)\,df} = \frac{4}{(\overline{A_n^{-1}})^2\overline{A_n^2}}, \tag{17}$$

since the integral in the numerator is simply $\frac{1}{2}$, and the integral in the denominator is $\overline{A_n^2}/2$. Eq. (17) is identical with (7). Hence, when a limiter is employed, the maximum degradation with narrow-band interference is 6 db, following the same argument used in connection with (7), and occurs with constant-amplitude interference. Actually, this conclusion is independent of interference bandwidth when the interference amplitude is constant, since $N_L(f)$ is proportional to $N(f)$ (no distortion), so that (16) reduces to a value of 4.

The only other example which will be treated in detail is the case where the interference is Gaussian noise and both noise and signal have rectangular spectra with the same center frequency $f_0$. The bandwidths are denoted by $B_N$ and $B_S$, and the powers by $N$ and $S$, respectively. The spectral density $N_L(f)$ of the interference at the limiter output is indicated in Fig. 3, using a result of Price.[16] The average of $A_n^{-1}$ in the denominator of (16) may be evaluated as shown in (3). The value of the integral in the denominator is either $SN/B_S$ or $SN/B_N$, depending on whether $B_S > B_N$ or $B_S < B_N$. It is then found that the expression for the degradation due to the limiter is either

$$\Lambda = \frac{8}{\pi}\int_{f_0-B_S/2}^{f_0+B_S/2} N_L(f)\,df \qquad (B_S > B_N) \tag{18}$$

or

$$\Lambda = \frac{8B_N}{\pi B_S}\int_{f_0-B_S/2}^{f_0+B_S/2} N_L(f)\,df \qquad (B_S < B_N). \tag{19}$$

Note that the integral in either (18) or (19) specifies the total output interference power contained within the bandwidth $B_S$ of the desired signal.

[13] J. L. Lawson and G. E. Uhlenbeck, "Threshold Signals," McGraw-Hill Book Co., Inc., New York, N. Y., p. 176; 1950.

[14] G. L. Turin, "An introduction to matched filters," IRE Trans. on Information Theory, vol. IT-6, pp. 311–329; June, 1960.

[15] David Middleton, "An Introduction to Statistical Communication Theory," McGraw-Hill Book Co., Inc., New York, N. Y., p. 683; 1960.

[16] R. Price, "A note on the envelope and phase-modulated components of narrow-band Gaussian noise," IRE Trans. on Information Theory, vol. IT-1, pp. 9–15; September, 1955.

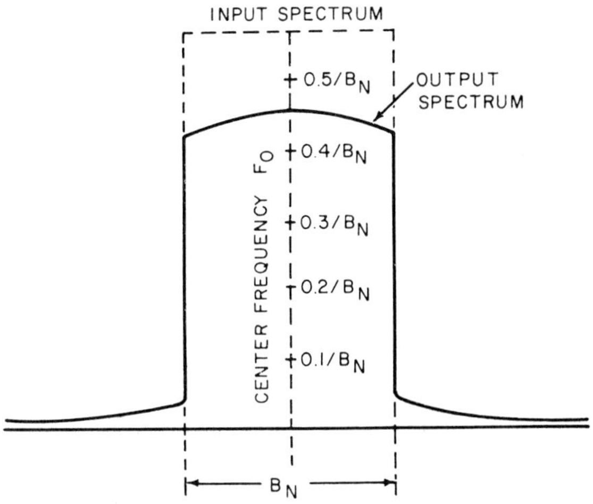


Fig. 3—Output spectrum of band-pass limiter.

Two extremes may be considered. First, let the signal bandwidth be much larger than the noise bandwidth, so that the "tails" of $N_L(f)$ are included in the integral of (18). The integral then is simply $\frac{1}{2}$, and $\Lambda = 4/\pi$ (1.0 db). Second, let the noise bandwidth be much larger than the signal bandwidth, so that (19) becomes

$$\Lambda = \frac{8}{\pi} \frac{B_N}{B_S} B_S(0.456/B_N) = 1.16 \tag{20}$$

or 0.6 db, the result obtained by Manasse, Price, and Lerner,[2] when the signal is assumed at the center of the noise spectrum. The transition between the two extremes is shown in Fig. 4. It is interesting to note that the least degradation occurs when the signal and noise have the same bandwidth, although from a practical point of view the variation with bandwidth is very small.

## Conclusions

The simplified analysis of the effect of an ideal band-pass limiter on signal-to-interference ratio has led to results in agreement with those obtained by more rigorous

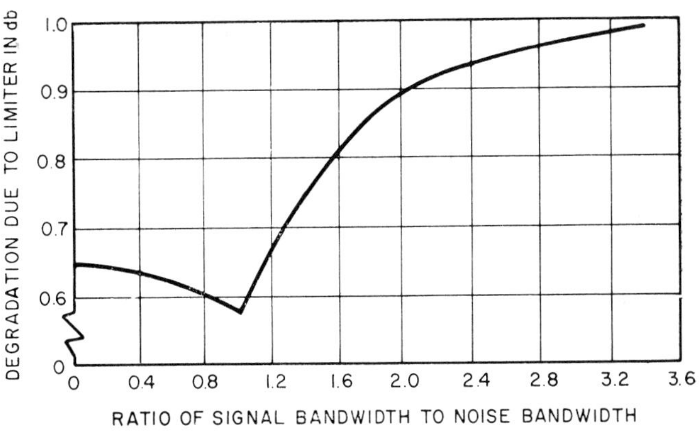


Fig. 4—Degradation in correlation system with Gaussian Interference.

techniques. In addition, the method obtains useful answers for non-Gaussian interference and may be applied to both ordinary band-pass systems and wide-band correlation-detection systems.

The most important conclusion is that the degradation in signal-to-interference ratio due to the presence of a limiter is quite dependent on the statistics of the interference amplitude. However, when the signal-to-interference ratio is low, the worst degradation (6 db) results for constant amplitude interference in both ordinary band-pass and wide-band correlation-detection systems. Amplitude fluctuations will reduce the degradation considerably; for example, the degradation with noise-like interference is about one db. The degradation (in db) may be expected to be negative for highly fluctuating interference (for example, impulsive interference). This indicates an important practical reason for incorporating a limiter into a communication system.

Finally, the result is obtained that with Gaussian noise interference the degradation due to a limiter in a wide-band correlation-detection system does not vary significantly with interference bandwidth. Previous analyses have been restricted to the case of wide-band interference only.

# Analysis of a Spread-Spectrum Multiple-Access System with a Hard Limiter

DOUGLAS R. ANDERSON, MEMBER, IEEE, AND PAUL A. WINTZ, MEMBER, IEEE

REFERENCE: Anderson, D. R., and Wintz, P. A.: ANALYSIS OF A SPREAD-SPECTRUM MULTIPLE-ACCESS SYSTEM WITH A HARD LIMITER,[1] TRW Systems, Redondo Beach, Calif. 90278, and Purdue University, Lafayette, Ind. 47907. Rec'd 10/14/67; revised 5/28/68, 11/12/68, and 1/2/69. Paper 68TP510-COM, approved by the IEEE Space Communication Committee for publication after sponsored presentation at the 1968 National Electronics Conference, Chicago, Ill., under title "A Satellite Communications System Using PN Codes." IEEE TRANS. ON COMMUNICATION TECHNOLOGY, 17-2, April 1969, pp. 285-290.

ABSTRACT: The detectability parameter (signal-to-noise ratio) at the output of a correlation detector is computed when the input is the hard-limited sum of a number of pseudonoise (PN) carriers plus noise. All pseudonoise carriers have the same amplitude and center frequency, but are phase modulated with different PN codes and have independent phase angles. The detectability parameter depends on the repeater bandwidth, the maximum number of channels, the number of active channels, the received signal-to-noise ratio, and the peak of the in- and out-of-phase cross correlations of the PN sequences.

## I. Introduction

ONE WAY to achieve both multiple access and random access in an amplitude limiting satellite communication system and also make efficient use of the satellite repeater is to have all the users simultaneously use the entire repeater bandwidth. This can be accomplished by assigning each user a distinct pseudonoise carrier. Each active user then modulates his message onto his pseudonoise (PN) carrier and transmits it through the satellite repeater to the receiving terminals. Each receiving station employs a phase coherent correlator capable of locking onto any one of the transmitted signals while rejecting the others. Once the receiving station is locked onto one of the PN carriers, the message can be recovered by a correlation detector.

A reasonable performance measure for multiple-access and random-access satellite communications systems is the signal-to-noise ratio (SNR) at the detector output. This parameter, which is also called the detectability parameter, depends on the repeater bandwidth, the maximum number of users (channels), the number of active users (channels), and the received SNR. Attempts to carry out a precise evaluation of the detectability as a function of these parameters have encountered severe mathematical difficulties due to the complexity of the signal at the output of the hard limiter. Aein [9] estimated the detectability parameter under the assumption that the intermodulation products generated in the hard limiter can be modeled by a white Gaussian noise process. In this paper we assume only the statistical independence of the carrier phases and then, by averaging over these phases as well as the receiver noise, determine a bound on the detectability parameter when the phase-coherent correlator is in lock with one of the transmitted signals. As an example we estimate the detectability parameter for the nearly optimum sequences suggested by Anderson [4].

## II. System Model

A model for a multiple-access satellite communication system is presented in Fig. 1. The $n$ active transmitters simultaneously transmit through the hard limiter to $n$ receivers. Each transmitter contains a PN sequence generator and a biphase modulator. The PN sequence generator for transmitter 1 generates the PN sequence $b_1 = b_1(t)$ as illustrated in Fig. 2. The biphase modulator phase modulates the sequence $b_1$ onto the carrier. The remaining $n-1$ transmitters are identical to the first except that a different PN sequence is used for each transmitter, i.e., the $i$th transmitter uses the sequence $b_i = b_i(t)$. As illustrated in Fig. 2, the $n$ transmitters need not be in either chip synchronization or in word synchronization. We do, however, assume that the chip durations $\Delta t$ and the word durations $T = (2^N - 1)\Delta t$ are the same for all transmitters. Hence, all $n$ sequences $b_i$ $(i = 1, \cdots, n)$ are the same length, and all of the transmitted signals occupy the same bandwidth.

The output of the $i$th transmitter is given by

$$s_i(t) = \cos\left[\omega t + b_i \pi + \varphi_i\right] \tag{1}$$

where $\omega$ is the carrier frequency (common to all transmitters), $b_i\pi$ represents the phase transitions due to the synchronization sequence, and $\varphi_i$ is a random phase. The $\varphi_i$ $(i = 1, 2, \cdots, n)$ are assumed to be independent, uniformly distributed random variables.

The $n$ transmitted signals are summed and hard-limited in the repeater so that the input to the receiver is given by

$$x(t) = s(t) + n(t) \tag{2}$$

where $n(t)$ is the receiver noise which we assume to be white with a power per unit bandwidth of $N_0$ W/Hz, and

$$s(t) = \operatorname{sgn} \sum_{i=1}^{n} \cos\left[\omega t + b_i \pi + \varphi_i\right]. \tag{3}$$

[1] This work was supported under NASA Grant NGR 15-005-006.

Reprinted from *IEEE Trans. Commun. Technol.*, vol. COM-17, pp. 285–290, Apr. 1969.

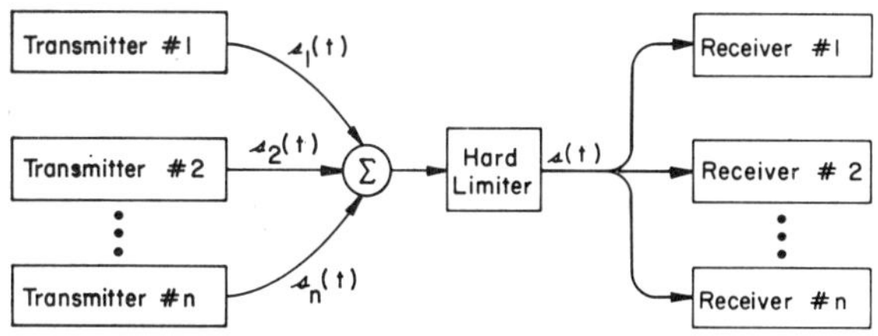


Fig. 1. System model.

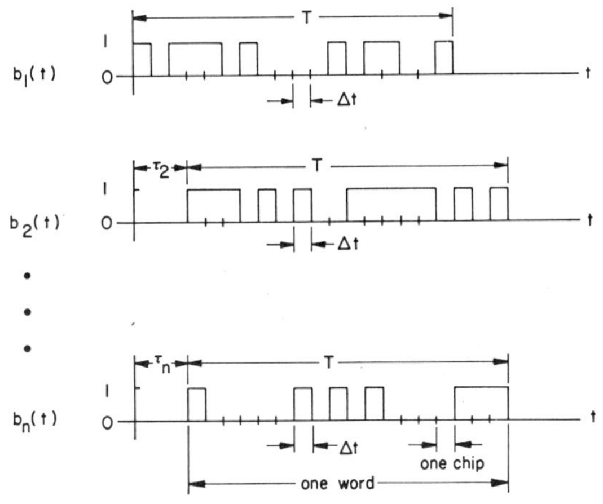


Fig. 2. Typical PN sequences.

Suppose that a typical receiver operates in a coherent mode and has achieved lock with the signal from transmitter 1. The correlator is coherent both in carrier phase and in chip and word synchronization. This is equivalent to assuming the availability of a reference signal

$$r(t) = s_1(t) = \cos [\omega t + b_1\pi + \varphi_1] \tag{4}$$

at the receiver. Hence, the output of the correlation detector is given by

$$\alpha = \frac{1}{T}\int_0^T x(t)r(t)\,dt. \tag{5}$$

In this paper we compute the mean and bound the variance of the random variable $\alpha$. This gives a bound on the detectability parameter (the SNR at the detector output)

$$d^2 = \frac{\bar{\alpha}^2}{\sigma_\alpha^2}, \quad \bar{\alpha} = E\{\alpha\}, \quad \sigma_\alpha^2 = E\{(\alpha - \bar{\alpha})^2\} \tag{6}$$

where $E\{\cdot\}$ is the expectation operator.

## III. Computation of $\bar{\alpha}$ and $\sigma_\alpha^2$

In this section we compute $\bar{\alpha}$ and we bound $\sigma_\alpha^2$. We start by noting that the received signal given by (3) is of the form

$$s(t) = \operatorname{sgn} \sum_{i=1}^{n} \cos [\theta_i], \quad \theta_i = \omega t + b_i\pi + \varphi_i. \tag{7}$$

Now, $\cos(\theta_i)$ is an even function for each $\theta_i$. Furthermore, $\operatorname{sgn} \sum_{i=1}^{n} \cos\theta_i$ is an even function in each $\theta_i$ $(i=1,2,\cdots,n)$ and can, therefore, be written in a Fourier cosine series (see Schumnitzky [14]), i.e.,

$$\begin{aligned} s(t) &= C_{1,0,0,\ldots,0}\cos\theta_1 + C_{0,1,0,\ldots,0}\cos\theta_2 + \cdots \\ &\quad + C_{0,0,\ldots,0,1}\cos\theta_n + \cdots \\ &\quad + C_{r_1,\ldots,r_n}\cos(r_1\theta_1)\cdots\cos(r_n\theta_n) + \cdots. \end{aligned} \tag{8}$$

Hence, when all $n$ transmitters are active, the output of the correlation detector is given by

$$\begin{aligned} \alpha &= \frac{C_{1,0,\ldots,0}}{T}\int_0^T \cos^2[\omega t + b_1(t)\pi + \varphi_1]\,dt \\ &\quad + \frac{C_{0,1,\ldots,0}}{T}\int_0^T \cos[\omega t + b_2(t-\tau_2)\pi + \varphi_2] \\ &\quad \cdot \cos[\omega t + b_1\pi + \varphi_1]\,dt + \cdots \\ &\quad + \frac{C_{0,0,\ldots,1}}{T}\int_0^T \cos[\omega t + b_n(t-\tau_n)\pi + \varphi_n] \\ &\quad \cdot \cos[\omega t + b_1\pi + \varphi_1]\,dt \\ &\quad + \frac{1}{T}\int_0^T (\text{sum of intermodulation products}) \\ &\quad \cdot \cos[\omega t + b_1\pi + \varphi_1]\,dt + \frac{1}{T}\int_0^T n(t) \\ &\quad \cdot \cos[\omega t + b_1\pi + \varphi_1]\,dt. \end{aligned} \tag{9}$$

Note that the reference signal is in phase and in chip and word synchronization with the first signal term, but is in neither phase nor chip synchronization with the other signal terms. For example, in the second term the reference is correlated with a signal term that consists of the last $\tau_2$ seconds of one word and the first $T-\tau_2$ seconds of the succeeding word. Also, the phase of the reference is statistically independent of the phase of the second signal term.

The expectation of $\alpha$ is the sum of the expectations of the terms in (9). For the first term we write

$$\begin{aligned} &E\left\{\frac{C_{1,0,\ldots,0}}{T}\int_0^T \cos^2[\omega t + b_1\pi + \varphi_1]\,dt\right\} \\ &= E\left\{\frac{C_{1,0,\ldots,0}}{T}\int_0^T \frac{1}{2} + \frac{1}{2}\cos[2\omega t + 2b_1\pi + 2\varphi_1]\,dt\right\} \\ &= \frac{1}{2}C_{1,0,\ldots,0} \end{aligned} \tag{10}$$

since the double-frequency term integrates to zero. The second through $n$th terms contain integrals of the form

$$\begin{aligned} I_j &= \int_0^T \cos[\omega t + b_j(t-\tau_j)\pi + \varphi_j]\cos[\omega t + b_1\pi + \varphi_1]\,dt \\ &= \int_0^T \frac{1}{2}\cos[b_j(t-\tau_j)\pi - b_1\pi + \varphi_j - \varphi_1]\,dt \\ &= \frac{1}{2}\cos[\varphi_j - \varphi_1]\int_0^T \cos[b_j(t-\tau_j)\pi - b_1\pi]\,dt \\ &\quad - \frac{1}{2}\sin[\varphi_j - \varphi_1]\int_0^T \sin[b_j(t-\tau_j)\pi - b_1\pi]\,dt \end{aligned} \tag{11}$$

where we have again used the fact that the double-frequency term integrates to zero. For $\varphi_j$ and $\varphi_i$ independent uniformly distributed random variables we find $E\{\cos[\varphi_j-\varphi_1]\}=E\{\sin[\varphi_j-\varphi_1]\}=0$ so that the expectation of the second through $n$th terms of (9) is zero. A similar argument holds for each intermodulation product term. Finally, the expectation of the last term of (9) is zero for zero mean noise. Hence we conclude that

$$\bar{\alpha} = \frac{1}{2} C_{1,0,\ldots,0}. \tag{12}$$

We next compute the variance of $\alpha$. First note that $\sigma_\alpha^2$ can be separated into two parts. The first part is due to the unwanted signal components; we denote this contribution by $\sigma_s^2$. The second part is due to the receiver noise; we denote this contribution by $\sigma_n^2$. Since the receiver noise is independent of the unwanted signal components and has zero mean, the noise-cross-unwanted signal term is zero. Hence $\sigma_\alpha^2=\sigma_s^2+\sigma_n^2$. We first compute $\sigma_s^2$ and then $\sigma_n^2$.

To compute $\sigma_s^2$ we first note that all the cross terms have zero mean. This can be shown by the following argument. By interchanging the normalized time integrations with expectation when finding the expected value of a cross term, we find the expected value of the cross term to be the result of two normalized time integrations with the expected value given by

$$\begin{aligned}\epsilon(t,\tau) = E\{&C_{r_1,\ldots,r_n}\cos[r_1(\omega t + b_1(t)\pi + \varphi_1)]\cdots\\ &\cdot\cos[r_n(\omega t + b_n(t-\tau_n)\pi + \varphi_n)]\\ &\cdot\cos[\omega t + b_1(t)\pi + \varphi_1]C_{r_1',\ldots,r_n'}\\ &\cdot\cos[r_1'(\omega\tau + b_1(\tau)\pi + \varphi_1)]\cdots\\ &\cdot\cos[r_n'(\omega\tau + b_n(\tau-\tau_n)\pi + \varphi_n)]\\ &\cdot\cos[\omega t + b_1(t) + \varphi_1]\}\end{aligned} \tag{13}$$

where neither all $r_i$ nor all $r_i'$ are 0 nor does $r_i=r_i'$ for all $i$.

Now by the independence of the $\varphi_i$ we have the following as a factor of the above whenever $r_i\neq r_i'$

$$E\{\cos[r_i(\omega t + b_i(t-\tau_j)\pi + \varphi_i)] \cdot \cos[r_i'(\omega\tau + b_i(\tau-\tau_i)\pi + \varphi_i)]\}, \quad i>1$$

$$\begin{aligned}E\{&\cos[r_1(\omega t + b_1(t)\pi + \varphi_1)]\cos[\omega t + b_1(t)\pi + \varphi_1]\\ &\cdot\cos[r_1'(\omega\tau + b_1(\tau)\pi + \varphi_1)]\\ &\cdot\cos[\omega\tau + b_1(\tau)\pi + \varphi_1]\}, \quad i=1.\end{aligned} \tag{14}$$

Since both of the last expectations are zero due to the uniform distribution of each $\varphi_i$ except when $|r_1+r_1'|$ or $|r_1-r_1'|$ is 2, $\epsilon(t,\tau)$ is zero. But then it must follow that the cross term in question has a zero expectation. That expectation is the result of integrating $\epsilon(t,\tau)$ with respect to $t$ and $\tau$, which assures a zero result even in the one case where $\epsilon(t,\tau)$ is not identically zero, namely, either $|r_1+r_1'|$ or $|r_1-r_1'|=2$.

Finally, we calculate the expected square of each correlation term $t^2_{r_1,\ldots,r_n}$ in $\sigma_s^2$. Using the same sort of reasoning as we did to reformulate the expectation of an arbitrary pair of correlation cross terms, we get the following expression for $E\{t^2_{r_1,\ldots,r_n}\}$, the mean square of any one of these terms.

$$E\{t^2_{r_1,\ldots,r_n}\} = \frac{1}{[(2^N-1)\Delta t]^2} \cdot \int_0^{(2N-1)\Delta t} dt \int_0^{(2N-1)\Delta t} d\tau\, Y(t,\tau) \tag{15}$$

where

$$\begin{aligned}Y(t,\tau) &= E\{C_{r_1,\ldots,r_n}\cos[r_1(\omega t + b_1(t)\pi + \varphi_1)]\cdots\\ &\quad\cdot\cos[r_n(\omega t + b_n(t-\tau_n)\pi + \varphi_n)]\\ &\quad\cdot\cos[\omega t + b_1(t)\pi + \varphi_1]\\ &\quad\cdot C_{r_1,\ldots,r_n}\cos[r_1(\omega\tau + b_1(\tau)\pi + \varphi_1)]\cdots\\ &\quad\cdot\cos[r_n(\omega\tau + b_n(\tau-\tau_n)\pi + \varphi_n)]\\ &\quad\cdot\cos[\omega\tau + b_1(\tau)\pi + \varphi_1]\} \\ &= C^2_{r_1,\ldots,r_n}\cos[((r_1+1)b_1(t)\cdots + r_nb_n(t-\tau_n))\pi]\\ &\quad\cdot\cos[((r_1+1)b_1(\tau) + \cdots + r_nb_n(\tau-\tau_n))\pi]\\ &\quad\cdot E\{\cos(r_1\omega t + r_1\varphi_1)\cdots\cos(r_n\omega t + r_n\varphi_n)\\ &\quad\cdot\cos(\omega t + \varphi_1)\cos(r_n\omega\tau + r_1\varphi_1)\cdots\\ &\quad\cdot\cos(r_n\omega\tau + r_n\varphi_n)\cos(\omega\tau + \varphi_1)\}.\end{aligned} \tag{16}$$

Then, by the independence of the $\phi_i$, we have

$$\begin{aligned}E\{&\cos(r_1\omega t + r_1\varphi_1)\cdots\cos(r_n\omega t + r_n\varphi_n)\cos(\omega t + \varphi_1)\\ &\cdot\cos(r_1\omega\tau + r_1\varphi_1)\cdots\cos(r_n\omega\tau + r_n\varphi_n)\cos(\omega\tau + \varphi_1)\}\\ &= \sum_{k=-\infty}^{+\infty} p(r_1,\cdots,r_n;k)e^{jk\omega(t-\tau)}\end{aligned} \tag{17}$$

where $p(r_1,\cdots,r_n;k)\geq 0$. Substituting the above in our formula for $Y(t,\tau)$ and, in turn, substituting that expression for $Y(t,\tau)$ into our expression for $E\{t^2_{r_1,\ldots,r_n}\}$, we obtain

$$\begin{aligned}E\{t^2_{r_1,\ldots,r_n}\} &= \frac{C^2_{r_1,\ldots,r_n}}{[(2^N-1)\Delta t]^2}\sum_{k=-\infty}^{+\infty} p(r_1,\cdots,r_n;k)\\ &\quad\cdot\int_0^{(2N-1)\Delta t} e^{jk\omega t}\cos[((r_1+1)b_1(t) + \cdots\\ &\quad + r_nb_n(t-\tau_n))\pi]\,dt\\ &\quad\cdot\int_0^{(2N-1)\Delta t} e^{jk\omega\tau}\cos[((r_1+1)b_1(\tau) + \cdots\\ &\quad + r_nb_n(\tau-\tau_n))\pi]\,d\tau\\ &\leq C^2_{r_1,\ldots,r_n}\sum_{k=-\infty}^{+\infty} p(r_1,\cdots,r_n;k)\\ &\quad\cdot\left|\frac{1}{(2^N-1)\Delta t}\int_0^{(2N-1)\Delta t}\cos[((r_1+1)b_1(t) + \cdots\right.\\ &\quad\left. + r_nb_n(t-\tau_n))\pi]\,dt\right|^2.\end{aligned} \tag{18}$$

Since the carrier frequency $\omega$ is much greater than the modulation bandwidth, we can assume that

$$\left| \int_0^{(2^N-1)\Delta t} e^{jk\omega t} \cos\left[((r_1+1)b_1(t) + \cdots + r_n b_n(t-\tau_n))\pi\right] dt \right|^2$$

has its peak at $k \neq 0$. Hence, combining (16) and (17),[2]

$$\begin{aligned}
\sigma_s^2 &= E\left\{ \left( \sum_{r_1=0}^{\infty} \sum_{r_2=0}^{\infty} \cdots \sum_{r_n=0}^{\infty}{}' t_{r_1,\ldots,r_n} \right)^2 \right\} \\
&= \sum_{r_1=0}^{\infty} \sum_{r_2=0}^{\infty} \cdots \sum_{r_n=0}^{\infty}{}' E\{t^2_{r_1,\ldots,r_n}\} \\
&\leq \sum_{r_1=0}^{\infty} \sum_{r_2=0}^{\infty} \cdots \sum_{r_n=0}^{\infty}{}' C^2_{r_1,\ldots,r_n} \left[ \sum_{k=-\infty}^{+\infty} p(r_1,\cdots,r_n;k) \right] \\
&\quad \cdot \left| \frac{1}{(2^N-1)\Delta t} \int^{(2^N-1)\Delta t} \cos\left[((r_1+1)b_1(t) + \cdots + r_n b_n(t-\tau_n))\pi\right] dt \right|^2 \qquad (19) \\
&= E\left\{ \frac{\omega}{2\pi} \int_0^{2\pi/\omega} dt \left[ \sum_{r_1=0}^{\infty} \sum_{r_2=0}^{\infty} \cdots \sum_{r_n=0}^{\infty}{}' \left| \frac{1}{(2^N-1)\Delta t} \cdot \int_0^{(2^N-1)\Delta t} \cos\left[((r_1+1)b_1(t) + \cdots + r_n b_n(t-\tau_n))\pi\right] dt \right| \cos(r_1\omega t + r_1\varphi_1) \cdots \cos(r_n\omega t + r_n\varphi_n) \cos(\omega t + \varphi_1) \right] \right\}.
\end{aligned}$$

We now define $\pi_c$ to be the peak of the in- and out-of-phase cross correlations of the $n$ PN sequences, i.e.,

$$\pi_c = \max_{r_2,r_3,\ldots,r_n} \left| \frac{1}{(2^N-1)\Delta t} \int_0^{(2^N-1)\Delta t} \cos\left[((r_1+1) \cdot b_1(t) + \cdots + r_n b_n(t-\tau_n))\pi\right] dt \right|. \qquad (20)$$

Therefore,

$$\sigma_s^2 \leq \pi_c^2 E\left\{ \text{power in fundamental of } \sum_{r_1=2}^{\infty} \sum_{r_2=1}^{\infty} \cdots \cdot \sum_{r_n=1}^{\infty} C_{r_1,\ldots,r_n} \cos[r_1(\omega t + \varphi_1)] \cdots \cos[r_n(\omega t + \varphi_n)] \right\}. \qquad (21)$$

[2] $\sum_{r_1=0}^{\infty} \cdots \sum_{r_n=0}^{\infty}{}' f(r_1,\cdots,r_n) = \sum_{r_1=0}^{\infty} \cdots \sum_{r_n=0}^{\infty} f(r_1,\cdots,r_n) - f(1,0,\cdots,0) - f(0,0,\cdots,0).$

Thus

$$\sigma_s^2 \leq \pi_c^2 \left[ \frac{1}{2} C^2_{0,1,0,\ldots,0} + \frac{1}{2} C^2_{0,0,1,0,\ldots,0} + \cdots + \frac{1}{2} C^2_{0,\ldots,0,1} \right] + \pi_c^2 \left[ \begin{matrix} \text{power in fundamental of} \\ \text{intermodulation products} \end{matrix} \right]. \qquad (22)$$

The contribution due to the receiver noise is the mean square value of the last term in (9); a straightforward computation yields

$$\sigma_n^2 = \frac{N_0}{2(2^N-1)\Delta t}. \qquad (23)$$

Therefore, we have

$$\begin{aligned}
\sigma_\alpha^2 &= \sigma_s^2 + \sigma_n^2 \\
&\leq \pi_c^2 \left[ \frac{1}{2} C^2_{0,1,0,\ldots,0} + \frac{1}{2} C^2_{0,0,1,\ldots,0} + \cdots + \frac{1}{2} C^2_{0,\ldots,0,1} \right] \\
&\quad + \pi_c^2 E\left\{ \begin{matrix} \text{power in fundamental of} \\ \text{intermodulation products} \end{matrix} \right\} \\
&\quad + \frac{1}{2} \frac{N_0}{(2^N+1)\Delta t}.
\end{aligned} \qquad (24)$$

We interpret $\bar{\alpha}^2$ as the average power in the "usable" signal component, and $\alpha^2$ as the average power in the remaining signal terms and the receiver noise term. Therefore, the detectability parameter is given by

$$d^2 = \frac{\bar{\alpha}^2}{\sigma_\alpha^2} \geq \frac{\frac{1}{2}\left[\frac{1}{2} C^2_{1,0,\ldots,0}\right]}{\pi_c^2 \left[ \frac{1}{2} C^2_{0,1,\ldots,0} + \cdots + \frac{1}{2} C^2_{0,\ldots,0,1} \right] + \pi_c^2 E\left\{ \begin{matrix} \text{power in fundamental} \\ \text{of modulation product} \end{matrix} \right\} + \frac{1}{2} \frac{N_0}{(2^N-1)\Delta t}}. \qquad (25)$$

But Shaft [6] has shown that

$$\begin{aligned}
\frac{1}{2} C^2_{1,0,\ldots,0} &= \cdots = \frac{1}{2} C^2_{0,\ldots,0,1} \\
&= \frac{1}{n}(0.88) \left[ \begin{matrix} \text{statistical average of total} \\ \text{received power in fundamental} \end{matrix} \right]
\end{aligned} \qquad (26)$$

and that

$$\begin{aligned}
E&\left\{ \begin{matrix} \text{power in fundamental} \\ \text{of modulation product} \end{matrix} \right\} \\
&= (0.12) \left[ \begin{matrix} \text{statistical average of total} \\ \text{received power in fundamental} \end{matrix} \right].
\end{aligned} \qquad (27)$$

Therefore, we can write

$$d^2 \geq \frac{\frac{1}{2n}(0.88)\left[\begin{array}{l}\text{statistical average of total}\\ \text{received power at fundamental}\end{array}\right]}{\left[\pi_c^2 \frac{n-1}{n}(0.88) + \pi_c^2(0.12)\right]\left[\begin{array}{l}\text{statistical average of total}\\ \text{received power at fundamental}\end{array}\right] + \frac{1}{2}\frac{N_0}{(2^N - 1)\Delta t}}. \tag{28}$$

For large $n$ we can use $(n-1)/n \approx 1$ in the first denominator term to obtain

$$d^2 \geq \frac{\frac{1}{2n}(0.88)\left[\begin{array}{l}\text{statistical average of total}\\ \text{received power at fundamental}\end{array}\right]}{\pi_c^2\left[\begin{array}{l}\text{statistical average of total}\\ \text{received power at fundamental}\end{array}\right] + \frac{1}{2}\frac{N_0}{(2^N - 1)\Delta t}}. \tag{29}$$

Next, we divide both numerator and denominator by the second denominator term to obtain

$$d^2 \geq \frac{\frac{1}{n}(0.88)(2^N - 1)\,\text{SNR}}{1 + 2\pi_c^2(2^N - 1)\,\text{SNR}} \tag{30}$$

where

$$\begin{aligned}\text{SNR} &= \left[\begin{array}{l}\text{statistical average of total}\\ \text{received power at fundamental}\end{array}\right]\Delta t/N_0\\ &= \left[\begin{array}{l}\text{statistical average of the (energy per}\\ \text{chip) SNR at the fundamental}\end{array}\right].\end{aligned} \tag{31}$$

Although we have assumed that all $n$ signals arriving at the repeater have equal signal strengths, the basic result of this section is valid for the more general case of unequal signal strengths provided we replace the limiter loss term [(0.88) in (26)–(30)] by the appropriate loss term. Shaft [6] has presented an algorithm for determining the limiter loss terms for up to 100 carriers with 100 different amplitudes. For this case the limiter loss terms are different for each carrier. By using the appropriate limiter loss terms in (30) we can compute the detectability parameter for each channel.

## IV. Example Using Anderson Codes

Anderson [4] has reported a strategy for choosing $M$ PN sequences of length $2^N - 1$ such that

$$\pi_c^2 \leq \frac{4(M-1)^2}{2^N - 1}. \tag{32}$$

Therefore, the detectability parameter for the system under consideration when using Anderson's PN sequences is bounded by

$$d^2 \geq \frac{\frac{1}{n}(0.88)(2^N - 1)\,\text{SNR}}{1 + 8(M-1)^2\,\text{SNR}}. \tag{33}$$

Now, $M$ is the total number of users ($n$ is the number of active users) and SNR is the SNR per chip. Therefore, for sufficiently small SNR the additive noise dominates and

$$d^2 \sim \frac{1}{n}(0.88)(2^N - 1)\,\text{SNR}$$
$$\text{SNR} \ll \frac{1}{8(M-1)^2}. \tag{34}$$

On the other hand, if the number of users is sufficiently large the crosstalk effect dominates the additive noise effect and we have

$$d^2 \sim \frac{(0.88)(2^N - 1)}{8n(M-1)^2}$$
$$\text{SNR} \gg \frac{1}{8(M-1)^2} \tag{35}$$

which is independent of the received SNR.

We also note that we can set $n = M$ in (33) and solve for $M$ to obtain a bound on the number of system subscribers in terms of the shift register length $2^N - 1$, receiver SNR, and the post-correlation detection SNR $d^2$.

Furthermore, it is shown in [4] that one can find a related family of binary synchronization sequences (not PN sequences) of length $2^N - 1$ which are $(2^N - 1)^{M-1}$ in number and still have a $\pi_c$ that satisfies the estimate (9).

## V. Discussion

In this section we discuss the accuracy of our estimate of the detectability parameter, and we relate these results to the results obtained by other researchers.

In Section II we presented an estimate for the detectability parameter. We obtained this estimate rather than attempting an exact analysis because of the fact that different pairs of maximal length sequences have different cross-correlation functions. All of these could be computed exactly and the resulting detectability parameter evaluated, but the resulting spectrum of detectability parameters would be more overwhelming than informative. Furthermore, a reasonable procedure for averaging with respect to the sequences is not apparent. Hence, a worst case analysis appears to be the only feasible approach. This, of course, raises the question of the sharpness of the estimate obtained. This, in turn, depends on the sharpness of the estimate of the peak of the cross correlations of each pair of sequence-addresses for each relative shift. But this estimate is quite accurately estimated by the quantity $2(M-1)/\sqrt{2^N - 1}$. (See [4].) We conclude that the estimate is reasonably sharp.

Perhaps the best way to compare this analysis with those of other authors is to note that this analysis is more deterministic while still accounting for the hard-limiting repeater. Aein [7], [10] has analyzed the effect of the hard-limiting repeater satellite on a number of channels each of which is operating in the information transmission mode with each channel using a different maximal length sequence address. However, he assumes that the channels, other than the one being monitored, are in effect independent equal-power white noise processes. This leads, among other consequences, to a more conservative estimate of the power lost in the intermodulation product terms ($\pi/4 \approx 0.78$ versus our 0.88). Blasbalg [11], [12] has analyzed a model comparable to Aein's. On the other hand, Wolf and Elspas [13] have analyzed a system comparable to ours in that the only statistical quantities in the model are the carrier phases (which they assume to be independent and uniformly distributed as we did), but they neglect the hard limiter.

Finally, we point out that our analysis for the synchronization mode of operation can be generalized to include the data transmission mode of operation. The analysis of Section III assumes that the correlation detector operates on one sequence period. (The integration in (5) is over $T=(2^N-1)\Delta t$ seconds.) In the data transmission mode of operation this correlation (integration) time is over an information bit. An information bit length is usually an integer multiple of chip lengths, but much less than the $2^N-1$ chip lengths comprising one period of the synchronization sequence. Therefore, for the data transmission mode, the SNR term in (30) is scaled by the ratio of the information bit length to the synchronization sequence length. Also, the periodic cross-correlation term $\pi_c^2$ must be replaced by a flip correlation term $\pi_f^2$. As a result, for a random binary data stream, $\pi_f^2$ depends on the ratio of the synchronization sequence length to the information bit length. Hence, the net effect is that for the data transmission mode of operation the right-hand side of (30) gets scaled by the ratio of the information bit length (in seconds) to the synchronization sequence length (in seconds). This is equivalent to scaling the right-hand side of (30) by the ratio of the system bandwidth to the information bandwidth, sometimes called the spread-spectrum processing gain.

## References

[1] W. Doyle, "Band-pass limiters and random walks," *IRE Trans. Information Theory (Correspondence)*, vol. IT-8, p. 380, October 1962.

[2] ——, "Elementary derivation for band-pass limiter S/N," *IRE Trans. Information Theory (Correspondence)*, vol. IT-8, p. 259, April 1962.

[3] I. Jacobs, "The effects of video clipping on the performance of an active satellite PSK communication system," *IEEE Trans. Communication Technology*, vol. COM-13, pp. 195–201, June 1965.

[4] D. R. Anderson, "A new class of cyclic codes," *SIAM J. Appl. Math.*, vol. 16, pp. 181–197, January 1968.

[5] M. Rosenblatt, *Random Processes.* New York: Oxford University Press, 1962.

[6] P. D. Shaft, "Limiting of several signals and its effect on communication system performance," *IEEE Trans. Communication Technology*, vol. COM-13, pp. 504–512, December 1965.

[7] J. M. Aein, "On the output power division in a captured hard-limiting repeater," *IEEE Trans. Communication Technology (Correspondence)*, vol. COM-14, pp. 347–349, June 1966.

[8] ——, "Normal approximations to the error rate for hard-limited correlators," *IEEE Trans. Communication Technology*, vol. COM-15, pp. 44–51, February 1967.

[9] ——, "Multiple access to a hard-limiting communication-satellite repeater," *IEEE Trans. Space Electronics and Telemetry*, vol. SET-10, pp. 159–167, December 1964.

[10] J. M. Aein and J. W. Schwartz, Eds., *Multiple Access to a Communication Satellite Repeater with a Hard-Limiting Repeater*, Institute for Defense Analyses, Arlington, Va., Rept. R-108, April 1965.

[11] H. Blasbalg, D. Freeman, and R. Keeler, "Random access communications using frequency shifted PN (pseudo-noise) signals," *1964 IEEE Internat'l Conv. Rec.*, pt. 6, pp. 192–216.

[12] ——, "Signal-to-noise ratio of a pulsed pseudo-noise system," in *Multiple Access to a Communication Satellite with a Hard-Limiting Repeater*, J. M. Aein and J. W. Schwartz, Eds., Institute for Defense Analyses, Arlington, Va., Rept. R-108, April 1965.

[13] J. K. Wolf and B. Elspas, "Mutual interference due to correlated constant-envelope signals," in *Multiple Access to a Communication Satellite with a Hard-Limiting Repeater*, J. M. Aein and J. W. Schwartz, Eds., Institute for Defense Analyses, Arlington, Va., Rept. R-108, April 1965.

[14] A. Schumnitzky, "Modulation products and optimum frequency conversion for an $n$-frequency input," *SIAM J. Appl. Math.*, vol. 13, no. 4, pp. 1019–1032, 1965.

# The Effect of Limiting a Biphase or Quadriphase Signal Plus Interference

JESS L. SEVY, Member, IEEE
TRW
Redondo Beach, Calif. 90278

Abstract

This paper analyzes the case of limiting an incoherent or coherent interference signal at the frequency of a biphase or quadriphase digital signal. The results give the IM products, interference, and attenuation of the digital signal, plus interference through a hard limiter.

Manuscript received July 19, 1968; revised August 19, 1968.

## I. Introduction

The effect of limiting a CW signal plus Gaussian noise has been analyzed by Davenport [1]; in this case the interference is within the signal bandwidth. Jones [2] analyzed the limiting of two CW signals plus noise, where one of the two sources of interference is within the bandwidth, the other outside it. Sevy [3] analyzed the limiting of two-, three-, and four-angle modulated signals, where there are one, two, or three sources of interference outside the signal bandwidth. Shaft [4] extended Sevy's work to include hard limiting of multiple-angle modulated signals plus noise. More detailed results of limiting of angle modulated signals and the demodulation of two-angle modulated signals are given in [5] and [6].

This analysis presents the effect of limiting noncoherent or coherent interference plus a biphase or quadriphase signal. Part of the problem associated with noncoherent interference, viz., CW or angle-modulated interference outside the signal bandwidth or Gaussian noise in the signal bandwidth, has already been solved [1]–[6]. These results will be quoted. The other part of the problem, incoherent and coherent interference at the same frequency as the signal, will be covered in this paper.

The reason that we are concerned with interference within the band of the signal is twofold. First, the interference may be unintentional radio-frequency interference (RFI) generated within the electronic equipment which processes the desired signal. Second, the interference may be intentional or unintentional sources of interference generated by neighboring transmitters sharing the same frequency as the desired signal.

Normally sources of interference are out of the band of the signal, the exception being Gaussian noise interference. The out-of-band sources of interference will only suppress the signal or reduce the signal-to-noise ratio. Here, usually the worst degradation to the signal under this condition is a 6 dB loss in power. When sources of non-Gaussian interference are within the signal's bandwidth, it is possible to have an infinite attenuation of the signal for the biphase carrier case and severe distortion of the signal's characteristic for the quadriphase carrier case.

## II. Theoretical Approach

The assumed characteristic of the hard limiter or TWT will be a $\nu$th-law full-wave (odd) device. For $\nu$ equal to zero, the transfer characteristic is a hard limiter. For $\nu$ greater than zero, the transfer characteristic is a soft limiter. The transfer characteristic is given by

$$g(x) = \begin{cases} ax^{\nu} & x > 0 \\ 0 & x = 0 \\ -a(-x)^{\nu} & x < 0 \end{cases}$$

where $\nu$ is less than one.

Reprinted from *IEEE Trans. Aerosp. Electron. Syst.*, vol. AES-5, pp. 387–395, May 1969.

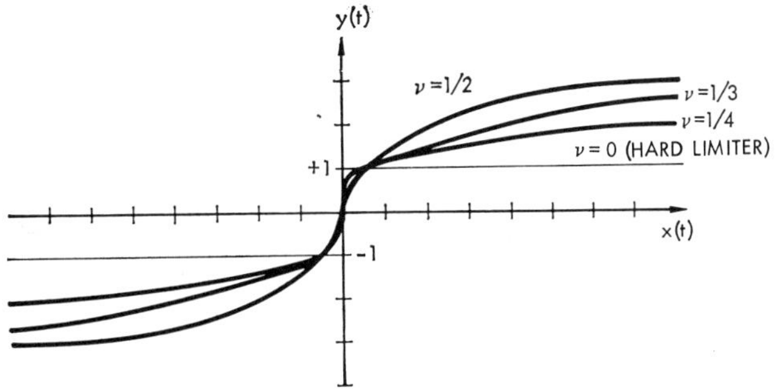


Fig. 1. $\nu$th law full wave (odd) transfer characteristics.

The transfer characteristic for the soft limiter with $\nu$ equaling $\frac{1}{2}$, $\frac{1}{3}$, and $\frac{1}{4}$ and for the hard limiter with $\nu=0$ is shown in Fig. 1.

The bilateral Laplace transform is [7]

$$f(w) = f_+(w) + f_-(w)$$

where

$$f_+(w) = \frac{a\Gamma(\nu+1)}{w^{\nu+1}}$$

$$f_-(w) = \frac{a\Gamma(\nu+1)}{(-w)^{\nu+1}}.$$

The inverse Fourier transform

$$g(x) = \frac{1}{2\pi}\int_{-\infty}^{\infty} f(jv)e^{jxv}dv$$

is the output of the nonlinear device. The autocorrelation function of the output of the nonlinear device is given by

$$\begin{aligned} R_y(t_1, t_2) &= E[g(x_1)g(x_2)] \\ &= \int_{-\infty}^{\infty}\int_{-\infty}^{\infty} g(x_1)g(x_2)p(x_1, x_2)dx_1dx_2 \\ &= \frac{1}{(2\pi j)^2}\int_{-\infty}^{\infty} f(w_1)dw_1 \int_{-\infty}^{\infty} f(w_2)dw_2 \\ &\quad \cdot \int_{-\infty}^{\infty}\int_{-\infty}^{\infty} p(x_1, x_2)\exp[w_1x_1 + w_2x_2]dx_1dx_2 \end{aligned}$$

where

$$w_k = jv_k, \qquad k = 1, 2.$$

The joint characteristic of $x_1$ and $x_2$ is

$$M_x(w_1, w_2) = \int_{-\infty}^{\infty}\int_{-\infty}^{\infty} p(x_1, x_2)\exp[w_1x_1 + w_2x_2]dx_1dx_2.$$

The output autocorrelation function becomes

$$R_y(t_1, t_2) = \frac{1}{(2\pi j)^2}\int_{-\infty}^{\infty} f(w_1)dw_1 \int_{-\infty}^{\infty} f(w_2)dw_2 M_x(w_1, w_2).$$

The input is assumed to be $m$ statically independent angle modulated signals plus Gaussian noise and is given by

$$\begin{aligned} x(t) &= \sum_{i=1}^{m} a_i(t) + n(t) \\ &= \sum_{i=1}^{m} A_i\cos[\omega_i t + \theta_i(t) + \alpha_i] + n(t) \end{aligned}$$

where $\alpha_i$ are uniformly distributed 0 to $2\pi$.

The joint characteristic function for $a_i(t_1)$ and $a_i(t_2)$ is given by

$$\begin{aligned} M_{a_i}(w_1, w_2) = E(\exp\{&w_1A_i\cos[\omega_i t_1 + \theta_i(t_1) + \alpha_i] \\ &+ w_2A_i\cos[\omega_i t_2 + \theta_i(t_2) + \alpha_i]\}). \end{aligned}$$

Using the Jacobi–Anger formula

$$\exp[z\cos\phi] = \sum_{m=0}^{\infty} \epsilon_m I_m(z)\cos m\phi,$$

the joint characteristic function becomes

$$\begin{aligned} &M_{a_i}(w_1, w_2) \\ &= \sum_{m_i=0}^{\infty}\sum_{n_i=0}^{\infty}(\epsilon_{m_i}\epsilon_{n_i}I_{m_i}(A_iw_1)I_{n_i}(A_iw_2) \\ &\quad \cdot E\{\cos m_i[\omega_i t_1 + \theta_i(t_1) + \alpha_i]\cos n_i[\omega_i t_2 + \theta_2(t_2) + \alpha_i]\}) \end{aligned}$$

where $\epsilon_0 = 1$, $\epsilon_{m_i} = 2$, $(m_i = 1, 2, 3, \cdots)$ are the Neumann numbers and $I_{m_i}(x)$ are the modified Bessel functions of the second kind. The expectation

$$\begin{aligned} &R_{a_im_i}(\tau) \\ &= E\{\cos m_i[\omega_i t_1 + \theta_i(t_1) + \alpha_i]\cos n_i[\omega_i t_2 + \theta_i(t_2) + \alpha_i]\} \\ &= \begin{cases} \frac{1}{2}\cos m_i\omega_i\tau E\{\cos m_i[\theta_i(t_1) - \theta_i(t_2)]\} & \\ -\frac{1}{2}\sin m_i\omega_i\tau E\{\sin m_i[\theta_i(t_1) - \theta_i(t_2)]\} & \text{for } m_i = n_i \\ 0 \quad \text{for } m_i \neq n_i & \end{cases} \\ &= E(\cos\{m_i\omega_i\tau + m[\theta_i(t_1) - \theta_i(t_2)]\}). \end{aligned}$$

The joint characteristic function for $a_i(t_1)$ and $a_i(t_2)$ is therefore given by

$$M_{a_i}(w_1, w_2) = \sum_{m_i=0}^{\infty} \epsilon_{m_i}{}^2 I_{m_i}(A_i w_1) I_{m_i}(A_i w_2) R_{a_i m_i}(\tau).$$

The joint characteristic function of a stationary Gaussian random process with zero mean is

$$M_n(w_1, w_2) = \exp\{\tfrac{1}{2}[R_n(0)w_1^2 + 2R_n(\tau)w_1 w_2 + R_n(0)w_2^2]\}$$

where

$$R_n(\tau) = E[n(t_1)n(t_2)]$$

$$\exp\{R_n(\tau)w_1 w_2\} = \sum_{k=0}^{\infty} \frac{R_n{}^k(\tau)w_1{}^k w_2{}^k}{k!}.$$

Therefore

$$M_n(w_1, w_2) = \exp\{\tfrac{1}{2}[R_n(0)w_1^2 + R_n(0)w_2^2]\} \cdot \sum_{k=0}^{\infty} \frac{R_n{}^k(\tau)w_1{}^k w_2{}^k}{k!}.$$

Since the input $x(t)$ is the sum of $n$ statistically independent signals plus noise, the joint characteristic function for $x_1$ and $x_2$ can be expressed as

$$M_x(w_1, w_2) = \prod_{i=1}^{m} M_{a_i}(w_1, w_2) M_n(w_1, w_2).$$

The output autocorrelation function may now be represented as

$$R_y(\tau) = \sum_{m_1=0}^{\infty} \sum_{m_2=0}^{\infty} \sum_{m_3=0}^{\infty} \cdots \sum_{m_m=0}^{\infty} \sum_{k=0}^{\infty} h^2_{m_1 m_2 m_3 \cdots m_m k} \cdot \epsilon_{m_1}\epsilon_{m_2}\epsilon_{m_3} \cdots \epsilon_{m_m} \cdot R_{a_1 m_1}(\tau) R_{a_2 m_2}(\tau) \cdots R_{a_m m_m}(\tau) \cdot R_n{}^k(\tau).$$

### III. Biphase Digital Signal

#### Incoherent Interference

The first type of incoherent interference that will be considered for the biphase digital signal is Gaussian noise interference. This case was discussed in a more general context (angle modulation) in [5]. Here the signal suppresses the noise by 3 dB for very large signal-to-noise ratios, and the noise suppresses the signal by 1 dB for very large noise-to-signal ratios.

The second type of incoherent interference that will be considered is an angle modulated signal which is outside the band of the desired signal. This signal usually interferes with the desired signal by suppressing its power. There may be IM interference in the band of the desired signal if the interfering signal is less than $2B$ away from the desired signal (the reader is referred to [3] and [6] for a more detailed discussion of this type of IM interference). The suppression type of interference is characterized by a 6-dB suppression of the interference by the signal at large signal-to-interference ratios (alternately, a 6-dB suppression of the signal by the interference at large interference-so-signal ratios).

The next type of incoherent interference which will be examined is coincident with the biphase carrier frequency. The phase of this signal is assumed to be statistically independent of the phase of the biphase carrier. The angle modulation of the interference is arbitrary, but statistically independent of the modulation of the biphase carrier.

The noiseless input to the limiter or TWT is given by

$$x(t) = a(t) + b(t)$$

where

$$a(t) = A \cos[\omega_c t + \theta(t) + \alpha] = Ap(t) \cos[\omega_c t + \alpha]$$

$$b(t) = B \cos[\omega_c t + \psi(t) + \beta]$$

where $p(t) = \pm 1$ with equal probability, $\psi(t)$ is an arbitrary function which is statistically independent of $p(t)$, and $\alpha$ and $\beta$ are uniformly distributed between 0 and $2\pi$ and are statistically independent. The two signals are statistically independent since

$$E(a^n b^k) = \int_{-\infty}^{\infty}\int_{-\infty}^{\infty}\int_0^{2\pi}\int_0^{2\pi} a^n b^k p[\theta(t), \psi(t), \alpha, \beta] d\theta d\psi d\alpha d\beta$$

$$= \frac{1}{4\pi^2}\int_{-\infty}^{\infty}\int_{-\infty}^{\infty}\int_0^{2\pi}\int_0^{2\pi} a^n b^k p[\theta(t)]p[\psi(t)] d\theta d\psi d\alpha d\beta$$

$$= E(a^n)E(b^k).$$

Therefore, the joint characteristic function for $x(t)$ becomes

$$M_x(w_1, w_2) = M_a(w_1, w_2) M_b(w_1, w_2).$$

The limiter or TWT limits each signal individually as if the carriers were separated in frequency. This is true even if the arbitrary function $\psi(t)$ is a switching function with equally likely values 0 or $\pi$, as long as $\psi(t)$ is statistically independent of $\theta(t)$. It is noted that $\psi(t)$ could equal $\theta(t+\tau)$ where $\tau$ is one bit time, and $\psi(t)$ would still be statistically independent of $\theta(t)$. This is true since the bits of $\theta(t)$ are statistically independent.

Intuitively, one would think that the limiter would limit the vector sum of the signals. This is not the case. The limiter limits each of the signals individually. Of course, there is the usual intermodulation generated when more than one signal is limited in a device with a nonlinear amplitude characteristic.

The output correlation function is given by

$$R_y(\tau) = \sum_{\substack{m_1=0 \\ m_1+m_2 \text{ odd}}}^{\infty} \sum_{m_2=0}^{\infty} h^2_{m_1 m_2} \epsilon_{m_1}\epsilon_{m_2} R_{am_1}(\tau) R_{bm_2}(\tau)$$

where

$$h_{m_1m_2} = \frac{aj^{(m_1+m_2-1)}}{2\pi} \int_{-\infty}^{\infty} v^{-1} J_{m_1}(Av) J_{m_2}(Bv) dv$$

is the coefficient evaluated previously for angle modulated interference out of band. Here, either the signal or interference is suppressed 6 dB for either large signal-to-interference ratios or large interference-to-signal ratios, respectively. The autocorrelation function is

$$R_{am_1}(\tau) = \begin{cases} \dfrac{A^2}{\epsilon_{m_1}} \cos m_1\omega_c\tau & \text{for } m_1 \text{ even} \\ \dfrac{A^2}{\epsilon m_1} R_p(\tau) \cos m_1\omega_c\tau & \text{for } m_1 \text{ odd.} \end{cases}$$

Assuming $b(t)$ is an independent biphase signal at the same bit rate, then the autocorrelation function for the interference becomes

$$R_{bm_2}(\tau) = \begin{cases} \dfrac{B^2}{\epsilon_{m_2}} \cos m_2\omega_c\tau & \text{for } m_2 \text{ even} \\ \dfrac{B^2}{\epsilon_{m_2}} R_{p_1}(\tau) \cos m_2\omega_c\tau & \text{for } m_2 \text{ odd.} \end{cases}$$

It is noted that all of the IM products which are generated by difference frequencies where the difference of the coefficients $m_1$ and $m_2$ is unity, fall back on the carrier frequency. These terms are out of phase with both the signals and are interference. These terms are sometimes called self-clutter or interfering clutter. For equal level signal and interference, the clutter is about 3 dB down from the signal for the hard limiter case. This result is obtained from [3, Table I].

### Coherent Interference

The signal and interference are given by

$$x(t) = a(t) + b(t)$$

where

$a(t) = A \cos(\omega_c t + \theta(t) + \alpha)$
$\quad = Ap(t) \cos(\omega_c t + \alpha)$
$b(t) = B \cos(\omega_c(t - \tau) + \alpha)$
$\quad = B \cos(\omega_c t + \alpha_0 + \alpha)$
$\theta(t) = 0$ or $\pi$ with equal probability
$p(t) = \pm 1$ with equal probability
$\alpha$ = uniform distribution from 0 to $2\pi$
$\alpha_0 = \omega_c\tau$ (modulo $2\pi$) which is the delay between the interference and the desired signal.

Here the interference is CW and has a fixed phase relation with the biphase carrier. Therefore,

$$x(t) = Ap(t) \cos[\omega_c t + \alpha] + B \cos(\omega_c t + \alpha_0 + \alpha)$$
$$= R(t) \cos[\omega_c t + \alpha + \alpha_0 + \zeta(t)]$$

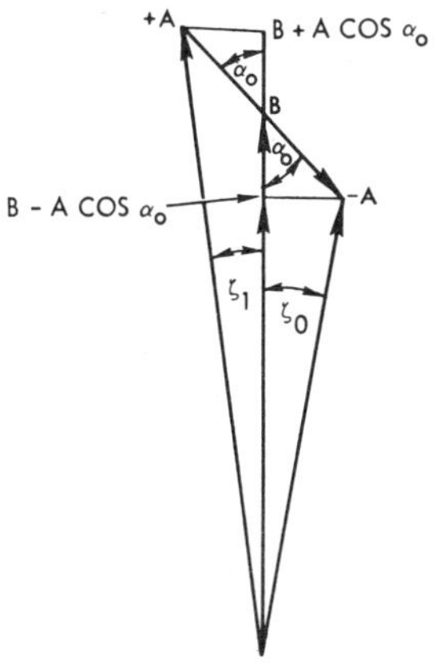


Fig. 2. Biphase signal plus interference.

where

$$R(t) = \sqrt{A^2 + 2p(t)AB \cos \alpha_0 + B^2}$$

$$\zeta(t) = \tan^{-1} \frac{p(t)A \sin \alpha_0}{B + Ap(t) \cos \alpha_0}.$$

Now for $\alpha_0 = 0$ or $n\pi$, $\zeta = 0$ (infinite attenuation of the biphase data); and for $\alpha_0 = n\pi/2$ ($n$ odd), $\zeta = p(t) \tan^{-1} A/B$ (no attenuation of the biphase data[1]) in the limiter.

At this point, if the interference is much greater than the signal, then $R(t) \cong B^2$ and $\zeta(t) \cong p(t)\, A/B \sin \alpha_0$. However, the approximation throws away the modulation or data of the desired signal. A diagram of the signal and interference is shown in Fig. 2.

Several interesting deductions may be made from the observation of Fig. 2. First a few assumptions will be made. It is assumed that the desired signal is much greater than thermal noise. It is further assumed that the interference is much greater than the desired signal. Therefore, the thermal noise will have little or no consequence when the composite signal is limited in a hard or soft limiter.

The first deduction is that the amplitude modulation is of no consequence, since the perfect limiter will remove it. There will be no signal suppression by the noise or the interfering signal. There will be noise suppression by the limiter (3 dB); however, it is assumed that interference is so strong compared to the noise that any noise contribution may be ignored. Here the in-phase noise is eliminated, and the quadrature noise remains at the same magnitude.

After limiting the composite signal plus interference signal, the signal will appear as a PSK carrier, being phase shifted $\zeta_1$ radians above the carrier phase and $\zeta_0$

[1] Assumes coherent in-phase and quadrature demodulation of the signal.

radians below the carrier phase. The angles $\zeta_1$ and $\zeta_0$ are given by

$$\zeta_1 = \tan^{-1}\frac{A \sin \alpha_0}{B + A \cos \alpha_0}$$

$$\zeta_0 = \tan^{-1}\frac{-A \sin \alpha_0}{B - A \cos \alpha_0}.$$

The two angles are slightly different in magnitude for $B \gg A$; however, the carrier state is never seen, only the extremes. Therefore, it appears as if the carrier is switching between $+(\zeta_1-\zeta_0)/2$ and $-(\zeta_1-\zeta_0)/2$.

It is noted at this time that the limited interference plus biphase signal is identical to a limited PSK signal shifted $\pm(\zeta_1-\zeta_0)/2$ with two exceptions, the noise suppression and signal-to-noise ratios. The noise suppression is nearly the same for a very strong interference or equivalently a PSK signal with a very strong carrier as compared to the noise. The signal-to-noise ratio of the interference plus biphase signal will vary with amplitude variations of the composite signal. However, it has been previously assumed that the signal is much greater than the noise, and that the interference is much greater than the signal. Thus, as far as limiting the composite signal is concerned, the noise is only a secondary contribution to the interference. If an in-phase and quadrature demodulator is placed after the limiter, then the noise will be the same as before less 3 dB (removal of amplitude variations), and the biphase signal will be reduced in power by $\sin^2 \alpha_0$. Therefore, the equivalent PSK signal will be constructed.

A typical PSK signal is given by

$$A \cos (\omega_c t + \theta(t) + \alpha)$$

where $\alpha$ is uniformly distributed from 0 to $2\pi$, $\theta(t) = \pi/2 \pm \theta_0$, and $+\theta_0$ or $-\theta_0$ each have probability of $\frac{1}{2}$ of occurring with $0 \le \theta_0 \le \pi/2$. For the biphase case, $\theta_0 = \pi/2$ and

$$A \cos (\omega_c t + \theta(t) + \alpha) = Ap(t) \cos (\omega_c t + \alpha)$$

where $p(t) \pm 1$ with equal probability. The PSK signal may be expanded yielding

$$A \cos (\omega_c t + \theta(t) + \alpha)$$
$$= Ap(t) \sin \theta_0 \cos (\omega_c t + \alpha) - A \cos \theta_0 \sin (\omega_c t + \alpha)$$

where again $0 \le \theta_0 \le \pi/2$ and $p(t) = \pm 1$. The vector diagram of the signal is shown in Fig. 3.

If the PSK signal is to be equivalent to the interference plus biphase signal, an additional carrier term will have to be added to the PSK carrier. Therefore, the modified PSK signal becomes

$$A \cos (\omega_c t + \theta(t) + \alpha) + B \sin (\omega_c t + \alpha)$$
$$= Ap(t) \sin \theta_0 \cos (\omega_c t + \alpha)$$
$$- (A + B) \cos \theta_0 \sin (\omega_c t + \alpha).$$

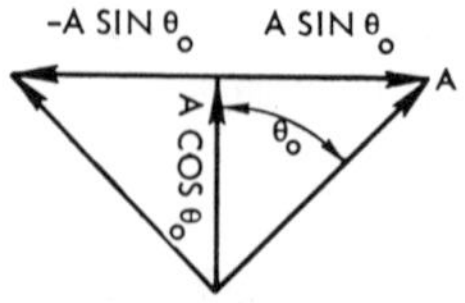


Fig. 3. Vector diagram of PSK signal.

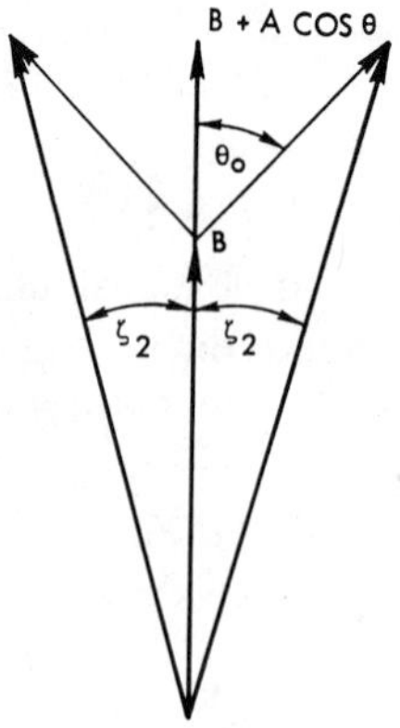


Fig. 4. Vector diagram of PSK signal with an addition carrier.

The vector diagram of this signal is shown in Fig. 4. Now for $B \gg A$ the $\zeta_2$ will approximately equal $\zeta_0$ and will equal $\zeta_1$. For this case $\theta_0$ equals $\alpha_0$. When $B$ is not much greater than $A$, then an equivalent $\theta_0$ will be chosen such that

$$\zeta_2 = \frac{\zeta_1 - \zeta_0}{2}.$$

The autocorrelation function for the PSK signal with an addition carrier is given by

$$\frac{A^2}{2} R_p(\tau) \sin^2 \theta_0 \cos \omega_c \tau + \frac{(A+B)^2}{2} \cos^2 \theta_0 \cos \omega_c \tau$$

$$+ \frac{A(A+B)}{4} \sin 2\theta_0 \sin \omega_c \tau \{E[p(t_1)] - E[p(t_2)]\}$$

$$= \left[\frac{A^2}{2} R_p(\tau) \sin^2 \theta_0 + \frac{(A+B)^2}{2} \cos^2 \theta_0\right] \cos \omega_c \tau$$

since

$$E[p(t_1)] = 0$$

and the autocorrelation function

$$R_p(\tau) = \begin{cases} \left(1 - \frac{|\tau|}{T}\right) & 0 \le \tau \le T \\ 0 & \text{elsewhere.} \end{cases}$$

The output of the limiter with noise added becomes

$$R_y(\tau) = \sum_{\substack{m=0 \\ m+k \text{ odd}}}^{\infty} \sum_{k=0}^{\infty} h_{mk}^2 R_{sm}(\tau) R_n^k(\tau)$$

where $h_{mk}$ is the coefficient that Davenport evaluates for the CW signal plus noise given previously, $R_n(\tau)$ is the autocorrelation function for the noise given previously, and $R_{sm}(\tau)$ is the autocorrelation function of the signal, given by

$$R_{sm}(\tau) = \begin{cases} \left[\dfrac{A^2}{\epsilon_m} \sin^2 \theta_0 + \dfrac{(A+B)^2}{2} \cos^2 \theta_0\right] \cos m\omega_c\tau & \text{for } m \text{ even} \\ \left[\dfrac{A^2}{\epsilon_m} R_p(\tau) \sin^2 \theta_0 + \dfrac{(A+B)^2}{2} \cos^2 \theta_0\right] \cos m\omega_c\tau & \text{for } m \text{ odd.} \end{cases}$$

Thus, for $\theta_0 = \pi/2$, the interference is orthogonal to the biphase PCM and there is no degradation of the signal. For $\theta_0 = 0$, the interference inphase with signal results in complete loss of the signal.

If the limiter is nonperfect, viz, $\nu \neq 0$, then the output biphase signal plus interference from the first zone is given by [7]

$$C(\nu, 1) R^\nu(t) \cos [\omega_c t + \alpha + \alpha_0 + \zeta(t)]$$

where

$$C(\nu, 1) = \frac{a\Gamma(\nu+1)}{2^\nu \Gamma\left[\dfrac{(\nu+1)}{2}\right] \Gamma\left[\dfrac{\nu+3}{2}\right]}.$$

The above equation represents the output signal for a noiseless biphase signal plus interference. The transform method breaks down when Gaussian noise is added to this signal and the second moments are computed.

## IV. Quadriphase Digital Signal

### Incoherent Interference

The quadriphase signal consists of two biphase digital signals which are orthogonal to each other. If the PCM signals are statistically independent, then the biphase signals are statistically independent. Here the two biphase signals are limited independently from a statistical point of view. However, since the two signals are orthogonal, no IM products are generated. Therefore, from a waveform point of view the limiter limits the composite signal as though the composite signal were one carrier. Intuitively, this is a satisfying result since the composite signal can be thought of as a carrier with four phases, $\pi/2$ apart.

If the composite signal is considered a single waveform, then the conclusions for the biphase carrier with Gaussian noise interference or out-of-band angle modulation interference are the same as the quadriphase carrier. The only difference to be noted is that when considering the individual biphase channels, these channels will be 3 dB down from the quadriphase carrier.

The next type of incoherent interference which will be examined is coincident with the quadriphase carrier frequency. The phase of this signal is assumed to be statistically independent of the quadriphase carrier. The angle modulation of the interference is arbitrary, but statistically independent of the modulation of the quadriphase carrier.

The noiseless input to the limiter or TWT is given by

$$x(t) = a(t) + b(t)$$

where

$$\begin{aligned} a(t) &= \frac{A}{\sqrt{2}} \cos [\omega_c t + \psi + \alpha(t)] \\ &\quad + \frac{A}{\sqrt{2}} \sin [\omega_c t + \psi + \beta(t)] \\ &= \frac{A}{\sqrt{2}} p(t) \cos [\omega_c t + \psi] + \frac{A}{\sqrt{2}} q(t) \sin [\omega_c t + \psi] \end{aligned}$$

is the quadriphase signal and

$$b(t) = B \cos [\omega_c t + \theta + \gamma(t)]$$

is the interference.

The modulating functions are given by

$p(t) = \pm 1$ with equal probability

$q(t) = \pm 1$ with equal probability, and statistically independent of $p(t)$

$\gamma(t) =$ an arbitrary function which is statistically independent of $p(t)$ and $q(t)$

$\psi, \theta =$ uniform distributions between 0 and $2\pi$ which are statistically independent.

The two signals are statistically independent since

$$E(a^n b^k) = E(a^n) E(b^k).$$

Therefore, the joint characteristic function for $x(t)$ becomes

$$M_x(w_1, w_2) = M_a(w_1, w_2) M_b(w_1, w_2).$$

The limiter or TWT limits each signal separately as if the carriers were at two different frequencies. This is true even if the arbitrary function $\gamma(t)$ is a switching function with equally likely values 0 or $2\pi$, or possibly 0, $\pi/2$, $\pi$, and $3\pi/2$, since $\gamma(t)$ is statistically independent of $\alpha(t)$ and $\beta(t)$. It is noted that $\gamma(t+T)$ could equal $\alpha(t)$ or $\beta(t)$ or their composite angle, as long as $\gamma(t)$ is delayed at least one bit and $\gamma(t)$ would still be statistically independent of $\alpha(t)$ and $\beta(t)$. This is true since the bits of $\alpha(t)$ and $\beta(t)$ are statistically independent.

Since the limiter limits the individual signals and not their vector sum, IM products are generated between the two signals. The output autocorrelation function is given by

$$R_y(\tau) = \sum_{\substack{m_1=0 \\ m_1+m_2 \text{ odd}}}^{\infty} \sum_{m_2=0}^{\infty} h^2_{m_1m_2}\epsilon_{m_1}\epsilon_{m_2}R_{am_1}(\tau)R_{bm_2}(\tau)$$

where

$$h_{m_1m_2} = \frac{aj^{(m_1+m_2-1)}}{2\pi}\int_{-\infty}^{\infty} v^{-1}J_{m_1}(Av)J_{m_2}(Bv)dv$$

is the coefficient evaluated previously for angle modulated interference outside the band.

The autocorrelation function for the signal is given by

$$R_{am_1}(\tau) = \begin{cases} \dfrac{A^2}{\epsilon_{m_1}}[R_p(\tau) + R_q(\tau)] \cos m_1\omega_c\tau & \text{for } m_1 \text{ odd} \\ \dfrac{A^2}{\epsilon_{m_1}} R_p(\tau) \cos m_1\omega_c\tau & \text{for } m_1 \text{ even.} \end{cases}$$

Assuming that $b(t)$ is an independent quadriphase signal at the same bit rate, then the autocorrelation for the interference becomes

$$R_{bm_2}(\tau) = \begin{cases} \dfrac{B^2}{\epsilon_{m_2}}[R_p(\tau) + R_q(\tau)] \cos m_2\omega_c\tau & \text{for } m_2 \text{ odd} \\ \dfrac{B^2}{\epsilon_{m_2}} \cos m_2\omega_c\tau & \text{for } m_2 \text{ even.} \end{cases}$$

Here all of the IM products which are generated by the difference frequencies, where the difference of the coefficients $m_1$ and $m_2$ is unity, fall back on the carrier frequency. These terms are out of phase with both the signals and are interference; they are called clutter. For the equal level signal and interference, the clutter is about 3 dB down from the signal for the hard limiter case. This result is obtained from [3, Table I].

### Coherent Interference

The signal and interference are given by

$$x(t) = a(t) + b(t)$$

where the signal is

$$a(t) = A \cos[\omega_c t + \gamma(t) + \psi]$$
$$= \frac{A}{\sqrt{2}} p(t) \cos[\omega_c t + \psi] + \frac{A}{\sqrt{2}} q(t) \sin[\omega_c t + \psi]$$

and the interference is

$$b(t) = B \cos[\omega_c(t - \lambda) + \psi]$$
$$= B \cos[\omega_c t + \psi_0 + \psi].$$

The interference is CW and has a fixed phase relation with the quadriphase carrier. The modulating functions are as follows:

$\gamma(t) = \pi/4$, $3/4\pi$, $5/4\pi$, or $7/4\pi$ with equal probability

$p(t)$, $q(t) = \pm 1$ with equal probability and are statistically independent

$\psi$ = a uniform distribution from 0 to $2\pi$

$\psi_0 = \omega_c\lambda$ (modulo $2\pi$) which is the delay between the signal and interference.

The composite signal may be written as

$$x(t) = R(t) \cos[\omega_c t + \psi + \psi_0 + \zeta(t)]$$

where

$$R(t) = \sqrt{A^2 \sin^2\left(\psi_0 + \frac{\pi}{4}\right) + \left[B + Ap(t) \cos\left(\psi_0 + \frac{\pi}{4}\right)\right]^2}$$

$$\zeta(t) = \tan^{-1}\left[\frac{Aq(t) \sin\left(\psi_0 + \frac{\pi}{4}\right)}{B + p(t)A \cos\left(\psi_0 + \frac{\pi}{4}\right)}\right].$$

For $\psi_0 = (4n+1)\pi/4$, $n = 0, 1, 2, \cdots$, there is infinite attenuation of the two phases

$$\tan^{-1}\left[\frac{-A \sin\left(\psi_0 + \frac{\pi}{4}\right)}{B - A \cos\left(\psi_0 + \frac{\pi}{4}\right)}\right]$$

and

$$\tan^{-1}\left[\frac{A \sin\left(\psi_0 + \frac{\pi}{4}\right)}{B + A \cos\left(\psi_0 + \frac{\pi}{4}\right)}\right].$$

However, there is no attenuation of the other two phases.

Similarly, for $\psi_0 = (4n+3)\pi/4$, $n = 0, 1, 2, \cdots$, there is infinite attenuation of the two phases

$$\tan^{-1}\left[\frac{-A \sin\left(\psi_0 + \frac{\pi}{4}\right)}{B + A \cos\left(\psi_0 + \frac{\pi}{4}\right)}\right]$$

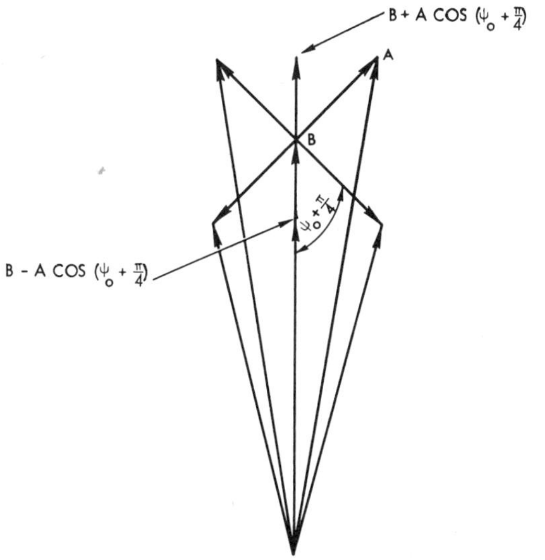


Fig. 5. Quadriphase signal plus interference.

and

$$\tan^{-1}\left[\frac{A\sin\left(\psi_0+\dfrac{\pi}{4}\right)}{B-A\cos\left(\psi_0+\dfrac{\pi}{4}\right)}\right].$$

The other two phases remain unattenuated. A diagram of the signal and interference is shown in Fig. 5.

It is assumed that the desired signal is much greater than noise and that the interference is much greater than the signal. Therefore, there will only be noise suppression (3 dB) by the composite signal and no signal suppression by the noise or interfering signal.

By observing Fig. 5 it is concluded that the amplitude modulation is of no consequence since it will be removed by the perfect limiter. In removing the amplitude modulation, the in-phase noise is also removed. The interference does not suppress the signal, but forms a new set of four angles which are less than the original angles. Therefore, the interference attenuates the quadriphase signal. This is a type of limiter suppression, although it is not the usual type of suppression referred to in the literature. The noiseless output of a nonperfect limiter, viz., $\nu \neq 0$ for a quadriphase signal plus interference in the first zone, is given by [1]

$$C(\nu, 1)R^{\nu}(t)\cos\left[\omega_c t+\psi+\psi_0+\zeta(t)\right]$$

where

$$C(\nu, 1)=\frac{a\Gamma(\nu+1)}{2^{\nu}\Gamma\left[\dfrac{\nu+1}{2}\right]\Gamma\left[\dfrac{\nu+3}{2}\right]}.$$

Therefore, the above equation represents the output signal for a noiseless quadriphase signal plus interference. The transform method breaks down when Gaussian noise is added to this signal and the second moments are computed. However, when $\nu=0$, there is no amplitude modulation, only angle modulation. Therefore, it is assumed that the signal is given by

$$B\cos\left[\omega_c t+\psi+\psi_0+\zeta(t)\right].$$

If the demodulator of the composite signal has an in-phase and quadrature reference signal, four output signals will be seen on one channel and a constant signal will be seen on the other channel. The four output signals consist of two positive signals and two negative signals, the positive signal usually denoting one and the negative signal usually denoting zero. When the interference is in phase with one of the biphase signals, one of the positive and one of the negative signals become zero. When this occurs there is a biphase signal on one channel and a constant signal on the other.

The quadriphase signal with coherent interference will normally yield a PSK signal with four unequal phases. In a degenerate form of this case two of the four quadriphase signals plus interference have the same phase, and two have different and unequal phases. Determining the performance of specific demodulators requires an analysis of output signal level and possibly of output feedback error signal as a function of the interference amplitude and phase relative to the desired quadriphase signal. This is a worthwhile problem, but is too detailed to be solved here. A noncoherent phase demodulator could be used if necessary and phase ambiguities could be resolved in a preamble.

The performance of the quadriphase signal plus coherent interference plus Gaussian noise is similar to that given previously for angle modulated signal plus noise. The only approximation used is that the amplitude modulation on the composite signal is ignored.

## V. Summary

The effect of limiting a Gaussian noise interference plus a biphase or quadriphase signal yields $-1$ dB signal suppression at large noise-to-signal ratios and $+3$ dB noise suppression at large signal-to-noise ratios. The effect of limiting an angle modulated interference out of the biphase or quadriphase signal band yields a 6 dB signal suppression at large interference-to-signal ratios and a 6 dB suppression of the interference at large signal-to-interference ratios. An additional effect of interfering IM products may exist if the signals are very close together [3].

Limiting a biphase or quadriphase plus incoherent interference which has the same carrier frequency yields

1) IM self-clutter 6 dB below the signal
2) IM interference clutter 6 dB below the signal for the equal level signal and interference case.

The total clutter level is 3 dB below the signal since the self-clutter is out of phase with the signal.

For coherent interference at the carrier frequency of the signal, the biphase signal level is attenuated as a function of the interference amplitude and phase relative to the signal. If the interference is in phase with the biphase signal, then complete attenuation of the digital data is noted. The addition of the interference is similar to the addition of a residual carrier.

The addition of coherent interference to a quadriphase signal yields an attenuation of the signal level and destroys the orthogonality of the signal as a function of the interference amplitude and phase. Since it is possible to have two, three, or four unequal angles, the conventional quadriphase demodulator may have some difficulty in demodulating the signal plus interference. The degree of difficulty will depend on the amplitude and phase of interference relative to the signal.

REFERENCES


[1] W. B. Davenport, Jr., "Signal-to-noise ratios in bandpass limiters," *J. Appl. Phys.*, vol. 24, pp. 720–727, June 1953.

[2] J. J. Jones, "Hard limiting of two signals in random noise," *IEEE Trans. Information Theory*, vol. IT-9, pp. 34–42, January 1963.

[3] J. L. Sevy, "The effect of multiple CW and FM signals passed through a hard limiter or TWT," *IEEE Trans. Communication Technology*, vol. COM-14, pp. 568–578, October 1966.

[4] P. D. Shaft, "Limiting of several signals and its effect on communication system performance," *IEEE Trans. Communication Technology*, vol. COM-13, pp. 504–512, December 1965.

[5] J. L. Sevy, "The effect of hard limiting an angle-modulated signal plus noise," *IEEE Trans. Aerospace and Electronic Systems*, vol. AES-4, pp. 24–30, January 1968.

[6] ——, "Interference due to limiting and demodulation of two angle modulated signals," *IEEE Trans. Aerospace and Electronic Systems*, vol. AES-6, pp. 580–587, July 1968.

[7] W. B. Davenport, Jr., "Signal-to-noise ratios in bandpass limiters," *J. Appl. Phys.*, vol. 24, pp. 720–727, June 1953.

[8] S. O. Rice, "Mathematical analysis of random noise," *Bell Sys. Tech. J.*, vol. 23, pp. 282–332, December 1944; vol. 24, pp. 46–156, January 1945.

# The Effects of Filtering and Limiting A Double-Binary PSK Signal

ROBERT K. KWAN, Member, IEEE
Northern Electric Laboratories
Ottawa, Ontario, Canada

Abstract

**This paper describes a digital computer simulation of a double-binary phase-shift keying system. This simulation program is used to investigate the effects of limiting action and of the shape and bandwidth of the filter on the system performance, expressed in terms of error probability**

Manuscript received October 13, 1968.

This paper was presented at the Canadian IEEE Symposium on Communications, Montreal, November 7, 1968.

## I. Introduction

This paper describes a digital computer simulation of a double-binary phase-shift keying (PSK) system which may be used for satellite communications.[1] A block diagram of the double-binary PSK system in a satellite environment is shown in Fig. 1; it consists of a modulator, up-path filter, limiter, noise source, down-path filter, and coherent demodulator. It is assumed that the up-path and the down-path filter are identical, and that they are either raised cosine or Gaussian filters. The input to the system is a random sequence of binary digits. The system performance is expressed in terms of error probability. The simulation program is used to investigate the effects of limiting action and of the shape and transmission bandwidth of the filter on the system performance. Curves relating the error probability and the filter bandwidth for various operating conditions of the limiter are presented. It is observed that

1) the system performs best without a limiter, except that a hard limiter is better when the 8.7-dB RF bandwidth of the Gaussian filter is less than 1.6 times the RF Nyquist bandwidth;
2) if limiting action is necessary, then a hard limiter is preferred;
3) a raised cosine filter is superior to a Gaussian filter up to twice the Nyquist bandwidth.

## II. Description of the Simulated System

The complete simulated system is shown in Fig. 1. It is assumed that the input message $s(t)$ is periodic and consists of a random sequence of $M$ bits. Each bit is spaced $\Delta$ seconds apart, corresponding to a signaling speed of $1/\Delta$ baud. The period of the random sequence is therefore $M\Delta$ seconds. This bit stream is fed into the signal splitter and is divided into two separate signals, $s_1(t)$ and $s_2(t)$. This separation is done by assigning the odd and even bits to separate channels, as indicated in Fig. 2. These two signals modulate their respective carriers $\cos \omega_c t$ and $-\sin \omega_c t$ and subsequently pass through the whitening filters. The outputs of these whitening filters are combined and put through the up-path filter with linear phase. Fig. 3(A) and (B) shows the transfer function $H(f)$ of the raised cosine and the Gaussian filter, respectively.

The limiter is characterized by its output versus input power characteristic. A typical power characteristic is shown in Fig. 4. The operating condition of the limiter is described by the ratio of its actual output power $P_{out}$ to the maximum output power $P_{max}$. This ratio when expressed in dB is referred to as the backoff power $P_b$ of the limiter,

$$P_b = -10 \log_{10} \frac{P_{out}}{P_{max}} \cdot \tag{1}$$

[1] The term "double-binary" is used to differentiate our modulation method from four-phase PSK. The advantage of this signal format is to avoid limiter capture by up-path thermal noise.

Reprinted from *IEEE Trans. Aerosp. Electron Syst.*, vol. AES-5, pp. 589–594, July 1969.

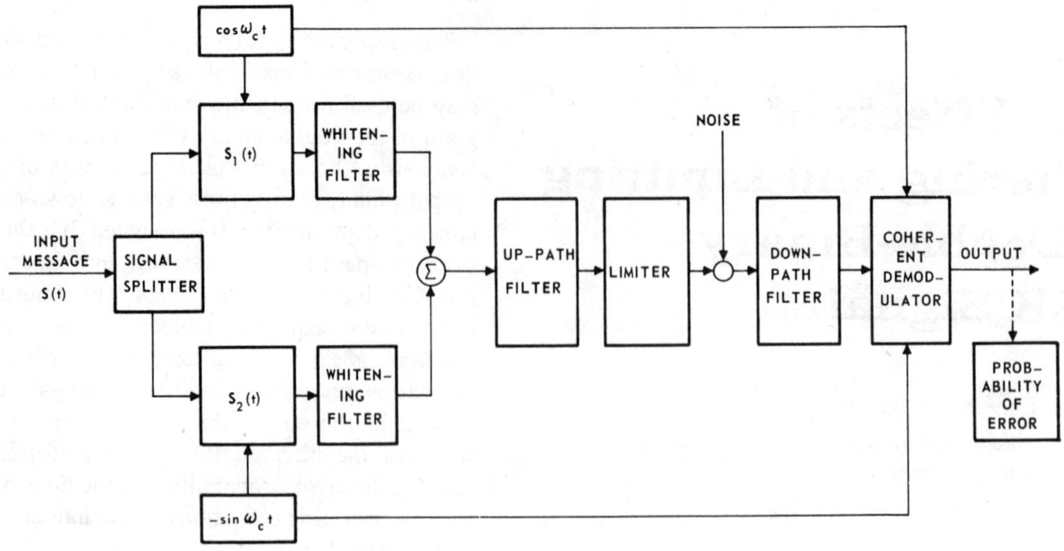


Fig. 1. A double-binary PSK system model.

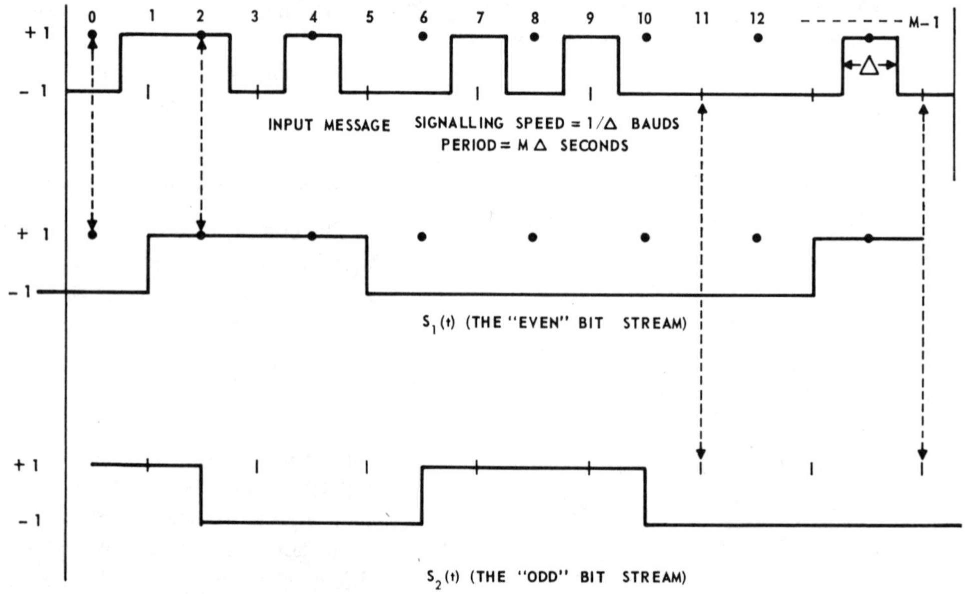


Fig. 2. Input message $s(t)$, $s_1(t)$, and $s_2(t)$.

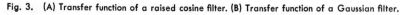

Fig. 3. (A) Transfer function of a raised cosine filter. (B) Transfer function of a Gaussian filter.

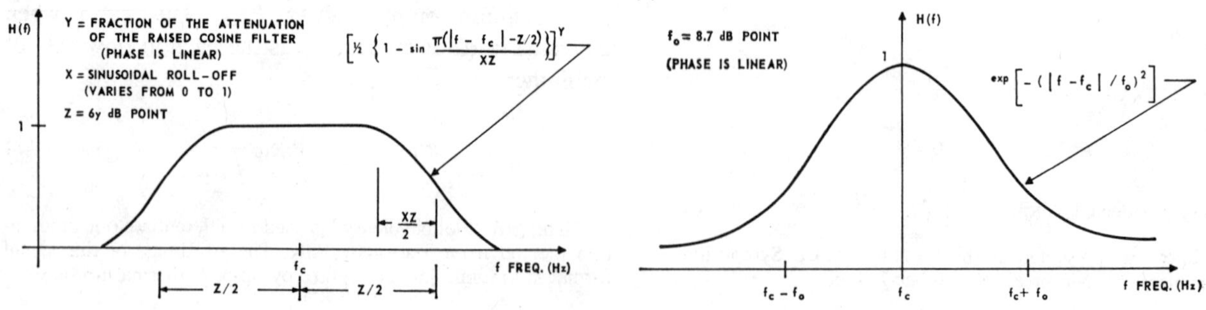

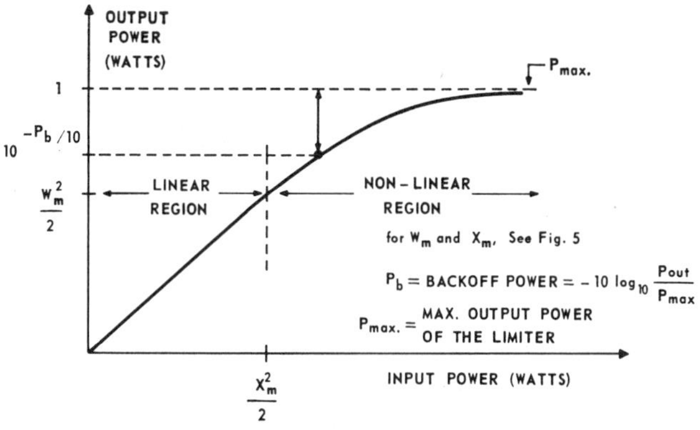


Fig. 4. The input versus output power characteristic of a limiter.

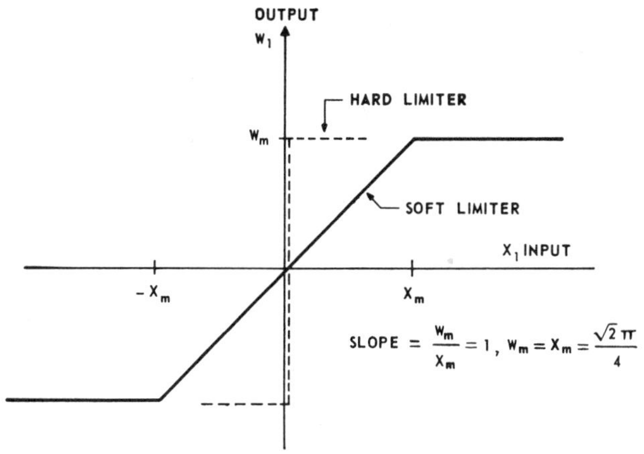


Fig. 5. The input versus output characteristic of an amplitude clipper.

When the backoff power is 0 dB, the limiter action is hard; otherwise it is soft.

The signal at the limiter output is corrupted by additive white, Gaussian noise, expressed in terms of carrier-to-noise ($C/N$) power ratio. With the limiter, $C$ is taken as $P_{max}$; with no limiter, $C$ is the mean sinusoidal carrier power numerically equal to $P_{max}$. $N$ is the noise power in the Nyquist bandwidth. The Nyquist bandwidth is the signaling speed $1/(2\Delta)$ for one phase. The contaminated signal then passes through the down-path filter (identical to the up-path one) followed by a coherent demodulator. The error probability is determined at the output and is used to characterize the system performance.

## III. The Simulation

The input message $s(t)$ consists of 64 bits. Each bit is spaced $\frac{1}{2}$ second apart, corresponding to a signaling speed of 2 bauds. When $s(t)$ is fed into the signal splitter, it is divided into two signals, the "even" bit stream $s_1(t)$ and the "odd" bit stream $s_2(t)$. The signaling speed of each phase is 1 baud and the Nyquist bandwidth is 1 Hz. These two signals modulate their respective carriers, $\cos \omega_c t$ and $-\sin \omega_c t$, and combine to give the resultant signal $\tilde{v}(t)$, which may be written as

$$\begin{aligned} \tilde{v}(t) &= s_1(t) \cos \omega_c t - s_2(t) \sin \omega_c t \\ &= \operatorname{Re}\left\{s_1(t) + j s_2(t)\right\} e^{j\omega_c t} \end{aligned} \tag{2}$$

where Re indicates real part and $j=\sqrt{-1}$. After passing through the whitening filter, the signals $s_1(t)$ and $s_2(t)$ may be represented by a train of impulses,

$$s_1(t) = \sum_{k=0,2,\cdots}^{M-1} A_k \delta(t - k\Delta) \qquad (k = \text{even}) \tag{3a}$$

$$s_2(t) = \sum_{k=1,3,\cdots}^{M-1} A_k \delta(t - k\Delta) \qquad (k = \text{odd}) \tag{3b}$$

where $A_k = \pm 1$ depending on the input message. Since $s_1(t)+js_2(t)$ is periodic, it has a Fourier series representation. The harmonics are then modified by the up-path filter with the appropriate transfer function $H(f)$.

1) *x Percent Raised Cosine Filter* [Fig. 3(A)]:

$$\begin{aligned} H(f) &= \left(\frac{1}{2}\left(1 - \sin \frac{\pi(|f-f_c| - z/2)}{xz}\right)\right)^y, \\ &\qquad \text{for } \frac{z}{2}(1-x) < |f-f_c| < \frac{z}{2}(1+x) \\ &= 1, \qquad \text{for } |f-f_c| < \frac{z}{2}(1-x) \\ &= 0, \qquad \text{for } |f-f_c| > \frac{z}{2}(1+x) \end{aligned} \tag{4}$$

where

$f$ = frequency in Hz
$f_c$ = the center frequency of the filter
$x$ = amount of sinusoidal rolloff which varies from 0 to 100 percent
$y$ = fraction of the attenuation
$z$ = the frequency where the $6y$-dB point of the filter occurs, and is chosen numerically equal to the Nyquist frequency.

Note that the total RF bandwidth of the raised cosine filter is $(1+x)$ times the Nyquist bandwidth.

2) *Gaussian Filter* [Fig. 3(B)]:

$$H(f) = \exp\left(-\frac{|f-f_c|^2}{f_0^2}\right) \tag{5}$$

where

$f$ = frequency in Hz
$f_c$ = the center frequency of the filter
$f_0$ = 8.7-dB point of the filter.

Since the Gaussian filter is not band-limited, it is characterized by its 8.7-dB bandwidth. The 8.7-dB RF bandwidth of the filter is $2f_0$ times the Nyquist bandwidth.

The up-path filter is followed by a limiter. In the simulation, the limiter consists of an amplitude clipper (as shown in Fig. 5) followed by a bandpass filter. If $W_1$ and $X_1$ are the output and input amplitude of the clipper, then the describing function[2] of this amplitude clipper can be written as

$$\frac{W_1}{X_1} = \begin{cases} \frac{2k}{\pi}\left(\theta + \frac{\sin 2\theta}{2}\right), & \text{for } X_1 > X_m \\ k, & \text{for } X_1 < X_m \end{cases} \quad (6)$$

where

$$k = \frac{W_m}{X_m}$$

and

$$\theta = \sin^{-1}\left(\frac{X_m}{X_1}\right).$$

In actual computation, the maximum output power of the limiter (i.e., under hard limiting) is 1 watt; this requires the value of $W_m$ to be $\pi\sqrt{2}/4$. We also let $k=1$ for convenience. The signal inside the limiter is processed in the following manner. For a hard limiter ($P_b=0$ dB), all the incoming harmonics are first converted to the time domain. This complex signal is divided by its envelope and subsequently multiplied by $\sqrt{2}$. As a result, the resulting time signal has a constant envelope with an output power of 1 watt. If a soft limiter ($P_b>0$ dB) is used, all the incoming harmonics are multiplied by a constant $\sqrt{P_{in}}(P_{in}=X_1^2/2)$ which can be determined from (6). These harmonics are converted to time domain and the amplitude of the complex time signal is then modified according to (6). The new complex time signal (due to hard or soft limiting) is converted back to the frequency domain and subsequently goes through the down-path filter and coherent demodulator.

The detection process of a coherent demodulator involves the multiplication of the output of the down-path filter by the corresponding carriers ($\cos \omega_c t$ and $-\sin \omega_c t$), followed by a low-pass filter. In actual computation, this amounts to sampling the output signal of the down-path filter once every second for each phase.

The error probability is computed in the following manner. Here we assume that the noise at various sampling instants is uncorrelated. For a $C/N$ ratio specified at the limiter output, we know the noise power in the Nyquist bandwidth. The noise power at the output of the down-path filter is found by computing the noise bandwidth of the filter. This noise power $\sigma^2$, together with each sample value $V_k(k=1, 2, \cdots, M)$ at the demodulator output, is used to calculate a set of error probabilities $P_k(k=1, 2, \cdots, M)$, according to

$$P_k = \frac{1}{\sqrt{2\pi\sigma^2}} \int_{-\infty}^{0} \exp\left(-\frac{(V - |V_k|)^2}{2\sigma^2}\right) dv. \quad (7)$$

The average probability of error is given by

$$P_e = \frac{1}{M} \sum_{k=1}^{M} P_k. \quad (8)$$

[2] See, for example, J. C. Gille, M. J. Pelegrin, and P. Decaulne, *Feedback Control System.* New York: McGraw-Hill, 1959, pp. 411–412.

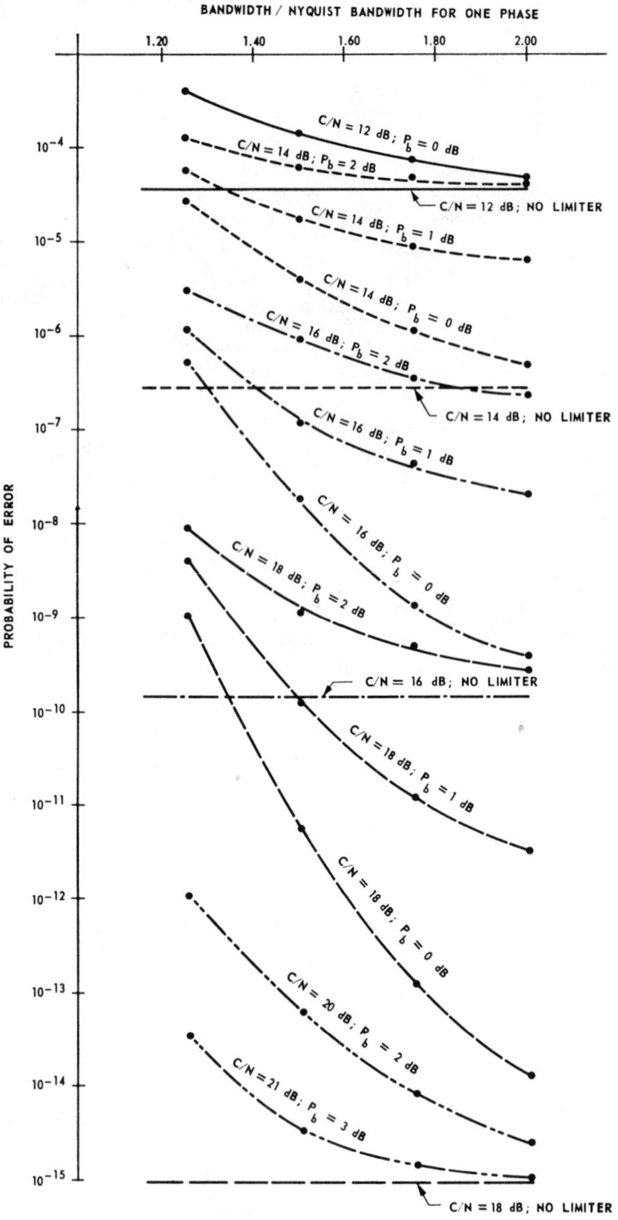


Fig. 6. Error probability versus normalized RF bandwidth of a raised cosine filter for various C/N ratios and backoff power: RF bandwidth $=(1+x)$ times Nyquist bandwidth; carrier power = 1 watt; signaling speed per one phase = 1 baud; Nyquist bandwidth = 1 Hz.

## IV. Results of the Simulation

### Raised Cosine Filter

Fig. 6 shows a set of curves relating the error probability ($P_e$) and the bandwidth of the raised cosine filter for a given $C/N$ power ratio (at the limiter output) and a given backoff power of the limiter. The curves are obtained by taking the average of two runs. The values of the parameters used in the simulation are as follows:

number of pulses in the input message $s(t)$: $M=64$
number of samples per pulse: $N=4$
pulse width in $s(t)$: $\Delta=\frac{1}{2}$ second
fraction of the attenuation of the up-path filter: $y_1=0.50$

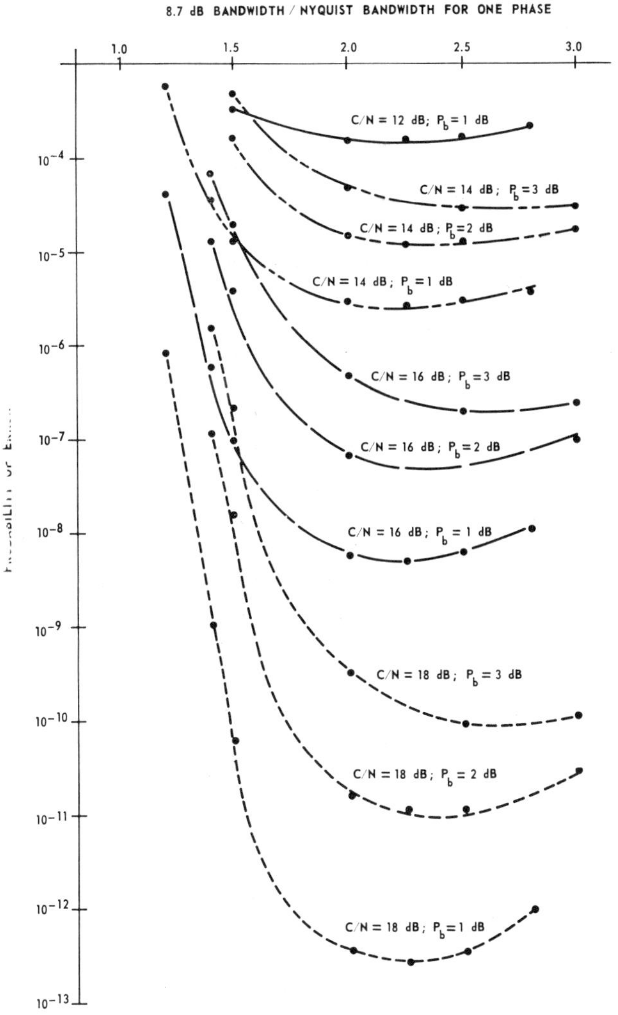


Fig. 7. Error probability versus normalized 8.7-dB RF bandwidth of a Gaussian filter for various C/N ratios and backoff power: 8.7-dB RF bandwidth $=2f_0$ times Nyquist bandwidth; carrier power $=1$ watt; signaling speed per one phase $=1$ baud; Nyquist bandwidth $=1$ Hz.

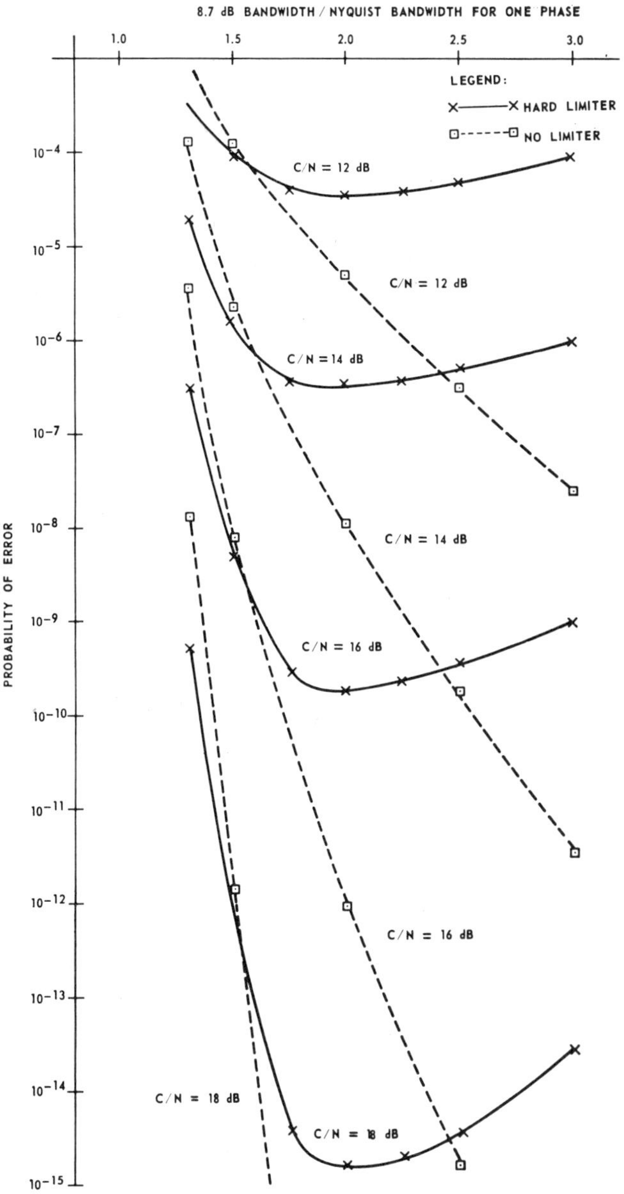


Fig. 8. Error probability versus normalized 8.7-dB RF bandwidth of a Gaussian filter with a hard limiter or without a limiter: 8.7-dB RF bandwidth $=2f_0$ times Nyquist bandwidth; carrier power $=1$ watt; signaling speed per one phase $=1$ baud; Nyquist bandwidth $=1$ Hz.

fraction of the attenuation of the down-path filter: $y_2=0.50$

$6y$-dB point of the raised cosine filter: $z=1$ [see Fig. 3(A)].

Note that for $z=1$, the Nyquist bandwidth corresponding to the signaling speed of one phase [$s_1(t)$ or $s_2(t)$] is unity. The total RF bandwidth of this bandpass filter is $(1+x)$ times the Nyquist bandwidth.

### Gaussian Filters

When Gaussian filters are used, the curves relating the error probability and the 8.7-dB bandwidth of the filter for various $C/N$ ratios and backoff powers of the limiter are presented in Fig. 7. The performance of the system when operated under hard limiting or without limiting is compared in Fig. 8. The values of the parameters used for Figs. 7 and 8 are: $M=64$, $N=4$, $\Delta=\frac{1}{2}$ second. The curves are obtained by averaging two runs.

## V. Discussions of Results

### Raised Cosine Filter

For a given $C/N$ ratio, we observe from Fig. 6 that:

1) the system performance, in terms of error probability, deteriorates as the backoff power of the limiter increases;
2) when the system does not have the limiter, the error probability is independent of the bandwidth of the filter; this is well known since there is no intersymbol interference at the sampling instants and the noise power $\sigma^2$ is constant;
3) under hard or soft limiting, the error probability decreases monotonically as the bandwidth increases.

### Gaussian Filter

For a given $C/N$ ratio, Figs. 7 and 8 indicate that

1) increase in backoff power results in increase of error probability;
2) when the system is without the limiter, the error probability decreases monotonically as the bandwidth increases; this can be seen from the fact that with no limiter, the signal power at the sampling instant ($\sim f_0^2$) increases more rapidly than the noise power ($\sim f_0$) as the 8.7-dB bandwidth of the Gaussian filter increases;
3) with a hard or a soft limiter, there exists an optimal bandwidth at which minimum error probability results; this optimal bandwidth occurs in between 1.8 and 2.2 times the Nyquist bandwidth.

The existence of the optimal bandwidth may best be explained by the impulse response of the Gaussian filter. It can be shown that the impulse response of (5) is

$$h(t) = \sqrt{\pi f_0^2} e^{-\pi^2 f_0^2 t^2} e^{j2\pi f_c t}.$$

The magnitude of the output envelope at the sampling instant is therefore

$$h(t = 0) = \sqrt{\pi f_0^2}.$$

In particular, if $f_0 = 1/\sqrt{\pi}$, then

$$h(t = 0)\big|_{f_0 = 1/\sqrt{\pi}} = 1.$$

Since the effect of hard limiting is to produce a constant (unit magnitude in this case) output envelope, the hard limiter either amplifies or attenuates the signal at the sampling instant depending on whether the 8.7-dB RF bandwidth ($=2f_0$) is less or greater than $2\sqrt{2}/\sqrt{\pi}$ ($\simeq 1.6$) times the Nyquist bandwidth. (Note that the $\sqrt{2}$ is used here because in the simulation, the mathematical operation of the hard limiter is to divide the complex time signal by its envelope and subsequently multiply by $\sqrt{2}$, as described before.) Consequently, an optimal bandwidth results. The foregoing argument may also be used to explain why the system performs better with a hard limiter when the 8.7-dB bandwidth is less than 1.6, as indicated in Fig. 8.

### Conclusions

The corresponding 8.7-dB bandwidth of a full (100 percent) raised cosine filter for $y_1 = y_2 = 0.50$ is 1.52 times the Nyquist bandwidth. Up to this bandwidth, the raised cosine is better than the Gaussian filter. Although the minimum error probability of the Gaussian filter is lower than that yielded by a full raised cosine filter, it is obtained at the expense of greater bandwidth.

It has been found that when a narrow-band raised cosine filter is used (bandwidth less than 1.3 times the Nyquist bandwidth), the error probability depends rather heavily on the input message used. Since the input message is a random sequence, a good estimate of the error probability will require a large number of runs.

In this simulation we employ the fast Fourier transform algorithm to transform time to frequency domain, and vice versa. This algorithm requires that the number of samples used be a power of 2. We have found that the use of a 64-pulse sequence and 4 samples per pulse is quite accurate. A longer pulse sequence and/or more samples per pulse can certainly be used for more accurate results, but at the expense of computing cost.

In this study, the complete raised cosine filter was split into two identical halves ($y_1 = y_2 = 0.50$). Other combinations are possible. In fact, the sum of $y_1$ and $y_2$ does not have to be unity. It would be of interest to determine the optimal combination of $y_1$ and $y_2$ in this system.

The model (Fig. 1) used in the simulation of the double-binary PSK system is simple, but may only be a fair approximation to a real system. A more realistic model would be to move the present noise source (in between the limiter and down-path filter) behind the down-path filter, followed by an additional (the third) filter and the coherent demodulator. This new model has more adjustable parameters and presents an interesting optimization problem.

ACKNOWLEDGMENT

The author wishes to thank Dr. W. F. McGee for suggesting the double-binary signal format used in this study, and for his many helpful comments.

# Effects of Phase Nonlinearities on Phase-Shift-Keyed Pseudonoise/Spread-Spectrum Communication Systems

R. A. LE FANDE

***Abstract*—The effective signal-to-noise ratio of a phase-shift-keyed pseudonoise/spread-spectrum signal passed through a communication link with phase nonlinearities $\varphi(f)$ is shown to be a fraction $\langle \cos \varphi(f) \rangle^2$ of the actual ratio, where $\langle \cdot \rangle$ denotes an average formed by weighting $\cos \varphi(f)$ by signal spectral power density across the passband.**

Signals with noiselike properties, i.e., pseudonoise (PN), are used in various satellite communications systems to permit many simultaneous accesses to the repeater. A PN carrier is generated by modulating a continuous wave (CW) signal by shifting the phase by $\varphi_{PN} = \pi C_{PN}(t)$, where $C_{PN}(t)$ is the binary ($C_{PN}(t) = 0$ or 1) output of a digital random sequence generator. The PN carrier is in turn biphase modulated by the digitized information, and the resulting signal is translated to the carrier frequency $\omega_0$ so that the final transmitted waveform is

$$e_S(t) = \cos [\omega_0 t + \varphi_{PN}(t) + \varphi_D] \tag{1}$$

where $\varphi_D$ is the phase shift derived from the input data. In a spread-spectrum PN system the keying or clock rate of the random sequence $f_C$ is much higher than that of the data $f_D$, so that the transmission bandwidth of the signal is much greater than the data bandwidth. Because of this property $\varphi_D$ may be taken to be constant during the detection period of a given data bit.

In a biphase system $\varphi_D = 0$ or $\pi$, so that

$$e_S(t) = \pm \cos [\omega_0 t + \varphi_{PN}(t)] = \pm e_{PN}(t), \quad 0 \leq t \leq T_D \tag{2}$$

where $e_{PN}(t)$ is the PN carrier and $T_D$ is the duration of a data bit.

The signals are a superposition of many frequencies as expressed in Fourier transform notation

$$e_{PN}(t) = \int_{-\infty}^{+\infty} E_{PN}(f) \exp (i\omega t)\, df \tag{3}$$

where $\omega = 2\pi f$ and $E_{PN}(f)$ is the Fourier transform of $e_{PN}(t)$

$$E_{PN}(f) = \int_{-\infty}^{+\infty} e_{PN}(t) \exp (-i\omega t)\, dt. \tag{4}$$

Here, and in the following expressions, members of the Fourier transform pair in the time domain and in the frequency domain are designated by lower case and capital letters, respectively.

The transmission of the PN signal through the communication link can result in the introduction of additional phase shifts $\varphi_E(f)$, that in general will be due to propagation delays and equipment imperfections, and so will be constant in time but may vary across the bandpass. In general, the effect of the link can be represented by a composite complex transfer function in the frequency domain $T(f) = A(f) \exp [i\varphi_E(f)]$. For the purpose of studying phase effects, $A(f)$ will be taken to be an ideal rectangular bandpass $A(f) = 1$, $|f| \leq f_B/2$, or $A(f) = 0$, otherwise, where $f_B$ is the bandwidth. In the actual case, of course, $A(f)$ and $\varphi_E(f)$ will be nonideal and interrelated. The received signal is then

$$e_S'(t) = \pm \int_{-\infty}^{+\infty} A(f) E_{PN}(f) \exp \{i[\omega t + \varphi_E(f)]\}\, df. \tag{5}$$

At the receiving terminal the spread signal is "collapsed" to the data bandwidth by mixing the receiver signal with a locally generated replica $e_R(t)$ of the PN carrier

$$e_R(t) = \int_{-\infty}^{+\infty} E_{PN}(f) \exp \{i[(\omega - \omega_{IF})t + \Delta\varphi(f)]\}\, df \tag{6}$$

where $\omega_{IF}$ is the intermediate frequency (IF) and $\Delta\varphi(f)$ is an adjustable phase shift. Without any loss of generality $\omega_{IF}$ may be set to zero.

Since the mixing process can be represented by multiplication followed by a low-pass (or IF) filter, the output of the mixer $e_0(t)$ is the IF component of $e_S'(t)e_R(t)$ so that

$$E_0(f) = [E_S'(f) * E_R(f)] H_{IF}(f)$$

where $H_{IF}(f)$ is the frequency response of the IF filter and the * represents convolution. Since $f_C \gg f_D$, the data bandwidth is very small compared to that of $E_S'$ or $E_R$, $H_{IF}(f)$ may be approximated by the Dirac impulse function $\delta(f)$, and the mixer output will consist of a signal that is approximately constant for the duration of the data bit. Thus

$$\begin{aligned} E_0(f) &= [E'_S(f) * E_R(f)]\delta(f) \\ &= \delta(f) \int_{-\infty}^{+\infty} E_S'(g) E_R(f-g)\, dg \\ &= \delta(f) \int_{-\infty}^{+\infty} E_S'(g) E_R(-g)\, dg \\ &= \delta(f) E_0. \end{aligned} \tag{7}$$

Thus $e_0(t) = E_0$, which is constant for the duration $T_D$ in this approximation.

By inspection of the Fourier transform integrals,

$$E_S'(f) = \pm A(f) E_{PN}(f) \exp [i\varphi_E(f)] \tag{8}$$

$$E_R(f) = E_{PN}(f) \exp [i\Delta\varphi(f)]. \tag{9}$$

Since $e_{PN}(t)$ is real, $E_{PN}(f)$ must be Hermitian, i.e., $E_{PN}(-f) = \bar{E}_{PN}(f)$, where $\bar{E}_{PN}(f)$ is the complex conjugate of $E_{PN}(f)$, so that $E_{PN}(+f)E_{PN}(-f) = |E_{PN}(f)|^2$ and

$$E_0 = \pm \int_{-\infty}^{+\infty} A(g) \, |E_{PN}(g)|^2 \exp \{i[\varphi_E(g) + \Delta\varphi(-g)]\}\, dg.$$

The output voltage $E_{OP}$ will be the real part of $E_0$ or

$$E_{OP} = \pm \int_{-\infty}^{+\infty} A(g) \, |E_{PN}(g)|^2 \cos [\varphi_E(g) + \Delta\varphi(-g)]\, dg. \tag{10}$$

Since

$$e(t - t_0) = \int_{-\infty}^{+\infty} E(f) \exp [i\omega(t - t_0)]\, df$$

a phase shift of the form $\varphi = \omega t_0$ is indistinguishable from a propagation delay time of $t_0$. Hence if the $\Delta\varphi(f)$ in the expression for $e_R(t)$ is derived by means of a phase lock system that minimizes the deviations of $\varphi_R(f)$ from such a linear dependence, and if $\varphi_E(f)$ is written as $\varphi_E(f) = \varphi_1\omega + \varphi(f)$, where $\varphi(f)$ is the minimized deviation of the link phase shifts from a linear characteristic, then $\Delta\varphi(f) = \varphi_1\omega$, $\Delta\varphi(-f) = -\varphi_1\omega$, and

$$E_{OP} = \pm \int_{-\infty}^{+\infty} A(g) \, |E_{PN}(g)|^2 \cos \varphi(g)\, dg. \tag{11}$$

If a weighted average of $\cos \varphi(f)$ is defined by

$$\langle \cos \varphi(f) \rangle = \frac{\int_{-\infty}^{+\infty} A(g) \, |E_{PN}(g)|^2 \cos \varphi(g)\, dg}{\int_{-\infty}^{+\infty} A(g) \, |E_{PN}(g)|^2\, dg}$$

Paper 70TP57-COM, approved by the Communication Theory Committee of the IEEE Communication Technology Group for publication without oral presentation. Manuscript received March 9, 1970.
The author is with the Satellite Communication Branch, Naval Research Laboratory, Washington, D. C. 20390.

Reprinted from *IEEE Trans. Commun. Technol.*, vol. COM-18, pp. 685–686, Oct. 1970.

then

$$E_{OP} = \pm \langle \cos \varphi(f) \rangle \int_{-\infty}^{+\infty} A(g) \mid E_{PN}(g) \mid^2 dg.$$

The desired result is that the value of $E_{OP}$ for a signal passed through a link with phase nonlinearities is identical to the result for $E_{OP}$ that would be obtained if the signal at the input to the link $e_S(t)$ were replaced by $e_S(t) \langle \cos \varphi(f) \rangle$ and the second signal passed through a link with only propagation delays or linear phase shifts.

Since the received noise $N$ is a signal of random phase with energy distributed uniformly in frequency, and since the phase function is still random after passing through the link with phase nonlinearities, the noise power output $N'$ is unchanged by the phase imperfections of the link.

The effect of the link phase nonlinearities can be expressed as a reduction in the signal-to-noise ratio (SNR) available to an equivalent link with no phase nonlinearities. The analysis presented here has shown that the signal available to the link, expressed as power in a unit impedance, is reduced from a value of $S = e_S^2(t)$ to an effective value of $S' = [e_S(t) \langle \cos \varphi(f) \rangle]^2$ by the phase nonlinearities. Then since the noise power is unaffected by the phase shifts, the reduced SNR is

$$S'/N' = (S/N) \langle \cos \varphi(f) \rangle^2.$$

The final result is that the equivalent degradation $L$ of the $S/N$ in decibels at the detector input introduced by nonlinear phase errors is

$$L\ (\mathrm{dB}) = -10 \log \left( \frac{S'/N'}{S/N} \right) = -20 \log \langle \cos \varphi(f) \rangle.$$

This formulation permits the evaluation of phase linearity specifications of link components directly in terms of additional signal strength required to obtain a given performance level. For instance, a specification of $\varphi(f) = 0.2$ radian overall tolerance on phase linearity corresponds to a maximum degradation of only 0.17 dB and hence may be needlessly restrictive and costly.

# Part X
# Synchronization

No consideration in a spread spectrum system's design is more critical than that of synchronization, how it is to be achieved, and once it is achieved, how it is to be maintained. Both direct sequence and frequency hopping systems must maintain synchronization to well within a chip time or they cannot work. Chirp signals, on the other hand, are usually synchronized on a pulse-to-pulse basis. To give an idea of the magnitude of the synchronization problem (and here we are referring to code sequence synch, not carrier synch) one needs only to note that most systems descriptions assume synchronization and avoid any discussion of how it is to be achieved or maintained. The papers reprinted here are devoted to analysis of the loops that are employed to track spread spectrum signals. These loops are usually considered to be one of two types, "delay lock" or "dither." The two are actually the same, but they are implemented somewhat differently.

Spilker and Magill's paper appeared in 1961, and its application was not considered to be for spread spectrum systems, although the results apply directly. The delay lock discriminators described here, and their descendents, employ two or more signal correlators spaced in time in such a way that the signals they output can be used to time synchronize a reference with respect to a received signal. The dithering loop is the same except that it employs a single correlator to alternately look at the same points in time and then act on the results in almost the same way as the delay lock loop. Dithering loops are discussed in Hartman's paper, which was published 13 years after Spilker and Magill's paper, even though dithering loops were in use even at the time of the earlier paper.

The remaining reprints included here (De Couvreur, and Sergo and Hayes) both are concerned with synchronization errors. De Couvreur analyzes the effect of random synchronization errors, and Sergo and Hayes analyze the effects that result from perturbing the synchronization loop.

No paper available to this author discusses the specific problems of gaining initial synchronization in spread spectrum systems, and this is the reason none is reproduced here. There are a number of papers that are concerned with carrier acquisition using phase-lock or Costas loops. The papers listed in the following section, Other Papers of Interest, contain information that is not adaptable to reproduction here, however.

## OTHER PAPERS OF INTEREST


1) J. J. Freeman, "The action of dither in a polarity coincidence correlator," *IEEE Trans. Commun.*, June 1974.
2) R. M. Gagliardi, "A geometrical study of transmitted reference communications systems," *IEEE Trans. Commun. Technol.*, Dec. 1964.
3) W. J. Gill, "A comparison of binary delay-lock tracking-loop implementations," *IEEE Trans. Aerosp. Electron. Syst.*, July 1966.
4) S. W. Golomb *et al.*, "Synchronization," *IEEE Trans. Commun. Syst.*, Dec. 1963.
5) S. S. Haykim and C. Thorsteinson, "A quantized delay-lock discriminator," *Proc. IEEE*, June 1968.
6) R. J. Huff and K. L. Reinhard, "A sampled-data delay-lock loop for synchronizing TDMA space communications systems," *FASCON '68 Rec.*
7) H. Kaneko, "A statistical analysis of the synchronization of a binary receiver," *IEEE Trans. Commun. Syst.*, Dec. 1963.
8) M. K. Simon, "Nonlinear analysis of an absolute value type of an early-late gate bit synchronizer," *IEEE Trans. Commun. Technol.*, Oct. 1970.
9) J. J. Spilker, Jr., "Delay-lock tracking of binary signals," *IEEE Trans. Space Electron. Telem.*, Mar. 1963.
10) R. B. Ward, "Application of delay-lock radar techniques to deep-space tasks," *IEEE Trans. Space Electron. Telem.*, June 1964.

# The Delay-Lock Discriminator—An Optimum Tracking Device*

J. J. SPILKER, JR.†, MEMBER, IRE, AND D. T. MAGILL†, MEMBER, IRE

*Summary*—**The delay-lock discriminator described in this paper is a statistically optimum device for the measurement of the delay between two correlated waveforms. This new device seems to have important potential in tracking targets and measuring distance, depth, or altitude. It operates by comparing the transmitted and reflected versions of a wide-bandwidth, random signal. The discriminator is superior to FM radars in that it can operate at lower power levels; it avoids the so-called "fixed error," and it is free of much of the ambiguity inherent in such periodically modulated systems. It can also operate as a tracking interferometer.**

**The discriminator is a nonlinear feedback system and can be thought of as employing a form of cross-correlation along with feedback. The basic theory of operation is presented, and a comparison is made with the phase-lock FM discriminator. Variations of performance with respect to signal spectrum choice, target velocity, and signal and interference power levels are discussed quantitatively. The nonlinear, "lock-on" transient and the threshold behavior of the discriminator are described. Performance relations are given for tracking both passive and actively transmitting targets. Results of some experimental measurements made on a laboratory version of the discriminator are presented.**

## Introduction

In many problems of position measurement, interferometry, and tracking, it is necessary to measure the delay difference between two versions of the same signal, *e.g.*, the transmitted signal and the returned signal reflected from a target. In the domain of pulse radar, emphasis in recent years has been placed on the improvement of positioning accuracy in the presence of noise, and this effort has led to the development of advanced, matched-filter and pulse-compression techniques.[1,2]

The purpose of this paper is to present an improved delay estimation technique which operates on wide-bandwidth, continuous signals in the presence of interfering noise. The delay-lock discriminator, which is described herein, provides an optimum, continuous measurement of delay by operating on a wide-bandwidth, random, continuous signal. Throughout most of this paper, the signal is considered to be either filtered Gaussian random noise, or a sine wave randomly modulated in frequency. The signals are usually nonperiodic. Operation with pulsed signals is also possible, although this possibility is not treated specifically.

The delay-lock discriminator is shown as it might be used in tracking Fig. 1. This tracking problem differs from the conventional pulse radar problem in that only a single target is to be tracked by each discriminator. (There may, however, be several discriminators.) The target is tracked continuously as a function of time rather than at periodic intervals. (Dispersive effects in the target return are to be neglected in this discussion.)

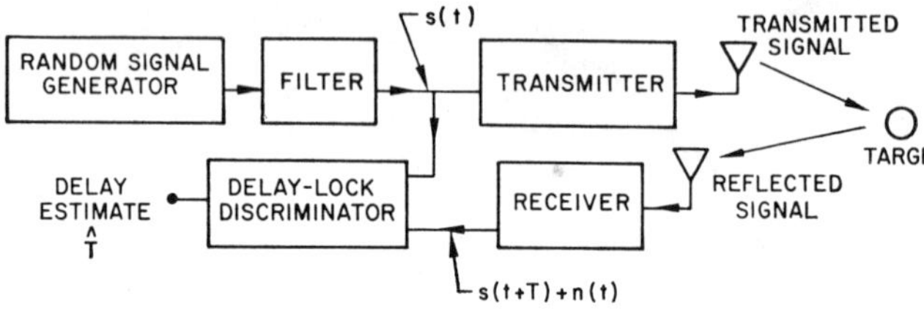


Fig. 1—Use of the delay-lock discriminator in tracking.

Although this radar uses a continuous signal, it differs from ordinary FM radars[3,4] in that, first, it avoids the so called "fixed error"; secondly, it is free of much of the ambiguity inherent in such periodically modulated systems; and finally, it can operate with multiple targets present at the same bearing from the antenna, thus providing range discrimination. The discriminator can be used in a second type of application: it can operate on a signal transmitted from the target which arrives via two separate receiving antennas. The delay difference in the two received signals is then measured by a method similar to that of a tracking interferometer.

Random-signal distance-measuring systems in themselves are not new. It is well known that when cross-correlations are made between the transmitted and received waveforms, the time difference can be accurately ascertained, if the received signal is sufficiently free of interference. These techniques have limitations, however, in that if the target is moving rapidly, the cross-correlation operation has limited useful integration time.

A somewhat different form of distance measuring technique employing random signals has been described by B. M. Horton[5] and was proposed for use as an altim-

* Received by the IRE, March 23, 1961; revised manuscript received, June 23, 1961.

† Commun. and Controls Res., Lockheed Missiles and Space Co., Palo Alto, Calif.

[1] C. E. Cook, "Pulse compression—key to more efficient radar transmission," Proc. IRE, vol. 18, pp. 310–316; March, 1960.

[2] Matched Filter Issue, IRE Trans. on Information Theory, vol. IT-6, pp. 310–413; June, 1960.

[3] D. G. C. Luck, "Frequency Modulated Radar," McGraw-Hill Book Co., Inc., New York, N. Y.; 1949.

[4] M. A. Ismail, "A precise new system of FM radar," Proc. IRE, vol. 44, pp. 1140–1145; September, 1956.

[5] B. M. Horton, "Noise-modulated distance measuring system," Proc. IRE, vol. 47, pp. 821–828; May, 1959.

Reprinted from *Proc. IRE*, vol. 49, pp. 1403–1416, Sept. 1961.

eter. This technique simply involves the direct multiplication of the transmitted and received signals, followed by a frequency-discrimination operation. Basically, this is a special type of correlation technique which is capable of operating over a relatively small range of delay. However, this system has a limitation on the dynamic range of delay which for many purposes would be overly restrictive.

Correlation techniques can be extended to cope better with time varying delays as shown in Fig. 2. A single element in the simple cross-correlation process is shown in Fig. 2(a). The fixed delay $T_m$ is one of a large set of delays to be tested for maximum cross-correlation. (Notice that the time shift $T$ is negative for a real delay.) The delay which produces the largest cross-correlation voltage $V_m$ is considered the best estimate over a given interval of time. However, the integration time $\tau$ is limited to relatively short periods of time over which the delay $T(t)$ does not fluctuate enough to change the cross-correlation significantly. This restriction on integration time can, in some situations, cause severe limitations on the accuracy of the delay estimate in the presence of interference.

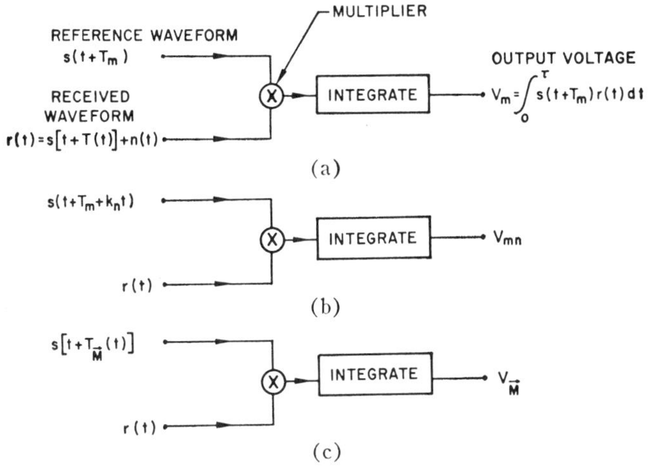


Fig. 2—Use of cross-correlation in delay estimation. Reference waveforms have: (a) Fixed delays $T$. (b) Fixed, plus linearly varying delays $T_m+k_n t$. (c) Time varying delay, $T_{\vec{M}}(t)$ chosen from a set of time functions $\tau$ sec long with bandwidth $W$.

A modified cross-correlation process is shown in Fig. 2(b). Here comparisons are made between the received signal and a two-dimensional set of fixed, plus linearly varying delays, and the integration time can be increased to time intervals over which the time delay is well approximated by a member of this set. Matched filter analogs to this technique have been discussed in the literature.[6]

The final stage of accuracy that can be achieved is shown in Fig. 2(c), where a multidimensional set of delay functions $T_{\vec{M}}(t)$ of length $\tau$ sec and bandwidth $W$ are used as comparison delay functions. It is clear, however, that to use large dimensions for $\vec{M}$ would be unfeasible in most practical problems.

The delay-lock discriminator provides an approximation to this last technique by generating its own comparison delay function $T_{\vec{M}}(t)$ through the use of cross-correlation and error feedback.

## Delay-Lock Discriminator

A block diagram of the delay-lock discriminator is shown in Fig. 3. As the figure shows, the discriminator is basically a nonlinear feedback system employing a multiplier, linear filter, and a controllable delay line.[7] The controllable delay line can have a number of implementations, *e.g.*, a ferrite-core delay line with magnetically controlled permeability and delay, or a servo-controlled electric or ultrasonic delay line. The ultrasonic lines are preferable for delays in the millisecond range or greater. In practice, it is often desirable to have an automatic gain control or limiter to maintain constant power at the discriminator input.

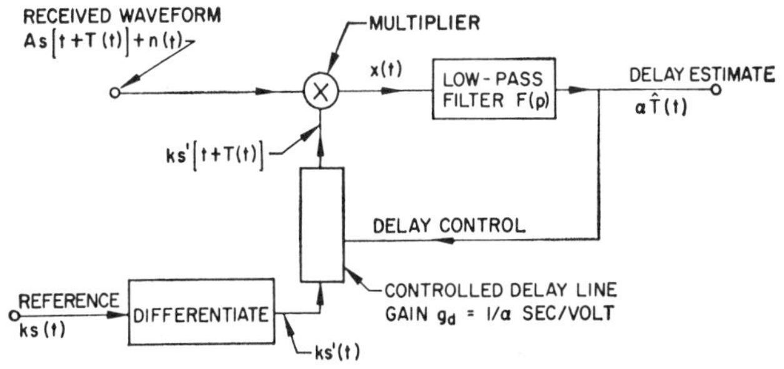


Fig. 3—Block diagram of the delay-lock discriminator. The symbols $k$, $\alpha$, are constants.

Through an analysis similar to that used by Lehan and Parks,[8] this discriminator, or a slightly modified version of it, can be shown to be optimum in that it provides the maximum likelihood (*a posteriori*, most probable) estimate of the delay. This derivation has been made by Spilker in unpublished work under the assumption of Gaussian random delay and interfering noise. In general, the truly optimum discriminator contains a second feedback loop which serves to reduce the effects of intrinsic or self-noise described in this section. It should be pointed out, however, that the maximum likelihood discriminator taking the form shown in Fig. 3 requires a nonrealizable loop filter $F(p)$. In this paper the configuration of elements of Fig. 3 is retained, but the loop filter is constrained to be realizable and is optimized for an important class of target delay functions;

[6] R. M. Lerner, "A matched filter detection system for complicated Doppler shifted signals," IRE Trans. on Information Theory, vol. IT-6, pp. 373–385; June, 1960.

[7] The output of a passive, lossless, delay line with an input $f(t)$ is actually $\sqrt{1+dT(t)/dt}\, f[t+T(t)]$ rather than just $f[t+T(t)]$ as shown in Fig. 3. The square root term is present to keep the output energy equal to the input energy. However, in most practical problems we have the relationship $dT(t)/dt \ll 1$, and this effect can be ignored.

[8] F. W. Lehan and R. J. Parks, "Optimum demodulation," 1953 IRE National Convention Record, pt. 8, pp. 101–103.

delay functions which can be approximated by a series of ramps fall into this class.

The operation of the discriminator can be analyzed by examining the multiplier output $x(t)$. The delay error may be defined as $\epsilon(t)=T(t)-\hat{T}(t)$. We can then write the Taylor series for the delayed signal

$$s(t+T) = s(t+\hat{T}) + \epsilon s'(t+\hat{T}) + \frac{\epsilon^2}{2} s''(t+\hat{T}) + \cdots$$

where the primes refer to differentiation with respect to the argument, and all derivatives of $s(t)$ are assumed to exist.[9] Initially, the delay error $\epsilon(t)$ is assumed to be small so that the Taylor series expansion of $s(t+T)$ about $s(t+\hat{T})$ converges rapidly. The multiplier output then has the series expansion

$$\frac{x(t)}{k} = A\left[s(t+\hat{T})s'(t+\hat{T}) + \epsilon(t)[s'(t+\hat{T})]^2 + \frac{\epsilon^2(t)}{2!} s''(t+\hat{T})s'(t+\hat{T}) + \cdots\right] + n(t)s'(t+\hat{T}). \quad (1)$$

For convenience, $s(t)$ is normalized to have unity power, and thus the received signal power is $P_s=A^2$. The term $(s')^2$ has a nonzero average value which will be defined as $P_d$, the power in the differentiated signal, and is dependent only upon the shape of the signal spectrum. We can then write $[s'(t)]^2 \triangleq P_d + s_2(t)$ where $s_2(t)$ has a zero mean. By making use of this last definition, we can rewrite (1) as

$$\frac{x(t)}{k} = AP_d\epsilon(t) + n_e(t), \quad (2)$$

where the first term is the desired error correcting term, and the second term $n_e(t)$ is an equivalent noise term caused by the interfering noise $n(t)$ and the remainder of the infinite series (distortion and intrinsic noise effects). If $\epsilon$ is small, $n_e(t)$ has little dependence upon $\epsilon(t)$.

The delay tracking behavior is evident from (2). Suppose that the input delay $T(t)$ is suddenly increased by a small amount. The error $\epsilon(t)$, assumed initially small, will also suddenly increase; the multiplier output will increase, and therefore the delay estimate $\hat{T}(t)$ will increase and tend to track the input delay. The discriminator output is indeed an estimate of the delay.

The representation of the multiplier output given in (2) permits the use of the partially linearized equivalent network shown in Fig. 4. The closed-loop transfer function $H(p)$ is

$$H(p) = \frac{F(p)}{1 + kAP_dF(p)/\alpha} \quad (3)$$

[9] RC filtered white noise for example is nondifferentiable. It seems, however, that for most physical systems parasitic effects cause the signal functions to be differentiable. See S. O. Rice, "Mathematical Analysis of Random Noise," in "Noise and Stochastic Process," edited by N. Wax, Dover Publications, New York, N. Y., pp. 193–195; 1954.

where $p$ is the complex frequency variable. This representation is equivalent to that shown in Fig. 3 because the input to the loop filter $F(p)$ is the same in both instances. The delay estimates thus obtained are identical.

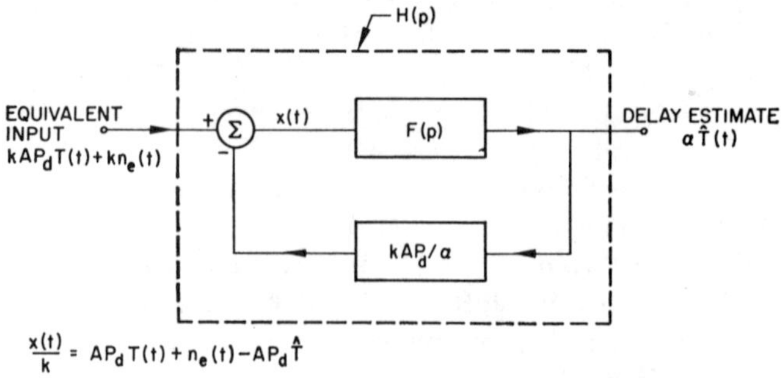


Fig. 4—Partially-linearized equivalent circuit for the delay-lock discriminator.

Notice that the equivalent transfer function $H(p)$ is still nonlinear because it is dependent upon the input signal amplitude $A$. In the initial part of this discussion, $A$ is assumed constant, and $H(p)$ is assumed linear. In a later paragraph, the effect of AGC or limiting the input signal on the loop transfer function is discussed.

The equivalent input noise $n_e(t)$ is dependent upon $\hat{T}(t)$. However, it can be seen that under conditions of small delay error, this effect can be neglected. This linearized equivalent circuit, then, has its greatest use under conditions of small delay error, *i.e.*, "locked-on" operation. Notice that if $n(t)$ is "white," the interfering noise component of $n_e(t)$ is also white.

To provide a relatively simple yet useful and rather general analysis of the discriminator operation, the signal $s(t)$ will be assumed to have the form of a random frequency, modulated sine wave

$$s(t) = \sqrt{2}\sin[\omega_0 t + \phi(t)] = \sqrt{2}\sin\left[\omega_0 t + \int_0^t \omega_i(t')dt'\right]. \quad (4)$$

The spectrum of this signal can have a wide range of shapes[10] depending upon the statistics of $\omega_i(t)$, but for convenience in calculation, the spectrum of $s(t)$ will be taken to be rectangular with bandwidth $B_s$ and center frequency $f_0$ as shown in Fig. 5. (It is assumed that $B_s<2f_0$ and that $\omega_i(t)$ has a zero average value.) Then we can write the expressions:

$$s'(t) = \sqrt{2}\,\omega_s(t)\cos[\omega_0 t + \phi(t)]$$

$$P_d = (2\pi)^2\left[f_0^2 + \frac{1}{3}\left(\frac{B_s}{2}\right)^2\right], \quad (5)$$

[10] D. Middleton, "An Introduction to Statistical Communication Theory," McGraw-Hill Book Co., Inc., New York, N. Y., pp. 604–625; 1960.

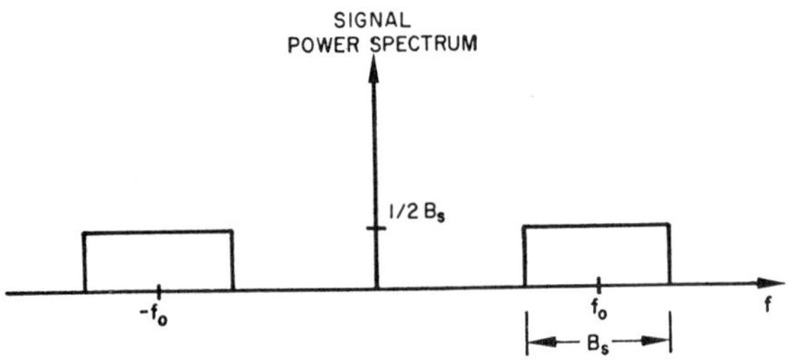


Fig. 5—Power spectral density of $s(t)$.

where we have defined $\omega_s(t)=\omega_0+\omega_i(t)$.

Define the quantities $a_n=E[s'(t)s^{(n)}(t)]$. Note that $a_n=0$ if $n$ is even.

In general, the input to the linearized equivalent circuit can be written as the sum of the equivalent inputs to the discriminator, signal and three types of interference noise terms,

$$\text{Signal term} = kAP_d\epsilon(t)$$

$$\text{Noise term} = kn_e(t) = k[n_d(t) + n_i(t) + n_n(t)] \quad (6)$$

where $n_d(t)$ represents a nonlinear distortion term (it is small for small $\epsilon$); $n_i(t)$ is an intrinsic or self-noise term, which is dependent upon the carrier characteristics, and $n_n(t)$ is an external interference term, which is dependent upon external noise at the discriminator input. By making use of (4) and (5), these noise terms can be evaluated as

$$n_d(t) = A\left[a_3\frac{\epsilon^3(t)}{3!} + a_5\frac{\epsilon^5(t)}{5!} + \cdots\right]$$

$$n_i(t) = A\left\{\epsilon(t)[(s'(t+\hat{T}))^2 - a_1] + \frac{\epsilon^2(t)}{2!}s'(t+\hat{T})s''(t+\hat{T}) + \frac{\epsilon^3(t)}{3!}[s'(t+\hat{T})s'''(t+\hat{T}) - a_3] + \cdots\right\}$$

$$n_n(t) = n(t)s'(t+\hat{T}) = \sqrt{2}\,n(t)\omega_s(t+\hat{T})\cos[\omega_0 t + \phi(t+\hat{T})]. \quad (7)$$

The distortion terms are taken as those terms of the form $\epsilon^n$ for $n\neq 1$.

The terms in the multiplier output with spectra centered about $\omega=2\omega_0$ have been neglected because they will be assumed to be above the passband of the loop filter. This is not possible for low-pass spectra, of course.

The importance of the intrinsic noise term in determining the performance of the discriminator is dependent upon how much of its spectrum passes through the low-pass loop filter. Notice that the intrinsic noise terms are present even if the interference $n(t)$ is absent. It can be seen from (6) and (7) that the intrinsic noise effect is relatively small for this type of signal if

$$|\omega_i(t)|/\omega_0 \leq B_s/2\omega_0 < 1,$$

and the bandwidth of the instantaneous frequency $\omega_i(t)$ is large compared to the closed-loop bandwidth. It should be pointed out that the operation of the discriminator is not restricted to the use of fixed envelope signals. However, the intrinsic noise contributions will generally increase if envelope fluctuations of the signal are allowed.

## Comparison with the Phase-Lock FM Discriminator

The operation of the delay-lock discriminator is analogous, in several respects, to the operation of the phase-lock FM discriminator (see Fig. 6 for a diagram of the phase-lock loop). It is desirable to investigate the differences and similarities of these two devices.

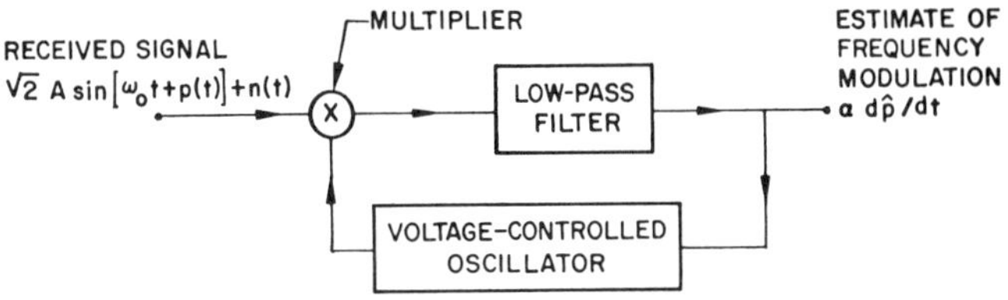


Fig. 6—Block diagram of the phase-lock discriminator.

For pure sine wave carriers (unmodulated carrier bandwidth of zero), delay modulation has a corresponding modulation in phase, *i.e.*,

$$\sin[\omega_0 t + \phi(t)] = \sin\omega_0[t + T(t)] \text{ if } \phi(t) = \omega_0 T(t).$$

Thus, if pure sine wave carriers are used, the delay line and its reference carrier input can be replaced by a differentiator and voltage-controlled oscillator. The differentiator can be lumped into the loop filter of the phase-lock loop. Theoretically, therefore, for the special case of a pure sine wave carrier, the delay-lock discriminator functions exactly as a phase-lock loop.[11]

The delay-lock discriminator normally operates with a wide bandwidth signal when used as a tracking device, and with this type of signal there is no longer a direct correspondence with the phase-lock discriminator operation. As might be expected, however, there are analogous features in both discriminators. For example, the delay-lock discriminator has a threshold error and lock-on performance which are analogous to those in the phase-lock loop.

## Discriminator Operating Curve

Thus far, it has been indicated that the discriminator will tend to track the delay variations of an incoming signal provided that the delay error magnitude, $|\epsilon|=|T-\hat{T}|$, is small. In this section we seek to determine how small this error must be and what occurs as the error becomes larger.

[11] In practice, the delay-lock discriminator uses a delay line with restricted dynamic range of delay. Thus, it can be operated only with the sine wave carriers having a limited peak phase deviation.

Assume that $s(t)$ is a stationary (wide sense), ergodic, random variable with zero mean, and that the delays $T(t)$ and $\hat{T}(t)$ are constant or slowly varying with time. Under these conditions, the loop filter when properly optimized forms the average of the multiplier output to obtain:

$$E[x(t)] = E\{[As(t+T)+n(t)]ks'(t+\hat{T})\}$$
$$= -kAR_s'(T-\hat{T})$$

where $n(t)$ and $s(t)$ are assumed independent, and $R_s'(\tau) = d/d\tau[R_s(\tau)]$, the derivative of the autocorrelation function of $s(t)$. The important component in the multiplier output is not always linearly dependent upon the delay error, but, more generally, is functionally dependent upon the error through the differentiated autocorrelation function, and thereby causes changes in the effective loop gain.

The multiplier output can be written using (6) and (7) as

$$\frac{x(t)}{k} = -AR_s'[\epsilon(t)] + n_i(t) + n_n(t) \quad (8)$$

where we have used the relationship

$$R_s'(\epsilon) = \sum_{n=1}^{\infty} a_n\epsilon^n/n!.$$

A further general statement can be made with respect to the effective loop gain for small $|\epsilon|$. The correction component of the multiplier output for small $|\epsilon|$ is $kA\epsilon(t)a_1$ where $a_1$, in general, is given by

$$a_1 = \int_{-\infty}^{\infty} \omega^2 G_s(f)df$$

and depends only on the shape of the signal spectrum.

## Threshold Error

To illustrate the nonlinear behavior of the discriminator, some exemplary signal spectra are shown in Fig. 7 along with their corresponding discriminator characteristics. If $s(t)$ is taken to have a rectangular band-pass spectrum as shown in Fig. 7(a), then, in the region $|\epsilon| < \frac{1}{4}f_0$, the discriminator curve is approximately linear and has a positive slope. However, if the error exceeds the threshold error[12] $\epsilon_T$, the point at which the slope of the discriminator curve first becomes zero, the slope becomes negative, and further small incremental increases in $\epsilon$ in this region produce decreases in $\hat{T}$. Thus, the discriminator is unlocked and temporarily unstable with respect to small noise perturbations. Notice that in Fig. 7(a) there are several possible positive-slope lock-on regions, a characteristic of band-pass signal spectra. The effective loop gain, however, dependent upon the magnitude of the slope in these regions, decreases considerably as the delay error moves several inverse bandwidths away from the origin.

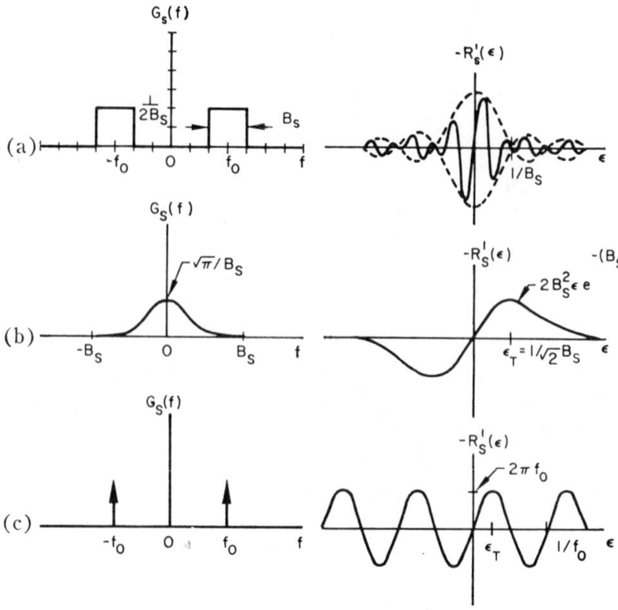


Fig. 7—Signal-power spectral density (unity-signal power) and the corresponding discriminator characteristics. (a) Rectangular band-pass spectrum $\epsilon_T = 1/4f_0$. (b) Gaussian low-pass spectrum $G(f) = (\sqrt{\pi}/B_s)\exp -(\pi f/B_s)^2$, $\epsilon_T = 1\sqrt{2}B_s$. (c) Pure sine-wave signal.

A Gaussian shape of low-pass signal spectrum is shown in Fig. 7(b). The discriminator curve for this signal spectrum has only one lock-on region, a characteristic which is also obtained using white noise passed through low-pass filters with poles on the negative real axis in the $p$ plane. The threshold error for this Gaussian spectrum is $\epsilon_T = 1/\sqrt{2}B_s$. These signals with low-pass spectra are, of course, assumed to be detected (AM, FM, or PM) versions of the actual transmitted RF waveform.

The last spectrum, Fig. 7(c), corresponds to a pure sine wave carrier and phase-lock loop type of operation. Obviously, there are an unlimited number of indistinguishable lock-on regions here, and each has the same loop gain and threshold error. The use of this type of carrier in a tracking problem has limitations unless the delay variations are restricted to values less than $1/f_0$.

## Dynamic Range

The dynamic range of the delay-lock discriminator is defined to be the maximum delay excursion of the controlled delay line, and is determined by the largest delay line control input voltage and the delay line gain. The maximum control input voltage in turn is determined by the signal amplitude, the loop filter dc gain, and the

[12] In general, the threshold error $\epsilon_T$ in the fundamental lock-on region about $\epsilon = 0$ is given by the smallest value of $\epsilon$ which can satisfy the equation

$$\int \omega^2 G_s(\omega)\cos\omega\epsilon d\omega = 0.$$

peak value of the discriminator curve. Thus, the dynamic range[13] $\Delta T$ is

$$\Delta T = kg_d A F(0) R_s'{}_{\text{peak}} = gR_s'{}_{\text{peak}}/P_d \tag{9}$$

where $g \triangleq kg_d P_d A F(0)$ is the dc loop gain. This value of $\Delta T$ relates to the fundamental lock-on region. The values for other regions, if they exist, will be correspondingly less.

## Delay Ambiguities and Interference from Other Targets

If a signal having a band-pass spectrum is used, there will exist ambiguities, in many situations, as to which lock-on zone the discriminator is using. An exception to this statement occurs if the ambiguity can be resolved by other means (such as knowledge of the exact target position at a certain instant of time, as might be the situation in tracking a rocket from its firing position). A means for resolving this ambiguity could be to control externally the bias on the controlled delay line and to observe some characteristic of the discriminator curve, *e.g.*, its slope or peak amplitude in a given lock-on region. The problem, then, is analogous to the resolution problem of radar.

Woodward[14] has defined a measure of time ambiguity for radar signals called the time resolution constant $T_c$. This constant is a measure of the width of the envelope of the discriminator characteristic; and for a rectangular signal spectrum, this time ambiguity has the value $T_c = 1/B_s$. It is difficult to determine the correct lock-on region from others that are separated in delay from it by less than $1/B_s$.

Of course, if a properly chosen low-pass signal spectrum is used, multiple lock-on regions will not exist, and hence ambiguities of this sort do not occur.

Considerations of a similar nature arise when one attempts to compute the interference caused by the presence of multiple targets. Suppose that the discriminator is locked on to a target with delay $T$, and an interfering target comes into view with delay $T_i$ and returned signal amplitude $A_i$. Then the multiplier output in the discriminator is $-[AR_s'(T-\hat{T})+A_iR_s(T_i-\hat{T})]$, and the discriminator will operate so as to minimize the sum of these two terms rather than the desired term $-AR_s'(T-\hat{T})$ alone. If the relative effect of the interfering target is to be small, then it is necessary to have the ratio $|A_iR_s'(T_i-\hat{T})/AR_s(T-\hat{T})|$ small for the desired accuracy maximum error $|T-\hat{T}|$. Thus, if a small effect only is to be caused by the second target, it must be separated from the desired target by a delay $|T_i-T| \gg 1/B_s$. It is also desirable that $R_s(\tau)$ decrease rapidly with increasing $\tau$ to make up for the differences in path attenuations from the target returns caused by a relatively close undesired target. Spectra with gradual cutoffs are therefore desirable because of the rapid falloffs of $R_s(\tau)$ for large $\tau$, *e.g.*, if $G_s(\omega) \sim \exp -(\omega/2B_s)^2$, then $R_s(\tau) \sim \exp -(B_s\tau)^2$.

## Lock-on Performance

Before a target can be tracked, the discriminator must lock on to the target delay so that the discriminator is operating in its linear region. This operation can be performed in practice by manually or automatically sweeping the bias on the delay line control throughout the expected range of the target delay. An alternative approach is to set the delay to correspond to the perimeter of some circular region surrounding the radar. Then targets will be tracked as they enter this region. In this subsection a short analysis is made of the nonlinear lock-on transient when the signal is first applied to the discriminator.

Two discriminator curves are shown in Fig. 8, one for a band-pass spectrum, the other for a low-pass spectrum. Both spectra have Gaussian shapes. If we assume that the received signal has a fixed delay $T$, and that the quiescent discriminator delay is zero, the steady-state conditions of the discriminator must then satisfy the equation

$$-gR_s'(T - \hat{T})/P_d = \hat{T} = (T - \epsilon). \tag{10}$$

It can be seen that solutions to this equation are given by the intersections of $-R_s'(\epsilon)$ and the straight line in Fig. 8. Recall that only the positive slope regions are stable zones with respect to noise perturbations.

A typical lock-on transient for the signal with a low-pass spectrum is as follows: when the input signal is first applied to the discriminator at $t=0$, the error $\epsilon(t)$ has its initial value $\epsilon(0+)=T$. As a result of this error, the loop filter input takes on a positive value, and $\hat{T}$ will begin to increase from zero and rise towards $T$. To describe the exact behavior of the loop, the loop filter must be specified.

If a simple low-pass RC filter is used as the loop filter, the lock-on transient is described by a first-order nonlinear differential equation. Referring to Fig. 3 and (8), and neglecting noise effects, one readily finds the differential equation to be

$$\left[\frac{1}{\omega_f}\frac{d\hat{T}}{dt} + \hat{T}\right] = \frac{F(0)}{\alpha} x(t) = -gR_s'(T - \hat{T})/P_d \tag{11}$$

where $\omega_c \triangleq 1/RC$. If $T(t) = T$ is a constant, and $\hat{T}(0) = 0$, then the transient response can be obtained by integrating

$$dt = d\hat{T}/\omega_f[-gR_s'(T - \hat{T})/P_d - \hat{T}(t)]. \tag{12}$$

[13] Notice that this dynamic range restriction is different from that encountered with phase-lock discriminators. Here it is the maximum delay excursion which is limited, whereas, with the phase-lock loop, the maximum frequency excursion is the quantity limited. The reason for this difference is that in the phase-lock loop, the multiplier output controls the *frequency* of the VCO.

[14] P. M. Woodward, "Probability and Information Theory with Applications to Radar," McGraw-Hill Book Co., Inc., New York, N. Y., pp. 115–118; 1953.

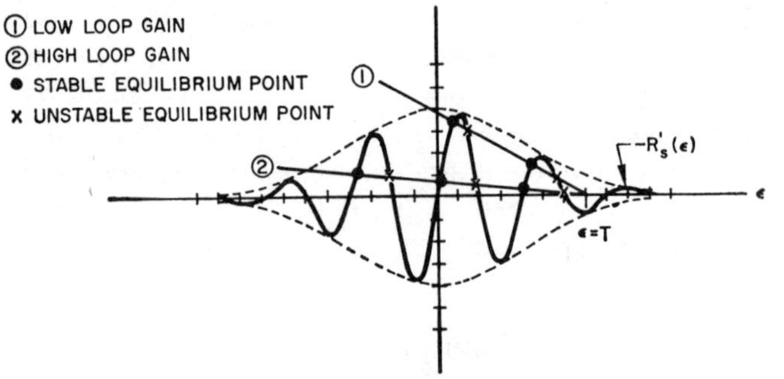

(a)

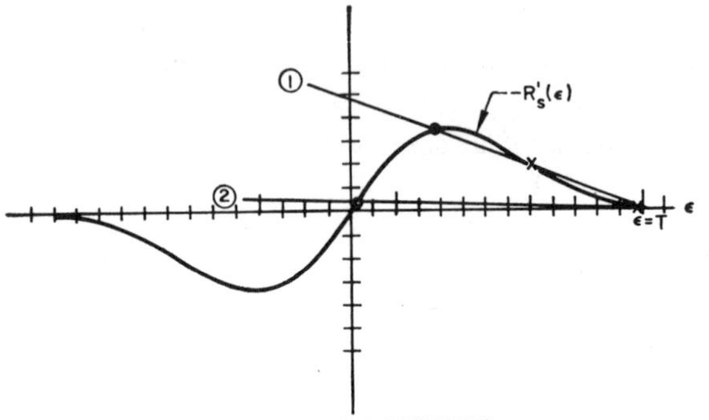

(b)

Fig. 8—Possible steady-state conditions. (a) Band-pass signal spectrum. (b) Low-pass signal spectrum.

Notice that the slope $d\hat{T}/dt$ is proportional to the difference between $-R_s'(T-\hat{T})$ and the straight line as shown in Fig. 8. Thus the slope becomes zero whenever the two curves cross. Of course if there are any zero slope points in negative discriminator slope regions, they are still unstable because of noise considerations neglected in (12).

If the Gaussian low-pass spectrum of Fig. 7(b) is assumed for the signal, and the loop gain is sufficient so that only one zero slope point exists, then the time $\tau$ required for the error to change from $\epsilon(0)=T$ to $\epsilon(\tau)=\epsilon_T$, the threshold condition, is given by

$$\tau = \int_0^\tau dt = \int_0^{T-\epsilon_T} \frac{d\hat{T}}{\omega_f[-gR_s'(T-\hat{T})/P_d - \hat{T}]}$$

$$\approx \int_0^{T-\epsilon_T} \frac{P_d\, d\hat{T}}{-\omega_f g R_s'(T-\hat{T})} \tag{13}$$

where the last expression assumed $-gR_s'(T-\hat{T}) \gg P_d\hat{T}$ in the region of interest. For the Gaussian spectrum (13) becomes

$$\tau = \hat{T}\int_{\epsilon_T} \frac{P_d e^{(B_s\epsilon)^2} d\epsilon}{\omega_f g 2B_s^2\epsilon} = \frac{P_d}{2B_s^2\omega_f g}\left[\ln y + \sum_{n=1}^{\infty} \frac{y^{2n}}{2n(n!)}\right]_{\epsilon_T B_s}^{TB_s}$$

where $y \triangleq B_s\epsilon$.

Now, by making use of the series representation

$$\frac{1}{2y^2}(e^{y^2}-1) = \frac{1}{2}\sum_{n=0}^{\infty}\frac{y^{2n}}{(n+1)!}$$

and the approximation $n(n!) \approx (n+1)!$ for $n \gg 1$, then for $y > 1$ we have

$$\tau \approx \frac{P_d}{4B_s^2\omega_f g}\left[\frac{1}{y^2}(e^{y^2}-1-y^2)\right]_{\epsilon_T B_s}^{TB_s} \tag{14}$$

Thus, with sufficiently large loop gain and the absence of interfering noise, the discriminator will eventually lock on even if the initial delay error is large. However, if $\epsilon(0)=T \gg 1/B_s$, the lock-on time will become extremely large and interfering noise effects will become of dominant importance.

Referring to (13) one sees that low-pass signals with autocorrelation functions which decrease rapidly with delay for large delays (desirable because of the effects of multiple targets) have lock-on times which increase extremely rapidly with initial delay error for large initial errors, *e.g.*, from (14),

$$\tau \sim e^{(TB_s)^2}/(TB_s)^2$$

for large $TB_s$ with the Gaussian signal spectrum.

## Accuracy of the Discriminator

In this section we return to the investigation of linear discriminator operation and the linearized equivalent representation shown in Fig. 4. The objective of this section is to determine the accuracy of the discriminator and the threshold value of input SNR. Intrinsic noise effects are assumed negligible compared to those caused by other error terms. Both band-pass and low-pass signal spectra are considered. The input signal amplitude is assumed fixed.

The target delay to be used is a ramp of delay beginning at $t=0$ and corresponds to a sudden change in velocity, *i.e.*,

$$T(t) = 0 \qquad \text{for } t < 0$$

$$= \frac{2v}{c}t \qquad t \geq 0,$$

where $v$ is the target velocity, and $c$ the velocity of light. The Laplace transform of the delay is $T(p)=2v/cp^2$. Although real targets, of course, cannot change velocity instantaneously in this manner, they can approximate this ramp well enough to make the results of this analysis useful. This sudden ramp of delay is also important in studying the discriminator response when the return from a constant velocity target is suddenly applied to the input. Furthermore, the general behavior of the transient errors and the steady-state errors with velocity inputs are of interest by themselves. The linearized analysis used here applies only if the delay error at the beginning of the transient $\epsilon(0)$ is much less than the threshold error.

Two loop filters are shown in Fig. 9. The first of these, a simple integrator, produces a closed-loop transfer function [obtained from (3)] which is given by

$$H(p) = \frac{\alpha}{kAP_d}\left(\frac{1}{1 + p/p_0}\right). \tag{15}$$

This filter has zero steady-state error to step inputs of delay, but a finite nonzero steady-state error to ramp inputs. The second loop filter, shown in Fig. 9(b), is composed of an integrator and an RC filter. The closed-loop transfer function for this filter is

$$H(p) = \frac{\alpha}{kAP_d}\,\frac{1 + \sqrt{2}\,p/p_0}{1 + \sqrt{2}\,p/p_0 + (p/p_0)^2}\cdot \tag{16}$$

This loop filter has been shown optimum for ramp inputs in the presence of white noise, in that it minimizes the total squared transient error plus the mean square error caused by interfering noise.[15] The frequency $p_0$ would then be chosen by relative weighting of the two types of errors. The frequency here will be chosen from other considerations, namely, to keep the peak transient error below a set value. This filter produces zero steady-state error in response to a ramp input.

The transient error is defined as the delay error $T(t) - \hat{T}(t)$ for a given delay function $T(t)$ in the absence of discriminator interference $n_e(t)$. The transient error for the simple integrator type of loop filter [Fig. 9(a)] with a ramp of delay as the input is shown in Fig. 10(a). The corresponding closed-loop frequency response is shown in Fig. 10(b). Notice that the error rises to a final steady-state value $\epsilon_t(\infty) = 2v/cp_0$ for a target radial velocity $v$, and a corresponding steady-state target position error $2v/p_0$. It is obviously desirable to have $\epsilon_t(\infty) < \epsilon_T$ and the position error small enough to obtain the required position accuracy. Suppose, then, that we choose $p_0$ to obtain the desired small steady-state transient error $\epsilon_t(\infty)$, *i.e.*, $p_0 = 2v/c\epsilon_t(\infty)$.

For this value of $p_0$, what is the lowest input SNR for which we can keep the delay errors below the threshold value $\epsilon_T$ most of the time? If the equivalent input noise, $n_e(t)$, is assumed Gaussian, and produces an rms error $\sigma_{\epsilon_n}$ in the delay estimate, then a reasonable condition for the discriminator to be said to operate above threshold is that $\sigma_{\epsilon_n} \le \epsilon_T/3$. For delay errors which are approximately Gaussian (transient errors are assumed much less than $\epsilon_T$), this condition corresponds to a probability of $|\epsilon| \ge \epsilon_T$ of less than or equal to 0.27 per cent at any instant of time.

The rms value of noise error for white noise inputs can be found from the expression

$$\sigma_{\epsilon_n}{}^2 = \int_{-\infty}^{\infty} k^2 G_{n_n}(f)\,|H(j\omega)/\alpha|^2 df = G_{n_n}(0)p_0/2(AP_d)^2$$

[15] R. Jaffe and E. Rechtin, "Design and performance of phase-locked circuits capable of near optimum performance over a wide range of input signal levels," IRE Trans. on Information Theory, vol. IT-1, pp. 66–72; March, 1955.

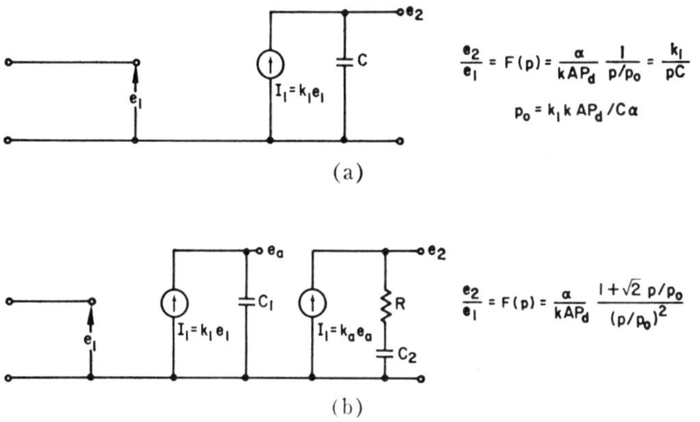


Fig. 9—Two loop filters and their transfer functions.

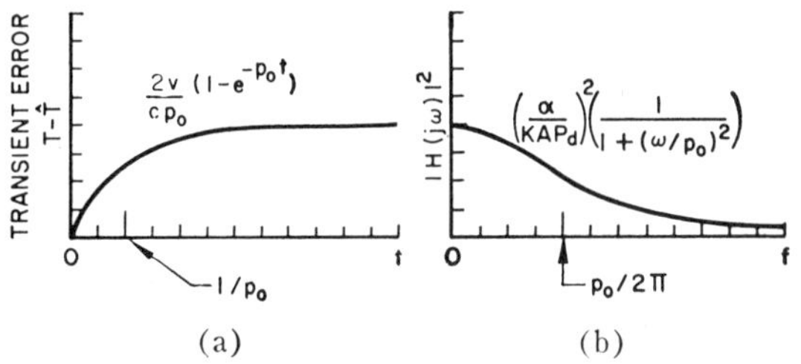


Fig. 10—Discriminator performance with the loop filter of Fig. 9(a). (a) Transient error in response to a ramp of delay. (b) Closed-loop frequency response.

where $G_{n_n}(f)$ is the power spectral density of the noise term $n_n(t)$. For the value of $p_0$ chosen, we have

$$\sigma_{\epsilon_n}{}^2 = \frac{G_{n_n}(0)v}{c\epsilon_t(\infty)(AP_d)^2}\cdot \tag{17}$$

The threshold occurs, then, when $G_{n_n}(0)$ has the value $c\epsilon_T{}^2\epsilon_t(\infty)(AP_d)^2/9v$. The power spectral density $G_{n_n}(0)$ is in turn related to the input noise spectral density. For white input noise $n(t)$ and a signal spectrum which is rectangular or Gaussian in shape, the spectrum of $G_{n_n}(f)$ is also white.

For white interfering noise $n(t)$ with power $P_n$ in a bandwidth $2B_s$ (both positive and negative frequency regions are used throughout this paper), the amplitude of this power spectral density is[16]

$$G_{n_n}(f) = P_d G_s(f) * G_n(f)$$

and

$$G_{n_n}(0) = P_d P_n/2B_s. \tag{18}$$

This last relation is valid regardless of the shape of the spectrum of $s(t)$ and has assumed that the spectrum of $s'(t+\hat{T})$ is the same as that of $s'(t)$.

Now by combining (17) and (18), the threshold input SNR can be found

$$(\text{SNR})_{\text{threshold}} = \left[\frac{A^2}{P_n}\right]_{\text{threshold}} = \frac{4.5(v/c)}{B_s P_d \epsilon_T{}^2 \epsilon_t(\infty)}\cdot \tag{19}$$

[16] The use of the asterisk indicates convolution in the frequency domain.

It is seen that, in general, the threshold SNR increases as the transient error $\epsilon_t$ is made smaller for fixed velocity $v$, just as expected.

To evaluate this expression, the power spectrum of $s(t)$ must be specified so that $\epsilon_T$ and $P_d$ can be determined. If $s(t)$ has a Gaussian low-pass spectrum,

$$G_s(f) = \frac{\sqrt{\pi}}{B_s} \exp - (\pi f/B_s)^2, \qquad \sigma \text{ is } \frac{B_s}{\sqrt{2}\pi}$$

for this spectrum, then

$$\epsilon_T = 1/\sqrt{2}B_s, \qquad P_d = (2\pi\sigma)^2 = 2B_s^2.$$

Thus the threshold SNR is

$$(\text{SNR})_{\text{threshold}} = \frac{4.5(v/c)}{B_s\epsilon_t(\infty)} \tag{20}$$

As an example, suppose $B_s = 1$ Mc, which makes $\epsilon_T = 0.707$ $\mu$sec, $\epsilon_t(\infty) = 0.1$ $\mu$sec (98.4 ft. transient error), $v = 2000$ mph, and ($v/c = 2.99 \times 10^{-6}$), then the threshold SNR is $1.36 \times 10^{-4}$ or $-38.6$ db.

The transient error for the loop filter depicted in Fig. 9(b) in response to the same ramp input of delay $T(t) = 2(v/c)t$ is shown in Fig. 11(a). The closed-loop frequency response is shown in Fig. 11(b). The peak transient error for this filter is $\epsilon_t(t_{\text{peak}}) = 0.91$ $(v/cp_0)$ and occurs at time $t_{\text{peak}} = 1.11/p_0$. Because the transient error is significant over a limited time interval only (about $2t_{\text{peak}}$) and has a limited rise time, it can be seen that in order to have the peak transient error from a real target be well approximated by that given in Fig. 11(a), the actual change in target velocity must occur over a time interval less than $t_{\text{peak}}$. In other words, the maximum target velocity transient considered here is the velocity change that can occur in a period of time $t_{\text{peak}}$.

The peak transient error will be set at $\epsilon_T/3$, *i.e.*, $p_0 = 2.72v/c\epsilon_T$. Threshold will be said to occur when the delay error caused by noise $\epsilon_n$ has an rms value $\sigma_{\epsilon_n} = \epsilon_T/3$. For Gaussian $\epsilon_n$, this condition corresponds to a probability of $|\epsilon| \geq \epsilon_T$ of 0.27 per cent when there is no transient error. The probability of $|\epsilon| \geq \epsilon_T$ at peak transient error is 2.3 per cent.

The mean square delay error caused by a white interfering noise input can be found using (16) as[17]

$$\sigma_{\epsilon_n}^2 = \int_{-\infty}^{\infty} k^2 G_{n_n}(f) \mid H(j\omega)/\alpha \mid^2 df$$

$$= 1.06 G_{n_n}(0) p_0/(AP_d)^2 = (\epsilon_T/3)^2. \tag{21}$$

Now by using (18), (21) and the relation for $p_0$, the threshold input SNR can be found as

$$(\text{SNR})_{\text{threshold}} = \left(\frac{A^2}{P_n}\right)_{\text{threshold}} = \frac{13.0(v/c)}{B_s P_d \epsilon_T^3} \cdot \tag{22}$$

[17] This integral has been evaluated using D. Bierens de Haan, "Nouvelles tables d'intégrales définés," Hafner Publishing Co., New York, N. Y., p. 47; 1957.

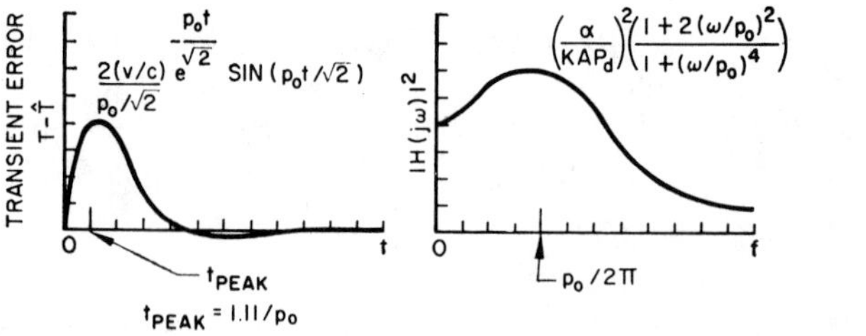


(a) (b)

Fig. 11—Discriminator performance with the loop filter of Fig. 9(b). (a) Transient error in response to a ramp of delay. (b) Closed-loop frequency response.

If the signal spectrum has a Gaussian shape as before $\sigma = B_s/\sqrt{2}\pi$, then (22) becomes

$$(\text{SNR})_{\text{threshold}} = 18.4(v/c). \tag{23}$$

As a second example, suppose $v = 2000$ mph ($v/c = 2.99 \times 10^{-6}$). Then the threshold (SNR) is $5.5 \times 10^{-5}$ or $-43$ db, an improvement of more than 4 db over that provided by the first filter.

## Tracking an Actively Transmitting Target

One of the more important applications of the delay-lock discriminator is to track a target which is itself transmitting a wide-bandwidth, random signal. Information on the target position can be obtained by estimating the delay difference $T(t)$ between the signals as they arrive at the two antennas as shown in Fig. 12. The signal received from one antenna is fed into the discriminator as the reference, and the other received signal is fed into the input. By comparing the delay differences for three such pairs of antennas, the target position (including range) can be determined as the intersection point of three hyperboloids.[18] Two pairs of antennas are sufficient to provide angular information.

As it concerns the operation of the delay-lock discriminator, this problem differs from the one just discussed only in that the noise-perturbed signal received in one antenna is used as the reference. As a result, a corresponding degradation in accuracy at low input SNR is to be expected. By referring to Fig. 13 and (2), one can write the low-frequency terms of the multiplier output as

$$x(t) = A_1 A_2 P_d \epsilon(t) + n_e(t) \tag{24}$$

where $n_e(t)$ is the equivalent linearized interference and has the representation

$$n_e(t) = A_1 A_2 [n_d(t) + n_i(t)] + A_1 s(t + T) n_2'(t + \hat{T})$$

$$+ A_2 s'(t + \hat{T}) n_1(t) + n_1(t) n_2'((t + \hat{T}), \tag{25}$$

[18] Actually, there are two intersections of the three hyperboloids, one on each side of the plane of the antennas. However, if the antennas are on the ground, it is usually easy to decide which point is correct.

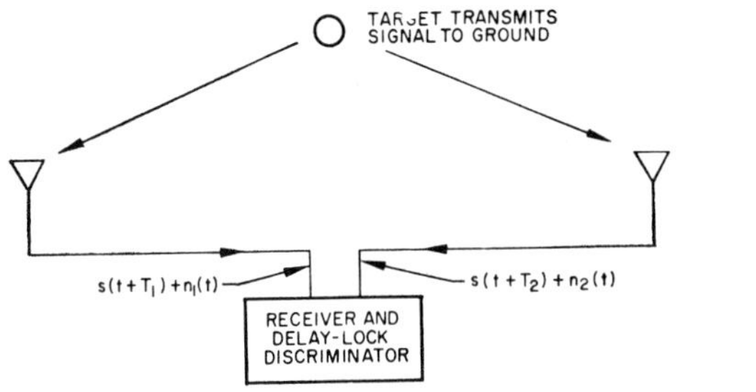


Fig. 12—Tracking a target which is transmitting a wide bandwidth signal.

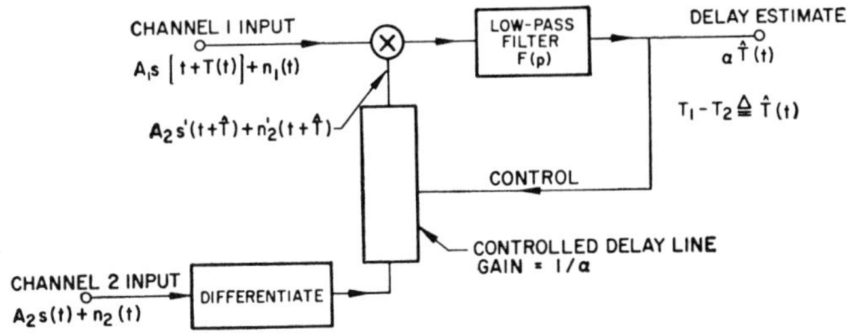


Fig. 13—Operation of the delay-lock discriminator with a noise perturbed reference.

where $n_d(t)$, $n_i(t)$ are the distortion and intrinsic noise components, respectively. Notice that in addition to the noise terms of (6) there are now two additional noise terms, another $S \times N$ term (signal times noise term) and a $N \times N$ term.

In many situations the dominant noise terms are generated in the two receiver amplifiers, and the noise terms $n_1(t)$ and $n_2(t)$ are independent of one another. If the spectra of the signal and these noise components have bandwidths much greater than the closed loop bandwidth of the discriminator, then $n_e(t)$ can be considered to have an approximately white spectrum, and the results of the previous section can be used to obtain the performance of this discriminator. Of course, if $n_1(t)$ and $n_2(t)$ contain components which are not independent, any dc and low-frequency noise components which might then exist must be taken into account.

If, for example, we take the signal and independent noise components to have rectangular spectra with bandwidths $B_s$, then the equivalent noise spectrum in the low-frequency region is

$$G_{n_n}(0) = \frac{1}{2B_s}(A_1{}^2 P_{dn_2} + A_2{}^2 P_d P_{n_1} + P_{dn2} P_{n_1}) = \frac{A_1{}^2 A_2{}^2 P_d}{2B_s}(r_1 + r_2 + r_1 r_2) \qquad (26)$$

where $P_{n1}$, $P_{dn2}$ are the average powers in $n_1(t)$, $n_2'(t)$, and $r_1$, $r_2$ are the noise-to-signal power ratios on channels 1 and 2, respectively.

If intrinsic noise effects are negligible, then threshold input SNR can be obtained by combining (26) with either (17) or (21), depending on which loop filter is used. Notice that constant $k$ in (15) and (16) now becomes $A_2$. Consider that the loop filter of Fig. 9(b) is used. Then by using (21), (26) and assuming equal SNR on both channels, the threshold SNR can be evaluated as

$$(\mathrm{SNR})_{\text{threshold}} = h + \sqrt{h + h^2} \qquad (27)$$

where

$h \triangleq 13.0(v/c)/B_s P_d \epsilon_T{}^3$, and $v$ is the radial velocity difference to the antennas. For $h \ll 1$, this relation becomes $(\mathrm{SNR})_{\text{threshold}} = \sqrt{h}$. As an example, suppose that $v = 2000$ mph. If the signal spectrum is low-pass and rectangular, then $\epsilon_T \cong \frac{1}{2}B_s$, $P_d = (2\pi B_s)^{2/3}$, and the threshold SNR is $4.85 \times 10^{-3}$ or $-23$ db.

## Effect of AGC or Limiting on the Discriminator Performance

As pointed out earlier, to control the discriminator loop gain it is desirable to feed the received data through a limiter or an amplifier with strong AGC. The use of an ideal AGC serves to maintain a constant average input power for the discriminator and has a relatively simple effect. Thus, the ideal AGC acts as a variable attenuator which produces no distortion of the input, but attenuates the amplitude of the signal component in its output. Its only effect is to vary the discriminator loop gain as a function of the input SNR. If the total input power to the discriminator is $A_t{}^2$ and only one channel has noise added and AGC control, then the effective loop gain is

$$\text{loop gain} = g = \frac{kA_t P_d g_d F(0)}{\sqrt{1 + P_n/P_s}}. \qquad (28)$$

The change in the loop gain, however, is important because it affects both the dynamic range of the discriminator and the closed-loop bandwidth. Here we encounter the problem: if a time invariant loop filter is to be used, what value of the loop gain should be assumed in designing the loop filter?

Once the discriminator has locked onto the signal, the most critical phenomenon is the occurrence of the threshold or loss of lock condition. While the discriminator is operating well above threshold at a fixed SNR, there is a linear relationship—the closed-loop transfer function $H(j\omega)$—between the true delay and the delay estimate. Thus we can follow the discriminator with a linear filter with a transfer function $H_2(j\omega)$, and the product $H_T(j\omega) = H(j\omega)H_2(j\omega)$ can be chosen so that it is optimum in some sense, *e.g.*, $H_T(j\omega)$ can be chosen as the realizable Wiener filter which allows some particular value of delay (negative, if a predictor is desired) in forming the estimate of the target delay. Consequently, one reasonable approach to this is to optimize the loop filter using the threshold value of loop gain, and then to choose a time invariant filter $H_2(j\omega)$, so that $H_T(j\omega)$ is optimum in the Wiener sense at large input SNR.

Now, if we consider that the single noisy channel has a limiter preceding the discriminator, it can be shown that the dominant effect is the change in the loop gain. However, the exact dependence of loop gain on input SNR is not always exactly the same as with perfect

AGC, because the limiter input and output SNR are not always equal. For example, Davenport[19] has shown that the signal power output of an ideal band-pass limiter for sine wave plus Gaussian noise inputs is related to the total limiter output power by the expression

$$P_{s\,\text{out}} = \frac{P_T}{1 + b(P_n/P_s)}$$

where $P_T$ is the band-pass limiter output power, $\pi/4 \leq b \leq 2$, and $b$ depends on the input SNR $P_s/P_n$. The loop gain varies with $P_{s\,\text{out}}$ roughly in the same manner as with AGC.

If the input to an ideal limiter is a Gaussian signal plus independent Gaussian noise, then the discriminator operating curve can be obtained using the results of Bussgang[20] which show that the cross-correlation between the input and output of the limiter is proportional to the autocorrelation function of the input. The discriminator operating curve can thus be shown to be

$$-R'(\tau) = \sqrt{P_s P_T}\,\frac{-R_s'(\tau)}{\sqrt{1+r}}$$

where $P_T$ is the limiter output power, $P_s$ is the signal power, and $R_s(\tau)$ is the autocorrelation function of the signal which has been normalized to unity power. In this way the loop gain is changed exactly as it was with the AGC. The loop gain change may not be the only effect, because in passing through the limiter the noise statistics change and harmonics of the signal are generated. In practice, however, the limiting operation can usually be done at an IF or RF frequency (before detection if $s(t)$ is to be low-pass) so that harmonic content is removed by band-pass filters and is of little concern.

It is sometimes convenient to limit both received data channels at the multiplier inputs; the reference channel is differentiated and delayed before amplitude limiting. With this type of operation the multiplier inputs are both binary random variables, and the multiplier circuit can be implemented by using an AND circuit. If both inputs to the receiver have stationary Gaussian statistics and the noise-to-signal power ratios on the two channels are $r_1$ and $r_2$, then the discriminator characteristic can be shown to be[21]

$$\frac{2}{\pi} P_T \sin^{-1}\left[R_s'(\tau)/\sqrt{(1+r_1)(1+r_2)R_s(0)R_s''(0)}\right]$$

where $P_T$ is the output power of each of the limiters, and $R_s(\tau)$ is the autocorrelation function of the signal. The ratio $R_s'(0)/\sqrt{R_s(0)R_s''(0)}$ is less than unity as can be shown using the Schwarz inequality. This discriminator characteristic is of roughly the same shape as obtained without limiting since $\sin^{-1}x \approx x$ for $|x| < 1$. The peak value of the loop gain varies in proportion to $[(1+r_1)(1+r_2)]^{-1/2}$.

If a band-pass limiter is used on both received input channels, then using Price's[22] (6) we can show that the cross-correlation is given by

$$R_{12}(\tau) = \frac{\left(\frac{\pi}{8}\right) P_T R_s(\tau)}{\sqrt{(1+r_1)(1+r_2)}}\left\{1 + \sum_{m=1}^{\infty} \frac{\left[\left(\frac{1}{2}\right)\left(\frac{3}{2}\right)\cdots\left(\frac{2m-1}{2}\right)\right]^2}{m!(m-1)!} \cdot \frac{\rho_s^{2m}(\tau)}{\sqrt{(1+r_1)(1+r_2)}}\right\}$$

where $R_s(\tau) \triangleq \rho_s(\tau)\cos[\omega_0\tau + \lambda(\tau)]$, *i.e.*, $\rho_s(\tau)$ is the envelope of $R_s(\tau)$. The discriminator characteristic, $-R_{12}'(\tau)$, is not greatly different in shape from $-R_s'(\tau)$. The loop gain is again attenuated by both noise-to-signal ratios $r_1$ and $r_2$.

### Experimental Version of the Discriminator

A laboratory model of the delay-lock discriminator has been constructed and tested. The objective of the experimental work was to demonstrate the basic principles of operation and to provide experimental verification of some of the theory of linear operation. Ferrite-core delay lines with magnetically controlled permeability[23] were used in these particular experiments as the variable delay elements.

A block diagram of the experimental delay-lock discriminator is shown in Fig. 14. In this experimental equipment, the reflection and transmission from the target were simulated by another delay line similar to the one used in the discriminator. An AGC amplifier was provided in the signal input channel to maintain constant input power to the discriminator. The loop filter $F(p)$ consisted of a RC low-pass filter with a time constant of 8.8 msec.

The phase delay vs control current characteristic of the delay lines used in the experimental discriminator is shown in Fig. 15. Note the nonlinearity and hysteresis effect present even for relatively small delay variations. Additional measurements have shown the slope of the curve (*i.e.*, the delay line gain) to vary as a function of carrier frequency approximately ±10 per cent of the value shown. The group delay (slope of the phase shift vs frequency curve) is expected to vary by about this same amount from the values shown.

The amplitude spectrum of the carrier measured at the output of the AGC amplifier is shown in Fig. 16(a).

[19] W. B. Davenport, Jr., "Signal-to-noise ratios in bandpass limiters," *J. Appl. Phys.*, vol. 24, pp. 720–727; June, 1953.

[20] J. J. Bussgang, "Cross-correlation functions of amplitude-distorted Gaussian signals," Mass. Inst. Tech., Cambridge, Mass., RLE TR No. 216, pp. 4–13; March, 1952.

[21] If $x_1$ and $x_2$ are limited forms of $y_1 \triangleq s + n_1$ and $y_2 \triangleq s' + n_2$, respectively, then it can be shown that $R_{x_1x_2}(\tau) = P_T\{4\,\Pr[y_1(t) > 0, y_2(t+\tau) > 0] - 1\}$, where $\Pr(y > 0)$ is the probability that $y > 0$. This probability can be evaluated by integrating the bivariate normal distribution to obtain the above result.

[22] R. Price, "A note on the envelope and phase-modulated components of narrow-band Gaussian noise," IRE Trans. on Information Theory, vol. IT-1, pp. 9–12; September, 1955.

[23] H. W. Katz and R. E. Schultz, "Miniaturized ferrite delay lines," 1955 Natl. IRE Convention Record, pt. 2, pp. 78–86.

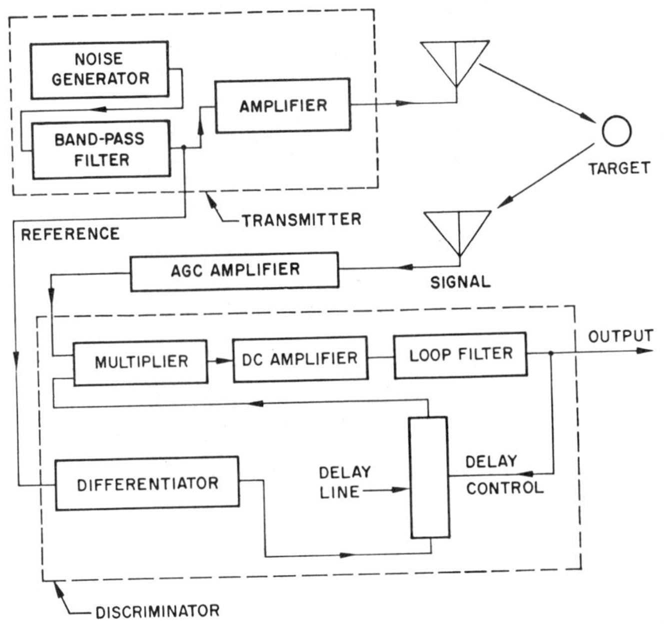


Fig. 14—Experimental system-block diagram.

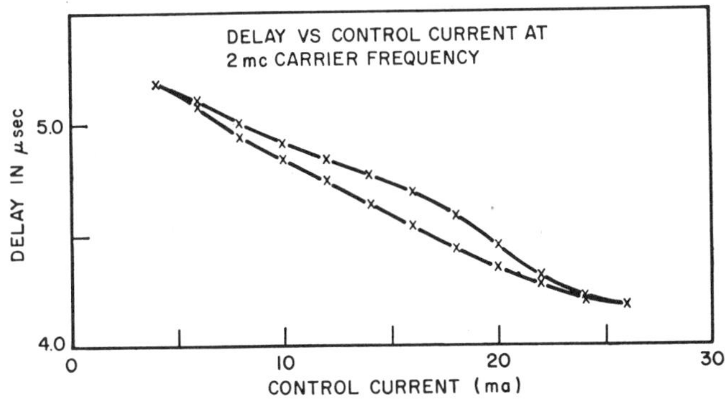


Fig. 15—Discriminator delay-line characteristic.

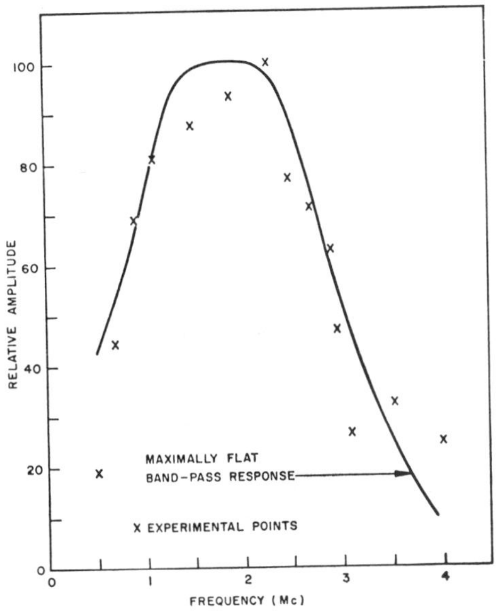


(a)

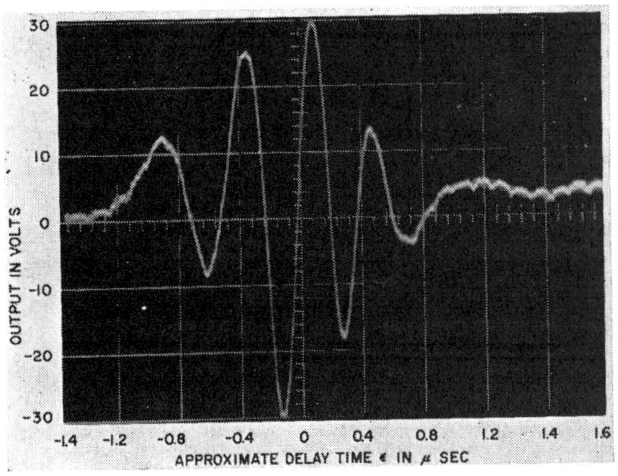


(b)

Fig. 16 (a) Amplitude spectrum of carrier. (b) Oscillogram of discriminator characteristic.

A maximally flat band-pass spectrum with the same 3 db points as the experimental data is plotted for comparison. This spectrum has a center frequency of 1.85 Mc.

The discriminator characteristic obtained from the experimental system is shown in Fig. 16(b). The horizontal axis is labelled "approximate delay" since much nonlinear distortion was produced by the delay line. Note that the delay variation presented is about $2\frac{1}{2}$ times that shown in Fig. 15. It should be pointed out, however, that the operating range for the measurements presented is the main lock-on region at the center of the oscillogram. This portion of the discriminator characteristic, which is quite linear, extends $\pm 0.12$ μsec about the $\epsilon = 0$ position. This wave corresponds to a center frequency of approximately 2.1 Mc for a symmetrical band-pass spectrum. Thus, the major linear region of the characteristic extends over a range of delay error $\epsilon$ that agrees to within 13 per cent of the value predicted by the maximally flat band-pass approximation to the experimental spectrum.

Measured open-loop and closed-loop amplitude responses are plotted in Figs. 17(a) and 17(b), respectively. The measured open-loop response coincides well with the theoretical response of an RC low-pass loop filter with a cutoff frequency of 18 cps. Using a linearized equivalent circuit similar to Fig. 4, we see that for such a simple filter the only effect of the feedback will be to multiply the cutoff frequency by a factor of $1+g$. The measured loop gain was $g=11$. The theoretical closed loop response plotted in Fig. 17(b) is that of a single real-axis pole with a cutoff frequency of 216 cps. The measured closed-loop response, plotted also in Fig. 17(b), again matches the theoretical curve closely.

Another check on the theory of linear operation of the delay-lock discriminator can be made by measuring the transient error for a triangular wave input. Figs. 18(a) and 18(b) show the discriminator responses for 13 ma, peak-to-peak inputs of frequencies 24 cps and 240 cps, respectively. Since a triangular wave is a summation of an infinite number of ramps, the transient error to a triangular wave can be found from the error to a ramp.

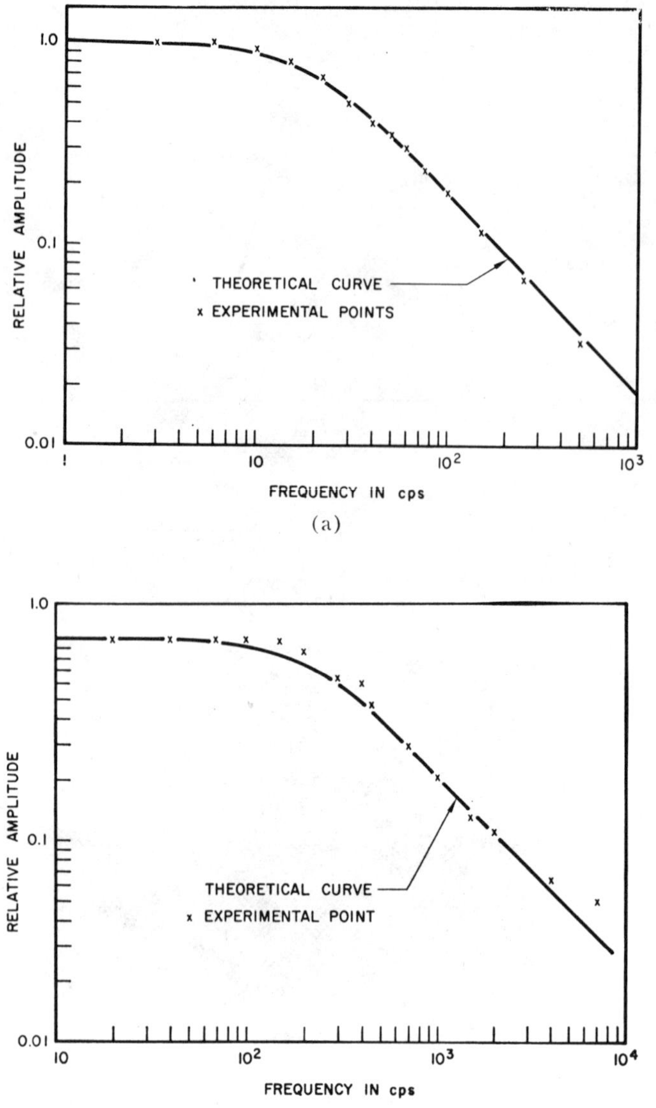


(b)

Fig. 17—(a) Open-loop amplitude response. (b) Closed-loop amplitude response.

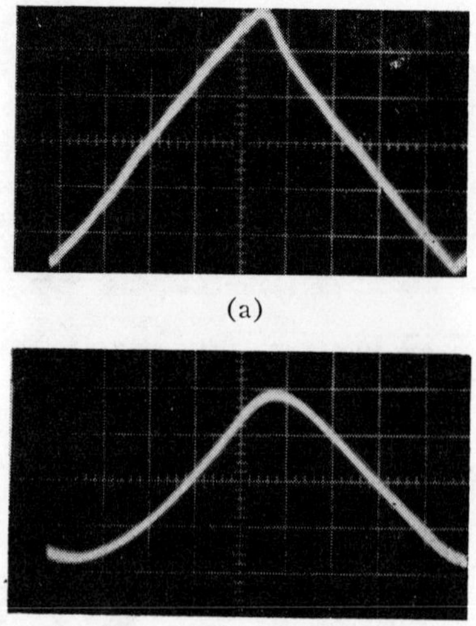

(a)

(b)

Fig. 18—Oscillograms of discriminator delay-line, control current for triangular wave control current in modulating delay line. (a) 24 cps input. Vertical scale is 2 ma per division, while the horizontal scale is 5 msec per division. (b) 240 cps input. Vertical scale is 2 ma per division, while the horizontal scale is 500 $\mu$sec per div.

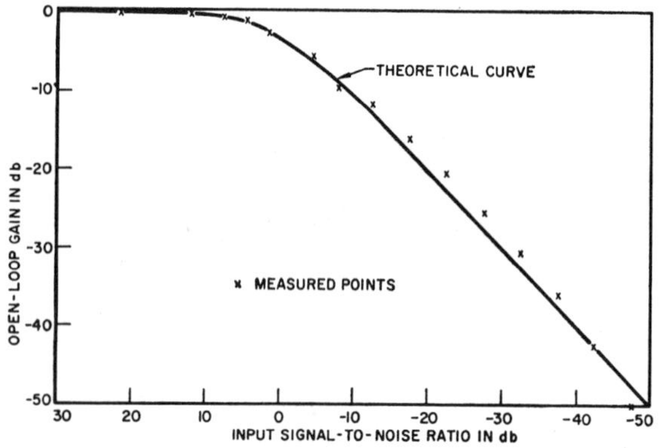


Fig. 19—Loop gain vs input signal-to-noise power ratio.

From elementary control theory, using a linearized equivalent circuit similar to Fig. 4, it is possible to find a simple expression for the delay error $\epsilon(t)$ to a ramp input of delay.

$$\epsilon(t) = \frac{at}{(1+g)} + \frac{agRC}{(1+g)^2}(1 - e^{-(1+g)t/RC}) \qquad (29)$$

where the input is

$$T(t) = at, \qquad t \geq 0$$
$$= 0, \qquad t < 0.$$

If we define $\epsilon'$ as the peak-to-peak output error in response to a triangular wave input, then it can be shown that[24]

$$\epsilon' = 2\epsilon(t = T_0/2) \qquad (30)$$

[24] Choose the time origin so that the input function is an even function of time.

where $T_0$ is the period of the triangular wave input. Further calculations using (29) and (30) predict a peak-to-peak amplitude of 11.6 ma for the 24 cps input, and a peak-to-peak amplitude of 8.0 ma for the 240 cps input. These predictions are in good agreement with the oscillograms of Figs. 18(a) and 18 (b).

The measured loop gain as a function of input, SNR power ratio, is plotted in Fig. 19. A theoretical curve based on (28) is plotted in the same figure and corresponds closely with the experimental points. This curve of loop gain is an indirect indication of closed-loop discriminator dynamic range and closed-loop bandwidth. A version of this discriminator, with a higher dc loop gain than that described here, has operated at input SNR ratios as low as $-40$ db.

## Discussion

On the basis of these results, the delay-lock discriminator appears to have good potential in tracking rapidly moving targets while using very low, received, SNR ratios. It is especially suited to tracking problems where the initial target position is known or where tracking is to begin only when the target enters a fixed perimeter. However, by the use of search techniques, targets of unknown initial position can be tracked.

By properly choosing the signal spectrum shape and bandwidth, good performance can be obtained with respect both to reducing the ambiguity in target position and discriminating against undesired targets.

In practice, where tracking is required over moderately long distances, the use of servocontrolled ultrasonic delay lines seems attractive. Delays in the millisecond range are attainable using such lines, and the linearity of delay vs control voltage can be made quite good. However, the response of the servosystem has to be taken into account in computing the closed-loop response. The presence of this servomotor within the loop may require some modification of the loop filter depending on the speed of response desired. Other delay techniques using such devices as magnetic recorders or shift registers might also be useful where long delays are desired.

The delay line also restricts the signal frequency spectrum that can be used because of its delay-bandwidth product limitations. At present, quartz delay lines can function at frequencies up to 100 Mc. However, the state of the art prevents direct discriminator operation at frequencies much above this with delays in the millisecond region. If transmission frequencies above this are to be used (a likely requirement) and delays are large, the transmitted signal can be formed by amplitude or frequency-modulating an RF sine wave with low-pass random energy. The low-pass random waveform can then be synchronously (or nonsynchronously) detected at the receiver, and the detected signal fed into the delay-lock discriminator. If synchronous detection is to be used, it should be noted that the phase of the local oscillator used for detection must follow the phase modulation of the carrier caused by the reflection from the moving target.

It is also possible to devise modified versions of the delay-lock discriminator which can operate directly on FM deviated signals and use video delay lines. Nonsynchronous forms of the discriminator can provide delay estimates which are free of the possible ambiguities caused by the fine structure of the signal autocorrelation function. In essence, this type of operation is made possible by ignoring the fine structure and working only with the envelope of the autocorrelation function. If the delay-lock discriminator is to be used in an interferometer, the delay variations generally are in the microsecond region or less, and the frequency limitations of the delay lines become greatly relaxed.

Further work is being carried out on the problems of locking-on and unwanted target discrimination. For example, reflections from undesired targets can be discriminated against in both range and velocity by making the closed-loop bandwidth relatively small. Then, if the undesired target passes rapidly enough through the range of the target to which the discriminator is locked, the interfering transients which result occur too rapidly to affect materially the discriminator output. Adaptive filtering techniques seem to be appropriate here; one loop filter can be employed during the lock-on transient, and another can be used after lock-on is established.

## List of Symbols

$A$ = signal amplitude
$B_s$ = signal bandwidth (cps)
$c$ = velocity of light (or of sound if sonic propagation is considered)
$e$ = 2.718
$E$ = expected value of a random variable
$f$ = frequency (cps)
$f_0$ = center frequency of the signal
$F(p)$ = loop filter transfer function
$g$ = loop gain
$G_s(f)$, $G_n(f)$ = signal, noise, power, spectral densities
$h$ = a constant
$H(p)$ = linearized equivalent transfer function
$k$ = reference signal amplitude
$n(t)$ = input noise waveform
$n_e(t)$ = equivalent noise
$p$ = complex frequency
$p_0$ = filter cutoff frequency in rad/sec
$P_s$, $P_n$ = signal, noise-average power
$r$ = input noise-to-signal power ratio
$R_s(\tau)$, $R_n(\tau)$ = signal, noise autocorrelation functions
$s(t)$ = signal waveform (unity power)
$t$ = the variable time
$T(t)$ = delay
$\hat{T}(t)$ = estimate of delay
$v$ = velocity of the target
$x(t)$ = multiplier output
$y$ = a variable
$\alpha$ = relative amplitude of the delay estimate
$\delta(f)$ = Dirac delta function
$\Delta T$ = dynamic range of the discriminator
$\epsilon(t)$ = delay error $T(t)-\hat{T}(t)$
$\epsilon_T$ = threshold delay error
$\rho(\tau)$ = envelope of the normalized autocorrelation function
$\sigma$ = standard deviation of a random variable
$\tau$ = a variable representing time
$\phi(t)$ = phase function
$\omega$ = angular frequency
$\omega_i(t)$ = instantaneous angular frequency

## Acknowledgment

The authors would like to acknowledge the valuable comments and suggestions of their associates in Communications Research at Lockheed Missiles and Space Company. Special thanks are expressed to M. R. O'Sullivan for his interesting and rewarding comments.

# Effect of Random Synchronization Errors in PN and PSK Systems

GILBERT A. DE COUVREUR, Member, IEEE
Department of Electrical Engineering
Sherbrooke University
Sherbrooke, Quebec, Canada

Abstract

**The effect of a constant synchronization error on PN systems has been studied by Gill [1]. His results are generalized here for random synchronization errors, and extended to PSK systems using decision directed channel measurements [2].**

**In both cases, it is shown that the effect of random synchronization errors is to reduce the effective input signal power and to introduce an additional self-noise. The effect is minimized when the synchronization error has zero mean and can easily be evaluated in terms of circuit parameters.**

Manuscript received April 25, 1969; revised June 16, 1969.

## Introduction

Products of two randomly delayed binary sequences are encountered in both PN systems and PSK systems using decision-directed channel measurements.

In PN systems, regardless of the type of message modulation, the received pseudorandom binary sequence $m(t)$ is multiplied by the locally generated sequence $m(t+\alpha)$, where $\alpha$ is the delay jitter at the output of the delay lock loop. In PSK systems using decision-directed channel measurements, the received message $m(t)$ is multiplied by the detected message $m(t+\alpha)$, where $\alpha$ is the jitter in the bit timing.

The expression for the spectrum of the product of two randomly delayed sequences is obtained in this paper for a Gaussian delay. The effect of the random delay, or random synchronization error $\alpha$, is then evaluated for both systems.

## Power Spectral Density of the Product of Two Randomly Delayed Binary Sequences

In both systems, it is necessary to evaluate the spectrum of $s(t, \alpha)$:

$$s(t, \alpha) = m(t)m(t + \alpha) \tag{1}$$

where, for good SNR, the jitter $\alpha$ can be considered to be Gaussian, with mean $m$ and variance $\sigma^2$.

The autocorrelation $R_S(\tau | \alpha)$ of $s(t, \alpha)$ is itself a random variable depending on $\alpha$:

$$R_S(\tau \mid \alpha) = E[m(t)m(t + \alpha)m(t + \tau)m(t + \tau + \alpha) \mid \alpha].$$

Therefore, the autocorrelation $R_S(\tau)$ is simply the expected value of $R_S(\tau | \alpha)$ with respect to $\alpha$:

$$R_S(\tau) = \int_{-\infty}^{\infty} R_S(\tau \mid \alpha) f(\alpha) d\alpha \tag{2}$$

where $f(\alpha)$ is the PDF of the jitter $\alpha$, assumed Gaussian.

The power spectral density $S(\omega)$ is obtained by Fourier transform:

$$S(\omega) = \int_{-\infty}^{\infty} \int_{-\infty}^{\infty} R_S(\tau \mid \alpha) f(\alpha) e^{-i\omega\tau} d\alpha \, d\tau$$

or

$$S(\omega) = \int_{-\infty}^{\infty} f(\alpha) \int_{-\infty}^{\infty} R_S(\tau \mid \alpha) e^{-i\omega\tau} d\tau \, d\alpha$$

and finally

Reprinted from *IEEE Trans. Aerosp. Electron Syst.*, vol. AES-6, pp. 98–100, Jan. 1970.

$$S(\omega) = \int_{-\infty}^{\infty} S(\omega \mid \alpha) f(\alpha) d\alpha \tag{3}$$

where $S(\omega|\alpha)$ is the power spectral density of $s(t, \alpha)$ for a fixed value of $\alpha$, as given by Gill [1]. This result can be used here, since both $m$ and $\sigma^2$ are much smaller than the bit period $T$.

For PN systems, where $m(t)$ is a PN sequence of length $P$,

$$S(\omega \mid \alpha) = 2\pi \left[1 - \frac{|\alpha|}{T}\,\frac{P+1}{P}\right]^2 \delta(\omega) + 2\pi \frac{P+1}{P}\left(\frac{\alpha}{T}\right)^2 \sum_{n \neq 0} \operatorname{sinc}^2\left(\frac{n\pi\alpha}{T}\right) \delta\left(\omega + \frac{2\pi n}{T}\right) \tag{4}$$

$$+ 2\pi \frac{P+1}{P^2}\left(\frac{\alpha}{T}\right)^2 \sum_{n \neq 0} \operatorname{sinc}^2\left(\frac{n\pi\alpha}{PT}\right) \delta\left(\omega + \frac{2\pi n}{PT}\right).$$

For PSK systems, where $m(t)$ can be represented by a random binary sequence,

$$S(\omega \mid \alpha) = 2\pi \left(1 - \frac{|\alpha|}{T}\right)^2 \delta(\omega) + 2\pi \left(\frac{\alpha}{T}\right)^2 \sum_{n \neq 0} \operatorname{sinc}^2\left(\frac{n\pi\alpha}{T}\right) \delta\left(\omega + \frac{2\pi n}{T}\right) + \frac{\alpha^2}{T} \operatorname{sinc}^2\left(\frac{\omega\alpha}{2}\right) \tag{5}$$

where

$$\operatorname{sinc} x = \frac{\sin x}{x}\cdot$$

The spectrum $S(\omega)$ given by (3) can therefore be evaluated for any statistics of the random delay $\alpha$. In particular, for a Gaussian delay it is found that for PN sequences,

$$S(\omega) = 2\pi \left\{1 - \frac{2(P+1)}{PT}\left[m \operatorname{erf}\left(\frac{m}{\sigma\sqrt{2}}\right) + \sigma\sqrt{\frac{2}{\pi}}\, e^{-(m^2)/(2\sigma^2)}\right] + \left(\frac{P+1}{PT}\right)^2 (\sigma^2 + m^2)\right\} \delta(\omega)$$

$$+ \pi \frac{P+1}{P} \sum_{n \neq 0} \frac{1}{n^2\pi^2}\left[1 - \cos\left(\frac{2n\pi m}{T}\right) e^{-2(n\pi\sigma/T)2}\right] \delta\left(\omega + \frac{2\pi n}{T}\right) \tag{6}$$

$$+ \pi(P+1) \sum_{n \neq 0} \frac{1}{n^2\pi^2}\left[1 - \cos\left(\frac{2n\pi m}{PT}\right) e^{-2[(n\pi\sigma)/(PT)]^2}\right] \delta\left(\omega + \frac{2\pi n}{PT}\right)$$

while for random sequences,

$$S(\omega) = 2\pi \left\{1 - \frac{2}{T}\left[m \operatorname{erf}\left(\frac{m}{\sigma\sqrt{2}}\right) + \sigma\sqrt{\frac{2}{\pi}}\, e^{-m^2/2\sigma^2} + \frac{\sigma^2 + m^2}{T^2}\right\} \delta(\omega)$$

$$+ \pi \sum_{n \neq 0} \frac{1}{\eta^2\pi^2}\left[1 - \cos\left(\frac{2n\pi m}{T}\right) e^{-2(n\pi\sigma/T)^2}\right] \delta\left(\omega + \frac{2\pi n}{T}\right) + \frac{2}{\omega^2 T}\left[1 - \cos(\omega m) e^{-\omega^2\sigma^2/2}\right] \tag{7}$$

where the error function erf $(x)$ is defined, as usual, by

$$\operatorname{erf}(x) = \frac{2}{\sqrt{\pi}} \int_0^x e^{-a^2} da.$$

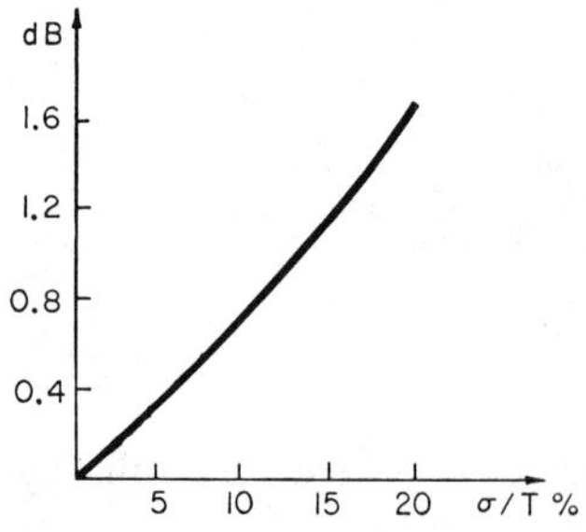


Fig. 1. Power loss in decibels.

### Effect on the Performance

In both expressions (6) and (7), the first term represents the reduced effective signal power, while the second and third terms represent the power in the additional self noise.

It is clear that the signal power is maximum when the mean $m$ of the delay is equal to zero, and that this condition also minimizes the noise contribution. In this case, the expressions (6) and (7) become, respectively, (8) and (10).

For PN sequences, with $P \gg 1$,

$$S_0(\omega) = 2\pi\left[1 - 2\frac{\sigma}{T}\sqrt{\frac{2}{\pi}} + \left(\frac{\sigma}{T}\right)^2\right]\delta(\omega) \tag{8}$$

$$+ \sum_{n\neq 0} \frac{1}{\pi n^2}\left[1 - e^{-2(n\pi\sigma/T)^2}\right]\delta\left(\omega + \frac{2\pi n}{T}\right)$$

$$+ (P+1)\sum_{n\neq 0} \frac{1}{\pi n^2}\left[1 - e^{-2(n\pi\sigma/PT)^2}\right]\delta\left(\omega + \frac{2\pi n}{PT}\right).$$

Usually, the second term is filtered out, while the noise power contributed by the third term is, for $\sigma/PT \ll 1$, approximately equal to

$$\frac{n}{P}\left(\frac{\sigma}{T}\right)^2.$$

This is normally much smaller than the input noise power. Therefore, the main effect of the random synchronization error is to reduce the effective input power by the factor

$$K_\alpha = 1 - 1.6\frac{\sigma}{T}\cdot \tag{9}$$

For random sequences (in PSK),

$$S_0(\omega) = 2\pi\left[1 - 2\frac{\sigma}{T}\sqrt{\frac{2}{\pi}} + \left(\frac{\sigma}{T}\right)^2\right]\delta(\omega)$$

$$+ \sum_{n\neq 0} \frac{1}{\pi n^2}\left[1 - e^{-2(n\pi\sigma/T)^2}\right]\delta\left(\omega + \frac{2\pi n}{T}\right) \tag{10}$$

$$+ \frac{2}{\omega^2 T}\left[1 - e^{-\omega^2\sigma^2/2}\right].$$

The second term is usually filtered out, while the noise power contributed by the third term in a bandwidth $B \ll 1/T$ is approximately equal to $2BT(\sigma/T)^2$. Here again, the main effect of the random timing error is to reduce the effective input signal power by the same factor $K_\alpha$ given by (9); this is represented in Fig. 1.

#### References

[1] W. J. Gill, "Effect of synchronization error in pseudorandom carrier communications," *Proc. 1st Ann. Communication Symp.* (Boulder, Colo., June 1965), paper G-6B-2, pp. 187–191.

[2] J. G. Proakis and P. R. Drouilhet, "Performance of coherent detection systems using decision directed channel measurement," M.I.T. Lincoln Laboratory, Lexington, Mass., Rept. 64G-1, June 27, 1963.

# Analysis and Simulation of a PN Synchronization System

JOHN R. SERGO, JR., MEMBER, IEEE, AND
JEREMIAH F. HAYES, MEMBER, IEEE

*Abstract*—**This paper analyzes the synchronization error which results when a pseudonoise synchronization signal in a coherent communication link is degraded by both additive white Gaussian noise and amplitude jitter produced by the reference carrier phase error. A synchronization system similar to a phase-locked loop is presented and simulated on a digital computer in order to find the distribution of the synchronization error. It is shown that the error is made up of two Gaussian components: one produced by the additive noise and one produced by the amplitude jitter. An approximate solution is also derived by appropriately bounding the reference phase error. The results are shown to be applicable to several similar systems found in the literature.**

## INTRODUCTION

Recently several authors [1], [5], [6], [10], [11] have investigated synchronization systems for coherent communication links. Generally these systems resemble phase-locked loops (PLL) and make use of the cross-correlation properties of pseudonoise (PN) or similar sequences. However, the noise behavior of such systems has been restricted to a given synchronization signal imbedded in additive noise. This paper analyzes the synchronization error which results when the synchronization signal is degraded by both a random amplitude modulation due to noise in the carrier tracking PLL and additive white Gaussian noise. The particular synchronization signal is taken as a modified PN sequence although the results are applicable to any sequence with a similar cross-correlation characteristic. We consider only the steady-state tracking characteristics and assume that acquisition has taken place.

The system that we shall consider is similar to the *two-channel* system considered by Lindsey [2], [3]. In a two-channel system a data signal $d(t)$ and a synchronization signal $s(t)$ jointly phase modulate a common carrier. Upon transmission the signal undergoes a phase shift $\theta$ and is further degraded by additive white Gaussian noise of single-sided spectral density $N_0$ W/Hz. The received signal is then given by

$$r(t) = [2P]^{1/2} \sin [\omega t + \theta + (\cos^{-1} m_D) d(t) + (\cos^{-1} m_s) s(t)] + n(t) \quad (1)$$

where $P$ is the received power and $m_D$, $m_s$ are modulation indices. The received signal is demodulated by tracking the carrier component of $r(t)$ with a narrow-band PLL [10] of one-sided bandwidth $B_L$. It is easily shown [3], [9] that the sync component after demodulation is given by

$$e(t) = [P_s]^{1/2} [\cos \varphi(t)] s(t) + n'(t) \quad (2)$$

where $P_s = Pm_D^2(1 - m_s^2)$, $\varphi(t)$ is the PLL error in tracking $\theta$, and $n'(t)$ is white Gaussian noise of single-sided spectral density $N_0$ W/Hz. Furthermore, if we take the PLL as a first-order loop operating in its linear region, then $\varphi(t)$ is Gaussian with correlation function $R_\varphi(\tau)$ given by [10]

$$R_\varphi(\tau) = \sigma_\varphi^2 \exp(-4B_L |\tau|) \quad (3)$$

where

$$\sigma_\varphi^2 = \frac{N_0 B_L}{P_C}, \quad P_C = Pm_D^2 m_s^2. \quad (4)$$

In this paper we analyze the performance of a sync system whose input is given by (2) with $s(t)$ taken to be a modified PN sequence. We assume $\varphi(t)$ to be Gaussian with variance and correlation function given by (3) and (4); finally we assume [10] that $\varphi(t)$ is independent of $n'(t)$.

The remainder of the paper is organized as follows. First, we analyze a sync system similar to a PLL, present a linear model, and briefly discuss its noise performance. Second, we present the results of computer simulation of the complete error signal.

## THE SYNCHRONIZATION SYSTEM

The synchronization system to be considered is shown in Fig. 1. The synchronization signal [9] $s(t)$ is given by PN $\times$ $2f_s$, where PN represents a pseudonoise sequence $T_{PN}$ seconds long consisting of $N$ bits ($\pm 1$) each $T$ seconds long, $T_{PN} = NT$, and $2f_s$ is the square wave clock ($\pm 1$) with one cycle per PN bit. The relationship between PN and $2f_s$ is shown in Fig. 2. The details of operation for the system are given in Appendix I. The input signal $e(t)$ given by

Paper 70TP40-COM, approved by the Communication Theory Committee of the IEEE Communication Technology Group for publication without oral presentation. This work was supported by NSF under Grant GK1528. Manuscript received June 13, 1969; revised January 15, 1970.

The authors were with the School of Electrical Engineering, Purdue University, Lafayette, Ind. They are now with Bell Telephone Laboratories, Inc., Holmdel, N. J. 07733.

Reprinted from *IEEE Trans. Commun. Technol.*, vol. COM-18, pp. 676–679, Oct. 1970.

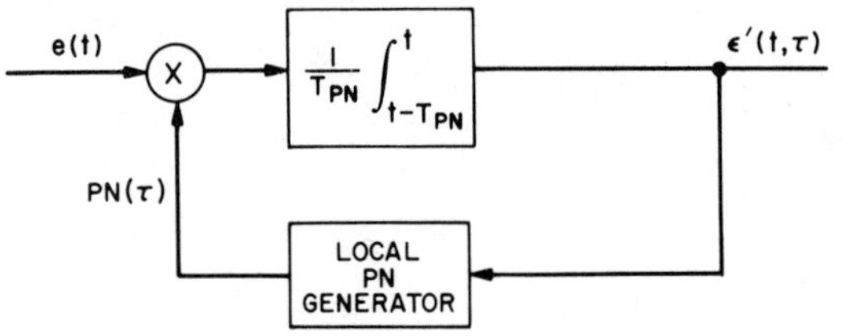


Fig. 1. PN synchronization system.

(2) is multiplied by a local PN sequence and integrated for $T_{PN}$ seconds to produce the error signal $\epsilon'(t,\tau)$ shown in Fig. 2. The local PN generator consists of a shift register driven by a voltage-controlled oscillator (VCO). The phase of the VCO is controlled by the error signal $\epsilon'(t,\tau)$. The PN generator produces one complete sequence PN$(\tau)$ each $T_{PN}$ seconds. Hence the starting point of the reference sequence is controlled by the error signal $\epsilon'(t,\tau)$.

Disregarding noise for the moment let $e(t) = [P_s]^{1/2} \times \text{PN} \times 2f_s$. In this case the error signal is given by

$$\epsilon'(t,\tau) = \frac{1}{T_{PN}} \int_{t-T_{PN}}^{t} [P_s]^{1/2} \times \text{PN} \times 2f_s(t_1 + \tau_1)\ \text{PN}\ (t_1 + \tau_2)\ dt_1,$$

$$\tau = \tau_1 - \tau_2. \quad (5)$$

(Note that the reference PN sequence is not modulated by the clock.) Integration of (5) shows that $\epsilon'(t,\tau)$ is a function of $\tau$ alone; i.e., $\epsilon'(t,\tau) = \epsilon(\tau)$. The function $\epsilon(\tau)$ is shown in Fig. 3. Note that $\epsilon(\tau)$ is a stable tracking characteristic [1] for a PLL with square wave input. For the case where $e(t)$ is noiseless it is clear that the loop will lock the incoming PN sequence to the local PN sequence at $\tau = 0$, thus achieving synchronization.

Next, if we assume perfect phase synchronization (i.e., $\varphi(t) = 0$), we have

$$e(t) = [P_s]^{1/2} \times \text{PN} \times 2f_s + n'(t). \quad (6)$$

If we assume the loop to be operating in the linear region $-T/2 < \tau < T/2$, we may use the linear equivalent model [9] shown in Fig. 4 (see Appendix I). It is shown in Appendix I that, for the linear model, $\tau$ is Gaussian with zero mean and variance $\sigma^2$ given by

$$\sigma^2 = \frac{N_0/P_s}{2(N+1)^2}\left[T_{PN} - \frac{1}{\omega_\tau}\left(1 - \exp\left(-\omega_\tau T_{PN}\right)\right)\right] \quad (7)$$

where $\omega_\tau = (N+1)K/2N\pi$ and $K$ is the combined multiplier-integrator constant of the loop.

Before proceeding with the analysis we point out that this loop closely resembles several systems previously analyzed [1], [5], [6], [11]. For example, when all nonessential elements are removed from the systems shown in Springett [1], they reduce basically to the system shown in Fig. 1. Van Horn [5] used a bank of delay lines to delay the input code by discrete amounts and correlate the delayed versions with a locally generated sequence in order to find the peak in the correlation function, exactly the function performed by the loop. Sage [6] similarly employed a continuous delay parameter, again similar to Fig. 2. The loop is also similar to delay lock loops [11], although the delay lock loop is somewhat more difficult to handle mathematically. However, all of the previous loops were analyzed with additive noise alone. In the remainder of this section we will find an approximate bound on noise performance when the input signal is given by (2); then exact results will be presented for the simulated loop.

In order to derive a bound on system performance when a random amplitude modulation is present, we begin with the approximation $\cos\varphi(t) \doteq 1 - \varphi^2(t)/2$; hence the error signal, using (2), is given by

$$\epsilon'(t,\tau) = \frac{[P_s]^{1/2}}{T_{PN}} \int_{t-T_{PN}}^{t} \left(1 - \frac{\varphi^2(t_1)}{2}\right) \text{PN} \times 2f_s(t_1+\tau_1)$$

$$\cdot\ \text{PN}(t_1+\tau_2)\ dt_1 + \frac{1}{T_{PN}}\int_{t-T_{PN}}^{t} n'(t_1)\ dt. \quad (8)$$

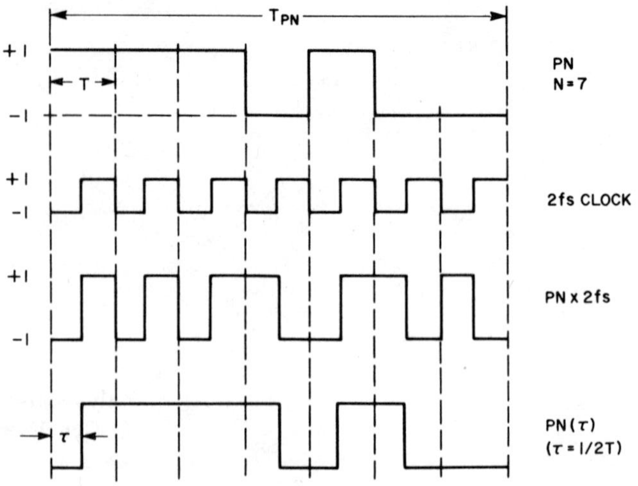


Fig. 2. Typical signals.

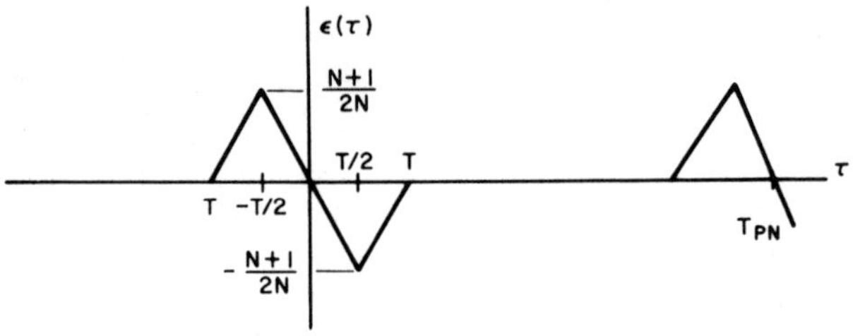


Fig. 3. Sync system error signal.

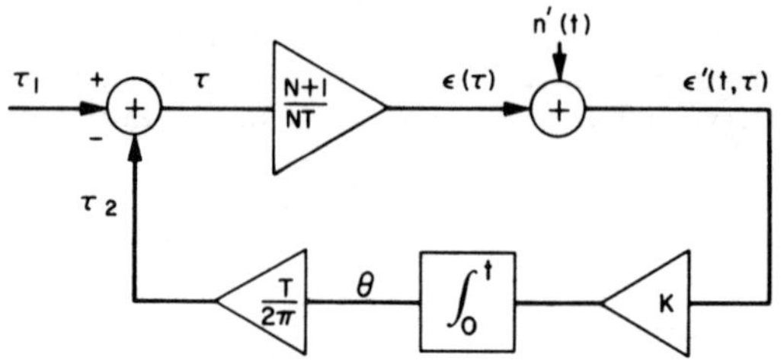


Fig. 4. Linear model.

The approximation for $\cos\varphi(t)$ relies on the linear operation of the carrier tracking loop; this is easily verified [4] by computing the variance $\sigma_\varphi^2$ for acceptable error probability. Furthermore, in most cases of practical interest [2]–[4] $\sigma_\varphi^2 \ll 1$; hence if we let

$$1 - \frac{\varphi^2(t)}{2} \rightarrow 1 - \left.\frac{\overline{\varphi^2(t)}}{2}\right|_{\sigma_\varphi^2=1} = \frac{1}{2} \quad (9)$$

we obtain an approximate bound on the error signal in the form of an energy loss. Although the bound for $\sigma_\varphi^2$ depends on the choice of the approximation for $\cos\varphi(t)$, this bound is somewhat arbitrary. However, computation of the variance [2] indicates that $\sigma_\varphi^2 = 1$ is well within the $4\sigma_\varphi$ limit for acceptable system performance. In this case $\tau$ is again Gaussian with zero mean and variance $\sigma_\tau^2 = 2\sigma^2$, where $\sigma^2$ is given by (7). Note that this bound is valid for both the case where the carrier phase error $\varphi(t)$ is slowly varying or rapidly varying.

## Simulation of the Sync Detector Error Signal

In order to determine more precisely the statistics of the error signal produced by (2), the expression

$$I = \frac{1}{T_{PN}}\int_0^{T_{PN}} \left(1 - \frac{\varphi^2(t)}{2}\right) \text{PN} \times 2f_s(t)\ \text{PN}\ (t+\tau)\ dt \quad (10)$$

was simulated on a CDC 6500 digital computer [9]. Note that this is simply the first term of the loop error signal given by (8)

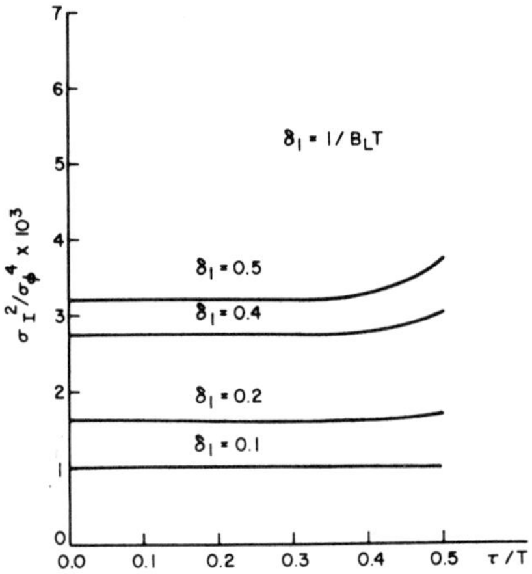


Fig. 5. Variance of sync error term.

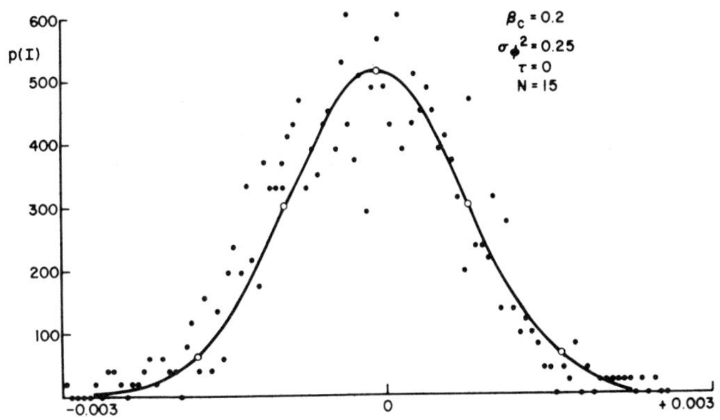


Fig. 6. Experimental density of sync error ($\tau = 0$).

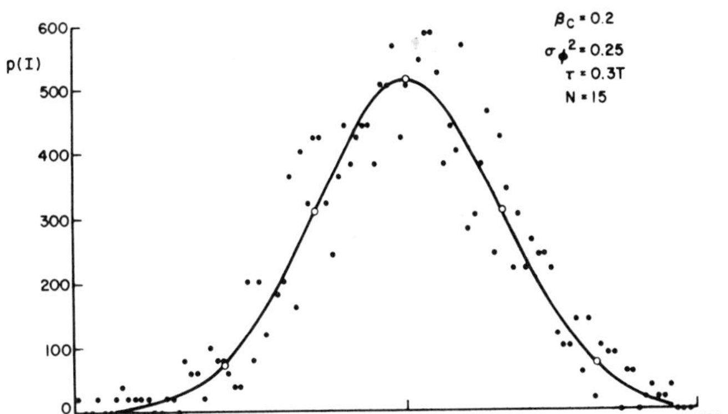


Fig. 7. Experimental density of sync error ($\tau = 0.3T$).

with $P_s = 1$ and $\tau_1 = 0$. Simulation of $I$ (to be discussed shortly) indicated that the variance of $I$, $\sigma_I^2$, was independent of $\tau$. It is shown in Appendix II that the mean and variance of $I$ are given by

$$E(I) = \left(1 - \frac{\sigma_\varphi^2}{2}\right)\epsilon(\tau) = \left(1 - \frac{\sigma_\varphi^2}{2}\right)\frac{N+1}{2N}\cdot\frac{\tau}{T/2} \tag{11}$$

$$\sigma_I^2 = \frac{\sigma_\varphi^4}{2}\int_0^{T_{PN}}\int_0^{T_{PN}}\frac{\exp(-8B_L\,|\,t_1 - t_2\,|)}{T_{PN}^2}\cdot\Gamma(t_1,t_2,\tau)\,dt_1\,dt_2 \tag{12}$$

where

$$\Gamma(t_1,t_2\tau) = \{PN \times 2f_s(t_1)\,PN\,(t_1 + \tau)\,PN \times 2f_s(t_2)\,PN\,(t_2 + \tau)\}.$$

We note from (12) that as $B_L$ becomes large the integrand of (12) approaches an impulse function and $\sigma_I^2$ becomes independent of $\tau$ since $\Gamma(t,t,\tau) = 1$.

In order to compute $\sigma_I^2$, (12) was evaluated on the digital computer. The results are shown in Fig. 5. Several values of $N$ were considered. In general, the results presented later improve as the number of bits $N$ in the PN sequence increase. The value $N = 15$ represents an intermediate value used in typical systems. The results shown in Fig. 5 are for $N = 15$. Note that the variance is constant (and thus independent of $\tau$) for $|\,\tau\,| \le 0.4T$ when $1/B_LT < 0.3$. Furthermore, note that the magnitude of $\sigma_I^2$ is quite small even for large values of $\sigma_I^4$. In particular $\sigma_I^2 < 3.7 \times 10^{-3}$ for $\sigma_\varphi^2 = 1$. This is quite small by comparison with normal values of $\sigma_n^2$, the variance of $n'(t)$, which is the additive noise term in $\epsilon'(t,\tau)$. In other words, the additive noise will normally dominate the amplitude degradation.

Following these preliminary calculations a Monte Carlo simulation of (10) was carried out. The details of the simulation can be found in [9].

For convenience we rewrite (3) as

$$R_\varphi(\epsilon_1) = \sigma_\varphi^2\exp\left(-\frac{5}{\beta_c}\left|\frac{\epsilon_1}{T}\right|\right), \quad \beta_c \triangleq \frac{5}{4B_LT}. \tag{13}$$

$\beta_c$ determines the time over which $\varphi(t)$ is correlated (taken as five correlation time constants) with respect to the bit time $T$.

In the simulation of $I$, 1000 samples were generated for each set of the parameters $\tau$, $\beta_c$, $\sigma_\varphi^2$, and $N$. Typical results are shown in Figs. 6 and 7. Superimposed on these simulated density functions is a Gaussian density function whose mean and variance are given by the sample mean and sample variance for that particular trial.

The following results were obtained. The sample mean and variance of the simulated density functions showed excellent agreement with the theoretical values given by (11) and (12). Inspection of the simulated density function indicated that $I$ was Gaussian. In order to verify this, a *chi square* goodness of fit test [7], [8] was applied to the sample density. This test showed that $I$ is Gaussian with the level of significance at 0.1 percent. Hence we see that the degradation produced by the phase error $\varphi(t)$ leads to a Gaussian term in the error signal with mean given by (11). For large values of $B_LT$ the variance of this term is independent of $\tau$ (see Fig. 5).

For small values of $B_LT$ where $\varphi(t)$ is correlated over a significant portion of the PN sequence time $T_{PN}$, it is clear that this term will not be Gaussian. In this situation two approaches can be taken: $\varphi(t)$ can be treated as a constant over the whole sequence length using the average value of $\varphi(t)$. However, as in the case of large values of $B_LT$, in practical situations the magnitude of the amplitude degradation is negligible compared to the additive noise term.

## Conclusions

We have presented and analyzed a simple synchronization system for a coherent communication system. We have considered the case where both an amplitude degradation and additive noise are present. Simulation results show that when the ratios of the data rate to the carrier loop bandwidth are small, then the sync error is made up of two independent Gaussian components: one due to amplitude degradation and one due to the additive noise. Furthermore, in practical cases the degradation caused by the amplitude degradation may be neglected when compared to the additive noise term.

## Appendix I

In this appendix we derive a simple linear model for the sync loop shown in Fig. 1. We then derive the statistics necessary to predict its behavior. Referring to Fig. 1 we take the input to be

$$e(t) = [P_s]^{1/2} \times PN \times 2f_s + n'(t). \tag{14}$$

Hence the error signal $\epsilon'(t,\tau)$ is given by

$$\epsilon'(t,\tau) = \frac{1}{T_{PN}}\int_{t-T_{PN}}^{t}(PN \times 2f_s(t_1 + \tau_1) + n'(t_1))PN(t_1 + \tau_2)\,dt_1 \tag{15}$$

where we have let $\tau_1$ be the starting time of the incoming sequence, $\tau_2$ be the starting time of the locally generated sequence, and define $\tau \triangleq \tau_1 - \tau_2$. Simplifying (15) we find

$$\epsilon'(t,\tau) = \epsilon(\tau) + \hat{n}(t) \tag{16}$$

where

$$\hat{n}(t) \triangleq \frac{1}{T_{PN}} \int_{t-T_{PN}}^{t} n'(t_1) PN(t_1 + \tau_2)\, dt_1 \tag{17}$$

where we realize that since $n'(t)$ is white, $\hat{n}(t)$ is independent of $\tau_2$ and hence of $\tau$. It is also easy to show that $\hat{n}(t)$ is zero-mean Gaussian with correlation function $R_{\hat{n}}(\epsilon_1)$ and spectral density $S_{\hat{n}}(\omega)$ given by

$$R_{\hat{n}}(\epsilon_1) = \frac{N_0}{2T_{PN}}\left[1 - \frac{|\epsilon_1|}{T_{PN}}\right] \tag{18}$$

$$S_{\hat{n}}(\omega) = \frac{N_0}{2}\left[\frac{\sin(\omega T_{PN}/2)}{\omega T_{PN}/2}\right]^2. \tag{19}$$

If we now restrict $\tau$ to the linear region (see Fig. 3) $-T/2 \leq \tau \leq T/2$ we may derive a linear model as follows. Let the error signal $\epsilon'(t,\tau)$ control the phase $\Theta$ of a VCO whose output is a square wave with period $T$; thus

$$\frac{d\Theta}{dt} = K[\epsilon(\tau) + \hat{n}(t)] \tag{20}$$

where $K$ is the VCO constant and $\tau$ is related to $\Theta$ by

$$\tau = \frac{T}{2\pi}\Theta. \tag{21}$$

Hence in the linear region

$$\epsilon'(t,\tau) = K\left[\frac{N+1}{NT}\tau + \hat{n}(t)\right] \tag{22}$$

and the linear model of Fig. 4 follows readily. Since $n'(t)$ is zero-mean Gaussian, $\tau$ is likewise zero-mean Gaussian in the linear model with variance $\sigma_\tau^2$ given by

$$\sigma_\tau^2 = \frac{1}{2\pi}\int_{-\infty}^{\infty} |H(\omega)|^2 S_{\hat{n}}(\omega)\, d\omega \tag{23}$$

where $|H(\omega)| = |\tau(\omega)/\hat{N}(\omega)|$ is found from the linear model as follows. Let $\tau_1 = 0$, $\tau = -\tau_2$; hence from Fig. 4

$$-\tau(\omega) = \frac{T}{2\pi}\frac{K}{j\omega}\left(\frac{N+1}{NT}\tau(\omega) + \hat{N}(\omega)\right) \tag{24}$$

$$\frac{\tau(\omega)}{\hat{N}(\omega)} = \frac{-K(T/2\pi)}{j\omega + (T/2\pi)[(N+1)/NT]K} \tag{25}$$

$$|H(\omega)|^2 = \left|\frac{\tau(\omega)}{\hat{N}(\omega)}\right|^2 = \frac{K_1^2}{\omega^2 + \omega_\tau^2} \tag{26}$$

where

$$\omega_\tau = \frac{N+1}{N}\cdot\frac{K}{2\pi}$$

$$K_1 = \frac{T}{2\pi}K.$$

Substituting (26) into (23) we obtain (7).

## Appendix II

In this appendix we derive the conditional mean and conditional variance of $I$ given by (10). Beginning with (10)

$$E(I) = \left(1 - \frac{\sigma_\varphi^2}{2}\right)\epsilon(\tau) = \left(1 - \frac{\sigma_\varphi^2}{2}\right)\left(\frac{N+1}{2N}\right)\left(\frac{\tau}{T/2}\right) \tag{27}$$

(see text following (5) for $\epsilon(\tau)$ and Fig. 3)

$$E(I^2) = \frac{2}{T_{PN}^2}\int_0^{T_{PN}}\int E\left[\left(1 - \frac{\varphi^2(t_1)}{2}\right)\left(1 - \frac{\varphi^2(t_2)}{2}\right)\right]\Gamma(t_1,t_2,\tau)\, dt_1\, dt_2 \tag{28}$$

where

$$\Gamma(t_1,t_2,\tau) = PN \times 2f_s(t_1)PN(t_1+\tau)PN \times 2f_s(t_2)PN(t_2+\tau)$$

noting that

$$E\left[\left(1 - \frac{\varphi^2(t_1)}{2}\right)\left(1 - \frac{\varphi^2(t_2)}{2}\right)\right] = 1 - \sigma_\varphi^2 + \frac{1}{4}R_\varphi 2(t_1 - t_2). \tag{29}$$

Substituting (4) into (29) we find

$$R_\varphi 2(t_1 - t_2) = \sigma_\varphi^4 + 2\sigma_\varphi^4 \exp(-8B_L|t_1 - t_2|). \tag{30}$$

Substituting (30) in (28) we find

$$E(I^2) = I_A + I_B$$

where

$$I_B = (1 - \sigma_\varphi^2)\frac{1}{T_{PN}^2}\int_0^{T_{PN}}\int \Gamma(t_1,t_2,\tau)\, dt_1\, dt_2 \tag{31}$$

$$I_A = \frac{1}{4}\frac{1}{T_{PN}^2}\int_0^{T_{PN}}\int R_\varphi^2(t_1 - t_2)\Gamma(t_1,t_2,\tau)\, dt_1\, dt_2. \tag{32}$$

Evaluating $I_A$ and $I_B$ we find

$$\sigma_I^2 = \frac{\sigma_\varphi^4}{2}\int_0^{T_{PN}}\int_0^{T_{PN}} \frac{\exp(-8B_L|t_1 - t_2|)}{T_{PN}^2}\Gamma(t_1,t_2,\tau)\, dt_1\, dt_2 \tag{33}$$

and (12) follows.

## References


[1] J. C. Springett, "Telemetry and command techniques for planetary spacecraft," Jet Propulsion Lab., Pasadena, Calif., Tech. Rep. 32-495, January 1965.
[2] W. C. Lindsey, "Optimal design of one-way and two-way coherent communication links," *IEEE Trans. Commun Technol.*, vol. COM-14, pp. 418–431, August 1966.
[3] ——, "Determination of modulation indexes and design of two-channel coherent communication systems," *IEEE Trans. Commun. Technol.*, vol. COM-15, pp. 229–237, April 1967.
[4] J. F. Hayes and W. C. Lindsey, "Power allocation—rapidly varying phase error," *IEEE Trans. Commun. Technol.* (Concise Papers), vol. COM-17, pp. 323–325, April 1969.
[5] J. H. Van Horn, "A theoretical synchronization system for use with noisy digital signals," *IEEE Trans. Commun. Technol.*, vol. COM-12, pp. 82–90, September 1964.
[6] G. F. Sage, "Serial synchronization of pseudonoise systems," *IEEE Trans. Commun. Technol.*, vol. COM-12, pp. 123–127, December 1964.
[7] H. Cramer, *Mathematical Methods of Statistics*. Princeton, N. J.: Princeton University Press, 1946, pp. 416–434.
[8] S. S. Wilks, *Mathematical Statistics*. New York: Wiley, 1962, p. 208.
[9] J. R. Sergo, "Power allocation in a coherent communication system," Ph.D. dissertation, Purdue University, Lafayette, Ind.; also School of Electrical Engineering, Purdue University Tech. Rep. TREE69-12, June 1969.
[10] A. J. Viterbi, *Principles of Coherent Communication*. New York: McGraw-Hill, 1966.
[11] J. J. Spilker, Jr., "Delay-lock tracking of binary signals," *IEEE Trans. Space Electron. Telem.*, vol. SET-9, pp. 1–8, March 1963.

# Analysis of a Dithering Loop for PN Code Tracking

**H. PETER HARTMANN**, Member, IEEE
AG Brown, Boveri & Cie.
Turgi, Switzerland

**Abstract**

**The tracking performance of a dithering loop in the presence of white Gaussian noise is analyzed and compared to the performance of a delay-lock loop. Performance curves are presented.**

Manuscript received March 22, 1973.

The work reported in this paper was carried out while the author was with Radiation Inc., a Division of Harris-Intertype Corporation, Melbourne, Fla.

## I. Introduction

There are two principal ways of implementing a tracking loop for a pseudo-random (PN) code: the delay-lock loop and the dithering loop. In a delay-lock loop, the incoming code is correlated with an early and a late version of the locally generated replica of the code, and the difference of the two demodulated correlation signals is the desired error signal. The performance of delay-lock loops has been analyzed in detail by Gill [1].

In a dithering loop, the incoming signal is *alternately* correlated with the early and late versions of the locally generated replica of the code (i.e., the local code is "dithered" back and forth), and the error signal is obtained by alternately inverting the demodulated correlation signal and low-pass filtering the resulting signal.

The block diagram of the dithering loop is given in Fig. 1. The received sequence is mixed with a locally generated replica of the PN code. The PN code generator is driven by a clock signal whose phase is switched back and forth in accordance with the binary signal $q(t)$. The dc component of the multiplier output is the desired error signal, which is applied to the clock VCO through the loop filter. The dithering loop may be considered to be a delay-lock loop in which the early and late local reference signals time-share the correlator and demodulator.

The bandwidth of the bandpass filter must be wide enough to pass the information signal in the presence of any carrier frequency shifts. A square-law envelope detector is shown as the demodulator in Fig. 1; alternatively, a linear envelope detector or a coherent detector could be used.

The major advantage of the dithering loop over the delay-lock loop is that only one correlator is required, as opposed to two in the case of the delay-lock loop. This eliminates the problems associated with gain imbalance and (in the case of coherent demodulation) differences in the phase characteristics.

On the other hand, the signal-to-noise performance of the dithering loop is approximately 3 dB worse because of the time-sharing of the early and late channels. When the dithering is periodic, the loop is vulnerable to jamming signals modulated at the dithering frequency; however, this can be combatted by randomly varying the dithering frequency.

In the following section, a model of the loop is derived which is then used to determine the tracking performance of the loop for the case of periodic dithering with the demodulator being a square-law envelope detector. An analytical expression for the percent tracking jitter is derived and plotted, and the results compared to those obtained by Gill [1] for the delay-lock loop.

## II. Analysis

For the analysis, we consider the dithering loop shown in Fig. 1. Let the received signal be

$$r(t) = s(t) + n(t) \tag{1}$$

Reprinted from *IEEE Trans. Aerosp. Electron. Syst.*, vol. AES-10, pp. 2–9, Jan. 1974.

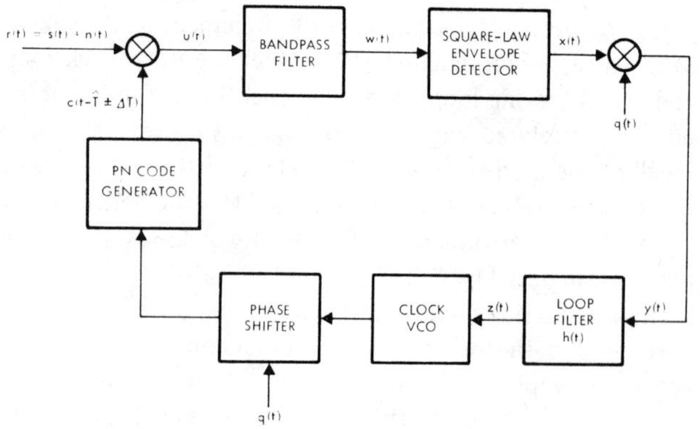


Fig. 1. Block diagram of the dithering loop.

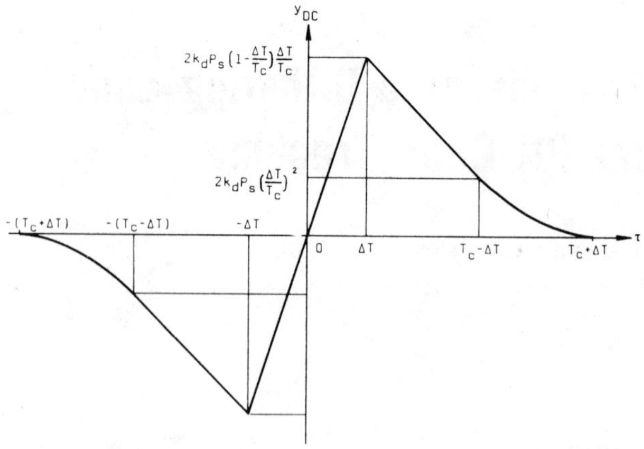


Fig. 2. Phase error characteristic of the dithering loop with square-law detector.

and

$$s(t) = \sqrt{2P_s}\, I(t-T)c(t-T)\cos\omega_0 t \tag{2}$$

where

$P_s$ = power of the received signal
$I(t)$ = information sequence
$c(t)$ = code sequence
$T$ = phase of received code clock
$\omega_0$ = carrier frequency
$n(t)$ = white Gaussian noise of density $N_0/2$ (double-sided).

The mixer output is given by

$$\begin{aligned} u(t) &= r(t)c(t-\hat{T} \pm \Delta T) \\ &= \sqrt{2P_s}\, I(t-T)c(t-T)c(t-\hat{T} \pm \Delta T)\cos\omega_0 t \\ &\quad + n(t)c(t-\hat{T} \pm \Delta T) \end{aligned} \tag{3}$$

where $\hat{T}$ is the phase of the locally generated code clock and $\Delta T$ is the amount of time dither.

If we assume that the bandpass filter is wide enough to pass the data, and that the dithering rate is equal to or lower than the data rate, the signal portion at the bandpass filter output is alternately

$$w_+(t) = \sqrt{2P_s}\, \frac{T_c - |\tau - \Delta T|}{T_c}\, I(t-T)\cos\omega_0 t \tag{4a}$$

and

$$w_-(t) = \sqrt{2P_s}\, \frac{T_c - |\tau + \Delta T|}{T_c}\, I(t-T)\cos\omega_0 t \tag{4b}$$

where $T_c$ is the chip duration and $\tau = T - \hat{T}$ is the clock phase error.

The output of the square-law envelope detector is given by

$$x(t) = k_d w^2(t) \tag{5}$$

where $k_d$ is the detector constant. We therefore have, alternately,

$$x_+(t) = k_d P_s \left(1 - \frac{|\tau - \Delta T|}{T_c}\right)^2 + 2\omega_0 \text{ terms} \tag{6a}$$

and

$$x_-(t) = k_d P_s \left(1 - \frac{|\tau + \Delta T|}{T_c}\right)^2 + 2\omega_0 \text{ terms.} \tag{6b}$$

The envelope detector has removed the data; note that the $2\omega_0$ terms are of no further consequence, and can be dropped because they will not pass the loop filter anyway.

The multiplication by $q(t)$ leaves the sign of $x_+(t)$ intact and inverts the sign of $x_-(t)$. The dc component of the resulting square wave is given by

$$\begin{aligned} y_{dc}(t) &= \tfrac{1}{2}\{x_+(t) - x_-(t)\} \\ &= \tfrac{1}{2}k_d P_s \left[-2\frac{|\tau - \Delta T|}{T_c} + 2\frac{|\tau + \Delta T|}{T_c} - 4\frac{\tau\Delta T}{T_c T_c}\right] \\ &= \tfrac{1}{2}k_d P_s \left[4\frac{\tau}{T_c} - 4\frac{\tau \Delta T}{T_c T_c}\right] \\ &= 2k_d P_s \left(1 - \frac{\Delta T}{T_c}\right)\frac{\tau}{T_c} \end{aligned} \tag{7}$$

The above expression applies only for $|\tau| \leqslant \Delta T$; the complete characteristic for $-T_c \leqslant \tau \leqslant T_c$ is shown in Fig. 2. In the tracking mode, the clock phase error $\tau$ is close to zero, and (7) applies for $y_{dc}$. Defining

$$k_1 \triangleq 2k_d P_s \left(1 - \frac{\Delta T}{T_c}\right) \tag{8}$$

and

$$\phi_e(t) \triangleq \frac{\tau}{T_c} \tag{9}$$

the expression for $y_{dc}$ simplifies to

$$y_{dc}(t) = k_1 \phi_e(t). \tag{10}$$

The loop filter output is given by the convolution of $y(t)$ and the filter impulse response $h(t)$. Since the loop filter is low-pass with bandwidth much lower than the dithering frequency, this is equivalent to convolving $y_{dc}(t)$ and $h(t)$.

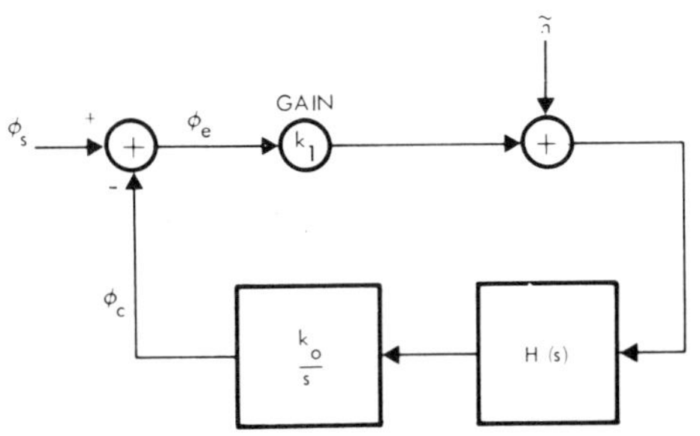


Fig. 3. Loop model for analysis.

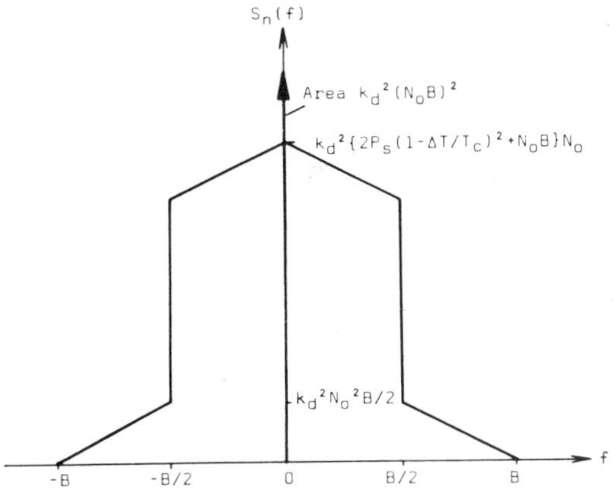


Fig. 4. Noise spectrum at envelope detector output.

Therefore,

$$z(t) = y(t)*h(t)$$
$$= y_{dc}(t)*h(t)$$
$$= k_1 \phi_e(t)*h(t) \tag{11}$$

where the asterisk denotes convolution. Finally, the phase of the clock VCO is given by

$$\phi_c(t) = \frac{\hat{T}}{T_c} = k_0 \int z(t)\, dt \tag{12}$$

where $k_0$ is the frequency slope of the VCO. Therefore,

$$\phi_c(t) = k_0 k_1 \int \phi_e(t)*h(t)\, dt \tag{13}$$

and, since

$$\phi_e(t) = \phi_s(t) - \phi_c(t) \tag{14}$$

where $\phi_s(t) = T/T_c$, we have

$$\phi_c(t) = k_0 k_1 \int \left\{\phi_s(t) - \phi_c(t)\right\}*h(t)\, dt. \tag{15}$$

Taking the Laplace transform of both sides, one finds

$$\Phi_c(s) = k_0 k_1 \left\{\Phi_s(s) - \Phi_c(s)\right\} \frac{H(s)}{s}. \tag{16}$$

Solving for $\Phi_c(s)$, one finds

$$\Phi_c(s) = \frac{k_0 k_1 H(s)/s}{1 + k_0 k_1 H(s)/s} \Phi_s(s), \tag{17}$$

which is the desired result. The block diagram of the corresponding feedback loop is shown in Fig. 3.

The noise at the output of the bandpass filter can be represented as

$$n_w(t) = \sqrt{2}\, n_c(t) \cos \omega_0 t + \sqrt{2}\, n_s(t) \sin \omega_0 t \tag{18}$$

where $n_c(t)$ and $n_s(t)$ are independent low-pass processes of density $N_0/2$ (double-sided) and bandwidth $B/2$ ($B$ = IF filter bandwidth). In addition to the thermal noise given by (18), there will be "self-noise" generated due to the fact that the received and local PN sequence are not in step because of the dithering. The self-noise can usually be neglected with respect to the thermal noise.

If one assumes, for simplicity, that the loop is tracking with zero error and, hence, the envelope of the signal term is constant, the noise out of the square-law envelope detector is given by

$$n(t) = k_d 2\sqrt{2P_s}\left(1 - \frac{\Delta T}{T_c}\right) \cos \omega_0 t \left\{\sqrt{2} n_c(t) \cos \omega_0 t + \sqrt{2} n_s(t) \sin \omega_0 t\right\} + k_d\left\{\sqrt{2} n_c(t) \cos \omega_0 t + \sqrt{2}\, n_s(t) \sin \omega_0 t\right\}^2$$
$$+ \text{signal} \times \text{noise term at } 2\omega_0 \tag{19}$$

Neglecting the $2\omega_0$ terms which are not passed by the loop filter, one finds

$$n(t) = k_d \left[2\sqrt{P_s}\left(1 - \frac{\Delta T}{T_c}\right) n_c(t) + n_c^2(t) + n_s^2(t)\right]. \tag{20}$$

The autocorrelation function of the noise is given by

$$R_n(\tau) = E\left\{n(t) n(t-\tau)\right\}$$
$$= k_d^2 \left[4P_s \; 1 - \frac{\Delta T}{T_c} \; ^2 R_{n_c}(\tau)\right.$$
$$+ E\left\{n_c^2(t) n_c^2(t-\tau)\right\}$$
$$+ E\left\{n_s^2(t) n_s^2(t-\tau)\right\}$$
$$\left. + 2E\left\{n_c^2(t) n_s^2(t-\tau)\right\}\right]. \tag{21}$$

Taking into account the fact that $n_c$ and $n_s$ are identical independent Gaussian random variables, and making use of the identity (for Gaussian random variables)

$$E\left\{x_1 x_2 x_3 x_4\right\} = E\left\{x_1 x_2\right\} E\left\{x_3 x_4\right\} + E\left\{x_1 x_3\right\} E\left\{x_2 x_4\right\} + E\left\{x_1 x_4\right\} E\left\{x_2 x_3\right\},$$

one finds

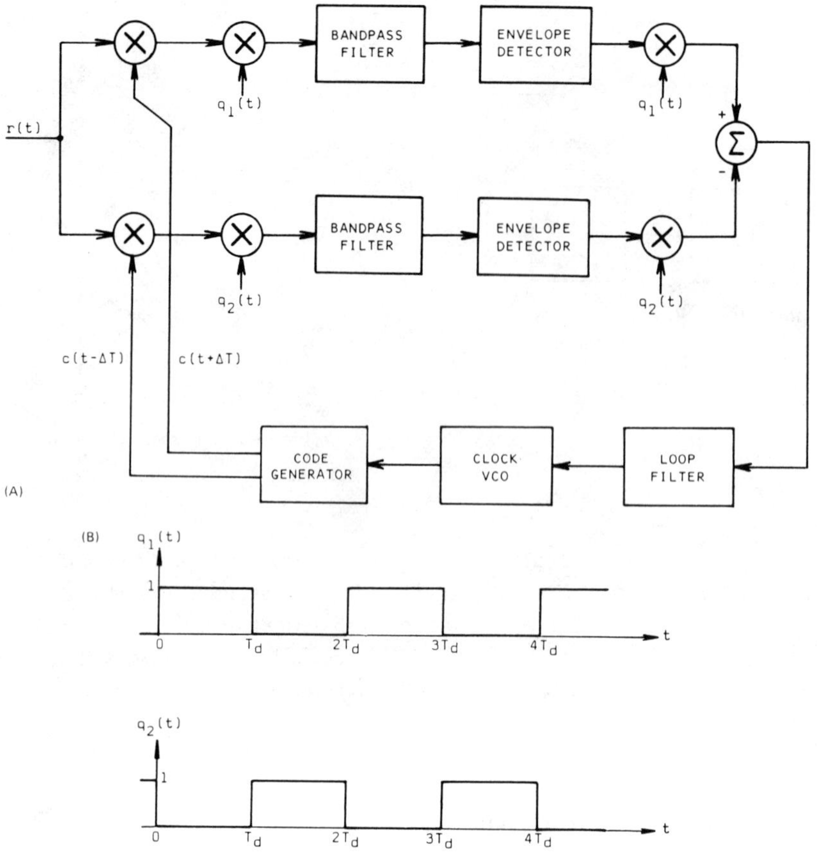


Fig. 5. (A) Block diagram of equivalent system. (B) Switching functions $q_1(t)$, $q_2(t)$.

$$R_n(\tau) = k_d^2\left[4P_s\left(1-\frac{\Delta T}{T_c}\right)^2 R_{n_c}(\tau) + 2\left\{R_{n_c}^2(0) + 2R_{n_c}^2(\tau)\right\} + 2R_{n_c}^2(0)\right]$$

$$= k_d^2\left[4P_s\left(1-\frac{\Delta T}{T_c}\right)^2 R_{n_c}(\tau) + 4R_{n_c}^2(\tau) + 4\sigma^4\right]. \qquad (22)$$

The noise spectrum is found by taking the Fourier transform of $R_n(\tau)$, and is shown in Fig. 4. If the signal term is taken into account, the area of the impulse at dc becomes

$$k_d^2\left\{P_s\left(1-\frac{\Delta T}{T_c}\right)^2 + N_0 B\right\}^2.$$

Note that the foregoing analysis is identical to the one presented in Chapter 12 of Davenport and Root [2], with the following correspondence:

| This Analysis | | Davenport and Root [2] |
|---|---|---|
| $\sqrt{2P_s}(1-\Delta T/T_c)$ | $\Longleftrightarrow$ | $P$ |
| $N_0/2$ | $\Longleftrightarrow$ | $A$ |
| $B$ | $\Longleftrightarrow$ | $B$ |
| $k_d$ | $\Longleftrightarrow$ | $a$ |

The system shown in Fig. 1 can be modeled as shown in Fig. 5(A), which shows two channels which are sampled alternately. The block diagram of Fig. 5(A) is essentially that of a delay-lock loop. The systems of Figs. 1 and 5 are equivalent as long as the switching rate is less than half the IF bandwidth, and transients due to the rise time of the IF filter can be neglected. When the transients can be neglected, the $q$ function multipliers at the inputs to the IF filters can be deleted, and the block diagram of Fig. 6 results.

When the loop is tracking without error, the signal portion at the filter outputs is given by [see (4)]

$$w_+(t) = w_-(t) = \sqrt{2P_s}\left(1-\frac{\Delta T}{T_c}\right) I(t-T)\cos\omega_0 t. \qquad (23)$$

The noise portions at the filter outputs are denoted by $n_+(t)$ and $n_-(t)$, respectively. We now show that $n_+(t)$ and $n_-(t)$ are uncorrelated for $\Delta T/T_c \geqslant 1/2$.

$$n_+(t) = \int_{-\infty}^{\infty} h(t-\sigma)n(\sigma)c_1(\sigma)\,d\sigma$$

$$n_-(t) = \int_{-\infty}^{\infty} h(t-v)n(v)c_2(v)\,dv. \qquad (24)$$

The cross correlation of $n_+(t)$ and $n_-(t)$ is given by

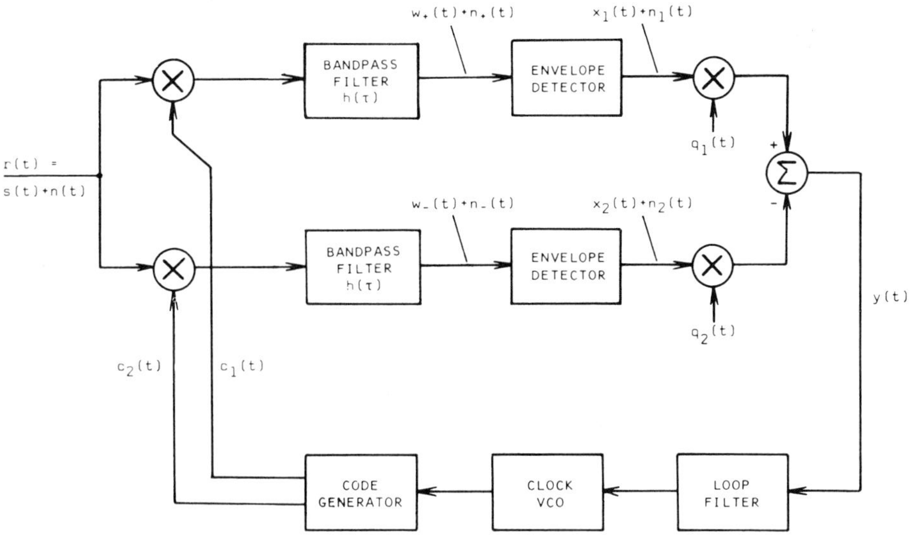


Fig. 6. Equivalent system for low switching rate.

$$R_{n_+n_-}(\tau) = E\{n_+(t)n_-(t-\tau)\}$$
$$= \iint_{-\infty}^{\infty} h(t-\sigma)h(t-\tau-v)\,\frac{N_0}{2}\,\delta(\sigma-v)$$
$$\cdot E\{c_1(\sigma)c_2(v)\}\,d\sigma dv$$
$$= \frac{N_0}{2}\int_{-\infty}^{\infty} h(t-\sigma)h(t-\tau-\sigma)$$
$$\cdot E\{c_1(\sigma)c_2(\sigma)\}\,d\sigma. \tag{25}$$

Now, $c_1(t)$ and $c_2(t)$ are simply the early and late versions of the code sequence, and one has

$$c_2(t) = c_1(t-2\Delta T). \tag{26}$$

Therefore,

$$E\{c_1(\sigma)c_2(\sigma)\} = E\{c_1(\sigma)c_1(\sigma-2\Delta T)\}. \tag{27}$$

Since the autocorrelation function of a PN code vanishes for $\tau \geqslant T_c$, one has, for $2\Delta T \geqslant T_c$,

$$E\{c_1(\sigma)c_2(\sigma)\} \equiv 0 \tag{28}$$

and, consequently,

$$R_{n_+n_-}(\tau) \equiv 0. \tag{29}$$

Q.E.D.

Since $n_+(t)$ and $n_-(t)$ are Gaussian, they are not only uncorrelated, but also independent. Therefore, the noises at the envelope detector outputs are also independent.

It remains to determine the spectrum of the noise at the output of the difference circuit. The autocorrelation function of $y(t)$ is given by

$$R_y(\tau) = E\{y(t)y(t-\tau)\}$$
$$= E[\{(x_1(t)+n_1(t))q_1(t) - (x_2(t)+n_2(t))q_2(t)\}$$
$$\cdot\{(x_1(t-\tau)+n_1(t-\tau))q_1(t-\tau)$$

Fig. 7. Auto- and cross-correlation functions of switching functions.

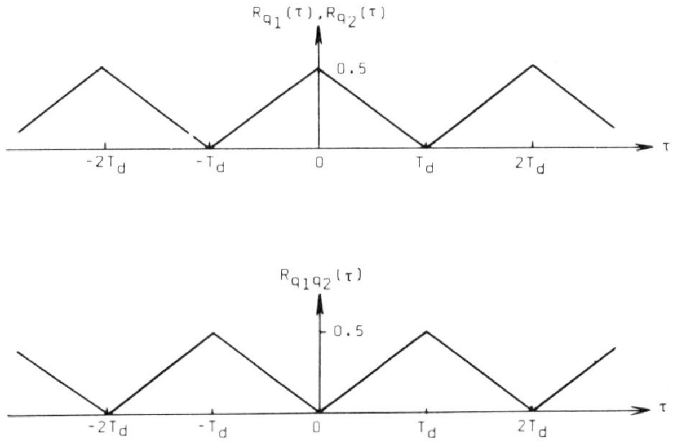


$$-(x_2(t-\tau)+n_2(t-\tau))q_2(t-\tau)\}]$$
$$= R_{x_1+n_1}(\tau)R_{q_1}(\tau) - R_{(x_1+n_1)(x_2+n_2)}(\tau)R_{q_1q_2}(\tau)$$
$$-R_{(x_2+n_2)(x_1+n_1)}(\tau)R_{q_2q_1}(\tau)$$
$$+R_{x_2+n_2}(\tau)R_{q_2}(\tau). \tag{30}$$

The auto- and cross-correlation functions of the switching functions $q_1(t)$ and $q_2(t)$ are shown in Fig. 7. Note that

$$R_{q_1}(\tau) = R_{q_2}(\tau) = \frac{1}{2} - R_{q_1q_2}(\tau). \tag{31}$$

For the purpose of the analysis it is convenient to choose the noises $n_1(t)$ and $n_2(t)$ as having zero mean; this can be achieved by defining

$$x_1 = x_+ + m_1 = k_d\left[P_s\left(1-\frac{\Delta T}{T_c}\right)^2 + N_0B\right] \tag{32a}$$

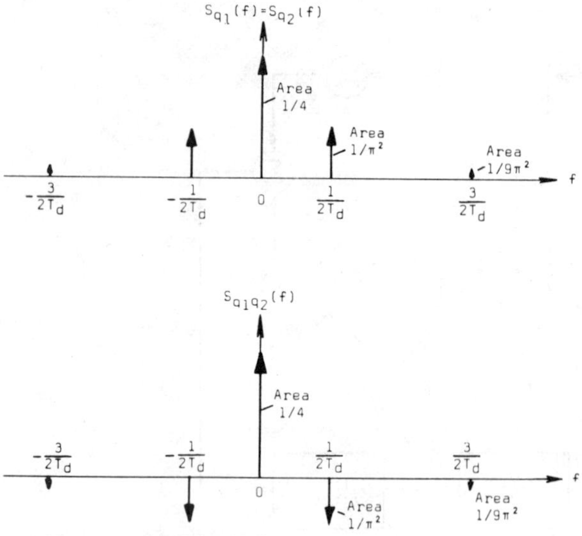


Fig. 8. Auto and cross spectra of switching functions.

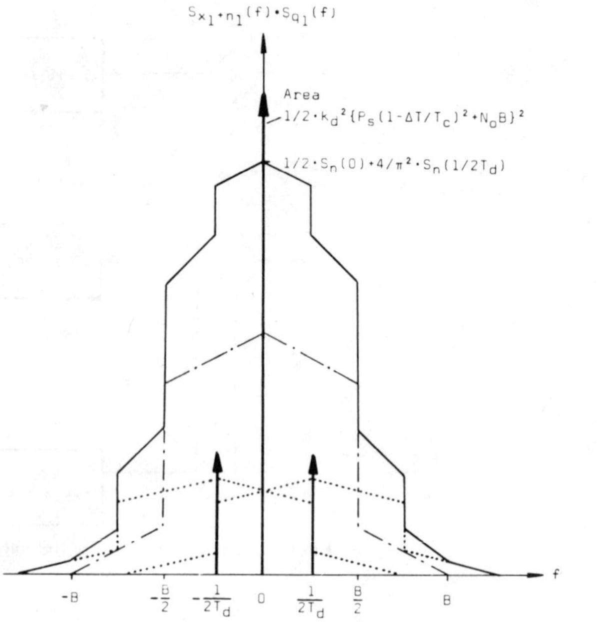


Fig. 9. Spectrum $S_{x_1+n_1}(f) * S_{q_1}(f)$.

and

$$x_2 = x_{-} + m_2$$

$$= k_d\left[P_s\left(1 - \frac{\Delta T}{T_c}\right)^2 + N_0 B\right]$$

$$= x_1 \tag{32b}$$

in the case of zero tracking error. With these definitions,

$$R_{(x_1+n_1)(x_2+n_2)} = R_{x_1x_2} + R_{x_1n_2} + R_{x_2n_1} + R_{n_1n_2}. \tag{33}$$

The cross terms $R_{x_1n_2}$ and $R_{x_2n_1}$ vanish because the signal and noise are independent and the noise is zero mean, and the last term, $R_{n_1n_2}$, vanishes because $n_1$ and $n_2$ are independent (as shown above) and zero mean. Therefore,

$$R_{(x_1+n_1)(x_2+n_2)}(\tau) = R_{x_1x_2}(\tau)$$

$$= k_d^2\left\{P_s\left(1 - \frac{\Delta T}{T_c}\right)^2 + N_0 B\right\}^2. \tag{34}$$

We finally find the autocorrelation

$$R_y(\tau) = R_{x_1+n_1}(\tau)R_{q_1}(\tau) + R_{x_2+n_2}(\tau)R_{q_2}(\tau)$$

$$- 2R_{x_1x_2}(\tau)R_{q_1q_2}(\tau). \tag{35}$$

The spectrum of $y(t)$ is given by

$$S_y(f) = \int_{-\infty}^{\infty} R_y(\tau)e^{-j2\pi f\tau}\,d\tau$$

$$= S_{x_1+n_1}(f)*S_{q_1}(f) + S_{x_2+n_2}(f)*S_{q_2}(f)$$

$$- 2S_{x_1x_2}(f)*S_{q_1q_2}(f) \tag{36}$$

where the asterisk denotes convolution. In the case of zero tracking error, one has

$$S_{x_1+n_1}(f) = S_{x_2+n_2}(f) \tag{37}$$

and, since $S_{q_1}(f) = S_{q_2}(f)$, one finds

$$S_y(f) = 2\{S_{x_1+n_1}(f)*S_{q_1}(f) - S_{x_1x_2}(f)*S_{q_1q_2}(f)\}. \tag{38}$$

The auto and cross spectra of the switching functions $q_1(t)$ and $q_2(t)$ can be found easily, and are shown in Fig. 8.

Convolution of the spectrum $S_{x_1+n_1}(f)$ with the impulsive spectrum $S_{q_1}(f)$ is most easily carried out graphically, since convolution with an impulse results simply in amplitude scaling and a frequency offset. The spectrum $S_{x_1+n_1}*S_{q_1}$ is shown in Fig. 9 for the case $1/2T_d = B/4$.

Since $R_{x_1x_2}(\tau)$ is a constant [see (34)], the corresponding spectrum $S_{x_1x_2}(f)$ is an impulse at dc, and the spectrum $S_{x_1x_2}*S_{q_1q_2}$ is thus simply an amplitude scaled version of $S_{q_1q_2}(f)$.

The spectrum of $y(t)$ is shown in Fig. 10. As expected, the dc terms cancel out when there is no tracking error; however, there are discrete components at the frequency $1/2T_d$ and its odd harmonics. These components may be considered to be interfering signals as far as the loop is concerned, and the loop bandwidth should be chosen such that their effect is minimized.

The spectral density at dc is given by

$$S_y(0) = \tfrac{1}{2}k_d^2\left\{2P_s\left(1 - \frac{\Delta T}{T_c}\right)^2 + N_0 B\right\}N_0$$

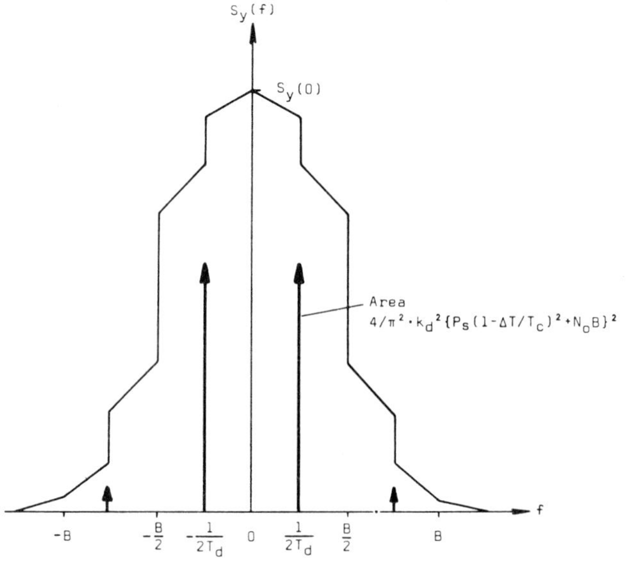


Fig. 10. Spectrum of $y(t)$.

$$+2\frac{2}{\pi^2}k_d^2\left\{2P_s\left(1-\frac{\Delta T}{T_c}\right)^2\right.$$

$$\left.+N_0B\left(1-\frac{1}{2T_dB}\right)\right\}N_0$$

$$=k_d^2\left\{\left(1+\frac{8}{\pi^2}\right)P_s\left(1-\frac{\Delta T}{T_c}\right)^2\right.$$

$$\left.+\left(\frac{1}{2}+\frac{4}{\pi^2}-\frac{2}{\pi^2}\frac{1}{T_dB}\right)N_0B\right\}N_0$$

$$=k_d^2\left\{1.811\left(1-\frac{\Delta T}{T_c}\right)^2P_s\right.$$

$$\left.+\left(0.905-\frac{1}{5T_dB}\right)N_0B\right\}N_0 \qquad (39)$$

where the approximation $\pi^2/2 \cong 5$ has been made.

The clock timing jitter is determined next. It follows from Fig. 3 that the normalized clock phase is given by

$$\Phi_c(s)=\frac{k_0k_1H(s)/s}{1+k_0k_1H(s)/s}\left(\Phi_s(s)+\frac{\tilde{n}(s)}{k_1}\right). \qquad (40)$$

When the loop bandwidth is narrow compared to the IF bandwidth, the normalized clock jitter is given by

$$\sigma_{\Phi_c}^2 \cong \frac{1}{k_1^2}2S_{\tilde{n}}(0)B_L \qquad (41)$$

where $B_L$ is the loop noise bandwidth. Since

$$S_{\tilde{n}}(0)=S_y(0), \qquad (42)$$

one finds

$$\sigma_{\Phi_c}^2 \cong \frac{1}{k_1^2}2S_y(0)B_L. \qquad (43)$$

Substituting $S_y(0)$ from (39) and recalling that

$$k_1=2k_dP_s\left(1-\frac{\Delta T}{T_c}\right), \qquad (8)$$

one finds

$$\sigma_{\Phi_c}^2=\tfrac{1}{2}\left[1.811\frac{N_0}{P_s}+\frac{0.905-1/5T_dB}{(1-\Delta T/T_c)^2}\frac{N_0^2B}{P_s^2}\right]B_L$$

$$=\left[0.905\frac{N_0B}{P_s}+\frac{0.453-1/10T_dB}{(1-\Delta T/T_c)^2}\left(\frac{N_0B}{P_s}\right)^2\right]\frac{B_L}{B} \qquad (44)$$

Finally, since

$$(S/N)_{\text{IF}}=\frac{P_s}{N_0B}, \qquad (45)$$

one finds

$$\sigma_{\Phi_c}^2=\left[0.905(S/N)_{\text{IF}}^{-1}+\frac{0.453-1/10T_dB}{(1-\Delta T/T_c)^2}\cdot(S/N)_{\text{IF}}^{-2}\right]\frac{B_L}{B}, \qquad (46)$$

which is the desired result.

### III. Discussion

It is seen from (46) that, for large IF signal-to-noise ratios, the first term dominates, while for small IF signal-to-noise ratios, the second term dominates. From (46), it would appear that the second term can be made arbitrarily small by choosing $1/T_d$ large enough; however, the dithering frequency $1/2T_d$ must be chosen small enough for the dithered signal to be passed by the IF filter [this assumption has been made in deriving (46)]. On the other hand, $1/2T_d$ cannot be chosen too small, because of the sinusoidal component present in the spectrum of $y(t)$ at this frequency. If $1/2T_d$ is too small, this component will not be sufficiently attenuated by the loop filter and will, therefore, interfere with the operation of the loop. A suitable compromise is

$$\frac{1}{2T_d}=\frac{B}{8}\cdots\frac{B}{4},$$

depending on the width of the loop filter.

The performance of the loop also depends on the ratio $\Delta T/T_c$. The loop gain is maximized for $\Delta T/T_c \to 0$, but only over an arbitrarily small region of the error signal. The linear range of the error signal, as well as its peak value, is maximized for $\Delta T/T_c = 1/2$ (see Fig. 2). Therefore, this value represents the most desirable choice from the point of view of acquisition. On the other hand, if the data are

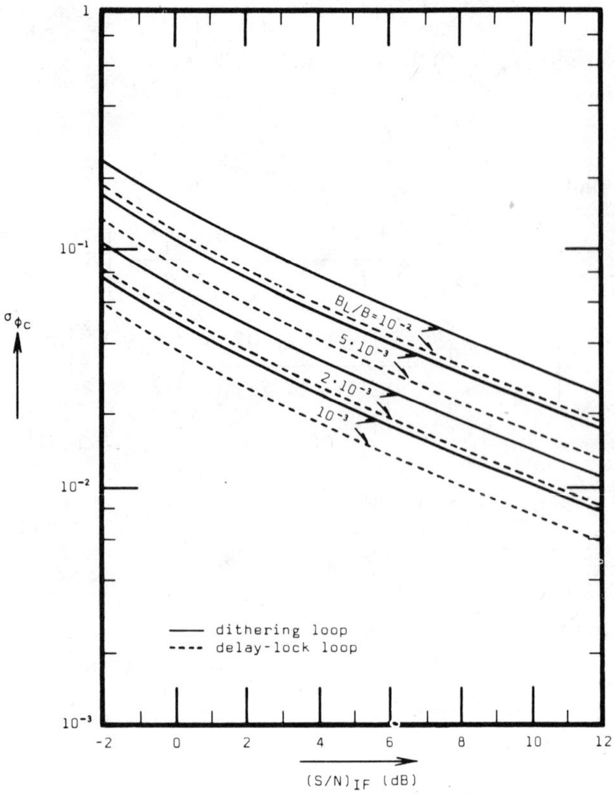


Fig. 11. Clock jitter versus IF signal-to-noise ratio ($T_dB = 2$, $\Delta T/T_c = 1/2$).

extracted from the same channel, the signal power is reduced by the factor $(1 - \Delta T/T_c)^2$, and it might be desirable to choose $\Delta T/T_c$ less than 1/2.

The performance of the loop is shown in Fig. 11 for the values $T_dB = 2$ and $\Delta T/T_c = 1/2$. The corresponding curves for the delay-lock loop, based on the expression (from Gill [1])

$$\sigma_{\Phi_c}{}^2 = [0.5(S/N)_{\mathrm{IF}}{}^{-1} + (S/N)_{\mathrm{IF}}{}^{-2}]\,\frac{B_L}{B}\,,$$

are also given.

The results have been derived under the assumption of white Gaussian noise at the input to the loop and, hence, bandlimited white Gaussian noise at the output of the bandpass filter. The former assumption does not always hold in practice (e.g., in jamming or multipath environments). However, the assumption of bandlimited Gaussian noise at the output of the bandpass filter will be closely approximated for any uncorrelated interfering signal as long as the processing gain or bandspread ratio, i.e., the ratio of the PN code rate to the information rate, is sufficiently large ($>$ 20 dB). Therefore, the curves of Fig. 11 are valid for any uncorrelated interfering signal; however, care must be taken in properly defining the signal-to-noise ratio in those cases.

**References**

[1] W.J. Gill, "A comparison of binary delay-lock tracking-loop implementations," *IEEE Trans. Aerospace and Electronic Systems*, vol. AES-2 pp. 415-424, July 1966.

[2] W.B. Davenport and W.L. Root, *Random Signals and Noise*. New York: McGraw-Hill, 1958.

# Part XI
# Miscellaneous

This part exists because the papers that are reprinted here contain information that is pertinent to spread spectrum system designers but that do not fit into one of the other parts. Turin's paper is included here because of the widespread use of matched filter correlators in spread spectrum receivers and because the receivers themselves are matched filter receivers in an overall sense. Gupta and Painter's paper on the effects of processing PN sequences, specifically the effect of filtering the sequence on the correlation functions, might have been included in part IX, RF Effects, because of the similarity of the effect on correlation, but the authors are not really addressing the RF channel.

The three papers that remain all address applications of devices that have recently become available and that are particularly useful in a spread spectrum context. A glance at any of the three will show that they contain information that is directly applicable. Two of the three discuss surface wave implementations of spread spectrum subsystems, and the third discusses similar implementation using charge transfer devices. To anyone who is interested in implementing a spread spectrum system, I recommend that they become familiar with these techniques, for they make systems practical that might not be so when any other implementation is contemplated.

## OTHER PAPERS OF INTEREST


1) C. R. Cahn, "performance of digital matched filter correlators with unknown interference," *IEEE Trans. Commun. Technol.*, Dec. 1971.
2) C. P. Hatsell and L. W. Nolte, "Detectability of burst-like signals *IEEE Trans. Aerosp. Electron. Syst.*, Mar. 1971.
3) J. Klapper, "The effect of the integrator-dump circuit on PCM/FM error rates," *IEEE Trans. Commun. Technol.*, June 1966.
4) R. E. Millett, "A matched-filter pulse-compression system using a nonlinear FM waveform," *IEEE Trans. Aerosp. Electron. Syst.*, Jan. 1970.
5) N. P. Muraka, "Spread spectrum systems using noise band shift keying," *IEEE Trans. Commun.*, July 1973.
6) S. M. Sussman and E. J. Ferrari, "The effects of notch filters on the correlation properties of a PN signal," *IEEE Trans. Aerosp. Electron. Syst.*, May 1974.
7) C. S. Weaver, "An adaptive communications filter," *Proc. IRE*, Oct. 1961.

# An Introduction to Matched Filters*

GEORGE L. TURIN†

*Summary*—**In a tutorial exposition, the following topics are discussed: definition of a matched filter; where matched filters arise; properties of matched filters; matched-filter synthesis and signal specification; some forms of matched filters.**

## I. Foreword

In this introductory treatment of matched filters, an attempt has been made to provide an engineering insight into such topics as: where these filters arise, what their properties are, how they may be synthesized, etc. Rigor and detail are purposely avoided, on the theory that they tend, on first contact with a subject, to obscure fundamental concepts rather than clarify them. Thus, for example, although it is not assumed that the reader is conversant with statistical estimation and hypothesis-testing theories, the pertinent results of these are invoked without mathematical proof; instead, they are justified by an appeal to intuition, starting with simple cases and working up to greater and greater complexity. Such a presentation is admittedly not sufficient for a completely thorough understanding: it is merely a prelude. It is hoped that the interested reader will fill in the gaps himself by consulting the cited references at his leisure.

Of course, one must always start somewhere, and here it is with the assumption that the reader is already familiar with the elements of probability theory and linear filter theory—that is, with such things as probability density functions, spectra, impulse response functions, transfer functions, and so forth. If he is not, reference to Chapters 1 and 2 of [57] and Chapter 9 of [7] will probably suffice.

The bibliography, although lengthy, is not meant to be complete, nor could it be. Aside from the inevitable inability of the author to be familiar with the entire unclassified literature on the subject, there is an extensive body of classified literature, much of it precedent to the unclassified literature, which of course could not be cited. Of the latter, it must be said regretfully, large portions should not have been classified in the first place, or should long since have been declassified.

No bibliography can satisfactorily reflect the influence of personal conversations with colleagues on an author's thoughts about a subject. The present author would especially like to acknowledge the many he has had over the years with Drs. W. B. Davenport, Jr., R. M. Fano, P. E. Green, Jr., and R. Price; this, without attributing to them in any way the inadequacies of what follows.

* Manuscript received by the PGIT, January 23, 1960.
† Hughes Research Laboratories, Malibu, Calif.

## II. Definition of a Matched Filter

If $s(t)$ is any physical waveform, then a filter which is matched to $s(t)$ is, by definition, one with impulse response

$$h(\tau) = ks(\Delta - \tau), \tag{1}$$

where $k$ and $\Delta$ are arbitrary constants. In order to envisage the form of $h(t)$, consider Fig. 1, in part (a) of which is shown a wave train, $s(t)$, lasting from $t_1$ to $t_2$. By reversing the direction of time in part (a), *i.e.*, letting $\tau = -t$, one obtains the reversed train, $s(-\tau)$, of part (b). If this latter waveform is now delayed by $\Delta$ seconds, and its amplitude multiplied by $k$, the resulting waveform—part (c) of Fig. 1—is the matched-filter impulse response of (1).[1]

The transfer function of a matched filter, which is the Fourier transform of the impulse response, has the form

$$\begin{aligned} H(j2\pi f) &= \int_{-\infty}^{\infty} h(\tau)e^{-i2\pi f\tau}\, d\tau \\ &= k\int_{-\infty}^{\infty} s(\Delta - \tau)e^{-i2\pi f\tau}\, d\tau \\ &= ke^{-i2\pi f\Delta}\int_{-\infty}^{\infty} s(\tau')e^{i2\pi f\tau'}\, d\tau', \end{aligned} \tag{2}$$

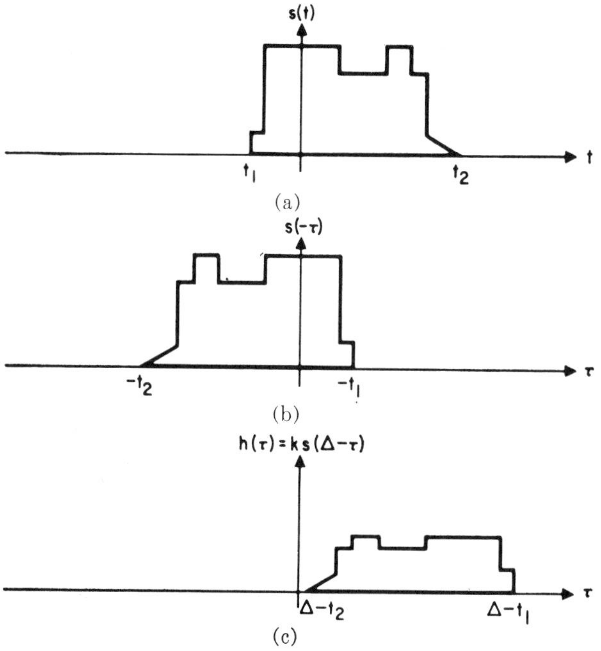


Fig. 1—(a) A wave train; (b) the reversed train; (c) a matched-filter impulse response.

[1] For some types of synthesis of $h(\tau)$—for example, as the impulse response of a passive, linear, electrical network—$\Delta$ is constrained by realizability considerations to the region $\Delta \geq t_2$. If $t_2 = \infty$, approximations are sometimes necessary. The problems of realization will be considered more fully later.

Reprinted from *IRE Trans. Inform. Theory*, vol. IT-6, pp. 311–329, June 1960.

where the substitution $\tau' = \Delta - \tau$ has been made in going from the third to the fourth member of (2). Now, the spectrum of $s(t)$, *i.e.*, its Fourier transform, is:[2]

$$S(j2\pi f) = \int_{-\infty}^{\infty} s(t)e^{-j2\pi ft}\,dt. \tag{3}$$

Comparison of (2) and (3) reveals, then, that

$$H(j2\pi f) = kS(-j2\pi f)e^{-j2\pi f\Delta} = kS^*(j2\pi f)e^{-j2\pi f\Delta}. \tag{4}$$

That is, except for a possible amplitude and delay factor of the form $ke^{-j2\pi f\Delta}$, the transfer function of a matched filter is the complex conjugate of the spectrum of the signal to which it is matched. For this reason, a matched filter is often called a "conjugate" filter.

Let us postpone further study of the characteristics of matched filters until we have gained enough familiarity with the contexts in which they appear to know what properties are important enough to investigate.

## III. Where Matched Filters Arise

### A. Mean-Square Criteria

Perhaps the first context in which the matched filter made its appearance [31], [55] is that depicted in Fig. 2.

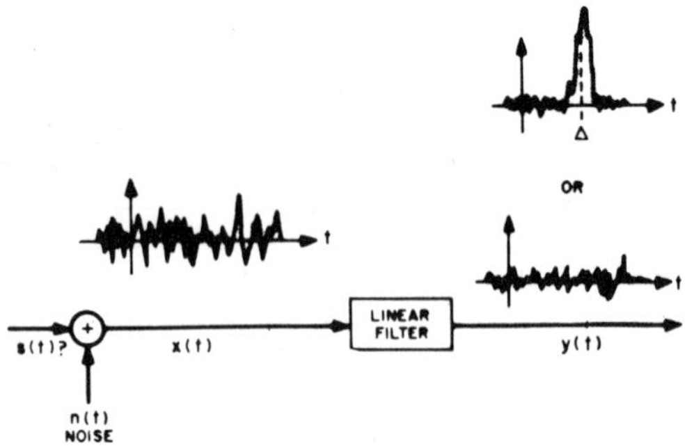


Fig. 2—Pertaining to the maximization of signal-to-noise ratio.

Suppose that one has received a waveform, $x(t)$, which consists either solely of a white noise, $n(t)$, of power density $N_0/2$ watts/cps;[3] *or* of $n(t)$ *plus* a signal, $s(t)$—say a radar return—of known form. One wishes to determine which of these contingencies is true by operating on $x(t)$ with a linear filter in such a way that if $s(t)$ *is* present, the filter output at some time $t = \Delta$ will be considerably greater than if $s(t)$ is absent. Now, since the filter has been assumed to be linear, its output, $y(t)$, will be composed of a noise component $y_n(t)$, due to $n(t)$ only, and, if $s(t)$ is present, a signal component $y_s(t)$, due to $s(t)$ only. A simple way of quantifying the requirement that $y(\Delta)$ be "considerably greater" when $s(t)$ is present than when $s(t)$ is absent is to ask that the filter make the instantaneous power in $y_s(\Delta)$ as large as possible compared to the average power in $n(t)$ at time $\Delta$.

Assuming that $n(t)$ is stationary, the average power in $n(t)$ at any instant is the integrated power under the noise power density spectrum at the filter output. If $G(j2\pi f)$ is the transfer function of the filter, the output noise power density is $(N_0/2)\,|\,G(j2\pi f)\,|^2$; the output noise power is therefore

$$\frac{N_0}{2}\int_{-\infty}^{\infty} |\,G(j2\pi f)\,|^2\,df. \tag{5}$$

Further, if $S(j2\pi f)$ is the input signal spectrum, then $S(j2\pi f)G(j2\pi f)$ is the output signal spectrum, and $y_s(\Delta)$ is the inverse Fourier transform of this, evaluated at $t = \Delta$; that is,

$$y_s(\Delta) = \int_{-\infty}^{\infty} S(j2\pi f)G(j2\pi f)e^{j2\pi f\Delta}\,df. \tag{6}$$

The ratio of the square of (6) to (5) is the power ratio we wish to maximize:

$$\rho = \frac{2\left[\int_{-\infty}^{\infty} S(j2\pi f)G(j2\pi f)e^{j2\pi f\Delta}\,df\right]^2}{N_0\int_{-\infty}^{\infty} |\,G(j2\pi f)\,|^2\,df}. \tag{7}$$

Recognizing that the integral in the numerator is real [it is $y_s(\Delta)$], and identifying $G(j2\pi f)$ with $f(x)$ and $S(j2\pi f)e^{j2\pi f\Delta}$ with $g(x)$ in the Schwarz inequality,

$$\left|\int f(x)g(x)\,dx\right|^2 \le \int |\,f(x)\,|^2\,dx \int |\,g(x)\,|^2\,dx, \tag{8}$$

one obtains from (7)

$$\rho \le \frac{2}{N_0}\int_{-\infty}^{\infty} |\,S(j2\pi f)\,|^2\,df. \tag{9}$$

Since $|\,S(j2\pi f)\,|^2$ is the energy density spectrum of $s(t)$, the integral in (9) is the total energy, $E$, in $s(t)$. Then

$$\rho \le \frac{2E}{N_0}. \tag{10}$$

It is clear on inspection that the equality in (8), and hence in (9) and (10), holds when $f(x) = kg^*(x)$, *i.e.*, when

$$G(j2\pi f) = kS^*(j2\pi f)e^{-j2\pi f\Delta}. \tag{11}$$

Thus, when the filter is matched to $s(t)$, a maximum value of $\rho$ is obtained. It is further easily shown that the equality in (8) holds *only* when $f(x) = kg^*(x)$, so the matched filter of (11) represents the only type of linear filter which maximizes $\rho$.

Notice that we have assumed nothing about the statistics of the noise except that it is stationary and white, with power density $N_0/2$. If it is not white, but has some arbitrary power density spectrum $|\,N(j2\pi f)\,|^2$, a derivation similar to that given above [9], [15] leads to the solution

$$G(j2\pi f) = \frac{kS^*(j2\pi f)e^{-j2\pi f\Delta}}{|\,N(j2\pi f)\,|^2}. \tag{12}$$

[2] This is a *density* spectrum: that is, if $s(t)$ is, *e.g.*, a voltage waveform, $S(j2\pi f)$ is a voltage density, and its integral from $f_1$ to $f_2$ (plus that from $-f_2$ to $-f_1$) is the part of the voltage in $s(t)$ originating in the band of frequencies from $f_1$ to $f_2$.

[3] This is the "double-ended" density, covering positive and negative frequencies. The "single-ended" physical power density (positive frequencies only) is thus $N_0$.

One can convince himself of this intuitively in the following manner. If the input, $x(t)$, of Fig. 2 is passed through a filter with transfer function $1/N(j2\pi f)$, the noise component at its output will be white; however, the signal component will be distorted, now having the spectrum $S(j2\pi f)/N(j2\pi f)$. On the basis of our previous discussion of signals in white noise, it seems reasonable, then, to follow the noise-whitening filter with a filter matched to the distorted signal spectrum, *i.e.*, with the filter $kS^*(j2\pi f)e^{-j2\pi f\Delta}/N^*(j2\pi f)$. The cascade of the noise-whitening filter and this matched filter is indeed the solution (12).[4]

So far we have considered only a detection problem: is the signal present or not? Suppose, however, we know that the signal is present, but has an unknown delay, $t_0$, which we wish to measure (*e.g.*, radar ranging). Then the first of the output waveforms in Fig. 2 obtains, but the peak in it is delayed by the unknown delay. In order to measure this delay accurately, we should not only like the output waveform, as before, to be large at $t = \Delta + t_0$ but also to be very small elsewhere.

More generally, we may frame the problem in the manner depicted in Fig. 3. A sounding signal of known form, $s(t)$, is transmitted into an unknown filter, the impulse response of which is $u(\tau)$. [In Fig. 2, this filter is merely a pair of wires with impulse response $\delta(t)$, the Dirac delta function.] At the output of the unknown filter, stationary noise is added to the signal, the sum being denoted by $x(t)$. We desire to operate on $x(t)$ with a linear filter, whose output, $y(t)$, is to be as faithful as possible an estimate of the unknown impulse response, perhaps with some delay $\Delta$.

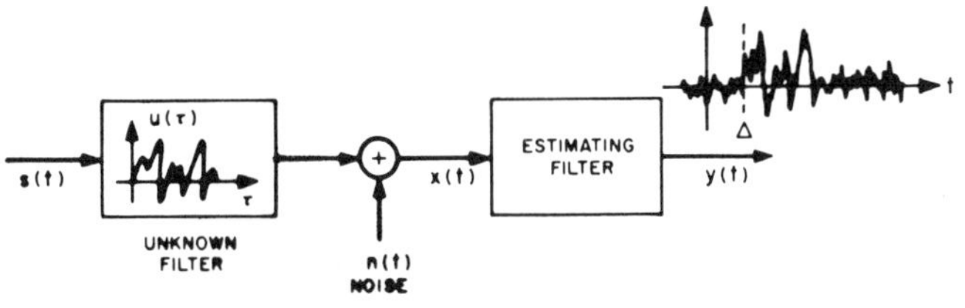


Fig. 3—Pertaining to mean-square estimation of an unknown impulse response.

The unknown filter may be some linear or quasi-linear transmission medium, such as the ionosphere, the characteristics of which we wish to measure. Again, it may represent a complex of radar targets, in which case $u(\tau)$ may consist of a sequence of delta functions with unknown delays (ranges) and strengths.

A reasonable mean-square criterion for faithfulness of reproduction is that the average of the squared difference between $y(t)$ and $u(t - \Delta)$, integrated over the pertinent range of $t$, be as small as possible; the average must be taken over both the ensemble of possible impulse responses of the unknown filter, and the ensemble of possible noises. Using such a criterion [51], one arrives at an optimum estimating filter which is in general relatively complicated. However, when the signal-to-noise ratio is small, and it is assumed that nothing whatever is known about $u(\tau)$ except possibly its maximum duration, the optimum filter turns out to be matched to $s(t)$ if the noise is white, and has the form of (12) for nonwhite noise. Further, in the important case when the sounding signal, $s(t)$, is also optimized to minimize the error in $y(t)$, the optimum estimating filter is matched to $s(t)$ for all signal-to-noise ratios and for all degrees of *a priori* knowledge about $u(\tau)$, provided only that the noise is white.[5]

### B. Probabilistic Criteria

In the preceding discussion, we have confined ourselves to mean-square criteria—maximization of a signal-to-noise power ratio or minimization of a mean-square difference. The use of such simple criteria has the advantage of not requiring us to know more than a second-order statistic of the noise—the power-density spectrum. But, although mean-square criteria often have strong intuitive justifications, we should prefer to use criteria directly related to performance ratings of the systems in which we are interested, such as radar and communication systems. Such performance ratings are usually probabilistic in nature: one speaks of the probabilities of detection, of false alarm, of error, etc., and it is these which we wish to optimize. This brings us into the realm of classical statistical hypothesis-testing and estimation theories.

Let us first examine perhaps the simplest hypothesis-testing problem, the one posed at the start of the section on mean-square criteria: the observed signal, $x(t)$, is either due solely to noise, or to both an exactly known signal and noise.[6] Such a situation could occur, for example, in an on-off communication system, or in a radar detection system. Adopting the standard parlance of hypothesis-testing theory, we denote the former hypothesis, noise only, by $H_0$, and the alternative hypothesis by $H_1$. We wish to devise a test for deciding in favor of $H_0$ or $H_1$.

There are two types of errors with which we are concerned: a Type I error, of deciding in favor of $H_1$ when $H_0$ is true, and a Type II error, of deciding in favor of $H_0$ when $H_1$ is true. The probabilities of making such errors are denoted by $\alpha$ and $\beta$, respectively. For a choice of criterion, we may perhaps decide to minimize the average of $\alpha$ and $\beta$ (*i.e.*, the over-all probability of error); this would require a knowledge of the *a priori* probabilities of $H_0$ and $H_1$, which is generally available in a communication system. On the other hand, perhaps one type of error is more costly than the other, and we may then wish to minimize an average cost [29]. When, as is often the case in radar detection, neither the *a priori*

[4] The weak link in this heuristic argument is, of course, that it is not obvious that an optimization performed on the output of the noise-whitening filter is equivalent to one performed on its input, the observed waveform; it can be shown, however, that this is so.

[5] Another approach to this problem of impulse-response estimation appears in [25].

[6] Here, however, we shall not initially restrict ourselves as before solely to additive combinations of signal and noise.

probabilities nor the costs are known, or even definable, one often alternatively accepts the criterion of minimizing $\beta$ (in radar: maximization of the probability of detection) for a given, predetermined value of $\alpha$ (false-alarm probability)—the Neyman-Pearson criterion [7].

What is important for our present considerations is that all these criteria lead to the same generic form of test. If one lets $p_0(x)$ be the probability (density) that *if* $H_0$ is true, the observed waveform, $x(t)$, could have arisen; and $p_1(x)$ be the probability (density) that *if* $H_1$ is true, $x(t)$ could have arisen; then the test has the form [7], [29], [33]:

$$\left.\begin{array}{lll} \text{accept} & H_1 & \text{if} \quad \dfrac{p_1(x)}{p_0(x)} > \lambda \\ \text{accept} & H_0 & \text{if} \quad \dfrac{p_1(x)}{p_0(x)} \leq \lambda \end{array}\right\}. \tag{13}$$

Here $\lambda$ is a constant dependent on *a priori* probabilities and costs, if these are known, or on the predetermined value of $\alpha$ in the Neyman-Pearson test; most importantly, it is *not* dependent on the observation $x(t)$. The test (13) asks us to examine the possible causes of what we have observed, and to determine whether or not the observation is $\lambda$ times more likely to have occurred if $H_1$ is true than if $H_0$ is true; if it is, we accept $H_1$ as true, and if not, we accept $H_0$. If $\lambda = 1$, for example, we choose the cause which is the more likely to have given rise to $x(t)$. A value of $\lambda$ not equal to unity reflects a bias on the part of the observer in favor of choosing one hypothesis or the other.

Let us assume now that the noise, $n(t)$, is additive, gaussian and white with spectral density $N_0/2$,[3] and further that the signal, if present, has the known form $s(t - t_0)$, $t_0 \leq t \leq t_0 + T$, where the delay, $t_0$, and the signal duration, $T$, are assumed known. Then, on observing $x(t)$ in some observation interval, $I$, which includes the interval $t_0 \leq t \leq t_0 + T$, the two hypotheses concerning its origin are:

$$\left.\begin{array}{ll} H_0: & x(t) = n(t), \quad t \text{ in } I \\ H_1: & x(t) = s(t - t_0) + n(t), \quad t \text{ in } I \end{array}\right\}. \tag{14}$$

Now, it can be shown [57] that the probability density of a sample, $n(t)$, of white, gaussian noise lasting from $a$ to $b$ may be expressed as[7]

$$p(n) = k \exp\left[-\frac{1}{N_0}\int_a^b n^2(t)\,dt\right], \tag{15}$$

where $N_0/2$ is the double-ended spectral density of the noise, and $k$ is a constant not dependent on $n(t)$. Hence the likelihood that, if $H_0$ is true, the observation $x(t)$ could arise is simply the probability (density) that the noise waveform can assume the form of $x(t)$, *i.e.*,

$$p_0(x) = k \exp\left[-\frac{1}{N_0}\int_I x^2(t)\,dt\right], \tag{16}$$

[7] The space on which this probability density exists must be carefully defined, but the details of this do not concern us here.

the region of integration being, as indicated, the observation interval, $I$. Similarly, the likelihood that, if $H_1$ is true, $x(t)$ could arise is the probability density that the noise can assume the form $n(t) = x(t) - s(t - t_0)$, *i.e.*,

$$\begin{aligned} p_1(x) &= k \exp\left[-\frac{1}{N_0}\int_I [x(t) - s(t - t_0)]^2\,dt\right] \\ &= k \exp\left[-\frac{1}{N_0}\int_I x^2(t)\,dt \right. \\ &\qquad \left. + \frac{2}{N_0}\int_I s(t - t_0)x(t)\,dt - \frac{E}{N_0}\right], \end{aligned} \tag{17}$$

where we have denoted $\int_I s^2(t - t_0)\,dt$, the energy of the signal, by $E$.

On substituting (16) and (17) in (13) and taking the logarithm of both sides of the inequality, the hypothesis-testing criterion becomes

$$\left.\begin{array}{lll} \text{accept} & H_1 & \text{if} \quad y(t_0) > \lambda' \\ \text{accept} & H_0 & \text{if} \quad y(t_0) \leq \lambda' \end{array}\right\}, \tag{18}$$

where we have set

$$y(t_0) = \int_I s(t - t_0)x(t)\,dt \tag{19}$$

and

$$\lambda' = \frac{N_0}{2}\log\lambda + 2E. \tag{20}$$

Changing variable in (19) by setting $\tau = t_0 - t$, one obtains

$$y(t_0) = \int_{-T}^{0} s(-\tau)x(t_0 - \tau)\,d\tau. \tag{21}$$

But one immediately recognizes this last as the output, at time $t_0$, of a filter with impulse response $g(\tau) = s(-\tau)$, in response to an input waveform $x(t)$. The filter thus specified is clearly matched to $s(t)$, and the optimum system called for by (18) therefore takes on the form of Fig. 4.[8]

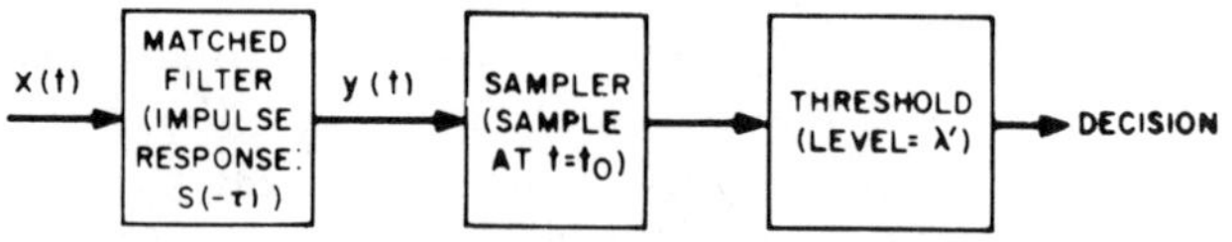


Fig. 4—A simple radar detection system.

[8] Notice that $s(-\tau)$, hence $g(\tau)$, is nonzero only in the interval $-T \leq \tau \leq 0$; hence the limits of integration. In order to realize $g(\tau)$, a delay of $\Delta \geq T$ must be inserted in $g(\tau)$—see (1) and footnote 1. This introduces an equal delay at the filter output, which must then be sampled at time $t_0 + \Delta$, rather than at $t_0$.

Notice also that $y(t_0)$ could be obtained by literally following the edicts of (19). That is, one could multiply the incoming waveform, $x(t)$, by a stored replica of the signal waveform, $s(t)$, delayed by $t_0$; the product, integrated over the observation interval, is $y(t_0)$, and is to be compared with the threshold, $\lambda'$. Such a detector is called a correlation detector. We shall in this paper, however, refer solely to the matched-filter versions of our solutions, with the understanding that these may be obtained by correlation techniques if desired.

The similarity between the solution represented in Fig. 4 and the one we obtained in connection with Fig. 2 is apparent: the matched filter in Fig. 4 in fact maximizes the signal-to-noise ratio of $y(t)$ at $t = t_0$, the sampling instant. That a mean-square criterion and a probabilistic criterion should lead to the same result in the case of additive, gaussian noise is no coincidence; there is an intimate connection between the two types of criteria in this case.

So far, we have considered that the signal component of $x(t)$, if it is present, is known exactly; in particular, we have assumed that the delay $t_0$ is known. Suppose now that the envelope delay of the signal is known, but not the carrier phase, $\theta$ [50]. Assuming that a probability density distribution is given for $\theta$, (13) reduces to

$$\left.\begin{array}{ll} \text{accept } H_1 \quad \text{if} & \dfrac{\int_0^{2\pi} p_1(x/\theta)p(\theta)\, d\theta}{p_0(x)} > \lambda'' \\ \text{accept } H_0 \quad \text{otherwise} & \end{array}\right\}. \qquad (22)$$

Here $p_1(x/\theta)$ is the conditional probability, given $\theta$, that if $H_1$ is true $x(t)$ will arise; $p(\theta)$ is the probability density of $\theta$. If $\theta$ is completely random, so $p(\theta)$ is flat, then carrying through the computations for the case of white, gaussian noise leads to the intuitively expected result that an envelope detector should be inserted in Fig. 4 between the matched filter and the sampler [38], [57]. Note, however, that the matched filtering of $x(t)$ is still the core of the test.

If the envelope delay is also unknown, and no probability distribution is known for it *a priori* other than that it must lie in a given interval, $\Omega$, a good test is [7]:

$$\left.\begin{array}{ll} \text{accept } H_1 \quad \text{if} & \dfrac{\max\limits_{\Omega} \int_0^{2\pi} p_1(x/\theta)p(\theta)\, d\theta}{p_0(x)} > \lambda''' \\ \text{accept } H_0 \quad \text{otherwise} & \end{array}\right\}, \qquad (23)$$

where it is implicit that the integral in the numerator depends on a hypothesized value of the envelope delay.[9] For a flat distribution of $\theta$, (23) yields a circuit in which the envelope detector just inserted in Fig. 4 remains, but is now followed not by a sampler, but by a wide gate, open during the interval $\Omega$. For all values of $t_0$ within this interval, this gate passes the envelope of $y(t_0)$ to the threshold; if the threshold is exceeded at any instant, then the maximum value of the gate output will also surely exceed it, and, by (23), $H_1$ must then be accepted.

As before, a matched filtering operation is the basic part of the test.[10]

We have been discussing, mostly in the radar context, the simple binary detection problem, "signal plus noise or noise only?" Clearly, this is a special case of the general binary detection problem, more germane to communications, "signal 1 plus noise or signal 2 plus noise?", where we have taken one of the signals to be identically zero. Let us now address ourselves to the even more general digital communications problem, "which of $M$ possible signals was transmitted?"

Let us first consider the case in which the forms of the signals, *as they appear at the receiver,* are known exactly. In this situation, a good hypothesis test, of which (13) is a special case, is of the form:

$$\left.\begin{array}{l} \text{accept the hypothesis, } H_m, \text{ for which} \\ \mu_m p_m(x) \ (m = 1, \cdots, M) \quad \text{is greatest} \end{array}\right\}. \qquad (24)$$

Here $p_m(x)$ is the probability that if the $m$th signal was sent, $x(t)$ will be received. The $\mu_m$'s are constants, independent of $x(t)$, which are determined solely by the criterion of the test. If the criterion is, for example, minimization of the over-all probability of error, $\mu_m$ is the *a priori* probability of transmittal of the $m$th signal [56], [57]. The $\mu_m$'s may possibly also be related to the costs of making various types of errors. If neither *a priori* probabilities nor costs are given, the $\mu_m$'s are generally all equated to unity, and the test is called a maximum-likelihood test [7].

If the noise is additive, gaussian, and white with spectral density $N_0/2$, then following the reasoning which led to (17), we have

$$p_m(x) = k \exp\left[-\frac{1}{N_0}\int_I x^2(t)\, dt + \frac{2}{N_0} y_m(0) - \frac{E_m}{N_0}\right], \qquad (25)$$

where, letting $s_m(t)$ be the $m$th signal,

$$y_m(t) = \int_{-T}^{0} s_m(-\tau)x(t-\tau)\, d\tau. \qquad (26)$$

We have arbitrarily assumed that the signals are received with no delay (this amounts to choosing a time origin), and that they all have the same duration, $T$. $E_m$ is the energy in the $m$th signal.

Taking logarithms for convenience, test (24) reduces to:

$$\left.\begin{array}{l} \text{accept the hypothesis, } H_m, \text{ for which} \\ y_m(0) + \left(\dfrac{N_0}{2}\log \mu_m - 2E_m\right) \text{ is greatest} \end{array}\right\}. \qquad (27)$$

[9] Here, for lack of knowing the true envelope delay, we have essentially used test (22), in which we have assumed that the envelope delay has that value which maximizes the integral in the numerator. This procedure is part and parcel of the estimation problem, which we have already considered briefly in the discussion of mean-square criteria, and which we shall later bring into the present discussion on probabilistic criteria.

[10] Note that if a correlation detector (see footnote 8) is to be used here, it must compute the envelope of $y(t_0)$ separately for each value of $t_0$ in $\Omega$. That is, (19) *and its quadrature component* must be obtained, squared and summed *for each* $t_0$ by a separate multiplication and integration process; $t_0$ is here a parameter (parametric time). In general, the advantages of using a matched filter to obtain $y(t_0)$, for all $t_0$ in $\Omega$, as a function of real time are obviously great. In a few circumstances, however—such as range-gated pulsed radar—the correlation technique may be more easily implemented, to a good approximation.

$y_m(0)$ is, as we have seen, the output at $t = 0$ of a filter matched to $s_m(t)$, in response to the input $x(t)$. Therefore, the optimum receiver has the configuration of Fig. 5, where the biases $B_m$ are the quantities $(N_0/2) \log \mu_m - 2E_m$. The output of the decision circuit is the index $m$ which corresponds to the greatest of the $M$ inputs.

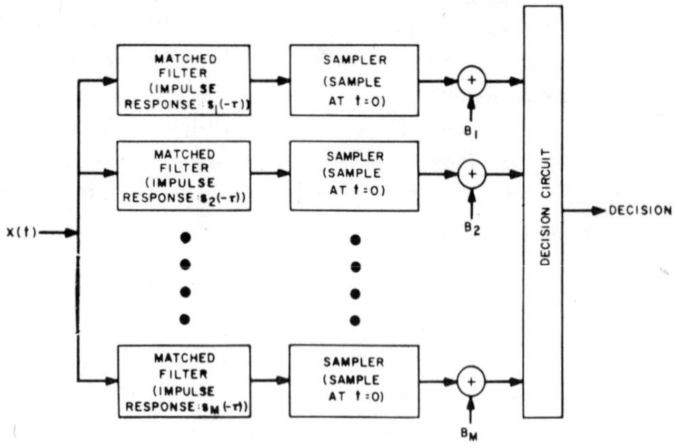


Fig. 5—A simple $M$-ary communications receiver.

If the forms of the signals $s_m(t)$, as they appear at the receiver, are not known exactly, but are dependent on, say, $L$ random parameters, $\theta_1, \cdots, \theta_L$, whose joint density distribution $q(\theta_1, \cdots, \theta_L)$ is known, then (24) takes the form:

$$\left.\begin{array}{l}\text{accept the hypothesis, } H_m, \text{ for which} \\ \mu_m \int \cdots \int q(\theta_1, \cdots, \theta_L) \\ \quad \cdot p_m(x/\theta_1, \cdots, \theta_L)\, d\theta_1 \cdots d\theta_L \quad \text{is greatest}\end{array}\right\}, \tag{28}$$

where $p_m(x/\theta_1, \cdots, \theta_L)$ is the conditional probability, given $\theta_1, \cdots, \theta_L$, that if $H_m$ is true, the observed received signal, $x(t)$, will arise.

Suppose there is only one unknown parameter, the carrier phase, $\theta$, which is assumed to have a uniform distribution. Then, as in the on-off binary case, it turns out that the only modification required in the configuration of the optimum receiver is that envelope detectors of a particular type[11] must be inserted between the matched filters and samplers in Fig. 5.

Test (28) may also be applied to the case of multipath communications. For example, one may consider the case of a discrete, slowly varying, multipath channel in which the paths are independent, and each is characterized by a random strength, carrier phase-shift, and modulation delay; if $P$ is the number of paths, there are then $3P$ random parameters on which the signals depend. It can be shown [50] that, for a broad class of probability distributions of path characteristics, an optimum-receiver arrangement similar to Fig. 5 still obtains. Instead of a simple sampler following the matched filter, however, there is in general a more complicated nonlinear device, the form of which depends on the form of the distribution, $q(\theta_1, \cdots, \theta_L)$, inserted in (28). If, for instance, it is assumed that the modulation delays of the paths are known, but that the path strengths and phase-shifts share joint distributions of a fairly general form [50], the device combines nonlinear functions of several samples, taken at instants corresponding to the expected path delays, of both the output of the matched filter and of its envelope. Again, if all the paths are assumed *a priori* to have identical strength distributions, their carrier phase-shifts assumed uniformly distributed over $(0, 2\pi)$, and their modulation delays assumed uniformly distributed over the interval $(t_a, t_b)$,[12] the form of the nonlinear device which should replace the $m$th sampler in Fig. 5 is given, to a good approximation, by Fig. 6 [12], [50]. The exact form of the nonlinear device, $F_m$, is determined by the assumed path-strength distribution.

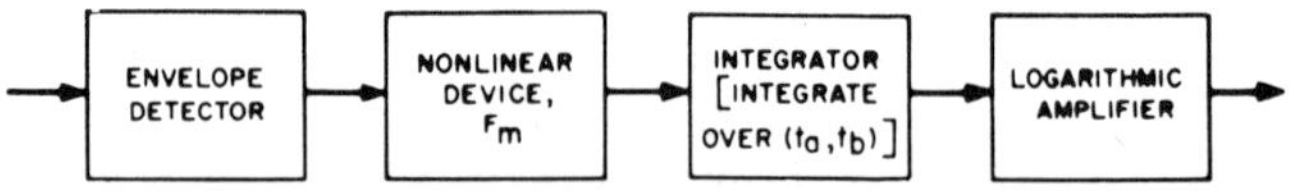


Fig. 6—A nonlinear device for use in Fig. 5 when the path delays are unknown.

The case in which the path modulation delays are known, and the carrier phase-shifts and strengths vary randomly *with time* (*i.e.*, are not restricted, as before, to "slow" variations with respect to the signal duration), has also been considered for Rayleigh-fading paths [36]. Again, at least to an approximation, the results can be interpreted in terms of matched filters. The operations performed on the matched filter outputs now vary with time, however.

In order to use test (28), it is necessary to have a parameter distribution, $q(\theta_1, \cdots, \theta_L)$. It may be, however, that a complete distribution of all the parameters is not available. Then it is often both theoretically and practically desirable to return to a test based on the tenet that the parameters for which no distribution is given are exactly known; in place of the true values of these parameters called for by the test, however, estimates are used. We have already come across such a technique in connection with (23); in that case, an *a priori* distribution of one parameter, phase, was used, but another parameter, modulation delay, was estimated to be that value which maximized the integral in the numerator.[9]

[11] Unlike the on-off binary case, in which any monotone-increasing transfer characteristic can be accommodated in the envelope detector by an adjustment of the threshold, in this case, except when all the biases are equal, the transfer characteristic must be of the log $I_0$ type [7], [38], [50]. In the region of small signal-to-noise ratios, however, such a characteristic is well approximated by a square-law detector.

[12] These distributions of phase shift and modulation delay may not, of course, be totally due to randomness in the channel, but may partially reflect a distribution of error in phase-base and time-base synchronization of transmitter and receiver; the original assumption of knowledge of the *exact* forms of the signals as they appear at the receiver implied perfect synchronization.

Let us, as a final topic in our discussion of probabilistic criteria, then, consider this problem of estimation of parameters. Clearly, estimation may be an end in itself, as in the case of radar ranging briefly considered in the section of mean-square criteria; on the other hand, it may be to the end discussed in the preceding paragraph.

The step from hypothesis testing to estimation may in a sense be considered identical to that from discrete to continuous variables. In the hypothesis test (24), for example, one inquires, "To which of $M$ discrete causes (signals) may the observation $x(t)$ be ascribed?" If one is alternatively faced with a continuum of causes, such as a set of signals, identical except for a delay which may have any value within an interval, the equivalent test would clearly be of the form:

$$\left.\begin{array}{ll}\text{accept the hypothesis, } H_m, & \text{for which} \\ \mu(m)p_m(x)\ (m_1 \leq m \leq m_2) & \text{is greatest}\end{array}\right\}, \tag{29}$$

where the notation is the same as that used in (24), except that $m$ is now a continuous parameter. Only one parameter has been explicitly shown in (29), but clearly the technique may be extended to many parameters.

To consider but one application of (29), let us again investigate the radar-ranging problem, in which the observation is known to be given by

$$x(t) = s(t - t_0) + n(t) \quad \begin{array}{c} a \leq t_0 \leq b \\ t \text{ in } I \end{array}, \tag{30}$$

where $s(t)$ is of known form, nonzero in the interval $0 \leq t \leq T$. Again let us imagine $n(t)$ to be stationary, gaussian and white with spectral density $N_0/2$. Then a little thought will convince one that the probability that $x(t)$ will be observed, if the delay has some specific value $t_0$ in the interval $(a, b)$, is of the form of the right-hand side of (17). Placing this in (29), identifying $m$ with $t_0$, and letting $\mu(m)$ be independent of $m$ (maximum-likelihood estimation) [7], it becomes clear that we seek the value of $t_0$ for which the integrals (19) and (21) are maximum. Remembering our previous interpretation of (21), it follows that a system which estimates delay in this case is one which passes the observed signal, $x(t)$, into a filter matched to the signal $s(t)$, and estimates, as the delay of $s(t)$, the delay (with respect to a reference time) of the maximum of the filter's output. Thus, in optimum radar systems, at least in the case of additive, gaussian noise, a matched filter plays a central part in both the detection and ranging operations. This is a dual rôle we have previously had occasion to note heuristically.[9]

The application of the technique of estimation of unknown signal parameters for use in a hypothesis test has been considered for ideal multipath communication systems [21], [36], [37], [41], [48], [50]. In fact, even if such estimation techniques are not postulated explicitly to start with, but some *a priori* distribution of the unknown parameters is assumed, it is on occasion found that operations which may be interpreted as implicit *a posteriori* estimation procedures appear in the hypothesis-testing receiver [21], [36]. Again, matched filters, or operations very close to matched filtering operations, arise prominently in the solutions.

It is perhaps not necessary to emphasize that the point of the foregoing discussion of where matched filters arise is not to paint a detailed picture of optimum detection and estimation devices; this has not been done, nor could it, in the limited space available. Rather, the point is to indicate that matched filters do appear as the core of a large number of such devices, which differ largely in the type of nonlinear operations applied to the matched-filter output. Having made this point, it behooves us to study the properties of matched filters and to discuss methods of their synthesis, to which topics the remainder of this paper will be devoted.

It seems only proper, however, to end this section with a caveat. The devices based on probabilistic criteria in which we have encountered matched filters were derived on the assumption that at least the additive part of the channel disturbance is stationary, white and gaussian. The stationarity and whiteness requirements are not too essential; the elimination of the former generally leads to time-varying filters, and the elimination of the latter, to the use of the noise-whitening pre-filters we have previously discussed [11], [30]. The requirement of gaussianness is not as easy to dispense with. We have seen that, within the bounds of linear filters, a matched filter maximizes the signal-to-noise ratio for any white, additive noise, and this gives us some confidence in their efficacy in nongaussian situations. But due care should nonetheless be exercised in implying from this their optimality from the point of view of a probabilistic criterion.

## IV. Properties of Matched Filters

In order to gain an intuitive grasp of how a matched filter operates, let us consider the simple system of Fig. 7.

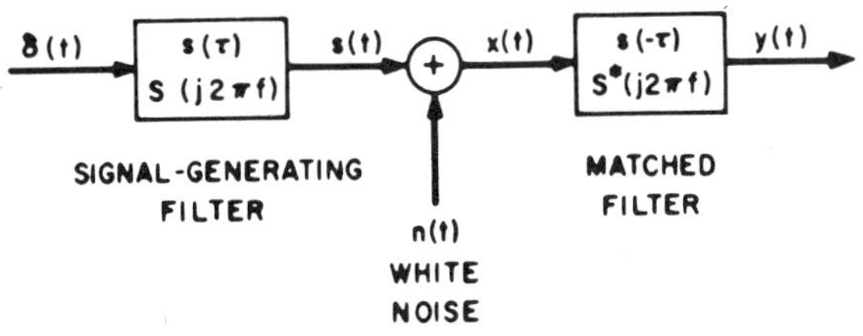


Fig. 7—Illustrating the properties of matched filters.

A signal, $s(t)$, say of duration $T$, may be imagined to be generated by exciting a filter, whose impulse response is $s(\tau)$, with a unit impulse at time $t = 0$. To this signal is added a white noise waveform, $n(t)$, the power density of which is $N_0/2$. The sum signal, $x(t)$, is then passed into a filter, matched to $s(t)$, whose output is denoted by $y(t)$.

This output signal may be resolved into two components,

$$y(t) = y_s(t) + y_n(t), \tag{31}$$

the first of which is due to $s(t)$ alone, the second to $n(t)$ alone. It is these two components which we wish to study. For simplicity of illustration, let us take all spectra to be centered around zero frequency; no generality is lost in our results by doing this.

The response to an input $s(t)$ of a linear filter with impulse response $h(\tau)$ is

$$\int_{-\infty}^{\infty} h(\tau)s(t - \tau)\,d\tau.$$

If $h(\tau) = s(-\tau)$, as in Fig. 7, then

$$y_s(t) = \int_{-\infty}^{\infty} s(-\tau)s(t - \tau)\,d\tau. \qquad (32)$$

This is clearly symmetric in $t$, since

$$\begin{aligned} y_s(-t) &= \int_{-\infty}^{\infty} s(-\tau)s(-t - \tau)\,d\tau \\ &= \int_{-\infty}^{\infty} s(t - \tau')s(-\tau')\,d\tau' = y_s(t), \end{aligned} \qquad (33)$$

where the second equality is obtained through the substitution $\tau' = t + \tau$. For the low-pass case we are considering, $y_s(t)$ may look something like the pulse in Fig. 8. The height of this pulse at the origin is, from (32),

$$y(0) = \int_{-\infty}^{\infty} s^2(\tau)\,d\tau = E, \qquad (34)$$

where $E$ is the signal energy. By applying the Schwarz inequality, (8), to (32), it becomes apparent that $| y_s(t) |$ cannot exceed $y(0) = E$ for any $t$.

The spectrum of $y_s(t)$, that is, its Fourier transform, is $| S(j2\pi f) |^2$. This is easily seen from the fact that $y_s(t)$ may be looked on, in Fig. 7, as the impulse response of the cascade of the signal-generating filter and the matched filter. But the over-all transfer function of the cascade, which is therefore the spectrum of $y_s(t)$, is just $| S(j2\pi f) |^2$. The spectrum corresponding to the $y_s(t)$ in Fig. 8 will look something like Fig. 9.

In Figs. 8 and 9 we have denoted the "widths" of $y_s(t)$ and $| S(j2\pi f) |^2$ by $\alpha$ and $\beta$, respectively. It has been shown [13] that for suitable definitions of these widths, the inequality,

$$\alpha\beta \geq \text{a constant of the order of unity}, \qquad (35)$$

holds. The exact value of the constant depends on the definition of "width" and need not concern us here. The important thing is that the "width" of the signal component at the matched-filter output in Fig. 7 cannot be less than the order of the reciprocal of the signal bandwidth.

In view of the above results, one might question the optimal character of a matched filter. In the preceding section we saw, for example, that in the radar case with gaussian noise we were to compare $y(t)$ with a threshold to determine whether a signal is present or absent (see Fig. 4). Now, if a signal component *is* present in $x(t)$, we seemingly should require, for the purpose of assuring

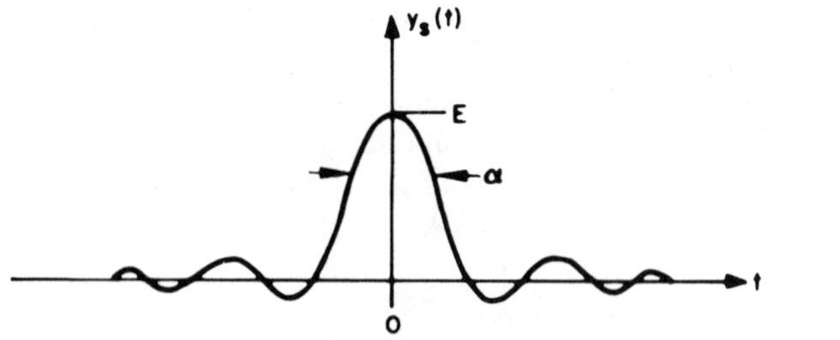


Fig. 8—The signal-component output of (32).

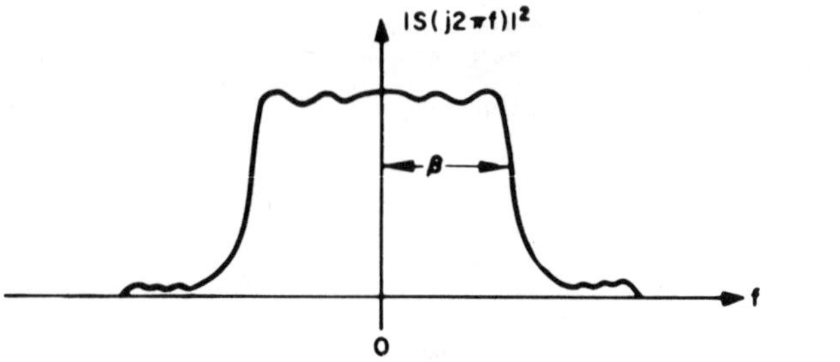


Fig. 9—The spectrum corresponding to $y_s(t)$ in Fig. 8.

that the threshold is exceeded, that the signal component of $y(t)$ be made as large as possible at some instant. Again, if $s(t)$ has been delayed by some unknown amount $t_0$, so that the signal component of $y(t)$ is also delayed, we saw that we could estimate $t_0$ by finding the location of the maximum of $y(t)$; in order to find this maximum accurately, one would imagine we would require that the signal component of $y(t)$ be a high, narrow pulse centered on $t_0$. In short, it appears that for efficient radar detection and ranging we really require an output signal component which looks very much like an *impulse*, rather than like the finite-height, nonzero-width, matched-filter output pulse of Fig. 8. Furthermore, we could actually obtain this impulse by using an inverse filter, with transfer function $1/S(j2\pi f)$, instead of the matched filter in Fig. 7. (To see this, note from Fig. 7 that the output signal component would then be the impulse response of the cascade of the signal-generating filter and the inverse filter, and since the product of the transfer functions of these two filters is identically unity, this impulse response would itself be an impulse.) We are thus led to ask, "Why not use an inverse filter rather than a matched filter?"

The answer is fairly obvious once one considers the effect of the additive noise, which we have so far explicitly neglected in this argument. Any physical signal must have a spectrum, $S(j2\pi f)$, which approaches zero for large values of $f$, as in Fig. 9. The gain of the inverse filter will therefore become indefinitely large as $f \to \infty$. Since the input noise spectrum is assumed to extend over all frequencies, the power in the output noise component of the inverse filter will be infinite. Indeed, the output noise component will override the output signal-component impulse, as may easily be seen by a comparison of their spectra: the former spectrum increases without limit as $f \to \infty$, while the latter is a constant for all $f$.

Thus, one must settle for a signal-component output pulse which is somewhat less sharp than the impulse delivered by an inverse filter. One might look at this as a compromise, a modification of the inverse filter which, while keeping the output signal component as close to an impulse as possible, efficiently suppresses the noise "outside" the signal band. In order to understand the nature of this modification, let us write the signal spectrum in the form

$$S(j2\pi f) = | S(j2\pi f) | e^{-i\psi(f)}, \tag{36}$$

where $\psi(f)$ is the phase spectrum of $s(t)$. Then the inverse filter has the form

$$\frac{1}{S(j2\pi f)} = \frac{1}{| S(j2\pi f) |} e^{i\psi(f)}. \tag{37}$$

Now, since the input noise at any frequency has random phase anyway, we clearly can achieve nothing in the way of noise suppression by modifying the phase characteristic of the inverse filter—we would only distort the output signal component. On the other hand, it seems reasonable to adopt as the amplitude characteristic of the filter, not the inverse characteristic $1/| S(j2\pi f) |$ of (37), but a characteristic which is small at frequencies where the signal is small compared to the noise, and large at the frequencies where the signal is large compared to the noise. In particular, a reasonable choice seems to be $| S(j2\pi f) |$.[13] Then the compromise filter is of the form

$$H(j2\pi f) = | S(j2\pi f) | e^{i\psi(f)} = S^*(j2\pi f), \tag{38}$$

a matched filter. [The last equality in (38) follows from (36) and the fact that, for a physical signal, $| S(j2\pi f) |$ is even in $f$.]

The compromise solution of (38), of course, as we have already seen, maximizes the height of the signal-component output pulse *with respect to the rms noise output.* This maximum output signal-to-noise ratio turns out to be perhaps the most important parameter in the calculation of the performance of systems using matched filters [20], [28], [33]–[35], [39], [52], [53], [57]; it is given by the right-hand side of (10):

$$\rho_0 = \frac{2E}{N_0}. \tag{39}$$

Note that $\rho_0$ depends on the signal *only through its energy,* $E$; such features of the signal as peak power, time duration, waveshape, and bandwidth do not directly enter the expression. In fact, insofar as one is considering *only* the ability of a radar detection system or an on-off communication system to combat white gaussian noise, it follows from this observation that all signals which have the same energy are equally effective.[14]

One may relate the output signal-to-noise ratio, $\rho_0$, to that at the input of the filter. Let the noise bandwidth of the matched filter—*i.e.*, the bandwidth of a rectangular-band filter, with the same maximum gain, which would have the same output noise power as the matched filter—be denoted by $B_N$. Then, for simplicity, one may think of the amount of input noise power within the matched filter "band" as being given by $N_{in} = B_N N_0$. Further, let the average signal power at the filter input be $P_{in} = E/T$, where $T$ is the effective duration of the signal. Then, letting $\rho_i = P_{in}/N_{in}$, (39) becomes

$$\rho_0 = 2B_N T \rho_i . \tag{40}$$

In this formulation of $\rho_0$, it is apparent that the matched filter effects a gain in signal-to-noise *power* ratio of $2B_N T$.

This last result seems at first to contradict our previous observation that, in the face of white noise, the signal bandwidth and time duration do not directly influence $\rho_0$. There is no contradiction, of course. For a given total signal energy, the larger $T$ is, the smaller the input average signal power $P_{in}$ is, and hence the smaller $\rho_i$ is. Any increase in the ratio of $\rho_0$ to $\rho_i$ caused by "spreading out" a fixed-energy signal is thus exactly offset by a decrease in $\rho_i$. Similarly, any increase in the ratio of $\rho_0$ to $\rho_i$ occasioned by increasing the signal bandwidth is also offset by a decrease in $\rho_i$; for, the larger the signal bandwidth, the larger $B_N$, and hence the larger $N_{in}$—that is, the greater the amount of input noise taken in through the increased matched-filter bandwidth.

However, in relation to the foregoing argument let us suppose that one is combating *band-limited* white noise of *fixed* total power, rather than true white noise, which has infinite total power. That is, suppose the interference is such that its total power $N_{in}$ is always caused, malevolently, to be spread out evenly over the signal "bandwidth" $B_N$, *whatever* this bandwidth is. Then, in (40), $\rho_i$ is no longer dependent on $B_N$, and it is clearly advantageous to make the signal and matched-filter bandwidths as large as possible; the larger the bandwidth, the more thinly the total interfering power must be spread, *i.e.*, the smaller the value of $N_0$ in (39) becomes. In this situation, of all signals with the same energy, the one with the largest bandwidth is the most useful.

An interesting way of looking at the functions of the pair of filters, $S(j2\pi f)$ and $S^*(j2\pi f)$, in Fig. 7 is from the point of view of "coding" and "decoding." The impulse at the input to the signal-generating filter has components at all frequencies, but their amplitudes and phases are such that they add constructively at $t = 0$, and cancel each other out elsewhere. The transfer function $S(j2\pi f)$ "codes" the amplitudes and phases of these frequency components so that their sum becomes some arbitrary waveform lasting, say, from $t = 0$ to $t = T$, such as is shown in Fig. 10. Now, what we should like to do at the receiver is to "decode" the signal, *i.e.*, restore all the amplitudes and phases to their original values. We have seen that we cannot do this, since it would entail an inverse filter; we compromise by restoring the phases,

[13] This is indeed the solution Brennan obtains in deriving weights for optimal linear diversity combination [2]; here we have essentially a case of coherent frequency diversity.

[14] As we shall see, for more complicated communication systems in which more than one signal waveform may be transmitted, parameters governing the "similarity" of the signals enter the performance calculations [20], [52].

so that all frequency components at the filter output have zero phase at the same time ($t = 0$ in Fig. 8) and add constructively to give a large pulse. This pulse has a nonzero width, of not less than the order of the reciprocal of the signal bandwidth, because we are not able to restore the amplitudes of the components properly.

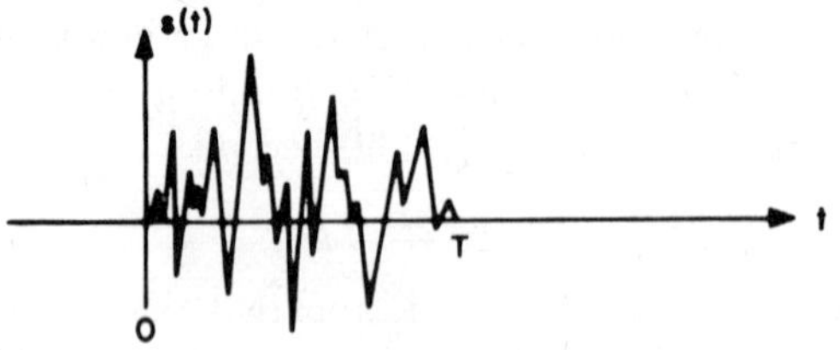


Fig. 10—A signal waveform.

In "coding," then, we have spread the signal energy out over a duration $T$; in "decoding," we are able to collapse this energy into a pulse of the order of $\beta T$ times narrower, where $\beta$ is some appropriate measure of the signal bandwidth. The "squashing" of the energy into a shorter pulse leads to an enhancement of signal-to-noise power ratio by a factor of the order of $B_N T$, already noted in connection with (40).

We thus see that the time-bandwidth product of teh signal or its matched filter, which we shall henceforth denote by $TW$, is a very important parameter in the description of the filter. It also turns out to be an index of the filter's complexity, as can be seen by the following argument. It is well known [43], that roughly $2TW$ independent numbers are sufficient (although not always necessary) to describe a signal which has an effective time duration $T$ and an effective bandwidth $W$. It follows that the complete specification of a filter which is matched to such a signal requires, at least in theory, no more than $2TW$ numbers. Therefore, in synthesizing the filter there theoretically need be no more than $2TW$ elements or parameters specified, whence the use of the $TW$ product as a measure of "complexity." (See footnote 20, however.)

Hopefully, this section has provided an intuitive insight into the nature of matched filters. It is now time to investigate the problems encountered in their synthesis.

## V. Matched-Filter Synthesis and Signal Specification

In considering the synthesis of matched filters, one must take account of the edicts of two sets of constraints: those of physical realizability, and those of what might be called practical realizability. The first limit what one *could* do, at least in theory; the second are more realistic, for they recognize that what is theoretically possible is not always attainable in practice—they define the limits of what one *can* do.

The constraints of physical realizability are relatively easily given, and may be found in any good book on network synthesis [19]. Perhaps the most important for us, at least for electrical filters, is that expressed in footnote 1, that the impulse response must be zero for negative values of its argument.[15] If the signal to which the filter is to be matched "stops"—*i.e.*, falls to zero and remains there thereafter—at some finite time $t_2$ (see Fig. 1), then we have seen that by introducing a finite but perhaps large delay, $\Delta \geq t_2$, in the impulse response, we can render the impulse response physically realizable. We must of course then wait until $t = \Delta \geq t_2$ for the peak of the output signal pulse to occur; put another way, we cannot expect an output containing the full information about the signal at least until the signal has been fully received. Suppose, however, that $t_2$ is infinite, or it is finite but we cannot afford to wait until the signal is fully received before we extract information about it. Then it may easily be shown, for example, that in order to maximize the output signal-to-noise ratio at some instant $t < t_2$, we should use that part of the optimum impulse response which is realizable, and delete that part which is not [58]. Thus, if the signal of Fig. 1(a) is to be detected at $t = 0$, the *desired* impulse response is proportional to that of Fig. 1(b); the best we can do in rendering this physically realizable is to delete that part of it occurring prior to $\tau = 0$. The output signal-to-noise ratio at the instant of the output signal peak (in this case, $t = 0$) is still of the form of (39), but now $E$ must be interpreted not as the total signal energy, but only as that part of the signal energy having arrived by the time of the output signal peak. Of course, we are no longer dealing with a true matched filter.

The constraints of practical realizability are not so easy to formulate: they are, rather, based on engineering experience and intuition. Let us henceforth assume that we are concerned with a true matched filter, *i.e.*, that the impulse response (1) is physically realizable. Even then, we are aware that the filter may not be practically realizable, because too many elements may be required to build it, or because excessively flawless elements would be needed, or because the filter would be too difficult to align or keep aligned, etc. In this light, the problem of realizing a matched filter changes from "Here is a desirable signal; match a filter to it" to "Here is a class of filters which I can satisfactorily build; which members of the class, if any, correspond to desirable signals?" In the former case we might here have neglected the question of how it was decided that the given signal is "desirable"; it would perhaps have sufficed merely to discuss how to realize the filter. But from the latter point of view the choice of a practical filter becomes inextricably interwoven with criteria governing the desirability of a signal, and one would therefore do well to design both the filter *and* the signal together to do the best over-all job. For this reason it is worthwhile to devote some time to answering the question, "What is a desirable signal?"

[15] Note that such a constraint is not necessary for optical filters [5], and filters—such as may be programmed on a computer—which use parametric rather than real time.

The answer, of course, depends on the application. Let us first consider the case of radar detection and ranging.

From the point of view of detection, we noted in the last section that in the face of white gaussian noise all signals with the same energy are equally effective, while if the interfering noise is band-limited and is constrained to have a given total power, then of all signals of the same energy those with the largest bandwidth are the most effective.

From the point of view of ranging there are at least three properties of the signal which we must consider: *accuracy*, *resolution*, and *ambiguity*. Let us first discuss these for the case of a low-pass signal. In this case, the matched-filter output has the form of the pulse in Fig. 8, but delayed by an unknown amount and immersed in noise. In order accurately to locate the position of the delayed central peak of the output signal pulse, we should like both to make $\rho_0$ of (39) large and also to make $\alpha$, the width of this peak, small. This latter requirement implies making the bandwidth large [see (35)], whether the noise is truly white, or is of the band-limited, fixed-power variety. Further, if several targets are present, so that the signal component of the matched filter output consists of several pulses of the form of Fig. 8, delayed by various amounts (see Fig 11), then making $\alpha$ very small will allow closely adjacent targets to be resolved. That is, if two targets have nearly the same delay, as, for example, targets 3 and 4 in Fig. 11, making $\alpha$ small enough will lead to the appearance of two distinct peaks in the matched-filter output, rather than a broad hump.

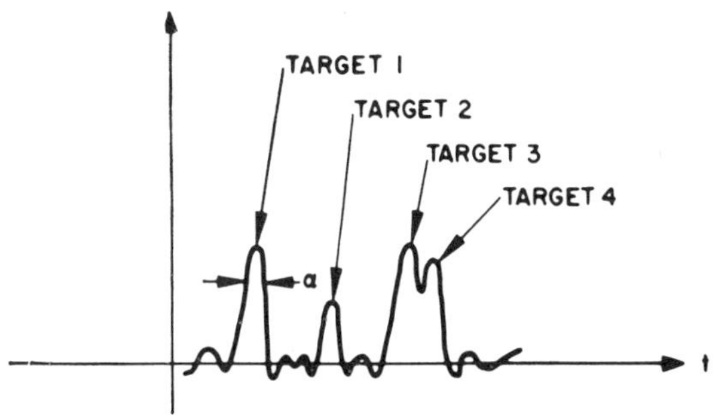


Fig. 11—The signal-component output of a matched filter for a resolvable multitarget or multipath situation.

The requirements of accuracy and resolution thus dictate a large-bandwidth signal. A more stringent requirement is that of lack of ambiguity. To explain this, let us again consider Fig. 8, the output signal component in response to a single target. As shown, there is but one peak, so even if the peak is shifted by an unknown delay there is hope that, despite noise, the amount of the delay can be determined unambiguously. However, suppose now that the waveform of Fig. 8 were to have many peaks of equal height, as would happen if the signal $s(t)$ were periodic [see (32)]. Then even without noise, it might not be totally clear which peak represented the unknown target delay; that is, there would be ambiguity in the target range, a familiar enough phenomenon in, say, periodically pulsed radars.

For the purposes of radar ranging then, what we require in the low-pass case is a large bandwidth signal, $s(t)$, for which, from (32),

$$y_s(t) = \int_{-\infty}^{\infty} s(\tau)s(t+\tau)\,d\tau \tag{41}$$

has a narrow central peak, and is as close to zero as possible everywhere else. The right-hand side of (41) may also be written as the real part of

$$2\int_0^{\infty} |S(j2\pi f)|^2 e^{j2\pi ft}\,df, \tag{42}$$

where $S(j2\pi f)$ is, as usual, the spectrum of $s(t)$. We see, therefore, that we are here concerned with a shaping of the energy density spectrum of the signal.

In the case of a band-pass signal with random phase, all we have said still holds, but now not with respect to $y_s(t)$, but with respect to its envelope; $y_s(t)$ itself now has a fine oscillatory structure at the carrier frequency. This envelope is expressible as the magnitude of (42) [57]. In other words, we now want the *envelope* of the matched-filter output, in the absence of noise, to have a narrow central peak and be as close to zero as possible elsewhere. As before, the minimum width attainable by the central peak is of the order of the reciprocal of the signal bandwidth.

We have thus far in the present paper neglected the possibility of doppler shift in our discussion of radar systems. It is worthwhile to insert a few words on this topic now; we shall limit ourselves, however, to consideration of narrow-band band-pass signals, which are the only ones for which we can meaningfully speak of a doppler "*shift*" of frequency. Suppose, in addition to being delayed, the target return signal may also be shifted in frequency. It turns out then that when additive, white, gaussian noise is present, the ideal receiver should contain a parallel bank of matched filters much like that in the communication receiver of Fig. 5. Each filter is matched to a frequency-shifted version of the transmitted signal, there being a filter for each possible doppler shift. (If there is a continuum of possible doppler shifts, we shall see that the required "continuum" of filters is well approximated by a finite set, in which the frequency shifts are evenly spaced by amounts of the order of $1/T$, the reciprocal of the duration of the transmitted signal.) The (narrow-band) outputs of the bank of matched filters are then all envelope detected and subsequently passed into a device which decides, according to the edicts of hypothesis-testing and estimation theories, whether or not a target is present, and if present, at what delay (range) and doppler shift (velocity).

Now, as in the case of no doppler shift, the detectability of the signal is still governed by (39) and (40). But a modification is required in our previous discussion of the demands of high accuracy, high resolution, and low ambiguity. Generalizing this discussion to the case of nonzero doppler shift, it is clear that we require the following: each target represented at the receiver input should excite *only* the filter in the matched-filter bank which corresponds to the target doppler shift (velocity), and, further, should cause a sharp peak to appear in this filter's output envelope *only* at a time corresponding to the delay of the target, and nowhere else. In order to state this requirement mathematically, let us compute the output envelope at time $t$ of a filter matched to a target return with doppler shift $\phi$, in response to a target return with zero doppler shift and zero delay. (We lose no generality in assuming these particular target parameters.) We first note that if the (double-sided) spectrum of the transmitted signal is $S(j2\pi f)$, then for the narrow-band band-pass signal we are considering, the spectrum of the signal after undergoing a doppler shift $\phi$ is approximately $S[j2\pi(f - \phi)]$ *in the positive-frequency region.*[16] A filter matched to this shifted signal therefore has the approximate transfer function $S^*[j2\pi(f - \phi)]$, again in the positive-frequency region. Then the spectrum of the response of this filter to a non-doppler-shifted, nondelayed signal is approximately $S(j2\pi f)\ S^*[j2\pi(f - \phi)]\ (f > 0)$; the response itself, at time $t$, is the real part of the complex Fourier transform

$$\chi(t, \phi) = 2 \int_0^\infty S(j2\pi f) S^*[j2\pi(f - \phi)] e^{j2\pi f t}\, df. \tag{43}$$

The envelope of the response is just $|\chi(t, \phi)|$, and it is this which we require to be large at $t = 0$ if $\phi = 0$, and small otherwise. That is, we require that $|\chi(t, \phi)|$ have the general shape shown in Fig. 12: a sharp central peak at the origin, and small values elsewhere [23], [44], [57].

Note that (42) is a special case of (43) for $\phi = 0$; hence, the magnitude of (42) corresponds to the intersection of the $|\chi(t, \phi)|$ surface in Fig. 12 with the plane $\phi = 0$. It follows therefore from our discussion of (42) that the central peak in Fig. 12 cannot be narrower than the order of $1/W$ in the $t$ direction. The use of an uncertainty relation of the form of (35) similarly reveals that the "width" of the peak cannot be less than the order of $1/T$ in the $\phi$ direction, where $T$ is the effective signal duration [57]. (From this is implied a previous statement, that when a continuum of doppler shifts is possible, a good approximation to the ideal receiver involves the use of matched filters spaced apart in frequency by $1/T$; for, a target return which has doppler shift $\phi$ will cause responses in filters matched to signals with doppler shifts in an interval at least $1/T$ cps wide centered on $\phi$.) More generally, one may show that the cross-sectional "area" of the central peak of the surface in Fig. 12—*i.e.*, the size of the $(t, \phi)$ region over which the peak has appreciable height—cannot be less than the order of $1/TW$ [44]. Thus, in order to attain a very sharp central peak it is

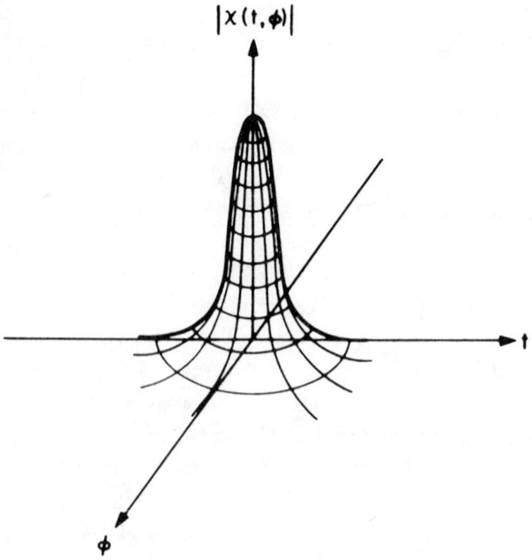


Fig. 12—A desirable $|\chi(t, \phi)|$ function.

necessary—but not sufficient, as we shall see—to make the $TW$ product of the signal very large. Elimination of spurious peaks in $|\chi(t, \phi)|$ away from the $(t, \phi)$ origin is much more complicated, and has been studied elsewhere [23], [45], [57].

So much for radar signals. The requirements on communication signals are somewhat different, in some ways laxer and in others more stringent. In the simplest case, on-off communication, in which we are concerned with only one signal, the situation is obviously much like radar, except that in general one need not worry about doppler shifts of the transmitted signal. In particular, for gaussian noise, the detectability of the signal, and hence the probability of error, will in this case depend solely on $\rho_0$ of (39) and (40).

It should be expressly noted, however, that the problems of ranging which we encountered in the radar case are not entirely absent in the communication case. For example, in on-off communication, in order to sample the output of the matched filter at the time its signal component passes through its maximum, we must know when this maximum occurs. In many transmission media, however, the transmitted signal is randomly delayed, thus necessitating a ranging operation, in communication parlance called synchronization. We are not interested in this synchronization time *per se*, as in radar ranging, and are therefore not necessarily interested in eliminating large ambiguous peaks in $y_s(t)$ of (41). If such subsidiary peaks are of the same height as the central one, as will occur if the signal is periodic, we will be just as happy to sample one of them, rather than the central peak. On the other hand, we should not like to synchronize on and sample a peak appreciably smaller than the central peak, for then we would lose in signal-to-noise ratio. Thus, roughly, we require that a spurious peak in $y_s(t)$ be either very large or nonexistent.

[16] In the negative-frequency region, the shifted spectrum has the approximate form $S[j2\pi(f + \phi)]$.

We may no longer even require the peaks in $y_s(t)$ to be narrow, for we are not interested in determining the exact location of the peak, but only in sampling the matched-filter output at or near this peak. Clearly, an error in the sampling instant will be less disastrous if the peak is broad than if it is narrow. On the other hand, a narrow peak *is* often desirable in a multipath situation. There are often several independent paths between the transmitter and receiver, which represent independent sources of information about the transmitted signal. It behooves us to keep these sources separate, *i.e.*, to be able to resolve one path from another: this is the same as the radar resolvability requirement, illustrated in Fig. 11. From the frequency-domain viewpoint, requiring the matched-filter output pulse width to be small enough to resolve the various paths is the same as requiring the signal bandwidth to be large enough to avoid nonselective fading of the whole frequency band of the signal.

Such are the considerations which must be given to the choice of a signal for an on-off communication system, or to each signal individually in multisignal systems. However, in systems of the latter type, such as in Fig. 5, one must also consider the relationships *between* signals. In the system of Fig. 5, for example, it is not enough to specify that each signal individually have high energy and excite an output in its associated matched filter which consists, say, of a single narrow pulse at $t = 0$; if this were sufficient, we could choose all the signals to be identical, patently a ridiculous choice. We must also require that the various signals be *distinguishable*. More precisely, if the signal component of $x(t)$ in Fig. 5 is, say, $s_i(t)$, then the signal component at the output of the $i$th filter should be as large as possible at $t = 0$, *and* at the same instant the signal components of the outputs of all other filters should be "as much different" from the $i$th filter signal output as possible.

The phrase "as much different" needs defining: one wishes to specify $M$ signals so that the over-all probability of error in reception is minimized. Unfortunately, this problem has not been solved in general for the phase-coherent receiver of Fig. 5. For the special case of binary transmission ($M = 2$), however, it turns out that if the two signals are *a priori* equally probable, one should use equal-energy antipodal signals, *i.e.*, $s_1(t) = -s_2(t)$ [20], [52]. For then, on reception of the $i$th signal with zero delay, the output signal component of its associated matched filter at $t = 0$ is, from (32),

$$y_s(0) = \int_{-\infty}^{\infty} s_i^2(\tau)\, d\tau = E \qquad (i = 1, 2), \tag{44}$$

where $E$ is the signal energy. The $k$th filter signal output at $t = 0$ is clearly

$$\int_{-\infty}^{\infty} s_k(-\tau)s_i(-\tau)\, d\tau = -E \qquad (i \neq k), \tag{45}$$

which is easily shown to be "as much different" from (44) as possible.[17]

If one considers the band-pass case in which the carrier phases are unknown, we have seen that the optimum system in Fig. 5 is modified by the insertion of envelope detectors between the matched filters and samplers. In this case a reasonable conjecture, which has been established for the binary case [20], [52], is that the $M$ signals be "envelope-orthogonal." That is, if the $i$th signal is received, the envelopes of the signal-component outputs of all but the $i$th filter should be zero at the instant $t = 0$. Now, if the spectrum of the $i$th signal is denoted by $S_i(j2\pi f)$, then the envelope of the signal-component output of the $k$th filter is:

$$2\left| \int_0^{\infty} S_k^*(j2\pi f) S_i(j2\pi f) e^{j2\pi ft}\, df \right|. \tag{46}$$

This, evaluated at $t = 0$, must therefore be zero for all $k \neq i$. There are several ways of assuring that this be so, the most obvious being the use of signals with nonoverlapping bands, so that $S_k^*(j2\pi f)\ S_i(j2\pi f) = 0$.[18] Another way involves the use of signals which are rectangular bursts of sine waves, the sine-wave frequencies of the different signals being spaced apart by integral multiples of $1/T$ cps, where $T$ is the duration of the bursts. A third method is considered elsewhere in this issue [49].

If random multipath propagation is involved and the modulation delays of the paths are known, then we have noted that the samplers in Fig. 5 should in general sample both the matched-filter outputs and their envelopes at several instants, corresponding to the various path delays. We may in this case conjecture, again for the situation of unknown path phase-shifts (*i.e.*, only envelope sampling), that for an optimum set of signals, (46) should vanish for $k \neq i$, but now at values of $t$ corresponding to all path delay *differences*, including zero. For, suppose the $i$th signal is sent. Then the spectrum

$$\sum_{l=1}^{L} S_i(j2\pi f) e^{-j2\pi f t_l} e^{-j\theta_l} \tag{47}$$

is received, where $t_l$ and $\theta_l$ are, respectively, the modulation delay and carrier phase-shift of the $l$th path [50].

[17] Since the writing of this paper, Dr. A. V. Balakrishnan has informed the author that he has proved the following long-standing conjecture concerning the general case of $M$ equiprobable signals. If the dimensionality of the signal space (roughly $2TW$) is at least $M - 1$, then the signals, envisaged as points in signal space, should be placed at the vertices of an $(M - 1)$-dimensional regular simplex (*i.e.*, a polyhedron, each vertex of which is equally distant from every other vertex); in this situation, (44) holds for all $i$, and the right-hand side of (45) becomes $-E/(M - 1)$. The problem of a signal space of smaller dimensionality than $M - 1$ has not been solved in general.

[18] If the signals $s_i(t)$ are of finite duration, then their spectra extend over all $f$, and nonoverlapping bands are therefore not possible. An approximation is achieved by spacing the band centers by amounts large compared to the bandwidths.

The envelope of the output signal component of the $k$th matched filter is then

$$\left| 2 \sum_{l=1}^{L} e^{-j\theta l} \int_{0}^{\infty} S_k^*(j2\pi f) S_i(j2\pi f) e^{j2\pi f(t-t_l)} \, df \right| . \quad (48)$$

Since the output envelopes of the matched filters are to be sampled at $t = t_r$ $(r = 1, \cdots, L)$, it seems reasonable to require that in the absence of noise these samples should all be zero for $k \neq i$. That is, (48) should be zero for all $k \neq i$ at all $t = t_r$. For lack of knowledge of the $\theta_L$'s, a sufficient condition for this to occur is that (46) be zero at all $t = t_r - t_l$.

An extension of this argument to the case of unknown modulation delays considered in connection with Fig. 6 leads similarly to a requirement that, for all $k \neq i$, (46) vanish over the whole interval $-A \leq t \leq A$, where $A = t_b - t_a$, $t_a$ and $t_b$ being the parameters referred to in Fig. 6. This may not be possible with physical signals, and some approximation must then be sought. Here is another unsolved problem.

A final desirable property of both radar and communication signals which is worth mentioning is one arising from the use of a peak-power limited transmitter. For such a transmitter, operation at rated average power often points to the use of a constant-amplitude signal, *i.e.*, one in which only the phase is modulated. A signal of this sort is also demanded by certain microwave devices.

Having thus closed parentheses on a rather lengthy detour into the problem of signal specification, let us recall the question on which we opened them. We had decided that the constraints of practical realizability had limited us to the consideration of filters which can, in fact, be built. Looking at any particular class of such filters—for example, those with less than 1000 lumped elements, with coils having $Q$'s less than 200—we ask, "Which members of this class are matched to desirable signals?" We have gotten some idea of what constitutes a desirable signal. Let us now briefly examine a few proposed classes of filters and see to what extent this question has been answered for these classes.

## VI. Some Forms of Matched Filters

It is not intended to give herein an exhaustive treatment of all solutions obtained to the problem of matched-filter realization; indeed, such a treatment would be neither possible nor desirable. We shall, rather, concentrate on three classes of solutions which seem to have attracted the greatest attention. Even in consideration of these we shall be brief, for details are adequately given elsewhere, in many cases in this issue.

### *A. Tapped-Delay-Line Filters*

Let us first consider matched filters for the class of signals generatable as the impulse response of a filter of the form of Fig. 13. The spectrum of a signal of this class has the form

$$S(j2\pi f) = F(j2\pi f) \sum_{i=0}^{n} G_i(j2\pi f) e^{-j2\pi f \Delta_i}, \quad (49)$$

which is, of course, the transfer function of the filter of Fig. 13. It is immediately clear that a filter matched to this signal may be constructed in the form of Fig. 14, for the transfer function of the filter shown there is

$$\begin{aligned} H(j2\pi f) &= F^*(j2\pi f) \sum_{i=0}^{n} G_i^*(j2\pi f) e^{-j2\pi f(\Delta_n - \Delta_i)} \\ &= S^*(j2\pi f) e^{-j2\pi f \Delta_n}. \quad (50) \end{aligned}$$

The filters of Figs. 13 and 14 are thus candidates for the filter pair appearing in Fig. 7.

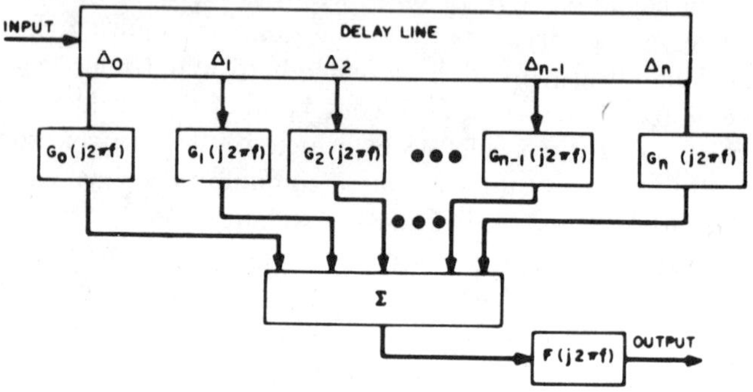


Fig. 13—A tapped-delay-line signal generator.

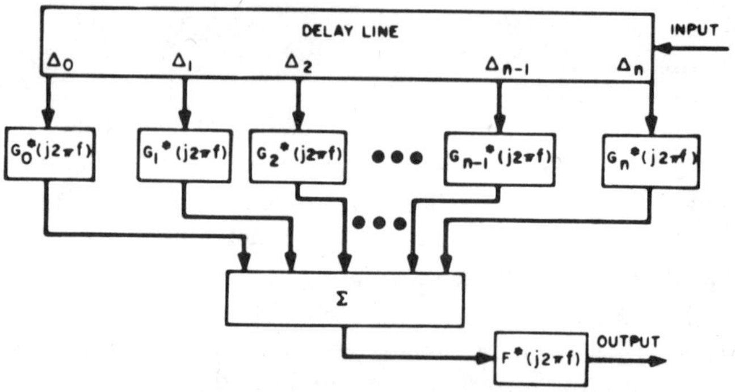


Fig. 14—A tapped-delay-line matched filter.

If $F(j2\pi f)$ and $G_i(j2\pi f)$ are assigned phase functions which are uniformly zero, then $F^*(j2\pi f) = F(j2\pi f)$ and $G_i^*(j2\pi f) = G_i(j2\pi f)$, and the two filters of Figs. 13 and 14 become identical except for the end of the delay line which is taken as the input. [The same identity of Figs. 13 and 14 is obviously also obtained, except for an unimportant discrepancy in delay, if $F(j2\pi f)$ and $G_i(j2\pi f)$ have linear phase functions, the slopes of all the latter being equal.] The advantages of having a single filter which can perform the tasks both of signal generation and signal processing are obvious, especially in situations such as radar, where the transmitter and receiver are physically at the same location.

Having defined a generic form of matched filter, we are still left with the problem of adjusting its characteristics [$F(j2\pi f)$, $G_i(j2\pi f)$ and $\Delta_i$, all $i$] to correspond to a desirable signal. A possibility which immediately comes to mind is to set

$$\left.\begin{aligned} F(j2\pi f) &= \begin{cases} \dfrac{1}{2W}, & |f| \leq W \\ 0, & |f| > W \end{cases} \\ G_i(j2\pi f) &= a_i \\ \Delta_i &= \frac{i}{2W} \end{aligned}\right\}. \tag{51}$$

For, the signal which corresponds to such a choice has, from (49), the spectrum

$$S(j2\pi f) = \begin{cases} \dfrac{1}{2W} \sum_{i=0}^{n} a_i e^{-j2\pi f(i/2W)}, & |f| \leq W, \\ 0, & |f| > W, \end{cases} \tag{52}$$

and the signal itself therefore has the form

$$s(t) = \sum_{i=0}^{n} a_i \frac{\sin \pi(2Wt - i)}{\pi(2Wt - i)}. \tag{53}$$

It is well known [43] that *any* signal limited to the band $|f| \leq W$ can be represented in a form similar to (53), but with the summation running over all values of $i$; the $a_i$'s are in fact just the values of $s(t)$ at $t = i/2W$. In (53) we therefore have a band-limited low-pass signal for which

$$s\left(\frac{i}{2W}\right) = \begin{cases} a_i, & i = 0, \cdots, n \\ 0, & \text{other integral values of } i \end{cases}. \tag{54}$$

Although $s(t)$ is not *uniformly* zero outside of $0 \leq t \leq n/2W$, it is seen from (53) and (54) that, at least for large $n$, the duration of $s(t)$ is effectively $T = n/2W$. The time-bandwidth product of the signal, which we have found to be a very important parameter, is thus approximately $TW = n/2$. Notice that this is proportional to the number of taps on the delay line and the number of multipliers, $a_i$, which in this case justifies the use of the $TW$ product as a measure of the complexity of the filter.

It would seem that we have here, in one swoop, solved the problem of signal specification and matched-filter design, for we now have means available for obtaining both any desired band-limited signal and the filter matched to it.[19] There are two drawbacks which mar this hopeful outlook, however, one practical and the other theoretical. The first is that, at least at present, we do not know how to choose the $a_i$'s so that $s(t)$ is desirable in the senses, say, of our discussions of (43) and (46). More basic is the fact that truly band-limited signals are not physically realizable; that is, the transfer function $F(j2\pi f)$ of (51) cannot be achieved, even theoretically. Using a realizable approximation to $F(j2\pi f)$ complicates the choice of the $a_i$'s: for even if we were aware of how to choose the $a_i$'s for the ideal $F(j2\pi f)$, it would not be clear how the use of an approximation would then affect the "desirability" of $s(t)$. This is not to say that the solution embodied in (51) should be discarded, but only that it must be further investigated to render it practically realizable.

Another possible choice of characteristics for the filters of Figs. 13 and 14 involves letting the pass bands of the filters $G_i(j2\pi f)$ be nonoverlapping, or essentially so [27]. [$F(j2\pi f)$ may here be considered to be unity, since limitation of the signal bandwidth is accomplished by the $G_i$'s.] The purpose here is to afford independent control of various frequency bands of $S(j2\pi f)$ [cf. (49)], to the end of satisfying whatever requirements have been placed on the signal spectrum by constraints on (43) and (46). If we are considering only one signal which is not subject to doppler shift, then we are concerned only with constraints on (42), a special case of (43). In this case, control of various frequency ranges of $S(j2\pi f)$ is a direct method of achieving the energy-spectrum shaping mentioned in connection with (42); further, the use of a long enough delay line in conjunction with enough filters, $G_i$, will result in the desired large $TW$ product.[20] For this special case, then, the use of a tapped delay line with nonoverlapping filters yields a possible desirable solution to our problem. More generally, however, when there are doppler shifts and/or many signals, we again must profess ignorance of how to select the $G_i$'s and $\Delta_i$'s properly. Again further investigation is called for.

A third choice of characteristics for the filters of Figs. 13 and 14, *viz.*,

$$\left.\begin{aligned} F(j2\pi f) &= \frac{\sin \pi f \Delta}{\pi f} e^{-j\pi f \Delta} \\ G_i(j2\pi f) &= b_i = \pm 1 \\ \Delta_i &= i\,\Delta \end{aligned}\right\}, \tag{55}$$

has received considerable attention [12], [27], [44]. Note that the impulse response of $F(j2\pi f)$ is a rectangular pulse of unit height, and width $\Delta$, starting at $t = 0$.[21] The impulse response of the filter of Fig. 13, *i.e.*, the matched signal, therefore has the form of Fig. 15—a low-pass sequence of positive and negative pulses, shown

[19] We have explicitly given only the low-pass case, in which, incidentally, the $F$ and $G$'s have the desirable zero phase functions. The band-pass case is obtainable by replacing the low-pass $F(j2\pi f)$ of (51) with its band-pass equivalent, letting the $a_i$'s be complex (*i.e.*, contain phase shifts), and letting $\Delta_i = i/W$, where $W$ is the band-pass band-width.

[20] If, in particular, the impulse responses of the filters $G_i$ all have an effective duration of $\Delta$, and the tap spacings in Fig. 13 are $\Delta_i - \Delta_{i-1} = \Delta$, then a "stepped-frequency" signal is obtained; that is, $s(t)$ is a continuous succession of nonoverlapping "pulses" of different frequencies. If, in addition, the bands of the $G_i$'s are adjacent and have widths of the order of $1/\Delta$, the $TW$ product for $s(t)$ and its matched filter is of the order of $n\Delta(n/\Delta) = n^2$. Here is a degenerate case in which we have generated a signal whose $TW$ product is of the order of $n^2$ with a filter comprising a number of parameters proportional to $n$; that is, in this case $TW$ is not a good measure of the filter's complexity, being much too large. The degeneracy involved here is not without its disastrous effects, however, as we shall see later when considering "chirp" signals.

[21] Needless to say, the $F(j2\pi f)$ can be eliminated in the signal-generator of Fig. 13, and the resulting filter driven by such a rectangular pulse, instead of an impulse. The $F(j2\pi f)$ is still required in the matched filter, however [40].

for $n = 10$. An equivalent band-pass case is obtained merely by using a band-pass equivalent of the $F(j2\pi f)$ in (55); the resulting signal is a sequence of sine-wave pulses of some frequency $f_0$, each pulse having either 0° or 180° phase. The search for a desirable signal is now simply the search for a desirable sequence, $b_0, b_1, \cdots, b_n$, of $+1$'s and $-1$'s.

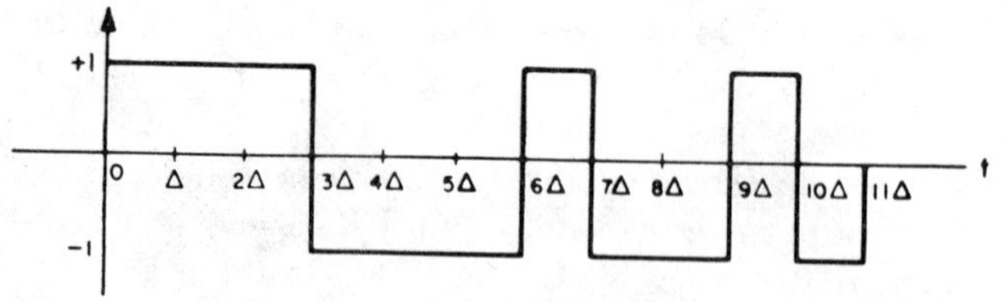


Fig. 15—A signal corresponding to (55).

Notice that $s(t)$ is a constant-amplitude signal, a property we have already seen to be important in some situations. For such signals, for the band-pass case implicit in (43), we easily may show that

$$| \chi(0, \phi) | = T \left| \frac{\sin \pi\phi T}{\pi\phi T} \right|, \tag{56}$$

where $T$ is the signal duration, equal to $(n + 1)\ \Delta$ in Fig. 15. This is the cross section of the $| \chi(t, \phi) |$ surface in the $\phi$ direction; it has the shape shown in Fig. 16. In view of our discussion of the properties of $| \chi(t, \phi) |$, this shape seems reasonably acceptable: a central peak of the "minimum" possible "width," with no serious spurious peaks.

The cross section of $| \chi(t, \phi) |$ in the $t$ direction—*i.e.*, $| \chi(t, 0) |$—can be made to have a desirable shape by proper choice of the sequence $b_0, b_1, \cdots, b_n$. Classes of sequences suitable from this point of view have, in fact, been found. The members of one such class [1], [47] have the desirable property that the central peak has a width of the order of $\Delta$ [the reciprocal of the "bandwidth" of $s(t)$] and is $(n + 1)$ times as high as any subsidiary peak. The sequence of Fig. 15, of length $n + 1 = 11$, is in fact a member of this class and has the $| \chi(t, 0) |$ shown in Fig. 17. Other members of the class with lengths 1, 2, 3, 4, 5, 7, and 13 have been found. Unfortunately, no odd-length sequences of length greater than 13 exist; it is a strong conjecture that no longer even-length sequences exist either.

If we for the moment redefine $| \chi(t, 0) |$ as the response envelope of the matched filter to the signal made periodic with period $(n + 1)\ \Delta$, we find that at least for the odd-length sequences we have just discussed, $| \chi(t, 0) |$ retains a desirable (albeit necessarily periodic) shape; for example, the new, "periodic" $| \chi(t, 0) |$ function for the sequence in Fig. 15 is shown in Fig. 18. This property is of interest in radar, where the signal is often repeated periodically or quasi-periodically.

Another class of binary sequences, $b_0, b_1, \cdots, b_n$, which have periodic $| \chi(t, 0) |$ functions of the desirable

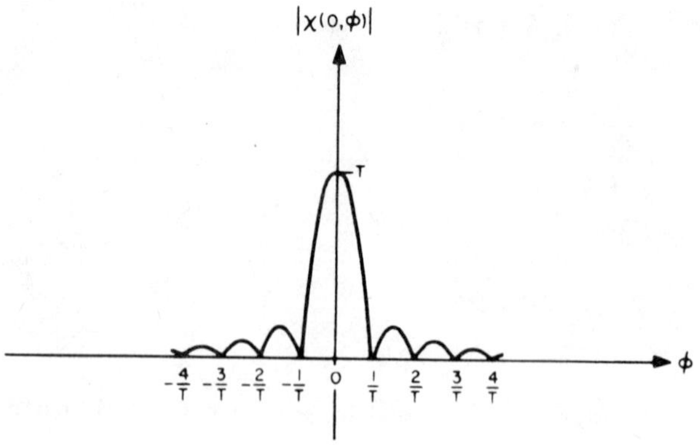


Fig. 16—The $|\chi(0, \phi)|$ function for the signal in Fig. 15.

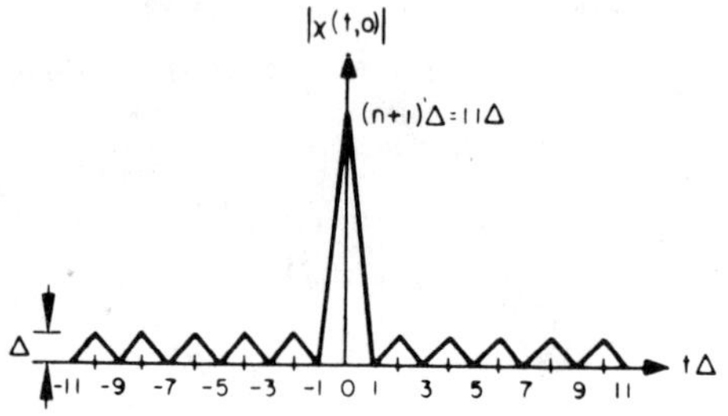


Fig. 17—The $|\chi(t, 0)|$ function for the signal in Fig. 15.

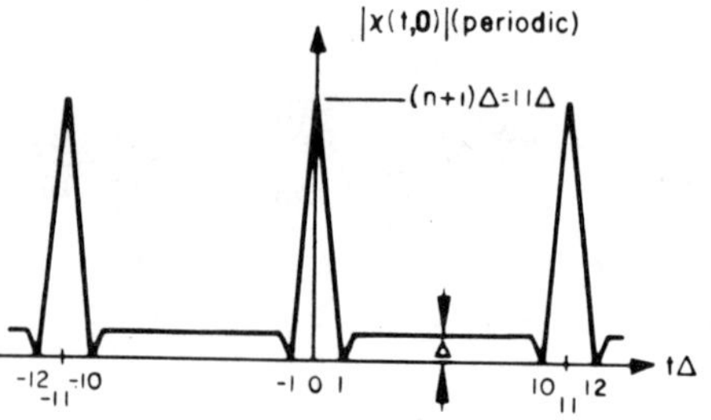


Fig. 18—The periodic $|\chi(t, 0)|$ function for the signal in Fig. 15.

form shown in Fig. 18 are the so-called linear maximal-length shift-register sequences. These have lengths $2^p - 1$, where $p$ is an integer; the number of distinct sequences for any $p$ is $\Phi(2^p - 1)/p$. where $\Phi(x)$, the Euler phi-function, is the number of integers less than $x$ which are prime to $x$ [59]. The class of linear maximal-length shift-register sequences has been studied in great detail [10], [16], [17], [42], [44], [46], [59], [61]. In general, their aperiodic $| \chi(t, 0) |$ functions leave something to be desired [26].

Other classes of binary sequences with two-level periodic $| \chi(t, 0) |$ functions such as shown in Fig. 18 have been investigated [18], [60].

So far we have discussed the desirability of certain binary sequences for use in (55) only from the point of view of the form of the $| \chi(t, \phi) |$ function along the coordinate axes. No general solution has been given for the form of the function off the axes, but certain conjectures can be made, which have been roughly corroborated by trying special cases. It is felt [44], at least for long linear shift-register sequences, that the central peak of $|\chi(t, \phi)|$ indeed has the minimum cross-sectional "area" of $1/TW$, and has subsidiary peaks in the plane of height no greater than the order of $1/\sqrt{n+1}$ of the height of the central peak [$(n+1)$ is the length of the sequence].

No general conclusions have been reached concerning the *joint* desirability, from the viewpoint of (46), of several of these binary codes.

The actual synthesis of matched filters with the characteristics of (55) is considered in detail elsewhere in this issue [24].

As a final example of a choice of characteristics of the filters of Figs. 13 and 14, let us consider

$$\left.\begin{aligned} F(j2\pi f) &= \frac{\sin \pi f a}{\pi f} e^{-i\pi f a} \\ G_i(j2\pi f) &= 1, \quad \text{all } i \\ \Delta_i &= i\,\Delta, \qquad \Delta > a \end{aligned}\right\}. \tag{57}$$

The impulse response of the signal-generating filter in this case is a sequence of $(n+1)$ rectangular pulses of width $a$, starting at times $t = i\Delta$. (Such a signal, of course, is more easily generated by other means.) The ambiguity function for the band-pass analog of this signal, which is often used in radar systems, is rather undesirable, having pronounced peaks periodically both in the $t$ and $\phi$ directions [44], [57], but the signal has the virtue of simplicity. The filter which is matched to the signal is often called a pulse integrator, since its effect is to add up the received signal pulses; alternatively, it is called a comb filter, since its transmission function, $|S(j2\pi f)|^2$, has the form of a comb with roughly $(\Delta/a)$ teeth of "width" $1/(n+1)\,\Delta$, spaced by $1/\Delta$ cps [14], [54].

## B. Cascaded All-Pass Filters

Another way to get a signal-generating and matched filter pair is through the use of cascaded elementary all-pass networks [27], [48]. An elementary all-pass network is defined here as one which has a pole-zero configuration like that in Fig. 19. Such a network clearly has a transfer function which has constant magnitude at all frequencies, $f$, on the imaginary axis.

Now, suppose that many (say, $n$) elementary all-pass networks are cascaded, as in Fig. 20, to form an over-all network with the uniform pole-zero pattern of Fig. 21. The over-all transfer function, $G(j2\pi f)$, will have a constant magnitude; its phase will be approximately linear over some bandwidth $W$, as shown by the upper curve of Fig. 22.[22] If some of the elementary networks of Fig. 20 are now grouped together into a network, $A$, with transfer function $G_A(j2\pi f)$, and the rest into a network, $B$, with transfer function $G_B(j2\pi f)$, both $G_A(j2\pi f)$ and $G_B(j2\pi f)$ still have constant magnitudes, but neither necessarily will have a linear phase function; however, the two phase

[22] We are again considering the "low-pass" case for convenience. The "band-pass" analog is obvious.

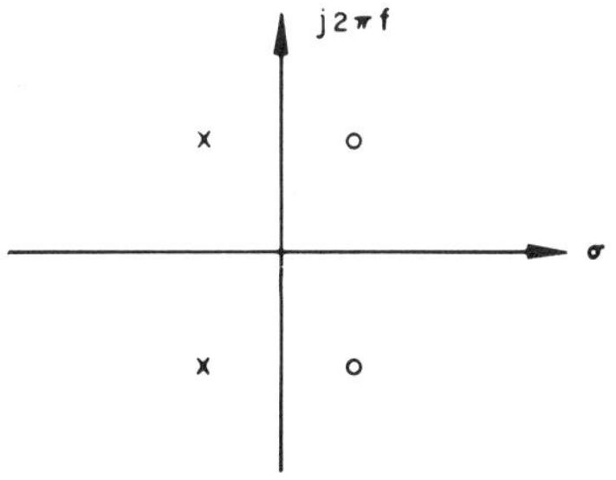


Fig. 19—The pole-zero configuration of an elementary all-pass network.

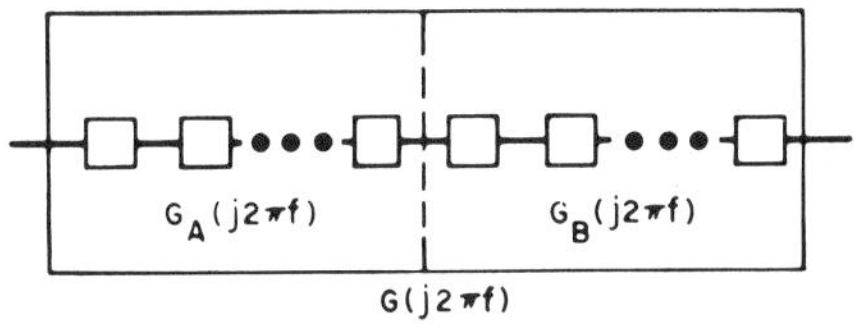


Fig. 20—A cascade of elementary all-pass networks.

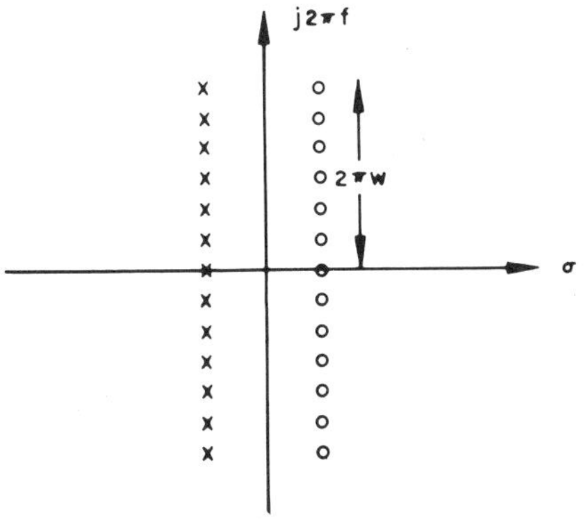


Fig. 21—The pole-zero configuration for the over-all network of Fig. 20.

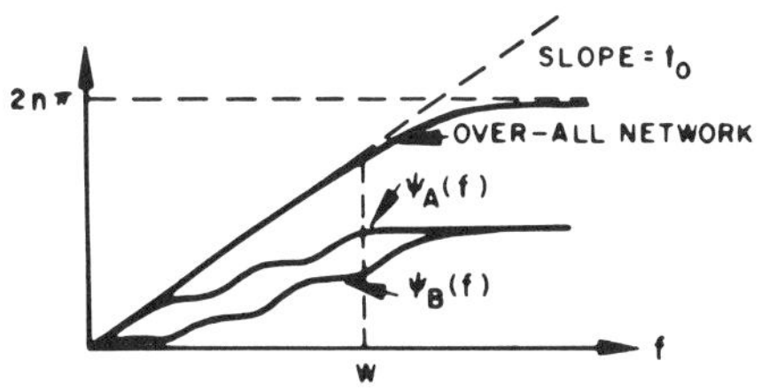


Fig. 22—Phase functions corresponding to the networks in Fig. 20.

functions must add to approximately a linear phase within the band $0 \le f \le W$ (see Fig. 22). *Within this band*, the relationship between the $A$ and $B$ transfer functions is

$$e^{-i\psi_A(f)}e^{-i\psi_B(f)} = e^{-i2\pi f t_0}, \tag{58}$$

where $t_0$ is the slope of the over-all phase function, and $\psi_A$ and $\psi_B$ are the phase functions of the $A$ and $B$ networks, respectively.

Suppose network $A$ is driven by a pulse of bandwidth $W$, such as might be supplied by the pulse-forming network, $F(j2\pi f)$, of (57) ($a \approx 1/W$). Then the output signal of network $A$ will have the spectrum $S(j2\pi f) = F(j2\pi f)e^{-j\psi_A(f)}$. From (58), therefore, over the bandwidth of $F(j2\pi f)$,

$$\begin{aligned} F^*(j2\pi f)e^{-j\psi_B(f)} &= F^*(j2\pi f)e^{j\psi_A(f)}e^{-j2\pi f t_0} \\ &= S^*(j2\pi f)e^{-j2\pi f t_0}. \end{aligned} \quad (59)$$

We hence have, at least approximately, a filter pair $F(j2\pi f)\, G_A(j2\pi f)$ and $F^*(j2\pi f)\, G_B(j2\pi f)$ which are matched.

The function of the filter $F(j2\pi f)$ is merely that of band limitation; therefore $F$ should be made as simple as possible, preferably with zero or linear phase. The problems of choosing $G_A(j2\pi f)$ so as to obtain a desirable signal, and of actually synthesizing the filters, are considered elsewhere in this issue [48].

### C. Chirp Filters

Let us now consider, as a final class of signals, signals of the form

$$s(t) = A(t) \cos (\psi_0 + 2\pi f_0 t + 2\pi k t^2), \quad 0 \le t \le T, \quad (60)$$

where $A(t)$ is some slowly varying envelope. Such signals, whose frequency—more correctly, whose phase derivative—varies linearly with time, have appropriately been called "chirp" signals.

In general, the spectrum of a chirp signal has a very complicated form. For the case of a constant-amplitude pulse, $A(t)$ = constant, an exact expression has been given [4]; this indicates, as one might expect, that in practical cases the spectrum has approximately constant amplitude and linearly increasing group time delay of slope $k$ over the band $f_0 \le f \le f_0 + kT$, and is approximately zero elsewhere. The corresponding matched filter then has approximately constant amplitude and linearly *decreasing* group time delay of slope $-k$ over the same band.

Chirp signals and the synthesis of their associated matched filters have been studied in great detail [3], [4], [6], [8], [22], [32], [44], [57]. The chief virtue of this class of signals is their ease of generation: a simple frequency-modulated oscillator will do. Similarly, chirp matched filters are relatively easy to synthesize. On the other hand, from the point of view of the ambiguity function, $|\chi(t, \phi)|$—*i.e.*, of radars in which doppler shift is important—a chirp signal is rather undesirable. The area in the $(t, \phi)$ plane over which the ambiguity function for a chirp signal with a gaussian envelope is large is shown in Fig. 23 [44], [57]. Along the $t$ and $\phi$ axes the "width" of the $|\chi(t, \phi)|$ surface is satisfactorily small: $1/W$ and $1/T$, respectively. But the surface, instead of being concentrated around the origin as desired, is spread out along the line $\phi = kt$; in fact, the area of concentration is very much greater than the minimum value, $1/TW$. This is equivalent to saying that it is very hard to determine whether the chirp signal has been given a time delay $t$ or a frequency shift $kt$, a fact which is obvious from an inspection of the signal waveform.

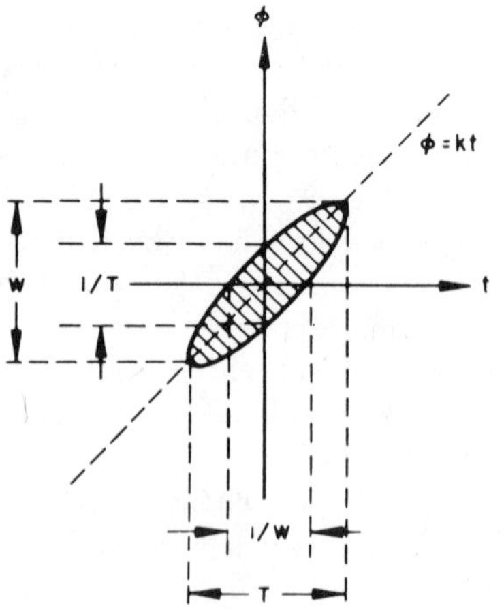


Fig. 23—The ambiguous "area" for a chirp signal.

## VII. Conclusion

It must be admitted that, in regard to matched filters, the proverbial "state of the art" is somewhat less than satisfactory. We have seen that there are two basic problems to be solved simultaneously: the specification of a desirable signal or set of them, and the synthesis of their associated matched filters. In regard to the former, we have but the barest knowledge of the freedom with which we can constrain the "desirability" functions (43) and/or (46) and still expect physical signals; we know even less how to solve for the signals once both desirable and allowable constraints are set. It was partially for these reasons that we attacked a different problem: of a set of physical signals corresponding to a class of filters which we can build, which are the most desirable? In even this we were stopped, except for some special cases.

Nor can we assume that we are very sophisticated in the area of actually constructing filters which we say, on paper, we can build. It has become apparent that the $TW$ product for a signal is a most important parameter; in general, the larger the product, the better the signal. But at the present time the synthesis of filters with $TW$ products greater that several hundred may be deemed exceptional.

Clearly, much more effort is needed in this field. One hopes that the present issue of the Transactions will stimulate just such an effort.

## VIII. Bibliography


[1] Barker, R. H., "Group synchronizing of binary digital systems," in "Communication Theory," W. Jackson, Ed., Academic Press, New York, N. Y.; 1953.
[2] Brennan, D. G., "On the maximum signal-to-noise ratio realizable from several noisy signals," Proc. IRE, vol. 43, p. 1530; October, 1955.
[3] Cauer, W., German Patent No. 892, 772; December 19, 1950.
[4] Cook, C. E., "Modification of pulse compression waveforms," *Proc. 1958 Natl. Electronics Conf.*, pp. 1058–1067.
[5] Cutrona, L. J., *et al.*, "Optical data processing and filtering systems," this issue, p. 386.
[6] Darlington, S., U. S. Patent No. 2, 678, 997; May 18, 1954.
[7] Davenport, W. B., Jr., and Root, W. L., "An Introduction to the Theory of Random Signals and Noise," McGraw-Hill Book Co., Inc., New York, N. Y.; 1958.
[8] Dicke, R. H., U. S. Patent No. 2, 624, 876; January 6, 1953.

[9] Dwork, B. M., "Detection of a pulse superimposed on fluctuation noise," Proc. IRE, vol. 38, pp. 771–774; July, 1950.
[10] Elspas, B., "The theory of autonomous linear sequential networks," IRE Trans. on Circuit Theory, vol. CT-6, pp. 45–60; March, 1959.
[11] Fano, R. M., "Communication in the presence of additive Gaussian noise," in "Communication Theory," W. Jackson, Ed., Academic Press, New York, N. Y., 1953.
[12] Fano, R. M., "On Matched-Filter Detection in the Presence of Multipath Propagation," unpublished paper, M. I. T., Cambridge, Mass.; 1956.
[13] Gabor, D., "Theory of communication," *J. IEE*, vol. 93, pt. III, pp. 429–457; November, 1946.
[14] Galejs, J., "Enhancement of pulse train signals by comb filters," IRE Trans. on Information Theory, vol. IT-4, pp. 114–125; September, 1958.
[15] George, T. S., "Fluctuations of ground clutter return in airborne radar equipment," *J. IEE*, vol. 99, pt. IV, pp. 92–99; April, 1952.
[16] Golomb, S. W., "Sequences with Randomness Properties," Glenn L. Martin Co., Baltimore, Md., Internal Report; June 14, 1955.
[17] Golomb, S. W., "Sequences with the Cycle-and-Add Property," Jet Propulsion Lab., C. I. T., Pasadena, Calif., Section Rept. 8–573; December 19, 1957.
[18] Golomb, S. W., and Welch, L. R., "Nonlinear Shift-Register Sequences," Jet Propulsion Lab., C. I. T., Pasadena, Calif., Memo. 20–149; October 25, 1957.
[19] Guillemin, E. A., "Synthesis of Passive Networks," John Wiley and Sons, Inc., New York, N. Y.; 1957.
[20] Helstrom, C. W., "The resolution of signals in white, gaussian noise," Proc. IRE, vol. 43, pp. 1111–1118; September, 1955.
[21] Kailath, T., "Correlation detection of signals perturbed by a random channel," this issue, p. 381.
[22] Krönert, R., "Impulsverdichtung," *Nachrichtentech.*, vol. 7, pp. 148–152 and 162, April, 1957; pp. 305–308, July, 1957.
[23] Lerner, R. M., "Signals with uniform ambiguity functions," 1958 IRE National Convention Record, pt. 4, pp. 27–36.
[24] Lerner, R. M., "A matched filter detection system for doppler-shifted signals," this issue, p. 373.
[25] Levin, M. J., "Optimum estimation of impulse response in the presence of noise," 1959 IRE National Convention Record, pt. 4, pp. 174–181.
[26] Lytle, D. W., "Experimental Study of Tapped Delay-Line Filters," Stanford Electronics Labs., Stanford Univ., Stanford, Calif., Tech. Rept. 361–3; July 30, 1956.
[27] Lytle, D. W., "On the Properties of Matched Filters," Stanford Electronics Labs., Stanord Univ., Stanford, Calif., Tech. Rept. 17; June 10, 1957.
[28] Marcum, J. I., "A Statistical Theory of Target Detection by Pulsed Radar," Rand Corporation, Santa Monica, Calif., Repts. RM-753 and RM-754; July, 1948, and December, 1947.
[29] Middleton, D., and Van Meter, D., "Detection and extraction of signals in noise from the point of view of statistical decision theory," *J. Soc. Indus. Appl. Math.*, vol. 3, pp. 192–253, December, 1955; vol. 4, pp. 86–119, June, 1956.
[30] Muller, F. A., "Communication in the Presence of Additive Gaussian Noise," Res. Lab. of Electronics, M. I. T., Cambridge, Mass., Tech. Rept. 244; May 27, 1953.
[31] North, D. O., "Analysis of the Factors which Determine Signal/Noise Discrimination in Radar," RCA Laboratories, Princeton, N. J., Rept. PTR-6C; June, 1943.
[32] O'Meara, T. R., "The Synthesis of 'Band-Pass', All-Pass Time-Delay Networks with Graphical Approximation Techniques, "Hughes Res. Labs, Culver City, Calif., Res. Rept. 114; June, 1959.
[33] Peterson, W. W., Birdsall, T. G., and Fox, W. C., "The theory of signal detectability," IRE Trans. on Information Theory, PGIT-4, pp. 171–212; September, 1954.
[34] Pierce, J. N., "Theoretical diversity improvement in frequency-shift keying," Proc. IRE, vol. 46, pp. 903–910; May, 1958.
[35] Price, R., "Error Probabilities for the Ideal Detection of Signals Perturbed by Scatter and Noise," Lincoln Lab., M. I. T., Lexington, Mass., Group Rept. 34–40; October 3, 1955.
[36] Price, R., "Optimum detection of random signals in noise, with application to scatter-multipath communication," IRE Trans. on Information Theory, vol. IT-2, pp. 125–135; December, 1956.
[37] Price, R., and Green, P. E., Jr., "A communication technique for multipath channels," Proc. IRE, vol. 46, pp. 555–570; March, 1958.
[38] Reich, E., and Swerling, P., "The detection of a sine wave in gaussian noise," *J. Appl. Phys.*, vol. 24, pp. 289–296; March, 1953.
[39] Reiger, S., "Error probabilities of binary data transmission in the presence of random noise," 1953 IRE Convention Record, pt. 9, pp. 72–79.
[40] Rochefort, J. S., "Matched filters for detecting pulsed signals in noise," 1954 IRE Convention Record, pt. 4, pp. 30–34.
[41] Root, W. L., and Pitcher, T. S., "Some remarks on statistical detection," IRE Trans. on Information Theory, vol. IT-1, pp. 33–38; December, 1955.
[42] Scott, B. L., and Welch, L. R., "An Investigation of Iterative Boolean Sequences," Jet Propulsion Lab., C. I. T., Pasadena, Calif., Section Rept. 8–543; November 1, 1955.
[43] Shannon, C. E., 'Communication in the presence of noise," Proc. IRE, vol. 37, pp. 10–21; January, 1949.
[44] Siebert, W. McC., "A radar detection philosophy," IRE Trans. on Information Theory, vol. IT-2, pp. 204–221; September, 1956.
[45] Siebert, W. McC., "Studies of Woodward's Uncertainty Function," Res. Lab. of Electronics, M. I. T., Cambridge, Mass., Quart. Prog. Rept.; April 15, 1958.
[46] Sloan, R. W., and Marsh, R. W., "The Structure of Irreducible Polynomials Mod 2 Under a Cubic Transformation"; July 7, 1953 (private communication).
[47] Storer, J. E. and Turyn, R., "Optimum finite code groups," Proc. IRE, vol. 46, p. 1649; September, 1958.
[48] Sussman, S., "A matched-filter communication system for multipath channels," this issue, p. 367.
[49] Titsworth, R. C., "Coherent detection by quasi-orthogonal square-wave pulse functions," this issue, p. 410.
[50] Turin, G. L., "Communication through noisy, random-multipath channels," 1956 IRE Convention Record, pt. 4, pp. 154–166.
[51] Turin, G. L., "On the estimation in the presence of noise of the impulse response of a random, linear filter," IRE Trans. on Information Theory, vol. IT-3, pp. 5–10; March, 1957.
[52] Turin, G. L., "Error probabilities for binary symmetric ideal reception through nonselective slow fading and noise," Proc. IRE, vol. 46, pp. 1603–1619; September, 1958.
[53] Turin, G. L., "Some computations of error rates for selectively fading multipath channels," *Proc. 1959 Natl. Electronics Conf.*, pp. 431–440.
[54] Urkowitz, H., "Analysis and synthesis of delay line periodic filters," IRE Trans. on Circuit Theory, vol. CT-4, pp. 41–53; June, 1957.
[55] Van Vleck, J. and Middleton, D., "A theoretical comparison of the visual, aural, and meter reception of pulsed signals in the presence of noise," *J. Appl. Phys.*, vol. 17, pp. 940–971; November, 1946.
[56] Woodward, P. M. and Davies, I. L., "Information theory and inverse probability in telecommunications," *Proc. IEE*, vol. 99, pt. III, pp. 37–44; March, 1952.
[57] Woodward, P. M., "Probability and Information Theory, with Applications to Radar," McGraw-Hill Book Co., Inc., New York, N. Y.; 1953.
[58] Zadeh, L. A. and Ragazzini, J. R., "Optimum filters for the detection of signals in noise," Proc. IRE, vol. 40, pp. 1123–1131; October, 1952.
[59] Zierler, N., "Several binary-sequence generators," *Proc. Am. Math. Soc.*, vol. 7, pp. 675–681; August, 1956.
[60] Zierler, N., "Legendre Sequences," Lincoln Lab., M. I. T., Lexington, Mass., Group Rept. 34–71; May 2, 1958.
[61] Zierler, N., "Linear recurring sequences," *J. Soc. Indus. Appl. Math.*, vol. 7, pp. 31–48; March, 1959.

# Correlation Analyses of Linearly Processed Pseudo-Random Sequences

S. C. GUPTA, SENIOR MEMBER, IEEE, AND J. H. PAINTER, MEMBER, IEEE

*Abstract*—**This paper develops a generalized technique for exact determination of time and frequency domain behavior of the cross-correlation function between input and any point of interest in a linear system, driven by a periodic pseudo-random binary waveform. The output autocorrelation function is also treated by a variation of the scheme. The technique is conceptually simple and offers exact solutions in closed form. The solutions are in such a form as to make possible, by inspection, the determination of when sequence periodicity may and may not be neglected. Sufficient examples are given to clarify the theory.**

## Introduction

THE KNOWLEDGE and use of pseudo-random (PN) sequences and waveforms generated therefrom are relatively recent. The first comprehensive documentation of the theory of PN sequences is presented by Golomb et al. [1]. Historically, PN sequences have been used in radar, telemetry, and command systems for spacecraft and for planetary tracking [2]–[5]. Of great value to these applications are the correlation properties of the sequences. Since the autocorrelation function of a PN sequence only has appreciable value for time displacements equal to integer multiples of the sequence period, sequences lend themselves quite naturally to measurement of time delay by cross-correlation methods. Since measurement of time delay is an inherent part of radar ranging or synchronization of coded telemetry signals, sequences have been used both as ranging waveforms and as basic telemetry waveforms.

Manuscript received February 14, 1966; revised August 1, 1966.
The authors are with Motorola, Inc., Government Electronics Division, Aerospace Center, Scottsdale, Ariz. S. C. Gupta is also with Arizona State University, Tempe, Ariz.

The correlation properties of unperturbed PN sequences are well treated in the literature [1]. Treatment of sequences or PN codes which have been processed, either linearly or nonlinearly, has received very little attention. Gilchriest [6] has derived expressions for the cross-correlation function of an unperturbed sequence with sequences which have been transmitted through simple high- or low-pass filters. The derivation of his expressions neglects PN sequence periodicity and requires considerable algebraic manipulation and time domain integration.

The problem to which this paper is addressed is to develop a generalized technique by which the time domain and frequency domain characteristics of the cross-correlation and autocorrelation functions of PN sequences which have been passed through an arbitrary linear system may be determined. Clearly, a general treatment must consider the periodicity of the PN sequence. In practical applications, only when the sequence period and the time constant of the linear system are not commensurate may periodicity be neglected.

It should be noted that treatment of the output autocorrelation function is included mainly for the sake of completeness. It is the cross-correlation function which is of greatest current practical significance. Cross-correlation processes are widely used to generate *error curves* for automatic sequence tracking [1]. The output auto-

Reprinted from *IEEE Trans. Commun. Technol.*, vol. COM-14, pp. 796–801, Dec. 1966.

correlation is generally used to ascertain the output power spectrum, which may be more easily found in the frequency domain without first determining the output autocorrelation.

As is shown in this paper, use of the Laplace transform and exploitation of the *straight line* property of the autocorrelation functions of PN sequences combine to give an elegant solution to the problem.

## Basic Technique

At any point in a linear system, initially at rest, correlation functions, resulting from a system driving function, may be obtained. Assume the system to be characterized by an input terminal $x$, point of interest $y$, and impulse response function $h(t)$, connecting points $x$ and $y$, as shown in Fig. 1.

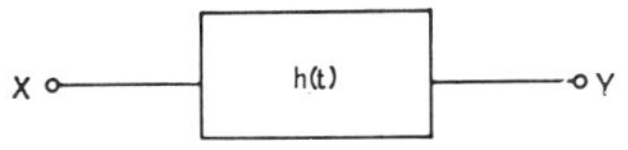


Fig. 1. System model.

The correlation functions at point $y$ are expressed as convolutions of the impulse response with the autocorrelation function existing at the system input, point $x$.

$$\phi_{yx}(\tau) = h(\tau)*\phi_{xx}(\tau) \tag{1}$$

$$\phi_{yy}(\tau) = h(\tau)*h(-\tau)*\phi_{xx}(\tau) \tag{2}$$

where $\phi_{xx}$ and $\phi_{yy}$ are the autocorrelation functions at the points $x$ and $y$, respectively, and $\phi_{yx}$ is the cross-correlation function between $y$ and $x$.

Pseudo-random sequences, or any repetitive binary signals, possess periodic autocorrelation functions composed of straight line segments only [1]. Hence, the second derivative of the input autocorrelation function $\phi_{xx}$ may be written as a finite sum of delta functions for each periodic interval $T$ of the sequence. In practice, the interval $T$ is chosen by time shifting $\phi_{xx}(\tau)$, to begin and end at a zero-crossing. Such a shift is not required mathematically but simplifies the notation for $\ddot{\phi}_{xx}{}^T(\tau)$ over the interval by precluding the need for first order delta functions. Since the system is time invariant, the shift in the input function may be rectified by a corresponding shift in $\phi_{yx}(\tau)$ and $\phi_{yy}(\tau)$. Over the interval, $\ddot{\phi}_{xx}(\tau)$ may be written as

$$\ddot{\phi}_{xx}{}^T(\tau) = \sum_{k=0}^{N} [\alpha_k \delta(\tau - kT_o)]; 0 \leq \tau < T \tag{3}$$

where $T_o$ is the least interval of variation of $\phi_{xx}(\tau)$. The index $k$ is not necessarily an integer.

Considering, first, the time domain, (1) and (2) may be operated upon to give

$$\ddot{\phi}_{yx}(\tau) \triangleq \psi_{yx}(\tau) = h(\tau)*\psi_{xx}(\tau) \tag{4}$$

$$\ddot{\phi}_{yy}(\tau) \triangleq \psi_{yy}(\tau) = h(\tau)*h(-\tau)*\psi_{xx}(\tau) \tag{5}$$

where

$$\psi_{xx}(\tau) \triangleq \ddot{\phi}_{xx}(\tau). \tag{6}$$

Interchange of the order of integration and differentiation is permissible due to the linearity of the system function and convergence of the integral.

By truncating $\phi_{xx}$ causally at the origin, the Laplace transform may be employed to give

$$\Psi_{yx}(s) = H(s)\Psi_{xx}(s) \tag{7}$$

$$\Psi_{yy}(s) = H(s)H(-s)\Psi_{xx}(s) \tag{8}$$

where $\Psi_{yx}(s)$ is a unilateral transform and $\Psi_{yy}(s)$ is bilateral.

Because $\phi_{xx}$ is defined as causal, the output correlation functions may be written as

$$\phi_{yx}(\tau) = \int_0^T \int_0^T \psi_{yx}(\tau) d\tau\, d\tau \tag{9}$$

$$\phi_{yy}(\tau) = \int_0^T \int_0^T \psi_{yy}(\tau)\, d\tau\, d\tau. \tag{10}$$

Then by the *integral property* of the Laplace transform [7],

$$\Phi_{yx}(s) = \frac{1}{s^2} \Psi_{yx}(s) \tag{11}$$

$$\Phi_{yy}(s) = \frac{1}{s^{2y}} \Psi_y(s). \tag{12}$$

Finally the transformed correlation functions are given

$$\Phi_{yx}(s) = \frac{1}{s^2} H(s)\Psi_{xx}(s) \tag{13}$$

$$\Phi_{yy}(s) = \frac{1}{s^2} H(s)H(-s)\Psi_{xx}(s). \tag{14}$$

By the *periodicity property* of Laplace transforms [7] $\Psi_{xx}(s)$ is given as

$$\Psi_{xx}(s) = \frac{\Psi_{xx}{}^T(s)}{1 - \exp(-sT)} = \frac{1}{1 - \exp(-sT)} \sum_{k=0}^{N} [\alpha_k] \times \exp(-skT_0). \tag{15}$$

## Time-Domain Results

### *The Cross-Correlation Function*

Since $\phi_{xx}$ is periodic and has been defined here as causal, $\phi_{yx}(\tau)$ as evaluated from the inversion of (13), will be composed of both a transient component and a component periodic in $T$. The transient component is easily obtained by inverting (13), evaluating residues at only the singularities of $H(s)$. The poles of $H(s)$ are the only poles which contribute to the transient response. The periodic component is conveniently obtained by evaluating the total $\phi_{yx}(\tau)$ over the first period only and subtracting from this total response the transient component for the first period [7]. Clearly, the periodic component is the desired *steady-state* cross-correlation function.

Assuming $H(s)$ represents a stable linear system, the singularities of $\Phi_{yx}(s)$ have a configuration like that of Fig. 2.

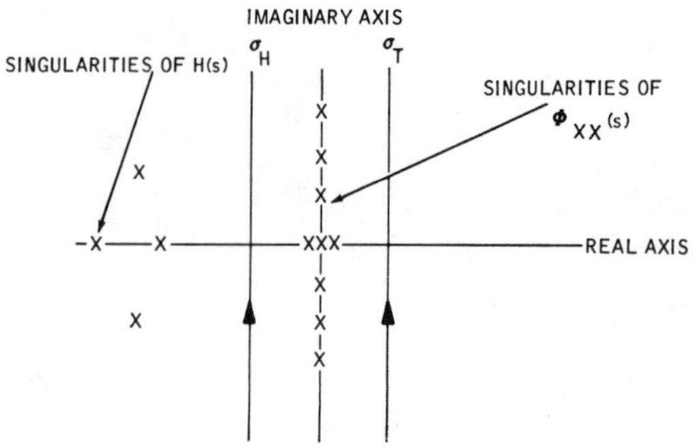


Fig. 2. Singularities of $\Phi_{yx}(s)$.

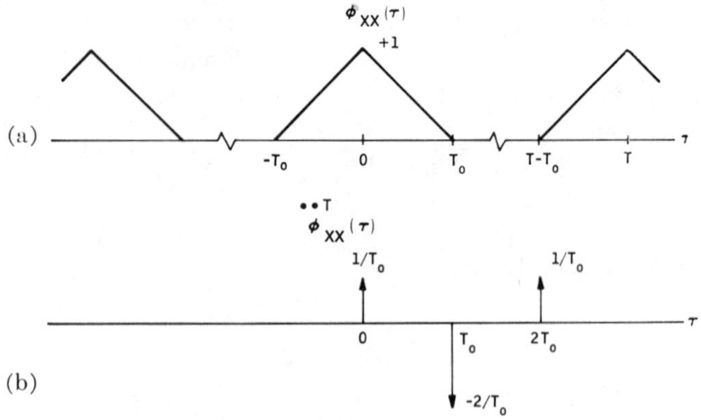

Fig. 3. (a) Input autocorrelation function. (b) Shifted second derivative.

The transient component $\phi_{yx}{}^{H}(\tau)$ is obtained by a contour integration along a contour enclosing only the singularities of $H(s)$.

$$\phi_{yx}{}^{H}(\tau) = \frac{1}{2\pi j}\int_{\sigma_H - j\infty}^{\sigma_H + j\infty} \frac{H(s)}{s^2[1-\exp(-sT)]} \times \left[\sum_{k=0}^{N} \alpha_k \exp(-skT_0)\right]\exp(s\tau)\, ds. \quad (16)$$

The total solution over the first period only is the inverse of $\Phi_{yx}{}^{T}(s)$, where

$$\Phi_{yx}{}^{T}(s) = [1-\exp(-sT)]\Phi_{yx}(s). \quad (17)$$

The singularities of this function include those of $H(s)$ plus poles at the origin. Lacking are the infinite number of imaginary singularities attributed to the periodicity of $\phi_{xx}(\tau)$.

$$\phi_{yx}{}^{T}(\tau) = \frac{1}{2\pi j}\int_{\sigma_T - j\infty}^{\sigma_T + j\infty} \frac{H(s)}{s^2}\left[\sum_{k=0}^{N} \alpha_k \exp(-skT_0)\right] \times \exp(s\tau)\, ds \quad (18)$$

where now the contour encloses the singularities of $H(s)$ and those at the origin. The periodic component $\phi_{yx}{}^{P}(\tau)$ is the difference,

$$\phi_{yx}{}^{P}(\tau) = \phi_{yx}{}^{T}(\tau) - \phi_{yx}{}^{H}(\tau);\ 0 \leq \tau < T. \quad (19)$$

It should be pointed out in passing that the periodic component evaluated above may be obtained directly, using the modified z-transform [7] without finding the first period and transient components.

*Example 1:* The first example will be a simple one wherein the linear system is a low-pass filter having transfer function

$$H(s) = \frac{A}{s+p}. \quad (20)$$

The input autocorrelation function is shown in Fig. 3(a), for a sequence whose length in elements is very great. The special case to be evaluated is one of the class for which periodicity may be neglected. The relations between filter and sequence parameters are chosen as

$$\frac{A}{p} = 1,\ pT_0 = 0.78,\ T \gg T_0. \quad (21)$$

As a first step, $\phi_{xx}(\tau)$ is shifted positively by $T_0$ and double differentiated over the first period, as shown in Fig. 3(b). Then, by inspection,

$$2\alpha_0 = \frac{2}{T_0} = -\alpha_1 = 2\alpha_2. \quad (22)$$

From (13) and (15)

$$\Phi_{yx}(s) = \left[\frac{1}{s^2}\right]\left[\frac{A}{s+p}\right]\left[\frac{1}{1-\exp(-sT)}\right] \times \left[\sum_{k=0}^{N} \alpha_k \exp(-skT_0)\right]. \quad (23)$$

From (16)

$$\phi_{yx}{}^{H}(\tau) = \sum_{k=0}^{N} \frac{1}{2\pi j}\int_{\sigma_H - j\infty}^{\sigma_H + j\infty} \times \left[\frac{1}{s^2}\right]\left[\frac{A}{s+p}\right]\alpha_k\left[\frac{\exp(-skT_0)}{1-\exp(-sT)}\right]\exp(s\tau)\, ds \quad (24)$$

where the summation and integration processes have been interchanged by the linear property of integration. It should be noted that the integrand of (24) satisfies Jordan's Lemma identically for $\tau \geq 0$. Then, taking residues at only the singularities of $H(s)$ gives

$$\phi_{yx}{}^{H}(\tau) = \sum_{k=0}^{N}\left[\frac{A\alpha_k}{p^2}\right]\left[\frac{\exp[-p(\tau-kT_0)]}{1-e^{pT}}\right]1(\tau). \quad (25)$$

Next, from (18)

$$\phi_{yx}{}^{T}(\tau) = \sum_{k=0}^{N}\frac{1}{2\pi j}\int_{\sigma_T - j\infty}^{\sigma_T + j\infty}\left[\frac{1}{s^2}\right]\left[\frac{A}{s+p}\right] \times \alpha_k \exp(-skT_0)\exp(s\tau)\, ds. \quad (26)$$

Taking residues at the singularities of $H(s)$ and at the origin gives

$$\phi_{yx}{}^{T}(\tau) = \sum_{k=0}^{N}\left[\frac{A\alpha_k}{p^2}\right] \times \{\exp[-p(\tau-kT_0)] + p(\tau-kT_0) - 1\}1(\tau-kT_0). \quad (27)$$

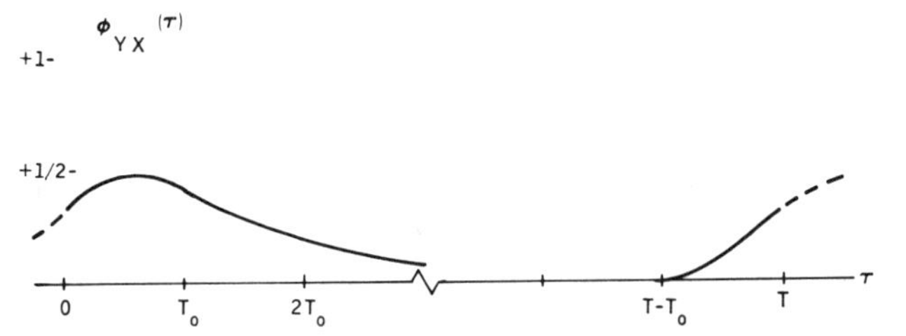


Fig. 4. Cross-correlation function of low-pass filtered long PN sequence.

The periodic component is then

$$\phi_{yx}{}^{P}(\tau) = \phi_{yx}{}^{T}(\tau) - \phi_{yx}{}^{H}(\tau) \tag{28}$$

$$= \exp\left[-p(\tau - kT_0)\right]\left[1(\tau - kT_0) - \frac{1(\tau)}{1 - e^{pT}}\right] +$$

$$[p(\tau - kT_0) - 1]1(\tau - kT_0) \; 0 \leq \tau < T.$$

For the parameters chosen in this example, the transient response is insignificant. Therefore, the steady state is given very accurately by the first period response, $\phi_{yx}{}^{T}(x)$. These results, which agree with Gilchrist's [6], are plotted in Fig. 4.

A second, slightly more complex example is given to explicitly show the results of a case where periodicity may not be neglected.

*Example 2:* The input autocorrelation function, shown in Fig. 5, is obtained from the modulo two addition of a PN sequence of length three (PN) and a clock sequence of alternating ones and zeroes ($2f_s$) with element lengths half that of the PN sequence.

For this example the linear system is a simple high-pass filter with transfer function

$$H(s) = \frac{s}{s + p}. \tag{29}$$

The response will be developed for the special case

$$pT_0 = 1/3. \tag{30}$$

The origin of $\phi_{xx}(\tau)$ is shifted to the point $A$ shown in Fig. 5, so that the period $T$ extends from $A$ to $A'$. Then

$$\Psi_{xx}{}^{T}(s) = \alpha_0 + \sum_{k=1}^{6} \alpha_K \exp\left[-\left(k - \frac{1}{4}\right)T_0 s\right] +$$

$$\alpha_7 \exp\left[-6T_0 s\right] \tag{31}$$

where

$$2\alpha_0 = -\alpha_1 = 2\alpha_2 = 4\alpha_3 = -2\alpha_4 = 4\alpha_5 = 2\alpha_6$$

$$= -2\alpha_7 = \frac{8}{3T_0}. \tag{32}$$

Inversion of $\Phi_{yx}(s)$ produces an appreciable transient response which may not be neglected. Subtracting the transient from the first period total response gives the function graphed in Fig. 6.

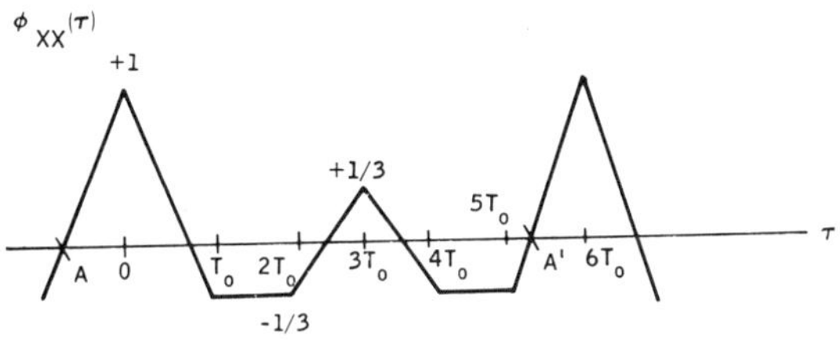


Fig. 5. Autocorrelation of PN $\oplus$ $2f_s$.

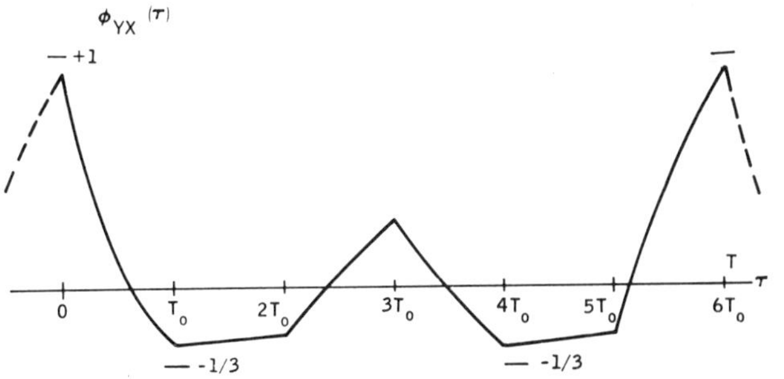


Fig. 6. Cross-correlation function of high-pass filtered PN sequence.

*The Autocorrelation Function*

The evaluation of the output autocorrelation function for a periodic input is, in general, much more difficult. Due to the term $h(-\tau)$ in (2), (14) must be treated as a bilateral Laplace transform and the inverse obtained for negative as well as positive time $\tau$. The difficulty in inverting $\Phi_{yy}(s)$ is due to the periodicity of $\Phi_{xx}(s)$. Because of periodicity, no convergence strip exists for $\Phi_{yy}(s)$ in the $s$-plane.

To make the problem amenable to a transform solution, $\phi_{xx}(\tau)$ is broken into two parts as

$$\phi_{xx}(\tau) \triangleq \phi_{xx+}(\tau) + \phi_{xx-}(\tau) \tag{33}$$

where

$$\left.\begin{aligned} \phi_{xx+}(\tau) &\equiv \phi_{xx}(\tau);\ \tau > 0 \\ &\equiv 0 \qquad ;\ \tau < 0 \\ \phi_{xx-}(\tau) &\equiv \phi_{xx}(\tau);\ \tau < 0 \\ &\equiv 0 \qquad ;\ \tau > 0 \end{aligned}\right\}. \tag{34}$$

Then

$$\Phi_{yy}(s) = H(s)H(-s)[\Phi_{xx+}(s) + \Phi_{xx-}(s)]. \tag{35}$$

Now define

$$\Phi_{yy+}(s) = H(s)H(-s)\Phi_{xx+}(s) \tag{36}$$

$$\Phi_{yy-}(s) = H(s)H(-s)\Phi_{xx-}(s). \tag{37}$$

The procedure to obtain the output autocorrelation function is analogous to that for the cross-correlation. Transient responses and total first period responses are obtained from the inversions of both (36) and (37). The periodic component is then obtained by subtraction.

The transient response to $\phi_{xx+}(\tau)$ is denoted $\phi_{yy+}{}^{H}(\tau)$ and is given by two separate expressions, one valid for positive $\tau$ and one for negative $\tau$.

$$\phi_{yy+}{}^H(\tau) = I_1{}^H(\tau) + I_2{}^H(\tau) = \frac{1}{2\pi j}\int_{\sigma_H - j\infty}^{\sigma_H + j\infty} \times \frac{H(s)H(-s)}{s^2(1-\exp(-sT))}\cdot \sum_{k=0}^{N} \alpha_k \exp(-skT_0)\exp(s\tau)\,ds. \quad (38)$$

$I_1{}^H(\tau)$ is evaluated by taking residues at the singularities of $H(s)$ only and is valid for positive $\tau$. $I_2{}^H(\tau)$ is obtained by taking residues at poles of $H(-s)$ only and is valid for negative $\tau$.

Likewise, the total first period response to $\phi_{xx+}(\tau)$ is denoted $\phi_{yy+}{}^T(\tau)$ and is given by two expressions.

$$\phi_{yy+}{}^T(\tau) = I_1{}^T(\tau) + I_2{}^T(\tau) = \frac{1}{2\pi j}\int_{\sigma_T - j\infty}^{\sigma_T + j\infty} \frac{H(s)H(-s)}{s^2} \times \sum_{k=0}^{N} \alpha_k \exp(-skT_0)\exp(s\tau)\,ds. \quad (39)$$

$I_1{}^T(\tau)$ is evaluated by taking residues at the poles of $H(s)$ and the origin and is valid for positive $\tau$. $I_2{}^T(\tau)$ is evaluated by taking residues at the poles of $H(-s)$ and is valid for negative $\tau$.

Following identical procedures, the transient and total first period responses to $\phi_{xx-}(\tau)$ may be obtained. These are denoted $I_3{}^H(\tau)$, $I_4{}^H(\tau)$, $I_3{}^T(\tau)$, and $I_4{}^T(\tau)$, respectively. The periodic component $\phi_{yy}{}^P(\tau)$, for positive $\tau$ is then given as

$$\phi_{yy}{}^P(\tau) = I_1{}^T(\tau) + I_3{}^T(\tau) - I_1{}^H(\tau) - I_3{}^H(\tau); \quad 0 \le \tau < T. \quad (40)$$

For negative $\tau$,

$$\phi_{yy}{}^P(\tau) = I_2{}^T(\tau) + I_4{}^T(\tau) - I_2{}^H(\tau) - I_4{}^H(\tau); \quad -T < \tau < 0. \quad (41)$$

Having obtained (40) and (41), the resulting $\phi_{yy}{}^P(\tau)$ may be shifted in time to properly orient the output autocorrelation function. Naturally, the shifted $\phi_{yy}{}^P(\tau)$ will be an even function.

In practice it is generally the output power spectrum that is required, rather than the output autocorrelation function. The output frequency domain results, however, may be derived without having an explicit representation for the output autocorrelation function, as is shown in the next section.

## Frequency Domain Results

It is desirable to be able to graph the frequency distribution of energy or power for the correlation functions derived above. Although the power spectra are basically the Fourier integrals of the autocorrelation or cross-correlation functions, they may be derived in several different ways. The simple derivation below makes use of the fact that the input autocorrelation function is composed of straight line segments and hence its second derivative is a series of delta functions.

The input autocorrelation is periodic. Hence $\phi_{xx}(\tau)$ may be expressed, using the Poisson formula [8], as

$$\phi_{xx}(\tau) = \frac{1}{T}\sum_{m=-\infty}^{\infty} \Phi_{xx}{}^T(n\omega_T)\exp(jm\omega_T\tau);\ \omega_T = \frac{2\pi}{T}. \quad (42)$$

$\Phi_{xx}{}^T(m\omega_T)$ is the Fourier transform of $\phi_{xx}{}^T(\tau)$. To obtain the transform of $\phi_{xx}{}^T(\tau)$, the second derivative of the input autocorrelation function is expressed as an even function over the interval $[-T/2, T/2]$ as

$$\ddot{\phi}_{xx}{}^T(\tau) = \sum_{k=-L}^{L} \alpha_k \delta[\tau - kT_0] \quad (43)$$

where now

$$2LT_0 = T \quad (44)$$

is the period of $\phi_{xx}(\tau)$. Then

$$\Phi_{xx}{}^T(m\omega_T) = \frac{-1}{(m\omega_T)^2}\sum_{k=-L}^{L} \alpha_k \exp(-jm\omega_T kT_0) \quad (45)$$

$$\phi_{xx}(\tau) = \frac{1}{T}\sum_{m=-\infty}^{\infty}\left[-\sum_{k=-L}^{L}\frac{\alpha_k\exp(-jm\omega_T kT_0)}{(m\omega_T)^2}\right]\times \exp(jm\omega_T\tau). \quad (46)$$

The Fourier transform of the autocorrelation function is then

$$\Phi_{xx}(\omega) = \frac{2\pi}{T}\sum_{m=-\infty}^{\infty}\left[-\sum_{k=-L}^{L}\frac{\alpha_k\exp(-jm\omega_T kT_0)}{(m\omega_T)^2}\right]\times \delta(\omega - m\omega_T) \quad (47)$$

$$= -\sum_{m=-\infty}^{\infty}\frac{1}{m}\left\{\frac{\alpha_0 + 2\alpha_k\sum_{k=1}^{L}\cos[m\omega_T kT_0]}{m\omega_T}\right\}\times \delta(\omega - m\omega_T).$$

$\Phi_{xx}(\omega)$ is the power density spectrum of the input waveform. The output power density spectrum is given as

$$\Phi_{yy}(\omega) = \Phi_{xx}(\omega)|H(\omega)|^2. \quad (48)$$

Likewise, the cross-spectral density is

$$\Phi_{yx}(\omega) = \Phi_{xx}(\omega)|H(\omega)|. \quad (49)$$

*Example:* The output power spectra will be derived for the sequence and linear system of example 1 of the previous section.

$$2\alpha_{-1} = 2\alpha_{+1} = \frac{2}{T_0} = -\alpha_0. \quad (50)$$

Then

$$\Phi_{xx}(\omega) = -\sum_{m=-\infty}^{\infty}\frac{1}{m}\left\{\frac{-\frac{2}{T_0} + \frac{2}{T_0}\cos[m\omega_T T_0]}{m\omega_T}\right\}\times \delta(\omega - m\omega_T)$$

$$= 4\pi\frac{T_0}{T}\sum_{m=-\infty}^{\infty}\frac{\sin^2\left(\frac{m\omega_T T_0}{2}\right)}{\left(\frac{m\omega_T T_0}{2}\right)^2}\,\delta(\omega - m\omega_T). \quad (51)$$

Now

$$\left.\begin{aligned} H(\omega) &= \frac{A}{j\omega + p} \\ |H(\omega)| &= \frac{A}{\sqrt{\omega^2 + p^2}} \\ |H(\omega)|^2 &= \frac{A^2}{\omega^2 + p^2} \end{aligned}\right\} . \tag{52}$$

Finally

$$\Phi_{yx}(\omega) = 2\pi\left[\frac{A}{\sqrt{\omega^2 + p^2}}\right] 2\,\frac{T_0}{T} \times \sum_{m=-\infty}^{\infty} \frac{\sin^2\left(\frac{m\omega_T T_0}{2}\right)}{\left(\frac{m\omega_T T_0}{2}\right)^2}\, \delta(\omega - m\omega_T) \tag{53}$$

$$\Phi_{yy}(\omega) = 2\pi\left[\frac{A^2}{\omega^2 + p^2}\right] 2\,\frac{T_0}{T} \times \sum_{m=-\infty}^{\infty} \frac{\sin^2\left(\frac{m\omega_T T_0}{2}\right)}{\left(\frac{m\omega_T T_0}{2}\right)^2}\, \delta(\omega - m\omega_T). \tag{54}$$

The results of (53) and (54) appear deceptively simple. It is to be expected that more complex system and input functions will result in spectra more complicated arithmetically but still simple, conceptually.

## Conclusion

This paper has presented a generalized technique for exact determination of the time and frequency domain behavior of the cross-correlation function between input and any point of interest in a linear system driven by a periodic pseudo-random binary sequence. The output autocorrelation function has also been treated very similarly. The technique employed the Laplace and Fourier transforms and exploited the *straight line property* of the autocorrelation function of PN sequences and other binary waveforms. Sufficient examples were included to clarify the technique. Existence of this simple general technique now offers quick results to problems previously requiring time-consuming effort and offers a fruitful approach for obtaining solutions in closed form.

## Nomenclature

| | |
|---|---|
| $x$, $y$ | Input and output terminals, respectively, of a linear system |
| $h(t)$ | Impulse response function of a linear system |
| $\phi_{xx}(\tau)$, $\phi_{yy}(\tau)$ | Autocorrelation functions of input and output signals at terminals $x$ and $y$, respectively |
| $\phi_{yx}(\tau)$ | Cross-correlation of output and input signals |
| $T$ | Period of a pseudo-random (PN) sequence in seconds |
| $T_0$ | The least interval of variation of $\phi_{xx}(\tau)$ in seconds; i.e., the length of a *bit* |
| $\ddot{\phi}$, $\psi$ | Second derivative with respect to time of correlation function |
| $(\ )^T$ | Denotes a function defined only for one sequence period $T$ |
| $\Phi(s)$, $\Psi(s)$ | Laplace transforms of $\phi(\tau)$, $\psi(\tau)$, respectively |
| $H(s)$ | Laplace transform of $h(t)$ |
| $\phi_{yx}{}^H$, $\phi_{yx}{}^P$ | Transient and periodic components, respectively, of the inverse transform of $\Phi_{yx}(s)$. |

## Acknowledgment

The authors wish to acknowledge the helpful cooperation of their colleague, C. D. McBiles, who led them to the problem which showed the need for an exact treatment of the correlation properties of linearly processed PN sequences.

## References

[1] S. W. Golomb, L. D. Baumert, M. F. Easterling, J. J. Stiffler, and A. J. Viterbi, *Digital Communications with Space Applications.* Englewood Cliffs, N. J.: Prentice-Hall, 1964.
[2] M. Easterling, "A skin tracking radar experiment involving the COURIER satellite," *IRE Trans. on Space Electronics and Telemetry*, vol. SET-8, pp. 76–84, June 1962.
[3] B. D. Martin, "Telemetering over interplanetary distances," *Proc. 1962 Nat'l Telemetering Conf.*, vol. 2, session 8–3.
[4 J. C. Springett, "Command techniques for the remote control of interplanetary spacecraft," *Proc. 1962 Nat'l Telemetering Conf.*, vol. 2, session 8–4.
[5] R. C. Tausworthe, "A precision planetary range-tracking radar," *IEEE Trans. on Space Electronics and Telemetry*, vol. SET-11, pp. 78–85, June 1965.
[6] C. E. Gilchriest, "Correlation functions of filtered PN sequences," Jet Propulsion Lab., Pasadena, Calif., Space Programs Summary 37-16, pp. 81–87, July 31, 1962.
[7] S. C. Gupta, *Transform and State Variable Methods in Linear Systems.* New York: Wiley, 1966.
[8] A. Papoulis, *The Fourier Integral and its Applications.* New York: McGraw-Hill, 1962.

# ACOUSTIC SURFACE WAVE SEQUENCE GENERATORS AND MATCHED FILTERS WITH ADJUSTABLE TAPS

D. A. Gandolfo, G. D. O'Clock, and C. L. Grasse
RCA Advanced Technology Laboratories, Van Nuys, CA 91409

Summary

A hybrid combination of an acoustic surface wave tapped delay line and semiconductor switching devices is used to generate bi-phase coded sequences and to serve as the matched filter for these sequences. The switches permit the phase of a tap to be changed by 180° so that complete code flexibility is achieved.

The usefulness of acoustic surface wave devices as sequence generators and matched filters for bi-phase codes has been widely recognized. In these devices each tap represents a digital bit and the polarity of the bit (i.e., "1" or "0") is determined by the phase of the tap which in turn is determined by the manner in which the tap is connected to the rf summing bus. Devices which generate and correlate a fixed sequence have been demonstrated in several laboratories; however, these fixed code devices have limited utility. In order for the surface wave correlators to realize the broad utility of which they are capable, means must be developed to achieve code flexibility, i.e., the ability to change the phase of a given tap by 180° in a controllable way. This paper describes our efforts toward that end.

We have developed code-flexible sequence generators and correlators such as the device pictured in Figure 1. This device is a composite consisting of an acoustic surface wave device and several diode switches mounted on a hybrid circuit board. The surface wave device is YZ $LiNbO_3$ with interdigital transducer/taps. It may be noted that some of the taps are hard-wired directly to the rf summing bus while others are connected to the summing bus through the diode switches. The hybrid circuit also incorporates diode bias connections. The operation of a single switchable tap is illustrated in Figure 2. TG (i.e., transmission gate) 1,2,3,4 are diode switches. With TG1,3 open and 2,4 closed the tap has a given polarity (e.g., digital "1"). With TG 2,4 open and 1, 3 closed the opposite polarity is obtained (digital "0").

In experiments with devices like that shown in Figure 1 we have observed controllable 180° phase shifts at given taps. The insets in Figure 1 show sequences generated by devices with switchable taps. The upper photo shows the sequence generated when three consecutive taps have the same polarity (....111....) while the lower photo shows the sequence when the polarity of the middle tap of the three is reversed (....101....). The phase shift between adjacent bits of opposite polarity is evident. It is also evident that there is very little difference in amplitude and distortion between those bits which are hard-wired directly to the summing bus and those which are connected through the diode switches.

A further series of experiments involved two devices similar to that pictured in Figure 1. One such device served as the generator of the bi-phase coded sequence while a second device served as the matched filter or correlator for this sequence. The results are summarized in Figure 3. Figure 3(a) shows the coded sequence generated by one of the devices while Figure 3(b) shows the correlation signal observed when the coded sequence is input to the correlator.

Several different semiconductor device types were considered for use as transmission gates and three of these were actually used successfully. These were discrete, beam-leaded PIN and Schottky barrier diodes and arrays of silicon-on sapphire diodes. Desireable characteristics include small foreward resistance, small capacitance and large reverse resistance. Since most systems envisioned require a large number of taps, availability in integrated arrays is also important and for this reason the SOS diodes are very attractive. The control

Reprinted from *IEEE Int. Microwave Symp. Dig.*, May 1971, pp. 60–61.

logic circuitry required to store the desired codes and to impress the appropriate biases on the transmission gates may also be implemented in the SOS format so that integrated circuits containing both functions are possible.

We believe these results to be significant because they demonstrate the feasibility of acoustic surface wave correlators with code-flexibility. These devices should be useful in a wide variety of communications systems where they may offer significant advantages over purely digital matched filters.

The authors are grateful to R. Geshner, J. Mitchell, P. Schnitzler and D. Kleitman for device fabrication, and to E. Schmitt and J. Vollmer for program support.

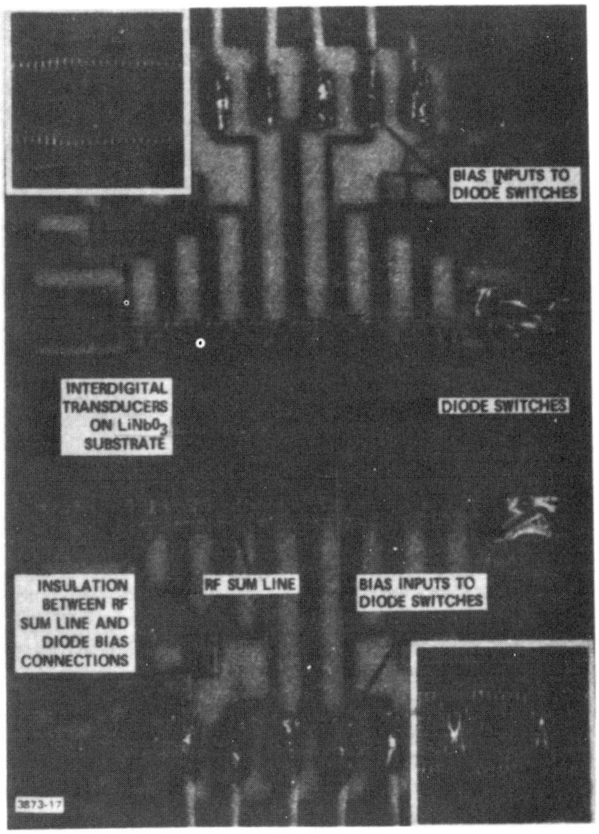


FIG.1 - Acoustic Sequence Generator with Adjustable Taps. Waveforms show (....111....) and, after phase reversal of one tap (....101....).

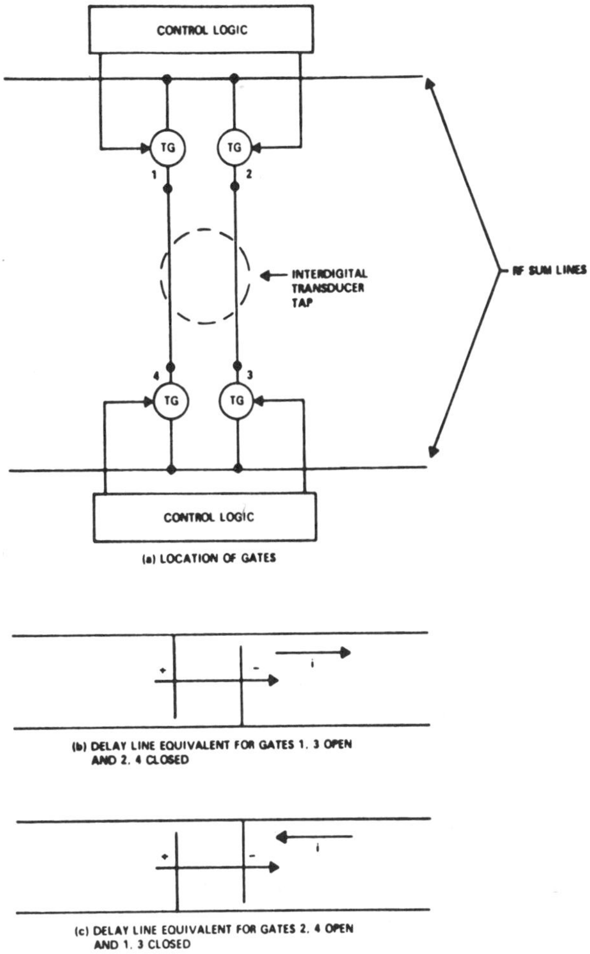


FIG. 2 - Operation of a Switchable Tap

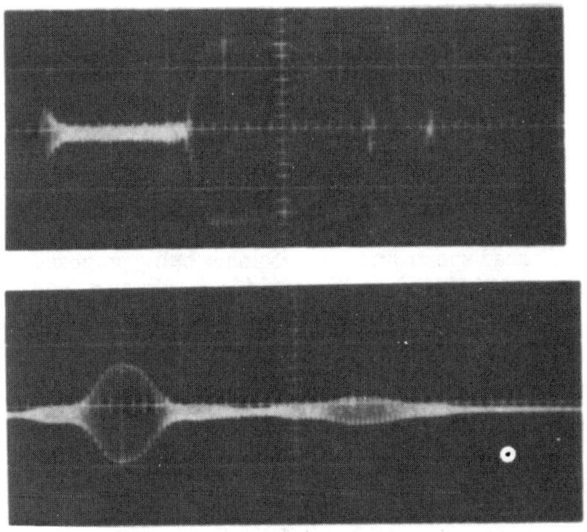

FIG. 3 - Coded Sequence (upper photograph) and Autocorrelation Function Obtained from Devices Similar to that in Figure 1.

# Application of Acoustic Surface-Wave Technology to Spread Spectrum Communications

DELAMAR T. BELL, JR., JERRY D. HOLMES, AND RICHARD V. RIDINGS

*Invited Paper*

*Abstract*—Spread spectrum transmission is being proposed for an increasing number of digital communication, navigation, and radar systems. One of the reasons is the simplicity and availability of surface-wave devices (SWD) for performing the necessary signal generation and processing. The properties of spread spectrum signals, the operation of SWD's, and their advantages and limitations when used in communication systems are discussed. Spread spectrum terminology and basic concepts are defined in terms common to both systems engineers and device designers.

## I. Introduction

SPREAD spectrum transmission is a form of signal processing which trades transmission bandwidth for enhanced detectability and interference rejection in various digital communication, navigation, and radar systems [1]. In this paper, we consider the advantages and limitations of the application of acoustic surface-wave technology to spread spectrum systems. As a continuing theme to this discussion, we shall consider techniques for transmitting a digital data signal occupying a bandwidth considerably larger than required for the specified data rate. Three principal reasons for artificially enlarging the bandwidth of an information signal will be discussed in Section II. First, spread spectrum techniques permit a communication link to exhibit an attenuation against average power limited interfering signals that are not correlated with the particular waveform used to spread the spectrum. Such interfering signals might be deliberate jamming, random natural events, or even other users of the same spectrum. Second, signal-to-noise improvement even against receiver noise may be obtained by certain systems which make use of several codes; i.e., a given message may be communicated with a given reliability with less energy

Manuscript received November 2, 1972; revised November 27, 1972.
The authors are with Texas Instruments Incorporated, Dallas, Tex. 75222.

Reprinted from *IEEE Trans. Microwave Theory Tech.*, vol. MTT-21, pp. 263–271, Apr. 1973.

consumed than would be possible with an uncoded signal. Finally, enhanced time resolution may be obtained with the increased bandwidth, as may be desired for range measurements and some forms of analog transmission.

A serious consequence of spectrum spreading is the complexity of the signal processing required to extract the useful information. One common modulation technique is to use coded sequences to transmit each bit of information. For other systems, a linear FM waveform has significant advantages [2]. In any case, some form of correlation or matched filtering [3]–[5] is required to synchronize the transmitter and receiver to extract the original information. The processing time and equipment expense of doing this filtering with digital techniques has limited spread spectrum applications to areas where system cost is a secondary consideration, such as secure communications and satellite data links [6], [7].

Surface-wave devices (SWD) have the potential to revolutionize spread spectrum systems. The necessary matched filtering can be performed at high rates with a simple microelectronic device of small size. For example, a signal waveform 50 chips long with 5-MHz chip rate would require a digital processor capable of handling 250 analog multiplications and additions per microsecond to perform real-time matched filtering. Equivalent signal processing can be performed by an SWD with dimensions of approximately 1.5 by 0.3 by 0.1 in. A signal with the same number of chips and a 50-MHz chip rate would require an even more complex digital processor, while the corresponding SWD matched filter is even smaller than the 5-MHz device.

It is the purpose of this paper to discuss spread spectrum communications, SWD's, and their combination into communication systems in terms meaningful to both systems engineers and device designers. To keep the discussion within bounds, all specific examples will consider phase-shift keyed (PSK) signals, although most of the techniques described apply equally to other waveforms. Section II describes advantages to expanding the bandwidth of a digital data signal: increased protection against certain classes of interference, increased communication efficiency, and improved time resolution. The significant properties and limitations of SWD's are covered in Section III, followed in Section IV by descriptions of applications to spread spectrum systems particularly suited to SWD's.

Several other papers in this special issue deal with more specialized aspects of SWD's in spread spectrum systems. Grant *et al.* [2] describe in detail the requirements for air-traffic-control systems as well as several illustrative systems using SWD's. Staples and Claiborne [26] review the status of programmable filters.

## II. Spread Spectrum Communications

Many possible waveforms can be used to spread the spectrum of a digital signal. A technique in common usage for many years involves PSK modulation of an RF carrier such that the transmitted waveform consists of a series of equal-length segments of carrier signal which differ only in phase. If the phase is 0 or 180°, the waveform is biphase PSK. For the sake of having a specific signal to discuss, this waveform will be assumed unless otherwise specified. Other waveforms of interest are linear and nonlinear FM, pulse-position modulation (PPM), frequency hopping, and various combinations.

A few definitions are in order. Fig. 1 shows a typical PSK signal of duration $T_B$. This signal is made up of $N_C$ equal-length chips which may have any prescribed phase with respect to a reference carrier (0 or 180° for biphase as shown). The phases are assigned according to some code sequence that in the general case defines a particular symbol. A collection of such codes can define an alphabet of symbols, in which case successful communication of a symbol results in the transmittal of several bits of information. In the simplest binary antipodal case, there is one symbol and the negative (or complement) of that symbol, resulting in 1 bit of information being communicated in the time $T_B$ by $N_C$ chips of code. In the nonspread spectrum case, $N_C=1$, that is, the symbol is uncoded.

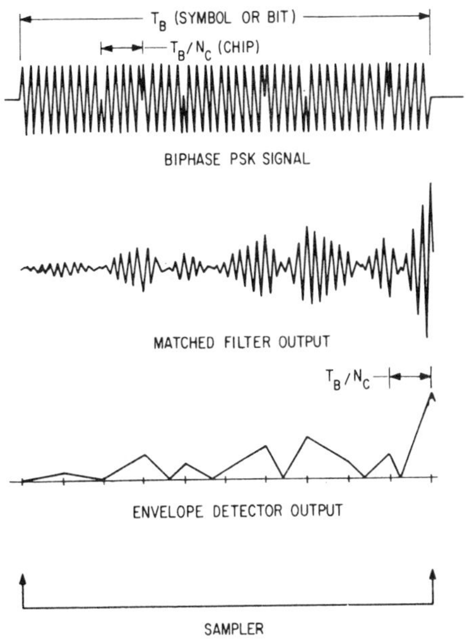


Fig. 1. Timing diagram for binary spread spectrum system.

A brief discussion of both correlation and matched filter techniques for the detection and decoding of a binary biphase signal will be used to illustrate the protection that spread spectrum offers against average power limited interference as well as the role of SWD's in implementing matched filter processing.

### *A. Interference Protection in Digital Communications*

*1) Signal Processing Techniques:* The signal waveform of Fig. 1, or its complement, is to be used to transmit a data symbol at some bit rate $f_B=1/T_B$ on a carrier $f_0$. That is, the transmitted waveform is given by

$$V_\pm(t) = \cos\left[2\pi f_0 t \pm \alpha_i(t)\right] \tag{1}$$

where $\alpha_i(t)=\pm\pi/2$ for each chip, depending on the code sequence being used, and the sign before $\alpha$ is determined by whether the symbol or its complement is desired.

The bandwidth is determined by the duration of the chip $T_B/N_C$ rather than the symbol duration. Thus, the bandwidth has been increased by a factor of $N_C$ resulting in a spread spectrum signal.

A conventional technique for detecting and decoding the data stream involves use of a correlation receiver in which locally generated replicas of the symbol and its complement are mixed with the arriving signal. If the locally generated signals are given by

$$W_\pm(t) = \cos\left(2\pi f_0 t \pm \alpha_i + \gamma\right) \tag{2}$$

where $\gamma$ is an arbitrary phase term, then the output of the

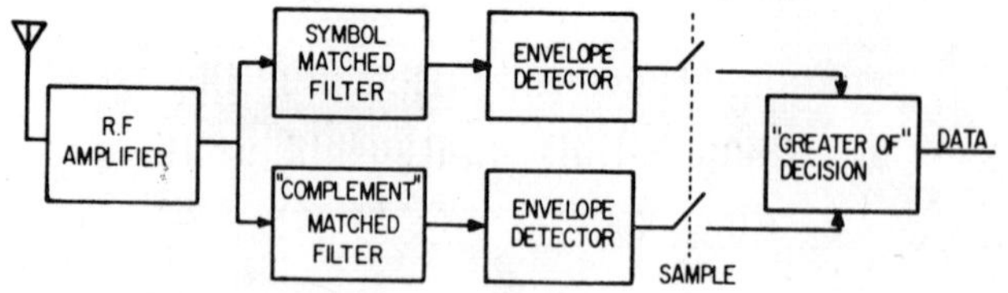


Fig. 2. Matched filter receiver, binary spread spectrum modulation.

mixers after filtering are given by

$$X = \cos\gamma, \qquad \text{reference same as signal}$$
$$= \cos(2\alpha_i - \gamma), \qquad \text{reference complement to signal.} \tag{3}$$

Provided that the local replicas are phase coherent with the incoming signal ($\gamma=0$), then the output is $+1$ at the mixer which has the same reference as the received signal and $-1$ otherwise. The system complexity required to achieve this coherence (i.e., synchronization) is the principal disadvantage of this technique.

An alternate approach to data detection for this type of signaling format is the use of a matched filter receiver. The complement to the symbol is now a different symbol rather than its own negative. The receiver contains a pair of matched filters, one for each symbol, as shown in Fig. 2. Here, SWD's are especially useful as they readily permit implementation of matched filters for complex signal structures such as those given in (1).

To illustrate the advantages of SWD's for matched filter application, it will be helpful to briefly review the elements of matched filter theory. Let $h(t)$ be the impulse response of a linear filter. For an arbitrary input signal $s_i(t)$, linear system theory gives the output signal $s_o(t)$ as

$$s_o(t) = \int_0^t s_i(\tau)h(t-\tau)\,d\tau. \tag{4}$$

For matched filter applications, there is a specific relationship between the input signal and the impulse response of the filter. They are matched in the sense that

$$h(t) = s_i(T-t) \tag{5}$$

i.e., the impulse response is the reverse time image of the signal with an arbitrary fixed time offset $T$.

Substitution of (5) into (4) yields

$$s_o(t) = \int_0^t s_i(\tau)s_i(T-t+\tau)\,d\tau. \tag{6}$$

When allowance is made for the time-limited nature of real signals, (6) is a time-shifted replica of the autocorrelation function of the signal $s_i(t)$.

The practical limitation to using this technique has been the implementation of the integral in (6). Digital techniques require a tremendous number of multiplication and addition steps at each sample point. The SWD is inherently an analog correlation device, thereby removing computation restrictions in the frequency and time ranges where it can operate (see Section III).

2) *Signal-to-Noise Improvement:* We assume that it is desired to detect the presence or absence of a signal whose exact waveform is known *a priori*. Further, assume that the signal has been corrupted by additive white noise and that one is constrained to use only a linear filter for improving the signal-to-noise ratio (SNR), a quantity which determines the reliability of the "presence–absence" decision. Many references [3]–[5], [8] show that the matched filter defined by (5) produces the maximum value for the peak signal-to-rms-noise ratio. This ratio is

$$\mathrm{SNR}_{\max} = \frac{2E}{N_0} \tag{7}$$

where $E$ is the total energy contained in the $s_i(t)$ signal and $N_0$ is the noise spectral density of the additive white noise at the input to the matched filter. The maximum value of the peak signal-to-rms-noise ratio thus depends only on the signal energy and the white-noise spectral density, independent of signal waveform.

For the receiver shown in Fig. 2, one would select different (rather than complementary) pseudorandom sequences to represent the two possible transmitted symbols. If these sequences are judiciously chosen, the performance of the receiver shown in Fig. 2 is given by [8, p. 298]

$$P_e = \tfrac{1}{2}\exp(-\rho/2) \tag{8}$$

where $P_e$ is the probability of bit error and $\rho$ is the SNR at the output of the matched filter whose corresponding symbol has been received at the time when a decision is made. This SNR is a maximum and given by

$$\rho = \frac{E}{N_0} = \tfrac{1}{2}\,\mathrm{SNR}_{\max} \tag{9}$$

only at time $t=T_B$, i.e., 1-bit duration after reception of the symbol. This implies that the samplers of Fig. 2 are synchronized to the reception time of the symbols, that is, the system has bit synchronization. Assuming such bit synchronization, the quantity which determines system performance is the SNR ratio $E/N_0$.

Now consider the effect of an average power limited noise-like jamming signal. This noise may be nonthermal noise, intentional jamming, or even a statistical representation of other users occupying the same channel. The noise spectral density in the receiver is given by

$$N_0 = N_{0R} + N_{0J} \tag{10}$$

where $N_{0R}$ and $N_{0J}$ are noise spectral density contributions due to receiver thermal noise and jammer, respectively. If the jammer is average power limited to $J$ W and adjusts its spectral occupancy to match the signal bandwidth, then

$$N_{0J} = \frac{J}{(N_C/T_B)} = \frac{JT_B}{N_C}. \tag{11}$$

Since $N_{0J}' = JT_B$ would define the jammer effect if the data signal occupied a bandwidth equal to its data rate, (11) shows that the effect of the bandwidth expansion has been to reduce the effect of the jammer by the factor $N_C$, which is also the bandwidth expansion factor.

### *B. Communications Efficiency: M-ary Transmission*

It is generally known in communications that the most efficient signals for binary communications are antipodal [8, ch. 7]: one signal is the negative of the other. Coherent PSK is an example of antipodal signaling since a phase shift of 180° is equivalent to changing the algebraic sign. Such signals are most efficient in the sense that bit error probability is minimized for a given bit energy-to-noise spectral density ratio.

If one permits the signal alphabet to become more complex than binary, a given number of information bits can be transmitted at a specified error rate with less total energy than required for the optimum antipodal binary signal. In exchange for a savings in required bit energy, one must pay in the form of increased bandwidth and equipment complexity. A thorough development of this concept is provided by Viterbi [9], [10]. Briefly, one constructs an alphabet of $M=2^k$ symbols. Transmission of one such symbol conveys

$$I = \log_2 M = k \tag{12}$$

bits of binary data. Such schemes are called $M$-ary coded transmissions. Each of the symbols consists of a sequence of $n$ elementary signals or chips. Typically, $n \gg k$ in order to permit alphabets to be constructed where each member is orthogonal (or nearly orthogonal) to all other members. Alphabets which have been found to have this property include those called orthogonal, biorthogonal, and transorthogonal codes [10].

Optimal processing at the receiver requires the incoming signal to be correlated with all $M$ possible waveforms. The receiver determines the most probable waveform to be that one having the highest value of correlation as measured by the $M$ receiver correlators. This decision minimizes the probability of error.

Surface-wave technology is important to $M$-ary communications because it permits a simple implementation of the parallel correlator function in the optimum receiver. Each SWD is matched to one particular alphabet symbol. All $M$ SWD's receive the incoming waveform simultaneously. The matched filter processing action of the SWD's is exactly that required by the optimum receiver. At the instant of peak correlation, the outputs of all $M$ SWD's are compared. The SWD having the greatest output voltage corresponds to the most probable signal waveform.

Justification for this added complexity comes from the ability to maintain a given bit error probability with less received energy per bit. Upwards of 3- to 6-dB energy savings can be realized if one goes to sufficiently large alphabets, say $M=32$ to $M=1024$ symbols. Realization of this energy savings requires an increase in bandwidth in keeping with Shannon's theory [11]. Typically, the bandwidth is expanded by a factor proportional to

$$\frac{2^k}{k} \tag{13}$$

which increases exponentially with $k$.

Limited experiments have been reported by Darby *et al.* [12] for the case of $k=1$, using a 13-chip Barker code and its inverse as the waveforms. A more ambitious scheme using four FM signals ($k=2$) in an air-traffic-control system is described in [2].

### C. Ranging

In many system applications it is desired not only to communicate data between two terminals, but also to estimate the distance between the terminals. Air-traffic-control [2] and collision-avoidance systems are examples. This can be accomplished either by active transponder ranging or by passive hyperbolic techniques [7], [13], [14]. In either case, for data communication systems, the quantity of interest is the time of arrival of pulses at a receiver. For a noncoherent system, the time of arrival of a pulse is estimated by the time at which

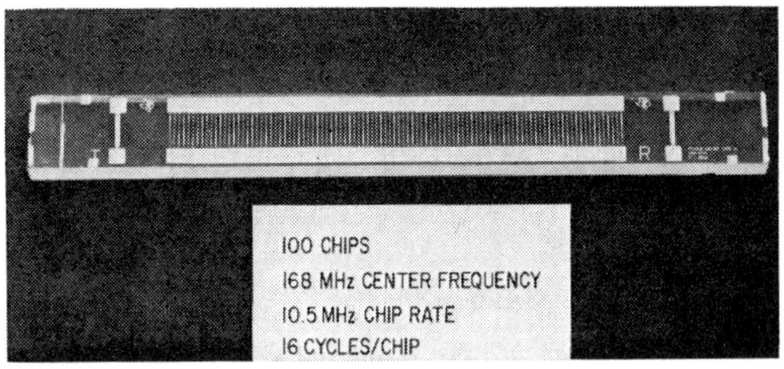


Fig. 3. 100-chip device on $ST$-cut quartz.

the envelope of the pulse (or the envelope of the processed pulse) exceeds some threshold. The rms error in such a measurement is given by [15]

$$\sigma_t = \frac{1}{\beta(2E/N_0)^{1/2}} \tag{14}$$

where $\beta$ is the effective bandwidth of the predetection pulse, $E$ is the energy in the pulse, and $N_0$ is the noise spectral density in the receiver, which is a function of receiver design. Equation (14) thus implies that accuracy can be improved by increasing $\beta$ or $E$. For a peak-power-limited transmitter, the received energy can be increased only by increasing the transmitted pulse duration $\tau$. For conventional (nonspread spectrum) pulses, the pulse duration is inherently tied to the bandwidth of the signal; increasing the pulse duration decreases the bandwidth, and vice versa. Thus, in (14) one effect tends to offset the other. Clearly, what is desired is a signal structure in which the pulse bandwidth is not tied to the pulse duration so that the two parameters may be selected more or less independently. This is precisely the situation with spread spectrum pulses where the time–bandwidth product for the pulse waveform exceeds unity. It is interesting to note that the use of spread spectrum pulses for measuring range precedes any human attempts at communication; bats have utilized frequency-swept signals in their sonic navigation system since before prehistoric times [16].

## III. Coded Surface-Wave Devices

### A. Design and Operation of Coded Devices

The matched filter operation described in the previous section is one of a class of filters, called transversal filters, which may be described as tapped delay lines. The application of SWD's to transversal filtering was reviewed very effectively by Squire *et al.* [17] and others [18]. While a great many techniques have been proposed for generating and detecting surface waves [19], the interdigital transducer [20] has proven to be the most practical, as indicated by its dominant role in more recent surveys of surface-wave technology [21]–[23], especially in application to spread spectrum and communications systems [24].

A typical coded SWD (as in Fig. 3) consists of $n$-pair interdigital transducers at each end of a multiply tapped center transducer. The interdigitated geometry of the transducers is shown more clearly in Fig. 4. A voltage applied between the pads results in a strong field between alternate fingers of the pattern. Since the substrate is piezoelectric, this field produces a periodically varying stress in the material. The resultant wave propagates on the surface away from the electrodes in both directions, in a manner similar to radiation from an endfire antenna. Conversely, as the wave passes under other electrodes, it produces a voltage which may be detected by

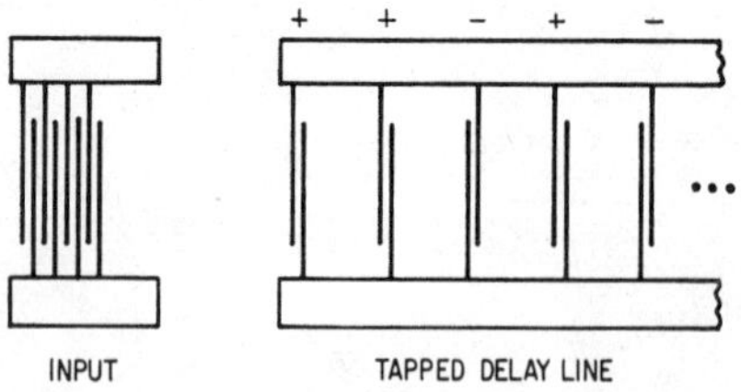


Fig. 4. Tapped delay line finger placement.

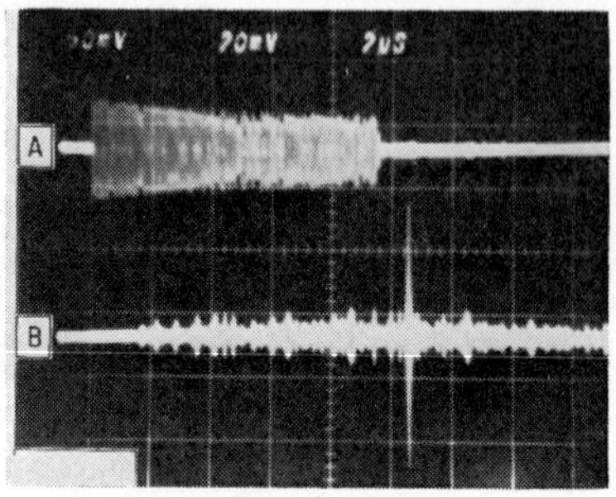


Fig. 5. 100-chip device waveforms. (a) Impulse response. (b) Correlation response.

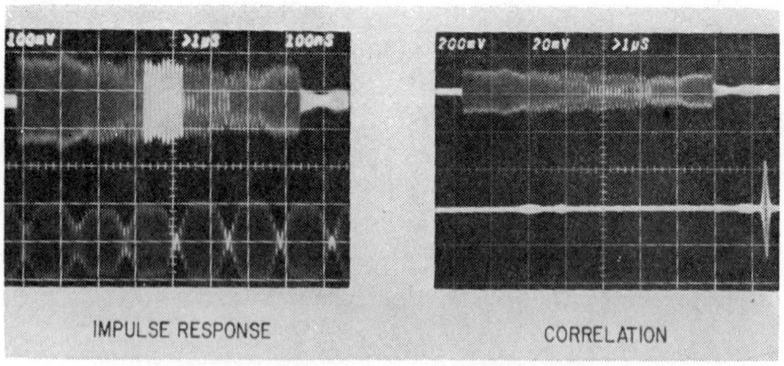


Fig. 6. 64-chip Frank polyphase code on *ST*-cut quartz. Center frequency: 120 MHz. Chip rate: 7.5 MHz.

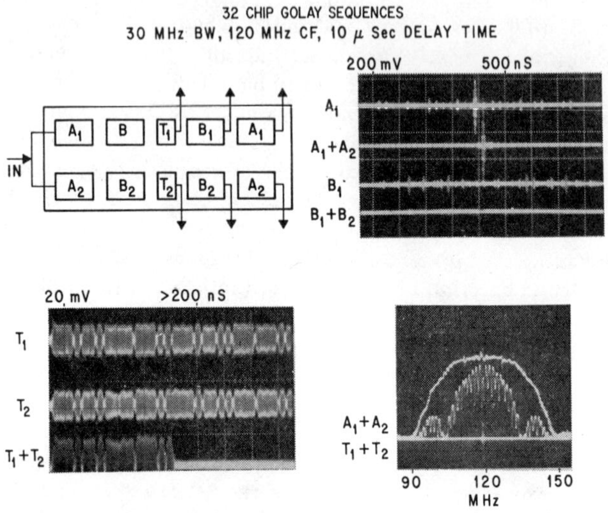


Fig. 7. 32-chip Golay complementary and orthogonal codes.

external circuitry, such as shown in Fig. 5, curve *A*, for the device illustrated in Fig. 3.

In a spread spectrum communication system, the generated signal is normally clipped, gated, and transmitted from a class *C* amplifier. In the receiver, the signal will be applied (usually after some signal conditioning) to a second device with the time inversed code. When the signal matches the coded device, a strong response results. At other times, only noise or the relatively weak sidelobe response results, as illustrated in Fig. 5(b). The operation of the system then depends on detecting the existence and timing of the main correlation peak.

The accessibility of the wave to tapping is key to very flexible code generation and transversal filtering. To first order, there is a one-to-one relation between the location of a tap on the substrate and the signal generated by the transducer (i.e., its impulse response) [25]. By proper design of the electrode placement and overlap, it is possible to generate signals of prescribed amplitude, phase, and frequency versus time, including all the standard weighted and unweighted biphase and polyphase codes. Most work to date has been done with codes of fixed center frequency, equal chip length, and fixed chip sequence, but even these restrictions are not necessary. For example, Grant *et al.* [2] describe the usefulness of programming chip sequence and Staples and Claiborne [26] review the current status of techniques for providing this capability.

The design of a device consists of two steps: specify the desired impulse response, then choose substrate material and finger geometry to realize this impulse response in a practical device [25]. Specification of the desired impulse response (code sequence, frequency, etc.) is primarily the responsibility of the communication system designer, who must be aware that some practical limitations exist due to fabrication techniques and choice of material. As will be discussed in the next section, these limitations affect the total time length, carrier frequency, fractional bandwidth, and allowable temperature variation.

Realization of a specified impulse response starts with a first-order design based only on the required impulse response and results in approximate numbers for overall device size, beamwidths, finger placement, impedance, insertion loss, etc. As more and more chips are added to the code sequence at higher frequencies, smaller and smaller levels of distortion become significant while the distortive effects become stronger. The early surface-wave equivalent circuit models [27] can be used to analyze the effect of electrical loading of the taps, but must be extended to include the effects of acoustic reflections at each electrode edge [28], [29]. While the details of the design can be complicated, it is possible to realize in practice almost any desired impulse response within the size and frequency limits which can be fabricated. For example, results have recently been published on a 127-chip biphase device [30], [31] and a 1000:1 FM pulse compressor [32].

Some representative codes should be mentioned before considering fabrication. The 100-chip code shown in Fig. 5 is a conventional biphase code taken from a set of such codes generated by random selection of the phase sequence. Only those codes with desirable auto- and cross-correlation properties are retained in the set. If the criteria are not too stringent, this technique results in a nearly unlimited supply of code sequences with fairly consistent correlation responses. A more deterministic approach to code selection is illustrated by the very limited number of Frank codes [33], noted for their extremely low nonperiodic sidelobes. The codes are all polyphase, with $n$ phases and $n^2$ chips. An example, with 64 chips and 8 phases, is shown in Fig. 6. Still another approach is to use Golay complementary sequences [34]. Two codes are generated, as shown in Fig. 7, which have sidelobes of opposite

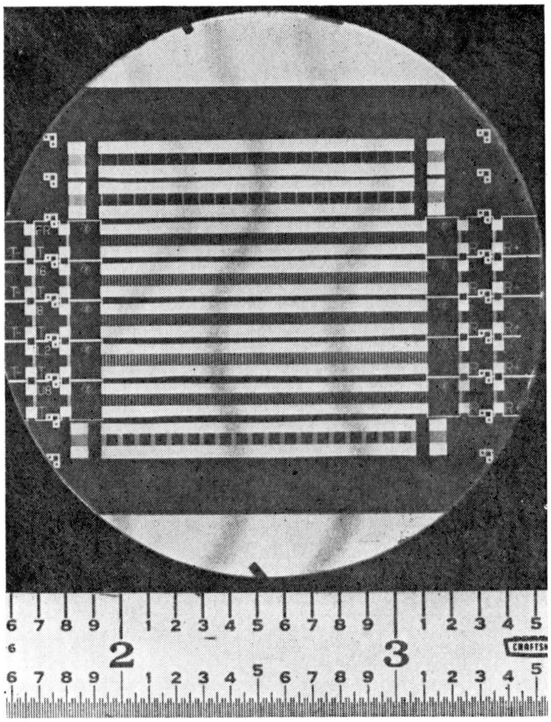


Fig. 8. PSK devices on 2-in slice of *ST*-cut quartz.

phase. When added, the sidelobes disappear, as shown in trace $A_1+A_2$. Orthogonal pairs also exist such that their cross correlation is zero [35] (trace $B_1+B_2$), allowing two sets of data to be transmitted on the two channels required. A variety of other codes have been summarized in the literature on radar signal design [36], as well as some special topics oriented to codes for spread spectrum applications [37], [38]. One last signal of interest is linear FM because of its good correlation properties and immunity to Doppler and phase errors. While waveform variability is somewhat limited, device design has been considerably developed for application to high resolution radar systems [39].

These examples are chosen more to demonstrate the variety of coding techniques that may be implemented with surface waves than to recommend particular codes. Each spread spectrum system will have its own requirements to be satisfied as determined by the number of distinct sequences required, allowable sidelobes, jamming environment, duty cycle, error rates, etc.

### *B. Performance Limitations*

The performance of SWD's has been improving at a rapid rate for several years as device designers become more familiar with the photolithographic techniques developed for integrated circuits. Progress is expected to continue at a rapid rate because the microelectronics industry is itself on the threshold of a revolution in circuit lithography as electron-beam and ion-etching techniques become practical. In perspective, it should be remembered that we are discussing applications in communication systems. Since large numbers of users are usually involved, the choice of technique becomes price sensitive as well as technology sensitive. With this in mind, let us look first at what can be done within the constraints of current mass production techniques.

The most highly automated production lines in the world for photolithography are those used for making integrated circuits. Fig. 8 shows a set of PSK devices built on a 2-in

TABLE I

TYPICAL LITHOGRAPHY LIMITATIONS

| Technique | Typical Equipment | Full Field Capabilities | | |
|---|---|---|---|---|
| | | Field Size (in) | Linewidth ($\mu$m) | Line Pairs |
| Large-scale photoplotting | Gerber photoplotter | 30 by 40 | 50 | 10 000 |
| Contact printing | Conventional production equipment, 3-in mask | 3.5 (diagonal) | 4 | 12 000 |
| High-resolution projection | Mann projection printer | 0.25 by 0.25 | 1 | 3100 |
| Electron beam | Production oriented | 0.300<br>0.050 | 2.5<br>0.5 | 1500<br>1250 |
| Electron beam | Scanning electron microscope | 0.004 | 0.1 | 500 |

quartz slice using such equipment. Both quartz and lithium niobate are readily available in this size. The codes shown are 10 $\mu$s on *ST* quartz. Longer codes (up to 13 $\mu$s) can be accommodated by deleting one of the end transducers and scraping more material at the top and bottom of the slice. While it is desirable to operate below 200 MHz, acceptable results can still be obtained at 300 MHz on *ST* quartz or 400 MHz on 41.5° *Z*-cut *X*-propagating lithium niobate [40]. For those production lines using 3-in slices, an additional 8–10 $\mu$s is available, but at slightly lower resolution.

Size restrictions are removed by going to custom fabrication, although increases above about 4 in involve some premium from materials suppliers and increasing difficulty in handling and fabrication. For example, a single code pattern longer than 3.5 in requires special equipment to generate and use. Maximum possible code length is a somewhat nebulous quantity usually not of practical interest in multiple-user communication systems because of the expense involved. For those interested, quartz may be obtained longer than 10 in and lithium niobate in lengths approaching 10 in. The corresponding delay times can be increased even more by such techniques as the wrap-around delay line [41], [42] with separate devices being driven from each delay line tap or by printing parts of the code on each side of the substrate [43].

Resolution restrictions can be eased by use of narrow field of view projection printing. Resolution of 1 $\mu$m (0.7–1.0-GHz fundamental) is paid for by a maximum field of 0.25 in from a given reticle. Larger patterns require joining several segments with placement errors of a fraction of a linewidth.

Further improvement in resolution can be obtained by using electron-beam techniques [44]–[46] for producing photomasks and/or devices. The very best resolution (0.14 $\mu$m) has been obtained using scanning electron microscopes [47] but over extremely limited fields of view. Machines designed especially for mask generation are capable of larger fields at somewhat worse resolution (e.g., 0.5 $\mu$m over 50 mil, for 2500 lines, and similar numbers of lines for larger fields) [48].

Several pattern generation and reproduction machines are compared in Table I in terms of field of view, resolution, and maximum number of line pairs (i.e., cycles of carrier signal) which can be produced without realignment.

For frequencies above 300 MHz and code sequences longer than 1 $\mu$s, intrinsic surface-wave attenuation can become important. Small losses can usually be ignored and larger losses can be compensated by weighting the taps. Weighting is less

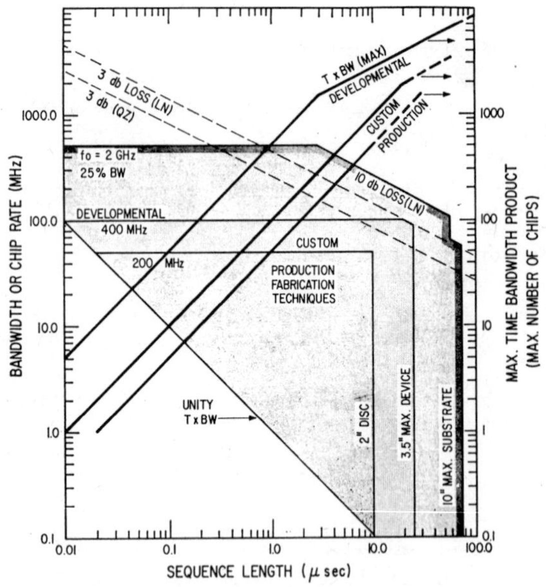


Fig. 9. Current fabrication capabilities for coded devices.

desirable since the same device cannot be used for both code generation and correlation, thereby making fabrication tolerances more stringent. A reasonable loss allowance for practical devices is 3 dB. Assuming that surface preparation has been properly done [49], then attenuation increases quadratically with frequency, with 1 dB/$\mu$s at 0.6 and 1.05 GHz for quartz and lithium niobate, respectively [50]–[53].

These restrictions can be summarized graphically as shown in Fig. 9. A 25-percent bandwidth has been assumed for practical reasons (insertion loss, spurious responses from device and electronics, etc.). Devices within the center shaded region are readily obtainable in large quantities. Devices in the lightly shaded region are also readily available but require more custom work. The outer shaded region contains those devices which are technically feasible and potentially producible in quantity but still in the development stage. Extrapolations outside this region entail considerable technical as well as economic risk. The top and right-hand boundary determine the maximum bandwidth and time lengths which may be obtained using the given level of technology. The product is the maximum chip length obtainable and is shown in the figure for each of the three regions.

## IV. Surface-Wave Solutions to Spread Spectrum Problems

### A. *Introduction*

A comparison of the needs of spread spectrum systems (Section II) with the capabilities of SWD's (Section III) shows the advantages and limitations of SWD's for this application. The decisive advantage is the capability to do matched filtering with a single simple device at high chip rates. Alternative digital techniques are expensive both in processing time and equipment. The main SWD limitations are due to finite substrate size, resulting in limited chip-sequence lengths and a minimum practical chip frequency. The match between requirements and capabilities has been best for certain types of synchronization, addressing functions, and ranging. These functions can be implemented in a variety of ways, of which several will be briefly described in Section IV-B.

Certain functions which can be performed by spread spectrum communication systems are particularly compatible with SWD's. It should be remembered that each of these functions is being carried out in a noisy environment with limited transmitted or received power. The noise may be natural, deliberate jamming, or incidental to shared occupancy of the channel with other users, but it must be circumvented.

In its simplest form, a communications system exists to transmit data. The presence of a correlation peak can be considered the successful transmittal of a symbol of information. The meaning of this symbol depends upon the organization of the system. Limitations of SWD's require that this symbol be communicated with a relatively short duration waveform.

One particularly useful type of information to send is synchronization information. Conventional digital spread spectrum systems spend a great deal of time acquiring synchronization due to the difficulty of performing correlation processing with digital circuits. Since correlation is a natural function for SWD's, they may be used to initialize and activate the sequence generator of a conventional digital system.

By allowing a variety of codes or adding higher level coding, this same technique can be used to identify or address individual users of the communication channel.

The narrow correlation peak can be used to advantage to make timing measurements. Range between users is the most important parameter based on time, but analog information can also be transmitted by PPM. The accurate timing required would not be possible with narrow-band systems, and the length of the waveforms required is usually within the capability of SWD's.

### B. *System Examples*

The wide variety of applications for SWD's in spread spectrum systems will be illustrated by a few examples for specific systems. Each system can perform one or more of the functions previously described. The dual waveform and on–off-keyed systems describe the transmission of 1 bit of information and hence are basic to understanding the other systems. Each of the other systems involves an extension of the waveform to improve system performance for some particular application.

*1) Dual Waveform Binary Communication System:* This is the approach discussed in Section II and shown in Fig. 2. Binary data is used to select one of two possible spread spectrum waveforms for transmission. These waveforms may be biphase or polyphase shift keyed, frequency hopped, or any combination. Maximum likelihood detection at the receiver results in a processing gain against certain types of jamming signals, as described in Section II-A.

*2) On–Off-Keyed Binary Communication System:* This approach is a special case of the dual waveform binary communication system just discussed with one of the two waveforms being no signal at all. Maximum likelihood detection reduces to the decision as to whether signal plus noise is present or noise only. Accurate control of the threshold level relative to the noise level is a more difficult implementation problem than the comparable problem of making greater-of decisions between two matched filter outputs in the case of dual waveform approach.

*3) Pulse-Position Modulation:* The narrow correlation peak response naturally suggests its use in encoding analog or digital data. Analog data would be encoded by continuously modulating the separation interval between consecutive pulses with the (sampled) analog signal in the transmitter.

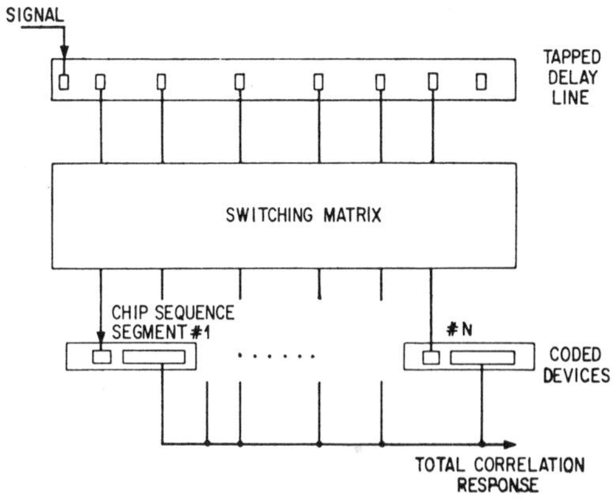


Fig. 10. Correlation of partly programmable code sequences.

The receiver would recover the analog samples by measuring the time between threshold crossings. Examples of useful analog information are sensor signals and round-trip travel time (range). Time–bandwidth-product processing gain is provided in this approach.

Digital data can be encoded in a number of ways. Straight binary PPM would have the interval between pulses constrained to one of two possible values. The receiver would investigate threshold crossing intervals in making binary decisions. $M$-ary coded PPM would have $M=2^k$ distinct possibilities for the interval between consecutive pulses. Upon measuring the pulse separation interval, the receiver would then have decoded $\log_2 M=k$ bit of information each time it received a new pulse. This technique is analogous to the approach discussed in Section II-B on communication efficiency in that each alphabet symbol conveys more than 1 bit of information.

Higher level coding is possible with PPM where groups of spread spectrum pulses are PPM encoded in unique patterns. The receiver is more complex in that it must decide if it has seen a pattern of individual pulses rather than one pulse The ability to compound the coding scheme through higher level PPM is virtually unlimited [54].

*4) M-ary Coded Transmission:* This is a generalized technique for communications involving the transmission of one of $M$ distinct symbols. This approach was discussed in Section II-B. One implementation was previously described for PPM. An alternative method uses separate codes for each symbol with separate surface-wave correlators for detection.

*5) Partly Programmable Codes:* Chip-sequence length and programming limitations can be partly circumvented with the system shown in Fig. 10. The chip sequence consists of several equal-length sequences in series. The signal to be correlated is applied to a delay line with taps at equal spaces corresponding to the short sequence length. Each tap is connected to an SWD with the chip sequence corresponding to that portion of the total sequence. The outputs of all SWD's are summed to produce the total correlation signal. If each of the $n$ taps is connected to any one of the $n$ SWD's (but only one) by means of a switching matrix, then there are $n!$ distinct sequences available to choose from. Thus, $n$ "easy" devices plus one "custom" device can be used to generate signals equivalent to $n!$ custom devices.

*6) SWD-Acquisition-Aided Conventional Spread Spectrum Communication System:* The shift-register version of spread spectrum communications can be modified to include an SWD in the receiver which is used to permit fast acquisition. Each transmitted message is preceded by a chip sequence which is matched to the SWD being addressed. The amplitude of the SWD response is an indication of the extent of agreement between the incoming signal and the SWD coded address. When this agreement reaches a threshold value, the decision is made that a legitimate preamble has been received and the receiver's code sequence generator is suitably initialized and activated.

## V. Summary

SWD's are becoming increasingly important in the development of communications systems based on spread spectrum concepts. Both PSK coding and linear FM waveforms are being used to increase the bandwidth of digital data in order to decrease the error rate and power requirements. Grant *et al.* [2] describe in detail how spread spectrum is applied to a particular operational problem—air-traffic control. We have been concerned here with the more general questions of why use spread spectrum, what are the advantages of SWD's, and some brief general descriptions of representative systems. A short review of the properties of spread spectrum signals showed the importance of matched filtering to successful operation of such systems. Advantages in improved SNR, communications efficiency, and time (or range) measurement pointed up potential application areas.

A broad look at SWD's showed that they are ideally suited to matched filtering operations. Fabrication processes were examined to determine current and potential limitations on chip rates, sequence lengths, and operating frequency. These results were summarized in Fig. 9 in terms of increasing sophistication and cost required for fabrication. In general terms, chip rates below 2 MHz are of debatable practicality and from 50 to 500 MHz involve increasing cost and risk using current technology. Total sequence lengths up to 10 $\mu$s are easily obtained below 200-MHz center frequency and can be extended to 25 $\mu$s with relatively little effort and to 75 $\mu$s in cases where substrate cost is not important. As the frequency is increased into the gigahertz range, acoustic attenuation becomes dominant for longer signals. With proper choice of parameters, it is relatively easy to achieve chip sequences of 1000, and the techniques required to reach 10 000 are clearly defined.

When spread spectrum system requirements were examined, it was seen that the best match to SWD capabilities occurred for the functions of preamble synchronization, including short data bursts; $M$-ary (or multiple code) transmission, for efficiency or discrete addressing; and timing measurements, for range or PPM. The examples of Section IV illustrated one or more of these functions in systems ranging from simple data channels to more sophisticated concepts employing higher level coding, multiple coded SWD's, and combination with conventional digital systems.

Analog matched filtering is not limited to SWD's. Charge transfer devices (CTD's) have the same capability as SWD's of sampling the signal at defined locations which allows for matched filtering. However, time delays up to 1 s and chip rates of less than 5 MHz make CTD's complementary to SWD's [55]–[57]. The systems of the future may well combine both devices to obtain much longer sequences or a wider range of rates.

## Acknowledgment

The authors wish to thank T. M. Reeder and M. G. Unkauf for helpful discussions and critical reading of the manuscript.

## References


[1] M. G. Unkauf, "Spread spectrum communications and modems," presented at the 1971 IEEE Ultrasonics Symp., paper M-1.

[2] P. M. Grant, J. H. Collins, B. J. Darby, and D. P. Morgan, "Potential applications of acoustic matched filters to air-traffic control systems," this issue, pp. 288–300.

[3] G. L. Turin, "An introduction to matched filters," *IRE Trans. Inform. Theory*, vol. IT-6, pp. 311–329, June 1960.

[4] *IRE Trans. Inform. Theory* (*Special Issue on Matched Filters*), vol. IT-6, June 1960.

[5] C. E. Cook and M. Bernfeld, *Radar Signals: An Introduction to Theory and Application*. New York: Academic Press, 1967.

[6] *Digital Communications with Space Applications*, S. W. Golomb, Ed. Englewood Cliffs, N. J.: Prentice-Hall, 1964.

[7] J. H. Painter, "Designing pseudorandom coded ranging systems," *IEEE Trans. Aerospace Electron. Syst.*, vol. AES-3, pp. 14–27, Jan. 1967.

[8] M. Schwartz, W. R. Bennett, and S. Stein, *Communications Systems and Techniques*. New York: McGraw-Hill, 1966, p. 67.

[9] A. J. Viterbi, "Phase-coherent communication over the continuous Gaussian channel," in Golomb, Baumert, Easterling, Stiffler, and Viterbi *Digital Communications with Space Applications*. Englewood Cliffs, N. J.: Prentice-Hall, 1964, pp. 106–134.

[10] ——, *Principles of Coherent Communication*. New York: McGraw-Hill, 1966, ch. 8.

[11] C. E. Shannon, "A mathematical theory of communication," *Bell System Tech. J.*, vol. 27, pp. 379–423, 623–656, 1948.

[12] B. J. Darby, P. M. Grant, and J. H. Collins, "Performance of surface acoustic wave matched filter modems in noise and interference limited environments," in *Conf. Proc., Ultrasonics Int.* (London, England), 1973.

[13] L. N. Ridenour, Ed., *M.I.T. Radiation Laboratory Series*. New York, N. Y.; McGraw-Hill, 1948–1949. See particularly *LORAN*, vol. 4, and *Electronic Time Measurements*, vol. 20.

[14] F. S. Stringer, "Hyperbolic radio navigation systems," *Wireless World*, vol. 75, pp. 353–357, Aug. 1969.

[15] M. I. Skolnik, *Introduction to Radar Systems*. New York: McGraw-Hill, 1962, pp. 468, 496.

[16] A. Novick, "Echolocation in bats: Some aspects of pulse design," *Amer. Sci.*, vol. 59, pp. 198–209, Mar.–Apr. 1971.

[17] W. D. Squire, H. J. Whitehouse, and J. A. Alsup, "Linear signal processing and ultrasonic transversal filters," *IEEE Trans. Microwave Theory Tech.*, vol. MTT-17, pp. 1020–1040, Nov. 1969.

[18] *IEEE Trans. Microwave Theory Tech.* (*Special Issue on Microwave Acoustics*), vol. MTT-17, Nov. 1969.

[19] R. M. White, "Surface elastic waves," *Proc. IEEE*, vol. 58, pp. 1238–1276, Aug. 1970.

[20] R. M. White and F. W. Voltmer, "Direct piezoelectric coupling to surface elastic waves," *Appl. Phys. Lett.*, vol. 7, pp. 314–316, Dec. 15, 1965.

[21] G. S. Kino and H. Matthews, "Signal processing in acoustic surface wave devices," *IEEE Spectrum*, vol. 8, pp. 22–35, Aug. 1971.

[22] G. S. Kino and J. Shaw, "Acoustic surface waves," *Sci. Amer.*, vol. 227, pp. 51–68, Oct. 1972.

[23] J. de Klerk, "Elastic surface waves," *Phys. Today*, vol. 25, pp. 32–39, Nov. 1972.

[24] J. H. Collins and P. M. Grant, "The role of surface acoustic wave technology in communication systems," *Ultrasonics*, vol. 10, pp. 59–71, Mar. 1972.

[25] C. S. Hartmann, D. T. Bell, Jr., and R. C. Rosenfeld, "Impulse model design of acoustic surface-wave filters," this issue, pp. 162–175.

[26] E. J. Staples and L. T. Claiborne, "A review of device technology for programmable surface-wave filters," this issue, pp. 279–287.

[27] W. R. Smith, H. M. Gerard, J. H. Collins, T. M. Reeder, and H. J. Shaw, "Analysis of interdigital surface wave transducers by use of an equivalent circuit model," *IEEE Trans. Microwave Theory Tech.*, vol. MTT-17, pp. 856–864, Nov. 1969.

[28] W. S. Jones, C. S. Hartmann, and T. D. Sturdivant, "Second order effects in surface wave devices," *IEEE Trans. Sonics Ultrason.*, vol. SU-19, pp. 368–377, July 1972.

[29] W. R. Smith, H. M. Gerard, and W. R. Jones, "Analysis and design of dispersive interdigital surface-wave transducers," *IEEE Trans. Microwave Theory Tech.*, vol. MTT-20, pp. 458–471, July 1972.

[30] G. S. Kino and J. Shaw, "Acoustic surface waves," *Sci. Amer.*, vol. 227, pp. 51–68, Oct. 1972.

[31] G. W. Judd, W. R. Jones, and T. W. Bristol, "An improved tapping transducer geometry for surface wave phase coded delay lines," in *Proc. 1972 IEEE Ultrasonics Symp.*, pp. 373–376.

[32] a) H. M. Gerard, W. R. Jones, W. R. Smith, and P. B. Snow, "Development of a broadband, low loss 1000:1 dispersive filter," in *Proc. 1972 IEEE Ultrasonics Symp.*, pp. 253–262.
b) H. M. Gerard, W. R. Smith, W. R. Jones, and J. B. Harrington, "The design and applications of highly dispersive acoustic surface-wave filters," this issue, pp. 176–186.

[33] R. L. Frank, "Polyphase codes with good nonperiodic correlation properties," *IEEE Trans. Inform. Theory*, vol. IT-9, pp. 43–45, Jan. 1963.

[34] M. J. E. Golay, "Complementary series," *IRE Trans. Inform. Theory*, vol. IT-7, pp. 82–87, Apr. 1961.

[35] C. C. Tseng, "Signal multiplexing in surface-wave delay lines using orthogonal pairs of Golay's complementary sequences," *IEEE Trans. Sonics Ultrason.*, vol. SU-18, pp. 103–107, Apr. 1971.

[36] C. E. Cook and M. Bernfeld, *Radar Signals: An Introduction to Theory and Application*. New York: Academic Press, 1967, ch. 8.

[37] R. Gold, "Study of correlation properties of binary sequences," U. S. Air Force Avionics Lab., Wright-Patterson AFB, Ohio, Tech. Rep. AFAL-TR-67-311, 1967.

[38] ——, "Optimal binary sequences for spread spectrum multiplexing," *IEEE Trans. Inform. Theory* (Corresp.), vol. IT-13, pp. 619–621, Oct. 1967.

[39] W. S. Jones, R. A. Kempf, and C. S. Hartmann, "Practical surface wave linear FM correlators for modern radar systems," *Microwave J.*, vol. 15, p. 43, May 1972.

[40] A. J. Slobodnik, Jr., and E. D. Conway, "New high-frequency, high-coupling low-beam-steering cut for acoustic surface waves on $LiNbO_3$," *Electron. Lett.*, vol. 6, pp. 171–172, Mar. 19, 1970.

[41] W. L. Bond, T. M. Reeder, and H. J. Shaw, "Wrap-around surface-wave delay lines," *Electron. Lett.*, vol. 7, pp. 78–80, 1971.

[42] T. M. Reeder, H. J. Shaw, and E. M. Westbrook, "Multimillisecond time delays with wrap-around surface-acoustic-wave delay lines," *Electron. Lett.*, vol. 8, pp. 356–358, July 13, 1972.

[43] C. F. Vasile and R. LaRosa, "1000 bit surface-wave matched filter," *Electron. Lett.*, vol. 8, pp. 479–480, Sept. 21, 1972.

[44] A. N. Broers and M. Hatzakis, "Microcircuits by electron beam," *Sci. Amer.*, vol. 227, pp. 34–44, Nov. 1972.

[45] G. R. Brewer, "The application of electron/ion beam technology to microelectronics," *IEEE Spectrum*, vol. 8, pp. 23–37, Jan. 1971.

[46] *IEEE Trans. Electron Devices* (Special Section on Computer Controlled Microfabrication), vol. ED-19, pp. 623–651, May 1972.

[47] A. N. Broers and M. Hatzakis, "Microcircuits by electron beam," *Sci. Amer.*, vol. 227, p. 44, Nov. 1972.

[48] R. R. Webster, G. L. Varnell, and D. R. Ch'en, "Production engineering measure for an electron-beam machine and microwave transistors," U. S. Army Electronics Command, Philadelphia, Pa., Contract DAAB05-71-C-3715, Quart. Reps., 1971–1972.

[49] D. T. Bell, Jr., "Growth, orientation, and surface preparation of quartz," in *Proc. 1972 IEEE Ultrasonics Symp.*, pp. 206–210.

[50] A. J. Budreau and P. H. Carr, "Temperature dependence of the attenuation of microwave frequency elastic surface waves in quartz," *Appl. Phys. Lett.*, vol. 18, pp. 239–241, Mar. 15, 1971.

[51] A. J. Slobodnik, Jr., P. H. Carr, and A. J. Budreau, "Microwave frequency acoustic surface-wave loss mechanisms in $LiNbO_3$," *J. Appl. Phys.*, vol. 41, pp. 4380–4387, Oct. 1970.

[52] A. J. Slobodnik, Jr., "Attenuation of microwave acoustic surface waves due to gas loading," *J. Appl. Phys.*, vol. 43, pp. 2565–2568, June 1972.

[53] ——, "Material dependence of acoustic surface wave propagation losses," presented at the 1972 IEEE Ultrasonics Symp., paper O-9.

[54] a) C. R. Cahn and S. E. Kosowski, "Integrated function (CNI) waveform study," Rome Air Develop. Cent., Rep. RADC-TR-69-424 (AD 865739), Jan. 1970.
b) R. V. Ridings, C. R. Reeves, and J. Aasterud, "Modulation waveform study," Rome Air Develop. Cent., Contract F30602-72-C-0102, Final Rep., Aug. 1972.

[55] D. D. Buss, W. H. Bailey, and D. R. Collins, "Matched filtering using tapped bucket-brigade delay lines," *Electron. Lett.*, vol. 8, pp. 106–107, Feb. 24, 1972.

[56] D. D. Buss, W. H. Bailey, D. R. Collins, and L. R. Hite, "Filtering using bucket brigade devices," *Data Commun. Des.*, May/June 1972.

[57] D. D. Buss, D. R. Collins, W. H. Bailey, and C. R. Reeves, "Transversal filtering using charge transfer devices," *IEEE J. Solid-State Circuits*, to be published.

# Transversal Filtering Using Charge-Transfer Devices

DENNIS D. BUSS, DEAN R. COLLINS, WALTER H. BAILEY, AND C. RICHARD REEVES

*Abstract*—Techniques are presented for making transversal filters using charge-coupled devices (CCD's) and bucket-brigade devices (BBD's). In a CCD transversal filter, the delayed signals are sampled by measuring the current flowing in the clock lines during transfer, and the sampled signals are weighted by a split electrode technique. In a BBD transversal filter, the delayed signals are "tapped" with a source follower whose load determines the weighting coefficient. Examples are given of CCD and BBD filters that are "matched" to particular signaling waveforms, and the limitations of charge-transfer devices (CTD's) in matched filtering applications are discussed. Finally, the application of CTD transversal filters to other signal processing functions is discussed.

## I. Introduction

Charge-transfer devices (CTD's), which include both charge-coupled devices (CCD's) [1]–[3] and bucket-brigade devices (BBD's) [4], [5], are uniquely applicable to many analog signal processing functions because they are capable of operating directly with analog signals. One of the most important signal processing functions for which CTD's can be used is the time delay of analog signals [6]. When CTD's are used in this application, the signal to be delayed is first sampled at a rate greater than twice the highest frequency in the signal. The analog samples are then clocked down the CTD shift register and appear at the output a delay time $T_d$ later. The delayed signal is finally reconstructed by passing the samples through an appropriate bandpass filter.

The alternatives to CTD's for analog time delay are acoustic delay lines for short time delay, or digital delay preceded by analog/digital conversion and followed by digital/analog conversion. Since CTD's can achieve hundreds of milliseconds of delay, they look very attractive for a large number of signal delay functions. However, the characteristics of CTD delay lines have been analyzed in great detail elsewhere in the literature [6]–[8], and therefore this paper will deal exclusively with the application of tapped CTD delay lines to transversal filtering [9].

A block diagram of a transversal filter is shown in Fig. 1. It consists of a sampling stage $S$ followed by $M$-delay stages $D$, each of which delays the signal by a time equal to an integral number (one in this paper) of clock periods $T_c$. The signal is nondestructively sampled at each delay stage, multiplied by the appropriate weighting coefficient $h_k$ $(k = 1, M)$, and the weighted signals are summed together to give the filter output. As can be seen from Fig. 1, the $h_k$ determine the impulse response, or Green's function, of the filter, i.e., the output that results when a single sample of unit amplitude is applied to the input. Moreover, when an arbitrary signal $v_{in}(t)$ is applied to the filter, the filter output is

$$v_{out}(nT_c) = \sum_{k=1}^{M} h_k v_{in}[(n - k + 1)T_c]\, T_c - kT_c) \quad (1)$$

$$\approx \int_0^{T_d} h(\tau) v_{in}(nT_c - \tau)\, d\tau \quad (2)$$

where $v_{in}(kT_c)$ represents the sampled input signal, and $T_d(=MT_c)$ is the total time delay of the filter. This output is approximately equal to the convolution of the input signal with the impulse response of the filter.

Operationally, CTD transversal filters can perform the same functions as surface wave device (SWD) transversal filters [10], except that SWD filters are limited in the time duration of the impulse response to a few tens of microseconds, whereas CTD filters can process signals having hundreds of milliseconds time duration. CTD filters, on the other hand, are limited in bandwidth to a few tens of megahertz.

The first CTD transversal filter utilized BBD's for

Manuscript received October 19, 1972. This work was supported in part by the Electronic Systems Division of the U. S. Air Force.
D. D. Buss, D. R. Collins, and W. H. Bailey are with Texas Instruments, Inc., Dallas, Tex. 75222.
C. R. Reeves was with Texas Instruments, Inc., Dallas, Tex. 75222. He is now with the Applied Research Laboratories, University of Texas at Austin, Austin, Tex.

Reprinted from *IEEE J. Solid-State Circuits*, vol. SC-8, pp. 138–146, Apr. 1973.

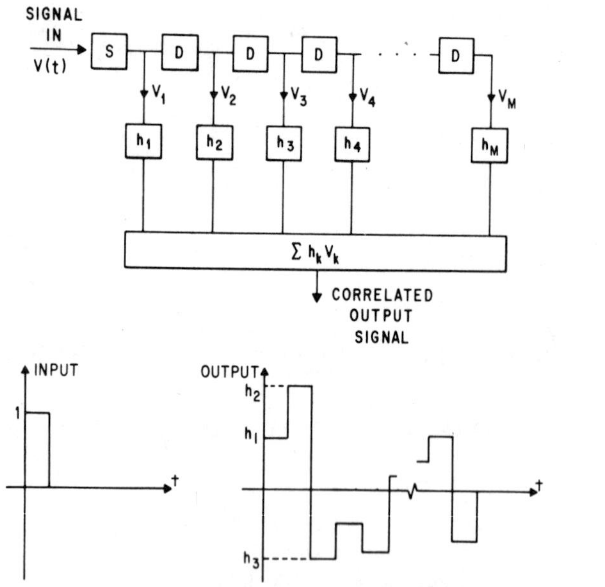


Fig. 1. Block diagram of a transversal filter. This consists of a sampling stage $S$, delay stages $D$, and taps with coefficients $h_k$, $k = 1, M$. The $h_k$ determine the response to a unit input as shown.

the delay element, and was designed to have a bandpass characteristic [11], [12] (see Section IV). A transversal filter, however, can have an arbitrary impulse response of finite time duration and therefore can be used to implement any linear filter. (Any system whose output is linearly related to the input is a linear filter.) In this sense, a transversal filter can be thought of as the fundamental building block of linear systems of which even the analog time delay is a special case.

Filters of the type described above are called sampled data filters [13] because a continuous input signal is sampled in time. Such filters have a wide range of applicability. However, before the advent of CTD's, many such filters required digital implementation. CTD's have the potential of revolutionizing certain sampled data filtering applications because they deal with the analog signals themselves. The potential advantages of performing sampled data filtering functions on a single CTD chip are overwhelming.

More complex sampled data filtering operations can be achieved by feeding the output of a delay line back to the input to achieve what is called a recursive filter. This type of filter is useful in generating an impulse response that is unbounded in time, and has been implemented using BBD's to achieve bandpass filtering [14].

In constructing a transversal filter, it is necessary to have, in addition to an analog time delay, a circuit for sampling, weighting, and summing the outputs, as shown in Fig. 1 and (1). This is accomplished in different ways, depending on whether CCD's or BBD's are used for the delay. Methods of sampling, weighting, and summing are described in Section II.

Since the impulse response of a CTD transversal filter can be selected arbitrarily, these filters can be "matched" to any desired signal waveform, in which case the filter is called a matched filter [15]–[18]. Matched filters are used to detect a given waveform in the presence of noise with optimum detection probability. CTD matched filters are useful, for example, in low data rate, spread spectrum communication systems. The design and operational characteristics of CTD matched filters are discussed in Section III.

CTD transversal filters also can be designed to achieve a particular spectral characteristic [19]. In order to obtain, for example, a bandpass filter, the impulse response of the filter is chosen to be the Fourier transform of the desired bandpass characteristic. Therefore, design of such bandpass filters is extremely flexible and relatively simple. Filters of this type are discussed in Section IV, together with other possible applications for transversal filters.

## II. Design of CTD Transversal Filters

In order to make a CTD transversal filter, it is necessary to nondestructively sample the delay line and to perform the weighted summation indicated in Fig. 1. This is achieved in different ways, depending on whether CCD's or BBD's are used, as is discussed in this section.

### A. CCD's

The principle used to nondestructively measure the charge under a CCD electrode is to integrate the current that flows in the clock line during charge transfer [15], [16]. This is illustrated in Fig. 2 for a three-phase (3-$\phi$) CCD. When a transferred charge $Q_k^t$ flows from under the $k$th $\phi_2$ electrode to under the $k$th $\phi_3$ electrode, the current that flows in the $k$th $\phi_3$ clock line can be separated into two portions: a portion that would flow if $Q_k^t$ were zero, plus a portion that is approximately proportional to $Q_k^t$.

If the CCD electrode is modeled by the oxide capacitance $C_{ox}$ in series with a voltage-independent depletion layer capacitance $C_d$, the charge $Q_k^c$ equal to the integral of the clock line current can be expressed by

$$Q_k^c = V_c \frac{C_{ox} C_d}{C_{ox} + C_d} + Q_k^t \frac{C_{ox}}{C_{ox} + C_d} \tag{3}$$

where $V_c$ is the voltage amplitude of the clock driver. When $C_{ox} \gg C_d$, as is the case for high-resistivity substrate material,

$$Q_k^c \simeq V_c C_d + Q_k^t. \tag{4}$$

In order to weight each sampled charge with an arbitrary coefficient $(-1 < h_k < +1)$, each $\phi_3$ electrode is split, as shown in Fig. 2. The upper portions of each $\phi_3$ electrode are connected together in a common clock line ($\phi_3^{(+)}$), and the lower portions are connected together in a common clock line ($\phi_3^{(-)}$). Identical voltage waveforms are applied to $\phi_3^{(+)}$ and $\phi_3^{(-)}$, but the currents in the two lines are measured separately, and the difference is applied to a differential amplifier external

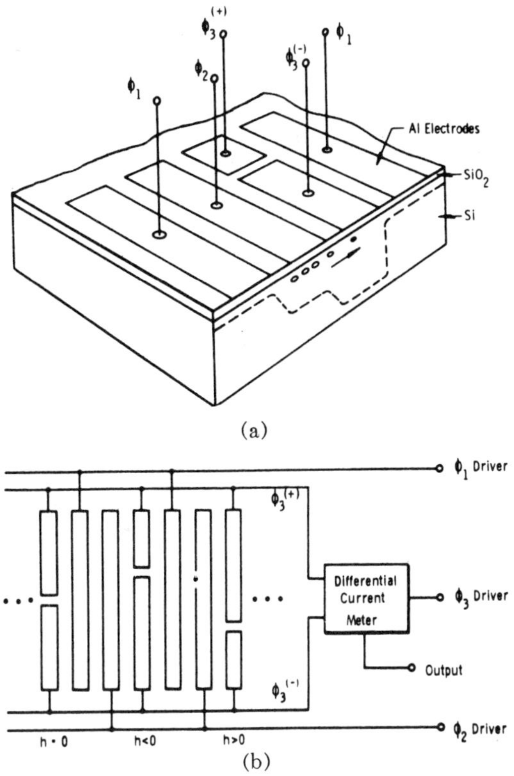


Fig. 2. Schematic of the electrode weighting technique for achieving the sampling, weighting, and summing operation indicated in Fig. 1. This technique is used with CCD filters.

to the chip. If the $k$th electrode is split so that a fraction $\frac{1}{2}(1 + h_k)$ is connected to $\phi_3^{(+)}$ (the $h_k$ are assumed normalized to unity) and a fraction $\frac{1}{2}(1 - h_k)$ is connected to $\phi_3^{(-)}$, then the output of the differential amplifier is

$$v_{\text{out}} \propto \sum_{k=1}^{M} \tfrac{1}{2}(1 + h_k)Q_k^c - \sum_{k=1}^{M} \tfrac{1}{2}(1 - h_k)Q_k^c = \sum_{k=1}^{M} h_k Q_k^c. \quad (5)$$

The device is operated such that zero signal corresponds to a charge midway between the maximum charge $Q_{\max}$ and the "fat zero" charge $Q_{fz}$. On this basis, the signal charge $Q_k^s$ can be either positive or negative, and is related to $Q_k^t$ by

$$Q_k^s = Q_k^t - \tfrac{1}{2}(Q_{\max} - Q_{fz}). \quad (6)$$

Inserting (4) and (6) into (5) shows that $v_{\text{out}}$ consists of a dc component plus a signal component.

$$v_{\text{out}} \propto [V_c C_d + \tfrac{1}{2}(Q_{\max} - Q_{fz})] \sum_{k=1}^{M} h_k + \sum_{k=1}^{M} h_k Q_k^s. \quad (7)$$

The dc component can be eliminated by capacitive coupling, leaving only the portion of $v_{\text{out}}$ which depends upon the $Q_k^s(t)$. The connection with (1) is established by relating the signal charge under the $k$th electrode to the input voltage $k - 1$ clock periods earlier:

$$Q_k^s(t) = (C_{\text{ox}} + C_d)v_{\text{in}}[t - (k - 1)T_c] \quad (8)$$

Equations (3)–(8) ignore the dependence of $C_d$ upon surface potential, which can introduce nonlinearity into the sampling weighting, and summing operation unless care is taken to avoid it. Two things can be done to insure linearity: 1) $C_d$ can be made small by utilizing a lightly doped substrate, and 2) by designing the input properly, the nonlinear relationship between $Q_k^s(t)$ and $v_{\text{in}}[t - (k - 1)]T_c$ can be made to exactly cancel the nonlinear relationship between $v_{\text{out}}$ and the $Q_k^s$.

The technique described above is called electrode weighting, and a CCD filter made using this technique is shown in Fig. 3. The gaps in the $\phi_3$ electrodes are clearly visible. A gap midway across the electrode corresponds to a weighting coefficient of zero, whereas a gap in the upper (lower) half of the electrode corresponds to a negative (positive) coefficient. The impulse response of this filter is an oscillatory function that increases in frequency from zero to half the clock frequency. The operation of filters of this type is discussed in Section III.

### *B. BBD's*

BBD transversal filters can be made using the electrode weighting technique discussed in Section II-A, as was first demonstrated by Sangster [11], [12]. However, because the signal charge in a BBD is stored on a diffused node, this node voltage can be tapped by applying it to the gate of the active transistor of a source follower, as is illustrated in Fig. 4 [17], [18]. BBD filters have been made using both the electrode weighting technique and the gate tapping technique, and the choice of the latter is one of convenience: it is easier to implement the peripheral electronics for the gate tapping technique.

In the circuit of Fig. 4, the current $i_k$ that flows in the $k$th source follower is proportional to the node voltage $v_k$ and to the conductance $G_k$ of the load transistor. The nodes for which $h_k > 0$ are connected to a common line $\Sigma^{(+)}$, and the nodes for which $h_k < 0$ are connected to a common line $\Sigma^{(-)}$. The current in $\Sigma^{(-)}$ is then subtracted from the current in $\Sigma^{(+)}$ in an external low-impedance differential amplifier to give the correlation output. This particular filter is matched to a 13-bit Barker-coded [20] p-n sequence (see Section III-A). Consequently, $|h_k| = 1$, and the $G_k$ are identical.

This technique is not limited, however, to filters having $|h_k| = 1$, since the conductance $G_k$ of the load transsistor can be varied to obtain arbitrary $h_k$. BBD chirp filters having 100 stages have been fabricated and are discussed in Section III-A.

A further advantage of the gate tapping method is that programmable filters are more easily implemented. A 20-stage filter having unity weighting coefficients ($|h_k| = 1$) has been fabricated. This filter is programmed by switching each source follower to $\Sigma^+$ or $\Sigma^-$, depending upon the state of MOS switches into which the code has been read. Programmability is very important for many system applications, but will not be discussed further.

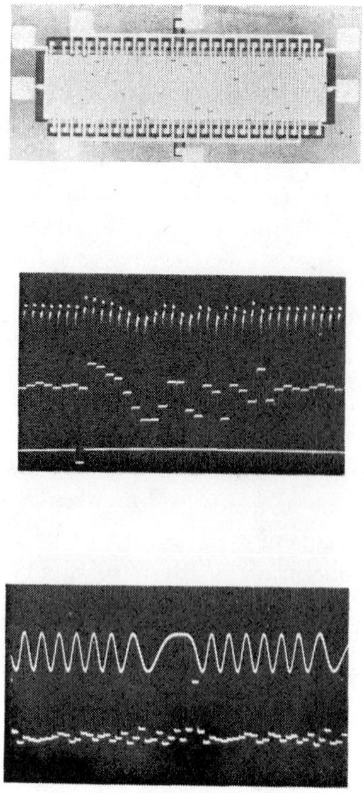

Fig. 3. CCD matched to a chirp signal, i.e., a sinusoid whose frequency decreases linearly with time. The impulse response is clearly visible in the electrode gaps shown in the photomicrograph. Top: CCD chirp filter; middle: impulse response of a 21-chip code; bottom: FM waveform and matched filter output.

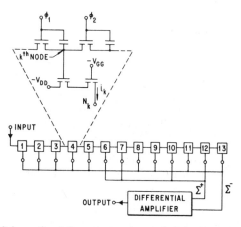

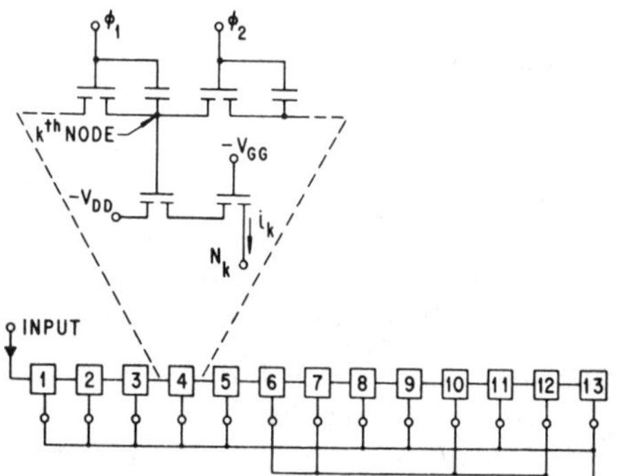


Fig. 4. Schematic of the gate tapping technique for achieving the sampling, weighting, and summing operation. The implementation of this filter is shown in Fig. 5.

## III. Matched Filters

The matched filtering theorem [9] states that in order to detect a signal in the presence of white additive noise with the optimum detection probability, a matched filter should be used, i.e., a filter whose impulse response is the time inverse of the signal to be received.

The principle of matched filtering is important in many applications, but one of the most apparent is in low data rate, spread spectrum communication systems, where it is desired to transmit a peak-power-limited signal over a noisy channel. The peak power limitation is overcome by spreading the energy in a low-power signal over a long time interval (up to several hundred milliseconds in some applications). The receiver in such a system must be capable of coherently integrating the received signal power for the time duration of the signal, and it requires a matched filter.

This section gives results on testing CTD matched filters and discusses their limitations.

### *A. Results*

As an example of a matched filter, consider a signaling scheme that utilizes a 13-bit Barker-coded [20] p-n sequence. A p-n sequence takes on one of two values, +1 or −1, and a Barker code is a particular sequence that has desirable autocorrelation properties. The 13-bit Barker code is

$$h_k = (-, -, -, -, -, +, +, -, -, +, -, +, -) \quad (9)$$

and the BBD filter shown in Fig. 4 is matched to this code.

The response of the filter to a negative impulse is shown in Fig. 5(a). From this figure it can be seen that the response to a positive impulse is the time inverse of the signal specified by (9), and when the signal itself is applied to the input, the correlation output results in a large peak, shown in Fig. 5(b). This correlation peak results from the constructive addition of signal voltages from the entire signal waveform, and therefore utilizes the energy of the waveform in the optimum way to overcome noise. The output from an ideal filter is shown in Fig. 5(c). The correlation peak is 13 times the input voltage level, and results in a signal-to-noise ratio ($S/N$) improvement of 13 to 1 (11.1 dB) over a single pulse signal scheme.

The devices whose results are shown here were fabricated on low-resistivity (1–2 Ω·cm) ⟨111⟩ n-type silicon using an oxide–nitride gate for low threshold voltage. The charge transfer efficiency (CTE) was found to be 99.5 percent per transfer, and a calculation of the output using this CTE is shown in Fig. 5(d). The height of the correlation peak is degraded by CTE from 13 to 11.87, so that the peak output power is only $(11.87)^2 =$ 140.9 times the input power. However, imperfect CTE also introduces correlation between the noise voltages on the different nodes, and calculations of this effect [18] indicate that the output noise power is decreased from 13 times the input noise power to 10.95 times the input noise power. The overall $S/N$ improvement is therefore 12.87, which represents a loss in sensitivity of only 0.04 dB.

In order to verify that the predicted sensitivity is in fact achieved, an experiment was performed in which a controlled amount of noise was added to the signal at the filter input. The filter output was fed to a thresholding device whose threshold was set to achieve a

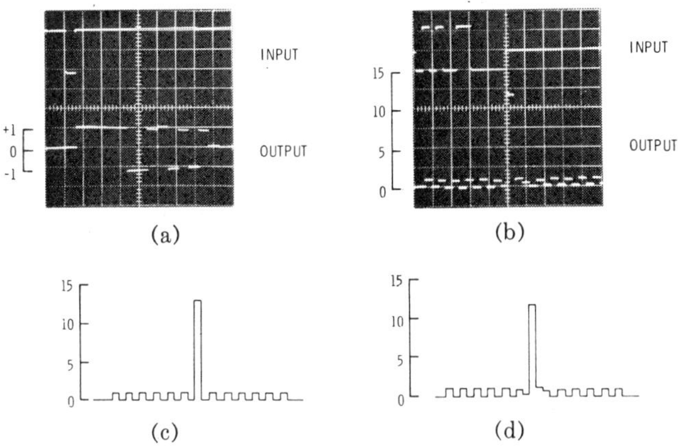


Fig. 5. (a) Impulse response of the filter shown in Fig. 4. (b) Correlation response of this filter. Note the correlation peak near the center of the photograph. (c) Ideal correlation response. (d) Calculated response assuming 99.5 percent CTE.

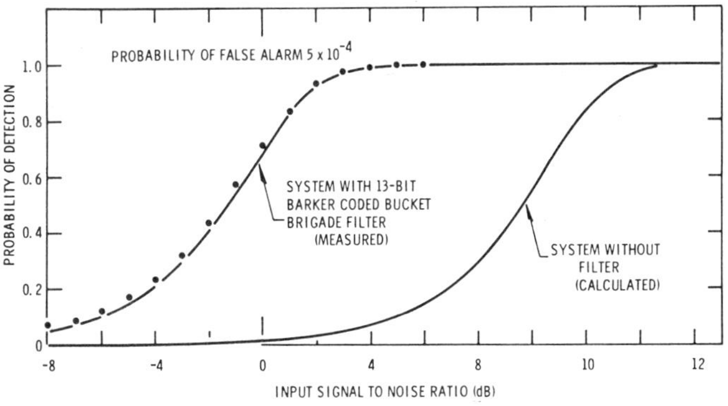


Fig. 6. Probability of detection versus input $S/N$ ratio achieved using the filter of Fig. 5. The detection threshold is set to give a false alarm probability of $5 \times 10^{-4}$. The solid line is calculated assuming Gaussian noise, and the points are measured.

given probability of false alarm ($P_{FA}$), i.e., the probability of the threshold being exceeded by noise alone in the absence of signal. The probability of detection ($P_D$), i.e., the probability of a threshold crossing when the signal is added, was then measured, and typical results are shown in Fig. 6. The solid lines represent calculations of $P_D$ versus input $S/N$ with and without the filter, and show that the 11.1-dB $S/N$ improvement is in fact achieved.

The CCD implementation of the 13-bit Barker-coded p-n filter is shown in Fig. 7. The electrode gaps are not present in the photomicrograph of the circuit because, since the weighting coefficients all have unit magnitude, the electrodes are connected entirely to either $\phi_3^{(+)}$ or $\phi_3^{(-)}$. The devices pictured here were processed on 20 Ω·cm ⟨111⟩ n-type silicon using a single-level three-phase CCD design. They had a CTE of 99.9 percent at 1 MHz, and were operated with essentially ideal performance from 10 kHz to 5 MHz.

In order to demonstrate the applicability of CTD matched filters to practical communication systems, two 100-stage BBD filters were designed to be matched to a chirp waveform. They are for use in a system that utilizes a signal of the form

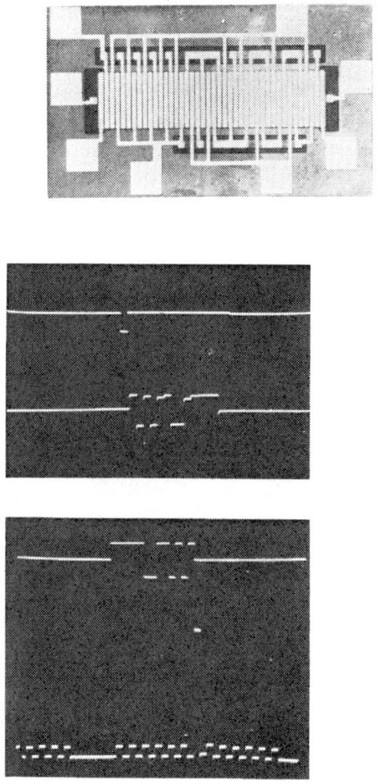

Fig. 7. CCD implementation of the 13-bit Barker-coded p-n filter. No interelectrode gaps are visible because $|h_k| = 1$. Top: 13-bit Barker code device; middle: impulse response; bottom: correlation response.

$$v(t) \;\alpha\; \cos\left[2\pi\left(f_1 t + \tfrac{1}{2}\frac{\Delta f}{T}t^2\right) + \phi\right], \qquad 0 < t < T. \quad (10)$$

This waveform "chirps" from frequency $f_1$ to frequency $f_1 + \Delta f$ in a time $T$, and the time–bandwidth product, which is a measure of pulse compression ratio or processing gain, is $T\Delta f = 50$. The receiver that was built to detect this waveform is shown in Fig. 8(a). The signal of (10) is mixed to baseband by multiplying by in-phase and quadrature sinusoids of frequency $f_0 = f_1 + \Delta f/2$. The baseband signal that "chirps" from $-(\Delta f/2)$ to $+(\Delta f/2)$ is then detected using the in-phase and quadrature matched filters whose respective impulse responses are given by the weighting coefficients.

$$h_k = \cos\left[\frac{2\pi}{25}(k - 50.5)^2\right]\exp\left[-2.648\left(\frac{k - 50.5}{49.5}\right)^2\right]$$

$$h_k = \sin\left[\frac{2\pi}{25}(k - 50.5)^2\right]\exp\left[-2.648\left(\frac{k - 50.5}{49.5}\right)^2\right],$$

$$k = 1{,}100 \qquad (11)$$

and are shown in Fig. 8(b). The receiver was tested by adding a controlled amount of noise to the signal, and by measuring the detection probability as a function of input $S/N$ and probability of false alarm. Fig. 8(c) shows the filter operating with 0-dB input $S/N$. The correlation peaks shown in the output are used to trigger a thresholding device. The filter has a theoretical improvement in $S/N$ of 18.7 dB down 1.3 dB from the

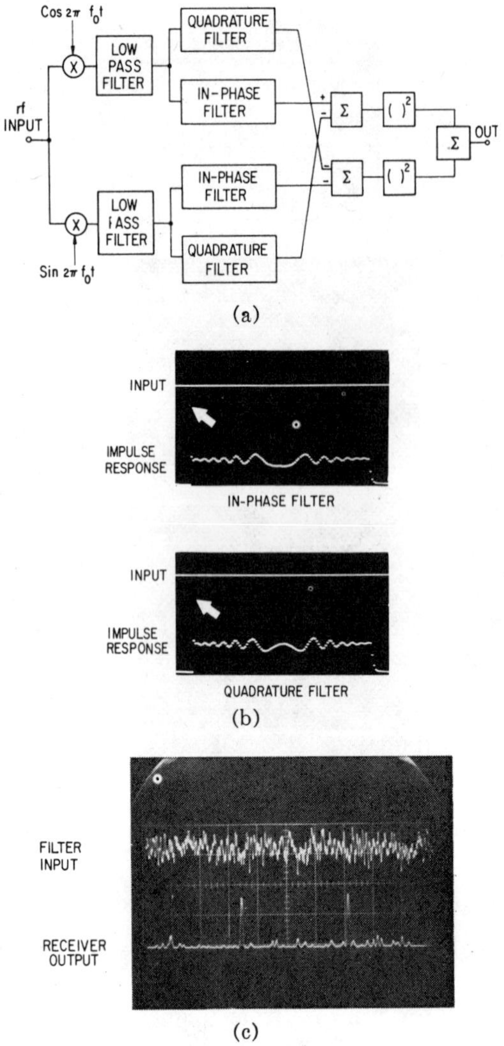


Fig. 8. (a) Block diagram of a receiver for chirp signals ($T_dW$ $=50$) that utilizes BBD matched filters. (b) Impulse responses of the two BBD filters used in the receiver. (c) Operation of the receiver at 0-dB input $S/N$. The top trace shows signal plus noise at baseband frequency at the input of one of the filters. The bottom trace shows the filter output in which two correlation peaks corresponding to two received signals rise unambiguously above the output noise.

ideal processing gain of 20 dB. This is because of the Gaussian weighting on the filter impulse responses, which introduces a mismatch between the signal and the filter. The Gaussian weighting results in lower processing gain, but significantly suppresses the sidelobes that are present at times different from the correlation peak. The measured processing gain was within 1.5 dB of the theoretical optimum in all cases tested.

### *B. Limitations*

The time duration ($T_d$) of signals that can be processed using CTD matched filters is ultimately limited by the storage time [3] of the devices (i.e., the time it takes a stored charge to be lost due to leakage). The storage time depends upon junction leakage in BBD's and upon inversion layer equilibration in CCD's, and it is typically on the order of 1 s for both devices.

The filter length (i.e., the number of delay stages $M$) is ultimately limited by CTE. The precise amount of loss due to imperfect CTE that can be tolerated depends upon the application. However, for matched filtering, imperfect CTE degrades the output noise power as well as the output signal power, so that the processing gain is only weakly affected. Calculations indicate that

$$M\epsilon < 2 \tag{12}$$

is acceptable for many matched filtering applications where $\epsilon$ is the loss per stage (i.e., three times the loss per transfer for a three-phase CCD, etc.).

The Nyquist sampling theorem requires that a signal having bandwidth $W$ be sampled at a frequency greater than $2W$, and combining this requirement with (12) gives the following limitation on the $T_dW$ product of signals that can be processed using CTD filters:

$$T_dW < 1/\epsilon. \tag{13}$$

To the extent that CTE can be predicted, the limitation imposed by (13) can be circumvented by selecting the weighting coefficients to invert the dispersion due to imperfect CTE. The dependence of CTE on signal amplitude makes it impossible to exactly invert this dispersion at all signal levels. However, the effectiveness of the technique is illustrated in Fig. 9, where a 13-bit filter with externally adjustable weighting coefficients is matched to an 11-bit Barker code. The device shown had singularly poor CTE (98 percent), and the degradation of circuit performance is shown in Fig. 9(a) and (b). In Fig. 9(c) and (d), however, the weighting coefficients have been adjusted to effectively invert the dispersion before adding.

When the CTE of a given design and process can be predicted, compensation can be designed into the filter. The required weighting coefficients are obtained by calculating the matrix of weighting coefficients that would be required to invert the dispersion at each node, and by multiplying this matrix by the desired weighting coefficients.

In addition to the limitation stated by (13), the signal bandwidth is limited to less than half the maximum clock frequency of the filter. For CCD's this limitation is currently approximately 20 MHz, whereas BBD's are limited to a few megahertz.

Another limitation on CTD transversal filters is the accuracy with which the weighting coefficients can be determined. Weighting coefficient error poses a severe limitation on many applications for transversal filters, but matched filters are usually operated in a high-noise environment, and the additional "noise" introduced by weighting coefficient error is usually inconsequential. To demonstrate this, an analysis of weighting coefficient error on p-n sequence filters has been performed, based on the assumptions that: 1) errors are uncorrelated, and 2) they contribute to the $S/N$ in the same way as other sources of noise. The result is

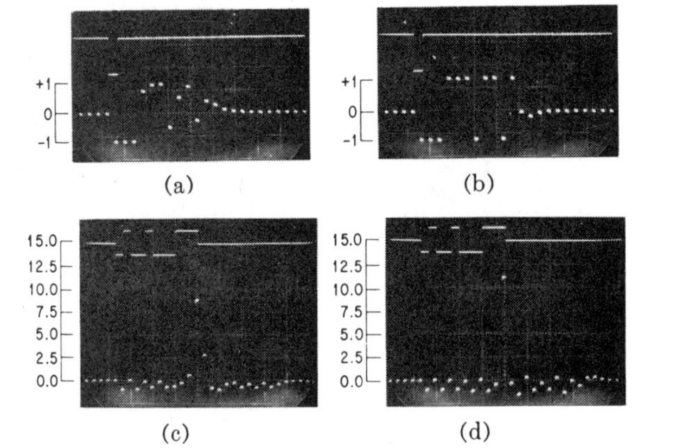


Fig. 9. Charge loss compensation in a BBD filter having poor CTE. The weighting coefficients are chosen to invert the dispersion due to loss. These results are measured on an 11-bit Barker-coded p-n filter. (a) Impulse response without charge compensation. (b) Correlation response without charge compensation. (c) Impulse response with charge compensation. (d) Correlation response with charge compensation.

$$\frac{S}{N}(\text{out}) = M \frac{\frac{S}{N}(\text{in})}{1 + \sigma_{\text{rms}}^2\left[1 + \frac{S}{N}(\text{in})\right]} \tag{14}$$

where $\sigma_{\text{rms}}$ is the fractional rms weighting coefficient error and is on the order of a few percent. This expression shows that the ideal processing gain (equal to the number of bits $M$ in the code) is achieved, unless $S/N(\text{in})$ is on the order of $\sigma_{\text{rms}}^{-2}$, which normally would not be the case.

## IV. Other Applications of Transversal Filtering

The use of a CTD transversal filter to achieve a desired spectral characteristic has been demonstrated using BBD's [11], [12], [19]. For this application, the impulse response of the filter is chosen to be the Fourier transform of the desired frequency characteristic, in much the same way that SWD spectral filters are designed [10]. The type of spectral characteristic that can be achieved is therefore limited by the finite time duration of the impulse response.

An example of a narrow-band filter characteristic is shown in Fig. 10(a). This is an example of a Dolph–Chebyshev filter, and is achieved using a 101-stage CCD whose impulse response is shown in Fig. 10(b). This class of filter is designed to optimize the tradeoff between the width of the passband and the rejection outside the passband. It has 29-dB out-of-band rejection and a 3-dB bandwidth of $4\frac{1}{2}$ percent of the center frequency. The center frequency is designed to be $\frac{1}{4}$ of the clock frequency $f_c$ and can be varied by varying $f_c$ [$=10$ MHz in Fig. 10(a)]. Filters of this type are not particularly sensitive to charge transfer loss. In this example, a loss per stage ($\epsilon$) of $10^{-3}$ reduces the minimum out-of-band rejection by less than 0.5 dB.

Filters of this type are potentially useful for a number of reasons. 1) The frequency of the passband of such

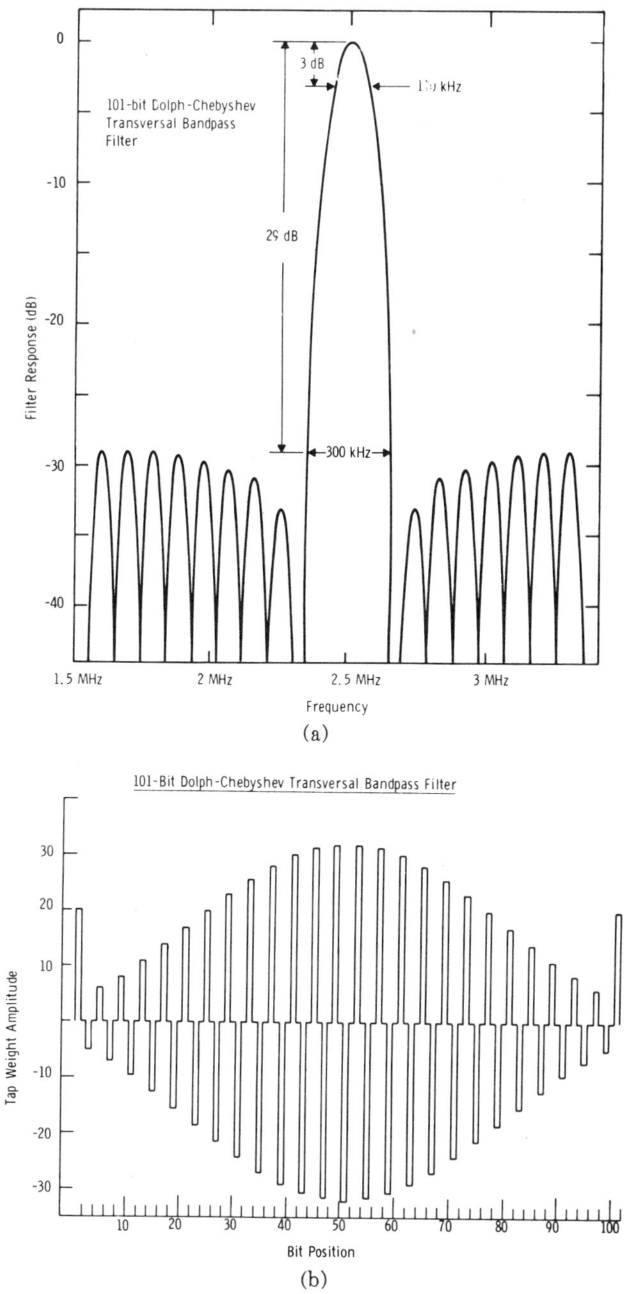


Fig. 10. (a) Frequency characteristic achievable using a 101-stage CCD filter clocked at 10 MHz. (b) Impulse response that gives this frequency characteristic. (The weighting coefficients are unnormalized.)

a filter can be tuned as described above. 2) The frequency characteristic of such a filter is extremely versatile. For example, the phase of the frequency characteristic can be specified in addition to the amplitude, and filters having linear phase across the passband can be constructed simply by making $h_k = h_{M-k+1}$. 3) CTD filters are potentially very-low-noise devices, and it may be possible to utilize them at low signal levels.

A transversal bandpass filter of the type described above is conceptually different from a recursive bandpass filter, which also can be effectively implemented using CTD's [6], [14]. The latter has an impulse response of infinite duration, and therefore filters can be designed having simultaneously a narrow passband and good out-of-band rejection. They are particularly useful in realizing high $Q$ filters, and out-of-band rejection is not limited by weighting coefficient error, as it is in transversal filters. On the other hand, a general frequency characteristic is not easily realizable, and filters of this type are not readily integrated because they require amplifiers having precisely determined gain.

Another potentially important application for CTD transversal filters is in performing Hilbert transforms for use, for example, in single-sideband modulation. Here the impulse response of the filter is determined by the following weighting coefficients (unnormalized):

$$h_k = \frac{1}{k - \dfrac{(M+1)}{2}}, \qquad k = 1, M; \quad M \text{ even.} \tag{15}$$

The output of the filter is

$$v_{\text{out}}(nT_c) = \sum_k v_{\text{in}}[(n - k + 1) + T_c]\left(k - \frac{M+1}{2}\right)^{-1} \tag{16}$$

which approximates the integral

$$v_{\text{out}}(t) = \int_0^{T_d} v_{\text{in}}(t - \tau)\left(\tau - \frac{T_d}{2}\right)^{-1} d\tau. \tag{17}$$

The ideal Hilbert transform is given in the time domain by

$$v_{HT}(t) = \frac{1}{\pi}\int_{-\infty}^{\infty} v(t - \tau)\,\frac{1}{\tau}\,d\tau \tag{18}$$

and differs from the CTD approximation in several ways. For one thing, (16) gives a signal that is the Hilbert transform of the input delayed by $T_d/2$. This is a necessary result of causality, and it requires that other signals that are to be processed together with the transformed signal must be delayed by a similar amount. In addition to being delayed, the CTD Hilbert transform is inexact because of two limitations. 1) The impulse response is not infinite in time duration, as is required by (18). This truncation introduces error, which is most severe when $v_{\text{in}}$ has frequency on the order of or less than $1/T_d$. 2) The integral is approximated by a summation that limits the frequency of $v_{\text{in}}$ to be less than $1/2T_c$.

The calculated spectral response of a 100-stage CTD Hilbert transformer is given in Fig. 11, ignoring the associated time delay. The real part is zero because of the symmetry of the impulse response about $t = T_d/2$. The imaginary part shows deviations from the ideal at low frequency, as expected.

## V. Conclusions

This paper has explored the potential of charge-transfer devices as transversal, sampled data filters. The mathematical description of such filters and their potential applications in signal processing have been studied extensively in the literature, and this paper has

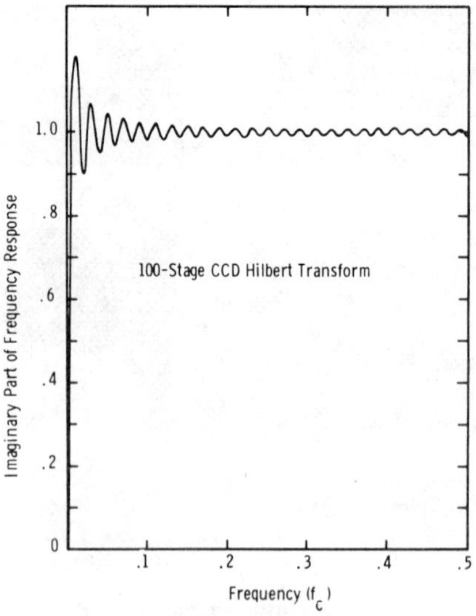


Fig. 11. Calculated response from a 100-stage CCD Hilbert transformer.

discussed the advantages and difficulties of implementing such a filter using CTD's.

Both CCD's and BBD's can be used for transversal filtering, and the sampling, weighting, and summing can be performed without adversely affecting charge transfer. Two techniques for performing sampling, weighting, and summing have been described: the electrode weighting method, for use primarily with CCD's, and the gate tapping method, for use primarily with BBD's.

CTD matched filters have been tested in spread spectrum receivers over a wide temperature range (−60°C to +80°C) and operate as predicted. In communication systems utilizing signals that are too long to be processed using SWD's ($T_d > 20\ \mu s$), CTD's are the only alternative to a digital computer. When CTD's can be used, their advantages in cost, power, size, and weight are overwhelming.

The principle advantages of CTD transversal filters in spectral filtering are tunability and flexibility in selecting the spectral characteristic. Weighting coefficient error and finite time duration of the impulse response make it difficult to achieve high $Q$ filters having high out-of-band rejection.

CTD filters have many other unique linear signal processing capabilities, of which the Hilbert transform is an example. Fully utilizing the wide range of these capabilities is a challenge to device designers and to system engineers.

## Acknowledgment

The authors are indebted to Dr. J. Holmes and Dr. A. McBride of Texas Instruments, Inc., Dallas, for consultation on matched filters for spread spectrum receivers, and to Dr. E. Hafner of the U. S. Army Electronics Command for pointing out the potential of CTD bandpass filters. They are also grateful to L. Hite, D. Splawn, and D. Awtrey for assistance in fabricating and testing the devices.

## References

[1] W. S. Boyle and G. E. Smith, "Charge coupled semiconductor devices," *Bell. Syst. Tech. J.*, vol. 49, pp. 587–593, Apr. 1970.
[2] G. F. Amelio, M. F. Tompsett, and G. E. Smith, "Experimental verification of the charge coupled device concept," *Bell Syst. Tech. J.*, vol. 49, pp. 593–600, Apr. 1970.
[3] For a recent review of CCD's, see M. F. Tompsett, "Charge transfer devices," *J. Vac. Sci. Technol.*, vol. 9, pp. 1166–1181, July/Aug. 1972.
[4] F. L. J. Sangster, "Integrated MOS and bipolar analog delay lines using bucket-brigade capacitor storage," in *1970 IEEE Solid-State Circuits Conf., Dig. Tech. Papers*, pp. 74–75, 185.
[5] For a recent review of BBD's, see L. Boonstra and F. L. J. Sangster, "Progress on bucket-brigade charge-transfer devices," in *1972 IEEE Solid-State Circuits Conf., Dig. Tech. Papers*, pp. 140–141, 228.
[6] W. J. Butler, C. M. Puckette, M. B. Barron, and B. Kurz, "Analog operating characteristics of bucket-brigade delay lines," in *1972 IEEE Solid-State Circuits Conf., Dig. Tech. Papers*, pp. 138–139, 226–227.
[7] C. N. Berglund, "Analog performance limitations of charge-transfer dynamic shift registers," *IEEE J. Solid-State Circuits*, vol. SC-6, pp. 391–394, Dec. 1971.
[8] W. J. Butler, M. B. Barron, and C. M. Puckette, "Practical considerations for analog operation of bucket-brigade circuits," this issue, pp. 157–168.
[9] G. L. Turin, "An introduction to matched filters," *IRE Trans. Inform. Theory*, vol. IT-6, pp. 311–329, June 1960.
[10] C. S. Hartmann, D. T. Bell, and R. C. Rosenfeld, "Impulse model design of acoustic surface-wave filters," *IEEE Trans. Microwave Theory Tech.* (Invited Paper), vol. MTT-21, pp. 162–175, Apr. 1973.
[11] F. L. J. Sangster," The bucket-brigade delay line, A shift register for analog signals," *Philips Tech. Rev.*, vol. 31, pp. 92–110, 1970.
[12] ——, "MOS integrated bucket-brigade transversal filters," presented at Eurocon 71, Lausanne, Switzerland, Oct. 18–22, 1971.
[13] B. Gold and C. M. Rader, *Digital Processing of Signals*. New York: McGraw-Hill, 1969.
[14] D. A. Smith, C. M. Puckette, and W. J. Butler, "Active bandpass filtering with bucket-brigade delay lines," *IEEE J. Solid-State Circuits*, vol. SC-7, pp. 421–425, Oct. 1972.
[15] D. R. Collins, W. H. Bailey, W. M. Gosney, and D. D. Buss, "Charge-coupled-device analogue matched filters," *Electron. Lett.*, vol. 8, pp. 328–329, June 29, 1972.
[16] ——, "Evaluation of the convolution integral using charge coupled devices," presented at the Device Res. Conf., Edmonton, Alta., Canada, June 21–23, 1972.
[17] D. D. Buss, W. H. Bailey, and D. R. Collins, "Matched filtering using tapped bucket-brigade delay lines," *Electron. Lett.*, vol. 8, pp. 106–107, Feb. 24, 1972.
[18] ——, "Bucket-brigade analog matched filters," in *1972 IEEE Solid-State Circuits Conf., Dig. Tech. Papers*, pp. 250–251.
[19] D. D. Buss, C. R. Reeves, W. H. Bailey, and D. R. Collins, "Charge transfer devices in frequency filtering," in *Proc. 26th Ann. Frequency Control Symp.*, June 6–8, 1972.
[20] R. H. Barker, "Group synchronizing of binary digital systems," in *Communication Theory*, W. Jackson, Ed. London: Butterworths, 1953, pp. 273–287.

# Bibliography

This bibliography is arranged by subject, although many of the papers referenced would fit very well into more than one category. Where this is true, the researcher is referred to the alternative section or category. Many of the papers listed are not specifically written with spread spectrum systems in mind, but are of interest in either designing or employing such systems. The following subject categories are used.



## *1. Antijamming (Interference Rejection)*


Aein, J. M. and Turner, R. D. "Effect of co-channel interference on CPSK carriers," *IEEE Trans. Commun. Technol.*, June 1966.

Bohrer, S. A. "Examples of frequency hopping performance analysis," Magnavox Res. Labs., Tech. Memo. MX-TM-6755-3006-66, Dec. 1966.

Cahn, C. R. "A note on signal-to-noise ratio in band-pass limiters," *IRE Trans. Inform. Theory*, Jan. 1961.

——. "Increasing frequency hopping rate of digital synthesizers," Magnavox Res. Labs., Rep. STN-14, Dec. 1964.

——. "Data coding to reduce vulverability to pulse jamming," Magnavox Res. Labs., Rep. STN-13, Nov. 1964.

——. "Comparison of frequency hopping and PN for AJ data transmission," Magnavox Res. Labs., Rep. STN-15, Dec. 1964.

Corneretto, A. "Spread spectrum communication system uses modified PPM," *Electron. Des.*, vol. 21, June 1961.

Costas, J. P. "Poisson, Shannon, and the radio amateur," *Proc. IRE* Dec. 1959.

Friedman, H. J. "Jamming susceptibility," *IEEE Trans. Aerosp. Electron. Sys.*, July 1968.

Gilmore, K. "The secret keepers," *Popular Electron.*, Aug. 1962.

Goodman, L. M., and Russell, S. B. "The TATS master—A net controller for tactical satellite communications." M.I.T. Lincoln Lab.

Houston, S. W. "Tone and noise jamming performance of spread spectrum *M*-ary FSK and 2, 4-ary DPSK waveform," *NAECON, '75.*

Jacobs, I. "The effects of video clipping on the performance of an active satellite PSK communication system," *IEEE Trans. Commun. Technol.*, June 1965.

Kadar, I., and Schreiber, H. H. "Performance of spread spectrum systems in a multipath environment," *WESCON '70 Rec.*

Levine, S. L. "Anti-jam communications systems," ASTIA Doc. AD445897, Apr. 1964.

Mason, J. F. "Air Force plans integrated avionics network," *Electron. Des.*, vol. 15, Aug. 1968.

Mattis, T. J. "Tactical satellite communications requirements," *Signal*, Sept. 1969.

Miadich, A. J. "On-board versus ground A. J. processing," TRW Systems Group., Corresp. 7323-2-257, June 1968.

Morchin, W. C. "Radar range in a jamming environment," *Microwave J.*, June 1968.

Pfanstiehl, A. "Intelligent noise," *Analog Sci. Fiction*, (circa) 1961.

Schmidt, H. J., and McAdam, P. L. "Anti-jam performance of spread spectrum coded systems," *NAECON, '75.*

Sevy, J. L. "The effect of limiting a biphase or quadriphase signal plus interference," *IEEE Trans. Aerosp. Electron. Syst.*, May 1969.

Sullivan, D. P. "Future trends in military communications satellite repeaters," TRW Systems Group, 1968.

Thorensen, R. "On the theory of jam-resistant communication systems, Magnavox Res. Labs., Rep. R-502, Apr. 1962.

Viterbi, A. J. "Maximum problems in coding for jammed channels," Magnavox Res. Labs., Rep. STM-27, June 1966.

——. "Bandspreading combats multipath and RFI in tactical satellite net," *Commun. Des. Dig.*, Dec. 1969.


## *2. Applications of Spread Spectrum Methods*


Allain, L. R. "First steps to radar-waveform design," *Microwaves*, Dec. 1965.

Allen, W. B., and Westerfield, E. C. "Digital compressed time correlators and matched filters for active sonar," *J. Acoust. Soc. Amer.*, Jan. 1964.

Anderson, G. C., and Perry, M. A. "A calibrated real-time correlator/averager/probability analyzer," *Hewlett-Packard J.*, Nov. 1969.

Barrow, B. B., Abraham, L. G., Jr., Stein, S., and Bitzer, D. "Tropospheric-scatter progagation tests using a rake receiver," presented at the IEEE Commun. Conv., June 7, 1965.

Bitzer, D. R., Chesler, D. A., Ivers, R., and Stein, S. "A rake system for tropospheric scatter," *IEEE Trans. Commun. Technol.*, Aug. 1966.

Blasbalg, H., Freeman, D., and Keeler, R. "Random access communications using frequency shifted PN (pseudo-noise) signals," IBM Corp.

Blasbalg, H., Najjar, H., D'Antonio, R., and Haddad, R. "Air–

ground, ground-air communications using pseudo-noise through a satellite," *IEEE Trans. Aerosp. Electron. Syst.*, Sept. 1968.

Brandon, W. T., Camera, A. G., and Wilson, Q. C. "A new approach to tactical aircraft-satellite communications," Tech. Rep. ESD-TR-68-296, Mitre Corp., 1968.

Chesler, D. "Performance of a multiple access RADA system," *IEEE Trans. Commun. Technol.*, Aug. 1966.

Cook, C. E. "Pulse compression—Key to more efficient radar transmission," *Proc. IRE*, Mar. 1960.

Corneretto, A. "Better radars designed using pulse compression," *Electron. Des.*, vol. 30, Aug. 1963.

Cushman, R. H. "Make the most of noise: Correlate it," *EDM*, Mar. 1, Apr. 15, 1971.

Crush, J. F., and Grossman, B. C. "Applications of spread spectrum technology to a low cost aircraft traffic control system," *Proc. Symp. Spread Spectrum Commun.*, Mar. 1973.

Cuccia, C. L. "Communication by satellite: A status report," *Microwave Syst. News*, Apr./May 1974.

Dayton, D. S. "Coming to grips with multipath ghosts," *Electronics*, vol. 27, Nov. 1967.

Diamond, P. M. "Satellite systems for integrated communications, navigation, and identification," Aerospace Corp., AF Rep. SAMSO-TR-70-160, 1970.

Dixon, R. C. "A spread spectrum ranging technique for aerospace vehicles," presented at SWIEEECO, Apr. 1968.

——. "Manipulating digital patterns with a new binary sequency generator," *Hewlett-Packard J.*, Apr. 1971.

Donn E. S. "Measuring digital error rate with pseudorandom signals," *Telecommunications*, Nov. 1971.

Drouilhet, P. R., Jr., and Bernstein, S. L. "TATS—A bandspread modulation-demodulation system for multiple access tactical satellite communication," *EASCON '69 Rec.*

Golomb, S. W., *et al. Digital Communications with Space Applications.* Englewood Cliffs, N.J.: Prentice-Hall, 1964

Hoff, L. E. "Design consideration of spread spectrm communication systems for the HF band," *Proc. Symp. Spread Spectrum. Commun.*, Mar. 1973.

Huang, R. Y., and Hooten, P. "Communication satellite processing repeaters," *Proc. IEEE*, Feb. 1971.

Hultberg, R. M., Jean, F. H., and Jones, M. C. "Time division access for military communications satellites," *IEEE Trans. Aerosp. Electron. Syst.*, Dec. 1965.

Judge, W. J. "Multiplexing using quasiorthogonal functions," presented at the AIEE Winter General Meeting, Jan. 1962.

Klauder, J. R., Price, A. C., Darlington, S., and Albersheim, W. J. "The theory and design of chirp radars," *Bell Syst. Tech. J.*, July 1960.

Price, R., and Green, P. E., Jr. "A communication technique for multipath channels," *Proc. IRE*, Mar. 1958.

Price, R. "Wideband analog transmission through multipath by means of a pseudo-noise carrier," presented at the URSI Spring Meeting, Apr. 30, 1962.

Rex, R. L., and Roberts, G. T. "Correlation, signal averaging, and probability analysis," *Hewlett-Packard J.*, Nov. 1969.

Roberts, L. G. "Picture coding using pseudo-random noise," *IRE Trans. Inform. Theory*, Feb. 1962.

Shepherd, S. G., and Seman, A. E. "Design with integrated circuits, pt. 2," *Electron. Des.*, July 19, 1965.

Springett, J. C. "Pseudo-random coding for bit and word synchronization of PSK data transmission systems," Jet Propulsion Labs.

Spoonemore, W. "UHF propagation experiment using a pseudonoise MODEM," Air Force Avionics Lab., Rep. TOD 0510, Proj. 7662-04, Jan. 1972.

Talamini, A. J., Jr., and Farnett, E. C. "New target for radar: Sharper vision with optics," *Electronics*, Dec. 27, 1965.

Ward, R. B. "Digital communications on a pseudo-noise tracking link using sequence inversion modulation," *IEEE Trans. Commun. Tech.*, Feb. 1967.

Ward, R. B., and Strubel, F. L. "Remote clock synchronization experiment progress 1968," LMSC/A946603 Lockheed MASC, Dec. 1968.

Wester, W. J., and Carter, H. G. "Spacecraft sequence generator utilizes integrated circuitry." *EDN*, Dec. 1964.

——. "Model 3721A correlator," Hewlett-Packard, Aug. 1969.

——. "Unified-carrier link proposed for lunar mission," *Electron. Des.*, Sept. 27, 1963.

——. "Range rider pseudo-noise transmission test sets," Int. Data Sciences, Data Sheets 1000, 1100, Sept. 1970.

——. "PN carrier modem brings privacy to commercial mobile radio networks," *Commun. Des. Dig.*, Jan–Feb. 1971.

——. "New methods for continuous, in service monitoring of microwave systems," Int. Microwave Corp., Cos Cob, Conn.

——. "System 5000/5100 digital communication test set," Tau-Tron, Inc., June 1971.

——. MX230a voice modem," Magnavox Res. Labs., Rep. R-2081A.

### *3. Coding*

Anderson, D. R. "A new class of cyclic codes," *SIAM J. Appl. Math.*, vol. 16, no. 1, 1968.

Anderson D. R. "Periodic and partial correlation properties of sequences," TRW Systems Group, Rep. I.C. 7353. 1-01, July 1969.

Baumert, L., Easterling, M., Golomb, S. W., and Viterbi, A. "Coding theory and its applications to communications systems," Jet Propulsion Labs., Rep. 32–67, Mar. 1961.

Birdsall, T. G., and Ristenbatt, M. P. "Introduction to linear shift-register generated sequences," Univ. Michigan Res. Inst., Tech. Rep. 90, Oct. 1958.

Blizard, R. B. "Quantizing for correlation decoding," *IEEE Trans. Commun. Technol.*, Aug. 1967.

Bluestein, L. J. "Interleaving of pseudo-random sequences for synchronization," *IEEE Trans. Aerosp. Electron. Syst.*, July 1968.

Braasch, R. H. "The distribution of (*n-m*) terms for maximal length linear pseudo-random sequences," *IEEE Trans. Inform. Theory*, July 1968.

Curry, R. C. "A method of obtaining all phases of a pseudo-random Sequence," *Proc. NAECON '67.*

De Vito, P. A., Carr, P. H., Kearns, W. J., and Silva, J. H. "Encoding and decoding with elastic surface waves at 10 Megabits per second," *Proc. IEEE*, Oct. 1971.

Dixon, R. C. "100 MHz PN code generator," TRW Systems Group, Rep. IOC 7325.3-19, July 1968.

Forney, G. D., Jr. "Coding and its application in space communications," *IEEE Spectrum*, June 1970.

Freymodsson, J. B. "A note on the run-length distribution of ones and zeros in maximal-linear shift register sequences," unpublished memo., Nov., 6, 1963.

Gold, R. "Study of correlation properties of binary sequences" Magnavox Res. Labs., Rep AFAL TR-66-234, Aug. 1966.

——. "Characteristic linear sequences and their coset functions," *J. SIAM Appl. Math.*, vol. 14, Sept. 1966.

——. "Optimal binary sequences for spread spectrum multiplexing," *IEEE Trans. Inform. Theory.*, Oct. 1967.

Golomb, S. W. "Sequences with randomness properties," Glenn L. Martin Co., June 1955.

——. *Shift Register Sequences.* San Francisco, Calif.: Holden-Day, 1967.

Gupta, S. C., and Painter, J. H. "Correlation analyses of linearly processed pseudo-random sequences," *IEEE Trans. Commun. Technol.*, Dec. 1966.

Haberle, H. "Modulation, synchronization and coding," presented at the Int. Conf. Digital Satellite Commun., London, Nov. 1969.

Hansen, J. C. "Modern algebra for coding," *Electro-Technol.*, Apr. 1965.

Horton, W. P. "Shift counters," Computer Control Corp.

Jacobs, I. M. "Practical applications of coding," *IEEE Trans. Inform. Theory*, May 1974.

Kahn, D. "Modern cryptology," *Sci. Amer.*, July 1966.

Lee, J., and Smith, D. R. "Families of shift-register sequences with impulsive correlation properties," *IEEE Trans. Inform. Theory*, Mar. 1974.

Lindholm, J. H. "An analysis of the pseudo-randomness properties of subsequences of long *m*-sequenes," *IEEE Trans. Inform. Theory*, July 1968.

Lindsey, W. C. "Coded noncoherent communications," *IEEE Trans. Space Electron. Telem.*, Mar. 1965.

O'Clock, G. D., Jr., Grasse, G. L., and Gandolfo, D. A. "Switchable acoustic surface wave sequence generator," *Proc. IEEE*, Oct. 1972.

Painter, J. H. "Designing pseudo-random coded ranging systems," *IEEE Trans. Aerosp. Electron. Syst.*, Jan. 1967.

Peterson, W. W. *Error Correcting Codes.* New York: Wiley.

Shannon, C. E. "Communication theory of secrecy systems," *Bell Syst. Tech. J.*, Vol. 28, p. 656, 1949.

Solomon, G. "Optimal frequency hopping sequences for multiple access," *Proc. Symp. Spread Spectrum Commun.*, Mar. 1973.

Swick, D. A. "Wideband ambiguity function of psuedo-random sequences: An open problem." *IEEE Trans. Inform. Theory*, July 1968.

Tausworthe, R. C. "Random numbers generated by linear recurrence modulo-two," *Math. Comput.*, vol. 19, Apr. 1965.

Titsworth, R. C. "Optimal ranging codes," *IEEE Trans. Space Electron. Telem.*, Mar. 1963.

Toerper, K. E. "Biphase Barker-coded data transmission," *IEEE Trans. Aerosp. Electron. Syst.*, Mar. 1968.

Viterbi, A. J. "On coded phase-coherent communications," Jet Propulsion Lab., Rep. 32-25, Aug. 1960.

Wainberg, S., and Wolf, J. K. "Subsequences of pseudo-random sequences," *IEEE Trans. Commun. Technol.*, Oct. 1970.

Watson, E. J. "Primitive polynomials (mod 2)," *Math. Comput.*, 1962.

White, R. C., Jr. "Experiments with digital computer simulative of pseudo-random noise generators," *IEEE Trans. Electron. Comput.*, June 1967.

Wolf, J. K. "On the application of some digital sequences to communication," *IEEE Trans. Commun. Syst.*, Dec. 1963.

Zierler, N. "Several binary-sequence generators," M.I.T. Lincoln Labs., Tech. Rep. 95, Sept. 1955.

——, "Linear recurring sequences," *J. Soc. Ind. Appl. Math.*, vol. 7, 1959.


## 4. Chirp (Pulse-FM)


Armstrong, D. B. "Solid state surface acoustic delay lines," Litton Industries, Tech. Note TN70-1, Jan. 30, 1970.

Berni, A. J., and Gregg, W. D. "On the utility of chirp modulation for digital signaling," *IEEE Trans. Commun.*, July 73.

Bert, A. G., Epsztein, B., and Kantrowicz, G. "Signal processing by electronbeam interaction with piezoelectric surface waves," *IEEE Trans. Microwave Technol.*, Apr. 1973.

Bell, D. T. Jr., Holmes, J. D., and Ridings, R. V. "Application of acoustic surface-wave technology to spread spectrum communications," *IEEE Trans. Microwave Theory Tech.*, Apr. 1973.

Burnsweig, J., and Wooldridge, J. "Ranging and data transmission using digital encoded FM-'Chirp' surface acoustic wave filters," *IEEE Trans. Microwave Theory Tech.*, Apr. 1973.

Collins, J. H., and Hagon, P. J. "Applying surface wave acoustics," *Electronics*, Nov. 10, 1969.

Cook, C. E. "Pulse compression—Key to more efficient radar transmission," *Proc. IRE*, Mar. 1960.

Coquin, G. A., and Tsu, R. "Theory and performance of perpendicular diffraction delay lines," *Proc. IEEE*, June 1965.

de Atley, E. "Surface acoustic waves offer cheap signal processing," *Electron. Des.*, Dec. 6, 1970.

Coquin, G. A., and Tsu, R. "Theory and performance of perpendicular diffraction delay lines," *Proc. IEEE*, June 1965.

Eveleth, J. H. "A Survey of ultrasonic delay lines operating below 100 Mc/s," *Proc. IEEE*, Oct. 1965.

——. "Dispersive and nondispersive ultrasonic delay lines," Anderson Labs., tech. note, undated.

Franklin, P. "Ultrasonics, microwaves join forces," *Microwaves*, Nov. 1968.

——. "Echo processor offers 12-s delay with 50-dB gain," *Microwaves*, Oct. 1969.

Gerard, H. M., Smith, W. R., Jones, W. R., and Harrington, J. B. "The design and applications of highly dispersive acoustic surface-wave filters," *IEEE Trans. Microwave Theory Tech.*, Apr. 1973.

Grant, P. M., Collins, J. H., Darby, B. J., and Morgan, D. P. "Potential applications of acoustic matched filters to air-traffic control systems," *IEEE Trans. Microwave Theory Tech.*, Apr. 1973.

Grasse, C. L., and Gandolfo, D. A. "400 MHz acoustic surface-wave pulse expansion and compression filter," *IEEE Trans. Microwave Theory Tech.*, June 1971.

Haavind, R. C. "Praetersonics: Microwaves of the future?" *Electron. Des.*, July 18, 1968.

Hagon, P. J., Micheletti, F. B., Seymour, R. N., and Wrigley, C. Y. "A programmable surface acoustic wave matched filter for phase-coded spread spectrum waveforms," *IEEE Trans. Microwave Theory Tech.*, Apr. 1973.

Kino, G. S., Ludvik, S., Shaw, H. J., Shreve, W. R., White, J. M., and Winslow, D. K. "Signal processing by parametric interactions in delay-line devices," *IEEE Trans. Microwave Theory Tech.*, Apr. 1973.

Klauder, J. R., Price, A. C., Darlington, S., and Albersheim, W. J. "The theory and design of chirp radars," *Bell Syst. Tech. J.*, July 1960.

Lean, E. G., and Broers, A. N. "Microwave acoustic delay lines," *Microwave J.*, Mar. 1970.

Martin, T. A. "The IMCON pulse compression filter and its applications," *IEEE Trans. Microwave Theory Tech.*, Apr. 1973.

Millett, R. E. "A matched-filter pulse-compression system using a nonlinear FM waveform," *IEEE Trans. Aerosp. Electron. Syst.*, Jan. 1970.

Morgan, D. P., and Sutherland, J. G. "Generation of pseudonoise sequences using surface acoustic waves," *IEEE Trans. Microwave Theory Tech.*, Apr. 1973.

Newhouse, P. D. "Simplify EMC design," *Microwaves*, May 1970.

Olson, F. A. "Today's microwave acoustic (bulk wave) delay lines," *Microwave J.*, Mar. 1970.

Riezerman, M. J. "Lazer-acoustic line reverses time functions," *Electron. Des.*, June 7, 1969.


## 5. Digital Transmission


Birch, J. N. "Design considerations for PCM and delta mod systems," Magnavox Res. Labs., ASAO Rep. TP 68-2174, 1968.

Cahn, C. R. "Performance of digital phase-modulation communication systems," *IRE Trans. Commun. Syst.*, May 1959.

——. "Application of Wagner code to digital data transmission system," Magnavox Res. Labs., Rep. STN-24, Dec. 1965.

——. "On transmitting digital data over an FM system," Magnavox Res. Labs., Rep. MX-TM-3091-70, Nov. 1970.

Creveling, C. J. "Comparison of the performance of PCM and PFM telemetry systems," NASA Goddard Space Flight Center, 1965.

Landau, H. J. "Sampling, data transmission, and the Nyquist rate," *Proc. IEEE*, Oct. 1967.

Lenden, A. "Correlative digital communication techniques," *IEEE Trans. Commun. Technol.*, Dec. 1964.

Lugannani, R. "Intersymbol interference and probability of error in digital systems," *IEEE Trans. Inform. Theory*, Nov. 1969.

Oliver, B. M., Pierce, J. R., and Shannon, C. E. "The philosophy of PCM," *Proc. IRE*, Nov. 1948.

Salz, J., and Koll, V. G. "Experimental digital multilevel FM modem," *IEEE Trans. Commun. Technol.*, June 1966.

Sanders, R. W. "Communication efficiency comparison of several communication systems," *Proc. IRE*, Apr. 1960.

Tjhung, T. J. "Band occupancy of digital FM signals," *IEEE Trans. Commun. Technol.*, Dec. 1964.

Wall, M. E., and Kuhn, T. G. "Wideband data transmission: Which medium is best?" *Microwaves*, Apr. 1966.

Whelan, J. W. "Analog-FM versus Digital-PSK transmission," *IEEE Trans. Commun. Technol.*, June 1966.

Wintz, P. A., and Totty, R. E. "Principles of digital communications," *Electro-Technol.*, Feb. 1967.

——. "Hybrid PCM improves noise performance when bandwidth is limited," *Commun. Des. Dig.*, Nov. 1969.

——. "Frame sync study points up optimum parameters for PCM transmission," *Commun. Des. Dig.*, Feb. 1970.


## 6. Direct Sequence


Cahn, C. R. "Spectrum reduction of biphase modulated (2-PSK) carrier," Magnavox Res. Labs., Rep. MX-TM-3103-71, 1971.

Gilchreist, C. E. "Pseudonoise system lock-in," Jet Propulsion Labs., Res. Summary 36-9.

Nilsen, P. W. "PN receiver carrier and code tracking performance," Magnavox Res. Labs., Rep. MX-TM-8-674-3043-68, 1968.

Sage, G. F. "Serial synchronization of pseudonoise systems," *IEEE Trans. Commun. Technol.*, Dec. 1964.

Ward, R. B. "Acquisition of pseudonoise signals by sequential estimation," *IEEE Trans. Commun. Technol.*, Dec. 1965.

Zegers, L. E. "Common bandwidth transmission of information signals and pseudonoise synchronization waveforms," *IEEE Trans. Commun. Technol.*, Dec. 1968.


Also see bibliography sections 1, 2, 3, and 5.

## 7. Frequency Hopping


Abramson, N. "Bandwidth and spectra of phase- and frequency-modulated waves," *IEEE Trans. Commun. Syst.*, Dec. 1963.

Cahn, C. R. "Noncoherent frequency hop sync mode performance," Magnavox Res. Labs., Rep. STN-12, Mar. 1964.

Cohen, S. A. "Interference effects of pseudo-random frequency hopping signals," *IEEE Trans. Aerosp. Electron. Syst.*, Mar. 1971.

George, O. H. "Performance of noncoherent *M*-ary FSK systems with diversity under the influence of Rician fading," presented at the IEEE Int. Conf. Commun., June 1968.
Huth, G. K. "Detailed frequency-hopper analysis," Magnavox Res. Labs., Rep. STN-29, Aug. 1966.
Kaplan, A. "Detection and analysis of frequency hopping radar signals," Sylvania Electron. Syst. W.D.L., Montain View, Calif.
Malm, R. and Schreder, K. "Fast frequency hopping techniques," *Proc. Symp. Spread Spectrum Commun.*, Mar. 1973.
Nossen, E. J. "Fast frequency hopping synthesizer," *Proc. Symp. Spread Spectrum Commun.*, Mar. 1973.
Schreiber, H. H. "Self-noise of frequency hopping signals," *IEEE Trans. Commun. Technol.* Oct. 1969.
Splitt, F. G. "Combined frequency and time-shift keyed transmission systems," *IEEE Trans. Commun. Syst.*, Dec. 1963.
Thomas, C. M. "A matched filter concept for frequency hopping synchronization," TRW Systems Group, Rep. IOC 7353.6-05.
Also see bibliography sections 1, 2, 3, 5, and 8.

### *8. Frequency Synthesis*

Barnum, J. L. "A multioctave microwave synthesizer," *Microwave J.*, Oct. 1970.
Burnell, R. W. "Phase-lock frequency synthesizer," TRW Systems Group, Rep. IOC 7325.2-99, July 1968.
Blachowicz, L. F. "Dial any channel to 500 MHz," *Electronics*, May 2, 1966.
Davis, M. G., Jr. "Phase-lock frequency synthesizer equivalent to Lincoln Labs' frequency synthesizer," TRW Systems Group, Rep. IOC 7325-18, Apr. 22, 1968.
Delaune, J. "MTTL and MECL avionics digital frequency synthesizers," Motorola, Rep. AN-532, July 1970.
Hekemian, N. C. "Digital frequency synthesizers," *Frequency*, July/Aug. 1967.
Illingworth, L. "Digital methods synthesize frequency," *Electron. Des.*, May 23, 1968.
Kahn, R. S. "Frequency synthesizer survey," Magnavox Res. Labs., Tech. Memo. MX-TM-8-672-3009-67, Feb. 1967.
Koeper, B. "Shift frequency automatically without transients," *EDN*, Nov. 11, 1968.
Lohrmann, D. R. and Sills, A. R. "Cut synthesizer current consumption," *Electron. Des.*, Dec. 5, 1968.
Maag, R. A. "Spurious output and acquisition time of an indirect frequency synthesizer," TRW Systems Group, Rep. IOC 7352.1-20, Feb. 1969.
Noordanus, J. "Frequency synthesizers—A survey of techniques," *IEEE Trans. Commun. Technol.*, Apr. 1969.
Renshler, E. and Welling B. "An integrated circuit phase-locked loop digital frequency synthesizer," Motorola, Rep. AN-463, Mar. 1963.
Stone, R. R., Jr., and Hastings, H. F. "A novel approach to frequency synthesis," *Frequency*, Sept./Oct. 1963.
——. "Modern methods of frequency synthesis," Antekna Tech. Bull. 20-02.
Also see bibliography section 7.

### *9. Information Transmission*

Berger, T. "Optimum PAM compared with information-theoretic bounds," *NEREM '66, Rec.*
Cahn, C. R. "Theoretical comparison of analog and digital modulations for voice," Magnavox Res. Labs., Rep. STN-23, Jan. 1966.
Cohen, W. "Signal-to-noise ratio in modulated systems, pts. 1 and 2," *Electro-Technol.*, Oct. 1965, Jan. 1966.
Develet, J. A. "Coherent FDM/FM telephone communication," *Proc. IEEE*, Sept. 1958.
Diaz, C. C. and Norvell, B. R. "Pulse modulation intelligibility," *Electro/Technol.*, Mar. 1966.
Gardenhire, L. W. "Selecting sample rates," *Instrum. Technol.*, Apr. 1964.
Hupert, J. J. "Frequency-modulation techniques," *Electro-Technol.*, Feb. 1965.
——. "Distortion in angle-modulation networks," *Electro-Technol.*, Sept. 1965.
Jayant, N.S. "Characteristics of a delta modulator," *Proc. IEEE*, Mar. 1971.
Landau, H. J. "Sampling, data acquisition, and the Nyquist rate," *Proc. IEEE*, Oct. 1967
Miller, G. A., and Licklider, J. C. R. "The intelligibility of interrupted speech," *J. Acoust. Soc. Amer.*, Mar. 1950.
Porter, J. A. "Prediction of speech intelligibility over voice communications systems," NASA, Rep. EB-65-R2001, 1965.
Schuchman, L. "Dither signals and their effect on quantization noise," *IEEE Trans. Commun. Technol.*, Dec. 1964.
Walsh, C. P. "Frequency-modulation principles," *Electro-Technol.*, Jan. 1965.
Weiner, D. D. and Leon, B. J. "The quasi-stationary resonse of linear systems to modulated waveforms," *Proc. IEEE*, June 1965.
Young, J. A. "Design parameters associated with multilevel transmission systems," *NEREM '66 Rec.*

### *10. Modulation/Demodulation*

Adashko, J. G. "Design of phase sensitive demodulators," *Electron. Des.*, Apr. 12, 1962.
Baghdady, E. J. "On the noise threshold of conventional FM and PM demodulators," *Proc. IEEE*, Sept. 1963.
Cahn, C. R. "Phase detector characteristic's effect on signal-to-noise ratio, general theory," STL, Rep. 10C, Apr. 1962.
——. "Analysis of correlation system with receiver filter," Magnavox Res. Labs., Rep. STN-20, Sept. 1965.
——. "Error bound for non optimally demodulated channel," Magnavox Res. Labs., addendum to Rep. STN-27, June 1966.
Chandler, J. P. "IC's fill need for low-drift phase-shift keyed detector," *EDN*, Jan. 15, 1969.
Channell, E. "The semiconductor ring modulator," *EDN*, Jan. 1964.
Cooper, P. W. "Correlation functions for the random binary wave," *IEEE Trans. Commun. Syst.*, Dec. 1963.
Costas, J. P. "Synchronous communications," *Proc. IRE*, Dec. 1956.
Datillo, J. A. "Incremental phase modulator," Magnavox Res. Labs., Tech. Rep. MX-TR-8-675-2002, Mar. 1967.
Develet, J. A. Jr. "An analytic approximation of phase-lock receiver threshold," TRW, Systems Group, Rep. 9332.6-2, Apr. 1962.
Eckstrom, J. L. "Coherent matched filter detection of quadratically phase-distorted carrier-band pulses, with application to trans-ionospheric signalling," *IEEE Trans. Space Electron. Telem.*, Mar. 1964.
Frankle, J. "Threshold performance of analog FM demodulators," *RCA Rev.*, Dec. 1964.
Gross, T. A. O. "Increasing the dynamic range of AM detectors," *EEE*, Nov. 1963.
Hess, D. T. "Equivalence of FM threshold extension receivers," *IEEE Trans. Commun. Technol.*, Oct. 1968.
Hirsch, S. R. "Convolution—A graphical interpretation," *EDN*, Feb. 1967.
Judge, W. J. "A passive correlator of arbitrarily large T-W product," Magnavox Res. Labs., Rep. R-502, Apr. 1962.
Katz, E. H., and Schreiber, H. H. "Design of phase discriminators," *Microwaves*, Aug. 1965.
Kivett, J. A., and Bowers, G. F. "A wideband modem for command and control of remote vehicles," *Proc. Symp. Spread Spectrum Commun.* Mar. 1973.
Kurth, C. "Analysis and synthesis of diode modulators," *Frequency*, Jan.-Feb. 1966.
Langenthal, I. M. "Correlation and probability analysis," Signal Analysis Industries Corp., Rep. TB14.
Levine, R. I. "Correlation—Theory and practice," Electron. *Products*, Nov. 1963.
Lowry, R. B. "PSK-FSK spread spectrum modulation/demodulation," *Proc. Symp. Spread Spectrum Commun.*, Mar. 1973.
Mouw, R. B., and Fukuchi, S. M. "Broadband double balanced mixer/modulators," pts. I and II," *Microwave J.*, Mar., May 1969.
Ogar, G. W. "Putting diode modulators to work," *Electron. Ind.*, July 1961.
Polson, J. H. "Wideband digital data link quadriphase demodulator," TRW Systems Group, Rep. 7322.05-202, Dec. 1968.
Schiff, M. L., and Dilley, D. M. "A surface acoustic wave spread spectrum modem," *Proc. Symp. Spread Spectrum Commun.*, Mar. 1973.
Stoll, A. W. "The electronic correlator," *Electron. Ind.*, Aug. 1965.
Stone, M. S. "Analytical considerations for multiphase modulation and demodulation," TRW Systems Group, Rep. 7323.2-245, Apr. 1968.
Stone, R. B., and White, G. M. "Correlation detector detects voice fundamental," *Electronics*, Nov. 22, 1963.
Urbach, W. G. Jr. "Produce fast and clean RF pulses," *Electron. Des.*, Sept. 1966.
Vizkanta, V. Z. "I-Q loop receivers," TRW Systems Group, Rep. IOC 7323.2-289, Sept. 1968.

Voyce, A. M. "Ultimate sensitivity of a detector," *EEE*, Jan. 1963.

### *11. Multiple Access*

Bedrosian, E., Feldman, N., Northrop, G., and Sollfrey W. "Multiple access techniques for communications satellites: I. Survey of the problem," Rand Corp. Rep. RM-4298-NASA, Sept. 1964.
Harman, W. H. "Multiple access and antijam capabilities of direct-sequence quadriphase on a linear channel," TRW Systems Group, Rep. IOC 7323.2-256, June 1968.
Udalov, S. "Pseudo-random pulse position multiplexing for random access," Magnavox Res. Labs., Rep. STN-8, Jan. 1964.
——, "Threshold criterion for virtual carrier multiplexing," Magnavox Res. Labs., Rep. STN-10, Jan. 1964.
Also see bibliography sections 1, 2, 3, 5, 6, and 9.

### *12. Phase Lock*

Davis, M. G., Jr. "On the measurement of phase detector scale factor," TRW Systems Group, Rep. IOC 7325-17, Apr. 1968.
Develet, J. A., Jr. "Threshold criterion for phase-lock demodulation," *Proc IEEE*, Feb. 1963.
Frankle, J. T., and Klapper, J. "Principles of phase lock and frequency feedback," RCA, Oct. 1967.
Frazier, J. P., and Page, J. "Phase-lock loop frequency acquisition study," *IRE Trans. Space Electron. Telem.*, Sept. 1962.
Gruen, W. J. "Theory of AFC synchronization," *Proc. IRE*, Aug. 1953.
Hoffman, L. A. "Receiver design and the phase-lock loop," *IEEE Electron. Space Exploration Lecture Ser.*, Aug. 1963.
Jaffe, R., and Rechtin, E. "Design and performance of phase-lock circuits capable of near-optimum performance over a wide range of input signal and noise levels," *IRE Trans. Inform. Theory*, Mar. 1955.
Janky, J. M. "Nomograms simplify phase-lock-loop analysis," *Microwaves*, Mar. 1970.
Lindsey, W. C., and Simon, M. K. "The effect of loop stress on the performance of phase-coherent communication systems," *IEEE Trans. Commun. Technol.*, Oct. 1970.
Lindsey, W. C., and Tausworthe, R. C. "A bibliography of the theory and application of the phase-lock principle," Jet Propulsion Lab., Tech. Rep. 32-1581.
Lohrmann, D. R. "Designing sampling phaselock loops," *Electron. Des.*, Nov. 8, 1970.
McAleer, H. T. "A new look at the phase-locked oscillator," *IRE Trans.*, June 1959.
Nash, G. "Phase-locked loop design fundamentals," Motorola, Rep. AN-535, Oct. 1970.
Preston, G. W., and Tellier, J. C. "The lock-in performance of an AFC circuit," *Proc. IRE*, Feb. 1953.
Sanneman, R. W., and Rowbotham, J. R. "Unlock characteristics of the optimum type II phase-locked loop," *IEEE Trans. Aerosp. Naval Electron.*, Mar. 1964.
Tausworthe, R. C. "Theory and practical design of phase-locked receivers," Jet Propulsion Lab., Tech. Rep. 32-819, Feb. 1966.
Van Trees, H. L. "Functional techniques for the analysis of the non-linear behavior of phase-locked loops," *Proc. IEEE*, Aug. 1964.
Viterbi, A. J. "Acquisition and tracking behavior of phase-locked loops," Jet Propulsion Lab., Ext. Publ. 673, July 1959.
——. "Phase-locked loop dynamics in the presence of noise by Fokker–Planck techniques," *Proc. IEEE*, Dec. 1963.
Young, W. D. "Receiver lock loop theory and application," STL, Rep. IOC 9331.2-258, Jan. 1962.
——. "Non-linear PLL's flunk test on vulnerability to noise and interference," *Commun. Des. Dig.*, Nov. 1969.

### *13. Ranging*

Horton, B. M. "Noise modulated distance measuring systems," *Proc. IRE*, May 1959.
Richardson, R. J. "Optimum transponder design for pseudonoise-coded ranging systems, weak signals," *IEEE Trans. Aerosp. Electron. Syst.*, Jan. 1972.
Rihaczek, A. W., and Golden, R. M. "Resolution performance of pulse trains with large time-bandwidth products," *IEEE Trans. Aerosp. Electron. Syst.*, July 1971.
Also see bibliography sections 2 and 3.

### *14. RF Effects*

Aein, J. M. "On the output power division in a captured hard-limiting repeater," *IEEE Trans. Commun. Technol.*, June 1966.
Benoit, A. "Signal attenuation due to neutral oxygen and water vapour, rain, and clouds," *Microwave J.*, Nov. 1968.
Blackman, N. M. "The output signal-to-noise ratio of a bandpass limiter," *IEEE Trans. Aerosp. Electron. Syst.*, July 1968.
Bussgang, J. J., and Leiten, M. "Analysis of phase-shift transmission through fading channels," *NEREM '65 Rec.*
Cahn, C. R., and Moore, C. R. "Bandwidth efficiency for digital communication via a hard limiting channel," *ITC Proc.*, vol. 8, 1972.
Cahn, C. R. "Effects of phase and amplitude distortion on PSK signal demodulation," Magnavox Res. Labs., Tech. Memo. MX-TM-3099-71, Mar. 1971.
Davenport, W. B., Jr. "Signal-to-noise ratios in band-pass limiters," *J. Appl. Phys.*, June 1953.
Doyle, W. "Elementary derivation for bandpass limiter *S/N*," *IEEE Trans. Inform. Theory*, Mar. 1962.
Eckstrom, J. L. "Coherent matched filter detection of quadratically phase distorted carrier-band pulses, with application to trans-ionospheric signalling," *IEEE Trans. Space Electron. Telem.*, vol. SET-10, Mar. 1963.
Elliott, R. S. "Pulse waveform degradation due to dispersion in wave-guide," *IRE Trans. Microwave Theory Tech.*, Oct. 1957.
Jacobs, I. "The effects of video clipping on the performance of an active satellite PSK communication system," *IEEE Trans. Commun. Technol.*, June 1965.
Jones, J. J. "Filter distortion and intersymbol interference effects on QPSK," SRS Div., Philco-Ford Corp., *Proc. NAECON '67.*
Karr, P. R. "The effect of phase noise on the performance of biphase communications systems," TRW Systems Group, Rep. 07791-6080-R000, Sept. 1966.
Kirlin, R. L. "Hard-limiter intermodulation with low input signal-to-noise ratio," *IEEE Trans. Commun. Technol.*, Aug. 1967.
Kwan, R. K. "The effects of filtering and limiting a double-binary PSK signal," *IEEE Trans. Aerosp. Electron. Syst.*, July 1969.
Kwon, S. Y., and Simpson, R. S. "Effect of hard limiting on a quadrature PSK signal," *IEEE Trans. Commun.*, July 1973.
Le Fande, R. A. "Effects of phase non-linearities on a phase shift keyed pseudonoise/spread spectrum system," *IEEE Trans. Commun. Technol.*, Oct. 1970.
Shaft, P. D. "Limiting of several signals and its effect on communication system performance," *IEEE Trans. Commun. Technol.*, Dec. 1965.
Staras, H. "The propagation of wideband signals through the atmosphere," *Proc. IRE*, vol. 49, July 1961.
Sunde, E. D. "Pulse transmission by AM, FM, and PM in the presence of phase distortion," *Bell Syst. Tech. J.*, Mar. 1961.
Weidner, M. Y. "Analysis of spread spectrum multiple access systems experiencing linear distortion," TRW Systems Group, Rep. IOC 7323.4-117, May 1968.
——. "Digital transmission study rates filtering effects on spread-spectrum PSK," *Commun. Des. Dig.*, Aug. 1969.

### *15. Synchronization*

Cahn, C. R. "Synchronization scheme with sequential detection," Magnavox Res. Labs. Tech. Memo. MX-TM-3084-70, Oct. 1970.
Carter, C. R., and Haykin, S. S. "A new synchronization technique for TDMA satellite systems," *Proc. Symp. Spread Spectrum Commun.*, Mar. 1973.
Cole, R., Jr. "Synchronization of a frequency-hopped spread spectrum signal," *Proc. Symp. Spread Spectrum Commun.*, Mar. 1973.
De Couvreur, G. A. "Effect of random synchronization errors in PN and PSK systems," *IEEE Trans. Aerosp. Electron. Syst.*, Jan. 1970.
Gagliardi, R. M. "Rapid acquisition signal design in a multiple-access environment," *Proc. Symp. Spread Spectrum Commun.*, Mar. 1973.
——. "A geometrical study of transmitted reference communications systems," *IEEE Trans. Commun. Technol.*, Dec. 1964.
Golomb, S. W., *et al.* "Synchronization" *IEEE Trans. Commun. Syst.*, Dec. 1963.
Kaneko, H. "A statistical analysis of the synchronization of a binary receiver," *IEEE Trans. Commun. Syst.*, Dec. 1963.
LaRosa, R. "Switchable and fixed-code surface wave matched filters," *Proc. Symp. Spread Spectrum Commun.*, Mar. 1973.
Lindsey, W. C. *Synchronization Systems in Communication and Control.* Englewood Cliffs, N.J.: Prentice-Hall, 1972.
Mifflin, R. W., and Wheeler, J. P. "Transmitted reference synchronization system," U.S. Patent 3 641 433, Feb. 8, 1972.
Ramsey, J. L. "Effective acquisition of FH TDMA signals in jamming," *Proc. Symp. Spread Spectrum Commun.*, Mar. 1973.

Sergo, J. R., and Hayes, J. F. "Analysis and simulation of a PN synchronization system," *IEEE Trans. Commun. Technol.*, Oct. 1970.
——. "Coherent system speeds sync acquisition in military TDMA systems," *Commun. Des. Dig.*, Jan. 1970.

### *16. Tracking*

Bruno, F. "Tracking performance and loss of a carrier loop due to the presence of a spoofed spread spectrum signal," *Proc. Symp. Spread Spectrum Commun.*, Mar. 1973.
Freeman, J. J. "The action of dither in a polarity coincidence correlator," *IEEE Trans. Commun.*, June 1974.
Gill, W. J. "A comparison of binary delay-lock tracking-loop implementations," *IEEE Trans. Aerosp. Electron. Syst.*, July 1966.
Hartman, H. P. "Analysis of a dithering loop for PN code tracking," *Proc. Symp. Spread Spectrum Commun.*, Mar. 1973.
Haykim, S. S., and Thorsteinson, C. "A quantized delay-lock discriminator," *Proc. IEEE*, June 1968.
Huff, R. J., and Reinhard, K. L. "A sampled-data delay-lock loop for synchronizing TDMA space communications systems," *EASCON '68 Rec.*
Simon, M. K. "Non linear analysis of an absolute value type of an early-late gate bit synchronizer," *IEEE Trans. Commun. Technol.*, Oct. 1970.
Spilker, J. J., Jr. "Delay-lock tracking of binary signals," *IEEE Trans. Space Electron. Telem.*, Mar. 1963.
Ward, R. B. "Application of delay-lock radar techniques to deep-space tasks," *IEEE Trans. Space Electron. Telem.*, June 1964.

### *17. Miscellaneous*

Burnell, R. W., and Ma, L. N. "Fourier analysis of an imperfect PSK signal," TRW Systems Group, Rep. IOC 7322.14-7, Oct. 1967.
Buss, D. D., Bailey, W. H., and Hite, L. R. "Spread-spectrum communications using charge transfer devices," *Proc. Symp. Spread Spectrum Commun.*, Mar. 1973.
Cahn, C. R. "Performance of digital matched filter correlators with unknown interference," *IEEE Trans. Commun. Technol.*, Dec. 1971.
Cheung, R., Ma, L. N., and Thornhill, A. "Experimental evaluation of a digital correlation detector with a large time-bandwidth product," *NAECON '75.*
Dixon, R. C. *Spread Spectrum Systems.* New York: Wiley, 1976.
——. *"Why Spread Spectrum," IEEE Commun. Soc. Dig.*, July 1975.
Glazer, B. G. "Spread spectrum concepts—A tutorial," *Proc. Symp. Spread Spectrum Commun.*, Mar. 1973.
Gooding, D. J. "Increasing the utility of the digital matched filter," *Proc. Symp. Spread Spectrum Commun.*, Mar. 1973.
Hancock, J. C. *An Introduction to the Principles of Communication Theory.* New York: McGraw-Hill, 1961.
Hatsell, C. P., and Nolte, L. W. "Detectability of burst-like signals," *IEEE Trans. Aerosp. Electron. Syst.*, Mar. 1971.
Klapper, J. "The effect of the integrator-dump circuit on PCM/FM error rates," *IEEE Trans. Commun. Technol.*, June, 1966.
Matthaei, G. L. "Acoustic surface-wave transversal filters," *IEEE Trans. Circuit Theory*, Sept. 1973.
Millett, R. E. "A matched-filter pulse-compression system using a nonlinear FM waveform," *IEEE Trans. Aerosp. Electron. Syst.*, Jan. 1970.
Mohanty, N. C. "Signal design for small correlation," Univ. Southern California, Rep. USCEE 438, Feb. 1973.
Muraka, N. P. "Spread spectrum systems using noise band shift keying," *IEEE Trans. Commun.*, July 1973.
Petrich, M. "On the number of orthogonal signals which can be placed in a WT-product," *J. Soc. Ind. Appl. Math.*, Dec. 1963.
Richardson, R. J. "The signal-suppression threshold of a frequency doubler," *IEEE Trans. Commun. Technol.*, Dec. 1964.
Ristenbatt, M. P. "Estimating effectiveness of covert communications," *Proc. Symp. Spread Spectrum Commun.*, Mar. 1973.
Sierra, H. M. "The matched filter concept," *Electro-Technol.*, Aug. 1964.
Solat, N. "Comparison of power spectra," Space General Corp., interoffice memo., Oct. 1963.
Stiffler, J. J. *Theory of Synchronous Communications.* Englewood Cliffs, N.J.: Prentice-Hall, 1971.
Sussman, S. M., and Ferrari, E. J. "The effects of notch filters on the correlation properties of a PN signal," *IEEE Trans. Aerosp. Electron. Syst.*, May 1974.
Torre, F. M. "A unified description and design format for spread spectrum waveforms," *Proc. Symp. Spread Spectrum Commun.*, Mar. 1973.
Turin, G. L. "An introduction to matched filters," *IRE Trans. Inform. Theory*, June 1960.
Weaver, C. S. "An adaptive communications filter," *Proc. IRE*, Oct. 1961.
Victor, W. K., and Brockman, M. H. "The application of linear servo theory to the design of AGC loops," Jet Propulsion Lab., Ext. Publ. 586, Dec. 1958.
——. "Spectrum analysis," Hewlett-packard, Rep. AN63, July 1964.
——. "Digital filter studies anticipate potential of spread spectrum designs," *Commun. Des. Dig.*, July/Aug. 1971.
——. *Reference Data for Radio Engineers.* Indianapolis, Ind.: Howard W. Sams, 1968,

# Author Index

# Subject Index

# Editor's Biography

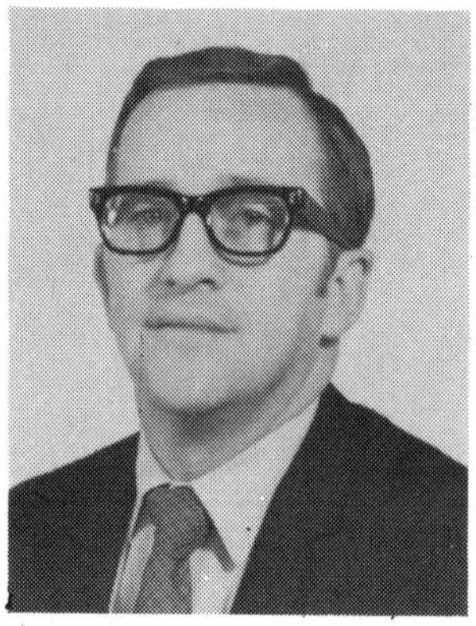

**Robert C. Dixon** (SM'75) is a private consultant, specializing in spread spectrum systems. He has 18 years experience in design and development of these systems. He has participated in more than 50 separate programs in this field as program manager, technical director, systems engineer, sub-system designer, and systems integrator. Mr. Dixon has worked at Hughes Aircraft Company as a Senior Technical Staff Assistant, at Northrop Corporation as a Senior Research Engineer, as a Senior Staff Engineer at Magnavox Research Labs, Staff Engineer at TRW, and Senior Staff Engineer at Hoffman Electronics. In these positions he contributed to the first producible spread spectrum system, the first troposcatter spread spectrum modem, the first spread spectrum comm-nav system for high performance aircraft, and the first satellite on-board spread spectrum demodulator. He has authored numerous technical papers and reports, and is the author of one book, *Spread Spectrum Systems* (Wiley-Interscience). Mr. Dixon has taught courses in spread spectrum systems at UCLA and at George Washington University.